TREATISE ON ANALYTICAL CHEMISTRY
A comprehensive account in three parts

PART I
THEORY AND PRACTICE

PART II
ANALYTICAL CHEMISTRY
OF THE ELEMENTS

PART III
ANALYTICAL CHEMISTRY IN INDUSTRY

TREATISE ON ANALYTICAL CHEMISTRY

Edited by I. M. KOLTHOFF
School of Chemistry, University of Minnesota

and PHILIP J. ELVING
Department of Chemistry, University of Michigan

with the assistance of ERNEST B. SANDELL
School of Chemistry, University of Minnesota

PART I
THEORY AND PRACTICE
VOLUME 4

INTERSCIENCE PUBLISHERS
a division of John Wiley & Sons, New York–London–Sydney

TREATISE ON ANALYTICAL CHEMISTRY

PART I
THEORY AND PRACTICE

VOLUME 4:

SECTION D-1
Magnetic Field Methods of Analysis

Chapters 38–41

SECTION D-2
Electrical Methods of Analysis

Chapters 42–52

With the cooperation of CHARLES N. REILLEY, *University of North Carolina*, as section advisor

AUTHORS OF VOLUME 4

RALPH N. ADAMS	JOHN W. MILLER
RALPH A. BROWN	L. N. MULAY
N. F. CHAMBERLAIN	ROYCE W. MURRAY
DONALD D. DEFORD	RICHARD PERTEL
PAUL DELAHAY	CHARLES N. REILLEY
N. H. FURMAN	SYLVAN RUBIN
J. WEST LOVELAND	IRVING SHAIN
FRANK W. MELPOLDER	NOBUYUKI TANAKA
LOUIS MEITES	BENJAMIN W. THOMAS

Acknowledgment

Considering the wide scope of the Treatise, the Editors have felt it desirable to consult with experts in specialized fields of analytical chemistry. For Section D-2, dealing with "Electrical Methods of Analysis," they have been fortunate in securing the cooperation of Dr. Charles N. Reilley, assisted by Dr. Royce W. Murray. Their constructive help in the preparation of this volume is acknowledged with gratitude.

Authors of Volume 4

Ralph N. Adams

Department of Chemistry, University of Kansas, Lawrence, Kansas; Chapter 47

Ralph A. Brown

Esso Research and Engineering Company, Linden, New Jersey; Chapter 40

N. F. Chamberlain

Research and Development, Humble Oil & Refining Company, Baytown, Texas; Chapter 39

Donald D. DeFord

Department of Chemistry, Northwestern University, Evanston, Illinois; Chapter 49

Paul Delahay

Department of Chemistry, Louisiana State University, Baton Rouge, Louisiana; Chapter 44

N. H. Furman

Professor Emeritus, Princeton University; Wake Forest College, Winston-Salem, North Carolina; Chapter 45

J. West Loveland

Research & Development, Sun Oil Company, Marcus Hook, Pennsylvania; Chapter 51

Louis Meites

Department of Chemistry, Polytechnic Institute of Brooklyn, Brooklyn, New York; Chapter 46

Frank W. Melpolder

Research Division, The Atlantic Refining Company, Glenolden, Pennsylvania; Chapter 40

John W. Miller

Research and Development Department, Phillips Petroleum Company, Bartlesville, Oklahoma; Chapter 49

L. N. Mulay

The Pennsylvania State University, University Park, Pennsylvania; Chapter 38

Royce W. Murray

Department of Chemistry, University of North Carolina, Chapel Hill, North Carolina; Chapter 43

Richard Pertel

Department of Chemistry, University of Houston, Houston, Texas; Chapter 52

Charles N. Reilley

Department of Chemistry, University of North Carolina, Chapel Hill, North Carolina; Chapters 42 and 43

Sylvan Rubin

Stanford Research Institute, Menlo Park, California; Chapter 41

Irving Shain

Department of Chemistry, University of Wisconsin, Madison, Wisconsin; Chapter 50

Nobuyuki Tanaka

Department of Chemistry, Faculty of Science, Tohoku University, Sendai, Japan; Chapter 48

Benjamin W. Thomas

Thomas Instrumentation and Research Co., Houston, Texas; Chapter 52

PART I. THEORY AND PRACTICE

CONTENTS—VOLUME 4

SECTION D-1: Magnetic Field Methods of Analysis

SECTION D-2:   Electrical Methods of Analysis

44. Chronoamperometry and Chronopotentiometry. By *Paul Delahay*. **2233**

52. Measurement of Capacity: Analytical Uses of the Dielectric Constant. By *Benjamin W. Thomas* and *Richard Pertel*........ 2631

SECTION D-1: Magnetic Methods

Part I
Section D-1

Chapter 38

ANALYTICAL APPLICATIONS OF MAGNETIC SUSCEPTIBILITY

By L. N. MULAY, *Magnetochemical Laboratory of the Materials Research Laboratory, Pennsylvania State University, University Park, Pennsylvania*

Contents

Contents (*continued*)

c. Chemical Shift Methods Using High-Resolution
N. M. R. Apparatus...................... 1804
8. Miscellaneous Techniques...................... 1806
III. Experimental Setup.................................. 1807
A. General Requirements of Laboratory.............. 1808
B. Apparatus Assembled in the Laboratory........... 1808
1. Commercially Available Components.......... 1808
a. Magnets and Direct-Current Sources......... 1809
b. Balances, Automatic Recording Devices, and
Helical Springs........................... 1811
2. Temperature Control....................... 1813
3. Requirements of Field Strength and Sensitivity of
Balance.................................... 1817
C. Gouy Magnetic Balance and Its Modifications..... 1818
D. Typical Assembly of the Gouy Balance............ 1820
1. Preparation of Sample for the Gouy Method.... 1823
a. Metallic and Certain Nonmetallic Solids..... 1823
b. Powdered Solids......................... 1824
c. Liquids and Solutions.................... 1825
2. Experimental Procedure..................... 1825
a. Measurements on Liquids and Solutions...... 1825
b. Measurement on Powdered Solids.......... 1826
3. Basis for Calculations of Magnetic Susceptibility. 1827
4. Calibration................................ 1828
E. The Faraday Balance and Its Modifications........ 1829
F. Typical Assembly of the Faraday Balance......... 1834
1. Calibration................................ 1835
IV. Analytical Applications of Magnetic Susceptibility..... 1836
A. Scope... 1836
B. Some Applications of Commercial Instruments..... 1836
1. Analysis of Oxygen: Oxygen Meters........... 1836
2. Permeameters: Carbon Content in Steel....... 1840
3. Coercimeters: Particle-Size Determination of Some
Ferromagnetics........................... 1841
4. Thermomagnetic Analysis: Determination of
Cementite in Steel........................ 1845
C. Some Applications of Magnetic Susceptibilities..... 1846
1. Applications to Inorganic Chemistry........... 1846
a. The Additivity Law and Paramagnetic Ions.. 1846
b. Determination of Purity and Analysis of Rare
Earths................................. 1847
c. Polymerization of Paramagnetic Ions........ 1848
d. Dissociation Phenomena.................. 1851
e. Study of Oxidation-Reduction Reactions *in*
situ.................................... 1852
f. Thermal Decomposition of Silver Oxide...... 1854
g. Structural Aspects of Coordination Complexes 1854
2. Applications to Organic Chemistry............. 1857
a. Free Radicals............................ 1857
b. Study of Reactions....................... 1860
c. Studies on Polymerization of Diamagnetic
Molecules............................... 1861

Contents (*continued*)

I. INTRODUCTION

Magnetism has been known since ancient times and the concepts of quantitative chemistry have been known for more than a century.   However, the application of magnetism to a study of analytical problems is of recent origin.

References to lodestone (leading stone) are found in the Vedas, the most ancient religious scriptures of the Hindus, dating back to some one thousand years B.C., in the Platonic dialogues of Socrates, and in the ancient literature of the Chinese.   Scientific studies of magnetism began with William Gilbert of Colshester (1540–1603), who showed that the earth itself behaves like a magnet, that iron ceases to be attracted while red hot, and that substances such as paper and cloth do not affect the force of attraction between a magnet and iron.   The early contributions of John Mitchell (1724–1793), of John Robison (1739–1805), and of Coulomb (1736–1806) helped to establish the well-known Coulomb's "inverse square" law.   Faraday is regarded as the founder of magnetochemistry; he based his investigations on the early researches of Ampère, Oersted, Arago, and Biot. Faraday showed that all matter is magnetic in one sense or the other; that is, that matter is either attracted or repelled by a magnetic field.   Today we know that the former category embraces para- and ferromagnetism and the latter corresponds to diamagnetism.   Stoner (208) has given an excellent historical introduction and many references to early work.

Faraday's genius established not only the laws of induction governing the relationship between electricity and magnetism, the laws of electrolysis, but it could foresee the close relationship between magnetism and the electromagnetic nature of radiation.   His experiments on the effect of magnetism on plane-polarized light were unsuccessful due to experimental limitations of his time; nevertheless, they planted the seed for the subsequent discovery of the Zeeman effect, which in turn directed the researches on nuclear magnetic resonance absorption spectroscopy.

The rigor of the mathematical analysis of magnetochemistry was developed in the past century by Poisson (1820), Weber (1854), and Ewing (1890). The theories of Langevin, Honda, Oxley, and Stoner established the present-day basis for a quantitative interpretation of magnetic properties of atoms in terms of electronic structure. G. N. Lewis showed the relationship between magnetism, electrons, and valence. This constitutes the basis for chemical interpretations of magnetic susceptibility.

The outstanding theoretical contributions of Van Vleck, Purcell, Bloch, and others in the United States are well known to physicists and physical chemists.

Thus far no reference to the accomplishments of the French school, notably of Pierre Curie, P. Pascal,* and Pacault (163) was made because it occupies a unique position in the history of magnetochemistry. As a matter of fact, the application of the Curie-Weiss law to a study of paramagnetism and of Pascal's constants to diamagnetism constitute the practical bases for the analytical applications of magnetic susceptibility measurements; these will be discussed later.

The first treatise in English dealing with physical principles and the applications of magnetochemistry was put forth in 1935 by S. S. Bhatnagar and K. N. Mathur (17) in India. This was followed by W. Klemm's *Magnetochemie* (114) and two editions of Selwood's *Magnetochemistry* (193), which is by far the most comprehensive and up-to-date contribution in this area. A number of books under the general title of "Electricity and Magnetism" have been published; however, only a few describe magnetism in relation to matter, and they have been written by a number of physicists. These deal with the basic theories and information vital to the magnetochemist (13,31,86,125a,154a,226). Information on magnetic properties of materials such as semiconductors and alloys is available in books and reviews (32,121) especially written in these areas and in solid-state physics (111). These works generally discuss the concepts of lattice and charge-carrier susceptibilities that contribute to the over-all susceptibility of a semiconductor (58). Some information on applications of magnetic susceptibility has appeared in *Technique of Organic Chemistry* (139) and other similar compilations and reviews (70,101,109,160,163,165,183). Most extensive tables of magnetic susceptibility constants are given by Foex, Gorter, and Smits (73); recent trends in magnetic susceptibility are discussed by Palmer (167). A recent review by this author (144) describes instrumentation and some analytical applications of magnetic susceptibility; important susceptibility constants have been reported separately

---

* An extensive list of references to Pascal's work is given by Bhatnagar and Mathur (17) and by Selwood (193).

(145). A major part of the review and these constants are included in this chapter.

In the inorganic area the applications include analysis of oxygen, of rare earths, study of complex compounds (81a), etc. In the organic area one deals with a study of some polymers, tautomerism, free radicals, reaction rates, and some simple structural problems. Some biochemical information on the components of blood is also obtained. The magnetic techniques are quick, nondestructive, and may be performed on a micro scale. In many instances the experiments may be conducted with inexpensive home-built apparatus that lends itself to automatic recording if desired. These advantages make the technique attractive for routine analysis and for basic and applied research.

II. THEORY OF MAGNETIC MEASUREMENTS

A. DEFINITIONS OF MAGNETIC PROPERTIES

"What is a magnetic field?" and "Why does a magnet attract iron?" are questions that cannot be answered precisely and in a simple fashion. Hence, using the approach of several texts on magnetism, and considering the limitations of this discussion, it will suffice to accept the phenomena of magnetism as commonly observed; we shall, therefore, define certain concepts within its own domain and in relation to the properties attributed to the fundamental particles of matter.

Magnetic field. The region surrounding a magnetized body, which is capable of inducing magnetism in other bodies, is termed a magnetic field.

Magnetic dipole. This is a macroscopic or microscopic magnetic system, in which the north and south poles of a magnet, equal and opposite in character, are separated by a short but definite distance. A magnetic dipole will tend to orient itself parallel to an applied magnetic field in the same way that an electric dipole would behave in an electric field.

Unit pole. Unlike an electric charge of either sign (+ or −), a single magnetic pole (north or south) cannot be isolated. However the purely fictitious concept of a unit pole helps to develop other useful quantitative aspects of magnetism. Hence, a unit pole may be defined as one that will repel an equal and similar pole placed 1 cm. away *in vacuo* with a force of 1 dyne. The repulsion or attraction is governed by Coulomb's law.

Pole strength. The strength, that is, the attractive (or repulsive) power of a magnet, is measured by the number of unit poles to which each pole is equivalent.

Intensity or strength of a magnetic field. If a unit pole is placed at a fixed point in vacuum in a magnetic field, it will be acted upon by a force that is taken as a measure of the intensity or strength of the magnetic field at that point. It follows from previous definitions that unit magnetic intensity exists at a point where the force on the unit pole is 1 dyne. The unit magnetic intensity was formerly called the "gauss," and this term is used even today by many manufacturers and users of magnets. According to the recommendations of the International Conference on Physics at London (1934), the unit is called the oersted. Some authors use the abbreviation "Oe" for the oersted. A smaller unit is the gamma, γ $(=10^{-5}$ oersted).

Magnetic flux or flux density. This is defined in terms of the lines of force of a magnet. The free path that would be traced by a unit pole in a magnetic field due to the forces acting on it is called the line of force. The number of lines of force per square centimeter is taken to be numerically equal to the strength or intensity of the field at that point. The total number of lines of force emanating from the (north) pole face of a magnet is called the total magnetic flux. The numbers of lines of force per unit area is termed the flux density. The unit of flux used for theoretical purposes is the maxwell. The number of lines of force emanating from a pole of strength m is $4\pi m$ maxwells.

Magnetic moment. This is a term most widely known to chemists and probably is the least understood with respect to its physical significance.

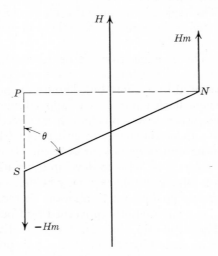

Fig. 38.1. Forces on a magnetic dipole, showing the "moment" or turning effect.

The "magnetic moment," as in the case of "moment of a force," refers to the turning produced under certain conditions. When a magnetic dipole is placed in a magnetic field it experiences a turning effect, which is proportional to a specific character, termed the magnetic moment.

If a field of strength H acts on a dipole $N-S$ of length l and strength m, its N and S poles will each experience a force of $+mH$ and $-mH$, respectively (Fig. 38.1). These two equal and opposite forces constitute a couple, the turning moment M of which is given by $M = $ force $\times$ distance; hence $M = mH \times PN = mH \times l \sin \theta = \mu H \sin \theta$.

Thus the quantity $\mu = ml$ defines the magnetic moment and serves as a measure of the turning effect. It is measured in dyne-cm. per oersted or in ergs per oersted. Although no practical unit for magnetic moment was formulated, experiments with the basic electrical and magnetic properties of fundamental particles have revealed the existence of a fundamental unit of magnetic moment, the Bohr magneton, which, like the charge of an electron, is just as real a quantity and may be placed amongst the "universal constants." The Bohr magneton, often abbreviated BM or designated μ_B, is equal to $eh/4\pi mc$, where $e = $ charge on the electron, $m = $ mass of the electron, $h = $ Planck's constant of action, and $c = $ velocity of light.

Substitution for their values gives $\mu_B = 0.917 \times 10^{-20}$ erg oersted^{-1}.

Coulomb's law and magnetic permeability. Magnetic permeability is best understood in terms of the Coulomb's law for magnetic attraction, which is treated in the same manner as electrical attraction.

If two poles of strength m_1 and m_2 are placed at a distance r cm. apart, the force between them is given by the inverse square law:

$$\text{force} = k \frac{m_1 m_2}{r^2}$$

The north and south poles are denoted by the positive and negative signs respectively. Hence, a positive value for the constant of proportionality k indicates repulsion, and a negative value, indicates attraction. This law is strictly true for a vacuum and is approximately true for air. However, in many media the force between magnetic poles is quite different than in a vacuum. Hence the concept of permeability is introduced to measure the extent to which a medium would be permeable to the magnetic (lines of) force. Thus,

$$\text{force} = \frac{m_1 m_2}{\mu \cdot r^2}$$

where μ is the magnetic permeability of the medium in which the poles are located. The same symbol μ is also used for the magnetic moment. For vacuum, μ is taken to be unity, and this equation furnishes the definition for the unit magnetic pole stated earlier. The term μ may be regarded as a constant of proportionality, depending on the nature of the medium and the units used for the measurement of force, distance, etc. It may be noted that in an analogous situation in electrostatics, one considers a constant K, termed the specific inductive capacity or the dielectric constant, for measuring the force between two electric charges q_1 and q_2 placed r cm. apart. In this case

$$\text{force} = \frac{q_1 q_2}{K \cdot r^2}$$

Intensity of magnetization. The amount of pole strength induced over the unit area represents intensity of magnetization. Thus,

$$I = \frac{m}{A}$$

where m is the induced pole strength over a total area of A sq. cm. An alternative definition is obtained by multiplying the numerator and denominator by the distance l cm. This gives

$$I = \frac{m \cdot l}{A \cdot l}$$

that is, the magnetic moment per unit volume.

Gauss's law and magnetic induction. According to the definition of field intensity, one unit line of force must pass through every sq. cm. If one considers a sphere of 1 cm. radius (with surface area of 4π sq. cm.) enclosing at its center a unit pole, it follows from the previous definition that 4π unit lines of force emanate from an unit pole. Gauss' law states that the total magnetic induction over a closed surface is 4π times the total amount of pole enclosed. Hence, for a pole m, $4\pi m$ maxwells emanate from its surface.

A bar of unmagnetized material when placed in a uniform magnetic field will become magnetized. Now, consider a unit surface A within the material at right angles to the direction of applied field, H, as in Fig. 38.2.

Fig. 38.2. Magnetization induced in unit area inside a sample in a magnetic field.

If I is the intensity of magnetization induced, there will be $4\pi I$ unit lines of force across the unit surface. In addition to this, there will be H lines of force of the applied magnetic field superimposed on the induced magnetization. Therefore, the magnetic induction B, representing the total number of lines of force across the unit surface, is given by

$$B = 4\pi I + H$$

If there is a vacuum in place of the magnetic material, one expects that $B = H$, because the magnetic permeability for vacuum is taken as 1. It also follows that for a magnetic material of permeability μ, the magnetic induction B will be given by

$$B = \mu H$$

Magnetic susceptibility. The intensity of magnetization I induced at any point in a body is proportional to the strength of the applied field H.

$$I \propto H, \; I = \kappa H \left(\text{or } \kappa = \frac{I}{H} \right)$$

where κ is a constant proportionality, depending on the material of the body. It is called the magnetic susceptibility per unit volume and may be verbally defined as the extent to which a material is susceptible to (induced) magnetization. For an isotropic body the susceptibility is the same in all directions. However, for anisotropic crystals, which are discussed in the next section, the susceptibilities along the three principal magnetic axes are different and the measurements on their powdered samples give the average of the three values.

Obviously, magnetic susceptibility is related to the magnetic permeability, and the following relationships may be derived.

As shown in the preceding section,

$$B = \mu H = 4\pi I + H$$

$$\mu = 4\pi \frac{I}{H} + 1$$

$$\mu = 4\pi \kappa + 1$$

$$\text{or} \quad \kappa = \frac{\mu - 1}{4\pi}$$

It should be noted that since κ is a ratio of the intensity I of induced magnetization to that of the applied field H, the susceptibility κ should be strictly a dimensionless quantity if I and H are measured in the same units.

This situation is comparable to that of specific gravity, in which the ratio of the density of a material to that of water, both measured in the same units, is expressed as a number without units.   However, magnetic susceptibility is still expressed in terms of c.g.s. units, more as a matter of convention than of scientific thought.* This is true because there exist, to start with, uncertainties both in the nature of measurement and in the units of magnetic permeability that have led to confusion as to whether B and H are quantities of the same kind.   In order to simplify matters, the convention of expressing susceptibility in some units will be followed here.

Mass (or specific) atomic and molar susceptibilities. If ρ is the density, then the susceptibility for 1 cc. or ρ g. of the material corresponds to the volume susceptibility, κ.   Hence, the susceptibility per gram of the material, called the mass or specific susceptibility, χ, is given by

$$\chi = \frac{\kappa}{\rho}$$

The atomic susceptibility χ_A and the molar susceptibility χ_M are simply defined as the susceptibility per g. atom and per g. mol, respectively. Hence,

$$\chi_A = \chi \cdot \text{atomic wt.}$$

$$\chi_M = \chi \cdot \text{molecular wt.}$$

Some authors (cf. References 75a, 171, 236) use the term "molal susceptibility"; this does not seem to have any relationship to "molal concentration," used for solutions, and corresponds to "molar susceptibility."

The magnetic susceptibilities are occasionally expressed in units of the rationalized Georgi system, based on the m.k.s. (meter, kilogram second) system.   For volume susceptibility, κ, the ratio of units,

$$\text{Georgi/c.g.s.} = 4 \pi$$

which makes the Georgi unit 12.56 times larger than the c.g.s. unit.   However, for conversion to mass susceptibility, χ, the Georgi system employs density in units of kg./m.^{3}, making the ratio of units for

$$\text{Georgi/c.g.s.} = 4 \pi \times 10^{-3}$$

Magnetic anisotropy. Many crystals, except those with cubic symmetry, show magnetic anisotropy.   The principal susceptibilities, that is,

---

* Some writers use the letters e.m.u. (electromagnetic units) in place of c.g.s., whereas others use a combination (e.m.u.-c.g.s.) to designate susceptibility.   Also see footnote on page 1766.

the susceptibilities along three mutually perpendicular axes of principal magnetism, are different. An anisotropic crystal when suspended in a magnetic field is found to rotate in such a manner that the axis of maximum susceptibility in the plane of rotation sets itself parallel to the direction of the applied field.

In the ultimate analysis the anisotropy of the unit cell in the crystal has its origin in (1) the anisotropy of the molecule and (2) the geometry of the molecules in the unit cell. The anisotropy of a crystal containing anisotropic molecules will depend largely on their relative orientation. A preferred orientation of molecules, such as in parallel layers, results in maximum anisotropy, whereas a random orientation will give a small anisotropy or occasionally result in an isotropic crystal if the anisotropies of individual molecules cancel one another. However, if the molecule itself is anisotropic, the crystal generally will exhibit a feeble anisotropic character.

B. TYPES OF MAGNETISM OBSERVED

Tables 38.I and 38.II summarize several aspects of the common and special types of magnetic behavior (cf. 160); some of these are described below.

1. Diamagnetism

This term refers to the phenomenon in which the intensity of magnetization induced in a body by an applied field is less than that produced in a vacuum by the same field. In practice, the net effect manifests itself as one of repulsion between the body and the applied field. Hence, the susceptibilities are shown with a negative sign. Such substances are called diamagnetics. Practically all organic and inorganic compounds with the exception of free radicals and compounds of elements of transition elements are diamagnetic. Diamagnetic susceptibility is independent both of temperature and of the applied field. Any significant change in diamagnetic susceptibility with temperature in most cases may be attributed to a change in the physical or chemical structure of the material.

2. Paramagnetism

If the intensity of the induced magnetization is greater in a substance than the applied field in vacuum, the substance is called paramagnetic and the phenomenon of attraction of the substance towards the magnetic field is observed. It is shown with a positive sign. Paramagnetism occurs especially among the transition group elements. Such substances are called paramagnetics. It may be noted that all substances, even

TABLE 38.I
Types of Magnetic Behavior Commonly Observed (Cf. 160)

	Type		
	Diamagnetism	Paramagnetism	Ferromagnetism
Effect of external field on substance	Feeble repulsion, $I < H$	Attraction $I > H$	Intense attraction, $I \gg H$
Examples	Most inorganic compounds, except those containing ions of transition elements; organic compounds, except free radicals; certain compositions such as stainless steel, special Cu–Ni alloys (e.g., 5¢ coin)	Salts and certain complexes of transition elements; "odd" electron molecules, such as NO_2 and oxygen; free radicals, such as triphenyl methyl	Metals such as iron, cobalt, nickel, and their alloys; $\gamma \cdot Fe_2O_3$
Comments on origin	Caused by orbital motion of electrons(s). Hence, it is a universal property. Most perceptible when all electrons are "paired," that is, when they have no permanent "spin" moment	Caused by spin and (usually) orbital momentum of (unpaired) electrons. The system contains permanent magnetic dipoles (moments) with no interaction	Caused by "domains" or lattice of particles containing electrons with parallel spins. Positive interaction amongst dipoles
Magnitude of specific susceptibility, χ at 20°C.	Negative and very small ($\sim 1 \times 10^{-6}$)	Positive and small ($\sim 100 \times 10^{-6}$). It is sufficiently large to mask the underlying diamagnetism	Positive and very large ($\sim 1 \times 10^2$)
Dependence of susceptibility on:			
(a) Temperature	None theoretically. Small dependence attributable to change in state of aggregation of system with temperature	$\chi \propto 1/T$ (Curie law) or $\chi \propto 1/(T + \theta)$ (Curie-Weiss law)	Dependence is complex. Beyond a certain temperature (Curie point), magnetization drops and shows paramagnetic behavior
(b) Field	None	None	Dependence described by hysteresis curves

TABLE 38.II. Special Types of Magnetic Behavior (Cf. 160)

Type	Effect of external field on substance	Examples	Origin	Magnitude of susceptibility at 20°C,	Dependence of susceptibility on temperature
Temperature-independent or Van Vleck paramagnetism	Feeble attraction	$KMnO_4$, Co(III) ammines	Atom with upper state separated from ground state by energy interval that is large compared with KT. System has no permanent magnetic moment	Positive and very small ($\sim 1 \times 10^{-6}$)	None
Pauli or free-electron paramagnetism	Feeble attraction	Metallic K and Na (vapors)	Paramagnetism of an "electron gas"	Positive and very small ($\sim 1 \times 10^{-6}$)	Very slight; generally for vapors, $\chi \propto 1/T$ (Curie law)
Antiferromagnetism	Feeble attraction	$KNiF_3$, MnSe, Ti_2O_3; ferrites	Two lattices of particles having electron spins in one lattice antiparallel to those in another lattice. Negative interaction amongst magnetic dipoles	Positive and very small ($\sim 1 \times 10^{-7}$ to 1×10^{-5})	Complex dependence. Up to a critical temperature (antiferromagnetic Curie point or Néel temperature), magnetization increases with temperature, then decreases
Ferrimagnetism	Feeble attraction	$FeCr_2O_4$,	Interpenetrating lattices with unequal numbers of electrons with antiparallel spins. Simultaneous unequal interaction amongst dipoles	Positive and small ($\sim 1 \times 10^{-3}$)	Positive dependence
Metamagnetism (may be regarded as a special case of antiferromagnetism with low Néel temperature). It shows field-strength dependence	Feeble attraction	$NiCl_2$ or $CoCl_2$ at liquid H_2 temperature	Parallel or antiparallel alignment of moments in domains	Positive and small ($\sim 1 \times 10^{-3}$)	Positive dependence

though paramagnetic, have an underlying diamagnetism, because such diamagnetism is a universal property; however, the magnitude of paramagnetism that manifests itself as a force of attraction is usually so great that it masks the feeble underlying and opposing diamagnetism. Paramagnetic susceptibility is independent of the applied field, but often is inversely proportional to the temperature. In some special cases paramagnetism independent of temperature arises; this is discussed in a later section.

3. Ferromagnetism

This falls under the category of attraction between a substance and an applied field; however, the forces of attraction are very great as compared with those of paramagnetism. Ferromagnetism is quite field-dependent, and ferromagnetic substances show typical hysteresis curves, as illustrated in Fig. 38.34. Hence, many ferromagnetic properties are measured at saturation, that is, by using high applied fields that cannot

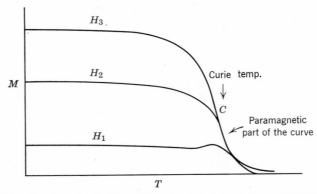

Fig. 38.3. Intensity of magnetization, M, $vs.$ temperature at three different fields for a ferromagnetic substance.

bring about any further increase in the intensity of induced magnetization at a given temperature. Ferromagnetic materials, when heated, start losing their magnetism gradually. Beyond a critical temperature, called the Curie temperature or the Curie point, these start behaving as regular paramagnetics (Fig. 38.3).

In nature, ferromagnetism* is restricted only to a few metals such as

* It must be noted that the term ferromagnetism and a new term "ferrimagnetism," suggested by Néel (155) to indicate ferromagnetism arising from atoms in two kinds of sites, have *no relation* with the valence-state nomenclature such as ferro(cyanide) and ferri(cyanide), employed by chemists. Cf. 125a

iron, although for several technological applications a number of alloys and compounds have been prepared.

4. Antiferromagnetism and Other Types of Magnetism

In a few compounds such as titanium sesquioxide, the induced magnetism increases with temperature up to a critical point called the "antiferromagnetic Curie temperature" or Néel point, beyond which the compounds behave like normal paramagnetics (Fig. 38.4). This phenomenon

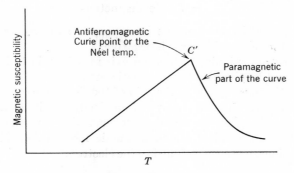

Fig. 38.4. Magnetic behavior of a typical antiferromagnetic.

is called antiferromagnetism, and is treated as a special case of ferromagnetism. Other types of magnetism are described briefly in Tables 38.I and 38.II.

C. PHYSICAL BASIS

The magnetic behavior of bulk matter often is explained in terms of the magnetic properties of the constituent molecules and atoms. In the ultimate analysis, one must consider the magnetic properties of the fundamental particles of matter. A discussion on these lines needs a thorough understanding of the electronic structure of atoms, in terms of the language of physics in general, and of spectroscopic nomenclature in particular. The reader is urged to clarify for himself the concepts of similar-sounding but often confusing terms, such as momentum and moment.

An attempt will be made here to present the physical basis of magnetic susceptibility by considering simply the magnetic effects arising from the two distinct types of motion of the electron, namely, its orbital rotation and spinning around itself. These effects often are expressed in terms of the turning moments or magnetic moments, although one does not know, in the classical sense, the precise magnitude of the strength of the poles of an electron and the distance separating them.*

In the following discussion the orbital and spin quantum numbers will be expressed in units of $h/2\pi$, where h is Planck's constant.

If l is the orbital quantum number, that is, the angular momentum of the electron, the magnetic moment μ_l for the orbital motion is given by

$$\mu_l = l \cdot \frac{eh}{4\pi mc}$$

$$= l \text{ Bohr magnetons}$$

This orbital magnetic moment can be expressed as a vector opposite to that of l since the electronic charge is negative.

Now, an electron spinning around an axis may be said to behave like a tiny magnet and to give rise to a magnetic moment. A theoretical value for the magnetic moment due to the spin of the electron cannot be derived, as nothing is known about the shape of an electron or its charge distribution. However, in order to obtain agreement with experimental results, and using wave mechanics, a spin magnetic moment, μ_s, given by the following relations, has been assigned to the electron.

$$\mu_s = 2 \sqrt{s(s+1)} \cdot \frac{eh}{4\pi mc}$$

$$= 2 \sqrt{s(s+1)} \text{ Bohr magnetons}$$

$$= 1.62 \times 10^{-20} \text{ erg oersted}^{-1}$$

Here $s = \frac{1}{2}$ represents the spin angular momentum of the electron. In vectorial presentation, μ_s has the same direction as s.

The observed magnetic moment arises from a combination of the orbital and spin moments. The resultant moment may be calculated theoretically by a vectorial addition of the two, taking into account various coupling mechanisms that arise in a system containing many electrons.

The effect of a magnetic field on different systems containing electrons may now be considered. Whether this effect will be one of attraction or of repulsion between the system and the applied field will depend on the presence or absence of unpaired electron(s) in the system. The ferric ion, for instance, is said to contain five unpaired electrons in its d shell, and a

---

* The magnetic susceptibility arising from electrons often is termed the "electronic susceptibility" to distinguish it from the susceptibility of the nucleus; the latter is of a very small magnitude ($\sim 10^{-10}$). The susceptibility of the nucleus is detectable at very low temperatures and may be ignored relative to the electronic susceptibility.

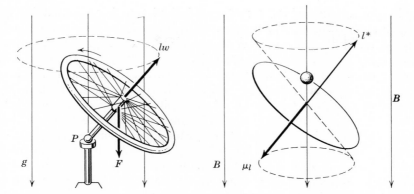

Fig. 38.5. A mechanical top precessing in a uniform gravitational field g is analogous to an electron orbit precessing in a uniform magnetic field. Reproduced by permission of Holt, Rinehart and Winston, Inc., from Semat and White, *Atomic Physics*.

free radical such as 2,2-diphenyl-1-picrylhydrazyl is said to contain one unpaired electron somewhere inside the molecule. Hence, such systems have a permanent magnetic moment to start with, and will be attracted appreciably toward an applied field. The magnetic moment of most paramagnetic systems may be expressed by the "spin only" formula mentioned earlier and correlated with the magnetic susceptibility.

There exist systems, comprising practically all inorganic and organic compounds, which do not contain any unpaired electrons. In these, the magnetism due to the spin of one electron is cancelled out in some fashion by that of another spinning in an opposite direction; as such these systems do not have any permanent magnetic moment. One would then ordinarily expect no effect due to an applied field. However, a very feeble yet significant repulsion is observed. This diamagnetic behavior is attributed entirely to the effect of the magnetic field on the orbital motion of the (paired) electrons, and the susceptibility in this case may be correlated with the radii of these orbits.

According to the classical theory, an electron carrying a negative charge and moving in a circular orbit is equivalent to a circular current. If a magnetic field is applied perpendicularly to the plane of the orbit the revolving electron will experience a force along the radius, the direction of which depends upon that of the magnetic field and of the moving electron. Application of the well-known Lenz's law, which predicts the direction of motion of a current-carrying conductor placed in a magnetic field, to this situation shows that the system as a whole will be repelled away from the applied field. An elaborate mathematical picture is presented by the Larmor (125) theorem, which describes the behavior of a system of particles, all having the same ratio of charge to mass, in the presence of a constant uniform field. According to this theorem, "the superimposed field leaves the form of the orbits and their inclination to the magnetic line of force, as also the motion in the orbit, unaltered and merely leads to the addition of a uniform 'precession' of the orbit about the direction of lines of force." At this juncture, it will be most appropriate to clarify the meaning of precession as applied to the orbital and spinning motions of an electron. Of these, the latter is rather easy to visualize by its comparison with the behavior of a spinning top or a gyroscope. As shown in Fig. 38.5, when a top originally spinning erect around an axis is subjected to an external force, F, it does not topple over completely but continues to spin around its own axis, PW, while this axis itself keeps on rotating in an orbit around the axis, P. This characteristic motion of the axis is termed the precession. This spin precession indeed arises in the case of a free (unpaired) electron subjected to a magnetic field, and forms the basis of the electron paramagnetic resonance techniques. Similarly, the precession of spins of certain nuclei, such as the protons, for example, forms the basis of nuclear magnetic resonance methods. It should now be possible to visualize the precession of the entire orbit of an electron around the direction of the applied field, as shown in Fig. 38.5. It is this type of orbital precession of an electron that gives rise to dimagnetism and forms the core of the mathematical theory of diamagnetism.

It is beyond the scope of this discussion to derive any equations for the atomic or molecular susceptibilities. However, some of the equations derived from classical and quantum mechanical considerations will be given here. Their applications to specific areas will be discussed in Section IV-B.

1. Diamagnetism

It will be appropriate to consider atomic and molecular diamagnetism separately and to point out the limitations in extending the classical derivation for the susceptibility of an atom to that of a molecule.

Atomic diamagnetism. According to the classical theory of Langevin (124a), the susceptibility per gram atom is given by

$$\chi_A = -\frac{Ne^2}{6mc^2} \sum r_i^2$$

where e and m refer to the charge and mass of the electron, respectively, c is the velocity of light, N is Avogadro's number, and r_i^2 is the sum of the mean square radii of the orbit of the ith electron projected perpendicular to the direction of the applied field. Diamagnetism thus depends only on the effective radii of the electronic orbits; the electrons in the outermost orbits contribute most to the atomic susceptibility. Langevin's (124a) equation also shows diamagnetism to be independent of temperature, but this is true in practice only to a first approximation. In many cases an increase in temperature causes a change in intramolecular forces, in hydrogen bonding, etc. This is sufficient to cause small changes in the diamagnetism. The negative sign of diamagnetism is a consequence of the Larmor precession (125); as such, all atoms possess the universal property of diamagnetism. It must be emphasized that the equation does not apply if the atom or ion contains a free unpaired electron or is not in a spherically symmetrical state.

The result of Van Vleck's quantum mechanical treatment (226) for the atomic susceptibility, χ_A, may be mentioned here briefly before proceeding to a discussion of molecular susceptibility.

$$\chi_A = -\frac{Ne^2}{6mc^2}\left\{\frac{h^2}{4\pi^2ze^2m}\right\}^2\left[\frac{5}{2}\,n^4l(l+1) - \frac{3}{2}\,n^2l(l+1) + {}^1\!/_2n^2\right]$$

where n and l are the principal and subsidiary quantum numbers respectively and z is the atomic number, h is Planck's constant of action, and other terms have the same meaning as before.

Molecular diamagnetism. Langevin's theory (124a) is strictly applicable to mononuclear systems; this implies that the electrostatic potential should be symmetrical about an axis parallel to the magnetic field. This stipulation is easily fulfilled by atoms; however, in considering molecules, the classical treatment may be extended only to linear molecules in the Σ state, on the following lines. The magnetic field is presumed to act along the molecular axis in the Z direction so that the cloud of electrons may be said to rotate freely around this axis with an angular velocity of $eH/2mc$. This gives

$$\chi_M = -\frac{Ne^2}{4mc^2}\sum\overline{x_i^2 + y_i^2}$$

Langevin's theory cannot be applied to other molecules, as the electric field acting on the electrons ceases to be spherically symmetrical. This is so because, in the classical treatment, if one refers the motion of electrons adequately to a rotating frame of coordinates, one cannot apply the equations of motion of a nonrotating system to a rotating one. Here the fixed nuclei, other than the one taken as the origin, produce an electric field that changes with rotation around the origin.   Any electrical assymmetry about the direction of the magnetic field will hinder free circulation of the electrons and will thus reduce the total diamagnetism.

Van Vleck (226) has treated this particular problem in terms of quantum mechanics, and the reduction in diamagnetism is ascribed to a mixing of the wave function for the ground state with that of some of the excited states brought about by the magnetic field.   He considers the lowering of the energy $E_n - E_0$ corresponding to the reduction in the total diamagnetic susceptibility.   This gives the following equation, which replaces the previous classical formula:

$$\chi_M = -\frac{Ne^2}{4mc^2} \sum_i \overline{x_i{}^2 + y_i{}^2} + \frac{Ne^2}{2m^2c^2} \sum_{n \neq 0} \frac{\left| (O \mid \mathfrak{m}_z \mid n) \right|^2}{E_n - E_0}$$

Here, in the second term, the summation is over the excited states, n, and the numerators and denominators represent the squares of the matrix elements of the electronic angular momentum component $\mathfrak{m}_z$ and the excitation energies, respectively.

In a generalized form for a polyatomic molecule with no resultant spin, Van Vleck (226) has derived the following equation for its molar susceptibility.   In this, the frequency of various transitions and the moments arising therefrom are considered.

$$\chi_M = -\frac{Ne^2}{6mc^2} \sum \overline{r^2} + \frac{2}{3} N \sum \frac{\left| m_0(n; n') \right|^2}{h\nu(n'; n)}$$

where $m_0(n; n')$ is a nondiagonal element of the matrix for the angular momentum of the system, $\nu(n'; n)$ is the frequency corresponding to $n'; n$ transition, and the other terms have their usual meaning.

The second term is always positive and is often called the temperature-independent paramagnetic term.   This should not be confused for paramagnetism arising from the spin of an unpaired electron.   It should be apparent that the temperature-independent paramagnetism corresponds to the decrease in diamagnetism discussed before.

In most cases, for instance in nitrous oxide, the second term vanishes. This reduces Van Vleck's equation to

$$\chi_M = -\frac{Ne^2}{6mc^2} \sum \bar{r}^2$$

which is identical with Langevin's equation.   Reference to the significance of the second term will be made later.

It may be now pointed out that the calculation of susceptibility even for the simplest element, hydrogen, is formidable, because the wave functions are not known. The first and second terms for hydrogen are -4.71×10^{-6} and about $+0.51 \times 10^{-6}$ respectively, which gives $\chi_M = -4.20 \times 10^{-6}$. This is in fairly good agreement with the experimental value of -4.005×10^{-6}, determined by Havens (90) and generally accepted as the most accurate value.

A major problem in the application of these equations is in computing $\Sigma \bar{r}^2$. Several workers, notably Stoner (209), Pauling (168), and Slater (202), have suggested theoretical and semiempirical derivations for this purpose.

It should be noted that an approximate method (17) for correlating the molar susceptibilities of isoelectronic compounds has been shown by this author (146) to be without any significance and to fail in many cases.

Significant advances in the theories of diamagnetism have been made recently by some workers (177a; cf. Reference 165).

2. Paramagnetism

For the sake of clarity, this topic is discussed under two categories, (1) normal temperature-dependent, and (2) temperature-independent paramagnetism, although a reference to the second must invariably be made in discussing the first category and, as seen before, in discussing molecular diamagnetism.

1. Normal paramagnetism.   According to the classical theory of Langevin (124a), the molar susceptibility is

$$\chi_m = \frac{N\mu^2}{3kT}$$

where μ is the permanent moment, T is the absolute temperature, N is Avogadro's number, and k is the Boltzmann constant. P. Curie had established experimentally prior to Langevin's work that the paramagnetic susceptibility χ_m is inversely proportional to the absolute temperature T, and the expression

$$\chi_m = \frac{C}{T}$$

is known as Curie's law; C is called the Curie constant.

Curie's law is generally applicable to a magnetically dilute system, that is, one in which magnetic interactions between neighboring molecules is negligible.

P. Weiss introduced the concept of a molecular field to account for molecular interactions and proposed the following modification

$$\chi_m = \frac{C}{T + \theta}$$

where θ is a constant known as the "Weiss constant." The magnetic susceptibility of many compounds is much better expressed by the Curie-Weiss law than by the Curie law alone. The significance of this is discussed by Selwood (193).

More precise derivations for χ_m include a term for the underlying diamagnetism. However, for all practical purposes this term, being small, may be neglected.

In paramagnetism, the magnetic moment μ may be regarded as a fundamental quantity relative to susceptibility, which varies inversely with temperature. Hence, in a comparison of experimental and theoretical results, the values of "effective Bohr magneton numbers," $\mu_{eff.}$, and the theoretical values may be used; $\mu_{eff.}$ is obtained very simply from Langevin's equation.

$$\mu_{eff.} = \sqrt{\frac{3k}{n\beta^2} \cdot \chi_M \cdot T} = 2.84 \sqrt{C}$$

where β is the Bohr magneton.

The magnetic moment, $\mu_{eff.}$, on the basis of classical theory, may be calculated from

$$\mu_{eff.} = g\sqrt{J(J + 1)}$$

in Bohr magneton units. Here g is the Lande splitting factor and J is the resultant angular momentum, which is a vector sum of L, the total angular momentum of the orbital motion of the electrons, and S, the corresponding spin angular momentum. For atoms in the S state for which the orbital moment $L = 0$, the magnetic moment is entirely due to the electron spins, so that $J = S$ and $g = 2$, giving

$$\mu_{eff.} = 2\sqrt{S(S + 1)}$$
$$= \sqrt{2S(2S + 2)}$$
$$= \sqrt{2ns(2ns + 2)}$$

Finally, this value equals $\sqrt{n(n + 2)}$, because S, the total spin momentum, is equal to the total number, n, of the unpaired electrons times s, the spin momentum for each electron, which is $1/2$ quantum unit. This formula is applicable to some ions of the transition group of elements. Moments calculated on the basis of this "spin only" formula are given in Table 38.III; values of the palladium and platinum group elements are given in Table 38.IV. In many cases the observed moments are greater than those calculated; the difference is ascribed to the orbital contribution (70,86).

It may be mentioned briefly now that, in the Langevin–Debye formula (226),

$$\chi = \frac{N\mu^2}{3kT} + \alpha$$

TABLE 38.III
Theoretical and Effective Bohr Magneton Numbers for Ions of First Transition Group (193)

Ion	$3d$ Electrons	Term	$\mu_{eff.}$	$\mu_{eff.}$ (obs.)
Sc^{+3} Ti^{+4} V^{+5}	0	$^1S_0$	0.00	0.0
Ti^{+3} V^{+4}	1	$^2D_{3/2}$	1.73	1.77–1.79
V^{+3}	2	$^3F_2$	2.83	2.76–2.85
V^{+2} Cr^{+3} Mn^{+4}	3	$^4F_{3/2}$	3.87	3.68–4.00
Cr^{+2} Mn^{+3}	4	$^5D_0$	4.90	4.80–5.06
Mn^{+2} Fe^{+3}	5	$^6S_{5/2}$	5.92	5.2–6.0
Fe^{+2}	6	$^5D_4$	4.90	5.0–5.5
Co^{+2}	7	$^4F_{9/2}$	3.87	4.4–5.2
Ni^{+2}	8	$^3F_4$	2.83	2.9–3.4
Cu^{+2}	9	$^2D_{5/2}$	1.73	1.8–2.2
Cu^{+} Zn^{+2}	10	$^1S_0$	0.00	0.0

TABLE 38.IV
Bohr Magneton Numbers for the Palladium and Platinum Group Elements (193)

Ion	μ
Ru^{+3}	2.09
Rh^{+3}	0.06
Pd^{+2}	0.07–0.13
Os^{+2}	0.27–0.50
Ir^{+3}	0.11
Pt^{+2}	0.0

the term α was introduced to account for magnetic effects other than those arising from the permanent magnetic moment of a molecule.

Van Vleck (226) has deduced an expression similar to the Langevin–Debye formula on the basis of quantum mechanics, which describes all aspects of paramagnetism:

$$\chi_M = \frac{N\mu^2}{3kT} + 2/3N \sum_{n' \neq n} \frac{\left| m^0(n; n') \right|^2}{h\nu(n'; n)} - \frac{Ne^2}{6mc^2} \sum \bar{r^2}$$

where the first term is identical with that of Langevin's expression for paramagnetism and is dependent on temperature. The symbols in the second and the third terms have the same meanings as those given in the preceding section. It will be recalled that the second term represents the contribution of the high-frequency elements to paramagnetism and is independent of temperature, whereas the third term, also independent of temperature, accounts for the underlying diamagnetism of the paramagnetic molecule. This term may be neglected in most cases.

2. Temperature-independent paramagnetism. It will be now in order to point out the physical significance of the temperature-independent term in Van Vleck's equation. One may imagine a resultant magnetic moment, μ_R, precessing regularly around a direction, J, in the absence of a field, but when J itself is made to precess about an applied field, H, the precession of μ_R ceases to be symmetrical and gives rise to a small increase in the magnetization parallel to H. An analysis of this situation shows this increase to be independent of temperature for a given L, S, J state.

Van Vleck's expression refers to only atoms with Russell-Saunders coupling, that is, in those cases in which the spin angular momenta, s, of the electrons can combine to form a resultant S and the orbital angular momenta, l, of electrons combine independently to give a resultant L. Application of Van Vleck's theory (226) to various paramagnetic systems is rather complex, but it accounts for departures from the Curie-Weiss law. It depends entirely on the magnitude of the spin multiplet intervals as compared to the Boltzmann distribution factor, kT. This gives rise to three specific situations in which the spin multiplet intervals may be (1) small, (2) great, or (3) nearly equal, as compared with kT. The meaning of this terminology is quoted from Van Vleck (226):

"We shall classify a state as 'normal' if its Boltzmann distribution factor $e^{-W/kT}$ is appreciably different from zero, i.e. if its excess of energy over the very lowest state is either smaller than or comparable with kT. An 'excited' state is one which has such a small Boltzmann factor that its probability of being occupied is negligible, and whose energy thus exceeds the energies of the normal states by an amount large compared to kT. An energy-level diagram illustrating graphically the delineation into normal and

Fig. 38.6. Energy-level diagram (Van Vleck (226)). Reproduced by permission of Oxford University Press.

excited states is given in [Fig. 38.6]. In order for the Langevin–Debye formula to be valid, it is vital for the electrical moment to involve no 'medium frequency' elements, which involve energy changes of the same order of magnitude as kT. Thus here and throughout the remainder of the volume, the equipartition allowance kT of energy enters as the unit for determining whether an energy change is 'large' or 'small' for our purposes, or in other words, whether a frequency is 'high' or 'low.' It is essential that the spacing between consecutive normal states or energy-levels be small compared to kT. In [Fig. 38.6] an interval such as b–c must be much less than kT. It is not necessary to demand that the energy-difference between two widely separated normal states, such as a–c in [Fig. 38.6], be small compared to kT, as ordinarily there will be selection principles which require that the matrix elements connecting two normal states be zero, or at least very small, unless the two states are adjacent, or nearly so (cf. the familiar selection rule, $\Delta j = 0, \pm 1$ for the inner quantum number, as a special example). It is clear that it is impossible to require that the energy-differences of two widely separated normal levels such as a–c be small compared to kT, as the equipartition theorem demands that at high temperatures the average excess of rotational energy over the very lowest state be kT itself. At very low temperatures the 'unit' kT will become much smaller, and the separation between adjacent normal states will become comparable with kT."

The final results of Van Vleck's calculations are as follows.

1. Multiplet intervals small compared to kT. Here, the high-frequency elements of the paramagnetic moment are absent. This gives

$$\chi_M = \frac{N\beta^2}{3kT}\left[4S(S+1) + L(L+1)\right]$$

The expression is used for calculating susceptibilities of ions of most transition-group elements (see Tables 38.III and 38.IV).

2. Multiplet intervals large compared to kT.

$$\chi_M = \frac{Ng^2\beta^2 J(J+1)}{3kT} + \frac{N\beta^2}{6(2J+1)}\left[\frac{F(J+1)}{h\nu(J+1;J)} - \frac{F(J)}{h\nu(J+1;J)}\right]$$

where β, the Bohr magneton, $= eh/(4\pi mc)$ and $F(J) = \dfrac{1}{J}[(S + L + 1)^2$

$- J^2][J^2 - (S - L)^2]$. This expression is used for most ions of the rare earth elements (see Table 38.V).

TABLE 38.V

Theoretical Effective Bohr Magneton Numbers for Tripositive Rare Earth Ions (Cf.226)

Tripositive ion	Term		Theoretical μ_{eff}.
La	$4f^0$	^1S	0.00
Ce	$4f^1$	$^2F_{5/2}$	2.56
Pr	$4f^2$	$^3H_4$	3.62
Nd	$4f^3$	$^4I_{9/2}$	3.68
Pm	$4f^4$	$^5I_4$	2.83
Sm	$4f^5$	$^6H_{5/2}$	1.55–1.65
Eu	$4f^6$	$^7F_0$	3.40–3.51
Gd	$4f^7$	$^8S_{7/2}$	7.94
Tb	$4f^8$	$^7F_6$	9.7
Dy	$4f^9$	$^6H_{15/2}$	10.6
Ho	$4f^{10}$	$^5I_8$	10.6
Er	$4f^{11}$	$^4I_{15/2}$	9.6
Tm	$4f^{12}$	$^3H_6$	7.6
Yb	$4f^{13}$	$^2F_{7/2}$	4.5
Lu	$4f^{14}$	^1S	0.00

3. Multiplet intervals comparable to kT. In this special case, the effect of the quantum number J is comparable with kT, and it is necessary to consider that the system containing N atoms is made of groups of atoms N_{J_1}, N_{J_2}, etc., with different values for J. The distribution of atoms amongst various groups is governed by the Boltzmann temperature factor and is proportional to $(2J + 1) \exp - W_j^0/kT$, where W_j is the energy of precession. Thus,

$$\chi_M = N \sum_{J=|L-S|}^{L+S} \frac{\{[g_j^2\beta^2 J(J + 1)/3kT] + \alpha_j\}(2J + 1)e^{-W_j^0/kT}}{\sum (2J + 1)e^{-W_j^0/kT}}$$

This expression is used particularly for ions of samarium and europium.

Van Vleck's theory and recent modifications (cf. Reference 86) are quite satisfactory in that they explain a number of experimental facts. According to the theory, Curie's law should be obeyed in the limiting cases in which the multiplet intervals are large or small compared to kT, neglecting the temperature-independent paramagnetic contribution to susceptibility arising from high-frequency elements. When the multiplet intervals are comparable to kT, a Boltzmann distribution of the normal states occurs, which results in serious departures from the Curie-Weiss law.

3. Ferromagnetism

This is by far the most complex area of magnetism.   It cannot be defined simply, but may be understood by its comparison with paramagnetism and in relation to the dependence of the intensity of magnetization both on the applied field and on the temperature, as depicted in Figs. 38.3 and 38.36.

The magnetization induced varies directly with the applied field in a ferromagnetic material and may attain 1000-fold value at lower field strengths; however, with certain limiting values for the applied field that can be obtained rather easily, a magnetic saturation is produced.   Hence, it is necessary to consider specific magnetization or the magnetic susceptibility of such materials at or above the saturation point.   The induction as a function of the applied field shows the typical hysteresis curve and the phenomenon of residual magnetism.   In this sense ferromagnetics are materials that can be permanently magnetized.

The magnetization produced at different values of magnetic fields may be destroyed by increasing the temperature.   However, even here ferromagnetics show the typical behavior shown in Fig. 38.3, in that at the Curie temperature the drooping curve up to the Curie point changes suddenly into the hyperbolic curve, which represents the characteristic behavior of a paramagnetic.

In ferromagnetism, it is necessary to distinguish between the susceptibility moment, $\mu = n(n + 2)$ Bohr magnetons, and the saturation moment, which is the maximum component of the magnetic moment in the direction of the applied field, given by $\mu = n$ where n = number of the unpaired electrons.   The saturation moment is obtained from specific magnetization σ, studied both as a function of temperature and of applied field strength.   Extrapolation of the σ versus T curve to $T = 0$ gives values for σ_0 corresponding to different fields.   These, when plotted against reciprocal field and extrapolated to zero (which amounts to finding σ_0 at infinite or "saturation" field), gives the value for $\sigma_{0,\infty}$, that is, for magnetic moment per unit mass.   From this, the magnetic moment per gram atom is computed.

It is important to recognize that, whereas paramagnetism is an atomic or a molecular property, ferromagnetism is a group effect.   The ferromagnetic moment arises from electron spins only; their orbital contribution is completely quenched.   Elements such as iron, cobalt, and nickel with incomplete low-energy levels, such as the $3d$ level, are ferromagnetic. The $4f$ level in gadolinium and other rare earths also is expected to produce the same effect; however, thermal vibrations prevent a complete alignment of spin moment.   In the group behavior of moments, therefore, a strong interaction between adjacent atoms or ions couples their moments parallel to each other in spite of thermal agitation; and ferromagnetism is produced. The nature of this interaction is discussed in the theories of Heisenberg, Zener, and in the domain theory of Néel. The scope of this work does not permit even a brief discussion of these theories. A survey in this area has been given recently by Néel (154a).

D. BASIC LAWS

The fundamental inverse square law of Coulomb which forms the basis for defining magnetic parameters, and the Curie-Weiss law, describing para- and ferromagnetic behavior, were considered in the previous sections. Other laws of a more direct practical application will be discussed here.

1. Additivity of Atomic Constants

P. Pascal studied a large number of gases and organic, metalloid, and complex compounds. The data he collected and the constants he derived for atomic susceptibilities on the assumption of an additivity law indeed stand out as a pioneering contribution to magnetochemistry. According to him, the molecular susceptibility χ_M of a compound could be expressed by

$$\chi_M = \sum n_A \cdot \chi_A + \lambda$$

where n_A is the number of atoms of susceptibility χ_A in the molecule and λ is a constitutive correction constant depending on the nature of chemical binding between the atoms. For ions, it is assumed that

$$\chi_m = \chi_{\text{cation}} + \chi_{\text{anion}}$$

which invalidates the necessity of a correction constant.

It must be pointed out that the derivation of Pascal's constants is purely empirical and is the result of a judicious mathematical juggling of numbers. Several attempts (49,85) have been made to attach a theoretical significance to the constitutive correction constant, and although some of these (216) have been partially successful, they have failed to change the empirical nature of his constants. Nevertheless, their usefulness lies in obtaining diamagnetic susceptibility corrections, which cannot otherwise be estimated for paramagnetic systems such as the free radicals, ions in solution, etc. and in allowing comparisons between the theoretical and experimental values of susceptibilities of atoms, ions, etc. A recent paper (177a) and a review (165) provide valuable information in the area of diamagnetism.

Tables 38.VI, 38.VII, 38.VIII, and 38.IX list the values for susceptibilities of atoms and the constitutive correction constants. This author and his collaborators (135) showed conclusively that the magnitude of the susceptibility of a cation depends on the nature of the anion and vice versa. The following generalizations apply to this dependence.

TABLE 38.VI
Atomic Susceptibility Constants[a]

Atom	$\chi\ (\times 10^{-6})$
Ag	-31.0
Al	-13.0
As(III)	-20.9
As(V)	-43.0
B	-7.0
Bi	-192.0
Br	-30.6
C	-6.0
Ca	-15.9
Cl	-20.1
F	-6.3
H	-2.93
Hg(II)	-33.0
I	-44.6
K	-18.5
Li	-4.2
Mg	-10.0
N, open chain	-5.57
Closed chain (ring)	-4.61
Monamides	-1.54
Diamides and imides	-2.11
Na	-9.2
O, alcohol or ether	-4.61
Aldehyde or ketone	$+1.73$
Carboxylic $=$ O in esters and acids	-3.36
3 O atoms in acid anhydrides	-11.23
P	-26.30
Pb(II)	-46.0
S	-15.0
Sb(III)	-74.0
Se	-23.0
Si	-20.0
Sn(IV)	-30.0
Te	-37.3
Tl(I)	-40.0
Zn	-13.5

[a] Many of the values listed are taken from Figgis and Lewis (70). See also References 167a and 170. For values for As and Sb in different organometallic compounds, see Reference 135.

TABLE 38.VII. Constitutive Correction Constants

(Groups containing only carbon atoms are listed first, then groups containing other atoms in the order of the symbols of these other atoms. For constitutive correction constants for cyclic systems, see Table 38.VIII)

Group	$\lambda \ (\times \ 10^{-6})$
C=C, ethylenic linkage	+5.5
C≡C, acetylenic linkage	+0.8
C=C—C=C, diethylenic linkage	+10.6
Ar—C≡C—Ar	+3.85
CH_2=CH—CH_2—, allyl group	+4.5
Ar—C≡C—	+2.30
C in one aromatic ring (e.g., benzene)	−0.24
C in two aromatic rings (e.g., naphthalene)	−3.1
C in three aromatic rings (e.g., pyrene)	−4.0
—C—Br, monobromo derivative	−4.1
BrC—CBr, dibromo derivative	+6.24
—C—Cl, monochloro derivative	+3.1
ClC—CCl, dichloro derivative	+4.3
CCl_2	+1.44
—$CHCl_2$	+6.43
—C—I, monoiodo derivative	+4.1
C=NR	+8.2
RC≡N	+0.8
RN≡C	0.00
C=N—N=C , azines	+10.2
RC≡C—C(=O)R′ or RC≡C—C(=O)OR′	+0.8
C bound to other C atoms with 3 bonds and in α, γ, δ, or ϵ position with respect to —C=O	−1.3
C bound to other C atoms with 4 bonds and in α, γ, δ, or ϵ position with respect to —C=O	−1.54
C bound to other C atoms with 3 or 4 bonds in β position with respect to a —C=O group	−0.5
—N=N—, azo group	+1.8
—N=O	+1.7

TABLE 38.VIII
Constitutive Correction Constants for Cyclic Systems[a]

Structure	$\lambda \ (\times \ 10^{-6})$
Benzene	−1.4
Cyclobutane	+7.2
Cyclohexadiene	+10.56
Cyclohexane	+3.0
Cyclohexene	+6.9
Cyclopentane	0.0
Cyclopropane	+7.2
Dicyclohexyl (C_6H_{11}–C_6H_{11})	+7.8
Dioxane	+5.5
Furan	−2.5
Imidazole	+8.0
Isoxazole	+1.0
Morpholine	+5.5
Piperazine	+7.0
Piperidine	+3.0
Pyramidon	0.0
Pyrazine	+9.0
Pyrazole	+8.0
Pyridine	+0.5
Pyrimidine	+6.5
α-Pyrone or γ-pyrone	−1.4
Pyrrole	−3.5
Pyrrolidine	0.0
Tetrahydrofuran	0.0
Thiazole	−3.0
Thiophene	−7.0
Triazine	−1.4
Urazol	0.0

[a] Most of the values listed are taken from Pacault (163). For the constitutive correction constants corresponding to other structural features, see Table 38.VII.

TABLE 38.IX
Diamagnetic Corrections for Various Ligands[a]

Ligand	$x \times 10^{-6}$
Dipyridyl	−105
Phenanthroline	−128
o-Phenylenebisdimethylarsine	−194
Water	−13

[a] The values listed are taken from Figgis and Lewis (70).

TABLE 38.X. Diamagnetic Susceptibilities per Gram-Ion[a]
(All values -1×10^{-6})
The underlying diamagnetism of paramagnetic ions is indicated by an asterisk (*).

Ion	Susceptibility	Ion	Susceptibility	Ion	Susceptibility	Ion	Susceptibility
Ag^+	24	$*Eu^{+2}$	22	Nb^{+5}	9	Se^{+4}	8
$*Ag^{+2}$	24?	$*Eu^{+3}$	20	$*Nd^{+3}$	20	Se^{+6}	5
Al^{+3}	2	F^-	11	$*Ni^{+2}$	12	SeO_3^{-2}	44
As^{+3}	9?	$*Fe^{+2}$	13	O^{-2}	12	SeO_4^{-2}	51
As^{+5}	6	$*Fe^{+3}$	10	OH^-	12	Si^{+4}	1
AsO_3^{-3}	51	Ga^{+3}	8	$*Os^{+2}$	44	SiO_3^{-2}	36
AsO_4^{-3}	60	Ge^{+4}	7	$*Os^{+3}$	36	$*Sm^{+2}$	23
Au^+	40?	Gd^{+3}	20	$*Os^{+4}$	29	$*Sm^{+3}$	20
Au^{+3}	32	H^+	0	$*Os^{+6}$	18	Sn^{+2}	20
B^{+3}	0.2	Hf^{+4}	16	Os^{+8}	11	Sn^{+4}	16
BF_4^-	39	Hg^{+2}	37	P^{+3}	4	Sr^{+2}	15
BO_3^{-3}	35	$*Ho^{+3}$	19	P^{+5}	1	Ta^{+5}	14
Ba^{+2}	32	I^-	52	PO_3^-	30	$*Tb^{+3}$	19
Be^{+2}	0.4	I^{+5}	12	PO_3^{-3}	42	$*Tb^{+4}$	17
Bi^{+3}	25?	I^{+7}	10	Pb^{+2}	28	Te^{-2}	70
Bi^{+5}	23	IO_3^-	50	Pb^{+4}	26	Te^{+4}	14
Br^-	36	IO_4^-	54	$*Pd^{+2}$	25	Te^{+6}	12
Br^{+5}	6	In^{+3}	19	$*Pd^{+4}$	18	TeO_3^{-2}	63
BrO_3^-	40	$*Ir^+$	50	Pm^{+3}	27[b]	TeO_4^{-3}	55
C^{+4}	0.1	$*Ir^{+2}$	42	$*Pr^{+3}$	20	Th^{+4}	23
CN^-	18	$*Ir^{+3}$	35	$*Pr^{+4}$	17	$*Ti^{+3}$	9
CNO^-	21	$*Ir^{+4}$	29	$*Pt^{+2}$	40	Ti^{+4}	5
CNS^-	35	$*Ir^{+5}$	20	$*Pt^{+3}$	33	Tl^+	34
CO_3^{-2}	34	K^+	13	$*Pt^{+4}$	28	Tl^{+3}	31
Ca^{+2}	8	La^{+3}	20	Rb^+	20	$*Tm^{+3}$	18
Cd^{+2}	22	Li^+	0.6	$*Re^{+3}$	36	$*U^{+3}$	46
$*Ce^{+3}$	20	Lu^{+3}	17	$*Re^{+4}$	28	$*U^{+4}$	35
Ce^{+4}	17	Mg^{+2}	3	$*Re^{+6}$	16	$*U^{+5}$	26
Cl^-	26	Mn^{+2}	14	Re^{+7}	12	U^{+6}	19
Cl^{+5}	2	Mn^{+3}	10	$*Rh^{+3}$	22	$*V^{+2}$	15
ClO_3^-	32	$*Mn^{+4}$	8	$*Rh^{+4}$	18	$*V^{+3}$	10
ClO_4^-	34	$*Mn^{+6}$	4	$*Ru^{+3}$	23	$*V^{+4}$	7
$*Co^{+2}$	12	$*Mn^{+7}$	3	$*Ru^{+4}$	18	V^{+5}	4
$*Co^{+3}$	10	$*Mo^{+2}$	31	S^{-2}	38?	$*W^{+2}$	41
$*Cr^{+2}$	15	$*Mo^{+3}$	23	S^{+4}	3	$*W^{+3}$	36
$*Cr^{+3}$	11	$*Mo^{+4}$	17	S^{+6}	1	$*W^{+4}$	23
$*Cr^{+4}$	8	$*Mo^{+5}$	12	SO_3^{-2}	38	$*W^{+5}$	19
$*Cr^{+5}$	5	Mo^{+6}	7	SO_4^{-2}	40	W^{+6}	13
Cr^{+6}	3	N^{+5}	0.1	$S_2O_8^{-3}$	78	Y^{+3}	12
Cs^+	31	NH_4^+	11.5	Sb^{+3}	17?	Yb^{+2}	20
Cu^+	12	NO_2^-	10	Sb^{+5}	14	$*Yb^{+3}$	18
$*Cu^{+2}$	11	NO_3^-	20	Sc^{+3}	6	Zn^{+3}	10
$*Dy^{+3}$	19	Na^+	5	Se^{-2}	48?	Zn^{+4}	10
$*Er^{+3}$	18						

[a] Most values are taken from Selwood (193), based on a compilation by W. Klemm (115).

[b] The value for Pm^{+3} (referred to as Il³ in the original) is from A. V. Jagannadham, *Proc. Rajasthan. Acad. Sci. (India)*, 1, 6 (1950).

1. The susceptibility of cations belonging to the same group may be expressed as a simple function of the total number of electrons in them; the susceptibility of a cation generally decreases with increasing valence of the anion.

2. The susceptibility of an anion in combination with a group of chemically related cations is generally a fixed quantity, and it decreases with the increasing valence of the group of cations with which it combines.

Klemm's (115) averaged values, listed in Table 38.X, may be used for all practical considerations in which minor variations in the susceptibilities of ion depending on the nature of oppositely charged ions are not of prime importance.

2. Wiedemann's Law

The mass susceptibility, χ, of a mixture of components with susceptibilities $\chi_1, \chi_2, \ldots \chi_n$ and weight fractions $p_1, p_2 \ldots p_n$ may be expressed by

$$\chi = \chi_1 p_1 + \chi_2 p_2 \ldots . \chi_n p_n$$

The law is obeyed quite closely by mechanical mixtures and solutions of diamagnetic substances in which little or no interaction takes place either between molecules or ions of the components or between these and the solvent. This stipulation makes it imperative that caution must be exercised in deducing the susceptibility of a solute from that of the solution. The application of the law to solid or liquid solutions containing paramagnetic ions becomes even more difficult as the interactions amongst ions or between ions and the solvent become quite pronounced. In such cases it is, therefore, necessary to ascertain that the system is "magnetically dilute."

E. TYPES OF INFORMATION OBTAINABLE FROM MAGNETIC MEASUREMENTS

The reader who has familiarized himself up to this point with the short account of the physical basis and theory of magnetochemistry would indeed be interested in knowing the scope of information obtainable from magnetic measurements. This is outlined below; the practical procedures to be followed for obtaining such information will be given later.

1. Qualitative aspects. Using any standard method, it is possible to determine whether the magnetic susceptibility of a material under test is dependent on (*1*) the temperature, (*2*) the field strength, or (*3*) both of these factors. This yields the qualitative information as to whether the material is dia-, para-, or ferromagnetic. In the area of geochemical studies a simple test with a magnet tells the nature of a mineral in respect to its "ferrous" (ferromagnetic) or nonferrous character.　The application of magnetic separation of minerals is well known.

　　2. Quantitative aspects.　Thermomagnetic analysis, which is discussed separately yields valuable information on the particle size distribution and activity of ferromagnetic catalysts, etc.

　　Measurements of magnetization and/or permeability give composition of alloys, the degree of precipitation of a metal in its alloy, the carbon content in steel, and so on.　The susceptibility of a paramagnetic system that includes solid and gaseous mixtures, solutions, and colloids and dispersed media, such as glass, yields the concentration of a transition metal, rare earth, or a paramagnetic gas involved in any of these systems.

　　A study involving dia- and paramagnetic measurements of organometals undergoing dissociation proves useful in detecting the presence and measuring the concentration of free radicals, the constants for the dissociation process, etc.　Similar studies in biological areas furnish the analysis of certain components of blood, whereas diamagnetic measurements alone are useful in characterizing and ascertaining the purity of organic and inorganic compounds and, to a moderate extent, in studying polymerization processes. It may be pointed out that with the advent of high-resolution nuclear magnetic resonance spectroscopy, a revival of investigations of diamagnetism of matter in its different physical states has taken place in recent years.

F. PRINCIPLES OF MAGNETIC MEASUREMENTS

　　Magnetic susceptibilities are generally measured by the so-called uniform field and nonuniform field methods.　Derived and related methods, to be discussed separately in the next section, include various induction and nuclear magnetic resonance methods.　A chart summarizing practical aspects, such as applicability, limitations, etc., of these methods will be given at the end of Section III (cf. Table 38.XII, p. 1838–1839).

　　The principles common to the conventional methods will be described first and the details of instrumentation will be deferred to Section III.

　　A body experiences an orienting effect in a magnetic field depending on its anisotropy and, to a lesser degree, on its shape factor.　This effect will be directly proportional to a product of its volume susceptibility, κ, its volume, V, and the applied field, H.　The body will experience a linear displacing force if the field is made nonuniform with a gradient $\partial H/\partial S$ in the S direction; the force may be given by

$$f = \kappa \cdot V \cdot H \cdot \partial H/\partial S$$

The details of this derivation are given in standard texts (13,208).

1. Uniform Field Method

In this method, developed by the French physicist Gouy (84), a long cylindrical sample is suspended such that one end lies in a region of strong uniform field and the other end lies in a region of negligible field. This is accomplished by a set up (Fig. 38.7) that permits a direct measurement of

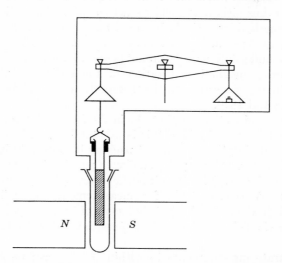

Fig. 38.7. Apparatus for the Gouy method. Reproduced from Lewis and Wilkins, *Modern Coordination Chemistry*, Interscience, 1960.

force. In this case, integration of $\kappa \cdot V \cdot H \cdot \delta H / \partial S$ over all layers between the limits of maximum field H and of negligible field ($H \simeq 0$) gives, for force, the relation

$$f = \frac{1}{2}\kappa \cdot H^2 \cdot A$$

where A is the cross-sectional area of the sample. This equation tacitly assumes that the atmosphere surrounding the sample has a negligible susceptibility and that the field at one end of the tube is negligible in comparison to that at the other. If these conditions are not fulfilled so that the atmosphere has a susceptibility of κ_0 and the field at the other end is H_0, then the equation for f becomes

$$f = \frac{1}{2}(\kappa - \kappa_0)(H^2 - H_0^2)A$$

It should be noted that the value of earth's magnetic field, in the neighborhood of 0.4 oersted acting at one end of the sample, is considered negligible for all practical purposes, in comparison with fields of a few thousand oersted applied at the other end. Even fields of about 100 oersted may be neglected if H is of the order of 10,000 oersted. The necessity of having a uniform field between the pole gap also arises from a practical consideration. If the field is not uniform the sample will experience a horizontal force, and it may tend to move toward one of the pole faces and thus vitiate an exact measurement of the vertical force.

The Gouy method is particularly suited for the measurement of dia- and paramagnetic susceptibilities of samples obtainable in the form of powdered solids, liquids, and solutions. It cannot be used for ferromagnetic measurements because a magnetic saturation of the entire sample cannot be attained. Modifications and a typical assembly of this method are described on pages 1818 and 1820.

The theory requires the sample to be in the form of a long homogeneous cylinder. In the case of solids, this is accomplished only to an approximation by powdering the sample and packing it uniformly in a glass tube of uniform diameter. The reproducibility of packing is rather difficult, and although corrections (75) for the air pockets can be introduced, the over-all accuracy cannot exceed $\pm 1\%$ for measurements on solids. Another limitation is introduced by the fact that some of the loosely bound particles in the magnetic field may orient preferentially due to their magnetic anisotropy.

More accurate measurements to within $\pm 0.1\%$ can be obtained with liquids, which do not pose the problems of packing, of anisotropic effects, etc. Usually 0.5- to 1-g. samples of solids, liquids, and of solutions of moderate concentration are required to obtain results with an analytical balance of sufficient accuracy. The use of a microbalance furnishes more refined measurements and allows the use of very small samples.

In all cases the Gouy method provides a measurement of volume susceptibility. Therefore, conversion to mass susceptibility requires an independent measurement of density; hence, the accuracy of this measurement finally determines the accuracy of the mass-susceptibility data.

2. Nonuniform Field Method

This is commonly known as the Faraday method, and its principle is illustrated in Fig. 38.8. If a sample of mass m with mass susceptibility χ is placed in a nonuniform field H with a gradient $\partial H/\partial s$, it will be subjected to a force along s, given by

$$f = m\chi H \, \partial H/\partial s$$

The nonuniform field may be obtained by inclining the poles of a magnet or by using pole pieces of special design Fig. 38.9 (see also Fig. 38.31). The

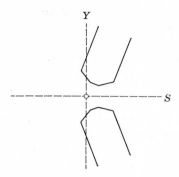

Fig. 38.8. Principle of the Faraday magnetic balance. The sample, shown here at the origin, is placed where the product $H \cdot \partial H / \partial s$ is a maximum. The sample is free to move along the s-axis, and may be suspended from a torsion arm. Reproduced from Selwood (193).

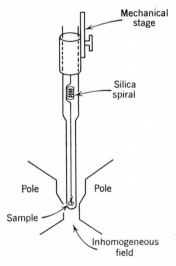

Fig. 38.9. Faraday balance using vertical suspension from a silica spiral spring (Selwood (193)).

force f may be measured either with a torsion arm suspended from a fiber or with a silica spring.

The Faraday method is applicable to the measurement of dia-, para-, and ferromagnetic susceptibilities. In the last case, a magnetic saturation of the sample can be achieved because the entire sample is enclosed in the field.

The method is particularly suitable for solids, which may be powdered and compressed into a tablet and placed at the region of maximum $H\partial H/\partial s$ in the magnetic field. The powdering and compressing technique destroys the anisotropic effects of individual particles. A few milligrams of the sample is required and a high degree of accuracy (to within $\pm 0.1\%$) may be obtained in the measurement of mass susceptibility that is directly furnished.

Measurement of susceptibilities on liquids is possible with this method; however, their handling is quite cumbersome. Efforts to enclose liquids in capsules sufficiently small to be surrounded by the limited region of uniform field gradient give rise to difficulties of sealing the samples and of calibrating the empty capsule.

Modifications of the Faraday method, to be described later, are also available for measurements on gases, liquids, and solutions.

In general, the accuracy of susceptibility measurements will depend on the particular method employed for the measurement of force. It also will depend on the precision with which the setting of the sample container is reproduced at the exact point of reference between the poles during the calibration and the making of final measurement on a sample.

G. DERIVED AND RELATED METHODS

1. The Quincke Method (179)

This method is related to the Gouy technique and is strictly applicable to liquids and solutions and, with some modifications, to gases. As shown in Fig. 38.10, the magnetic force acting on the sample in the capillary is measured in terms of the hydrostatic pressure. In the actual experiment, the change, Δh, in the height of the meniscus with the field off and on is measured with a cathetometer. Paramagnetic liquids show an increase in

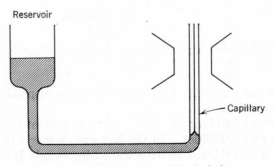

Fig. 38.10. Principle of the Quincke balance.

height; diamagnetic liquids show a decrease. If ρ and ρ_0 are the densities of the liquid and the gas above the liquid, respectively, then the hydrostatic pressure $g(\rho - \rho_0)\Delta h$ is balanced by the magnetic force $1/2\, H^2\, (\kappa - \kappa_0)$, where H is the applied field, κ is the volume susceptibility of the liquid, and κ_0 is the volume susceptibility of the gas over the meniscus. With solutions exposed to air the gas will consist of a mixture of air and the vapor of the liquid. Hence,

$$\frac{2g(\rho - \rho_0)\Delta h}{H^2} = \kappa - \kappa_0 \tag{1}$$

From this χ, the susceptibility per g., is given by

$$\chi = \frac{\kappa}{\rho} = \frac{2g\Delta h}{H^2} + \chi_0 \frac{\rho_0}{\rho} \tag{2}$$

where χ_0 and ρ_0 are the gram susceptibility and the density of the gas over the mensicus.

For practical purposes, the second term may be ignored when the reservoir is of a large diameter compared with the capillary and the susceptibility of the gas, χ_0, is small. This gives a simpler relation

$$\chi = \frac{2g\Delta h}{H^2}$$

and is found advantageous in that an independent measurement of the density of the liquid is not required. It is not usually necessary to find the value of the applied field, H, since the factor $2g/H^2$ can be eliminated by making measurements on a sample (subscript s) and on a reference (subscript r) under identical conditions:

$$\frac{\chi_s}{\chi_r} = \frac{\Delta h_s}{\Delta h_r}$$

Fields of about 25,000 oersted are recommended. Accuracy of about 1% in the susceptibility measurement, which is comparable to that of the Gouy method, is easily obtained, particularly at room temperature that can be regulated to a high degree of accuracy.

Equation (1) shows that the susceptibility κ_0 of a gas above the meniscus also may be determined by the Quincke method. In practice, a reference liquid such as water in an atmosphere of hydrogen gas may be used in the initial experiment. Hydrogen gas has a susceptibility of only 0.02% of water (κ_0). The experiment is repeated with a sample gas. If Δh_0 and Δh_g are the changes in the height of the meniscus of the liquid in the two experiments produced by the same magnetic field, the susceptibility κ of the gas is given by

$$\kappa = \kappa_0 \frac{\Delta h_0 - \Delta h_g}{\Delta h_0}$$

Several modifications of the Quincke method applicable to liquids and gases are described in the literature (17,193).

2. The Rankine Method (181): Susceptibility of Gases

The measurement of susceptibility of a gas involves some difficulties. The volume susceptibilities of liquids and solids range from 10^{-6} to 10^{-3} c.g.s. units per cc., whereas the susceptibilities of gases and vapors are found to be much smaller ($\sim 10^{-10}$ c.g.s. units per cc. at NTP). Measurements on a compressed gas, which is expected to have a larger volume susceptibility, are limited by the degree to which it may be compressed and the size of the vessels that may be used for measurements. Furthermore, most gases are diamagnetic and even a trace (1 part in 1000) of oxygen (from air), which is markedly paramagnetic ($\kappa = 0.162 \times 10^{-6}$ c.g.s. units), is enough to vitiate the measurements of diamagnetic susceptibilities by about 10%. Therefore, all gases and vapors must be purified and particularly freed from oxygen prior to measurement.

Many methods for measuring the susceptibility of gases are related to the Gouy and the Faraday techniques. Soné (206), for instance, used a partitioned glass tube with the Gouy technique; in one part air under pressure of known susceptibility was placed and the other end was evacuated and sealed off. Air was then replaced by the gas and the forces on the sample were measured with a sensitive balance using an optical system. Stossel (210) also used the Gouy principle for measurement on gases; however, it appears that for the measurement of small forces the sensitivity and stability of a balance have to be stretched to extreme limits. On the other hand, modifications of the Faraday method have been accomplished with ease. The methods introduced by Glaser (80), Bitter (20), Havens (90), Lallemand (124), Néel (154), Reber and Boeker (184), Vaidyanathan (224), and Rankine (181) fall in this category. Review of these and several other modifications are to be found in the literature (13,17,193,208). Each method has its characteristic advantages. However, considering the general usefulness for routine susceptibility measurements and analytical applications, the Rankine method (181) and its modifications will be considered here.

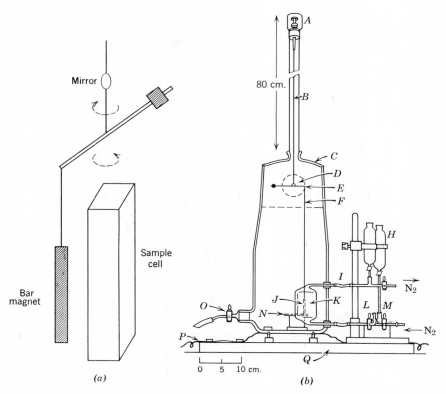

Fig. 38.11a. Principle of the Rankine magnetic balance. The quartz fiber with the mirror twists in either direction, depending on the dia- or paramagnetic nature of the sample in the cell.

Details (b) of the Rankine balance (28). Key: A, torsion head; B, 6.5-μ tungsten fiber; C, lid; D, lens; E, beam; F, 4.0-μ tungsten fiber; H, solution reservoirs; I, ground wire; J, magnet; K, cell; L, oxidizing agent; M, solution inlet; N, damping plate; O, to pump; P, balancing wire; and Q, slate slab. Reproduced by permission from the *Journal of Scientific Instruments*.

In this method, instead of keeping the magnet fixed and observing the displacement of the sample, the sample is fixed and the displacement of a small permanent magnet is observed. A bar magnet placed parallel to a sample surface induces a polarity on the surface that exerts a force on the magnet and displaces it. As in previous methods the force is an attraction for a paramagnetic sample and a repulsion for a diamagnetic. The force is measured with a torsion arm suspended from a quartz fiber and is designed to minimize the effect of the earth's magnetic field and other stray

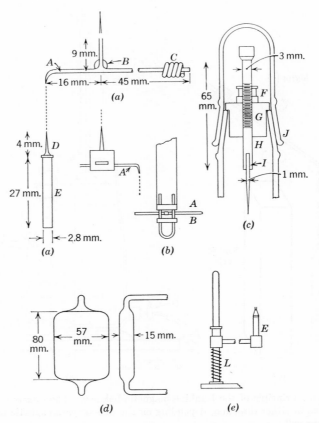

Fig. 38.12.   Details of Bockris and Parsons' modification of the Rankine balance (28): (a), beam and magnet; (b), beam support; (c), cell; and (e), magnet support. Key: A, 1-mm. quartz rod beam; B, aluminized plane mirror; C, silver wire counterpoise; D, silver pin; E, magnet; F, locking nuts; G, Tufnol bushing; H, brass rod; I, quartz rod; J, B29 joint; and L, spring. Reproduced by permission from the *Journal of Scientific Instruments.*

fields.   The method is quite sensitive and uses a magnet of only a few hundred oersted.   The method is used for measuring the susceptibilities of a sample relative to the known susceptibility of a reference.

An important modification of the Rankine balance is described in detail by Bockris and Parsons (28).   The major improvements consist of (1) the use of tungsten fibers that facilitate construction of the equipment and the sensitivity; (2) the use of a photoelectric cell for measurement of small deflections; and (3) the use of a small, powerful Alomax magnet.

The balance was constructed particularly for investigating free radicals of half-life time of more than 1 minute. Volume susceptibility changes of 0.0004×10^{-6} c.g.s. units could be followed. Considering this sensitivity, it appears to be quite useful for studying the small dia- and paramagnetic susceptibilities of gases.

The apparatus and its details are shown in Figs. 38.11 and 38.12. Reference to the original paper should be made for further details. The entire system is placed in a glass enclosure and is evacuated. Samples (liquids or gases) are changed easily through the inlet and outlet connected to the flat-faced cell, which is held rigidly inside the vessel. A light beam reflected from the mirror on the torsion head is focussed onto a photocell, which is operated differentially. When the beam illuminates both parts of the cell equally, no deflection is observed on the galvanometer. Small displacements of the balance produce proportionate deflection on the galvanometer.

The apparatus is calibrated by filling the cell with oxygen, nitrogen, etc. Benzene, water, and acetone also may be used.

3. Modified Rankine Balance

The original study of the magnetic moment of iron in biological systems such as hemoglobin and related materials, by Haurowitz (89), by Coryell and his co-workers (51), and by Pauling (170, 171), has led to many magnetochemical studies of biological systems. A fast and sensitive instrument for the measurement of magnetic susceptibilities of rapid biochemical reactions has been developed recently by Brill and his co-workers (34; see also Reference 25); in this writer's opinion it represents a major accomplishment in the area of instrumentation. The instrument was developed for measuring the rapid changes in the magnetic moment of iron-containing proteins during the course of their chemical reactions.

A part of the apparatus is shown in Figs. 38.13 and 38.14. A differential cell (Fig. 38.15) is employed. The interchange of solutions between the two half cells produces twice the change in the force on the magnet that is produced by one half cell, as in the original Rankine balance. A nonmagnetic counterweight of the same mass and moment of inertia as the magnet is suspended from a lateral fiber identical to the one shown in Fig. 38.13. The small Alnico bar magnet hangs inside the two-compartment cell to which it would be stiffly coupled in the absence of a magnetic field produced by the astatizing coil. The stiffness and damping effects maintain the symmetrical situation between the coil and cell and prevent a coupling between the magnet and the earth. These effects are added by a

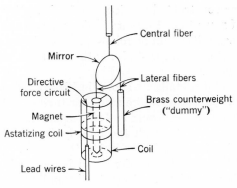

Fig. 38.13. Rankine balance (34). Reproduced by permission from the *Review of Scientific Instruments.*

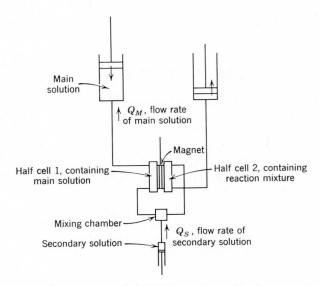

Fig. 38.14. Schematic of a flow experiment (34). Reproduced by permission from the *Review of Scientific Instruments.*

servomechanism in order to decrease the response time of the suspension. Several precautions are taken to discriminate against vibrational disturbances and accelerations of the earth. Displacements of the magnet as small as 10^{-8} cm. are detected by an optical system and recorded on a fast Esterline Angus recording milliammeter. The original article (34) must be consulted for a detailed analysis of the problems involved in the measure-

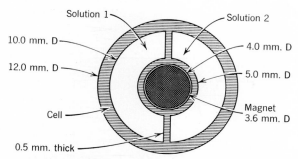

Fig. 38.15. Details of a magnetic susceptometer for a flow system (Brill *et al.* (34)). Reproduced by permission from the *Review of Scientific Instruments.*

ment of susceptibilities of a flow system and the steps taken to overcome major difficulties.

The instrument described can detect in one measurement a change in volume magnetic susceptibility of 5×10^{-12} e.m.u. The response time has been adjusted to a fraction of a second using an electronic servo system. The time of resolution of the flow system was found to be limited to five seconds by the flushing time of the cell. This low resolution of the flow system has been attributed to the sharpness of the corners of the cell and to their remoteness from the entrance and exit tubes. A feasibility is indicated of accomplishing (during a 1-second measurement) a time resolution of hundredths of a second and of detection of a change of 1.5×10^{-12} e.m.u. corresponding to the r.m.s. Brownian force arising from air resistance to the motion of the magnet. The method is indeed very promising for studying chemical and biochemical reactions.

4. Induction Methods

These may be classified into (*1*) direct-current, (*2*) alternating-current, and (*3*) radio-frequency methods. In all cases the principle is to measure the change in inductance of a solenoid with the introduction of a sample. These methods seem to have some advantages over the Gouy and Faraday methods in that they do not use bulky and expensive magnets and do not involve cumbersome procedures for measuring force. However, in the discussion to follow it will be seen that each method has limitations that restricts its use to highly specialized areas.

a. D.-C. Induction Method

Amongst the large number of induction methods a technique developed by Barnett (11) is simple and effective. The diagram is shown in Fig.

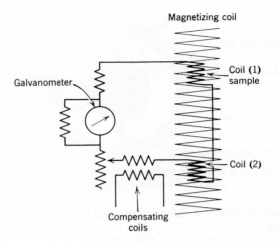

Fig. 38.16.   A simple, effective induction method, as described by S. J. Barnett.   Reproduced from Selwood, *Magnetochemistry* (193).

38.16.   A field of about 75 to 200 gauss is produced by the long magnetizing coil, which encloses identical secondary coils (1) and (2), connected in opposition.   The sample is quickly displaced from coil (1) to coil (2), which changes the mutual inductance of the two coils.   This is measured in terms of the deflection produced by the induced current in the shunted ballistic galvanometer.   An identical effect may be obtained by reversing the current in the magnetizing coil.   The deflection is proportional to the volume susceptibility of the material.

The method unfortunately requires samples as large as 15 cc. and detects volume susceptibilities of the order of 10^{-5}.   It is apparent that the susceptibilities of only those ferromagnetics that are easily saturable below 400 gauss can be determined by this method.   Selwood (195,195a) has developed a similar apparatus for thermomagnetic analysis.

b. A.-C. Induction Method

A technique has been developed by Broersma (38) especially for the measurement of diamagnetic susceptibilities.   In this, the effect of a sample is studied on the flux produced by a primary coil carrying an alternating current.   The induced e.m.f. is given by

$$V = -\,i\omega M_0 I(1 + f_0 K) - i\omega\phi_0 f_0 \kappa / 2\sqrt{2} \tag{3}$$

Here ϕ_0 is the flux produced by the current, I, of frequency ω; f_0 refers to

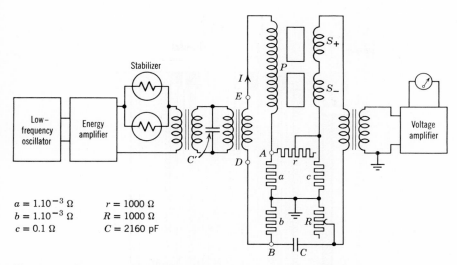

Fig. 38.17. Circuit diagram of Broersma's apparatus (38). Reproduced by permission from the *Review of Scientific Instruments*.

the maximum filling factor of the vessel, determined from its shape; and κ is the volume susceptibility. The coefficient of mutual inductance,

$$M_0 = \mu_0 n N_s S_s \tag{4}$$

and is determined by the physical characteristics of the coils. In equation (4), n = the number of primary turns per meter, N_s = the total number of turns in the secondary coil, S_s = the cross-sectional area, and μ_0 = the permeability in vacuum. M_0 is adjusted to 0.25 mh, f_0 is made 0.45, and a current I of 50 amp. is used. A description of the apparatus (Figs. 38.17 and 38.18) and its operation are quoted from Broersma's paper (38):

"The solenoid P of length 0.36 m. consists of 90 turns of capillary wire. The two secondary coils S_+ and S_- are composed of four sections of 350 turns each. By adjusting the number of turns, the voltage difference between the two coils can be reduced to 10^{-3} of the main voltage. A small piece of metal, M, placed in between the coils, reduces the voltage in phase with the primary current. A horizontal copper plate, outside the primary, cuts the induced voltage down to 10^{-5} of its original size.

"The circuit diagram [Fig. 38.17] shows that the primary current flows through two small resistances, a and b, of 10^{-3} ohm each. The voltages across these resistances are branched off by means of potentiometers. The upper part, containing a variable resistance r and a small resistance c, produces a voltage in phase with the primary current. The lower part consists of an air condenser C of about 2000 $\mu\mu$f. and a decade resistance R. The voltage across R:

$$V_{\text{comp}} = i\omega \cdot bRC \cdot I$$

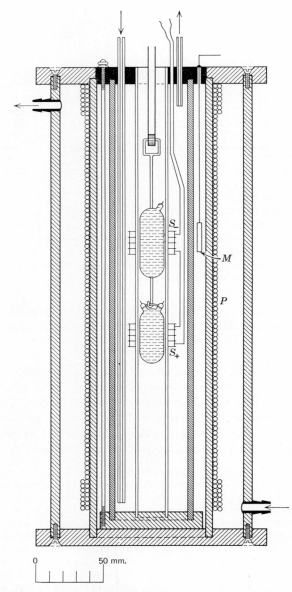

Fig. 38.18. Inductance apparatus of Broersma.   Drawing supplied by Prof. Broersma.

compensates for the e.m.f. in the secondary coil. Its value is correct within 10^{-5}, at least as concerns voltages of the same phase and for the circuit elements employed.

"Both the voltage given by [the equation above] and the first term [in equation (3)] are proportional to the current and the frequency. Therefore they cancel in the equilibrium condition:

$$M_+ - M_-(1 + f_{-\kappa}) = bC \cdot R$$

When a substance has to be measured, the lower cell is filled and placed in one of the coils. After R has been adjusted, the sample is brought into the second coil and another reading of R is taken. The difference of both settings then represents twice the effect of the sample. Hence the volume susceptibility can be measured as a change of R, as long as b and C remain constant and M and f reproduce. The upper container serves to compensate for a large part of the diamagnetic effect, of which the values do not vary strongly.

"As the factors b, R, C, M, and f for a spherical sample were known, an absolute measurement within 2 per cent could be performed. More precisely, the proportionality constant can be found from a calibration with a known substance. A great many results were obtained this way. Comparison with those found with a torsion balance showed agreement within 0.1 per cent. By employing relays, most of the measurement is made automatic, with the exception that every 5 seconds a galvanometer reading must be taken. After that, the sample moves and a part of R is short-circuited. R consists of two resistances in series, one to adjust the zero point and one to measure the effect. A measurement takes 8 minutes, filling included. Nine cc. of substance is required.

"Some of the auxiliary apparatus is indicated in [Fig. 38.17]. An RC generator supplies a signal of constant frequency and small distortion to the energy amplifier, which has an output of 200 v. The common point of the primary and secondary circuit has to be grounded. This necessitates the use of an input transformer which also reduces the effect of the amplifier noise. A twin-T network limits the band width to 1 c.p.s.

"A galvanometer, whose field coils are supplied with a.c., is used as null-instrument. The galvanometer gets a deflection when a phase relation between field and measuring current exists. The band width is 3 c.p.s.; the scale is linear. Two galvanometers are used: one in phase with e.m.f. and one 90 degrees out of phase. The phase is adjusted by utilizing the phase change, occurring in the filters employed, near their resonance point."

Broersma (38) has measured the susceptibility of a large number of organic compounds using the inductance apparatus. Average time for a single measurement was about 8 minutes; the torsion (Faraday) or Gouy methods required about 25 minutes. The method is particularly suited for measurements on diamagnetic materials. An obvious limitation is that it cannot be used for measurements over a range of temperature. Norder (159) has utilized features of Broersma's (38) and Selwood's (195) apparatus for measurement of magnetic susceptibility during adsorption and desorption processes.

Among other a.-c. induction methods, the following may be mentioned.

1. A mutual inductance bridge and a cryostat for low-temperature measurements of magnetic susceptibilities is described by Ericson, Roberts, and Dobbs (65) and by Fritz, Rao, and Seki (75a).

2. Pillinger and his co-workers (175) have developed an electronic a.-c. mutual inductance bridge (Cf. Jennings (104)) for measuring small susceptibilities at low temperatures on samples of about 1 cc. A precision of $\pm 2 \times 10^{-7}$ e.m.u./cm.^{3} is indicated.

5. Microvibrational Method

In this novel technique (237) a steady magnetic field is modulated by an a.-c. current and the periodic force acting on a sample placed in the field is translated into a periodic displacement of an elastic strip. The force is measured dynamically in terms of a compensating electrostatic force, an electronic circuit being used as a null detector. An accuracy of 10^{-4} dyne in the measurement of force is obtained. An attractive feature of the technique is that a small, inexpensive relay electromagnet is employed, which is energized by currents of about 0.1 amp. to give small fields of about 70 oersted. Sufficient space is available between the pole gap to accommodate large temperature-control devices. Measurements on a paramagnetic sample ($\sim$0.1 g.) are reported. The method provides a delicate test for the presence of ferromagnetic impurities.

6. Radio-Frequency Methods

During the last decade a few radio-frequency techniques were developed, notably by Effemy and his co-workers (64) in England and by A. Pacault and his co-workers (166) in France. Joussot-Dubien (107) has modified the latter technique for low-temperature (70°K.) measurement. The technique of the English workers will be reviewed here as the latter workers do not furnish any details of instrumentation and operation.

A substance of volume susceptibility κ, when placed in the tuning coil of a high-frequency critical oscillator (2.5 Mc./second) causes a change in its frequency, which is measured by the heterodyne beat method, that is, by beating the oscillator against another of fixed frequency. If the change in frequency is Δf at a frequency f, the cross-sectional area of the tuning coil is A, and that of the test substance A'; then

$$\kappa = \frac{1}{2\pi} \cdot \frac{\Delta f}{f} \cdot \frac{A}{A'}$$

Reference to the original paper should be made for details of circuitry and of the precautions to be taken in the operation.

The ultimate limitation on the sensitivity is imposed by the stability of the oscillator, which must be of the order of 1 in 10^8 c.p.s. This necessitates a control of the temperature (30°C.) within ± 0.001°C., both of the critical oscillator and of the sample. This makes it almost impossible to measure susceptibilities at different temperatures.

The apparatus is quite adequate for measurement of dia- and paramagnetic susceptibilities near room temperature, although it was designed especially for the changes in susceptibility of liquids of the order of about 0.0004×10^{-6}, caused by the generation *in situ* of short-lived (0.05 second) free radicals at very low concentrations ($\sim 0.005 M$). Considering the fact that some of the conventional magnetic methods do not permit a study of short-lived free radicals, the radio-frequency method is unique for work on free radicals. The authors (64) point out other possibilities of adapting the same technique for the precise measurements of dielectric constants, paramagnetic relaxation studies, and radio-frequency titrations.

7. Nuclear Magnetic Resonance Methods

a. The Broad-Line Technique

It is expected that the reader is familiar with the principles of nuclear magnetic resonance absorption in general and with the broad-line or low-resolution techniques in particular. For the sake of clarity, the phenomenon will be outlined briefly.

When the Larmor precessional frequency of a nucleus placed in a steady magnetic field is matched by or, so to speak, is brought into resonance with that of an applied rotating radio-frequency field, the nucleus will absorb magnetic energy. This will cause a change in the orientation of the nuclei relative to the steady field, that is, the nuclei in the lower energy state and originally parallel to the field will "flip" to an antiparallel position and vice versa. Although a stimulated emission of energy takes place in the opposite process, that is, in going from the high-energy, "antiparallel" state to the low-energy "parallel" state, a net absorption of energy occurs, because the population of the nuclei in the lower energy state is greater than the one in the higher energy state. The relation between the frequency ν of resonance and the steady applied field H is given by

$$\nu = \frac{\mu}{I} \cdot H$$

where μ and I are the spin magnetic moment and the spin angular momentum of the nucleus; the ratio μ/I is termed the gyromagnetic ratio. The nuclei that are commonly studied and are useful for susceptibility measure-

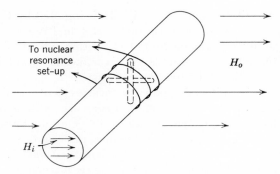

Fig. 38.19. A possible arrangement for probing the internal field for susceptibility measurements in Feher and Knight's broad-line N.M.R. method (69). Reproduced by permission from the *Review of Scientific Instruments*.

ments are the protons for which the gyromagnetic ratio is 2.67×10^4 second^{-1} gauss^{-1}.

The purpose of the broad-line nuclear magnetic resonance techniques is, in general, to study (*1*) the total absorption of energy by nuclei, surrounded by different magnetic environments inside bulk matter, and (*2*) to obtain useful information about their relative positions, the nature of molecular motion, etc.

In a technique developed by Feher and Knight (69) the mass susceptibility of a material is determined by probing into the internal field, which is easily performed by measuring the magnetic field or the frequency at which a resonance occurs of known nuclei placed inside the sample for this purpose. The term "electronic susceptibility" used by them to designate "magnetic susceptibility" arising from electrons should not be confused with "electric susceptibility," which arises in electric polarization, dielectric constants, etc.

The following theoretical considerations are employed in this method.

The internal field H_i of a sample subjected to an external magnetic field H_0 depends on its shape and susceptibility by the relation

$$H_i = H_0(1 - N_s \chi_s \cdot \rho)$$

where N_s is the demagnetizing shape factor for the sample, χ_s is its mass susceptibility, and ρ is its density. If, as shown in Fig. 38.19, two long, needle-shaped capillary tubes sealed with water inside are placed in a test tube containing the sample, so that one is parallel to the applied field and the other is at right angles, two resonance absorption lines at two different frequencies will be observed for the protons in water. This is true because the fields in the two cavities would be different. If f is the resonant frequency for protons corresponding to the field H_0, which may be found from a "blank" experiment, and Δf is the difference in the two frequencies observed under the conditions of the experiment, then

$$\chi_s = \frac{1}{\rho(1.9\pi)} \frac{\Delta f}{f}$$

The authors illustrated the technique with reference to manganese sesquioxide, which was powdered and placed in a test tube of about 20 mm. I.D. The capillaries were 18 mm. long and 1.5 mm. O.D. The resonance was observed with a Pound spectrometer (178). Δf was found to be 13.0 kc.

The method shows a promise for a general application and is quite sensitive; the sensitivity is determined by the strength of the applied field and its homogeneity. The use of commercial magnets giving fields of the order of 10^4 gauss with homogeneities over a cc. of 10^{-3} gauss give a sensitivity of 10^{-7} to 10^{-8} c.g.s. units in the measurement of mass susceptibility. This is better than most conventional methods. The packing of the powdered material apparently has no effect on the measurements and is decidedly a factor in favor of this method. The method is open to several modifications for measurement of susceptibilities over a range of temperature using small samples, etc. The authors suggest an alternate method using only one capillary tube that does not require the resolving of the two absorption lines to give the value of Δf, but instead measures the amplitude of the absorption line.

b. Spin Lattice Relaxation-Time Method for Paramagnetic Susceptibilities

A nucleus subjected to magnetic resonance, as outlined in the preceding section, experiences relaxation phenomena. During the absorption of energy the temperature of the spin system may be said to rise and eventually to come into a thermal equilibrium with its environment, loosely termed the "lattice." The rate at which this equilibrium is established is a measure of the spin lattice relaxation time. This may be defined in many other ways. Mathematically, if W is the mean of W_+ and W_-, the probabilities per unit time for an upward and a downward transition for a given nucleus by interaction with other molecular degrees of freedom, then the spin lattice relaxation time, T_1, is defined by

$$T_1 = \frac{1}{2W}$$

If n is the difference between the populations of n_+ and n_- the number of nuclei in the "parallel" and "antiparallel" states relative to the applied steady field H_0, $n_{eq.}$, the equilibrium value for excess number n, is given by

$$n_{eq.} = \frac{\mu H_0}{kT} (n_+ + n_-)$$

where μ is the magnetic moment of the nucleus; k is the Boltzmann constant, and T is the absolute temperature. The spin lattice relaxation time T_1 may now be defined by

$$n - n_{eq.} = (n - n_{eq.})_0 \, e^{t/T_1}$$

This may be verbally stated to mean that a lapse of time T_1 reduces the difference between the excess population n and its equilibrium by a factor of e.

The spin lattice relaxation time T_1 should be distinguished from another type of relaxation process involving the rate (T_2) at which magnetic energy is exchanged between two adjacent nuclei.

A number of workers (24,50) established that the spin lattice relaxation time T_1 for protons in water (which is about 3.6 seconds) is considerably reduced by the addition of paramagnetic salts. This is attributed to the diffusional Brownian motion of water molecules, which is altered by the magnetic effects of the paramagnetic ion. The dependence of T_1 on the effective magnetic moment is given by

$$\frac{1}{T_1} = \frac{4\pi^2 \gamma^2 \eta N_p \mu^2}{kT}$$

where N_p is the number of paramagnetic molecules or ions per cubic centimeter; η is the viscosity of the solution, which for all practical purposes, and especially for dilute solutions, may be taken to be equal to that of the solvent; γ is the magneto gyric ratio, which for protons is 2.67×10^4 sec.$^{-1}$ gauss^{-1}; k is the Boltzmann factor; and T is the absolute temperature.

A number of methods reviewed by Pople, Schneider, and Bernstein (177) are available for the measurement of T_1. It is possible in many cases to use a high-resolution nuclear magnetic resonance apparatus, or to build electronic instruments such as the "spino echo" apparatus (43) for the precise measurement of T_1.

c. Chemical-Shift Methods Using High-Resolution N.M.R. Apparatus

This method (66) is applicable to solutions of paramagnetic ions; less than 0.03 ml. of solution is required. It is based on the principle that the chemical shift, $\Delta H/H$, depends on the volume susceptibility of the solution, $\Delta H/H = {}^2/_3 \Delta\kappa$, where $\Delta\kappa$ is the change in volume susceptibility. For aqueous solutions of paramagnetic salts, an aqueous solution of 2% tertiary butyl alcohol of the same concentration is used as an external reference. From a measurement of the chemical shift the volume susceptibility of a paramagnetic solution can be calculated.

Another method based on that of Reilley and his co-workers has been developed recently (126a; references to this and relevant material are given in Reference 177). The sample is placed in an inner cylindrical tube and is surrounded by a reference standard, such as tetramethyl silane or benzene, in an outer tube. The resonance from the reference displays two maxima whose separation (measured in c.p.s.) is found to be a linear function of the volume susceptibility of the sample in the inner tube. Calibration is done with liquids of known susceptibility. In the author's opinion, this and the Evans method (66) have many limitations and do not seem to have the reliability and accuracy that are provided by the classical methods.

Frei and Bernstein (74a) have also described a method that takes advantage of the differences in chemical shifts arising from differences in the shape factors for a sphere and a cylinder. A reference liquid such as water is enclosed in a small glass bulb and separately in a small capillary tube. These are placed in a conventional spinning N.M.R. sample tube containing the sample. The volume susceptibility of the sample is calculated from the following equation:

$$\delta \text{ cyl (ref)} - \delta \text{ sph (ref)} = [g \text{ cyl} - g \text{ sph}][\kappa \text{ ref} - \kappa \text{ sample}]$$

where δ is the chemical shift in parts per million, κ is the volume susceptibility in c.g.s. units, and g is the geometric shape factor.

$$[g \text{ cyl} - g \text{ sph}] = [2\pi/3 - 0]$$

For ideal geometry, $2\pi/3 = 2.094$; however, using several compounds of known susceptibility and making appropriate plots, a value of 2.058 was obtained for a particular setup. Frei and Bernstein claim that the accuracy approaches that of classical methods and can be obtained readily with any N.M.R. spectrometer of sufficient resolution and stability.

This seems to be quite a promising method among the several N.M.R. techniques that are now available. A modification with several advantages has been developed by this author (149).

8. Miscellaneous Techniques

During the past few years entirely novel techniques, some using a combination of the principles outlined in Sections II-F and II-G, have been developed to meet special requirements.

An ingeneous method is available (79) for studying biological and chemical processes that occur within small particles 1 to 100 μ in diameter. The force on a single diamagnetic 10-μ particle can be made to be of the order of 10^{-9} dynes in an inhomogeneous field. Forces of this nature are measured in terms of the velocity that the particle assumes in hydrodynamic motion, depending on the viscosity of the medium. A microscope is used for measuring the velocity (of the order of 1 μ/second) in an inhomogeneous field of a particle suspended in a medium. Susceptibility differences as small as 0.04×10^{-6} have been measured for blood cells in salt solutions and also for polystyrene latex. In the writer's opinion this represents a significant advance in micro techniques. Another method (238) uses a torsion balance with very delicate quartz suspension fibers (0.5 μ diameter) for measuring susceptibilities of particles about 1 μ in diameter. A stereo microscope is used to observe the displacement of the sample in a pulsed field of 2000 oersted in $1/_{60}$ second. Appreciable motion of the suspension system is avoided during this small duration.

Another unique method also uses high pulsed fields (207). The magnetic force on the sample is converted to a stress wave through the apparatus and excites a voltage on two piezoelectric crystals, which is then measured.

Measurements of carrier susceptibility of semiconductors by means of a torsion pendulum balance (77) has been accomplished with an accuracy of 0.03%. Mercier and Bovet (138) employ a torsion pendulum with sample in two symmetrical cavities. The period of the pendulum is determined very precisely. For small amplitudes of oscillation in the magnetic field this period is found to be proportional to the magnetic susceptibility.

In a bubble method (136), which is somewhat related to the Quincke method, the force due to a field on an air bubble surrounded by a liquid is measured. This force is equal and opposite to that which would be experienced by the same volume of liquid when surrounded by air and kept in the same region of the field. The force is measured by tilting the "spirit level" type tube enclosing the bubble; the tilt is controlled by a micrometer and is adjusted to bring the bubble in its original position in the absence of the field. The susceptibility of air and density of air have been assumed to be negligible in the calculations of susceptibilities of some liquids; this is not always true. Several refinements in calculations and in the technique will have to be made to obtain better precision and accuracy than that reported.

A ballistic circuit (158) for the measurement of magnetic susceptibilities below 1°K. and a magnetic analog of a Wheatstone bridge (98) for susceptibility measurements have been reported. This bridge is inexpensive, portable, easy to operate, and quite unique in its construction. It appears to be capable of measuring diamagnetic susceptibilities as small as 10^{-7} c.g.s. unit. A transistorized device using two coils in a differential circuit (88) has been described for geological use. Measurements on detached samples or outcrops of rocks are possible on the field. A special apparatus for measurements on glasses up to their annealing temperature has been constructed (9). A magnetic torsion balance is described by Korovkin et al. (117).

Last of all, mention may be made of magnetometers, which generally seem to escape the attention of magnetochemists. Some of them can be adapted readily for measurement of dia-, para-, and ferromagnetic susceptibilities, although some writers design them for specific uses such as measuring the magnetization of ferromagnetics over a range of temperature.

In some magnetometers (5) the torque is balanced by means of an electric current passing through the coil of a moving-coil meter movement that replaces the normal torsion-head and wire; in others (2) a transducer is employed to convert the torque into a measurable electric current.

A number of magnetometers employ some sort of a vibration of the sample in the magnetic field (74,128). An elaborate setup is described by Foner (74), who lists references to several other vibration techniques. In his apparatus changes as small as 10^{-5} to 10^{-6} e.m.u. have been detected, and a stability of 1 part in 10^4 is attained. It minimizes or eliminates errors in other methods and is useful for measuring magnetic susceptibility as a function of temperature, magnetic field, and crystallographic orientation.

Most magnetometers are useful for thermomagnetic analysis, which has been extensively studied by Selwood and his co-workers (194–196). The construction of an apparatus for studying magnetizations between 2 and 1200°K. is given by Rimet (185). A special null-method astatic magnetometer for geomagnetic measurements also has been described (7).

III. EXPERIMENTAL SETUP

A. GENERAL REQUIREMENTS OF LABORATORY

The Gouy and Faraday techniques, which depend on an accurate measurements of change in weight, naturally require a location free from vibrations of the floor. Usually any location in a basement, away from elevators and stairways, is preferred. In the author's laboratory, a concrete pillar resting on a solid foundation was available. This has been very advantageous in supporting a "single-pan" microbalance for refined measurements of diamagnetic susceptibilities with the Gouy technique. Many balance manufacturers (Mettler, Sartorius, etc.) provide vibration-proof tables and designs for masonry supports. These are quite adequate for most purposes.

The location also should be free from electrical and magnetic disturbances arising in the vicinity of electric generators, air compressors, machine shops, and laboratories using high-voltage equipment.

B. APPARATUS ASSEMBLED IN THE LABORATORY

1. Commercially Available Components

Since preassembled equipment for measuring magnetic susceptibilities is not commercially available,* it becomes necessary to construct such equipment either with readily available or with home-made units.

a. MAGNETS AND DIRECT-CURRENT SOURCES

The introduction of nuclear magnetic resonance techniques during the last decade has greatly improved the availability of permanent and electromagnets with interchangeable pole faces and variable pole gaps. Some of the manufacturers of electromagnets (*1* to *6*) and of permanent magnets (*7* and *8*) are: (*1*) Harvey Wells, Framingham, Massachusetts; (*2*) Varian Associates, Palo Alto, California; (*3*) Pacific Electric Motor Co., Oakland 21, California; (*4*) Newport Instruments Ltd., Newport-Pagnell, Buckinghamshire, England; (*5*) Alpha Scientific Laboratories, Berkeley, California; (*6*) Universal Scientific Co., Parekh St., Bombay 4, India; (*7*) Indiana Steel Co., Valparaiso, Indiana; and (*8*) Crucible Steel Company of America, Pittsburgh, Pennsylvania.

When cost is not a problem it is indeed advantageous to buy a commercial magnet and a matching d.-c. power supply. However, it is possible to build at low cost electromagnets to give moderate fields of about 5000 oersted. A number of publications (13,26) describe the construction of such magnets. It is even possible to convert a large transformer into a workable electromagnet merely by cutting a pole gap in the core of the transformer at a suitable place. One such design is described by Broersma (36).

A d.-c. supply obtained from a generator may be used for energizing electromagnets. However, the fluctuations in the average supply are

---

* An exception to this appears to be an apparatus based on an inductance method (166), which is reported to be available in France.

usually so large that they ruin the precision of measurements. Devices for compensating such variations are described, but are cumbersome to build. A battery supply always is advantageous, but this requires constant maintenance and limits prolonged use of the batteries.

Several circuits for stabilized power supplies have been described in the literature (3,14,23). A circuit especially adaptable for energizing an electromagnet is described by Figgis and Nyholm (71). Here again, if the cost of such equipment is not of consequence, it is preferable to buy matching regulated power supplies from commercial sources (Varian Associates,

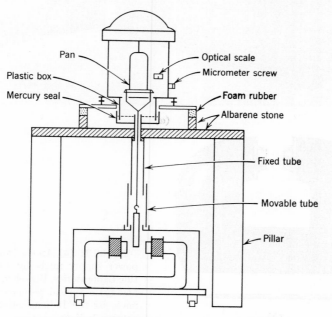

Fig. 38.20. Construction details of author's Gouy balance.

Alpha Scientific Instruments Co., etc.). These units provide regulation of current to within 1 part in 10^4 or better, which is more than adequate for the magnetic susceptibility measurements. It should be noted that regulation of current may not necessarily regulate the field in the pole gap. Devices for regulation of the magnetic field itself are described in the literature (13,26) and should be adopted, particularly with home-made electromagnets. Fortunately, the special construction designs used by manufacturers of electromagnets usually provide a regulation of magnetic field that is quite adequate for magnetic susceptibility measurements.

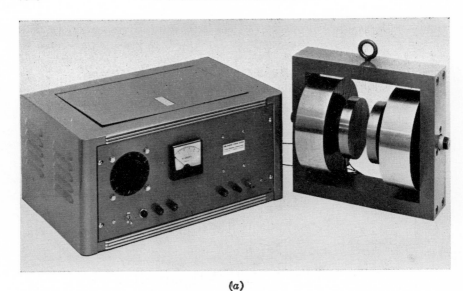

(a)

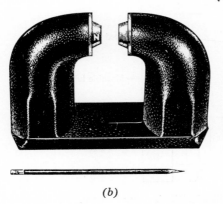

(b)

Fig. 38.21. (a) An electromagnet and power supply made by Alpha Scientific Laboratories, Berkeley, California, and (b) a typical permanent magnet, made by the Indiana Steel Co., Valparaiso, Indiana.

A set up, shown in Figs. 38.20 and 38.27, has been in satisfactory operation in the author's laboratory for some time. This arrangement provides the use of one electromagnet mounted on a movable platform and equipped with interchangeable pole caps for the Gouy, Faraday, etc., techniques. It has proved useful for other magnetic work, such as magnetic anisotropy and magnetic resonance studies. Fig. 38.21a shows a relatively inexpensive electromagnet and its power supply, suitable for susceptibility work.

Permanent magnets constructed from alloys such as Alnico, Permendur, etc., which have a high remanence and high coercive power, provide fields as high as 10,000 oersted in a pole gap of 2.5 cm. with tapered poles about 5 cm. in diameter. Fig. 38.21*b* shows a typical permanent magnet. Small permanent magnets giving fields of about 2000 oersted may be retrieved from "war surplus" magnetron magnets. The cost of a permanent magnet not involving an exceptional degree of field homogeneity (required for nuclear magnetic resonance work, etc.), is usually less than the combined cost of a comparable electromagnet and a stabilized source for direct current required for energizing it. This and the availability of a steady field over long periods constitute major advantages of a permanent magnet. On the other hand, some mechanical device for moving the permanent magnet over a sufficient distance is required to permit a measurement of force on the sample with and without the field. Permanent magnets have a disadvantage in that they cannot be used for studying the susceptibility as a function of field strength, which is useful for detecting the presence of ferromagnetic impurities in the sample. However, the field of a permanent magnet can be varied, within moderate limits, by passing a current through coils surrounding the magnet. Some variation in the field also may be obtained through the use of magnetic shunts. The usefulness of permanent magnets lies especially in studies of changes in magnetic susceptibility occurring as a function of time in certain photochemical and polymerization processes, and those involving free radicals, etc.

The choice of field strength depends on the size of the sample, the dimensions of the sample tube, and on the sensitivity of the technique for measuring force. Large forces obtained at higher fields can be measured with more precision than small forces; as such no upper limit may be placed on the magnetic field. However, taking into consideration even the most sensitive technique of measuring force, a lower limit at about 2000 oersted is desirable for routine work.

b. Balances, Automatic Recording Devices, and Helical Springs

A number of analytical, semimicro, and micro balances in the single- and double-pan styles are manufactured by Ainsworth and Sons, Cahn Instrument Co., Fisher Scientific Co., and Testing Equipment Co. in the U.S.A.; by E. Mettler in Switzerland; by Sartorius Werke A. G. in Germany; and by Stanton Instruments in England. A balance using a double-cantilevered beam also is made by the Testing Equipment Co. These manufacturers and several others not listed here also make equipment for the automatic recording of weight, and many provide a suspension for attaching to the bottom of the pan that is useful for the Gouy method (Fig. 38.20). The criteria for the choice of a balance will be discussed later.

For studying a continuous change in magnetic susceptibility as a function of temperature or the changes that may occur as a function of time in chemical and physical processes, it is convenient to have an automatic recording device. Robertson and Selwood (186; cf. 195) describe equipment for thermomagnetic analysis, especially of ferromagnetics. It is generally possible to convert any balance, such as the spring, the double-pan, or the single-pan devices, to automatic recording without too much difficulty. Gordon and Campbell (83) present an excellent review of a number of ingenious methods adapted by investigators and manufacturers for this purpose. These may be divided into (1) the deflection and (2) the null methods. In the first category, the deflection of the beam or of a pointer attached to the spring is proportional to the change in weight and is converted into a signal, which is then recorded. In the null method the force required to restore the balance to equilibrium is converted into an appropriate signal and then recorded. Considering the magnitude of changes in weight (which can be controlled by adjusting the magnetic field) in the Faraday and Gouy techniques, the deflection methods seem to be quite adequate and easier to adapt for automatic recording than the null methods.

In the phototube method the deflection controls the amount of light entering the photocell; the proportional current generated is then amplified and recorded on a potentiometric-type recorder, such as the Brown, Varian, Leeds and Northrup, etc. A Sartorius phototube device has been successfully adapted by the author (149) for measuring and recording the deflections in the Gouy- and Faraday-type balances. In the electronic methods, the deflection is made to cause a proportionate change in the capacitance of the parallel-plate condenser or in the mutual inductance of a coil-plate or coil-coil assembly. These changes are measured with a suitable capacitance or inductance bridge and are converted to a d.-c. signal, which is then displayed on a recorder through conventional electronic circuitry. Methods using novel techniques such as a strain gauge (12) also have been used. However, incorporating a differential transformer or a variable permeance transducer in a balance has a number of advantages (Cf. 83). These are commercially available, are inexpensive, and their connection to the recorder does not involve complicated circuitry.

Automatic recording of changes in torsion is somewhat complicated as compared with other techniques of measuring force. Nevertheless this has been accomplished by many workers (cf. Reference 83) and by the Sharples Corporation, Bridgeport, Pennsylvania.

Vacuum microbalance techniques have been reviewed by Katz (108), and may be used in magnetic balances. Quartz helical springs for such work are obtainable from the Worden Laboratories, Houston, Texas, and Microchemical Specialities, Berkeley, California.

2. Temperature Control

Production of temperatures above room temperature is obtained easily with an electric cylindrical furnace, the coils of which are wound noninductively to prevent stray magnetic fields. The temperature regulation is accomplished simply with adequate relay mechanisms or by motor-driven rheostats to within 0.10°C. of the desired temperature.

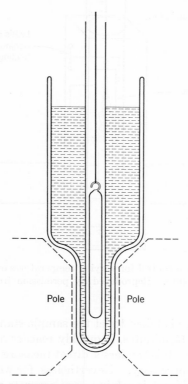

Fig. 38.22. Typical Dewar flask for low-temperature susceptibility measurements. Reproduced from Selwood (193).

In the low region, temperatures provided by freezing mixtures, low-boiling liquids, and liquefied gases (60,191) also are easily obtained, using a setup as shown in Fig. 38.22. The temperature of the sample remains constant as long as the freezing agent is maintained at an adequate level above the sample tube.

It is easier to measure the temperature of the atmosphere immediately surrounding the sample tube with a thermocouple than of the sample it-

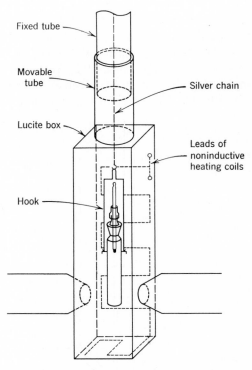

Fixed tube

Movable tube

Silver chain

Lucite box

Leads of noninductive heating coils

Hook

Fig. 38.23. Temperature control for varying temperatures over a narrow range, used with author's Gouy balance. Reproduced by permission from *Analytical Chemistry* (144).

self. However, if care is taken to let the sample stand at a fixed temperature for about 10 to 15 minutes, it quickly reaches a thermal equilibrium with its surroundings; this renders a direct measurement of the temperature of the sample unnecessary. Nevertheless, for work in a narrow range such as −10 to 60°C., not involving very accurate measurement of temperature, a small thermometer dipped right into the sample has been found to be useful in the author's laboratory. The details of this arrangement are shown in Fig. 38.23. This eliminates the somewhat cumbersome use of a thermocouple and potentiometer, normally required for large temperature ranges and more accurate measurement. This set up was used by the author with a Gouy balance in studying the changes in the magnetic susceptibility, as a function of acidity and temperature, of aqueous solutions containing paramagnetic ions. The tube containing the sample was weighed at room temperature and the weights used were left unchanged.

It was removed and cooled to a desired temperature in an air jacket, using an adequate freezing agent. Any condensed moisture was wiped off the tube, which was then suspended inside the plastic box and weighed quickly with the magnetic field off and on. The preliminary adjustment of weight helped to make these weighings quickly within a few seconds, during which the temperature change was found to be less than 1°C. Similar procedure was followed at high temperatures, which were obtained by heating the air inside the plastic box with electric coils that were wound noninductively on an asbestos board and placed at the bottom and back of the box, as shown in Fig. 38.23. The current was controlled by a Variac (variable transformer). An advantage of this method, which is restricted to the temperature range −10 to 60°C., is that it did not become necessary to widen the pole gap to accommodate a heating furnace, which would have weakened the magnetic field and affected the accuracy of susceptibility measurements.

The production of any intermediate temperature not furnished by a freezing agent calls for the construction of special cryostats. The following general principles have been used in their construction. A few references to their typical applications are cited as examples.

1. The sample is surrounded by a double-walled metal or glass jacket through which a liquid at the desired temperature is circulated. This provides only a limited temperature range. Low-temperature baths (−35 to about 65°C., with a regulation of 0.01°C.) are made by the Wilkens-Anderson Co., Chicago 51, Illinois.

2. A metal block (copper or lead) surrounding the sample is cooled by a cooling agent (e.g., liquid nitrogen) and simultaneously heated by electricity. Regulation of heat gives a desired temperature between that of the coolant and room temperature. A cryostat of this type was described by the author (147) for nuclear magnetic resonance studies. It can be used without the r.-f. coil for the Faraday magnetic susceptibility technique since the temperature gradient over a sample height of about 2 cm. is quite negligible.

3. A coolant such as liquid air is injected into a spiral opening in the metal block; the rate of flow controls the temperature. More sensitive control may be obtained by passing oxygen through a liquid nitrogen condenser and allowing the liquified oxygen to drip into the metal block. The rate of oxygen gas passing through the condenser controls the rate of cooling (Cf. Selwood (193)).

4. Liquid air or nitrogen is boiled under the sample so that cold vapors rise over a jacket surrounding the sample. Fig. 38.24 shows this arrangement (Cf. Selwood (193); Bose (30)).

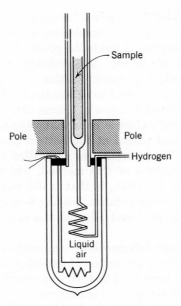

Fig. 38.24. Apparatus for automatically controlled low-temperature measurements. Reproduced from Selwood (193).

5. The sample is surrounded by a double-walled jacket, which, in turn, is surrounded by a coolant (liquid nitrogen). The space inside the jacket is filled with helium gas, which acts as a heat transfer medium. Regulation of the pressure of helium gas by a vacuum pump (and some heating) controls the temperature (203). Figgis and Nyholm (71) use air for heat transfer. Other descriptions of cryostats adaptable for susceptibility work may be found in books on experimental techniques (60).

6. For work in the temperature region furnished by liquid helium, principles *1* to *4* are difficult to adapt, as liquid helium boils off very quickly (the specific heat is only 1.25 cal./g.). Hence, a new conduction technique* originally developed for nuclear and electron magnetic resonance experiments may be used for magnetic susceptibility measurements. One end of a copper tube is immersed to variable extents in liquid helium and thus produces different temperatures at the other end, inside of which a small sample is placed. This limits the over-all volume over which a uniform temperature can be maintained; the technique appears promising for

* Such cryostats presumably are in operation in the Physics Department and Gordon McKay Laboratories of Harvard University. Any description of this and similar cryostats has escaped this author's attention.

the Faraday-type magnetic balance, which uses samples of very small volume.

In general, the production and control of temperatures between $-190°C$. and room temperature is easily accomplished with liquid nitrogen alone, and several references to such cryostats other than the ones cited above are to be found in the literature (18). It may be noted that the use of liquid hydrogen for obtaining temperatures down to $-163°C$. is rather hazardous, and it cannot be merely substituted in place of liquid nitrogen without introducing adequate safety precautions in the nitrogen cryostat. A design using liquid hydrogen originally developed by Aston and his co-workers (6) for N.M.R. experiments appears to be adaptable for the Gouy and Faraday techniques. Scott (192) describes an elaborate cryostat that uses liquid helium, hydrogen, and nitrogen to give temperatures from 1.6 to 300°K. It is particularly useful for the Faraday technique. Another cryostat (72) originally developed for EPR work may also be used conveniently for temperatures between 4.2 and 77°K.

The choice of a design for a cryostat depends on the specific nature of the magnetic study, the temperature range, the precision of temperature regulation, and, finally, the particular technique used for the susceptibility measurement. One important criterion for techniques using a magnet is to make the cryostat as narrow as possible so that a small pole gap for obtaining high magnetic fields can still be used. A Dewar flask with an oval cross section to fit into narrow pole gaps is described by Broersma (37). A helium Dewar with incorporated magnet pole tips is described by Edwards, Terhue, and Lazazzera (63).

3. Requirements of Field Strength and Sensitivity of Balance

Paramagnetic susceptibilities that are very large in comparison with the diamagnetic produce appreciable changes in the weight of a sample on application of a magnetic field. Changes produced by paramagnetic samples of a few tenths of a gram placed in a field as low as 3000 oersted may be measured with an analytical balance with a sensitivity of $±0.2$ mg. However, accurate measurements of diamagnetic susceptibilities on samples of the same size call for a better accuracy ($±0.01$ mg.) in weighing and the use of higher fields. A happy compromise for measurements on both para- and diamagnetics in fields ranging from 3000 to 7000 oersted is to be found in the use of a semimicro balance with a loading capacity around 50 g. or better. The changes in weight may be observed conveniently merely by adjusting the rider or the chain, with the conventional double-pan balances, or the optical (deflection) scale of the single-pan balance.

In studying a variation in the magnetic susceptibility of a system it is advantageous to restrict the changes in weight to the range provided by the rider, the chain, or the optical scale. This is readily done by adjusting the field strength of the electromagnet.

The single-pan balance has a number of advantages over the conventional double-pan type, and was first adapted for the Gouy technique by the author (146) in 1950. Many single-pan models are equipped with a good damping system (usually air), which facilitates a quick weighing within a few seconds. The enclosed gram and centigram weights are handled by a remote control and thus are protected. An optical deflection system is employed to read the milligrams; the fraction up to one hundredth or better of a milligram may be read off from an external vernier arrangement in the semimicro and micro versions of the single-pan balance. The built-in optical deflection scale incorporates the advantages of the external microscope method of observing deflections used in the sensitive Theorell (220, 220b) and Michaelis (139) modifications of the Gouy technique. Apart from these mechanical merits, some single-pan balances (e.g., the Mettler) facilitate weighing under conditions of constant load and hence, of constant sensitivity. This feature appears desirable if a necessity arises to study samples varying in sizes from a few tenths of a gram to several grams.

C. GOUY MAGNETIC BALANCE AND ITS MODIFICATIONS

Several modifications of this balance have recently appeared in the literature; a review of important modifications prior to 1956 is presented by Selwood (193). The novelty in these modifications lies partly in the use of a permanent magnet in place of an electromagnet and in the techniques used for suspending the sample and for measuring forces. Hilal and Fredericks (97), for instance, use a method in which changes of the order of a few milligrams are measured with a magnet–solenoid arrangement to a high degree of accuracy not obtainable by the conventional method of swings. The magnet–solenoid method is to be found in some recording balances made by the A.R.A.M. Company in Lyon, France, and by the Fisher Scientific Company, and the Niagara Electron Labs. in the U.S.A. There is indeed no limit to implementing ingenious devices in an ordinary or a susceptibility balance to meet special requirements.

A unique Gouy type recording apparatus using an Ainsworth model UMD Chainomatic balance has been reported recently (46). An unusual feature is the addition of a quartz spring that is always kept under tension. The resulting change in transducer output is amplified with a Sanborn Carrier preamplifier. A basic advantage of the Ainsworth balance is that it permits a complete evacuation of the balance and the weighing chamber and thus minimizes errors due to the buoyancy effects. In the particular Gouy balance setup it has a further advantage in that a correction is avoided for κ_0, the volume susceptibility of the medium surrounding the sample appearing in the following expression, force $= g\Delta w = \frac{1}{2}AH^2(\kappa-\kappa_0)$, where Δw is the change in weight of sample on applying the magnetic field H, κ is the volume susceptibility of the sample under investigation, and A is its cross-sectional area.

A Gouy balance suitable for studies of adsorption of (paramagnetic) gases on adsorbents such as silica, alumina, etc., based on the work of Juza and his co-workers, is described in the literature (193). The method may be regarded as a differential method in that the force of attraction on the sample (A) is counterpoised by a weight (B) similar in size to the sample. Any adsorption in chamber (A) naturally changes the susceptibility of the sample and produces a change in weight in the magnetic field, which may be applied temporarily. The change in weight itself may be followed by using the electromagnetic force device coupled to the (magnetic) counterpoise in chamber (B).

Other modifications developed by Theorell (220a,221b), shown in Fig. 38.25, are found to be excellent for studying reactions involving changes in paramagnetism and dimagnetism. These can be followed easily, as they produce significant changes in magnetic forces acting on the sample, which is suspended horizontally from a bifilar suspension. However, with sufficient sensitivity changes in diamagnetism, for example, those resulting during polymerization of styrene, etc., also could be followed. A high-field electromagnet is employed for convenience and increased sensitivity. The horizontal sealed tube holds the reaction mixture. The changes in susceptibility are followed by observing the displacement of the tube with a micrometer microscope. Selwood (193) calibrated a similar apparatus by filling the tube with a dichromate solution that was gradually undergoing reduction with sucrose. This involved a change from the diamagnetic $Cr_2O_7^-$ to the paramagnetic Cr^{+3} ion. A modification by Howland and Calvin (100) for work on microgram quantities is shown in Fig. 38.26.

Instrumentation of a Gouy balance with temperature control is reported by Earnshaw (61) and others (200).

Servomechanical networks have been also adapted by Hedgcock and Muir (93) for the Gouy method, which can be used in conjunction with the Faraday method also. In the instrument described, a sensitive electrodynamic balance is operated as a null instrument by allowing it to form part of a servomechanical network. The feedback system provides a stiffness of balance movement of 8×10^4 dynes/degree deflection. The sensitivity is such that changes of 10^{-9} e.m.u./g. are detected in the susceptibility of

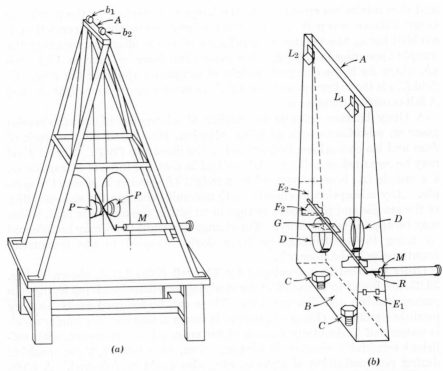

Fig. 38.25. Theorell's (220) magnetic deflection balance (*a*), and details (*b*). Reproduced by permission from *Arkiv för Kemi, Mineralogi och Geologi*.

large metallic samples having electrical resistances less than 10^{-9} ohm/cm. The effects of eddy currents in such samples induced by the magnetic field are eliminated. The balance appears to be versatile for measurement on other samples and at different temperatures. Henry and Rogers (95) described a special Gouy balance for short-length specimens and discuss the errors involved. A simple Gouy balance for lecture demonstration and student use utilizes a Westphal balance (131).

D. TYPICAL ASSEMBLY OF THE GOUY BALANCE

In the author's laboratory a Gouy magnetic balance, shown in Fig. 38.27, was assembled from the following units in order to obtain simplicity in its operation and to permit a maximum flexibility in its application to a variety of research problems. Fig. 38.20 shows the arrangement used for enclosing the suspension system to prevent the effects of drafts of air.

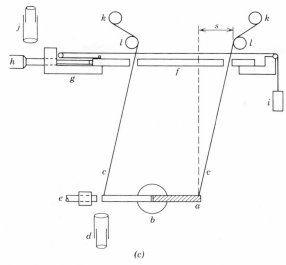

(c)

Fig. 38.25c. Schematic drawing of another sensitive balance, which was made by Theo-rell and Ehrenberg (221b). This view, illustrating the main principles of the apparatus, is in the direction of the central magnetic field, although the front magnet pole is not shown. Key: the tube (a) between the poles (b) is suspended by two thin wires (c). Its position relative to the fixed screw (e) is observed in the microscope (d). The upper ends of the wires are kept in position by a score in each of the cylinders (l) and are fixed on the unroll-ing cylinders (k). These four cylinders are mounted on the slide (f), whose movement in the guide (g) is controlled by the micrometer (h). The slide is maintained firmly against the head of the micrometer by the lead weight (i). The displacement (s) of the slide is read on the micrometer with the aid of a reading glass (j). Reproduced by permission from Arkiv för Fysik.

1. A Newport type-A electromagnet with adjustable pole gap and inter-changeable straight and Faraday pole caps, giving a maximum field of about 13,000 oersted in a 1.5-cm. gap (approximate cost $1200).

2. A matched Newport type-B d.-c. power supply operating off a 110 v. 60-cycle main, giving a maximum current of 8 amp. at 100 v. and a regulation of 1 part in 10^4 (approximate cost $1700).

3. A Sartorius semimicro balance, with a sensitivity of 0.02 mg. under normal working conditions. Range on optical scale 100 mg.; loading capacity 100 g. (approximate cost $1000). A thin silver chain is attached to the bottom of the pan.

4. A Sartorius photoelectric recording device (approximate cost $600) and a Leeds and Northrup recorder ($800). The recording device is best used in conjunction with a Sartorius analytical balance.

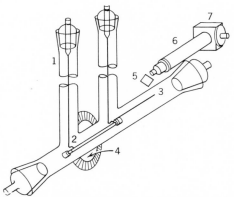

Fig. 38.26. Apparatus used by Howland and Calvin (100) to measure the magnetic susceptibility of aqueous ions of the actinide elements.   Key: *1*, 140-cm. glass suspension fiber; *2*, thin-wall capillary with control partition; *3*, pointer; *4*, magnet pole face (only one shown); *5*, mirror; *6*, microscope; and *7*, filar micrometer.   Reproduced by permission from *Nucleonics* (53).

Fig. 38.27. Recording Gouy magnetic balance in author's laboratory.   Reproduced by permission from *Analytical Chemistry* (144).

5. A home-made cryostat for regulating temperatures from −190 to 200°C. The arrangement facilitates displacement of air by nitrogen gas, whenever required for accurate work (148).

1. Preparation of Sample for the Gouy Method

a. METALLIC AND CERTAIN NONMETALLIC SOLIDS

Samples of metals, alloys, glass, polymers, etc., may be obtained in narrow, long, uniform cylinders. The length should be such that the suspended end of the rod would lie in a field that is negligible in comparison with the field applied at the lower end. Usually a length between 10 and 15 cm. is adequate. The diameter must be such that the rod will move freely inside the cryostat, fitted into the smallest possible gap. Rods, a few millimeters in diameter, are suitable for work over a wide temperature range; however, rods 2 to 3 cm. in diameter may be used with advantage for measurement at room temperature by suspending them directly in the pole gap.

For most purposes, a sample tube made of Pyrex glass is quite adequate. For very accurate measurements allowance must be made for the temperature dependence of its small paramagnetic susceptibility (92), which arises from certain impurities. The sample containers may be made from rather thin-walled tubing of uniform diameter (available from the Wilmad Glass Co., Buena, New Jersey) with hooks for suspension. A stirrup made of Pyrex glass, copper, or silver wire may be used for supporting the tube.

The general considerations for determining the size of the tube are the same as mentioned previously for rods of metals, alloys, etc. An etched mark may be made at the top of the tube, where the field is known to be negligible. This fixes the volume of the sample and of the reference to be used. For measurements on powdered solids a tube about 5 mm. in diameter and 15 cm. long is convenient; for liquids and solutions a tube of the same length and about 2 cm. in diameter is suitable for work of moderate precision.

For accurate work on solutions a semidifferential method is used (cf. Reference 139). This employs a tube partitioned at the center, where the field is applied (Fig. 38.28). The pure solvent is sealed in the bottom part with a reservoir half filled. This allows for the expansion of the solvent at higher temperatures and prevents the formation of a bubble of vapor at the septum on cooling. The solution is placed in the upper compartment. It is easy to see that the magnetic pull on the two ends of this compensation tube will be in opposite directions and will be almost cancelled if the sus-

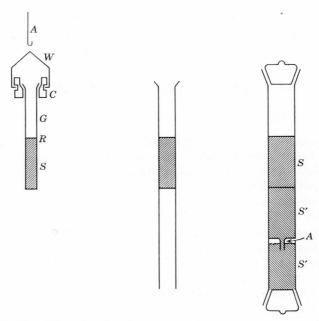

Fig. 38.28. Gouy tubes of various types.

Simple Gouy tube (*left*): *A*, suspension from balance; *W*, wire loop; *C*, collar; *G*, Gouy tube; *R*, reference mark; and *S*, specimen.

Double-ended Gouy tube (*center*) to eliminate δ.

Double-ended Gouy tube (*right*) to eliminate δ and solvent correction: *S*, solution; *S'*, solvent; and *A*, air bubble to permit expansion and contraction of solvent. Reproduced from Lewis and Wilkins, *Modern Coordination Chemistry*.

ceptibility of the contents in the two compartments is the same. Thus by keeping the solvent unchanged in the lower compartment and by varying the concentration of the solution in the upper compartment, changes in weight corresponding to a difference in the susceptibilities of the two is obtained. This difference may be taken to correspond to the susceptibility of the solute under conditions of magnetic dilution and in the absence of interactions between the solute and the solvent.

The limits of error in the differential method of evaluating the susceptibility of a solute are considerably lower than in the method employing separate measurements on the solvent and solution.

b. Powdered Solids

Some comments on the size of powdered solids, etc., appear on p. 1786. Finely ground powder should be used so that a maximum filling is obtained in a fixed volume. Experiments show that under normal conditions of working a loose packing or a tight ramming of the powder in the tube does not appreciably affect the susceptibility measurements, provided corrections, to be described below, are made for the presence of air pockets. However, the ramming method may be preferred to the first as it facilitates a maximum filling and minimizes the chances of preferential orientation of the particles in the field. In this method, small and nearly equal portions of the powder are introduced in the tube and are packed by pounding, after each addition, with the flat end of a ramrod that snugly fits the tube. By equalizing the portions and the number of strokes used in pounding, it is generally possible to obtain uniform packings and a reproducibility of weight to within 1%.

c. Liquids and Solutions

These do not pose the problems of packing and may be used in conjunction with sample containers described previously. The sample tube may be sealed in the case of very volatile liquids. A dry box with an atmosphere of nitrogen or special reservoirs and burets in which the flow of liquids is controlled by the pressure of nitrogen gas may be used for filling easily oxidizable samples, such as the solutions of Cr(II) and Fe(II). Sealing the tube is desirable in this case and also with reactive substances like the free radicals; this requires calibration of each tube used for individual experiments. In many cases a tube with a good ground-glass stopper or with a high-vacuum stopcock is quite adequate.

2. Experimental Procedure

For the sake of simplicity and brevity a procedure will be described for making measurements at room temperature relative to the author's equipment.

The experimental procedure is based on finding the susceptibility of a sample relative to the known susceptibility of a reference. A pure liquid such as benzene, acetone, or distilled water free from dissolved oxygen and carbon dioxide is recommended as a reference.

a. Measurements on Liquids and Solutions

A Pyrex sample tube of 25 ml. capacity and 0.8 cm. internal diameter is used conveniently for work on pure liquids and solutions; a smaller tube is used if the size of the available sample is small. The stopper is lightly greased to prevent evaporation of liquids during weighings; however, it must be handled carefully during the entire operation so that errors in the weight of the tube are not caused by loss of grease or by picking up of dust particles.

The empty tube is suspended between the poles of the magnet as shown in Fig. 38.20, with its lower tip in the center of the pole gap. It is weighed and the balance beam is left in the released position so that the milligram reading is displayed on the optical scale of the single-pan balance. A suitable current, say 2 amp. (which, in the author's setup, produces a field of 3000 oersted in a pole gap of 3 cm. of the electromagnet), is passed for a minute or two and the weight is noted. A decrease in weight due to the predominating diamagnetism of glass is readily observed on the optical scale. Care must be taken to avoid prolonged passage of current, which produces heating effects and thereby introduces buoyancy errors in weighing.

The procedure is repeated at other field strengths obtained by passing higher currents, say 4, 6, and 8 amp. The change in weight, ΔW_t, corresponding to each amperage, is noted.*

A reference liquid is enclosed in the sample tube up to a mark (enclosing a volume of about 25 ml.) and is weighed as before without the magnetic field. Care is taken to avoid the formation of air bubbles. The sample is weighed in magnetic fields corresponding to the exact amperages used previously for the empty tube. The change in weight, ΔW_{t+r}, corresponding to each setting, is noted. The reproducibility in current settings is facilitated by a sensitive lamp and scale galvanometer connected across a small resistor (1 to 10 ohms) placed in series with the ammeter in the electromagnet circuit.

The tube is dried and is filled up to the same mark with the sample. The weighing procedure with the magnetic field off and on is repeated as before. This gives the change in weight, ΔW_{t+s}, corresponding to the same fields used before for the reference.

b. MEASUREMENTS ON POWDERED SOLIDS

The general procedure used here is the same as that described previously, except that a smaller sample tube (volume 1.5 ml., internal diameter $\sim$ 4 mm.) facilitates handling powdered samples of about 0.3 g. The powder is packed in the tube as described before; a liquid is used as a reference.

---

* ΔW_t is proportional to the square of the field strength and should be, therefore proportional to the square of the amperage, provided the electromagnet is operated within the linear range of the field-current curves. A good check on the satisfactory performance of the balance and the electromagnet is obtained by ensuring that a linear plot is obtained for ΔW_t versus the square of amperage.

3. Basis for Calculations of Magnetic Susceptibility

The following symbols are used: W = weight, d = density, κ = volume susceptibility, χ = gram susceptibility, ΔW = change in weight on applying the magnetic field, and V = actual volume up to the mark = W_r/d_r. The subscripts r, s, and t correspond to the reference, sample, and the tube.

$$\kappa_{air} = 0.029 \times 10^{-6} \text{ c.g.s. units}$$

For measurements at a fixed field corresponding to a known current,

$$\Delta W_r = W_{t+r} - W_t$$

$$\Delta W_s = W_{t+s} - W_t$$

If the sample and reference are filled to the same mark in a tube of cross-sectional area, A, and are subjected to the same magnetic field, H, under identical conditions of the Gouy experiment, the following equations hold when the tube is surrounded by air:

$$\text{Force } (s) = g \cdot \Delta W_s = (1/2) A H^2 (\kappa_s - \kappa_{air})$$

$$\text{Force } (r) = g \cdot \Delta W_r = (1/2) A H^2 (\kappa_r - \kappa_{air})$$

$$\frac{\Delta W_s}{\Delta W_r} = \frac{\kappa_s - \kappa_{air}}{\kappa_r - \kappa_{air}}$$

$$= \frac{\chi_s d_s - \kappa_{air}}{\chi_r d_r - \kappa_{air}}$$

Hence

$$\chi_s = \left(\frac{\chi_r d_r - 0.029 \times 10^{-6}}{\Delta W_r} \right) \frac{\Delta W_s}{d_s} + \frac{0.029 \times 10^{-6}}{d_s}$$

or

$$\chi_s = (\text{tube constant}) \frac{\Delta W_s}{d_s} + \frac{0.029 \times 10^{-6}}{d_s}$$

This equation is used readily in computing the susceptibility of a *liquid sample relative to a liquid reference,* as liquids can be "packed" up to a mark in the tube under identical conditions. The evaluation of a constant for a tube and its repeated use in a series of measurements simplify the calculation of susceptibility.

With solids it is almost impossible to powder them to the same particle size and to pack them uniformly up to a mark in the tube; this introduces variations in the volume of paramagnetic air held in the pockets of the sample. Hence, a correction must be made for the susceptibility of air pockets in the powdered solid by including the contribution, $\kappa_{air} \cdot (1 - W_s/V \cdot d_s)$, due to the air enclosed per cc. of the solid–air mixture.

The *susceptibility* of a *powdered solid* relative to a *liquid reference* is thus computed from the following relationship, which is based on a derivation by French and Harrison (75).

$$\chi_s = \left(\frac{\chi_r d_r - 0.029 \times 10^{-6}}{\Delta W_r} \right) \cdot \frac{\Delta W_s}{W_s} \cdot \frac{W_r}{d_r} + \frac{0.029 \times 10^{-6}}{d_s}$$

$$= (\text{tube constant}) \frac{\Delta W_s}{W_s} \cdot \frac{W_r}{d_r} + \frac{0.029 \times 10^{-6}}{d_s}$$

For a higher degree of accuracy, another correction must be included to account for the situation that the volume of the solid packed up to a mark will be less than that of the reference liquid by an amount equal to the volume of the meniscus. In this case,

$$V \cdot d_r = W_r - C$$

where C, the correction for a meniscus of height h cm. for a tube of radius between 2 and 4 mm., is given by

$$C = 0.054 \frac{W_s}{h} - 0.0037$$

The final equation is then

$$\chi_s = (\text{tube constant}) \frac{\Delta W_s}{W_s} \cdot \frac{(W_r - C)}{d_r} + \frac{0.029 \times 10^{-6}}{d_s}$$

4. Calibration

It is customary to use distilled water as a calibrating agent. However, distilled water contains appreciable amounts of dissolved air, which is paramagnetic. The author prefers the use of "conductance water," which is boiled just prior to its use to drive off all air. The susceptibility of water is taken to be -0.720×10^{-6} c.g.s. units per gram.

Some authors (4) recommend benzene as a reference, but its susceptibility depends on whether it is saturated with air ($\chi = -0.7020 \times 10^{-6}$ c.g.s. units) or with nitrogen ($\chi = -0.7081 \times 10^{-6}$ c.g.s. units). Several authors (156) have investigated the susceptibility of solutions of nickel chloride. The molar susceptibility of this salt is found to be $4433 \pm 12 \times 10^{-6}$ at 20°C. The variation of the volume susceptibility of a 0.1M

nickel chloride solution with temperature, as reported by Michaelis (139), is given in Table 38.XI.

TABLE 38.XI
Magnetic Susceptibilities of 0.1M Nickel Chloride

Temperature, °C.	κ ($\times$ 10^{-6})
18	0.0446
20	0.0443
22	0.0440
24	0.0437
26	0.0434
28	0.0432

Although the susceptibility of a mixture is not a linear function of concentration in some cases, the susceptibility per gram of nickel chloride at 20°C. is given by the following relationship:

$$\chi = [34.21p - 0.720\ (1 - p)] \times 10^{-6}$$

where p is the weight fraction of $NiCl_2$ in the solution. The susceptibility of this solution is found to be independent of concentration near 30% $NiCl_2$ by weight. Hence, such a solution may be used conveniently for calibration.

Figgis and Lewis (70) recommend mercury tetrathiocyanatocobalt, $Hg[CO(CNS)_4]$, as an all-round calibrant for solids. It has a molar susceptibility of 16.44 $\times$ 10^{-6} ($\pm0.5\%$) at 20°C. and is said to have exceptionally good packing properties. Recently, Curtis (54) suggested *tris*-ethylenediamine nickel(II) thiosulphate as a calibrating agent. It has a molar susceptibility of 10.82 $\times$ 10^{-6} ($\pm0.4\%$) at 20°C.

E. THE FARADAY BALANCE AND ITS MODIFICATIONS

Critical reviews of several modifications of this method appear in the literature (193; cf. also 130). The novelty in most modifications lies in the force-measuring techniques. The original Faraday method used a torsion head to measure the force on a sample placed in a nonuniform field. The sample suspended from a torsion arm is free to move horizontally. The torsion head is twisted to return the sample to the original place; the twist is a measure of the force required to just balance the magnetic force at the zero position. Important modifications of this torsion method are named after Curie-Chéneveau (47), Curie-Wilson (234), and Oxley (162). In the Curie-Chéneveau method a small permanent magnet is moved toward and away from the sample to produce the gradient. An elaborate

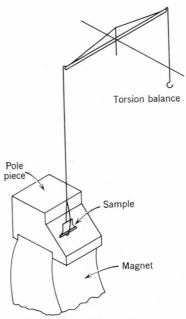

Fig. 38.29. Magnetic susceptibility measurement using a sensitive quartz torsion balance and an inhomogeneous field. Reproduced by permission from *Nucleonics* (53).

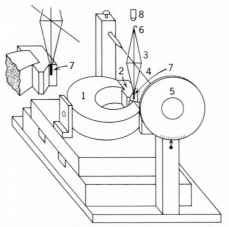

Fig. 38.30. Cunningham and Wallman magnetic susceptibility apparatus for solids. Key: *1*, 5-inch Alnico No. 5 magnet; *2*, specially cut pole piece to give uniform dH/dx; *3*, quartz frame; *4*, torsion fiber; *5*, torsion wheel; *6*, pointer; *7*, sample tube; and *8*, microscope. Reproduced by permission from *Nucleonics* (53).

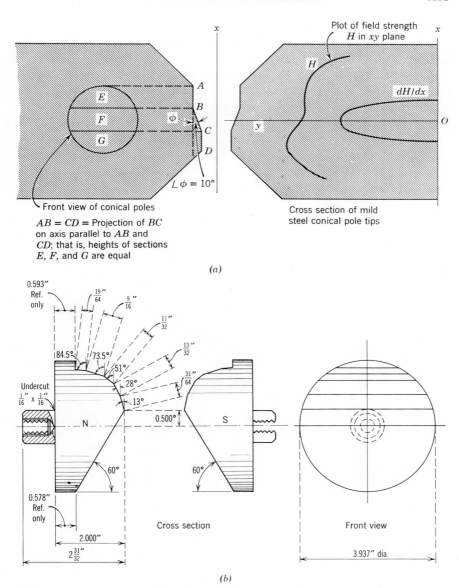

x

A

E

B

F

ϕ

C

G

D

$\angle\phi = 10°$

Front view of conical poles

$AB = CD =$ Projection of BC on axis parallel to AB and CD; that is, heights of sections E, F, and G are equal

Plot of field strength H in xy plane

x

H

dH/dx

y

O

Cross section of mild steel conical pole tips

(*a*)

0.593″ Ref. only

$\frac{19}{64}''$

$\frac{9}{16}''$

$\frac{11}{32}''$

$\frac{13}{32}''$

184.5°

173.5°

51°

Undercut $\frac{1}{16}''$ x $\frac{1}{16}''$

28°

$\frac{31}{64}''$

13°

0.500″

N

S

60°

60°

0.578″ Ref. only

Cross section

Front view

2.000″

$2\frac{31}{32}''$

3.937″ dia.

(*b*)

Fig. 38.31. Details of the pole gap (*a*) for the Faraday balance used in author's apparatus, which is similar to Sucksmith's design (211).

Details (*b*) of modified pole faces used in the author's apparatus. These provide a large uniform $H \cdot dH/ds$ region and are based on a design by Heyding and his co-workers (96).

modification of special significance is described by Sacconi and Cini (189) and recently by other workers (56). Some of the microtechniques (53) are shown in Figs. 38.29 and 38.30.

Sucksmith (211) used a sensitive method in which the sample is suspended from a phosphor bronze ring equipped with an optical system. The displacement of the sample is magnified several hundred times with this system. Chandrasekhar (45) has introduced special damping devices

Fig. 38.32. Photograph of the Faraday balance apparatus in the author's laboratory.

in the Sucksmith balance. Other workers (229) have replaced the optical system by a flat spiral spring that is linked to a displacement transducer. The voltage from this is recorded or read on an oscillograph. Improvements (205) for handling variable loads (1 to 80 mg.) have been incorporated in the Sucksmith balance.

Milligan and Whitehurst (141) and Jacobsen and Selwood (103) have described magnetic balances in which a quartz helical spring is used for measuring small changes in force. In the writer's opinion, this is by far the simplest and most sensitive force-measuring device that can be adapted readily for the Faraday technique.

Most of the modifications mentioned thus far use permanent or electro-magnets with inclined poles or poles of special design (211) (cf. Fig. 38.31) to produce a nonuniform field with a uniform field gradient. A new design for 4-inch pole faces is now available (96) to produce constant gradients in the 1- to 1.4-cm. region. These certainly improve the over-all precision and accuracy of the Faraday method and have been incorporated into the author's apparatus (Figs. 38.31 and 38.32). Larger poles, of different shape, are described by Garber et al. (76).

Other sensitive methods have been developed by Smith (204), Cini (48), and Pacault and his co-workers (164). In a recent modification (198) of the Curie-Chéneveau method, a small permanent magnet with straight pole faces is used. The required gradient is obtained by moving the permanent magnet vertically toward or away from the sample.

A quartz helix spring and a measuring microscope are used for measuring the force on the sample. The magnetic susceptibility of a sample relative to that of a standard is simply calculated from the following:

$$\chi = \frac{(d_1 - d_2)(m_2 - m_3)}{(m_1 - m_3)(d_2 - d_3)} \chi_s$$

where d is the deflection, i.e., one half the difference of maximum-to-mini-mum deflection observed during the movement of the magnet, and m is the mass in grams. χ_s is the susceptibility of the standard in e.m.u./g. and the subscripts 1, 2, and 3 refer, respectively, to the measurements of the sample plus pan, the standard plus pan, and the pan alone. The chief advantages of the method are that (1) submilligram amounts of the sample are required for paramagnetic substances having a susceptibility of from 1 to 50 × 10⁶ e.m.u./g.; (2) small samples, about 10 mg., are required for weakly paramagnetic and diamagnetic substances to obtain a precision of better than 2%; and (3) an inexpensive small permanent magnet and a simple experimental setup are needed.

A continuation of work with this equipment has led to a method of measuring magnetic susceptibility that has been claimed to be an absolute method not requiring a standard substance (222). The susceptibility χ is shown to be a function of the area, a, under the curve of sample displace-ment versus the distance of the magnet from the sample and of the max-imum applied field, $H_{max.}$:

$$\chi = 2g \frac{a}{h} \cdot H_{max.}{}^2$$

Here g is acceleration due to gravity and h is the measured static deflection of the helix. In the experimental procedure the area a of the curve (which resembles the first differential of a Gaussian curve) is measured with a planimeter and $H_{max.}$ is measured with a Gaussmeter. The usefulness of this method has been verified by other workers (42). With regard to the claim that it is an absolute method not requiring any standards (but requiring a precise measurement of H), it may be remembered that, if an exact measurement of the field H is made, for instance, in the Gouy technique, then it does not become necessary even here to use a standard. In this case the volume susceptibility κ (and hence the mass susceptibility $\chi = \kappa/$density) can simply be calculated from the basic equation, $g\Delta w = {}^{1}/_{2} AH^{2} \cdot \kappa$, where the symbols have the same meaning as used previously. It is important to note that in the magnetic susceptibility methods the purpose of employing a standard with known susceptibility κ is to avoid a measurement of the magnetic field H and other parameters, such as the area A of the cross section of the sample. This is possible because these factors cancel out in considering the ratio of changes in weight due to magnetic field of the sample to standard $\Delta W/\Delta W_{s}$, which equals the ratio of the susceptibility of the sample to standard κ/κ_{s}.

Garber and his co-workers (76) provide an elaborate description of a Faraday balance designed to give a reproducibility of better than 0.15%; this was particularly used for measurements of magnetic susceptibility of copper, silver, and gold.

A null technique especially useful for paramagnetics has been developed (201). It can be used over a wide range of magnetic field strengths without any readjustments and automatically detects the presence of ferromagnetic impurities. The balance is semiautomatic, uses small single crystals, and subtracts the contributions from (ferromagnetic) impurities and antiferromagnetic components. Another torque method (174) originally designed for ferromagnetic anisotropy measurements on crystals is expected to be useful for susceptibility measurements. This employs a light beam–mirror–phototube network.

An electromagnetic servo balance employing a differential transformer has been designed to handle large forces (5 g.) for ferromagnetic materials (41). It readily measures forces as small as 0.02 mg. This paper (41) lists several references to servo balances.

Special adaptations are described for measurements at very high temperatures (223,228).

F. TYPICAL ASSEMBLY OF THE FARADAY BALANCE

In the author's laboratory the same electromagnet and d.-c. power supply described previously under the Gouy technique are employed; the usual flat pole faces are replaced by those of a special design having the characteristics shown in Fig. 38.31b. The entire apparatus is similar to the one shown schematically in Fig. 38.9. A quartz spiral spring (made by Worden Laboratories, Houston, Texas) with a light-weight marker is suspended in the top tube, which is held rigidly in a sturdy table support. The spring is attached to a valve with bellows made by Kopp Scientific Industries, New York 13, N. Y. A vernier screw at the top allows centering the sample in the field. The lower tube is easily detachable through the ground-glass joint; this permits a free access to the Pyrex (or quartz) bucket that holds the sample. This tube may be replaced with a tubular heating furnace or a suitable cryostat—if measurements of susceptibility are to be made over a range of temperature. A photograph of the author's apparatus (not showing the microscope for reading deflections) is given in Fig. 38.32.

1. Calibration

The theory of the Faraday method requires that the sample be placed in a region of fairly high field where the product $H \cdot \partial H / \partial x$ is constant over the volume of the sample. This region may be located by the following procedures. A sample of known susceptibility χ and mass m (for instance, potassium chloride: $\chi = -0.516 \times 10^{-6}$ c.g.s. units, $m \simeq 0.3$ g.) is placed at different points along the x axis with the help of the vernier screw at the top. At each position the electromagnet is energized with the same current to give an intense field. The deflection of the spring is noted with a cathetometer (micrometer microscope). The force f acting on the sample is proportional to this deflection. Since

$$f = m\chi H \frac{\partial H}{\partial x}$$

$$H \cdot \frac{\partial H}{\partial x} = \frac{f}{m \cdot \chi}$$

Thus a value for $H \cdot \partial H / \partial x$ in units (mm.) of the observed deflection is obtained as a function of x. From the appropriate curve the region of uniform $H \cdot \partial H / \partial x$ is located. The vernier screw at the top is then adjusted so that the sample bucket is always located in this region.

As with the Gouy method, by using a reference such as pure potassium chloride or sucrose the susceptibility of a sample is found from the following relation. In this the subscripts r and s stand for the reference and for the sample and d represents the deflection of the spring in arbitrary units, such as "divisions" on the cathetometer.

$$\chi_s = \frac{d_s}{d_r} \cdot \frac{m_r}{m_s} \cdot \chi_r$$

IV. ANALYTICAL APPLICATIONS OF MAGNETIC SUSCEPTIBILITY

A. SCOPE

The applications of the magnetic technique are numerous, as will be seen from the next few sections and from Table 38.XII. For convenience some applications of commercial instruments will be described first; these fall in the area of inorganic chemistry. Secondly, some selected applications of magnetic susceptibility will be described in the areas of inorganic, organic, and biological chemistry, and geological applications will be mentioned briefly. With sufficient ingenuity it should be possible for the analyst to use the magnetic technique to attack many other problems not represented by these examples.

Several techniques are related to a study of paramagnetic and ferromagnetic properties; these methods have many technological applications. Diamagnetism seems to be somewhat limited in this respect; however, the applications in the area of organic chemistry have been quite significant. Although the techniques of nuclear and electron magnetic resonance spectroscopy developed during the last decade are finding new applications every day, the relatively simple technique of magnetic susceptibility continues to be useful in certain respects. This technique has proved helpful as an exploratory tool and, in several cases, the magnetic studies have preceded the more elaborate N.M.R. and E.P.R. investigations.

B. SOME APPLICATIONS OF COMMERCIAL INSTRUMENTS

As stated previously, commercial equipment of general applicability for measuring magnetic susceptibility is not available. However, instruments such as oxygen meters, permeameters, coercimeters, etc., designed for specific applications, are marketed by some manufacturers.

1. Analysis of Oxygen: Oxygen Meters

Among the many physical methods that are adaptable for a continuous analysis and recording of oxygen content in a sample of gas, the ones most widely used are based on a measurement of oxygen's magnetic susceptibility and on special effects produced in a magnetic field.

Most methods take advantage of the fact that, among the few paramagnetic gases known, oxygen has a large magnetic susceptibility of 0.142 $\times$ 10^{-6} at 20°C. and standard pressure. All other gases such as nitrogen, carbon dioxide, etc., which are constituents of air, are diamagnetic. This facilitates an analysis of oxygen in air and in other samples containing diamagnetic gases. Magnetic susceptibility data on oxygen have been used in conjunction with the electron magnetic resonance technique to study atomic recombination of oxygen. Krongelb and Strandberg (120) found that the surface recombination coefficient for oxygen atoms on quartz is 3.2×10^{-4} per collision and the second-order volume recombination process is about 5×10^{15} cm.^{6} mole^{-2} second^{-1}.

1. The Hays oxygen analyzer, marketed by the Hays Corp., Michigan City, Indiana: the apparatus is based on the inverse relation between the paramagnetism of oxygen and its temperature. It is similar to an apparatus developed by Klauer, Turowski, and Wolff (112). Fig. 38.33*a* shows two electrically self-heated, identical nickel coils (*3A* and *3B*) on the outside of a glass tube (1). The winding (*3A*) is placed between the poles of a small permanent magnet (4). The two windings form two legs of a Wheatstone bridge. The sample gas flows from the entrance (5) to the exit (6) and oxygen is attracted into tube (1) by the magnetic field. The gas is heated by coil (*3A*), which decreases its susceptibility. Cooler gas entering at (*3A*) pushes the heated gas away from the field, as shown by the arrow. This flow, often termed the "magnetic wind," cools coil (*3A*) and heats coil (*3B*). This difference in temperature changes the resistance of the two coils and produces an unbalance of the Wheatstone bridge. This is converted into a voltage unbalance, amplified and transmitted to an indicator or a recorder. The unbalance is found to be proportional to the oxygen content of the gas. The instrument is thus adaptable to an "enclosed" or a "flowing" sample of gas containing oxygen. An internal view of the instrument is shown in Fig. 38.33*b*. Several references to a similar oxygen meter and applications are given by Selwood (193) and Krupp (122).

2. The Beckman oxygen analyzer, marketed by the Beckman Co., Fullerton, California: As shown in Fig. 38.34*a*, it measures directly the volume susceptibility of a gas in an inhomogeneous field, similar to the one employed in the Faraday technique. One end of a test body in the form of a glass dumbbell is placed between the poles of an Alnico permanent magnet. The test body is supported on a silica fiber, which acts as a tension suspension. This measures the torque of the system about the axis of the suspension in terms of the deflection of a small mirror attached to the fiber. The torque is proportional to the magnetic field strength, its gradient, and the difference in the volume susceptibilities of the test body and the gas

TABLE 38.XII

Summary of Important Aspects of Methods of Measuring Magnetic Susceptibilities

Method	General field requirements	Applicable to	Physical nature of sample	Approx. minimum and convenient size of sample	Accuracy	Temperature control
Gouy	Uniform field. Recommended and easily available range with electromagnets is 3000 to 15,000 oersteds; permanent magnets	Dia- and paramagnetic only	Powdered solids, pure liquids and solutions. (Adaptable for a gas surrounding a known sample)	Solids, 0.5 g.; liquids, 5 ml. (macro scale). Few mg. or γ can be handled in special apparatus	Generally $\pm 1\%$, may be improved to $\pm 0.1\%$. (Separate density measurement required; accuracy depends on packing)	Possible over a wide range. Temperatures from liquid H_2 or N_2 levels to several hundred degrees may be obtained easily
Quincke	Same as Gouy	Same as Gouy	Pure liquids and solutions. (Adaptable for measuring x of a gas above the meniscus of a known liquid)	~ 5 ml.	Generally $\pm 0.1\%$	Limited range, depending on f.p. and b.p. of system

Rankine	Low fields, 15 to 100 oersted	Same as Gouy	Pure liquids and solutions. (Adaptable to flow systems and gases)	~2 ml.	Same as Quincke	Same as Quincke
Faraday	Field strength range same as for Gouy, but giving nonuniform field with a constant field gradient	Dia-, para-, and ferromagnetic materials	Generally useful for powdered solids. (Liquids may be handled in special containers)	Few mg. (micro-techniques are also available)	±0.1%	Possible over a wide range (same as for Gouy; liquid He may be used)
Induction[a]	External fields not required except in a study of ferromagnetics	Generally to dia- and paramagnetics. Ferromagnetics may be studied in special apparatus	Solids and liquids	Solids, 0.5 g.; liquids, 5 ml.	Generally better than ±0.1%, but depends on dielectric characteristics	Control over a wide range is rather difficult with the r-f method, but is adaptable in other inductance methods

[a] Alternating current, including radio-frequency and direct-current methods. Most N.M.R. techniques also fall in this category. See pages 1801 to 1805.

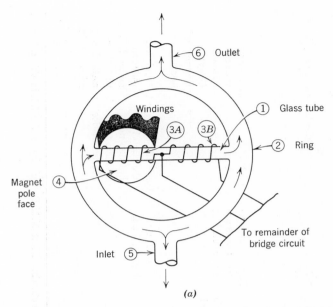

Fig. 38.33. Hays Corporation's oxygen analyzer (*a*) based on the "magnetic wind" principle, and (*b*) internal view of Hays analyzer (opposite page). Reproduced by permission from *Analytical Chemistry* (144).

surrounding it.   A change in the susceptibility of this gas, resulting from a change in its oxygen content, produces a nearly proportional deflection (cf. 172).   A portable table model of this instrument is shown in Fig. 38.34*b*.

2. Permeameters: Carbon Content in Steel

The basic idea is to measure the permeability of a sample in terms of the magnetic coupling that it can establish between two inductance coils.   In a low-frequency a.-c. permeameter designed by Rogers and his co-workers (187), a primary and a secondary solenoid are wound around the sample holder.   A small alternating current at 5 c.p.s. is sent through the primary, and the induced current, after conversion to a direct current through a rectifier, is recorded on a microammeter.   A calibration curve is obtained for samples of the same size but containing different amounts of carbon. From this the carbon content of the unknown sample, shaped to the same size, is determined.

The Isthmus permeameter (123), shown schematically in Fig. 38.35, is based on the same general principle, except that the sample is first mag-

Fig. 38.33*b*

netized and then withdrawn from the secondary, which is connected to a galvanometer. The results obtained have found wide use in the determination of the concentration of copper in alloys containing a 1:1 ratio of iron and nickel.

Several other variations such as the Carbanalyser (235) and the Carbometer and Siemens Ferrometer (219) are described in the literature. Abbott and Kilgour (1) describe a permeameter suitable for comparing permeabilities in the range $\mu = 1 \pm 0.00001$ to $\mu = 1 \pm 0.00002$. It can be adjusted to cover other ranges and is said to be useful for testing materials such as phosphor bronze, copper, filled rubber, etc.

3. Coercimeters: Particle-Size Determination of Some Ferromagnetics

The coercive force, like the Curie point, is known to depend on the particle size of the magnetic material. The dependence, however, is quite marked and as such is used in an empirical fashion for the determination of

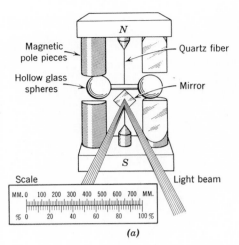

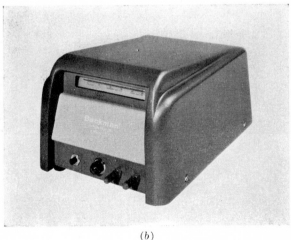

(b)

Fig. 38.34. Schematic view (a) of Beckman oxygen analyzer measuring system and (b) table-model analyzer. Reproduced by permission from *Analytical Chemistry* (144).

the (average) particle size of a ferromagnetic material. The coercive force in this connection may be defined as the field of force necessary to reduce I, the intensity of magnetization, to zero in a $I-H$ curve. Alternatively, in a typical hysteresis curve (Fig. 38.36) representing B versus H, the negative intercept (Ox) on the H axis is taken as a measure of the coercive force. This merely represents the force necessary to reduce the induction B to zero.

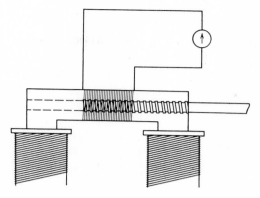

Fig. 38.35. The Isthmus permeameter. From Selwood (193).

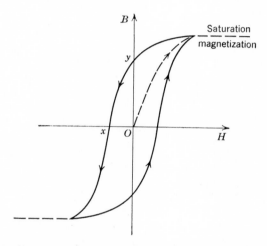

Fig. 38.36. Plot of magnetization (B) versus applied field (H), showing the hysteresis curve for a typical ferromagnetic. Remanence is represented by Oy; coercive force is represented by Ox.

The curves of coercive force H_c versus the applied field H_m are described by

$$H_m/H_c = C_1 + C_2 \cdot H_m$$

where C_1 is a constant and C_2 is the reciprocal of the coercivity. A similar equation,

$$H_m/B_r = d_1 + d_2 \cdot H_m$$

may be written to describe the curves for residual induction B_r versus H_m, employing d_2 for the reciprocal of retentivity.

In a coercimeter described by Doan (59), the sample is first magnetized in a strong magnetic field and then is placed in a variable field, the strength of which is balanced against the residual magnetism of the sample. This is accomplished by moving a secondary coil attached to a galvanometer (Fig. 38.37).

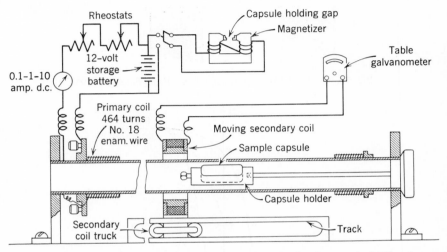

Fig. 38.37. A form of coercimeter for determining coercive force, principally of powdered specimens. Reproduced by permission from *U. S. Bureau of Mines Reports of Investigations*, No. 3400.

Another technique for determining (average) particle size was devised by Knappworst (116), who described a method of measuring the susceptibility and the intensity of spontaneous magnetization. Generally, a determination of particle size from the bulk paramagnetism by Curie law requires a knowledge of the mass of the fraction of spontaneously magnetizable material. This is overcome by plotting the susceptibility χ as a function of $1/H$. In this plot the deviation from the horizontal corresponds to $Isp \cdot (VH/KT) = c$, where Isp is the spontaneous magnetization and V is the volume. For known Isp the volume is evaluated. The method is applicable to particle sizes in the range 15 to 100 A. It must be pointed out, however, that very small particles of ferromagnetics do not give the magnetizations expected for larger particles. The dependence of saturation magnetization on particle size is quite complex.

4. Thermomagnetic Analysis: Determination of Cementite in Steel

Several applications dependent on thermomagnetic analysis of materials are available. The general effort is directed toward elucidating the mechanism of heterogeneous catalysis. Since thermomagnetic analysis is dealt with extensively by Selwood (193–195a) and by Bozorth *et al.* (32), a few instrumental applications will be mentioned here.

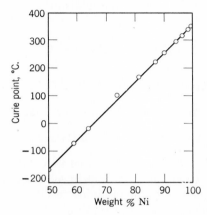

Fig. 38.38. Curie point *vs.* concentration for nickel-copper alloys. From Selwood (193).

One application is the detection and microdetermination of cementite (Fe_3C) in steel. A "magnetic balance" made by the General Electric Co. is employed (cf. Reference 193). This is in reality an apparatus for determining the Curie point of a sample, which is mixed with an inert support like silica and enclosed in a small tube. The sample is then exposed to varying fields from an electromagnet and to variable temperature from a noninductive electric oven. The force of attraction of the sample above and below the Curie point is measured. This enables the detection and determination of cementite in steel in an empirical way. Marian (133) discusses other procedures for the determination of cementite, carbon, and iron.

More refined apparatus adaptable to automatic recording, as constructed by Selwood (cf. References 186,195,195a), is found to be versatile for research.

Another application refers to the determination of components in copper–nickel alloys. According to Marian (133) and Ross (188), the Curie point as well as specific magnetization are linear with concentration, as shown in Fig. 38.38.

Thermomagnetic analysis is found useful in studies of reactions in the solid state of materials such as certain carbides and oxides of iron and cobalt. For instance, the Hagg carbide, Fe_2C, shows a distinct Curie point of 208°C. in a curve of magnetic moment versus temperature, which is found to be reversible in the range 0 to 300°C. However, heating this carbide at 580°C. for two hours and a subsequent run of the thermomagnetic curve lowers its Curie point to 208°C. This information, coupled with the corresponding x-ray analysis, helped to establish the following reaction in the solid state:

$$3Fe_2C \rightleftharpoons 2Fe_3C + C$$

C. SOME APPLICATIONS OF MAGNETIC SUSCEPTIBILITIES

1. Applications to Inorganic Chemistry

a. The Additivity Law and Paramagnetic Ions

Wiedemann's additivity law may be used to determine the concentration and oxidation state of paramagnetic ions in solution, in solid mixtures, and in glass. The method is capable of giving results to within 1% or better, depending on the accuracy of the susceptibility measurement. An obvious limitation is that there should not be any interaction between the solvent and the solute. In the case of paramagnetic ions a further limitation is imposed, in that the system must be magnetically dilute, that is, free from spin-spin interactions between adjacent ions. As a matter of fact, in recent years, the technique has been profitably used for studying the nature of such interactions and to derive valuable structural information. This will be discussed later.

In the case of a diamagnetic salt in solution, its concentration $(p\%)$ may be obtained by measuring the specific susceptibility (χ_s^g) of the solution and using the following relationship.

$$\chi_s^g = p \cdot \frac{\chi_{\text{cation}} + \chi_{\text{anion}}}{\text{mol. wt. salt}} + (100 - p)\chi_{H_2O}^g$$

χ_{cation} and χ_{anion} represent the gram ionic susceptibilities. Some of these values are listed in Table 38.X. The specific susceptibility of water $(\chi_{H_2O}^g)$ is taken as -0.720×10^{-6}.

In the case of a paramagnetic ion, χ_{cation} will be dependent on the temperature and its effective magnetic moment. In many cases χ_{cation} may be calculated from

$$\chi_{\text{cation}} = \frac{N \cdot \mu_{\text{eff.}}{}^2}{3KT}$$

Some of the typical values for $\mu_{\text{eff.}}$ are given in Table 38.III.

Solid mixtures, for instance, aluminum oxide, supporting paramagnetic ions are analyzed similarly (137). The specific susceptibility of the particular support used is determined separately.

It is remarkable that in some cases the determination of the ratio of paramagnetic ions in two different oxidation states dispersed in colloidal systems such as glass has given results with as much precision as that of the spectroscopic methods. According to deJong (105), a glass containing 0.08% total iron in the Fe^{+3} and Fe^{+2} states gave the following results for the percentage of Fe^{+3}: 44.5 to 47% from the ultraviolet spectrum, 44% from the infrared spectrum, and 45.5% from the magnetic susceptibility data, which was treated according to the additivity law, assuming that the magnetic moment for Fe^{+3} is 5.91 and for Fe^{+2} is 4.90 Bohr magnetons. It must be pointed out that the limited studies in this area were undertaken not merely to find the concentration of the paramagnetic ions, but to unravel structural aspects of glasses containing these ions. Bishay (19) has recently studied the color and magnetic properties of iron in glasses of various types. His paper lists a number of references to magnetic studies on glass. Iron-containing glasses have been studied by Banerjee (10).

b. DETERMINATION OF PURITY AND ANALYSIS OF RARE EARTHS

The shielding of $4f$ electrons in rare earths makes the interactions between their adjacent ions negligible. This corresponds to the ideal situation of "magnetic dilution" and in many cases permits a magnetic analysis of rare earths.

The purification of rare earths formerly was based on fractional crystallization. A plot of magnetic susceptibility versus fraction number was found quite useful in determining purity. A horizontal plateau in such plots indicated the isolation of a pure rare earth salt.

Although elegant techniques of ion exchange are used nowadays for the separation of rare earths, a determination of magnetic susceptibility is found to be an excellent criterion for purity in addition to that of "spectroscopic purity." As a matter of fact, the two criteria are quite different. It is known, for instance, that a trace of a ferromagnetic impurity in copper can be detected only by the magnetic technique. The choice of the criterion for purity naturally depends on the final use of the material in question.

The magnetic criterion has been applied successfully to the diamagnetic lanthanum and lutetium oxides.

The analysis of rare earths is dependent on the application of the additivity law, discussed previously. It has proved particularly useful for analysis of binary mixtures of lanthanum oxide (diamagnetic) and gadolinium oxide (paramagnetic). In general, an analysis of a binary mixture is facilitated if the two components have widely different susceptibilities. Accuracy better than 1% may be achieved by a careful control of temperature during susceptibility measurements and by studying the solutions of their soluble salts instead of the solid oxides. Many texts (112a,236) list the magnetic susceptibilities of rare earth oxides.

c. POLYMERIZATION OF PARAMAGNETIC IONS

The magnetic susceptibility method has proved useful in studying the polymerization of paramagnetic ions in solution. A few typical examples are Fe(III) and Cr(III), studied by the author (150,152,153), and Mo(V), investigated by Sacconi and Cini (190).

It seems that the technique is particularly useful for studying systems in which large changes in magnetic susceptibility of a solution take place due to conversion of a paramagnetic species to a diamagnetic one (or to one of a very low magnetic moment) or vice versa. Only relatively simple systems not containing too many species of varying magnetic properties can be studied effectively. The magnetic method has another limitation, in that its applicability is rather doubtful in studying polymerization of diamagnetic ions.

The magnetic work on the dimerization of Fe(III) in solution will be illustrated in some detail.

The following pH-dependent equilibrium proposed by Hedstrom (94) was investigated:

$$2Fe_3 + 2H_2O \underset{}{\overset{K_{22}}{\rightleftharpoons}} \left[Fe \overset{\overset{\displaystyle H}{\displaystyle O}}{\underset{\underset{\displaystyle H}{\displaystyle O}}{\diamondsuit}} Fe \right]^{+4} + 2H^+$$

The magnetic susceptibilities were measured for a solution containing $0.061M$ $Fe(ClO_4)_3$ at a constant ionic strength ($3M$ $NaClO_4$) at different acidities. Solutions containing other concentrations of iron were also investigated.

The problem was to find the dimerization constant K_{22}. It became necessary, first of all, to find the specific susceptibility of $Fe(ClO_4)_3$ in solution and then to find the susceptibility per gram atom of total iron in solution from the following data:

P_1 = Wt. fraction of $Fe(ClO_4)_3$ = 0.0173
P_2 = Wt. fraction of H_2O = 0.6570
P_3 = Wt. fraction of $NaClO_4$ = 0.2940
χ_1 = Specific susceptibility of $Fe(ClO_4)_3$ (unknown)
χ_2 = Specific susceptibility of H_2O = -0.720×10^{-6}
χ_3 = Specific susceptibility of $NaClO_4$ (calculated from

$$\frac{\chi_{Na^+} + \chi_{ClO_4^-}}{\text{mol. wt. } NaClO_4} = -0.3550 \times 10^{-6}\Bigg)$$

$\chi_{sol.}$ = Specific susceptibility of the solution (pH = 0.39, stored for several weeks), measured by the Gouy technique = 0.0856×10^{-6}

According to the additivity law, $\chi_{sol.} = \chi_1 P_1 + \chi_2 \cdot P_2 + \chi_3 P_3$; substituting the appropriate quantities and solving for χ_1 gave $\chi_1 = 38.4 \times 10^{-6}$. The molar susceptibility χ_m for $Fe(ClO_4)_3$, calculated from $\chi_m = \chi_1 \times$ molecular weight of $Fe(ClO_4)_3$, was found to be $13,600 \times 10^{-6}$ c.g.s. units. This result is converted to $\chi_{Fe(t)}$, susceptibility per g. atom (of total) iron in solution, using Pascal's relation, according to which $\chi_{Fe(t)} = \chi_{Fe(ClO_4)} + 3\chi_{ClO_4^-}$.

$$\chi_{Fe(t)} = 13,600 \times 10^{-6} - 3(-34 \times 10^{-6})$$
$$= 13,702 \times 10^{-6} \text{ c.g.s. units}$$

Now, $\chi_{Fe(t)} = f\chi_{Fe^{+3}} + (1 - f)\chi_{dimer}$

It was assumed that the dimer is diamagnetic* and, since diamagnetic susceptibilities are negligible in comparison with paramagnetic susceptibilities (making $\chi_{dimer} \simeq 0$), the following result was obtained:

$$f = \text{wt. fraction of } Fe^{+3} \text{ ions} = \frac{\chi_{Fe(t)}}{\chi_{Fe^{+3}}}$$

* This assumption was based on the observation that the magnetic moment per g. atom of total iron decreases rapidly to half the original value ($\mu = 5.82$ Bohr magnetons, pH $\simeq 0$) with increasing concentration of the dimer (at pH $\simeq 3$), indicating that, to cause such a large decrease, the dimeric species must have a negligible magnetic moment ($\mu \sim 0$, that is, diamagnetic). Other arguments supporting this assumption are discussed by the author (150).

A solution of the same composition at pH = 0, at which all iron is expected to be in the form of (hexaaquo) Fe^{+3} ions, gave for $\chi_{Fe^{+3}}$ a value of $14{,}500 \times 10^{-6}$. This gave $f = 13{,}702/14{,}500 = 0.9448$, and $(1 - f)$, the weight fraction of the dimer, equal to 0.0552.

Thus, the procedure involved evaluation of $\chi_{Fe(t)}$ as a function of the pH and the corresponding f value; in all cases $\chi_{Fe^{+3}}$ was taken as 14,500. The dimerization constant, K_{22}, could then be calculated in each case from the f and $(1 - f)$ values; the average value of 7.5×10^{-2} was obtained from a study of a number of solutions stored for long periods of time. The method was extended to study the temperature dependence of K_{22} by measuring the susceptibilities of the solution over a range of temperatures (-10 to $60°C.$). From this the energy of formation of the dimer was estimated to be about 9.8 kcal./mole. Independent spectrophotometric studies by Milburn (140) gave results in good agreement with this estimate. Recently Brownlow (40) studied the magnetic properties of hydrolyzed species adsorbed on ion-exchange resins and confirmed the existence of species such as the dimer with subnormal magnetic moments.

It is remarkable that an independent technique of measuring the effective magnetic moment of paramagnetic ions from the data on spin-lattice relaxation times, T_1, for proton magnetic resonance (39) indicated that the dimeric ions are diamagnetic ($\mu = 0$), and gave values between 10^{-2} and 10^{-3} for the dimerization constant K_{22}, in agreement with the magnetic susceptibility data. The experimental work involved measuring the spin-lattice relaxation time, T_1, for protons in solutions containing the Fe^{+3} and the dimeric species; the reciprocal of T_1 is known to be proportional to $\mu_{eff.}^2$ of the paramagnetic ion, as discussed above (pages 1803 and 1804).

The success of these two independent magnetic methods, apart from yielding the same magnitude for the dimerization constant K_{22}, is further seen from the fact that entirely unrelated techniques of ultraviolet spectrophotometry (150,153) and electrometric titration (94) gave results in satisfactory agreement with these magnetic methods.

Recently the magnetic method was used by Miyake (142) to study the slow decoloration of thiocyanate iron(III) complexes in acidic solutions. This was also investigated spectrophotometrically. The magnetic data could be interpreted to support the idea that the decoloration was caused simply by a reduction of iron(III) to iron(II) by NCS^- ions, but such a simple model of the reduction could not explain the observed decoloration because the decrease in absorbance was too small, being only about 20%. In order to eliminate this discrepancy, the formation of a dimeric complex of Fe(III) and Fe(II) during the decoloration reaction has been proposed. This dimer possesses only one unpaired electron and, therefore, explains the small magnetic moment observed and also the significant absorbance due to iron(III). The author considered some structures for the dimer and concluded that the dimeric structure

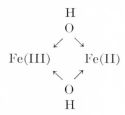

$$\text{Fe(III)} \quad\quad \text{Fe(II)}$$

is more likely than the corresponding structure with SCN bridges. The possibility of the formation of binuclear and polynuclear species of Co(III) also has been investigated by the susceptibility method (212).

A significant contribution by Earnshaw and Lewis (62) dealing with the theoretical and experimental aspects of polynuclear complexes may be mentioned here. They studied the magnetic properties of a number of binuclear complexes of iron(III) and chromium(III), with one and two bridging groups. In certain cases involving oxo or ol bridges, magnetic interaction is observed through a reduction in magnetic moment of the metal ion. This has been attributed to the possibility of π bonding between the metal ion and the oxygen of the bridge. Additional evidence for such bonding has been obtained from a study of IR spectra.

The author (152) also observed a small decrease in the magnetic moment of Cr(III) during hydrolysis; this has been attributed to polymeric species of Cr(III).

The solutions of sodium triphenyl boron, $NaBPh_3$, in tetrahydrofuran are found to be diamagnetic (143). This surprising result may be explained by its apparent dimerization. The tri-1-naphthyl boron anion (91) apparently dimerizes in solution.

d. Dissociation Phenomena

Magnetic susceptibility also has been used to study some dissociations. Bodenstein and his co-workers (29) found by cryoscopic measurements that chlorine hexoxide in carbon tetrachloride solution was mainly in the form Cl_2O_6. Goodeve and Richardson (81) showed that small amounts of ClO_3 also are present in the liquid. The compound in the gas phase is known to exist entirely as ClO_3, which contains 41 electrons. It must, therefore, contain at least one unpaired electron and show paramagnetism. The dimer Cl_2O_6, on the other hand, contains an even number of electrons and will be diamagnetic on the assumption that it is in $^1\Sigma$ state with completely paired spins. The molar magnetic susceptibility of Cl_2O_6 was calculated by adding the experimental atomic values, and that of ClO_3 was calculated by using Van Vleck's formula:

$$\chi_m = \frac{4N\beta^2 S(S + 1)}{3KT} + N\alpha$$

where the symbols have their usual meaning. $N\alpha$ is a small additional term, representing the underlying diamagnetism, etc., which could be neglected.

Measurements of magnetic susceptibility of liquid chlorine hexoxide over a temperature range of -40 to $10°C$. showed that the diamagnetism of the liquid was less than that calculated for Cl_2O_6, indicating that a paramagnetic contribution was presumably made by ClO_3; furthermore, the susceptibility was temperature-dependent, pointing again toward the presence of paramagnetic species and an increased dissociation of the dimers. The percentage of ClO_3 by weight varied from 0.721 at $-40°C$. to 1.001 at $10°C$. The dissociation constant was found to vary from 2.54×10^{-3} to 4.91×10^{-3} over the same range. From this the heat of dissociation was shown to be about 1.73 ± 0.5 kcal./mole.

e. STUDY OF OXIDATION-REDUCTION REACTIONS *in situ*

An important application of magnetic susceptibility to a study of oxidation-reduction reactions occurring in a Leclanché dry cell is described by Selwood (193). The problem was to find if the reduction of manganese in the pyrolusite employed as a depolarizer in the cell occurs during the discharge of the cell or during its recovery. For this purpose an apparatus, shown in Fig. 38.39, was employed. A small dry cell was suspended horizontally by two fine copper wires that also acted as a conductor for discharging the cell. One end of the cell was placed between the poles of a magnet with a field of about 9,000 oersted. Changes in the magnetic susceptibility of manganese during discharge and recovery were expected to produce proportional displacements. These were observed by a micrometer microscope. The deflection during discharge was plotted as a function of the coulombs withdrawn (Fig. 38.40). In the system studied manganese was the only paramagnetic constituent of the cell. Since the magnetic susceptibilities are virtually linear with the oxidation state of manganese in a magnetically dilute system such as the one provided by the disperse structure of pyrolusite, the deflections observed could be interpreted in terms of the change in the oxidation state of manganese in the cell. It was found that the cell contents became more paramagnetic during discharge of the cell and that all reduction of the manganese occurs only during the discharge.

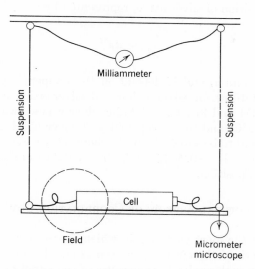

Fig. 38.39. Schematic diagram of Selwood's apparatus for following magnetic changes in the manganese dioxide of a dry cell during discharge. From Selwood (193).

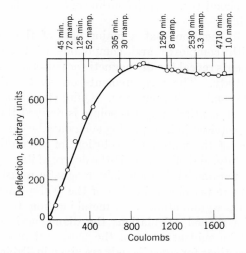

Fig. 38.40. Deflection *vs.* discharge for a dry cell. From Selwood (193).

f. THERMAL DECOMPOSITION OF SILVER OXIDE

Tobisawa (223) describes a magnetic technique for studying the susceptibilities at extremely high temperatures ($\sim$1200°C.). He studied the rate of decomposition of silver oxide, represented by

$$\frac{dn}{dt} = a_i t^{bi}$$

where the constants a_i and bi depend on the temperature. The decomposition temperatures for silver oxide and silver oxide containing some carbonate are 354 and 372°C. Metallic silver was shown to be diamagnetic up to 1100°C. and the susceptibility of silver obtained from decomposition was found to be -0.48×10^{-6}, whereas the susceptibility of silver oxide was shown to be -0.21×10^{-6}. These data were used to calculate the rate of decomposition.

g. STRUCTURAL ASPECTS OF COORDINATION COMPLEXES

This is by far the most vast area in which magnetic susceptibilities and the moments derived therefrom have been used. It is impossible to indicate even briefly such applications because of the variety of the complexes and of the bonding they involve. Reference must be, therefore, made to a recent article (70), and to books (44,51a,57,81a,85a,86,110,113,134,169,215) dealing with their chemistry. A brief outline of some rudimentary concepts will be presented here.

It will suffice to mention that a major part of the magnetochemical studies deals with complexes and compounds of transition elements. Simple measurements reveal the diamagnetic or paramagnetic nature of the material under study. The measurements on solid materials permit a study over a wide range of temperature. Quite often studies are made on solutions and the susceptibility of the solute is derived therefrom. Great caution must be exercised in interpreting such data because of the possibility of dissociation of the material in solution, of interaction between the solvent and the solute, and of changes in the degree of its magnetic dilution.

In the case of paramagnetic materials, magnetic measurements over a range of temperature permit evaluation of the Weiss constant and of the magnetic moment per gram atom of the metal ion from the measured molar susceptibility. In refined calculations the diamagnetic susceptibility of the ligands must be subtracted from the measured molar susceptibility. Diamagnetic corrections for some ligands are given in Table 38.IX and may be calculated, somewhat approximately, by using Pascal's atomic and correction constants given in Tables 38.VI and VII. For simple ions and ligands of low molecular weight, the diamagnetic correction often may be neglected.

Generally the theoretical spin-only formula

$$\mu_{\text{eff.}} = \sqrt{n(n+2)}$$

gives a rough agreement with experiment and allows an estimate of the number of unpaired electrons, n, in the molecule.

Van Vleck's equations, which take into account the orbital contributions, may be employed to calculate the moments of rare earth ions, in which the unpaired electrons in the $4f$ level are well shielded from the influence of surrounding ions and ligands. Hence, the electrons are free to orient with the applied field. Table 38.V lists moments for the tripositive rare earth ions. The transition metal ions differ in this respect because the orbital moments of their ions are not free to move and to orient themselves with the applied field. Their magnetic properties are modified by interactions with the surrounding ions and molecules. In certain cases "quenching" of the orbital moment is incomplete and many deviations from the "spin-only" formula are observed. Table 38.III lists the range of values observed for the magnetic moments of transition metal ions and the moments calculated by the spin only value.

Pauling's theory (169) is used in deducing the type of bonding in complex compounds. Generally, Hund's rule is applied; this assumes that electrons fill all the available orbitals before pairing off. Table 38.III shows that the magnetic moment rises from zero to 5.9 for Fe^{+3} and Mn^{+2} ($n = 5$) and falls back to zero. The agreement between theory and experiment is satisfactory up to five unpaired electrons; ions with six, seven, and eight d electrons show somewhat higher magnetic moments than those expected from the spin-only formula. These deviations may be attributed to incomplete quenching of orbital moments. A discussion of spin-orbit coupling is given by Figgis and Lewis (70).

Table 38.XIII illustrates the relationship between the magnetic moment and the nature of bonding in complexes of manganese based on the valence-bond theory; these complexes are particularly selected because manganese displays significant variation in its oxidation state, in coordination number, and in chemical bonding in these complexes. Different values of magnetic moment have been reported by some workers for the same compound; however, their comparison with the theoretical moments indicates the presence of the unpaired electrons, shown in the second column of Table 38.XIII.

A study of coordination compounds has stimulated by far the most activity in the area of magnetic susceptibility. The earlier interpretations

TABLE 38.XIII

Magnetic Moments of Some Manganese Complexes[a]

	Unpaired electrons, n	$\mu = \sqrt{n(n+2)}$	Example	Orbitals used in bond formation				Description of structure
				3d	4s	4p	4d	
Mn(VII)	0	0.00	MnO_4^{-} [b]					sp^3 tetrahedral
Mn(VI)	1	1.73	MnO_4^{-2}					sp^3 tetrahedral
Mn(II)	1	1.73	$Mn(CN)_6^{-4}$					"Inner" orbital d^2sp^3 octahedral
Mn(III)	2	2.83	$Mn(CN)_6^{-3}$					Same
Mn(II)	3	3.88	$MnPy_2Cl_2$ [c]					dsp^2 square planar
Mn(III)	4	4.90	$Mn(Acac)_3$					"Outer" orbital sp^3d^2 octahedral
Mn(II)	5	5.92	$Mn(dipy)_3Br_2$					Same
Mn(II)	5	5.92	$Mn(kojate)_2$					sp^3 tetrahedral

[a] Key to abbreviations: Py = Pyridine; Acac = acetylacetone; kojic acid = 2-hydroxymethyl-5-hydroxy γ-pyrone.
[b] $KMnO_4$ shows a feeble temperature-independent paramagnetism. This does not affect the electronic and structural assignments. See Bates (13).
[c] Kleinberg, Argensinger, and Griswold (113) and Cox and his co-workers (52) state that this compound is a nonelectrolyte and has a planar structure. Conflicting evidence, however, is found in the literature (Cf. Selwood (193)).

of the results in terms of the valence-bond theory, however, must be treated with caution. Thus, at one time a diamagnetic tetracoordinated Ni(II) complex was interpreted as indicating a square planar complex, whereas a paramagnetic Ni(II) complex was interpreted as a tetrahedral complex.

Ni(II) [↑↓|↑↓|↑↓|↑↓|..] [..] [..|..] dsp^2, square planar

Ni(II) [↑↓|↑↓|↑↓|↑|↑] [..] [..|..|..] sp^3, tetrahedral

In terms of the rapidly growing approach of crystal field theory (8,57,106, 127,132,161,173,213), the square planar Ni(II) complexes may be either diamagnetic or paramagnetic, the former occurring with strong-field ligands, and the latter with weak-field ligands. Crystal field theory indicates that tetrahedral Ni(II) complexes should always be paramagnetic. The work of Holm (99), who gives several references, may be cited as representative in the area. The new approach stems, in reality, from the early and pioneering work of Van Vleck (226) and Bethe (16).

As was pointed out in Section IV (p. 1851), many polynuclear species show subnormal magnetic moments and may even show completely diamagnetic behavior (190; Cf. 150,153). This may arise from exchange interactions between electrons on adjacent metal ions or may be due to π bonding between a metal ion and the bridging group in the polynuclear species (62).

2. Applications to Organic Chemistry

a. FREE RADICALS

Many organic and organometallic molecules are known to dissociate into free radicals under conditions of dissolution of solids, pyrolysis, and photolysis. From the magnetic point of view, free radicals are entities containing unpaired electrons and, as such, behave as paramagnetics. The stable free radicals are easily studied by the magnetic susceptibility technique; absence of an orbital contribution to magnetic moment somewhat simplifies the calculation of the magnetic moment by the "spin-only" formula. A study of free radicals with extremely short lives of the order of microseconds can be studied very effectively by the newer technique of electron paramagnetic resonance.

Free radicals are highly reactive and particularly are autoxidizable in the dissolved state, although they might be somewhat stable in the solid state. The solid state does not pose serious problems in the measurement of their susceptibilities. These can be measured by the Gouy method. However, since the magnetic state of a free radical in solution is usually quite different from that in the solid, measurements for the two states provide a vast amount of analytical and structural information about the free radicals. Their study in solution naturally calls for a number of precautions; these include (1) a prevention of autooxidation by carrying out the magnetic measurements in an inert atmosphere, (2) prevention of interaction with the solvent wherever possible, and (3) prevention of the loss of solvent by evaporation, a normal precaution to be exercised in all work dealing with solutions.

A vast number of magnetic studies have been reported in the literature on free radicals in systems such as hexaaryl and hexaalkyl ethane, organometallics, semiquinones, porphyrins, highly conjugated systems, metal ketyls, etc. Dainton, Wiles, and Wright (55) have shown that solutions of potassium in ethers are diamagnetic, unlike solutions of alkali metals in ammonia and amines (67,214). The literature has been reviewed by many authors, notably by Selwood (193), Hutchison (101), Walling (231), Wheland (233) and Klemm (114). An account of the electron paramagnetic resonance studies is given by Ingram (102), by the Varian Associate staff (227), and by others (25,225). Only one application of the magnetic susceptibility data will be outlined here with reference to a classical study of the dissociation of hexaaryl ethane.

The studies of chemical and optical properties and of apparent molecular weights showed that the hexaaryl ethanes probably dissociate into the corresponding triaryl methanes. These methods have been shown to be in error. In some cases, solutions are known to exhibit color even after a complete disappearance of the free radical and, hence, the assumption that only the free radicals are colored and the corresponding intensity calculations give rise to erroneous results. The dissociation constant at 20°C. for the hexaphenyl ethane by the colorimetric method is found to be $4.1 \times 10^{-4.22}$ in benzene, 19.2×10^{-4} in carbon disulfide, and 1.2×10^{-4} in propionitrile. The heat of dissociation was found to be about 11 kcal. per mole. The magnetic method gives 2×10^{-4} for the dissociation constant in benzene (20°C.); this is about half the value obtained from the colorimetric method.

The experimental procedure and the nature of calculations are given below for determining the dissociation constant of hexaphenyl ethane:

$$\phi_3 C\!-\!C\phi_3 \rightleftharpoons 2\phi_3\dot{C}$$

A known weight of chloromethane is dissolved in benzene and is shaken with silver to form the hexaphenyl ethane. It is assumed that the reaction is complete without any loss of solvent. The percentage of ethane (5.49% found in an experiment) is calculated from the stoichiometry

The specific susceptibility of benzene is taken as -0.708×10^{-6}. From the measured specific susceptibility of the solution (-0.700×10^{-6}), and using Wiedmann's law, the specific susceptibility χ_g of ethane is found to be -0.56×10^{-6}. The apparent molar susceptibility, χ_m, for the partly dissociated ethane is found to be -272×10^{-6} from $\chi_m = \chi_g \times$ molecular weight. Using Pascal's empirical constants, the molar diamagnetic susceptibility for the ethane is calculated to be -325×10^{-6}. The apparent diamagnetic molar susceptibility, as measured, is seen to be less than the calculated value; the difference is attributed to a paramagnetic contribution due to the formation of the free radical $\phi_3\dot{C}$ from the hexaphenyl ethane. The molar paramagnetism representing partial dissociation is thus $-272 - (-325) \times 10^{-6} = 53 \times 10^{-6}$. The degree of dissociation, α, is calculated from the ratio of molar paramagnetic susceptibility (53×10^{-6}) obtained for partial dissociation to that expected (2532×10^{-6}) for complete dissociation of the hexaphenyl ethane; α is thus equal to 2.1%.

The value 2532×10^{-6} is arrived at in the following way. One mole of hexaphenyl ethane on complete dissociation gives 2 moles of the triphenyl-methyl free radicals. The molar susceptibility, χ'_m, correspondong to one unpaired electron is calculated from its magnetic moment, $(\mu = \sqrt{n(n+2)}$ $= 1.73$ Bohr magnetons. The simple relation used here is $\mu = 2.84 \sqrt{\chi'_m \cdot T}$, where T is the absolute temperature; 2.84 is the numerical value of the constant, $3K/N\beta^2$; and K, N, and β correspond to the Boltzmann constant, the Avogadro number, and the Bohr magneton, respectively. Using 1.73 for μ and $293.16°$ A. for the temperature, χ'_m is seen to be 1266×10^{-6}. For 2 moles we obtain 2532×10^{-6}.

The magnetic method is based on certain assumptions. For instance, in using the formula $\mu = 2.84 \sqrt{\chi'_m \cdot T}$, it is assumed that the Weiss constant for the triphenyl methyl radical is zero. Although some experimental evidence indicates that the Weiss constant is not too large for such systems, it is not entirely negligible in many cases. This poses the problem of having to explain, in the first place, any appreciable interactions not suspected to be present in such magnetically dilute systems, and secondly, of making adequate corrections to the values calculated for χ'_m.

Another inherent difficulty is in finding accurately the diamagnetism of the (paramagnetic) organic free radicals in these solutions.

This is commonly done by using Pascal's empirical constants (Tables 38.VI and 38.VII) or by measuring the molar susceptibility of the corresponding methane and subtracting from it the atomic susceptibility of hydrogen. However, neither of these methods are capable of allowing for the anomalously large diamagnetism of certain free radicals. This diamagnetism may be as large in magnitude as the paramagnetism of the free radical itself. It stems from the possibility of motion of electrons over large distances in many resonant structures which, according to current theories, are said to stabilize the free radicals with respect to the ethane. The resonance stabilization may be accompanied by a large increase of molecular anisotropy. These considerations have been used particularly to explain the strange observation (196) that hexa-*p*-biphenylethane and hexa-*p*-*tert*-butylphenylethane were found to be only 70% dissociated and the apparent degree of dissociation was not seen to depend on temperature.

In spite of some shortcomings, the magnetic susceptibility method has proved very useful not only in analytical respects but also in testing the theories of free radical stability.

b. STUDY OF REACTIONS

The oxidation of styrene (27) and the reversible reduction of duroquinone (139) are typical examples of reactions studied *in situ* by the magnetic method. A horizontal Gouy magnetic balance (Fig. 38.25), designed by Theorell, is sound to be quite adequate for such studies.

Work of Michaelis (139) on the reduction of duroquinone will be described. In this case it was possible to avoid the correction for diamagnetism of the free radicals produced in the reaction, because the system was found to return to its original value of diamagnetic susceptibility. This behavior resulted from the reversible nature of the reduction of the diamagnetic duroquinone.

In one experiment a small amount of duroquinone (~0.2 g.) was dissolved in a mixed alkaline solvent (about 8 ml. of water, 2 ml. of pyridine or alcohol, and 1 ml. of about $1N$ sodium hydroxide) and was placed in the horizontal specimen tube. Glucose (0.08 g.) was added as a reducing agent. At first the solution was diamagnetic, but during reduction the diamagnetic susceptibility gradually decreased to a minimum, indicating the formation of paramagnetic free radicals (Fig. 38.41). The difference between the maximum and minimum diamagnetic susceptibilities could be attributed, without making any corrections, to the maximum formation of the free radical that was formed in equilibrium with the quinone and semiquinone. At the end of about 2 hours, the magnetic susceptibility was found to return to its original diamagnetic state and remain constant. In practice this was taken as the minimum value for the diamagnetic susceptibility because, at the time of the first measurement, the reduction might already have started.

It was found that 0.0142 molar concentration of duroquinone produced

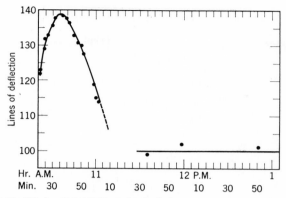

Fig. 38.41. Michaelis' (139) method of slow reduction of duroquinone.

a maximum concentration of 0.00757 mole per liter of the free radical. The concentration of the free radical was calculated according to the procedure discussed previously, with the exception that no correction for its diamagnetism had to be applied.

Glucose was found to be particularly suitable for studying slow reductions in the pH range of 10.5 to 12, whereas methyl glyoxal with traces of potassium cyanide was found suitable for reductions under acidic conditions (pH 3 to 5). The speed of the reductions could be controlled by adjusting the concentration of the reducing agent. Recently, reductions with several other monosaccharides have been also investigated (217).

c. STUDIES ON POLYMERIZATION OF DIAMAGNETIC MOLECULES

The work of Farquaharson (68) is quite representative in this area; rather extensive reviews (193) also are available.

The polymerization of 2,3-dimethylbutadiene will be considered. Suppose that $\chi_{m,M}$ and $\chi_{m,P}$ represent the molar susceptibilities of the monomer and a polymer containing n molecules of the monomer; then according to concepts of additivity,

$$\chi_{m,P} = n\chi_{m,M} + (n - 1)\lambda$$

where $n - 1$ corresponds to the new bonds formed between n molecules and λ is the constitutive correction constant for each bond. The specific susceptibility of the polymer χ_P is now given by

$$\chi_P = \frac{n\chi_{m,M} + (n - 1)\lambda}{n \times \text{mol. wt. of monomer}}$$

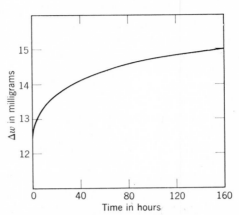

Fig. 38.42. Polymerization of 2,3-dimethylbutadiene; apparent change in weight on application of the magnetic field *vs.* time. From Selwood (193).

The polymerization of 2,3-dimethylbutadiene does show a hyperbolic curve expected for the above inverse relationship between χ_P and n. In general, by using Pascal's values for the specific bonds involved in polymerization, it is possible to find the degree of polymerization, n. The sensitivity of the method decreases rapidly with increases in n because the change in $\chi_{m,P}$ with respect to n varies inversely with n^2, which is seen by differentiating the above expression. The specific susceptibilities of 2,3-dimethylbutadiene and its final polymerized product are -0.670×10^{-6} and -0.7305×10^{-6}, respectively. Fig. 38.42 shows the change in diamagnetic susceptibility with time. Although the initial and final products are diamagnetic, a possibility exists for the formation of free radicals, which may induce the polymerization. Investigations showed that the induction period for the polymerization of 2,3-dimethylbutadiene is about 3 hours in the absence of any accelerator. During this period the molar susceptibility of the monomer decreases (instead of increasing) from -60×10^{-6} to about 42×10^{-6}; the sharp decrease is, therefore, attributed to the formation of paramagnetic free radicals. Simple calculations show that this decrease could be attributed to the formation of 0.7% of species with one unpaired electron. This has been verified indirectly by the addition of the same amount of benzoyl peroxide, an accelerator that results in a polymerization with no initial decrease in susceptibility.

A significant new development in organic polymers is reported by some Russian workers (15). Polymers containing nitrogen and polar groups in a conjugated chain in a macromolecule show a rapid decrease in paramagnetic susceptibility, which falls off rapidly with increasing field. This is said to be similar to a ferromagnetic behavior. The cloud of strongly interacting unpaired electrons is said to unite the whole structure into a single electronic unit. Preliminary experiments show that polyamino-quinones can act as extremely effective catalysts for decomposition of hydrogen peroxide and other oxidation-reduction reactions. Somewhat similar observations are reported by Krause (118). The polymers obtained from a reaction of benzidine and chloranil gave polymers with high susceptibility ($\sim$1.28 $\times$ 10^6), showing a dependence on the applied field. The polyaminoquinones show strong internal hydrogen bonds and form complexes with metals. The susceptibility and further E.P.R. data have been used to propose definite structures for the polyaminoquinones. Additional comments on the magnetic properties of (polymeric) nucleic acids are given on page 1875.

d. Quantitative Determination of Keto and Enol Forms in an Equilibrium Mixture

In many keto–enol equilibria, represented by

$$\begin{array}{cc} O & OH\ \ H \\ \| & |\ \ \ \ | \\ R\!-\!C\!-\!CH_2\!-\!R' \rightleftharpoons R\!-\!C\ =\ C\!-\!R' \end{array}$$

one may wish to find the relative proportions of the two tautomers. It is well known that many chemical methods of analysis do not provide accurate results. For instance, in the bromination method the enol content is obtained by quantitatively brominating its —C=C— bond. This is apt to shift the equilibrium to the enol side under the conditions of experiment and, therefore, lead to erroneous results. Hence, a method truly nondestructive with respect to the sensitive equilibrium is desired. Measurement of magnetic susceptibility of the equilibrium mixture provides an answer in many cases. A classical example is that of ethyl benzoylacetate, which was reported by Bhatnagar and Mathur (17), using Pascal's uncorrected constants, and by Hutchison (101), who employed the corrected constants. The molar susceptibility χ_m for the ketonic structure

is found to be

$$\chi_m(\text{keto}) = 11\chi_C + 12\chi_H + \chi_{=O'} + \chi_{-O-} + \chi C_{=O} + 6\lambda_{C(aro)} + \lambda_{C\alpha4} + \lambda_{C\gamma4}$$

$$= (-11 \times 6.00 - 12 \times 2.93 + 1.73 - 4.61 - 3.36 - 6 \times 0.24 -$$

$$- 1.54 - 1.54) \times 10^{-6}$$

$$= -111.9 \times 10^{-6}$$

The molar susceptibility for the enol structure

is given by

$$\chi_m(\text{enol}) = 11\chi_C + 12\chi_H + 2\chi_{-O-} + \chi_{=O} + 6\lambda_{C(aro)} + \lambda_{C=C} + \lambda_{C\alpha4} +$$

$$\lambda_{C\gamma4} + \lambda_{C\beta3} + 2\lambda_{C\alpha3}$$

$$= (-11 \times 6.00 - 12 \times 2.93 - 2 \times 4.61 - 3.36 - 6 \times 0.24 + 5.5 -$$

$$1.54 - 1.54 - 0.48 - 2 \times 1.29) \times 10^{-6}$$

$$= 115.8 \times 10^{-6}$$

The molecular weight of the compound is 192. The specific susceptibility found experimentally is -0.6001×10^{-6}, which gives a molar susceptibility of -115.2×10^{-6}, indicating that the equilibrium mixture exists largely in the enolic form. This is in agreement with other physical and chemical evidence. The exact percentage p of the enol form is calculated on the basis of additivity from

$$-115.8 \times 10^{-6} \times p + [-111.9 \times 10^{-6}](100-p) = -115.2 \times 10^{-6} \times 100$$

This gives $p = 84.6\%$.

These determinations call for an accuracy of at least 0.1% or better, which also is true of other physical methods. One can then distinguish between two structures having a difference of about 3 units in their molar susceptibilities. An error of $\pm 1\%$ leads to erroneous results; this may be illustrated in the following manner. Suppose that the specific susceptibility measured was either -0.6061×10^{-6} or -0.5941×10^{-6}, which represent values with an error of about $+1\%$ and -1%, respectively, in -0.6001×10^{-6} considered previously. These would lead to values of -116.3×10^{-6} and -114.1×10^{-6} for the molar susceptibility of the compound. This would mean that corresponding to these two cases the percentage of the enolic form is about 113% or 56.4%!

It may be pointed out that much of the confusion in magnetochemistry (particularly in those areas involving an application of the feeble diamagnetic properties) stems from a lack of accuracy and also of precision in the magnetic measurements.

e. DETERMINATION OF STRUCTURES

An interesting application of diamagnetism, independent of any assumptions involving the use of Pascal's constants, is to be found in the work of Pink and Ubbelhode (176), which has been reviewed by Hutchison (101). It refers to the problem of finding whether cyclooctatetraene is a nonplanar fourfold conjugated system. Thermal data showed that the eight-membered ring has a rather low resonance energy and favored such a structure (A). Now, from a structural point of view, the difference between this and cyclooctane (B) corresponds to 8 hydrogen atoms and 4 —C=C— bonds.

$$
\begin{array}{cc}
\overset{\displaystyle CH=CH}{\diagup\qquad\diagdown} & \overset{\displaystyle CH_2-CH_2}{\diagup\qquad\diagdown} \\
CH\qquad\qquad CH & CH_2\qquad\qquad CH_2 \\
\parallel\qquad\qquad\parallel & \mid\qquad\qquad\mid \\
CH\qquad\qquad CH & CH_2\qquad\qquad CH_2 \\
\diagdown\qquad\diagup & \diagdown\qquad\diagup \\
CH=CH & CH_2-CH_2 \\
(A) & (B)
\end{array}
$$

Considering the analogous cyclohexene (C) and cyclohexane (D),

$$
\begin{array}{cc}
\overset{\displaystyle CH_2}{\diagup\quad\diagdown} & \overset{\displaystyle CH_2}{\diagup\quad\diagdown} \\
CH_2\qquad CH & CH_2\qquad CH_2 \\
\mid\qquad\parallel & \mid\qquad\mid \\
CH_2\qquad CH & CH_2\qquad CH_2 \\
\diagdown\quad\diagup & \diagdown\quad\diagup \\
CH_2 & CH_2 \\
(C) & (D)
\end{array}
$$

a difference of 10.2×10^{-6} is found in their measured molar susceptibilities, which, according to Pascal's concepts, may be taken to correspond to $2\chi_H - \lambda_{C=C}$. Therefore, 4 times 10.2×10^{-6} ($=40.8 \times 10^{-8}$) may be taken to correspond to $8\chi_H - 4\lambda_{C=C}$. This is the difference between cyclooctane (B) and cyclooctatetraene (A), which show a difference of 39.5×10^{-6} between their measured molar susceptibilities, in close agreement with 40.8×10^{-8}. Hence, cyclooctatetraene may be pictured to be a conjugated nonaromatic ring.

The conclusion is supported even by using Pascal's constants. Assumption of an aromatic ring gives

$$\chi_m = 8\chi_C + 8\chi_H + 8\lambda_{C(arom)} = -73.36 \times 10^{-6}$$

whereas assumption of a nonaromatic system gives

$$\chi_m = 8\chi_C + 8\chi_H + 2\lambda \underset{\diagup}{\overset{\diagdown}{C}} = -50.2 \times 10^{-6}$$

The measured value of molar susceptibility of cyclooctatetraene is found to be -51.9×10^{-6}, in close agreement with the conjugated nonaromatic structure.

It may be pointed out that McDonnell and his co-workers (129) considered the possibility that cyclooctatetraene might exist partially in the form of paramagnetic biradicals, which would diminish the apparent diamagnetism of the molecule and make it appear less aromatic in character. To verify the presence of paramagnetism they measured the susceptibility as a function of temperature. They found no such dependence down to about 98°K. This could be interpreted (1) to show a complete absence of paramagnetic biradicals or (2) that the paramagnetic state of the biradical (with resultant spin $= 2 \times 1/2 = 1$ for two unpaired electrons) lies slightly higher than the diamagnetic state (with resultant spin $= 0$ for paired electrons), so that it could compensate any increase in paramagnetism with a decrease in temperature. It is believed that the probability of such a coincidental compensation is very small and hence the previous conclusions remain unchanged.

f. Application of Magnetic Anisotropy to Structural and Bonding Problems

Magnetic anisotropy has been used occasionally to elucidate several structural problems, especially of organic compounds. Excellent accounts in this area have been given by Selwood (193), Michaelis (139), and Ray (183). It must be pointed out that the technique is rather involved and quite cumbersome. To start with, one generally must face the problem of growing a single crystal that is sufficiently large for easy handling. Each edge of the crystal should be at least 2 to 3 mm. wide. Secondly, if values of principal molecular susceptibilities are to be used in the interpretations, complete x-ray diffraction data become necessary.

In spite of these limitations, the work (151–151b) on magnetic anisotropy of ferrocene will be briefly outlined, as it represents, in the author's opinion, an interesting application to the electronic bonding problem in this fascinating compound. The original publications should be consulted for details of experimentation and arguments concerning the bonding, and for references not given here.

The Krishnan flip-angle method (119), with several modifications including those suggested by Gordon (82), was used. Fourteen different

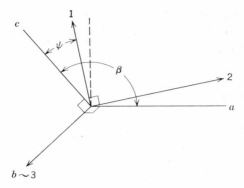

Fig. 38.43. Relationship of the crystal axes (*a*, *b*, *c*) to the principal magnetic axes (*1*, *2*, *3*) in ferrocene. Reproduced by permission of the *Journal of the American Chemical Society* (153).

crystals of ferrocene varying in size from 25 to 165 mg. were used in conjunction with four different quartz fibers (15 to 20 μ in diameter). The following values of crystal anisotropy, in units of 10^{-6}, were obtained:

$$\chi_1 - \chi_2 = 37.0 \pm 0.4; \ \chi_1 - \chi_3 = 40.9 \pm 0.3; \ \chi_2 - \chi_3 = 3.9 \pm 0.3;$$

$$\psi = 24 \pm 1°$$

Here ψ is the angle between the *c*-crystal axis and the direction of χ_1, as shown in Fig. 38.43.

Using the average value for the magnetic susceptibility (that is, $(\chi_1 + \chi_2 + \chi_3)/3$), the principal susceptibilities for ferrocene were found to be, in units of 10^{-6},

$$\chi_1 = -99, \chi_2 = -136, \chi_3 = -139.9$$

From a knowledge of the crystal-structure data, and employing the method of Lonsdale and Krishnan, the following values for the principal molecular susceptibilities (Fig. 38.44), in units of 10^{-6}, were obtained.

$$K_1 = -105, K_2 = -112, K_3 = -158, \psi = 22°$$

The agreement in the ψ values was regarded as a check on the determined values of the molecular direction cosines and the crystal susceptibilities. These results establish that the susceptibility K_3 at right angles to the plane of the ring is quite large as compared to the other two values. This can be attributed only to a circulation of π electrons in the rings and was substantiated by theoretical calculations of susceptibility arising from such circulation. This conclusion naturally supports the view that the π

electrons are free to circulate in the rings and that one π electron is enough to take part in each of the so-called "metal-to-ring" $d\pi$ — $p\pi$ bonds. The anisotropy studies do not favor the possibility of a complete donation of

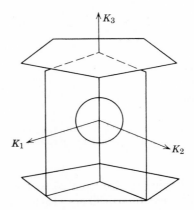

Fig. 38.44. Molecular axes for the magnetic anisotropy of ferrocene. Reproduced by permission of the *Journal of the American Chemical Society* (153).

π electrons (six from each ring) to the iron, as suggested by early workers, since in that case K_3 would have been much smaller than the observed value.

3. Applications to Biochemistry

Applications of magnetic studies to biochemical problems deal predominately with structural aspects of components of blood and a study of their reactions. In recent years studies on other biological components, such as ribonucleic acid (RNA) and deoxyribonucleic acid (DNA) have been reported. The general trend has been to study the nuclear and electron magnetic resonance spectra.

a. Study of Components of Blood

The pioneering work in this area has been due to Haurowitz, Pauling, Coryell, and their co-workers (51,89,170,171,218).

The heme, which is an iron porphyrin complex, may be said to be the essential constituent of hemoglobin and related compounds. The terms ferri and ferroheme refer to the ferric, Fe(III), and ferrous Fe(II), complexes of iron.

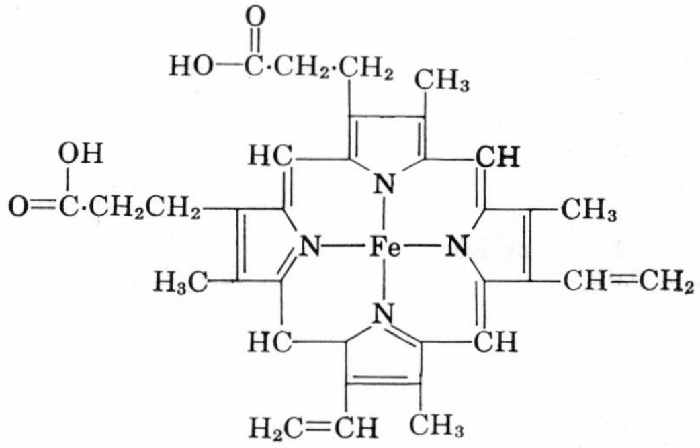

$$\begin{array}{c}
O \\
\| \\
HO{-}C{\cdot}CH_2{\cdot}CH_2 \quad CH_3
\end{array}$$

Heme: iron porphyrin complex

The general procedure has been to study the magnetic susceptibility of such components or their derivatives and to obtain the magnetic moment per gram atom of iron in these compounds. The magnetic criteria outlined previously under coordination compounds have been used to determine the valence state of iron and the bond type in these complexes.

In most cases an octahedral d^2sp^3 bonding is observed. Ferriheme chloride (hemin) has a magnetic moment of about 5.8 Bohr magnetons for iron, which corresponds to the theoretical value 5.92 Bohr magnetons for the $5d$ electrons in Fe(III). The iron in ferrohemoglobin, which is regarded as a conjugated protein containing native globin and the ferroheme, is found to have a moment of about 4.91 Bohr magnetons. This corresponds to the theoretical value of 4.9 Bohr magnetons for the $4d$ unpaired electrons in Fe(II).

The magnetic moments observed for some derivatives of iron protoporphyrin and porphyrin are shown below, using Rawlinson's (182) scheme.

A magnetic moment in the neighborhood of 2.83 Bohr magnetons corresponding to two unpaired electrons has not been reported in any of the derivatives.

It may be pointed out that the magnetic moment observed for iron in many derivatives depends on the experimental conditions employed. It has been now well established that the dimerization and polymerization of Fe(III) ions in solution at moderate acidities is sufficient to depress the average magnetic moment per gram atom of iron (150,153). Hence the magnetic moments observed in many cases, for instance, in hematin, need a cautious interpretation. The effect of pH on the magnetic moment of iron in ferrihemoglobin will be discussed under magnetic titrations.

Magnetic moments varying between 2 and 5.89 Bohr magnetons have been observed in ferrihemoglobin derivatives containing imidazole, ammonia, azide, and ethanol groups. Some studies are reported on hemochromogens, which are compounds of ferroheme and denatured globin.

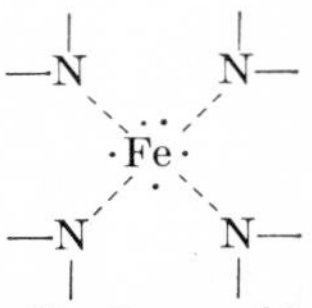

Hemin (ferriheme chloride)
$n = 5$, $\mu = 5.91$

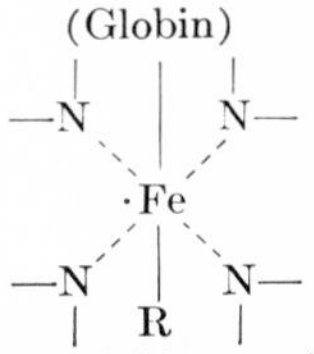

Ferrihemoglobin cyanide, or
ferrihemoglobin hydrosulfide
$n = 1$, $\mu = 2.50$ (R=CN)
$\mu = 2.26$ (R=SH)

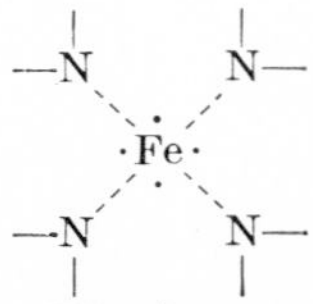

Ferroheme
$n = 4$, $\mu = 4.90$

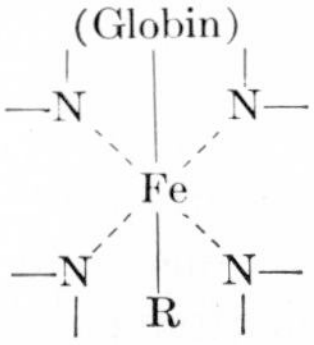

Oxyhemoglobin (R is —O=O)
or carbonmonoxyhemoglobin (R is =CO)
$n = 0$, $\mu = 0$

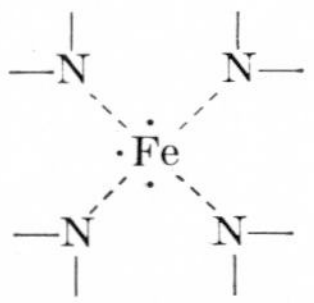

Hematin (ferriheme hydroxide)
$n = 3$, $\mu = 3.88$

Myoglobin, catalase, and other iron-containing compounds also have been investigated. The work has been reviewed by Selwood (193), by Haurowitz and Kittel (89), and by others (78,126,157,170). In a recent study, Brill and Williams (35) have correlated the absorption spectra of ferric porphyrin complexes with the magnetic moment of iron in these complexes. An analysis of the absorption spectra has been used to estimate the amounts of low-spin and high-spin complexes that exist in equilibrium mixtures. Magnetic, oxidation-reduction, and other chemical properties have been used to elucidate the nature of groups binding the iron in the hemoproteins, catalase, peroxidase, hemoglobin, and myoglobin. Brill and Williams' work gives an extensive bibliography in this area.

b. Magnetokinetic Studies

The work of Brill and his co-workers (33) on a magnetokinetic study of the reaction between ferrimyoglobin and methyl hydrogen peroxide represents an unique application of their "magnetic susceptometer," devised for studying kinetics of reactions and flow systems. A brief description of the apparatus is to be found under the experimental section.

In earlier work, Theorell and Ehrenberg (221) used a specially modified Gouy method for their studies on the red compound formed by the reaction between horse ferrimyoglobin and methyl hydrogen peroxidase. Because of the instability of this compound at the ferrimyoglobin concentration of 650 μM, some of the compound had reverted to ferrimyoglobin during the relatively long time required for making measurements with the Gouy balance. These authors made appropriate corrections for the ferrimyoglobin present, using spectrophotometric technique, and obtained a tentative value of 3000×10^{-6} c.g.s. units for the paramagnetic susceptibility of the red compound. According to Griffith (87), who introduced other corrections, the revised value is 3300×10^{-6} c.g.s. units.

The flow-system type susceptometer has many advantages over the Gouy method. It is capable of handling much smaller concentrations of the paramagnetic material and has a response of a few tenths of a second. In a kinetic study with this apparatus, methyl hydrogen peroxidase was injected into a sample of ferrimyoglobin and the changes in the magnetic susceptibility were followed on a recorder. The susceptibility of the reaction product was calculated from

$$\chi_{\text{compound}} = \chi_{\text{unreacted}} - \Delta\chi$$

where

$$\Delta\chi = \frac{10^3 \cdot \Delta\kappa(\text{final})}{(\text{ferrimyoglobin})}$$

and represents the observed change in molar susceptibility. The molar susceptibility of the unreacted ferrimyoglobin existing in two forms was calculated on the basis of additivity relation, using, at 20°C., $\chi_{\text{Fe}} = 13{,}980 \times 10^{-6}$ for the brown form and $\chi_{\text{FeOH}} = 11{,}330 \times 10^{-6}$ for the red alkaline form.

In the final analysis, Brill and his co-workers (33) calculated the magnetic susceptibility of the reaction product to be $(3300 \pm 500) \, 10^{-6}$ c.g.s. units. The rate constants for the reaction between ferrimyoglobin and methyl hydrogen peroxidase were obtained as a function of temperature, using the magnetic and spectrophotometric techniques. Significant differences were observed, particularly at low temperatures, in the results obtained by the two techniques. The authors point out that the magnetically determined rate constants would not be expected to obey the Arrhenius relation if two or more magnetic processes contribute to the observed kinetic curve. They considered the possibility of production and disappearance of free radicals, which was previously postulated by other workers in the reaction between ferrimyoglobin and hydrogen peroxide. Thus the production and disappearance of free radicals affected the time course of magnetic susceptibility, whereas the spectrophotometric method generally followed the over-all conversion of ferrimyoglobin to the reaction product. The original paper contains several interesting aspects of this work and discussions on other reactions.

c. Determination of Hemoglobin Concentration

The method was developed by Taylor and Coryell (218). It is quite promising, as it gives results more accurately than the conventional gasometric methods based on the determination of carbon monoxide capacity. The hemoglobin solution is reduced to ferrohemoglobin using sodium dithionite, $Na_2S_2O_4$. Ferrohemoglobin is paramagnetic. This is then saturated with carbon monoxide and converted to carbonmonoxyferrohemoglobin, which is diamagnetic. The difference between their susceptibilities, therefore, represents the paramagnetic contribution of the ferrohemoglobin. The observed difference depends on the concentration of ferrohemoglobin, which in turn corresponds to the original concentration of hemoglobin. A change in molar susceptibility of $12,290 \times 10^{-6}$ at 24°C. corresponds to one heme; the effective magnetic moment of ferrohemoglobin is taken to be 5.46 Bohr magnetons. In these experiments the diamagnetism of water, dissolved salts, and proteins cancels out, since the entire change in magnetic properties arises from a change in the state of iron, except for the negligible diamagnetism of added carbon monoxide.

A divided glass tube (18 mm. in diameter, 30 cm. long) was used to measure the difference between the susceptibility of the hemoglobin solution and of water using the Gouy technique. About 0.3 to 0.6 g. of sodium dithionite was used for reducing 30 ml. of the solution to ferrohemoglobin. In the actual experiments, the apparent change in weight of the solution on application of the magnetic field is determined. Since this is proportional to the magnetic susceptibility, a calculation of the actual susceptibility is avoided. Representing the change in weight for the ferrohemoglobin by ΔW_{Hb}, for the carbonmonoxy hemoglobin by ΔW_{HbCO}, and for the solution being studied by ΔW, the "molal susceptibility" per heme at 24°C. for the solution under investigation is given by

$$\chi_M = \frac{(\Delta W - \Delta W_{HbCO})}{(\Delta W_{Hb} - \Delta W_{HbCO})} \times 12,290 \times 10^{-6}$$

d. MAGNETIC TITRATIONS

It was pointed out previously that it is possible to carry out a magnetic study of chemical processes in which large changes in susceptibility arise due to conversion of a paramagnetic species into a diamagnetic one (or to species with relatively small paramagnetism) and vice versa. Such study is particularly facilitated if the susceptibility changes in the reagent and its products are very small. A number of magnetic titrations of oxyhemoglobin and ferrihemoglobin with diamagnetic reagents, such as sodium dithionite, sodium hydroxide, and potassium cyanide, have been described by Coryell and his co-workers (51). The Gouy technique, which allows handling of large samples (20 to 30 ml.) is very convenient for such titrations.

Oxyhemoglobin, which is diamagnetic, on reduction with sodium dithionite gives hemoglobin, which is paramagnetic. In the experimental procedure, a solution of oxyhemoglobin is introduced in a cylindrical sample tube ($\sim$25 ml.), which is closed with a rubber cap. Small volumes, about 0.5 ml., of sodium dithionite solution of a suitable concentration are injected each time from a syringe through the rubber cap. The magnetic

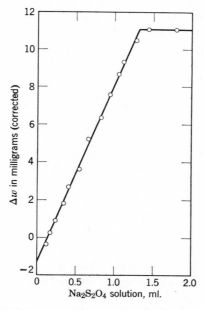

Fig. 38.45. Magnetic titration of oxyhemoglobin with sodium dithionite. From Selwood (193).

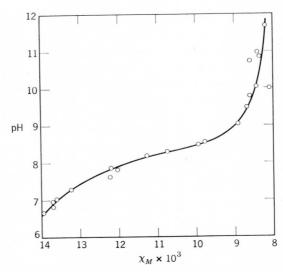

Fig. 38.46. Magnetic titration of ferrihemoglobin. From Selwood (193).

field is applied and the change in weight ΔW is determined after each addition of the reagent. Appropriate corrections are made for the effect of the added reagent on the observed ΔW values. This correction is determined by performing a separate experiment with the reagent or by using Pascal's constants. It is not necessary to apply corrections for the changes in susceptibility that occur during the oxidation of sodium dithionite itself, because such changes are diamagnetic and quite small. These fall well within the limits of experimental error involved in the Gouy method. A curve for the titration of oxyhemoglobin with sodium dithionite is shown in Fig. 38.45. The changes in ΔW are seen to be quite linear with the volume of the reagent, and a sharp end point is obtained; the curves and the limits of error are comparable to those obtained in the conventional conductometric type of titrations.

The magnetic titration of ferrihemoglobin is shown in Fig. 38.46. The pH was adjusted by the addition of suitable alkali and the same experimental method as before was used. The reaction was shown to be first order in hydroxide ion, and equilibrium constants were calculated. The calculation of the molar susceptibility from the changes in weight facilitated a calculation of the over-all change in the magnetic moment per gram atom of iron during the reaction. The magnetic moment at the point of inflection, which is somewhat affected by the ionic strength, was found to correspond to a species with three unpaired electrons.

c. Other Biochemical and Biological Studies

During the past few years some workers (180) have studied magnetic susceptibilities of carcinogenic compounds in efforts to examine the co-existence of antimitotic and carcinogenic action. They report that the susceptibility of chloramine, triethylenemelamine, urethan, myleran, 6-mercaptopurine, and several others show very high susceptibility. The observed values are higher than the calculated ones and range from 7.5×10^{-6} or 12×10^{-6}. This is ascribed to a spread of one or more π electrons in these molecules. Much work in this area appears to be purely speculative in nature.

In 1959 Bliumenfeld (21,22) reported work on the electron spin resonance in nucleic acids. Since then a number of workers have studied both the electron resonance and magnetic moments of a wide variety of preparations of nucleic acids. Shulman and his co-workers (199) showed that the electron spin-resonance spectra reported by earlier workers exhibit a ferromagnetic rather than paramagnetic behavior. This has been attributed to trace quantities of iron, which were shown to be present in amounts sufficient to explain the observed magnetism, assuming that the magnetic ions exist as concentrated ferromagnetic aggregates rather than as dispersed paramagnetic centers. The entire field has been reviewed critically in a recent article (232), whose authors suggest that the iron found in nucleoproteins is present in the living cells, although not in the concentrated ferromagnetic form. The latter, an oxide–hydroxide type material approximating Fe_3O_4 in composition, may be precipitated during the extraction of nucleic acids or may even form quite slowly in intact but dried organisms. These views are supported by findings of Wacker and Vallee (230).

Another interesting development is reported by Senftle and Thorpe (197), who studied the magnetic susceptibility of normal liver and transplantable hepatoma tissue. It was shown that the difference is probably due in large part to the amount of water held by the cells in the two types of tissue and on adsorbed oxygen. The water in the normal cells appears to be bound, whereas that in the tumor tissues appears to be partially free.

4. Geochemical Applications

Applications of magnetic susceptibility in the geochemical area are fewer in number and somewhat less specific than in the pure chemical and biochemical areas. However, it may be mentioned that magnetic susceptibility measurements on samples collected at different depths may be used to locate similar strata below ground, as in regions of oil wells. This is accomplished by plotting magnetic susceptibility as a function of depth. Variations in susceptibility in different strata are related to similar variations from other wells in adjacent areas. Tectonic structures favorable to accumulation of mineral deposits may be located by this method. Valuable information on the orientation of the earth's magnetic field in past ages has been obtained by measuring the orientation of magnetized impurities at different depths, under the ocean floor, and in sedimentary rocks. Many workers have tried to correlate the magnetic properties of minerals with their geochemical history. Several geochemical and geophysical journals and monographs, published by the American Institute of Mining and Metallurgical Engineers, describe magnetic analysis of minerals in the field, which are helpful for magnetic prospecting. Selected references are given by Selwood (193) and Kauffmann (109).

ACKNOWLEDGMENTS

The author is grateful to the following for permission to reproduce figures, numerical data, or quotations from their work: Professors S. Broersma, B. N. Figgis, J. Lewis, J. H. Van Vleck, A. Pacault, and P. W. Selwood, and to the American Physical Society and other scientific organizations mentioned in the text. He is indebted also to the staff of Professor H. Theorell's magnetic laboratory in Stockholm, Sweden, for a demonstration of their apparatus and techniques.

He is thankful to his wife, Dr. Indumati Mulay, for her invaluable help in the compilation of references and for bringing to his attention the interesting magnetic work on biological systems.

The encouragement and support received from the P. R. I. and the American Cancer Society at the University of Cincinnati are also gratefully acknowledged.

REFERENCES

1. Abbott, A., and R. Kilgour, *J. Sci. Instr.*, **31**, 155 (1954).
2. Aldenkamp, A. A., C. P. Marks, and H. Zijlstra, *Rev. Sci. Instr.*, **31**, 544 (1960).
3. Amey, W. G., W. R. Clark, F. M. Kranz, and A. J. Williams, Jr., Communication and Electronics Paper **54–295**, 1 (1954).
4. Angus, W. R., and W. K. Hill, *Trans. Faraday Soc.*, **40**, 185 (1943).
5. Archenhold, W. F., A. C. Brown, and J. E. Thompson, *J. Sci. Instr.*, **36**, 505 (1959).
6. Aston, J. G., B. Bolger, R. Trambarulo, and H. Segall, *J. Chem. Phys.*, **22**, 460 (1954).
7. Atanasiu, G., and S. Patrascu, *Rev. Phys. Bucarest*, **4**, 273 (1959).
8. Ballhausen, C. J., *Introduction to Ligand Field Theory*, McGraw-Hill, New York, 1962.

9. Bamford, C. R., and H. Charnock, *Phys. Chem. Glass*, **1**, 143 (1960).
10. Banerjee, B. K., *Indian J. Phys.*, **33**, 201 (1959).
11. Barnett, S. J., *J. Appl. Phys.*, **23**, 975 (1952).
12. Bartlett, E. S., and D. N. Williams, *Rev. Sci. Instr.*, **28**, 919 (1957).
13. Bates, L. F., *Modern Magnetism*, Cambridge University Press, London, 1961.
14. Bell, J. S., and P. G. Wright, *Electronic Engr.*, **32**, 394 (1960).
15. Berlin, A. A., L. A. Blymenfeld, and N. N. Semenov, *Izvest. Akad. Nauk. S.S.R., Otdel. Khim. Nauk.*, **1959**, 1689.
16. Bethe, H., *Ann. Phys.*, **3**, 133 (1929).
17. Bhatnagar, S. S., and K. N. Mathur, *Physical Principles and Applications of Magnetochemistry*, Macmillan, London, 1935.
18. Birss, R. R., and E. W. Lee, *J. Sci. Instr.*, **37**, 225 (1960).
19. Bishay, A., *J. Am. Ceram. Soc.*, **44**, 16 (1961).
20. Bitter, F., *Phys. Rev.*, **35**, 1572 (1930).
21. Bliumenfeld, L. A., *Biophysika*, **4** (3), 515 (1959).
22. Bliumenfeld, L. A., A. E. Kalmanson, and Pei-Ken Sheng, *Dokl. Akad. Nauk. S.S.R.*, **124**, 1144 (1959).
23. Block, R. B., *U.S. At. Energy Comm. Rept.*, **AECU-4554** (1959), *Nuclear Sci. Abstr.*, **14**, 678 (1960).
24. Bloembergen, N., E. M. Purcell, and R. V. Pound, *Phys. Rev.*, **73**, 679 (1948).
25. Blois, M. S., Jr., H. M. Brown, R. M. Lemmon, R. O. Lindblom, and M. Weissbluth, *Free Radicals in Biological Systems*, Academic Press, New York, 1961.
26. Bloom, A. L., and M. E. Packard, *Science*, **122**, 738 (1955).
27. Boardman, H., and P. W. Selwood, *J. Am. Chem. Soc.*, **72**, 1372 (1950).
28. Bockris, J. O'M., and D. F. Parsons, *J. Sci. Instr.*, **30**, 362 (1953).
29. Bodenstein, M., P. Hartek, and E. Padelt, *Z. anorg. Chem.*, **147**, 233 (1925).
30. Bose, A., *Indian J. Phys.*, **21**, 275 (1947).
31. Bozorth, R. M., *Ferromagnetism*, D. Van Nostrand, New York, 1951.
32. Bozorth, R. M., J. H. Van Vleck, and several other authors, *Magnetic Properties of Metals and Alloys*, American Society for Metals, Cleveland, 1959.
33. Brill, A. S., A. Ehrenberg, and H. Den Hartog, *Biochem. Biophys. Acta*, **40**, 313 (1960).
34. Brill, A. S., H. Den Hartog, and V. Legallais, *Rev. Sci. Instr.*, **29**, 383 (1958).
35. Brill, A. S., and R. J. P. Williams, *Biochem. J.*, **78**, 246 (1961).
36. Broersma, S., *Am. J. Phys.*, **24**, 500 (1956).
37. Broersma, S., *Rev. Sci. Instr.*, **24**, 993 (1953).
38. Broersma, S., *Rev. Sci. Instr.*, **20**, 660 (1949); and *Magnetic Measurements on Organic Compounds*, Martinus Nijhoff, The Hague, 1947; *J. Chem. Phys.*, **17**, 873 (1949).
39. Broersma, S., *J. Chem. Phys.*, **26**, 1405 (1957).
40. Brownlow, C. E. A., *Nature*, **194**, 176 (1962).
41. Butera, R. A., R. S. Craig, and Cherry, L. V., *Rev. Sci. Instr.*, **32**, 708 (1961).
42. Candela, G. A., and R. E. Mundy, *Rev. Sci. Instr.*, **32**, 1056 (1961).
43. Carr, H. Y., and E. M. Purcell, *Phys. Rev.*, **94**, 630 (1954).
44. Cartmell, E., and G. W. A. Fowles, *Valency and Molecular Structure*, 2nd ed., Academic Press, New York, 1962.
45. Chandrasekhar, B. S., *Rev. Sci. Instr.*, **27**, 967 (1956).
46. Chen, W. K., F. B. Koch, and J. M. Sivertson, *Rev. Sci. Instr.*, **31**, 1157 (1960).
47. Chéneveau, C., *Phil. Mag.*, **20**, 357 (1910).
48. Cini, R., *Ricerca Sci.*, **29**, 506 (1959).

49. Clow, A., *Trans. Faraday Soc.*, **33**, 381 (1937).
50. Conger, R. L., and P. W. Selwood, *J. Chem. Phys.*, **20**, 383 (1952).
51. Coryell, C. D., F. Stitt, and L. Pauling, *J. Am. Chem. Soc.*, **59**, 633 (1937).
51a. Cotton, F. A., and G. Wilkinson, *Advanced Inorganic Chemistry*, Interscience div., Wiley, New York, 1962.
52. Cox, E. G., A. J. Shorter, W. Wardlaw, and W. J. R. Way, *J. Chem. Soc.*, **1937**, 1556.
53. Cunningham, B. B., *Nucleonics*, **5**, 62 (1949).
54. Curtis, N. F., *J. Chem. Soc.*, **1961**, 3147.
55. Dainton, F. S., D. M. Wiles, and J. Wright, *J. Chem. Soc.*, **1960**, 4283.
56. Day, M. C., L. D. Hulett, and D. E. Willis, *Rev. Sci. Instr.*, **31**, 1142 (1960).
57. Day, M. C., Jr., and J. Selbin, *Theoretical Inorganic Chemistry*, Reinhold, New York, 1962.
58. Desirant, M., and J. L. Michiels, *Solid State Physics*, Part I, Vol. III (*Magnetic and Optical Properties*), Academic Press, New York, 1960.
59. Doan, D. J., *U.S. Bur. Mines, Invest., Tech. Papers, No.* **3268**, 91 (1935).
60. Dodd, R. E., and P. L. Robinson, *Experimental Inorganic Chemistry*, Elsevier, London, 1957.
61. Earnshaw, A., *Lab. Practice*, **10**, 157, 294 (1961).
62. Earnshaw, A., and J. Lewis, *J. Chem. Soc.*, **1961**, 396.
63. Edwards, D. F., R. W. Terhue, and V. J. Lazazzera, *Rev. Sci. Instr.*, **29**, 1049 (1958).
64. Effemy, H. G., D. F. Parsons, and J. O'M. Bockris, *J. Sci. Instr.*, **32**, 99 (1955).
65. Ericson, R. A., L. D. Roberts, and J. W. T. Dobbs, *Rev. Sci. Instr.*, **25**, 1178 (1954).
66. Evans, D. F., *J. Chem. Soc.*, **1959**, 2003.
67. Evers, E. C., *J Chem. Educ.*, **38**, 591 (1961).
68. Farquaharson, J., and P. Ady, *Nature*, **143**, 1067 (1939).
69. Feher, G., and W. D. Knight, *Rev. Sci. Instr.*, **26**, 293 (1955).
70. Figgis, B. N., and J. Lewis, "The Magnetochemistry of Complex Compounds," in *Modern Coordination Chemistry*, Editors. J. Lewis and R. G. Wilkins, Eds., Interscience, New York–London, 1960.
71. Figgis, B. N., and R. S. Nyholm, *J. Chem. Soc.*, **1959**, 331.
72. Flourney, J. M., L. H. Baum, and S. Siegels, *Rev. Sci. Instr.*, **31**, 1133 (1960).
73. Foex, G., C. J. Gorter, and L. J. Smits, *Tables Constantes Selectionnées Diamagnetisme et Paramagnetisme*, Masson et Cie, Paris, 1957.
74. Foner, S., *Rev. Sci. Instr.*, **30**, 549 (1959).
74a. Frei, K., and H. J. Bernstein, *J. Chem. Phys.*, **37**, 1891 (1962). The method has been modified by this author; see Reference 149.
75. French, C. M., and D. J. Harrison, *J. Chem. Soc.*, **1953**, 2538.
75a. Fritz, J.J., R. V. Rao, and S. Seki, *J. Phys. Chem.*, **62**, 703 (1958).
76. Garber, M., W. G. Henry, and H. G. Hoeve, *Can. J. Phys.*, **38**, 1595 (1960).
77. Geist, D., *Z. Phys.*, **158**, 359 (1960).
78. George, P., and R. L. J. Lyster, "A Survey of the Crevice Configuration for the Heme in Hemoglobin," in *Conference on Hemoglobin*, Publication 557, National Academy of Sciences and National Research Council, Washington, D.C., 1958.
79. Gill, S. J., G. P. Malone, and M. Downing, *Rev. Sci. Instr.*, **31**, 1299 (1960).
80. Glaser, A., *Ann. Physik.*, **75**, 459 (1924).
81. Goodeve, C. F., and F. D. Richardson, *J. Chem. Soc.*, **1937**, 294.
81a. Goodenough, J. B., *Magnetism and the Chemical Bond*, Interscience (Wiley), New York, 1963.

82. Gordon, D. A., *Rev. Sci. Instr.*, **29**, 929 (1958).

83. Gordon, S., and C. Campbell, *Anal. Chem.*, **32**, 271R (1960).

84. Gouy, L. G., *Compt. rend.*, **109**, 935 (1889).

85. Gray, F. W., and J. H. Cruickshank, *Trans. Faraday Soc.*, **31**, 1491 (1935).

85a. Graddon, D. P., *An Introduction to Coordination Chemistry*, Pergamon, London, 1961.

86. Griffith, J. S., *The Theory of Transition Metal Ions*, Cambridge University Press, London, 1961.

87. Griffith, J. S., *Biochim. Biophys. Acta*, **28**, 439 (1958).

88. Gruns, Y. E., and E. A. Suvorov, *Izvmerit Technika*, **1959**, 37.

89. Haurowitz, F., and H. Kittel, *Ber.*, **66B**, 1046 (1993).

90. Havens, G. G., *Phys. Rev.*, **41**, 337 (1932); **43**, 992 (1333).

91. Heal, H. G., *Recent Studies in Boron Chemistry, Roy. Inst. Chem. (London), Monogr.* **1** (1960).

92. Heer, C. V., and C. Rausch, *Phys. Rev.*, **90**, 530 (1953).

93. Hedgcock, F. T., and W. B. Muir, *Rev. Sci. Instr.*, **31**, 390 (1960).

94. Hedstrom, B. O. A., *Ark. Kemi*, **6**, 1 (1953).

95. Henry, W. G., and J. L. Rogers, *Phil. Mag.*, **1**, 223, 227 (1956).

96. Heyding, R. D., J. B. Taylor, and M. L. Hair, *Rev. Sci. Instr.*, **32**, 161 (1961).

97. Hilal, O. M., and G. E. Fredericks, *J. Chem. Soc.*, **1954**, 785.

98. Hilsum, C., and R. C. Rose Innes, *Nature*, **182**, 1082 (1958).

99. Holm, R. H., *J. Am. Chem. Soc.*, **82**, 5632 (1960).

100. Howland, J. J., and M. Calvin, *U.S. At. Energy Comm. Rept.*, **AECD-1895** (1949); Cf. Cunningham, B. B., *Nucleonics*, **5**, 62 (1949).

101. Hutchison, C. A., "Magnetic Susceptibilities" in *Determination of Organic Structures by Physical Methods*, E. A. Braude and F. C. Nachod, Academic Press, New York, 1955.

102. Ingram, D. J. E., *Spectroscopy at Radio and Microwave Frequencies*, 1955; *Free Radicals as Studied by Electron Spin Resonance*, 1958, Butterworths Scientific Publications, London.

103. Jacobsen, P. E., and P. W. Selwood, *J. Am. Chem. Soc.*, **76**, 2641 (1954).

104. Jennings, L. D., *Rev. Sci. Instr.*, **31**, 1269 (1960).

105. Jong, J. de, *J. Soc. Glass Tech.*, **38**, 84 (1954).

106. Jorgensen, C. K., *Absorption Spectra and Chemical Bonding in Complexes*, Addison Wesley, Reading, Mass., 1962.

107. Joussot-Dubien, J., *Compt. rend.*, **248**, 3165 (1959).

108. Katz, M. J., *Vacuum Microbalance Techniques*, Plenum Press, New York, 1961.

109. Kauffmann, A. R., "Magnetic Methods of Analysis," in *Physical Methods in Chemical Analysis*, W. G. Berl, Ed., Academic Press, New York, 1951. (Volumes of a new edition have been appearing since 1961, and may contain additional information.)

110. Kirschner, S., *Advances in the Chemistry of the Coordination Compounds*, Macmillan, New York, 1961.

111. Kittel, C., *Introduction to Solid State Physics*, Wiley, New York, 1960.

112. Klauer, F., E. Turowski, and V. Wolff, *Angew. Chem.*, **54**, 494 (1941); *Z. tech. Physik.*, **22**, 223 (1941).

112a. Kleber, A., *Rare Earth Research*, Macmillan, New York, 1961.

113. Kleinberg, J., W. J. Argensinger, and E. Griswold, *Inorganic Chemistry*, D. C. Heath and Co., Boston, 1960.

114. Klemm, W., *Magnetochemie*, Akademische Verlagsgesellschaft, Leipzig, 1936.

115. Klemm, W., *Z. Anorg. u. allgem. chem.*, **244**, 377 (1940); **246**, 347 (1941).

116. Knappworst, A., *Z. Electrochem.*, **63**, 278 (1959).

117. Korovkin, K. N., N. A. Oks, E. A. Bylina, and V. B. Erdokimov, *Zhur. fiz. Khim.*, **35**, 677 (1961).

118. Krause, A., *Izvest. Akad. Nauk. S.S.S.R. Otdel. Khim.*, **1959**, 2260.

119. Krishnan, K. S., B. C. Guha, and J. S. Banerjee, *Phil. Trans. Roy. Soc. (London)*, **A213**, 235 (1933).

120. Krongelb, S., and M. W. P. Strandberg, *J. Chem. Phys.*, **31**, 1196 (1959).

121. Krumhaul, J. A., *J. Appl. Phys.*, **30**, 1183 (1959).

122. Krupp, H., "Theorie der thermomagnetischen Sauerstaffmessung," Dissertation, Technische Hochschule, Karlsruhe, 1953; *Z. Angew. Phys.*, **6**, 541 (1954).

123. Kussman, A., *Z. Metall Kunde*, **26**, 25 (1934).

124. Lellemand, A., *Compt. rend. sci. Paris*, **194**, 1726 (1932).

124a. Langevin, P., *Ann. de chim. et Phys.*, **5** (8), 70 (1905); *J. Phys.*, **4**, 468, 678 (1905).

125. Larmor, J., *Aether and Matter*, Cambridge University Press, London, 1900.

125a. Lax, B., and Button, K. J., *Microwave Ferrites and Ferrimagnetics*, McGraw-Hill, New York, 1962.

126. Lemberg, R., and G. W. Legge, *Hematin Compounds and Bile Pigments*, Interscience, New York–London 1949.

126a. Li, N. C., L. Johnson, and J. Shoolery, *J. Phys. Chem.*, **65**, 1902 (1961).

127. Liehr, A. D., *J. Chem. Educ.*, **39**, 135 (1962).

128. Lubell, M. S., and A. S. Venturino, *Rev. Sci. Instr.*, **31**, 207 (1960).

129. McDonnell, F., R. C. Pink, and A. R. Ubbelohde, *Trans. Faraday Soc.*, **46**, 156 (1950).

130. McGuire, T. R., "Magnetic Properties," in *Method of Experimental Physics*, K. L. Horowitz and V. A. Johnson, Eds., Academic Press, New York, 1960.

131. McMillan, J. A., *Am. J. Phys.*, **27**, 352 (1959).

132. Manch, W., and W. C. Fernelius, *J. Chem. Educ.*, **38**, 192 (1961).

133. Marian, V., *J. Phys. Radium*, **8**, 313 (1937); *Ann. Phys.*, **7**, 45a (1937).

134. Martell, A. E., and M. Calvin, *Chemistry of the Coordination Compounds*, Prentice-Hall, Englewood Cliffs, N. J., 1956.

135. Mata Prasad, C. R. Kanekar, and L. N. Mulay, *J. Chem. Phys.*, **19**, 1440 (1951).

136. Mathai, A. O., *J. Sci. Instr.*, **37**, 71 (1960).

137. Matsunaga, Y., *Bull. Chem. Soc. Japan*, **31**, 745 (1958).

138. Mercier, R., and D. Bovet, *Bull. Soc. vandoise and Sci. nat.*, **66**, 181 (1957).

139. Michaelis, L., "Determination of Magnetic Susceptibilities," in *Techniques of Organic Chemistry*, A. Weissberger, Ed., Interscience, New York–London, Vol. I, Part II, 1949.

140. Milburn, R. M., *J. Am. Chem. Soc.*, **79**, 537 (1957).

141. Milligan, W. O., and H. B. Whitehurst, *Rev. Sci. Instr.*, **23**, 618 (1952).

142. Miyake, C., *Bull. Chem. Soc. Japan*, **33**, 867 (1960); **34**, 471, 475 (1961).

143. Moeller, C. W., and W. K. Wilmarth, *J. Am. Chem. Soc.*, **81**, 2638 (1959).

144. Mulay, L. N., *Anal. Chem.*, **35**, 343R (1962).

145. Mulay, L. N., "Magnetic Susceptibilities," in *Handbook of Analytical Chemistry*, L. Meites, Ed., McGraw-Hill, New York, (1963).

146. Mulay, L. N., *Proc. Ind. Acad. Sci.*, **34A**, 245 (1951).

147. Mulay, L. N., *Rev. Sci. Instr.*, **28**, 279 (1957).

148. Mulay, L. N., A. Attalla, and Sr. Mary Eleanor Fox (to be published); Cf. doctoral dissertations of Attalla and Sr. Fox, Univ. of Cincinnati (1962).
149. Mulay, L. N., and L. K. Keys (to be published).
150. Mulay, L. N., and M. C. Naylor, *Advances in the Chemistry of the Coordination Compounds*, S. Kirschner, Ed., Macmillan, New York, 1961.
151. Mulay, L. N., and Sr. Mary Eleanor Fox, *J. Am. Chem. Soc.*, **84,** 1308 (1962).
151a. Mulay, L. N., and Sr. Mary Eleanor Fox, *J. Chem. Phys.*, **38,** 760 (1963).
151b. Mulay, L. N., and Sr. Mary Eleanor Fox, *Proceedings 7th International Conference on Coordination Chemistry, Stockholm*, June, 1962, p. 54.
152. Mulay, L. N., and W. E. Querner, unpublished results (Cf. Ref. 110, p. 532).
153. Mulay, L. N., and P. W. Selwood, *J. Am. Chem. Soc.*, **76,** 6207 (1954); **77,** 2693 (1955).
154. Néel, L., *Compt. rend. acad. sci. Paris*, **194,** 1726 (1932).
154a. Néel, L., "French Contributions to the Field of Magnetism," in H. P. Kallmann, S. A. Korff, and S. G. Roth, Eds., *Physical Sciences*, New York Univ. Press, New York, 1962, Chapter 12.
155. Néel, L., *Ann. Phys.*, **3,** 137 (1946).
156. Nettleton, H. R., and S. Sugden, *Proc. Roy. Soc. (London)*, **A173,** 313 (1939).
157. Neurath, H., and D. J. E. Ingram, *The Proteins*, Academic Press, New York, 1954.
158. Nicol, J., *Rev. Sci. Instr.*, **31,** 211 (1960).
159. Norder, W. A., *Rev. Sci. Instr.*, **31,** 849 (1960).
160. Nyholm, R. S., *J. Inorg. & Nuclear Chem.*, **8,** 402 (1958).
161. Orgel, L. E., *Transition Metal Chemistry*, Methuen and Co., London, 1960.
162. Oxley, A. E., *Phil. Trans. Roy. Soc. (London)*, **A214,** 109, (1914); **A215,** 79 (1915).
163. Pacault, A., *Rev. Sci. acad. sci. Paris*, **84,** 169 (1946); **86,** 38 (1948); *Bull. Soc. Chim. France*, **D371** (1949).
164. Pacault, A., J. Duchene, and J. Baudet, *Compt. rend. acad. sci. Paris*, **250,** 3641 (1960).
165. Pacault, A., J. Hoarau, and A. Marchand, "Recent Advances in Diamagnetism," in *Advances in Chemical Physics*, I. Prigogine, Ed., Interscience, New York–London, 1961.
166. Pacault, A., J. Joussot-Dubien, and B. Lemanceau, *Compt. rend. acad. sci. Paris*, **237,** 1156 (1953); *J. Chim. phys., France*, **1956,** 198.
167. Palmer, T. M., *Proc. Inst. Radio. Engrs., Aust.*, **21,** 739 (1960).
167a. Pascal, P., *Chimie Générale*, Masson et Cie, Paris, 1949.
168. Pauling, L., *Proc. Roy. Soc. (London)*, **A114,** 181 (1927).
169. Pauling, L., *Nature of the Chemical Bond*, Cornell Univ. Press, Ithaca, N.Y., 1960.
170. Pauling, L., "The Electronic Structure of Hemoglobin," in *Haemoglobin*, F. J. W. Roughton and J. C. Kendrew, Eds., Interscience, New York–London, 1949. This gives references to earlier work.
171. Pauling, L., and C. D. Coryell, *Proc. Natl. Acad. Sci. U.S.*, **22,** 159, 210 (1936); *J. Phys. Chem.*, **43,** 825 (1939).
172. Pauling, L., R. E. Wood, and J. H. Sturdivant, *J. Am. Chem. Soc.*, **68,** 795 (1946).
173. Pearson, R. G., *J. Chem. Educ.*, **38,** 164 (1961).
174. Penoyer, R. F., *Rev. Sci. Instr.*, **30,** 711 (1959).
175. Pillinger, W. L., P. S. Jastram, and J. G. Daunt, *Rev. Sci. Instr.*, **29,** 159 (1958).
176. Pink, R. C., and A. R. Ubbelhode, *Trans. Faraday Soc.*, **44,** 708 (1948).
177. Pople, J. A., W. G. Schneider, and H. J. Bernstein, *High-Resolution Nuclear Magnetic Resonance*, McGraw-Hill, New York, 1959.

177a. Pople, J. A., *J. Chem. Phys.*, **37**, 53, 60 (1962).
178. Pound, R. V., and W. D. Knight, *Rev. Sci. Instr.*, **21**, 219 (1950).
179. Quincke, G., *Ann. Physik.*, **24**, 347 (1885); **34**, 401 (1888).
180. Rabotti, G. C., and G. Mayr, *Giorn. ital. chemioterap.*, **5**, 75 (1958).
181. Rankine, A. V., *Proc. Phys. Soc.*, **46**, 391 (1934).
182. Rawlinson, W. A., *Austr. J. Exptl. Biol. Med. Sci.*, **18**, 185 (1940).
183. Ray, P., Ed., *Magnetism, Report of the Symposium* (1954), Indian Assn. for the Cultivation of Science, Jadavpur, Calcutta, India, 1957.
184. Reber, R. K., and G. F. Boeker, *J. Chem. Phys.*, **15**, 508 (1947).
185. Rimet, G., *J. Phys. Radium*, **22**, 121A (1961).
186. Robertson, R. F. S., and P. W. Selwood, *Rev. Sci. Instr.*, **22**, 146 (1951).
187. Rogers, B. A., K. Wentzel, and J. P. Riott, *Trans. Am. Soc. Metals*, **29**, 969 (1941).
188. Ross, W. H., *Phys. Rev.*, **46**, 46 (1934).
189. Sacconi, L., and R. Cini, *J. Sci. Instr.*, **31**, 56 (1954).
190. Sacconi, L., and R. Cini, *J. Am. Chem. Soc.*, **76**, 4239 (1954).
191. Sanderson, R. T., *Vacuum Manipulation of Volatile Compounds*, Wiley, New York, 1948.
192. Scott, W. R., *J. Sci. Instr.*, **38**, 436 (1961).
193. Selwood, P. W., *Magnetochemistry*, 2nd ed., Interscience, New York–London, 1956.
194. Selwood, P. W., *Proc. Intern. Conf. on Structure and Properties of Thin Films, Bolton Landing, N.Y.*, **1959**, 490;   *J. Am. Chem. Soc.*, **83**, 1033, 2853 (1961).
195. Selwood, P. W., in *Advances in Catalysis*, A. Farkas, Ed., Academic Press, New York, 1957, Vol. IX, p. 93.
195a. Selwood, P. W., *Adsorption and Collective Paramagnetism*, Academic Press, New York, 1962.
196. Selwood, P. W., and R. M. Dobres, *J. Am. Chem. Soc.*, **72**, 3860 (1950).
197. Senftle, F. E., and A. Thorpe, *Nature*, **29**, 410 (1961).
198. Senftle, F. E., M. D. Lee, A. A. Monkewicz, J. W. Mayo, and T. Pankey, *Rev. Sci. Instr.*, **29**, 429 (1958).
199. Shulman, R. G., W. M. Walsh, Jr., H. J. Williams, and J P. Wright, *Biochem. Biophys. Res. Comm.*, **5**, 52 (1961).
200. Simek, M., and O. Navratil, *Chem. listy*, **53**, 1276 (1959).
201. Singer, J. R., *Rev. Sci. Instr.*, **30**, 1123 (1959).
202. Slater, J. C., *Phys. Rev.*, **32**, 349 (1928); **36**, 57 (1930).
203. Smith, A. L., and H. L. Johnston, *Rev. Sci. Instr.*, **24**, 420 (1953).
204. Smith, E. V., *J. Sci. Instr.*, **38**, 466 (1961).
205. Soling, H., *Acta Chem. Scand.*, **12**, 1005 (1958).
206. Soné, T., *Phil. Mag.*, **39**, 305 (1920); *Sci. Repts. Tohoku Imp. Univ.*, **11**, 139 (1922).
207. Stevenson, R., *Rev. Sci. Instr.*, **32**, 28 (1961).
208. Stoner, E. C., *Magnetism and Matter*, 1934; and *Magnetism and Atomic Structure*, Methuen, London, 1926.
209. Stoner, E. C., *Proc. Leeds Phil. Lit. Soc., Sci. Sect.*, **1**, 484 (1929).
210. Stossel, R., *Ann. Physik.*, **10**, 393 (1931).
211. Sucksmith, W., *Phil. Mag.*, **8**, 158 (1929).
212. Sutcliffe, L. H., and J. R. Weber, *J. Inorg. Nuclear Chem.*, **12**, 281 (1960).
213. Sutton, L. E., *J. Chem. Educ.*, **37**, 498 (1960).
214. Symons, M. C. R., *Quart. Rev.*, **13**, 99 (1959).
215. Syrkin, Y. K., and M. E. Dyatkina, *Structure of Molecules*, Butterworths Scientific Publications, London, 1950.

216. Tai Yuan Yang, *J. Chem. Phys.*, **16**, 865 (1948).

217. Takaki, H., C. Miyake, and T. Morita, *Nippon Kagaku Zasshi*, **79**, 645 (1959).

218. Taylor, D. S., and C. D. Coryell, *J. Am. Chem. Soc.*, **60**, 1177 (1938).

219. Thal, W. S., *Z. Tech. Phys.*, **15**, 469 (1934).

220. Theorell, H., *Arkiv. Kemi. Mineral.*, **A16** (No. 1), 1 (1943).

221a. Theorell, H., and A. Ehrenberg, *Arch. Biochem. Biophys.*, **41**, 442 (1952).

221b. Theorell, H., and A. Ehrenberg, *Arkiv. Fysik.*, **3**, 299 (1951).

222. Thorpe, A., and F. E. Senftle, *Rev. Sci. Instr.*, **30**, 1006 (1959).

223. Tobisawa, S., *Bull. Japan Chem. Soc.*, **32**, 1173 (1959).

224. Vaidyanathan, V. I., *Indian J. Phys.*, **1**, 183 (1926).

225. Vanngard, T., and B. Malmstrom, *Electron Spin Resonance and Biochemistry*, P. A. Nordstet and Sons, Stockholm, 1959, Vol. 37.

226. Van Vleck, J. H., *Electric and Magnetic Susceptibilities*, Oxford University Press, London, 1932; "The Magnetism of Some Rare Earth Compounds," in H. P. Kallmann, S. A. Korff, and S. G. Roth, Eds., *Physical Sciences*, New York Univ. Press, New York, 1962, Chapter 11.

227. Varian Associates Staff, *N.M.R. and E.P.R. Spectroscopy*, Pergamon, New York, 1960.

228. Vertman, A. A., and A. M. Samarin, *Zavodskaya Lab.*, **24**, 309 (1958).

229. Vickery, R. C., and W. C. Sexton, *Rev. Sci. Instr.*, **31**, 647 (1960).

230. Wacker, W. E. C., and B. L. Vallee, *J. Biochem.*, **234**, 3257 (1959).

231. Walling, C., *Free Radicals in Solution*, Wiley, New York, 1957.

232. Walsh, W. M., Jr., R. G. Shulman, and R. D. Heidenreich, *Nature*, **192**, 1041 (1961).

233. Wheland, G. W., *Advanced Organic Chemistry*, Wiley, New York, 1949.

234. Wilson, E., *Proc. Roy. Soc.* (*London*), **A96**, 429 (1920).

235. Work, H. K., and H. T. Clark, *Am. Inst. Mining Met. Engrs. Tech. Publ., No.* **1132** (1939).

236. Yost, D. M., H. Russell, and C. S. Garner, *The Rare Earth Elements and Their Compounds*, Wiley, New York, 1947.

237. Yousef, Y. L., and R. K. Gigris, and H. Mikhail, *J. Chem. Phys.*, **23**, 959 (1955).

238. Yu, S. P., and A. H. Morrish, *Rev. Sci. Instr.*, **27**, 9 (1956).

NUCLEAR MAGNETIC RESONANCE AND ELECTRON PARAMAGNETIC RESONANCE

By N. F. Chamberlain, *Manufacturing Research and Development, Humble Oil & Refining Company, Baytown, Texas*

Contents

Contents (*continued*)

I. INTRODUCTION

   Magnetic resonance spectrometry is based on transitions between the additional energy levels produced by the action of a magnetic field on susceptible atomic particles. Nuclear magnetic resonance (NMR) utilizes the energy levels of atomic nuclei, whereas electron magnetic resonance (EMR) utilizes those of electrons. The technique is applicable to only those nuclei that possess magnetic moments, or to only those electrons whose spins are not paired and whose magnetic moments are therefore not cancelled. Fortunately, a sizable number of nuclei important to chemists have magnetic moments and are susceptible to study by this technique. Likewise, unpaired electrons occur in free radicals and in certain transition metal species, both of which are important to the chemist.

The existence of nuclear and electron magnetic moments was demonstrated, long before the discovery of magnetic resonance spectrometry, by the characteristic splitting of the lines of optical spectra (Zeeman effect) and by atomic and neutron beam experiments. The first direct observations of signals produced through the magnetic resonance of nuclei were made in 1945 by Felix Bloch at Stanford University and E. M. Purcell at Harvard University (12,13,97). This discovery was of such importance that it was rewarded by the 1952 Nobel prize in physics for these two men. The full impact of this discovery on analytical chemistry could not be envisioned at that time, however. Advances in both instrumentation and applications of magnetic resonance have come with breathtaking speed, challenging the ingenuity and firing the imagination of the physicist, the electronics specialist, and the analytical chemist.

The importance of magnetic resonance to the analyst is not only in the indication of the presence of a given nucleus or of an unpaired electron, but also in the concurrent indication of the surroundings in which that nucleus or electron is found in the sample under study. The resonance of a nucleus is modified significantly by the electron cloud that surrounds it and by neighboring atoms and molecules, thus indicating the chemical functional group in which the nucleus is located, its spatial arrangement in the molecule, its rate of exchange with like nuclei, and/or the rate of rotation or interconversion of the portion of the molecule in which it is located. Electron resonance frequently indicates the molecular structure of that portion of a radical over which the unpaired electron is distributed, or identifies the metal ion and the valence state involved.

The differences between magnetic energy levels of nuclei (and of unpaired electrons) are dependent on the strength of the magnetic field to which the particles are subjected. With presently attainable fields, the frequency equivalent of the transition energies for nuclei lies in the radio frequency portion of the electromagnetic spectrum, between 1 and 60 Mc. Conventional radio transmitting and receiving equipment is used for stimulation and detection of the transitions. The energy transitions for unpaired electrons, on the other hand, for fields of a few kilogauss, lie in the microwave portion of the spectrum. The 10 Gc. band is the currently popular region. Therefore, for electron magnetic resonance it is necessary to employ microwave plumbing and apparatus. Otherwise, the two techniques are similar and interpretation of the information obtained is similar.

II. PRINCIPLES OF MAGNETIC RESONANCE SPECTROMETRY

In view of the number of excellent monographs that describe the theory of magnetic resonance in considerable detail (4,67,69,77,93,103,130), it is considered unnecessary to present the detailed theory here. Only those principles that are essential to an understanding of the analytical applications of magnetic resonance will be discussed in this chapter. Oversimplification of theory will be employed in some instances.

A. MAGNETIC RESONANCE

1. The Basic Experiment

A magnetic resonance spectrometer consists basically of a direct-current or permanent magnet, a radio-frequency or microwave transmitter and receiver, and means for subjecting the sample to the influence of both the static and alternating fields simultaneously under precisely controlled conditions. A block diagram showing the relationship of these components in a nuclear magnetic resonance (NMR) spectrometer is presented in Fig. 39.1 (see also Fig. 39.5). The sample, contained in a suitable glass tube, is inserted into a coil connected to the radio-frequency transmitter and receiver. This coil, in turn, is mounted in the air gap of the magnet. When the strength of the static magnetic field is set at the proper ratio to the frequency of the alternating field, nuclei of a particular isotope in a particular magnetic environment will produce a signal in the receiver. If the static-field strength is varied slowly while the alternating-field frequency is held constant, groups of nuclei in different magnetic environments will pass through the resonance condition in succession. This produces a spectrum of applied static magnetic field strength (conventionally the abscissa) versus resonance signal intensity (conventionally the ordinate; see Fig. 39.4). Since the strength of the applied static magnetic field is related to the energy of the resonance transition, the magnetic resonance spectrum may be considered a plot of transition energy versus intensity. In this respect it is analogous to an optical spectrum.

Normally only one isotope is observed in a single scan because the variation in field strength required to include the resonances of different isotopes is usually much greater than the variation required to encompass all the resonances of a single isotope. Furthermore, the magnetic environment of a nucleus is related to its chemical and physical environment. Therefore, a nuclear magnetic resonance spectrum indicates the distribution of the nuclei of a single isotope among the chemically or physically different

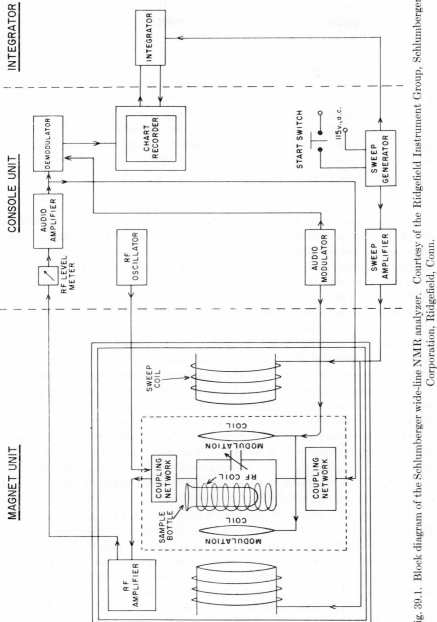

Fig. 39.1. Block diagram of the Schlumberger wide-line NMR analyzer. Courtesy of the Ridgefield Instrument Group, Schlumberger Corporation, Ridgefield, Conn.

environments in the sample. A high-resolution NMR spectrum shows primarily the distribution among the chemically different environments (chemical functional groups), whereas a wide-line NMR spectrum shows the gross distribution among physically different environments (such as hindered *vs.* free rotation, neighbors in crystals, etc.). A wide-line electron magnetic resonance spectrum indicates the number and relative concentrations of paramagnetic species with different g factors (related to electronic structure and to crystal fields). A high-resolution EMR spectrum shows, in addition to the different species, the distribution of the unpaired electronic charge among the various magnetic nuclei with which it is associated in a given molecule. All magnetic resonance spectra indicate the total concentration of the observed nuclei or electrons in the sample.

2. The Resonance Phenomenon

Unpaired electrons, being spinning electric charges, generate magnetic fields that are not cancelled out by their molecular surroundings. They thus may be considered to be tiny magnets, and they exhibit a measurable magnetic moment. Likewise, atomic nuclei with net spin angular momenta (due to unpaired protons and/or unpaired neutrons) also generate magnetic fields and exhibit magnetic moments. Spin angular momenta are quantized in half-integral multiples of the modified Planck constant, $h/2\pi$, so that the nuclear-spin quantum number, I, may have values of 0, $^1/_2$, 1, $^3/_2$, etc., in units of $h/2\pi$. The nuclear magnetic moment has $(2I + 1)$ observable components (parallel to an applied field) that are related to the angular momentum by the expression $m\mu/I$, where m, the magnetic quantum number, has the values of $I, I - 1, \ldots, -(I - 1), -I$, and where μ is the maximum observable component of the magnetic moment and is the experimental value commonly referred to as the magnetic moment. When $I = 0$, the nucleus has no net spin and therefore no magnetic moment, and does not exhibit magnetic resonance. The only nuclei of interest to this technique, then, are those for which $I \neq 0$. The electron-spin quantum number, S, has the value $^1/_2$, so that the electron magnetic moment has only two components parallel to the applied field.

The energy of a magnetic dipole in a magnetic field is equal to the work required to move one of the poles against the field a distance equal to the component of the moment arm parallel to the field. This is the product of the parallel component of the dipole moment and the field strength. Therefore, when a nucleus with a dipole moment is placed in a magnetic field of strength H, it can assume any one of the $(2I + 1)$ energy levels given by $m\mu H/I$. When I is replaced by S, the same relationship holds for the unpaired electron. The levels are equally spaced with differences of

$\mu H/I$ by the selection rule that m must change by ± 1. The quantum of energy, $h\nu$, can excite transitions between the energy levels if it has the same magnitude as the level spacing:

$$h\nu = \mu H/I = g\beta H \tag{1}$$

where ν is the frequency of the electromagnetic radiation supplying the quantum of energy, g is the *splitting factor* or *g factor*, and β is the nuclear magneton or the Bohr magneton, depending on whether the nucleus or the electron is being considered.

When a dipole aligned with a magnetic field is subjected to a torque perpendicular to the field, it will move out of alignment and will precess about the axis of the field like a gyroscope that is pushed from the vertical position. The rate of precession is the Larmor frequency:

$$2\pi\nu = \omega = \gamma H \tag{2}$$

The perpendicular torque is supplied by an alternating magnetic field rotating at the angular frequency ω, which in turn is a component of a field oscillating linearly at the frequency ν. In nuclear magnetic resonance an isotope normally is identified by its precession frequency in a given magnetic field or by its gyromagnetic ratio, γ. In electron magnetic resonance, on the other hand, the factor g (equation (1)) normally is used to define the position of the resonance and thus indicate gross differences in environment. In the absence of secondary disturbing influences, each isotope with a net spin would be characterized by a single precession frequency for a given applied field (128). The free electron also would have a single precession frequency under these conditions.

For simplicity, the remaining discussion of principles will be concerned with the simplest of all magnetic nuclei, the proton, but the general ideas presented also apply to other nuclei and to unpaired electrons.

When a sample containing protons (hydrogen nuclei) is placed in a magnetic field, the protons are permitted to align themselves either with or against the field ($I = {}^1/_2$). At equilibrium the protons will distribute themselves between the two energy states in accordance with the Boltzmann distribution. For a field of 10,000 gauss at room temperature there will be an excess of about 8 protons per million in the low energy state. If the sample is now irradiated at right angles to the static magnetic field with an alternating magnetic field of the proper frequency, ν, there will be a net transfer of energy from the alternating field to the sample, which will effect a net transfer of the excess protons from the low to the high-energy state. This energy transfer can be detected directly as a loss in power of the irradiating field (nuclear absorption), or it can be detected indirectly by

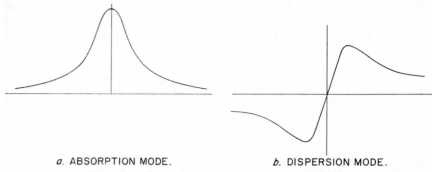

a. ABSORPTION MODE.   *b*. DISPERSION MODE.

Fig. 39.2. Shapes of the magnetic resonance signals.

means of a signal induced into a separate receiving coil that is placed at right angles to both fields (nuclear induction). There is more involved in this phenomenon than the simple absorption and release of energy by transitions between energy levels, and the reader is advised to consult one of the comprehensive monographs for a more complete picture (4,67,93). In addition to causing transitions between the nuclear energy levels, the radio frequency (rf) field also causes the nuclei to precess in phase, so that their combined signals are picked up by the receiving coil. Without this phase coherence, the signals would be far too weak to be observable.

The magnetic resonance phenomenon gives rise to two separate and distinct signals that are present simultaneously in the primary composite signal. They are illustrated in Fig. 39.2. These signals are analogous to optical absorption and dispersion. The absorption mode is the result of actual absorption of incident radiation (from the rf field), which produces a change in the distribution of nuclei among the permitted energy levels. This signal, therefore, is directly dependent on energy-level populations. The dispersion-mode signal, on the other hand, is the result of refraction of incident radiation and is not dependent on energy-level populations in the same way.

The absorption-mode signal is 90° out of phase with the applied radio-frequency field, whereas the dispersion-mode signal is in phase with the rf field. Since one wishes to observe only one of these signals at a time, it is necessary to select the desired signal by proper phasing of the receiving apparatus with respect to the rf field. This can be done by the introduction of "leakage" voltage at the sample probe, the phase and amplitude of which can be adjusted to favor one signal so strongly that the other is effectively eliminated. It is better, however, to introduce the phase-determining voltage in a phase-sensitive detector at a later stage in the signal-amplifying system. The proper use of phase-sensitive detectors eliminates a number of errors in measurements of the signal intensities, which are difficult to avoid when leakage voltage is introduced at the sample probe (134). Because the absorption-mode signal is easier to measure and to interpret by familiar means, it is the mode favored for most magnetic spectroscopic work. When maximum sensitivity is required, the dispersion-mode signal is favored.

B. RELAXATION

If the protons to be observed by magnetic resonance did not interact with their surroundings, application of the static magnetic field would cause all of them to be aligned in the direction of the static field. Application of the alternating field at the proper frequency would then cause the nuclei to be deflected from the direction of the static field and to precess in phase at the normal frequency. At the same time, however, the energy absorbed from the alternating field would quickly establish equal populations in the allowed directions with and against the field, at which time absorption of energy would cease and the observation of an absorption signal no longer would be possible. Thus the continued observation of an absorption signal requires that the protons interact with their surroundings in such a way as to establish and maintain a satisfactory population difference between the two energy states. This interaction is called *relaxation.*

On the other hand, the width of an observed resonance line is proportional to the frequency of transition between energy states (the inverse of the lifetime in a given state). As a signal broadens, its fine structure disappears, reducing the amount of information it conveys. Its signal/noise ratio also drops until, in the limiting case, the signal no longer can be observed. If the relaxation interaction is too strong, the transition rate will be speeded up until the signals are broadened beyond usefulness.

It is necessary, then, that the interaction of the protons with their surroundings be strong enough to maintain an acceptable population difference but not so strong as to broaden the signals excessively. An understanding of the various relaxation mechanisms and the factors that control them is necessary to the successful application of the magnetic resonance technique.

1. Spin-Lattice Relaxation

The physical system (the sample) in which the nuclei under observation are located is called the lattice, the molecules of which will be undergoing random motion to a degree depending on the physical state of the system. All magnetic particles (including observed nuclei) in this lattice produce local magnetic fields that affect the neighboring nuclei under observation as a function of their relative orientations and separations. Thus the thermal motion of the lattice elements gives rise to fluctuating fields at each observed nucleus, with the total energy spread over a wide range of frequencies in a manner analogous to blackbody radiation. That component which is at the proton precession frequency will induce net transitions from the upper to the lower spin state at a rate that is proportional to the strength of the component. The energy given up during these transitions appears as additional thermal motion of the lattice. This process is called spin-lattice relaxation.

The spin-lattice interaction is a first-order process characterized by a time T_1. This may be considered the characteristic time with which the nuclei return to the Boltzmann distribution of spin-state populations after the normal distribution has been temporarily upset. When the mobility of the lattice is low, as in crystalline solids or viscous liquids, the most probable frequency of the lattice fields will be lower than the precession frequency, the spin-lattice interaction will be weak, and T_1 will be long. As the mobility of the lattice components increases due to lower viscosity, higher temperatures, etc., a point will be reached at which the most probable frequency of the fluctuating lattice fields will equal the precession frequency. At this point the spin-lattice interaction will be at its strongest and T_1 will be at a minimum. Further increase in lattice mobility will move the most probable frequency higher than the precession frequency and will spread out the lattice-field frequencies over a wider range. This will again weaken the spin-lattice interaction and cause T_1 to rise again. Thus, as the mobility of the lattice components increases (viscosity decreases, temperature increases, etc.), T_1 decreases to a minimum and then increases again (Fig. 39.3).

The fluctuating magnetic fields produced by the thermal motion of ordinary weakly magnetic nuclei are strong enough to provide the relaxation rates required for the observation of signals. If the mobility of the lattice is high enough the lines will be narrow enough (long T_1) to provide high resolution. High-resolution signals cannot be observed with solid or viscous samples, however, because of the very low values of the spin-spin relaxation time, T_2, to be discussed in the next section. The strongly fluctuating lattice fields produced by unpaired electrons severely reduce T_1 and seriously broaden the resonance lines. For this reason only very small quantities of paramagnetic species can be permitted in samples that are to be observed by high-resolution nuclear resonance.

In addition to the motion of nuclei which is a consequence of their being attached to molecules in motion, nuclei that possess nonspherical charge

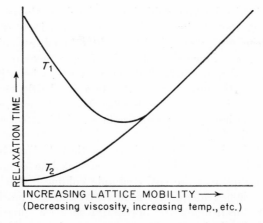

Fig. 39.3. Variation of relaxation times T_1 and T_2 with lattice mobility.

distributions can be set into separate motion by fluctuating electric fields in the sample. Nuclei with $I > \frac{1}{2}$ have nonspherical charge distribution; that is, they have an electric quadrupole moment. Experience shows that the frequency of the fluctuating magnetic field set up by this motion is frequently of the same order as the precession frequency of protons, and results in a serious broadening of proton resonance lines. This broadening can be reduced by either speeding up or slowing down the rate of motion of the offending nuclei by a proper choice of solvents (123), temperature, or proton-exchange catalysts (Reference 103, Chapter 5). It also can be eliminated by double irradiation (Section II-C-3).

2. Spin-Spin Relaxation

When two neighboring nuclei in different energy states are precessing at the same frequency, the magnetic field generated by each can cause a transition in the other, just as the applied rf field causes similar transitions. In this case, there can be a mutual exchange of energy states, or spin states, which reduces the lifetime of each nucleus in its spin state but does not change the relative populations of the energy levels. This phenomenon is known as spin-spin relaxation and the attendant reduction in lifetime of the spin states produces broadening of the resonance lines.

The phenomenon just described is a direct dipole-dipole interaction between like nuclei (Section II-E-1). The strength of this interaction is high when the nuclei are held in fixed space relation, as in crystalline solids, and the line broadening produced under these conditions is great. As the mobility of the lattice increases this interaction is weakened by averaging of the local fields, and line broadening is correspondingly decreased. Interactions between unlike nuclei also produce line broadening, but by a different mechanism. Since the precession frequencies are different there is no interchange of spin states, but the unlike dipoles still create local variations in the static magnetic field. These local field variations result in a spread of precession frequencies for the observed nuclei, the spread appearing as a broadening of the resonance lines. This effect also is reduced as the lattice mobility increases.

Inhomogeneity in the applied static magnetic field likewise results in a spread of precession frequencies that appears as line broadening. This inhomogeneity occurs over the entire sample volume rather than in localized portions. It is not adequately reduced by thermal motion within the sample, but is reduced along the horizontal axes by spinning the entire sample about its vertical axis. The inhomogeneity remaining along the vertical axis of cylindrical samples must be tolerated.

All of these line-broadening factors are lumped together and described by the characteristic relaxation time T_2, which is called the spin-spin relaxation time. The mutual interchange of spin states and the changes in precession frequency experienced by a nucleus as it wanders around among the various field strengths result in a loss of phase coherence among the precessing nuclei. Thus T_2 may be considered the characteristic time with which nuclei precessing in phase will lose phase coherence when the rf field is removed. T_2 increases continuously with increasing mobility of the lattice.

3. Combined Effect

The qualitative effect of lattice mobility on T_1 and T_2 is shown in Fig. 39.3. When lattice mobility is low, the low values of T_2 broaden the lines so much that high-resolution spectra cannot be observed. When lattice mobility is high, T_1 and T_2 are equal and long, and high-resolution spectra may be observed. Adequate molecular mobility for the observation of high-resolution spectra occurs in liquids of low viscosity and in gases. Since all the direct dipole interactions fall off as the cube of the distance between dipoles, effective reduction of these interactions requires mobility of the individual segments of large molecules. For this reason it is not possible to obtain high-resolution spectra for large molecules that have severely restricted internal rotation, even though they may be examined in solutions of low viscosity. On the other hand, this characteristic permits a study of the relative mobilities of different parts of such a molecule.

C. SATURATION

1. The Saturation Phenomenon

The net upward transitions produced by the rf field, H_1, are in dynamic equilibrium with the concurrent downward transitions produced by spin-lattice relaxation. The deviation of the spin-state populations from the Boltzmann distribution is a function of the magnitude of H_1, the time during which H_1 is applied to the resonant nuclei (proportional to the inverse of the scan rate), the relaxation time T_1, and other factors to be identified later. This deviation reduces the intensity of the absorption-mode signal from the value it would have had if the spin-state populations had remained at the Boltzmann distribution. This loss in signal intensity is known as saturation.

The over-all effect of saturation on the absorption-mode signal at constant scan rate and variable H_1 may be visualized as follows. As H_1 increases, the rate of transition and the degree of phase coherence both increase, tending to increase the signal amplitude. Simultaneously, the difference between spin-state populations decreases, tending to reduce the signal amplitude. At low values of H_1 the amplitude-increasing factors predominate and at high values the population change predominates. Finally, at very high values of H_1, the populations of the two energy levels will be essentially equal and no further absorption of power can take place. At this point the absorption-mode signal disappears entirely. Thus, the absorption-mode signal amplitude increases to a maximum and then decreases to zero as H_1 increases continuously.

Under conditions of slow passage, where the observed nuclei are always at equilibrium with their surroundings, the observed absorption-mode signal intensities are (Reference 93, pp. 23, 37–40):

$$\text{Peak height} = C \left(\frac{I+1}{3I}\right)\left(\frac{N\mu^2}{kT}\right)\left(\frac{H_1 T_2}{1 + \gamma^2 H_1^2 T_1 T_2}\right) \tag{3}$$

$$\text{Band area} = C' \left(\frac{I+1}{3I}\right)\left(\frac{N\mu^2}{kT}\right)\left[\frac{H_1}{(1 + \gamma^2 H_1^2 T_1 T_2)^{1/2}}\right] \tag{4}$$

where

C and C' are proportionality constants

I = spin quantum number

N = number of protons per unit volume (which can be the effective sample volume)

μ = maximum component of the nuclear magnetic moment

k = Boltzmann constant

T = absolute temperature
H_1 = amplitude of effective radio frequency field
γ = gyromagnetic ratio
T_1 and T_2 = relaxation times

These equations show that at very low constant values of H_1, band area is proportional to N while peak height depends on N and on T_2. Band area is thus an accurate measure of the relative number of protons contributing to various bands in a spectrum, whereas peak height is usable only when T_2's are identical.

At higher values of H_1 both signals become significantly dependent on a saturation parameter $S = \gamma^2 H_1^2 T_1 T_2$. At high values of H_1, band area becomes independent of H_1 but dependent on $(T_1 T_2)^{1/2}$. At the same time the drastic reduction in peak height makes measurement of the band area difficult and uncertain. Accurate measurements of the relative intensities of absorption-mode signals can therefore be made only at low values of the saturation parameter, well below that required for maximum signal amplitude. For slow passage this means extremely low values of H_1.

The amplitude (peak height) of the dispersion-mode signal continues to increase linearly with increasing H_1 up to a point that depends on the values of T_1 and T_2, and then it becomes independent of H_1, neither increasing nor decreasing thereafter. This signal amplitude still is dependent on T_2, however. The area from the zero-crossing point to the turning point of either half of the dispersion-mode signal is independent of both T_1 and T_2, and is proportional to H_1. Thus when maximum sensitivity is required, H_1 can be increased to large values and the signals can be observed in the dispersion mode. A special case results from observation of the dispersion mode under conditions of high rf amplitude and scan so rapid that negligible relaxation takes place during passage through the resonance. This technique, called adiabatic rapid passage, produces a signal envelope resembling the absorption mode while providing the sensitivity of the dispersion mode. It has been used successfully for the study of C^{13}, which has weak signals (in natural abundance) and long relaxation times. It is not generally applicable to the study of hydrogen because the fast scans required destroy the needed resolution.

2. Determination of Saturation Error

It is convenient to consider the slow-passage condition when studying the saturation phenomenon, but it is better to produce the actual spectra under conditions of intermediate passage, in which the nuclei are at incomplete equilibrium with their surroundings during resonance. An adequate signal/noise ratio usually requires a value of H_1 that is high enough to make the saturation parameter significant in determining relative signal intensities. Under these conditions the errors due to saturation depend on both the saturation parameter, S, and the rate at which the resonance is scanned, dH/dt (134).

Precise determination of the saturation error requires measurement of (dH/dt), H_1, T_1, and T_2. Scan rate is measured easily and can be preset accurately with modern instrumentation. The measurement of H_1 is time-consuming (about 30 minutes), but it need be measured only infrequently as the components of the rf transmitter age. The measurement of T_1 and T_2 also is time-consuming, and since they vary for different samples and even for different resonances within a sample, their routine determination is impractical. Therefore it is impractical to determine the precise saturation error for each resonance.

It is relatively easy to determine the *maximum possible error* for each resonance, however. This is the error that would apply if $S = \infty$ (T_1 and T_2 infinitely large). This error is determined from equation (5).

$$\frac{A}{A_0} = \frac{1 - \exp(-\gamma^2 H_1^2/2r)}{\gamma^2 H_1^2/2r} \tag{5}$$

where A = observed signal intensity (band area); A_0 = signal intensity at zero saturation; and r = scan rate, $\gamma dH/2\pi dt$, in c/s per second. It is usually convenient to adjust H_1 and r to produce low maximum errors (3% or less) rather than to apply calculated corrections to each intensity.

H_1 may be measured by the method of Anderson (Reference 130, pp. 164–168), or calculated from equation (5) (when $S \gg 1$) and a series of intensity measurements at constant H_1 and different scan rates. The latter method, worked out by R. B. Williams (137a), is simple and rapid and is directly applicable to the range of H_1 values normally used in high-resolution NMR.

3. Double Irradiation

The intentional saturation of selected resonances during the observation of related resonances in the same sample can be accomplished by the simultaneous application of two rf fields to the sample. A high-amplitude field is applied at the frequency of the resonance to be saturated while a field of normal amplitude is applied at the frequency of the resonance to be observed. The frequencies must be sufficiently well separated so that the high-amplitude field does not adversely affect the observed resonances. This technique can be helpful in a number of ways.

Saturation of the resonance of a nucleus that is spin coupled to another nucleus (see Section II-E) can eliminate completely the spin coupling between these nuclei and eliminate all spin-spin multiplicity due to this coupling. This results in a considerable simplification of the spectrum and aids materially in interpretation (2). Saturation of the resonance of an unpaired electron that is spin coupled to a nucleus under observation by NMR can increase the intensity of the NMR signal by a factor of up to 1000 or so (30,84). The increase may be due to an increase in the population of nuclei in a lower energy state or to the creation of an excess in an upper energy state (11). This technique has permitted the observation of nuclear resonance signals that are otherwise too broad or too weak to observe (29), and may prove of considerable value in the study of the nuclear resonances of isotopes of low abundance, such as carbon-13. It also may be useful in studies involving the interaction of paramagnetic species and associated hydrogen-containing materials (14,88,125).

Observation of a partially saturated electron spin resonance while producing transitions in associated nuclei makes it possible to observe the hyperfine splittings associated with the electron-nuclear coupling when the electron resonance itself is too broad to permit the observation of hyperfine structure (see Section VI-B-1).

D. CHEMICAL SHIFT

In Section II-A it was pointed out that, in the absence of secondary disturbing influences, each nucleus with a net spin would be characterized by a single characteristic precession frequency for a given applied magnetic field. Fortunately for the analyst, there are secondary disturbing influences that can be related directly to molecular structure. High-resolution nuclear magnetic resonance is concerned primarily with the observation and interpretation of these secondary influences.

1. Definition and Measurement

The static magnetic field applied to a sample is modified not only by the bulk magnetic properties of the sample (an effect that can be compensated or corrected), but also by the electron clouds surrounding the nuclei. Consequently, each nucleus experiences a static magnetic field that is a function of the nature of the electron cloud surrounding that nucleus and neighboring nuclei, and therefore a function of the chemical environment of that nucleus. The precession frequency is determined by the static field at the nucleus. A nuclear magnetic resonance spectrum is normally produced at a fixed radio (precession) frequency by slowly varying the strength of the applied static

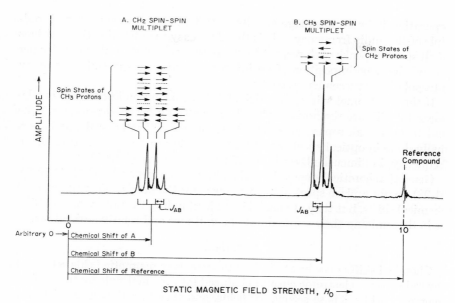

Fig. 39.4. High-resolution NMR spectrum of protons in ethyl ether.

field so that each environmentally different type of nucleus of a given iso-tope is brought into resonance successively along an abscissa that represents increasing magnetic field strength. The displacement of the "center" of an individual resonance multiplet (Section II-E) from some arbitrarily chosen position along this horizontal axis is called the chemical shift, illustrated in Fig. 39.4. When the resonance of a group of equivalent nuclei consists of a single sharp line, the chemical shift is simply measured to the center of the line. When the resonance consists of a multiplet, as in Fig. 39.4, a generally adequate estimate of the chemical shift can be made by measuring to the "center of area" of the multiplet. When necessary, the chemical shifts can be calculated more precisely from the spectral measurements by one of several methods outlined in the literature (3,38,63; 93, Chapter 6; 130, Chapter 10). Such calculations are too time-consuming to be used in general analytical work, but they can be very valuable in special cases.

The separation between resonance peaks, which is needed for chemical shift determination, may be measured with high accuracy in frequency units by the audio sideband method (5; 69, pp. 41–44; 93, pp. 74–77; 102,122). The static field sweep is modulated at accurately known audio frequencies, by means of a stable variable-frequency oscillator, so as to pro-duce images of a reference peak at selected points in the spectrum. The separation between an image and its parent peak will be an integral multiple of the audio frequency. It is therefore easy to determine the positions of all spectral peaks with respect to the parent reference peak, in cycles per second, by superimposition of an image peak on each spectral peak or by interpolation between image peaks.

If the spectrometer has very high stability and sweep linearity it is adequate to calibrate the horizontal scale occasionally for preset sweep widths and to read peak separations directly from the calibrated scale, as is normally done in optical spectrometry. The scale can be calibrated either in frequency, in dimensionless units, or in both (Section III-B-3).

General theoretical expressions that have been derived (68,71,73,79,90, 91,98) do not replace spectral measurement for the precise determination of chemical shifts, but they are useful in understanding the nature of the shifts or in determining their approximate magnitudes and relative directions.

2. Origin

Chemical shifts may be attributed to secondary magnetic fields set up by several types of electronic currents induced into the molecule by the applied magnetic field. These secondary fields, and therefore the chemical shifts, are directly proportional to the strength of the applied field. The electronic currents may be divided arbitrarily (90) into those that would be produced by spherical electron clouds (local isotropic diamagnetic current), those currents that account for the fact that most molecular electronic clouds are not spherically symmetrical (paramagnetic currents), and interatomic currents. The spherically symmetrical or diamagnetically isotropic electron clouds set up currents that oppose the applied field no matter what the direction of orientation of the field with respect to the molecule. These currents produce a positive shielding of the nucleus and require the application of a higher static field in order to achieve resonance at the fixed radio frequency. They therefore produce an upfield shift in resonance position. The field produced by the isotropic diamagnetic currents is directly proportional to the electron density. Thus, in the absence of other influences, the resonance of a given nucleus may be expected to move to lower fields with increasing electronegativity of adjacent groups. This has been found to be true for H^1, F^{19}, and trisubstituted P^{31}. For tetrasubstituted P^{31} other influences are stronger, so that the resonances actually shift to a higher applied field with increasing electronegativity of adjacent groups (24).

The anisotropic diamagnetic currents allow for the fact that electrons can actually circulate in a molecule in some directions more easily than in others. This sets up an asymmetric magnetic field that may either oppose or assist the applied magnetic field and thus shift magnetic resonances to either higher or lower field positions.   These anisotropic currents may be assumed to circulate axially around bonds such as C≡C, in the planes of groups such as the carbonyl, or in closed circuits around molecular paths such as aromatic rings.   They also may be assumed to flow around single nuclei as the result of mixing of the ground state and low-lying excited states of the atom by the magnetic field.   These last "local paramagnetic circulations" produce fields that always assist the applied field and cause the resonance of the affected nucleus to occur at lower applied field positions.   Although they are not expected to occur to a significant extent around hydrogen atoms, the paramagnetic currents around larger atoms are important in determining the chemical shifts for both the larger nuclei and for adjacent hydrogen nuclei.

An excellent discussion of the isotropic and anisotropic electronic circulations about atoms and their effect on chemical shift is presented by Jackman (Reference 69, pp. 14–20 and Chapter 7).   A detailed chart of the effects of benzene ring currents on nearby groups is given by Johnson and Bovey (71).

3. Range and Uses

The magnitude of the total range of the chemical shifts for an isotope is roughly a function of the nuclear charge.   The range varies from about 20 p.p.m. for hydrogen-1 to 700 p.p.m. for phosphorus-31, and may be as high as 1% for isotopes of uranium.   The chemical shift is used analytically as the primary means of identification of functional groups containing or affecting the observed isotope.   It also is an important indication of the relative spatial positions of the functional groups.   These identifications are based at present on empirical correlations between chemical structure and chemical shift.   A convenient form for the presentation of these correlations is a chart such as that in Fig. 39.15.   This permits rapid searching for either the functional groups that could produce an observed shift or the shift that would be expected from a given functional group.

E. SPIN-SPIN INTERACTIONS

1. Direct Dipole Interactions

When nuclei with magnetic moments are held in a relatively fixed space relationship, as in crystalline solids, the magnetic field at a given nucleus may be directly modified by the magnetic fields produced by neighboring nuclei.   The resulting splitting of the magnetic resonance lines is of the order of several gauss, which is wide enough to make these splittings visible in spite of the considerable line broadening produced by these same dipole-dipole interactions (Section II-B). The spacing between the lines is a function of the distance between the dipoles and the angle between the applied magnetic field and a line drawn between the centers of the dipoles. The number of lines observed in a given multiplet of this kind depends on the number of dipoles directly interacting on each other and on the degree of broadening of the lines. Analysis of the wide-line NMR spectra of single crystals and polycrystalline aggregates (including powders) of the same substance have led to improved knowledge of the number of magnetic nuclei of a given kind that are closely associated together in crystalline solids and of the distances and angles between these nuclei. Since this technique has not been widely used for analytical work, however, it will not be discussed further here. The reader is referred to the more detailed discussion of this subject by Andrew (Reference 4, Chapter 6) and to several later papers (55,113,120,133).

2. Indirect Dipole Interactions

a. ORIGIN AND MEASUREMENT

For liquids of low viscosity or for gases the rapid thermal movement of the molecules causes the direct dipole interactions to be effectively averaged to zero so that they are not observed. There remains, however, a residual coupling between magnetic nuclei that are bound closely together in the same molecule. This coupling has been successfully attributed to indirect coupling of the nuclei through the bonding electrons (59; 93, Chapter 8; 99). The coupling appears to be a combination of interactions between the nuclear moments and the electron spin moments and between the nuclear moments and the electron orbital moments. For covalent bonds, as in HD, the coupling produced by electron spin interactions is the stronger by an order of magnitude. It may be visualized as follows: the spin state and energy of the bonding electron localized momentarily on nucleus A is determined by interaction with nucleus A. Since the spins of the two bonding electrons are paired, this results in the orientation of the bonding electron at nucleus B in the opposite state. The magnetic energy level of B is then modified by interaction with its bonding electron. Thus the energy of B has been modified indirectly by the magnetic moment of A.

For strongly ionic bonds the electron orbital interactions may become important. They result from anisotropic orbital electron circulations induced by the nuclear moments—circulations that do not average to zero even with rapid tumbling.

The energy (Hamiltonian) of the indirect nuclear spin coupling (specifically, that resulting from nuclear spin–electron spin interactions) can be expressed in the form

$$h J_{AB} I_A \cdot I_B \tag{6}$$

where h is Planck's constant, J_{AB} is the coupling constant, expressed in cycles per second, and I_A and I_B are the nuclear spin vectors. The coupling constant is independent of the strength of the applied magnetic field, but does vary with some important molecular parameters and with the isotope.

In the simplest cases J is the separation, in cycles per second, between adjacent peaks in a spin-spin multiplet (next section and Fig. 39.4). In more complex cases J must be calculated from the spectral measurements (3,38,63; 93, Chapter 6; 130, Chapter 10).

b. Spin-Spin Multiplets

Without indirect spin-spin interactions between magnetic nuclei, all of the nuclei of a single chemically equivalent type within a sample would resonate at a single position identified by a chemical shift. The effect of the spin-spin interactions is to split this signal into a multiplet that, in the simplest cases, is characteristic of the number and the spin quantum number of nuclei contributing the spin-coupled perturbations. Since the perturbations are functions of the spin states of the perturbing nuclei, the total number of *first-order* perturbations and the relative probability for each can be determined very simply from a diagram of the possible spin states of the perturbing groups. Thus, in Fig. 39.4, the pair of equivalent protons in the methylene group, which can exist in three spin states with probabilities of $1:2:1$, causes the resonance of the methyl group to be split into three peaks with intensities in the ratio of $1:2:1$. Likewise, the three equivalent protons of the methyl group, which have four possible spin states in the ratio $1:3:3:1$, split the methylene resonance into four peaks in the ratio $1:3:3:1$.

Close observation of the spectrum in Fig. 39.4 will show that the peak ratios are not quite those given in the paragraph above. This is because the spin-spin multiplets are functions of the ratio of the coupling constant to the relative chemical shift between the two mutually coupled groups, J/δ. When this ratio is less than 0.05 (chemical shift is large compared to the coupling constant), the number of peaks in multiplet A generated by spin-spin perturbations from a group of equivalent nuclei B will be $(2nI + 1)$, where n is the number of equivalent nuclei of spin I in group B. When $n = 1$, the peaks of multiplet A will all be of equal intensity. When

$n > 1$, the peaks will be distributed symmetrically about the midpoint of the group.

When $I = 1/2$, as with H^1, F^{19}, P^{31}, and others (128), the number of peaks produced in multiplet A by the n equivalent nuclei in group B reduces to $(n + 1)$, and the peak intensities are proportional to the *coefficients* of the binomial expansion $(x + 1)^n$. The separations between peaks in multiplet A will be equal, and will be equal to the peak separations in multiplet B (Fig. 39.4). Fortunately, the occurrence of spin-spin multiplets that approximately follow these simple rules is sufficiently frequent to make them very valuable in the interpretation of NMR spectra.

As J/δ increases, the intensities of the inner peaks (on the sides between the two multiplets) are enhanced at the expense of the outer peaks, destroying the symmetry of the multiplets. Additional peaks also may appear at values of J/δ greater than 0.1. Such multiplets frequently must be analyzed mathematically.

c. Magnitude and Uses

The spin coupling constant is proportional to $\gamma_A \gamma_B$, so that it varies with the isotopes involved. For proton-proton interactions, J ranges from 20 to less than 1 c.p.s., requiring very high resolution for observation of the multiplets. For couplings between protons and C^{13} nuclei, J is 100 to 200 c.p.s., while for proton–P^{31} couplings it may be several hundred c.p.s. Proton couplings are strongest for those protons that are most closely bound together, and decrease rapidly with increasing numbers of bonds between protons. For some other isotopes, particularly F^{19}, the strengths of the spin-spin interactions do not follow quite so simple a rule. Proximity in space seems to be more important for fluorine couplings than proximity in bonds (124). The constant for coupling between vicinal protons or geminal protons is a function of the angle between the carbon-hydrogen bonds involved and of the electronegativity of adjacent groups (8,9,61,72). The coupling between hydrogen and C^{13} also has been found to be a function of the C—H bond length (82).

Spin-spin multiplets supply very valuable information concerning the spatial arrangements of functional groups in molecules, because they give direct information concerning those groups that are most closely associated with each other and the number of equivalent nuclei in each of the groups. They also provide information concerning bond lengths and bond angles under special circumstances. The absence of spin-spin multiplicity indicates groups that are relatively isolated from all other magnetic groups in the molecule. Spin coupling of the unpaired electron in free radicals with the protons or other magnetic nuclei with which it may be associated in the molecule often indicates the location and the degree of localization of the unpaired electron. A decisive choice between two alternate molecular structures frequently can be made on the basis of spin coupling alone.

3. Spin-Decoupling

If the lifetime of a nucleus in each of its allowed spin states is reduced sufficiently, the information carried from it to adjacent nuclei (and vice versa) will be only an average of the spin states, so that the perturbations normally due to the spin coupling will disappear. The spins of the two affected groups of nuclei are then said to be decoupled. This decoupling can result from rapid interchange of one group of the nuclei involved, such as is common in the labile protons of alcohols, acids, etc. It also can be produced by the intentional limitation of the lifetime of a given group by "double irradiation" (Section II-C-3). When one of the coupled nuclei has an electric qradrupole, spin decoupling can be achieved by means of the fluctuating electric fields set up in highly polar solvents. This technique has proved useful in the study of compounds containing N^{14} (18,121,123).

III. EXPERIMENTAL TECHNIQUE

A. INSTRUMENTATION

Although the specifications for the various components differ with the technique and the problem, the instrumentation for both nuclear and electron magnetic resonance consists of the same general unit assemblies. These are a static magnetic field, an alternating magnetic field, a sample probe, a signal detection and display system, a scanning system, stabilizing systems, and elementary computational systems. Their general relationships are indicated in Figs. 39.1 and 39.5, 39.6, and 39.7.

1. Static Magnetic Field

The static magnetic field is required to orient the magnetic nuclei or the electrons and to establish the basic magnetic energy levels and precession frequencies. Since the observed line width depends on the homogeneity of the static magnetic field, and the precision of the measurements depends in part on the stability of this field, it is necessary that both of these factors be maintained at levels high enough to permit precise observation of the narrowest lines that are to be observed. High-resolution nuclear magnetic resonance requires a field that is homogeneous to 1 part in 200 million over the sample volume, and which is stable to 1 part per billion for at least 10 seconds. It is preferable that the stability be 2 parts per billion or better

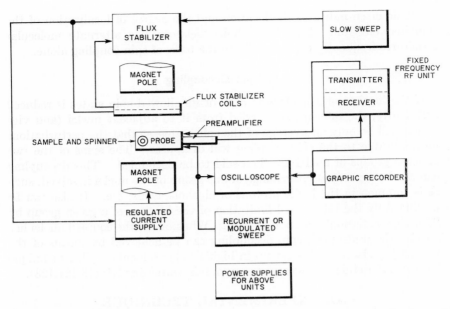

Fig. 39.5. Block diagram of a typical high-resolution NMR spectrometer. Courtesy of Varian Associates, Instrument Division.

for periods of days. This gives the highest precision of measurement on a long-term basis, a feature that is highly desirable for analytical work. Alternatively, resonance stability may be achieved by maintaining the ratio of alternating-field frequency to static-field strength constant, at $\gamma/2\pi$, within the above limits (see equation (2)).

This degree of homogeneity and stability is extremely difficult to obtain, requiring the utmost care in the design and construction of the magnet and stabilizing systems and in alignment of the magnet pole faces. The final degree of adjustment of homogeneity can be obtained most easily by the use of electric "shimming" coils, which compensate for the last vestiges of gradients in the magnetic field. Spinning the sample reduces the effects of residual horizontal gradients by averaging.

For wide-line nuclear magnetic resonance work, field homogeneity of the order of 1 part in 10^4 or 10^5 is adequate, since line widths in this case are of the order of several gauss. This degree of homogeneity and the stability commensurate with it are relatively easy to attain with either permanent or electromagnets.

The field requirements for electron spin resonance are quite similar to those for nuclear resonance. For the highest resolution, field homo-

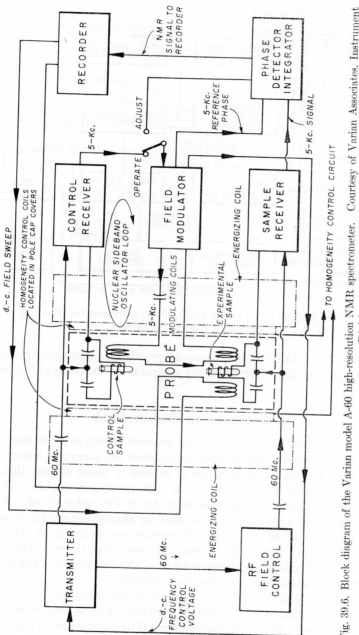

Fig. 39.6. Block diagram of the Varian model A-60 high-resolution NMR spectrometer. Courtesy of Varian Associates, Instrument Division.

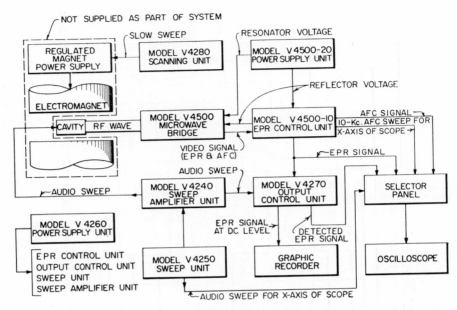

Fig. 39.7. Block diagram of the Varian EMR (EPR) spectrometer.   Courtesy of Varian Associates, Instrument Division.

geneities of 1 part in 10^8 or 10^9 are necessary, whereas homogeneity and stability of 1 part in 10^5 or 10^6 is entirely adequate for the study of free radicals in solids.

2. Alternating Magnetic Field

A magnetic field alternating at the precession frequency is required to supply energy for causing transitions between the magnetic energy levels and to force the nuclei or electrons to precess in phase so that their combined signals may be observed. For high-resolution nuclear resonance work, the amplitude of this field must be of the order of 10^{-3} to 10^{-1} mgauss, whereas for wide-line work and for highest sensitivity it may be higher by a factor of 10. Radio-frequency power input to the sample probe is less than 1 watt. In electron spin resonance the rf power input to the sample cavity is of the order of 10 mw., the amplitude of the resulting magnetic field depending on cavity characteristics.

The magnitude of the alternating magnetic field must be stable to 1% or better for 1 to 10 minutes, and should preferably have a long-term stability of a few per cent. Such stability is achieved by careful design and by good regulation of all voltages. The frequency stability of the alternating magnetic field should be the same as the stability required for the static magnetic field, 1 part in 10^9 for high resolution and 1 part in 10^6 for wide-line work. This is easily achieved at radio frequencies by crystal control, and is achieved at microwave frequencies by cavity-controlled stabilizing circuits.

The alternating voltage for nuclear resonance work is generated by a conventional multistage crystal-controlled rf generator employing receiving components. The rf output is preferably controlled by means of a precision attenuator to facilitate setting H_1 at selected levels, and is coupled into the sample probe by conventional coaxial transmission line. The corresponding voltage for electron spin resonance is generated by a cavity-stabilized klystron, is also controlled by precision attenuators, and is coupled to the sample cavity and measuring circuits by a suitable wave-guide.

3. Sample Probe

The sample probe provides the means for holding the sample at a selected fixed spot in the static field while it is irradiated by the alternating field, and for picking up the resulting signal. It must be free from vibration, nonmagnetic, and free from impurities that will adversely affect the required homogeneity. Probes used for NMR usually provide also for rapid recurrent (sawtooth) sweep, audio-frequency modulation of the static field, spinning of the sample about its vertical axis, and phasing and magnitude of the leakage voltage (Section II-A). Means for controlling the sample temperature also may be provided.

NMR probes may be classed in two ways according to the construction of the rf section. In single-coil probes (Figs. 39.1 and 39.6) both the transmitter and the receiver are coupled through a suitable network to the same coil, which is wound around the sample holder with its axis perpendicular to the static field. Leakage magnitude and phase may be controlled by an rf bridge when phase detection is not employed. In crossed-coil probes, used in all commercial high-resolution instruments prior to 1961, the receiver is connected to the coil wound around the sample holder while the transmitter is connected to a separate pair of coils set on each side of the sample holder and perpendicular to both the receiver coil and the static field. Leakage magnitude and phase are controlled by a pair of paddles that distort the field produced by the transmitter coil.

Probes used for EMR consist of microwave cavities with provision for inserting the sample at the optimum position, for modulating the static field, for optimum coupling of the rf energy, and for tuning when necessary.

It also may provide means for controlling the sample temperature and for irradiating the sample, while in place, with ultraviolet light. The magnitude and phase of the leakage voltage are not controlled in the EMR sample probe, but are controlled in an external microwave bridge circuit.

4. Signal Detection and Display System

The signals produced by resonating nuclei or electrons are very small, requiring amplifications of the order of 10^5 (100 db.) or greater in order to produce signals that can be displayed satisfactorily on oscilloscopes or recorded on conventional recorders. Careful design and maintenance of the equipment are required to achieve and maintain a satisfactory signal/noise ratio at these amplifications. NMR spectrometers employ conventional superheterodyne amplifying and detecting systems. Phase-sensitive detection may be used at the radio frequency or at the audio modulation frequency (when employed) or both.

EMR spectrometers usually employ crystal detectors operating at the microwave frequency in a microwave bridge system. The noise introduced by a crystal is inversely proportional to the frequency of the detected output signal. The best signal/noise ratio, therefore, is achieved by modulating the microwave signal so as to produce an alternating signal output from the crystal. This modulation also produces a broadening of the resonance lines proportional to the modulating frequency, limiting the modulating frequency to about $1/10$ of the width (at half height) of the narrowest line to be observed (Reference 67, pp. 72–80). A typical modulating frequency is 100 kc., making conventional rf amplification and detection usable after the crystal.

While an oscilloscope display of the signal has been found quite convenient for adjustment of the instrument, the permanent records produced by conventional strip chart or $X-Y$ recorders are much more desirable for general usage. The $X-Y$ record is much more convenient and versatile when the spectrometer has the required stability and operating features to permit its efficient use.

5. Scanning System

Since the nuclei or electrons in a sample do not all experience the same magnetic field simultaneously, it is necessary to scan either the magnitude of the static magnetic field or the frequency of the alternating magnetic field to bring them all into resonance. In most applications it has been found more convenient to scan the magnitude of the static field. The rate and range of scan must be controllable at the convenience of the operator to permit him to observe only that portion of the spectrum which is of immediate interest.   The scan rate, once set, must be constant to 1% or better if precision chemical shift and intensity measurements are to be obtained.   It is most convenient to establish a direct relation between the position of the recorder pen along the horizontal axis and the relative magnitude of the static magnetic field, so that the horizontal axis is directly and precisely related to the applied static field.   The width of the scan will vary from a few parts per million (a few milligauss) for high-resolution studies of hydrogen to about 1% (22 to 50 gauss) for extremely wide NMR and EMR work.

6. Stabilizing and Control Systems

a. RESONANCE POSITION STABILIZATION

The required stability of the observed resonance positions for high-resolution NMR may be obtained in two ways: by separate stabilization of the static and alternating magnetic fields or by stabilization of their ratio. Both systems are in successful use.   Stabilization of the frequency of the alternating field is quite simply achieved by crystal or cavity control, but precise stabilization of the static magnetic field is much more difficult to achieve.   It requires such drastic steps as control of the temperature around the magnet, insulation of the magnet yoke and pole faces, precise control of the magnet-cooling water temperature and flow rate (115), elimination of vibration, and the use of feedback stabilization circuits that sense directly the changes of strength of the magnetic field.

Two types of feedback field-stabilizing systems have been used successfully.   One uses coils as a sensing element and responds to the rate of change of the magnetic field (96,127).   This system is quite useful for detecting rapid rates of change, but it is not sensitive to the slow drift that produces long-term instability of the field.   The second system uses a suitable nuclear resonance signal as an absolute sensing element and is sensitive to absolute deviation from the preset field value (135).   This system is by far the most satisfactory from both long- and short-range standpoints.   It can be used in conjunction with or, in some forms, instead of the coil sensing system.

Although separate stabilization of the alternating and static fields has proved satisfactory for many applications, the highest degree of stability has been achieved by control of the ratio of alternating field frequency to static field strength.   This ratio is controlled at $\gamma/2\pi$ by means of a nuclear resonance signal that may be incorporated into a voltage-controlled oscillator (7), a resonance-controlled coherent oscillator (52,94), or a nuclear sideband oscillator (131, and Fig. 39.6).   These systems are fast acting and drift free, and may require less temperature, current, and voltage control than the separately stabilized systems.

b. Spectral Base-Line Stabilization

When the phase of the observed signal is selected by the introduction of properly phased leakage from the rf field to the receiver pickup coil, large voltages that are subject to the instabilities of the rf generating system are carried through the rf detector into the d.-c. signal system. When a radio-frequency phase-detection system is used to determine signal phasing, it is not practical to eliminate all stray leakage at the sample probe. Both systems, then, introduce voltages that can lead to instability of the spectral base line but that are no longer needed once the phasing of the signal has been properly established. The instabilities actually experienced have been of the order of 10 to 100% of the signal voltage, and *must* be eliminated before accurate intensity measurements can be made. Audio-frequency modulation of the static field modulates the signal voltage but not the leakage or phasing voltage. Subsequent audio-frequency phase-sensitive detection can then pass the signal while completely rejecting the now un-desired leakage, thus eliminating base-line variations due to leakage. This system is simple and very successful (52; 130, Chapter 15; 137).

c. Temperature Control

It is sometimes necessary to study samples at precisely controlled temperatures that may fall within a wide range both below and above ambient. The sample cell holder can be encased in a nonsilvered vacuum jacket, and air or nitrogen at controlled temperature can be passed through the annulus between holder and sample tube (23,112; 130, p. 149). Alternatively, the entire sample probe may be immersed in a temperature-controlled medium (Reference 130, pp. 19,244).

Control of the magnet cooling water is accomplished by conventional refrigeration and flow-control systems. Ambient temperature is controlled by air conditioning and by insulation and/or housing of the magnet.

7. Computing Systems

Since it is the areas under the absorption bands rather than the peak heights that are directly proportional to the number of nuclei being observed (Section II-C-1), it is advantageous to use integrating computers to provide the proper intensity measurements. Electronic integrators with either graphic or digital readout have been found desirable for this service because of their speed and accuracy. Digital readout is convenient for absorption bands that are well separated, but graphic readout is more convenient for the determination of the intensity of overlapping bands.

8. Commercial Instruments

Although a number of wide-line and medium high-resolution NMR instruments have been built by individuals, the difficulty of achieving the high magnetic field homogeneity and stability required for the highest resolution has prompted the purchase of such equipment in general. The highest sensitivity and resolution and the greatest versatility are achieved with instruments such as the Varian HR-60, illustrated in Figs. 39.5 and

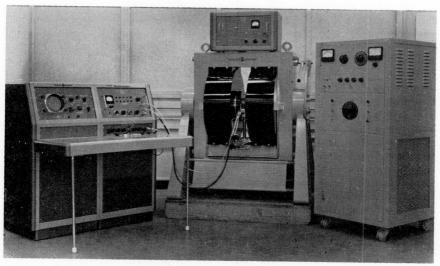

Fig. 39.8. The Varian HR-60 high-resolution NMR spectrometer. Magnet insulation is not shown. Courtesy of Varian Associates, Instrument Division.

39.8. This instrument employs separate stabilization of the alternating and static magnetic fields, using the coil-sensed feedback system for stabilization of the static field. It can be used to study any of the isotopes that can be observed at high resolution, and sample temperature-control equipment can be furnished for use with it. This type of instrument can be operated and maintained only by highly trained technicians or technical personnel.

A more specialized instrument, which is much simpler to operate and maintain, is the Varian A-60 spectrometer, illustrated in Figs. 39.6 and

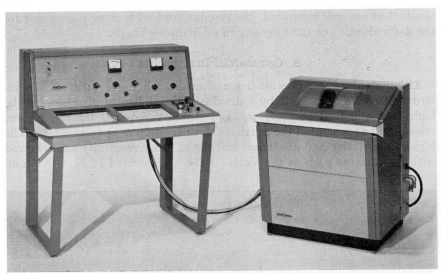

Fig. 39.9.   The Varian A-60 high-resolution NMR spectrometer.   Courtesy of Varian
Associates, Instrument Division.

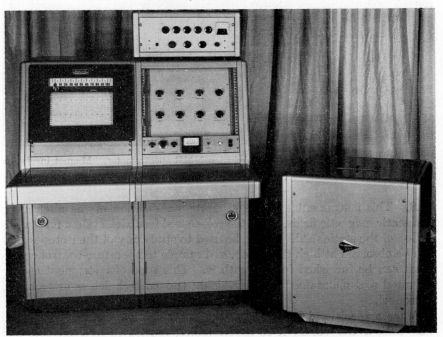

Fig. 39.10.   The Schlumberger NMR analyzer.   Courtesy Ridgefield Instrument Group,
Schlumberger Corporation, Ridgefield, Conn.

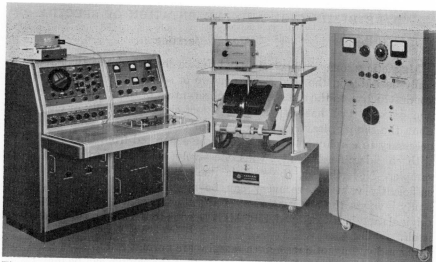

Fig. 39.11. The Varian model V 4500 EMR (EPR) spectrometer.   Courtesy of Varian
Associates, Instrument Division.

39.9.   This instrument thus far is limited to the observation of hydrogen-1 at room temperature and above, but it is capable of performing all of the qualitative and quantitative studies that are of routine importance to the analytical chemist.   It employs a hydrogen resonance signal in a nuclear sideband oscillator to provide absolute stabilization.   The exceptionally high degree of stability achieved very materially improves the efficiency of the production and interpretation of high-resolution spectra of hydrogen.

A wide-line nuclear resonance spectrometer, which also has the advantage of simplicity of maintenance and simplicity of operation, is the Schlumberger NMR Analyzer, illustrated in Figs. 39.1 and 39.10.   This instrument records and measures the intensities of the wide-line resonances of observable isotopes, and is designed to provide quantitative data with the highest degree of simplicity and automation.   It is especially well suited to routine analyses of several types for process control or research (Section V).

Although electron spin resonance spectrometers can be built successfully by anyone skilled in microwave technology, commercial instruments for this technique are also available.   The Varian spectrometer (Figs. 39.7 and 39.11) has been provided with a cavity with a slotted window to permit irradiation of the sample with light while the electron resonance is being observed.   Electron resonance spectrometers are also being marketed by Strand Laboratories (Model 601 EMR spectrometer) and Elion Instruments, Inc. (Electrospec 200).

B. DETERMINATION AND PRESENTATION OF SPECTRA

1. Sample Preparation

Magnetic resonance spectrometry has two characteristics that are especially desirable in the study of expensive or sensitive samples. First, it is nondestructive to the sample. The observation of the magnetic resonance phenomenon itself has no permanent effect either physically or chemically upon the sample, leaving it available for other studies. Sometimes it is necessary to employ solvents that can be separated from the sample only with considerable difficulty, thus effectively nullifying further use of the sample. Nevertheless, the sample itself is not destroyed and, if it is sufficiently valuable, recovery can be accomplished. Of course, if the study involves the observation of chemical changes within the sample, the original sample is destroyed, but this is not due to the method of observation itself.

Secondly, magnetic resonance samples are normally studied in glass containers that may be sealed, if desired, so that the sample can be maintained under vacuum or under any convenient atmosphere desired. This feature is especially important in the study of samples that are extremely sensitive to oxygen or to water vapor, and that must be maintained under controlled atmospheres during observation. Such samples can be sealed for an indefinite period in the sample tubes and can be studied periodically for as long an elapsed time as is necessary.

High-resolution spectra, either nuclear or electron, can be obtained only on liquids of low viscosity. Solid samples must be melted or dissolved in suitable solvents, and liquids of high viscosity must be heated or diluted to reduce their viscosity to a suitable level. The rapid molecular motion permitted by such solutions is absolutely essential to the averaging out of localized magnetic field variations that otherwise would broaden the spectral lines beyond the limits required for high resolution. Gaseous samples also permit the required rate of molecular tumbling, but the low concentrations of molecules obtainable at reasonable gas pressures do not provide sufficient sensitivity for the study of a very large number of compounds in the gas state.

Wide-line spectra, either nuclear or electron, may be observed in gaseous, liquid, or solid samples. Since the line width is not limited by field homogeneity in such cases, much larger samples can be used to provide much higher sensitivity than is available in high-resolution spectrometry, and there is no necessity for averaging the localized magnetic field differences. In fact, one of the desirable characteristics of wide-line spectrometry is that it is able to observe the large localized magnetic field variations brought about by dipole–dipole interactions, and it can indicate over what percentage of the nuclei these interactions have been averaged out by relatively rapid tumbling or by interconversion of rotational or conformational isomers.

The sample volume normally employed for high-resolution spectrometry is 0.2 to 0.5 ml. Samples of smaller volume can be handled, when necessary, by dilution to the required volume in a suitable solvent, by the use of special plugs in the sample cells (129,129a), or by the use of very small capillary tubing properly suspended in the sample probe (108). Use of the capillary cell permits observation of pure liquid samples in the microliter range, making possible the observation of undiluted larger fractions from gas chromatographic columns. Considerably increased sensitivity may be obtained in wide-line spectrometry by using samples up to 50 ml. in volume.

The ideal solvent for use in magnetic resonance work must be able to dissolve an appreciable amount of the sample to be studied (10% or more), must be chemically inert and magnetically isotropic, and should contain none of the nuclear or electronic species being observed. Carbon tetrachloride approaches this ideal for the multitude of compounds that will dissolve satisfactorily in it, but, unfortunately, there are many compounds that it simply does not dissolve satisfactorily, even at elevated temperatures. Furthermore, the analysis of reaction mixtures and completely unknown materials that have been extracted from plant streams, etc., requires that the analyst be familiar with the spectroscopic properties and the solvent effects of a wide variety of materials that may be encountered. When it is necessary to use solvents that may be chemically reactive with the sample or that are electrically polar or magnetically anisotropic, the analyst must always be on guard for specific solvent effects, which can change materially the appearance of the spectrum of the sample (32,62,85,109,116). These changes can be due to simple physical association of sample and solvent molecules or to varying degrees of chemical bonding, including hydrogen bonding. Observation and interpretation of such solvent effects is facilitated by observation of the sample in a number of different solvents or at different concentrations in the same solvent. These effects sometimes can be used to considerable advantage in separating normally overlapping resonances (32,116).

2. Referencing

a. EXTERNAL REFERENCING

Just as optical spectrometry employs absolute wavelength and mass spectrometry employs absolute mass, magnetic resonance could employ absolute static magnetic-field strength to designate peak position. If this property were used, however, it would be necessary to express the field strength to 9 significant figures, 3 to 5 of which would not change for a given series of spectra! This would also entail measurement of the magnetic-field strength for each point in each spectrum, a measurement that can best be made by reference to the magnetic resonance of a known material. The "reference compound" method for determining field strength is actually employed, but the use of excessively large numbers is eliminated by simply describing the spectral peak positions in terms of displacement from this reference peak. The reference compound thus employed must be kept entirely separate from the sample by placing it in a separate container, which is preferably concentric with the sample container. The reference material may be placed either in an annular space between two concentric cells (140) or in a small capillary tube mounted or dropped into the center of the sample tube (80). This technique is known as external referencing, and serves to establish the strength of the applied static magnetic field *external* to the sample.

Benzene is an accepted external reference compound for hydrogen resonances. Water has been used but is undesirable because of its relatively large resonance shift with temperature. Phosphoric acid (85% H_3PO_4) has served as the usual external reference for P^{31} resonances.

b. Solvent Effects

The magnetic field actually experienced by a given nucleus *within* the sample depends not only on the strength of the applied field but also on the structure of the sample molecule and a group of factors that will be called solvent effects. For neat liquids the sample becomes its own solvent. Only gases are free from solvent effects. The solvent effects appear to be due to the following factors (17,26).

1. Bulk diamagnetic susceptibility of the sample plus solvent (15). The precise contribution of this factor could be calculated readily if means were available to determine the susceptibility of the gross sample rapidly with an accuracy of $\pm 0.001 \times 10^{-6}$ (in cgs electromagnetic units (emu)). Available susceptibility data and methods are inadequate, however.

2. Preferential orientation of sample molecules with magnetically anisotropic or electrically polar solvent molecules (16,25). These effects can be calculated when the average orientations are known, but this is not usually the case. These orientations depend on both the structures and the shapes of the sample and solvent molecules.

3. Hydrogen bonding. Increasing degree of H-bonding produces an increasing shift of resonance of the labile hydrogen to the lower field (111), due, perhaps, to the effect of the electric field set up in the H-bond (92). The resonance position of labile hydrogen is very sensitive to the degree of H-bonding. Resonances of hydrogens in adjacent groups are affected to a much smaller but still measurable extent. These effects are calculable only roughly.

4. van der Waals forces. Contribution to the solvent shift is calculable only roughly at present.

For some isotopes, like phosphorus-31, the resonance displacements due to magnetic susceptibility and solvent effects are minor compared to the displacements due to the differences in molecular structure, so that the chemical shifts based on external references are sufficiently accurate for analytical work. For isotopes like fluorine-19 and hydrogen-1, however, the solvent and/or susceptibility effects are large enough to interfere seriously with the establishment of a reliable correlation between chemical shift and molecular structure. In order to study successfully the molecular structure of organic molecules through the resonances of fluorine or hydrogen, it is necessary to reduce the solvent and susceptibility effects to negligible levels.

c. INTERNAL REFERENCING

Virtually complete elimination of solvent and bulk susceptibility effects can be accomplished by observing each sample at a number of different concentrations in the same relatively inert and isotropic solvent and then extrapolating all data to infinite dilution in the solvent. All samples are thus subjected to exactly the same magnetic susceptibility and solvent effects, so that these effects cancel out between spectra. The same result can be obtained by observing the sample at a single high dilution in an ideal solvent and using a reference material that is dissolved in the sample (122). In this case the molecule of the reference compound experiences the same magnetic susceptibility effect as does the molecule of the sample, so that the magnetic susceptibility effect is cancelled out. If there is no solvent interaction with either the reference or the sample, or if the solvent interaction with the reference and sample is the same, the solvent effects also are cancelled out.

Less accurate but still very useful chemical shift data can be obtained in a wide variety of solvents and a full range of concentrations when a proper choice of internal reference material is made (32). This method does not eliminate the effects of hydrogen bonding, but uses them to identify labile hydrogens. Tetramethylsilane has proved to be the most nearly ideal and the most popular internal reference compound now in use for referencing hydrogen resonances. Cyclohexane has proved to be a good second choice for this purpose. Unfortunately, however, neither of these materials will dissolve universally in all of the samples or solvents that must be used for the successful study of organic materials by hydrogen resonance. No generally available compound has been agreed upon as a satisfactory reference for aqueous solutions. CF_3COOH and CCl_3F have been used successfully as internal references for F^{19} resonances (1,48), whereas 85% H_3PO_4 has served as the usual external reference for P^{31} resonances (1,49).

3. Presentation of Data

Although rapid changes in both instrumentation and technique have made it difficult to standardize presentation of the data, determined efforts are being made to standardize before the literature can become loaded with a wide variety of data-presentation forms. General agreement appears to have been reached on a number of important points. High-resolution magnetic resonance spectra are recorded in the absorption mode, oriented so that the magnetic field increases horizontally toward the right, with peaks pointing up as they do in mass spectra rather than down as they do in optical spectra.

No general agreement has yet been reached on the exact form of the scales to be used to indicate peak locations and separations, although it appears that two scales will be desirable. Since chemical shifts vary directly with magnetic-field strength (or alternating-field frequency), it is generally agreed that these data should be expressed in dimensionless units (parts per million) so that the numbers designating chemical shifts for a given isotope will *not* change with changes in the basic operating frequency of the spectrometer. Thus a given hydrogen chemical shift measured from a given reference point in p.p.m. would remain the same whether measured at 30, 40, or 60 Mc. Spin coupling constants, on the other hand, are independent of the magnetic field and operating frequency. It is generally agreed that these values should be expressed in cycles per second. Rapid and accurate measurement of both spin coupling constants and chemical shifts from a suitable spectrum, then, are facilitated by the presence of both a frequency scale and a dimensionless scale on the spectrum. Calculated data may conveniently be reported on the back of a spectrum so that the reader may benefit from the calculations made by the author.

Linear scales can be applied accurately only to those spectra produced on spectrometers of extremely high stability. For spectrometers of lesser stability, accurate peak-separation measurement is achieved by the audio sideband techniques (Section II-D-1).

Comprehension and future use of a spectrum are materially enhanced by placing thereon a complete interpretation of the spectrum in terms of the chemical structures from which it arose. This is easily done for the spectra of pure compounds by labeling the various functional groups in the structure diagram and the spectral features to which they give rise with corresponding letters, using spin-splitting diagrams to clarify complex spin-splitting patterns when possible (Figs. 39.12 and 39.16). Since such interpretations are subject to change with increasing knowledge, it has been considered unwise to employ them on spectra being produced and distributed for permanent record. Each recipient of such spectra would be expected to provide his own interpretation. Nevertheless, interpretations are very helpful on spectra published to illustrate a point or to prove a molecular structure.

To make possible reproduction of a spectrum by other experimenters, it is desirable that all of the pertinent operating variables be specified on the spectrogram. These variables include the nature and concentration of the solvent, the sample temperature, the basic spectrometer frequency, the isotope observed, the scan rate, the reference compound used, the referencing method employed, a time constant of the recording circuit, and the amplitude of the radio frequency field. This information also makes it possible to determine at a later date the degree of saturation that may have prevailed during production of the spectrum and to estimate the amount of fine structure that may have been modified by a fast scan rate. If the approxi-

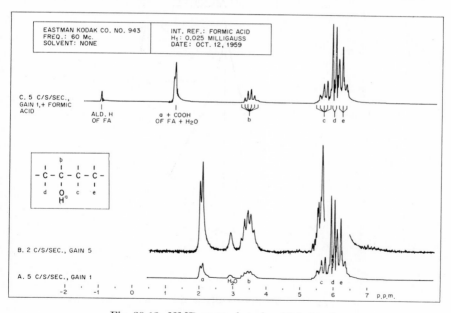

Fig. 39.12. NMR spectral study of 2-butanol.

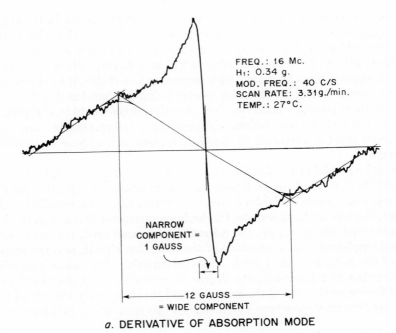

FREQ.: 16 Mc.
H_1: 0.34 g.
MOD. FREQ.: 40 C/S
SCAN RATE: 3.31g./min.
TEMP.: 27°C.

NARROW
COMPONENT =
1 GAUSS

——12 GAUSS——
= WIDE COMPONENT

a. DERIVATIVE OF ABSORPTION MODE

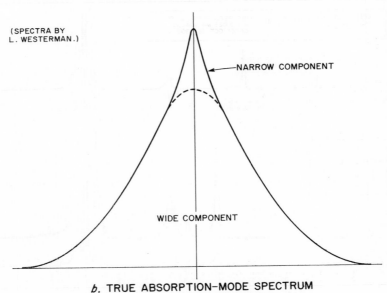

(SPECTRA BY
L. WESTERMAN.)

NARROW COMPONENT

WIDE COMPONENT

b. TRUE ABSORPTION–MODE SPECTRUM

Fig. 39.13. Wide-line NMR spectra of hydrogen in a hydrocarbon polymer.

mate degree of resolution is not obvious from the presence of relatively sharp peaks in the spectrum, it may be desirable to indicate separately the degree of resolution to which the spectrometer was adjusted at the time the sample was run. This may be done by specifying the width of one of the lines of the quartet of acetaldehyde as recorded on the spectrometer just prior to the production of the sample spectrum.

An informal spectrogram suitable for "in-lab" use is presented in Fig. 39.12. This was produced with a high-stability spectrometer with an $X-Y$ recorder synchronized with the scan.

Wide-line NMR spectra and EMR spectra are normally presented as derivatives of the absorption mode in order to emphasize the relatively small inflections often encountered in the presentation of the true absorption mode (Fig. 39.13). The audio or low rf modulation of the magnetic field, which is used to produce the derivative pattern, also makes possible the use of phase-sensitive detection to improve the signal/noise ratio. The true absorption-mode signal can be reproduced by electronic or graphic integration of the derivative signal. Elaborate scales are not required for these spectra, as a rule; instead, only an indication of the separation between the various peaks that may be observed or an indication of the total width of the scan is sufficient. The identification of the sample and the designation of the magnitude of important operating variables also is desirable on these spectra.

The Schlumberger NMR Analyzer used for elemental analysis records a modified absorption-mode spectrum to facilitate integration of the signal intensity while still providing the advantages of audio phase-sensitive detection (105). A modulation amplitude larger than the width of the spectrum plus a wide scan produce positive and negative absorption envelopes in succession. Both envelopes are recorded and are integrated electronically. The value of the total integral, without regard to polarity, is presented as a bar at the end of the spectrum. Two complete spectra with their integral values are shown in Fig. 39.14.

IV. APPLICATIONS OF HIGH-RESOLUTION NUCLEAR MAGNETIC RESONANCE

High-resolution spectra may be defined as those in which the observed widths of the resonance lines are smaller than the major resonance shifts caused by differences in the chemical environment of the observed nucleus. The effect of molecular structure on resonance shifts, both chemical shifts and spin–spin splittings, is shown clearly in spectra of this type, making them of great value in structure determinations. The high-resolution tech-

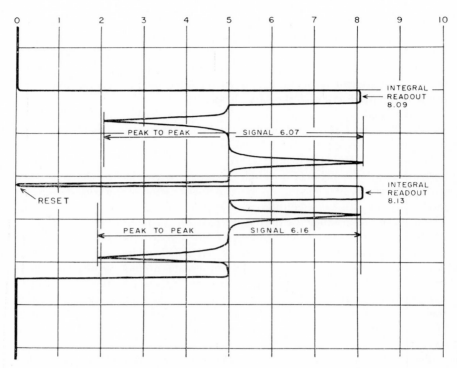

Fig. 39.14. Typical spectrum and integrated intensity measurement from the Schlumberger NMR analyzer. Courtesy of Ridgefield Instrument Group, Schlumberger Corporation, Ridgefield, Conn.

nique can be applied to only those isotopes that possess a nuclear magnetic moment but do not have a nuclear quadrupole moment, or to those isotopes whose quadrupole moment can be satisfactorily decoupled from the nuclear moment to prevent nuclear resonance broadening. Those that have been observed successfully to date are H^1, F^{19}, P^{31}, B^{11}, N^{14}, C^{13}, O^{17}, Si^{29}, Co^{59}, and Pb^{207} (24).

A. HYDROGEN RESONANCE

1. Characteristics

Hydrogen-1 is the most important isotope for study by high-resolution nuclear magnetic resonance for a number of reasons. It is the most easily detectable stable isotope, so that it can be studied in lower concentration than other isotopes. It occurs in most organic compounds, making its

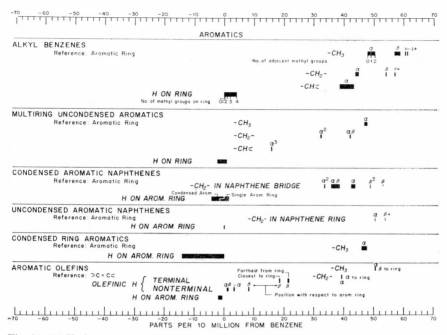

Fig. 39.15. Hydrogen magnetic resonance chemical shifts. Reproduced by permission from *Analytical Chemistry*, **31**, 56 (1959).

resonance especially useful in this field. Its resonance shifts follow a logical and predictable pattern under the influence of electron-withdrawing or electron-donating groups and under the influence of magnetically anisotropic groups. Its spin–spin couplings also follow a regular and predictable pattern. It is possible to associate a given functional group with a relatively narrow region of the total hydrogen chemical shift spectrum (Fig. 39.15), making it possible to identify hydrogen-containing functional groups with a minimum of ambiguity and uncertainty. On the other hand, hydrogen has the smallest range of chemical shifts of all the isotopes—about 20 p.p.m. total—with most of the resonances concentrated in a range of 10 p.p.m. The observation of such small shifts requires the highest quality of equipment and, at least until recently, highly skilled operators. Major improvements in equipment are now beginning to reduce the skill required for operation. Hydrogen resonance lines are usually sharp except when molecular motion is restricted, but the small chemical shift frequently prevents complete resolution of the lines, making interpretation and quantitative measurements more difficult.

2. Uses

a. DETERMINATION OF MOLECULAR STRUCTURE

The most frequent and perhaps the most obvious use for the high-resolution NMR of hydrogen is the determination of the functional groups in
and the structure of hydrogen-containing molecules. A procedure for ex-
tracting the structure information made available by this technique is as
follows.

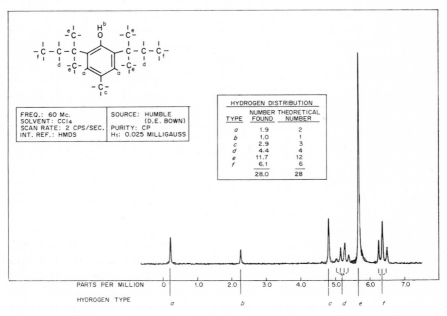

Fig. 39.16. NMR proof of structure of 1-hydroxy-2,6-bis(*tert*-pentyl)-4-methyl benzene.

1. Determine the high-resolution absorption-mode spectrum of the compound under conditions that will provide accurate quantitative as well as
qualitative data. This requires attention to sample preparation, instrument stability and resolution, saturation error, signal phasing, and, when
phase detection is not used, to errors due to improper leakage voltage (134).

2. Identify the individual resonance bands and individual spin-spin
multiplets. This is a trial-and-error procedure that may be illustrated by
reference to Fig. 39.16.

a. Identify the major groupings of peaks in the spectrum. In Fig.
39.16 these are indicated as *a*, *b*, *c*, *d*, *e*, and *f*.

b. Using the spin-spin multiplet rules (number of peaks, peak separations, and intensity relations), determine which peak groups are spin-spin multiplets and exactly which peaks belong to each multiplet, if possible. In Fig. 39.16, group *d* is the typical 1:3:3:1 quartet and group *f* is the matching 1:2:1 triplet produced by an ethyl group with a relatively large chemical shift between methyl and methylene hydrogens. It is apparent, therefore, that these two groups are the complete spin-spin multiplets of this mutually coupled five-spin system. All the other peaks in this spectrum appear to be singlets, and each one can be assumed to arise from a different functional group.

3. Measure the chemical shifts. For most structure work it is adequate to measure the chemical shifts to an accuracy of ±0.1 p.p.m., making it possible to read them directly from the spectra recorded by high-stability spectrometers, or by relatively rough measurement with the audio sideband method. It is not generally necessary to calculate the precise chemical shift for a spin-spin multiplet. An estimate of the shift based on the center-of-area of the multiplet is entirely adequate for most analytical work.

4. Measure the resonance band intensities. Intensities should be measured as accurately as is feasible, since this measurement is relatively easy to make with an electronic integrator or by a direct summation of ordinates of the resonance bands. Assuming that all instrumental factors have been brought under proper control, the remaining source of quantitative error will be band overlap. Since the shapes of the overlapping resonance bands are not always known, it is not always possible to calculate the contributions of one band to another. In such circumstances it has been found quite useful and informative to assume that the proper demarcation between the bands is a vertical line dropped from the lowest point of the valley to the base line. The intensities may be recorded either as a hydrogen distribution normalized to 100% or, if the total number of hydrogens in the proposed molecule or the number of hydrogens in any of the functional groups thought to be involved is known accurately, the intensities may be presented as numbers of hydrogens, as in Fig. 39.16.

5. Identify the functional groups present in the sample, using correlations of chemical shift with chemical structure. Useful correlations of this type have been published as charts (32) and as tables (24,69,93,103). Within the accuracy of the data included in these charts and tables, there usually will be more than one functional group which corresponds to a given shift. In the most difficult cases it is advisable to list all of the functional groups that could have given rise to each of the resonances observed in the spectrum and then eliminate those that are not admissible on the basis of the remaining NMR data or other available data. For example, in Fig.

39.16 the singlet at 0.2 p.p.m. (*a*) could be attributed, on the basis of chemical shift alone, to hydrogens on single or multiple aromatic rings, to hydrogens on a furan ring alpha to the oxygen, to any one of several types of labile hydrogens, such as OH, and to hydrogens on a quinone ring. The labile hydrogen assignment is ruled out immediately by the addition of acid to the sample, which caused *b* to move but had no effect on *a*. Thus, peak *b* is identified as arising from the labile OH hydrogen, whereas peak *a* is shown to arise from some other hydrogen type. The absence of multiplicity in peak *a* makes it quite unlikely that it represents hydrogen attached to condensed aromatic rings. The absence of a band representing hydrogen on a furan ring beta to the oxygen, and the absence of any other bands that could be expected to arise from alkyl substituents on a furan ring, effectively rule out the furan ring. The quinone ring is ruled out principally by the quantitative data. The presence of resonances *c*, *d*, *e*, and *f*, which may be attributed to alkyl substituents on a benzene ring, however, confirm that peak *a* most likely arises from hydrogens on a single highly substituted benzene ring. Identities of the functional groups that give rise to the other resonances may be similarly deduced and a tentative structure devised.

6. Determine the spatial positions of the hydrogen groups. This is done with the aid of both the chemical shift correlations and the spin-spin multiplet information. The C^{13}—H multiplets arising from C^{13} in natural abundance also are helpful. The identity and number of the individual functional groups finally determined from the spectrum of Fig. 39.16 and from a knowledge of the chemical reactions involved in the production of this sample are listed in Table 39.I. The relative number of units of each functional group present is determined directly from the quantitative NMR

TABLE 39.I

Functional Groups Deduced from Spectrum of Fig. 39.16

Band	Functional group[a]	Number groups	Remarks and conclusions[a]
a	Aromatic ring	1 ring	Isolated hydrogens (no relative shift and no spin splitting)
b	OH	1	Typical of pure phenols
None	CH_2 α to aromatic ring	0	—
c	CH_3 α to aromatic ring	1	Apparently isolated
d	CH_2 β to aromatic ring	2	Spin coupled to *f* (adjacent to *f*)
e	CH_3 β to aromatic ring	4	Isolated (gem-dimethyl or *tert*-butyl)
f	CH_3 γ to aromatic ring	2	Spin coupled to *d* (adjacent to *d*)

[a] See Fig. 39.15.

hydrogen distribution measurements.   The total number cannot always be determined in this way, since it is possible that the actual sample molecule is a polymer of the structure deduced.   The ambiguity that may remain in this regard can be cleared up quickly by determination of the molecular weight.

There doesn't seem to be any other way to arrange the functional groups listed in Table 39.I except in the monomeric compound shown in Fig. 39.16.   In this case the structure identification appears to be positive and complete, even to the details of structure of the large alkyl groups.

7. Check the theoretical hydrogen distribution of the proposed compound against the measured hydrogen distribution of the sample.   This often leads to the convincing results shown in Fig. 39.16.

b. Multicomponent Quantitative Analyses

Extensive improvements in spectrometer stability plus the addition of electronic integrators has made possible the complete quantitative determination of the components in an increasing variety of multicomponent mixtures.   In this area NMR is not often directly competitive with optical or mass spectrometry, but it is applied in those cases for which it is particularly well suited or those cases that are not adaptable to optical or mass analysis. The absolute proportionality between resonance-band intensity and the number of atoms of the observed isotope contributing to that band, combined with the possibility of completely indirect chemical shift calibration, gives NMR a tremendous advantage in those cases in which the individual components of the mixture are not known or the pure compounds are not available for the calibration of other spectrometric devices.   In a number of actual cases, NMR has been able to identify all of the major components present in a new reaction mixture and to provide the quantitative distribution of these components from an examination of only the reaction mixture itself, without preparation of the pure components for calibration.

Best results are obtained from spectra that have sharp, well-separated bands for all key functional groups required for the analysis.   Acceptable results, at reduced accuracy, may be obtained from less than ideal spectra, however.   With present instrumentation, the NMR intensity measurements are not generally sufficiently accurate to permit the use of simultaneous equations for determining the composition.   The spectrum generally must contain a sufficient number of accurately measurable resonance bands that are unique to individual components to permit calculation by successive elimination of components.   Alternatively, the spectra calculated for various theoretical mixtures of the known components can be matched to the observed spectrum by trial-and-error calculation.   Analyses thus obtained may be in error by 1 to 10% (arithmetic) for a given component, but they are usually far less expensive and time-consuming than the best alternative method.

A general calculation method that can be used with either unique or overlapping bands is convenient even though the data may not be accurate enough for precise solution of the simultaneous equations. For a mixture of j components that produces an NMR spectrum of i separately measurable resonance bands, let

H_{ij} = moles of type i hydrogen per mole of compound j. Determined from molecular structure.

H_{is} = moles of type i hydrogen in the effective sample volume. Directly proportional to the area of the ith resonance band in the NMR spectrum.

M_j = moles of compound j in effective sample volume. To be calculated.

H_s = total moles hydrogen in effective sample volume. May be chosen as 1.

M_s = total moles of all compounds in effective sample volume. To be calculated.

X_j = mole fraction of compound j in sample.

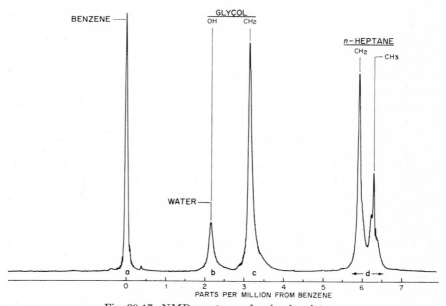

Fig. 39.17. NMR spectrum of a simple mixture.

Then

$$\sum_{j} H_{ij} M_j = H_{is} \tag{7}$$

$$\sum_{i} H_{is} = H_s \tag{8}$$

$$\sum_{j} M_j = M_s \tag{9}$$

$$X_j = M_j/M_s \tag{10}$$

When H_s is chosen as 1, the expanded form of equation (8) is the fractional hydrogen distribution of the sample.

An example of an ideal case for multicomponent analysis by NMR is presented in Fig. 39.17. This is a simple spectrum of sharp, well-separated bands in which all bands except one are unique to a single component. Application of equations (7) and (8) to this sample leads to the following array:

H_{is}		Relative areas		Benzene		Water		Ethylene glycol		Heptane
H_{as}	=	A_a	=	$6M_1$	+	$0M_2$	+	$0M_3$	+	$0M_4$
H_{bs}	=	A_b	=	$0M_1$	+	$2M_2$	+	$2M_3$	+	$0M_4$
H_{cs}	=	A_c	=	$0M_1$	+	$0M_2$	+	$4M_3$	+	$0M_4$
H_{ds}	=	A_d	=	$0M_1$	+	$0M_2$	+	$0M_3$	+	$16M_4$
H_s	=	1	=	$6M_1$	+	$2M_2$	+	$6M_3$	+	$16M_4$

From which

Component	Relative number moles	Mole fraction
Benzene	$M_1 = A_a/6$	$X_1 = A_a/6T$
Water	$M_2 = (A_b/2) - (A_c/4)$	$X_2 = (A_b/2T) - (A_c/4T)$
Ethylene glycol	$M_3 = A_c/4$	$X_3 = A_c/4T$
Heptane	$M_4 = A_d/16$	$X_4 = A_d/16T$
Total	T	1.00

$$\sum_{j} M_j = (8A_a + 24A_b + 3A_d)/48 = T$$

A wide range of mixtures of this type has been analyzed with a precision of $\pm 0.5\%$ and little or no bias.

Indirect calibration of chemical shifts leaves uncertainties of the order of ± 0.2 p.p.m., due principally to uncompensated solvent effects. This uncertainty is sometimes as large as the separation between closely spaced but well-resolved peaks in the spectra of multicomponent mixtures. When this situation prevents proper assignment of the peaks to specific compounds, it may be necessary to calibrate directly by addition of small amounts of some of the individual pure compounds to the sample (33). When spectrometers of extremely high stability are used, it is frequently possible to locate the resonance bands produced by a specific compound by superimposing the spectrum of that pure compound on the sample spectrum. The variations in key bands in the spectra of a series of fractions produced by separation techniques (distillation, chromatography, etc.) indicate which bands should be identified together and thus simplify their assignment to specific compounds.

c. Characterizations

Many multicomponent mixtures and many molecules of very high molecular weight are so complex that the complete determination of their composition or structure is unjustified. A great deal can be deduced about the properties of such mixtures or molecules from a knowledge of the functional groups present and their quantitative distribution. The collection of such information is called characterization of the sample. In the case of complex mixtures it leads to a knowledge of the compound types present, and sometimes permits determination of the structure of the "average molecule." Characterizations have proved very helpful in predicting and following the processing of petroleum fractions and in determining the probable origin of unexpected or undesirable by-products or waste materials.

The most complete and satisfactory characterization of complex hydrocarbon mixtures has been done with a combination of NMR and mass spectrometry. Mass spectrometry can determine the percentages of compounds containing 0, 1, 2, etc. naphthene or aromatic rings. It also can provide a measurement of the average molecular weight or average carbon number of the sample. MS does not, however, provide much information concerning the branchiness of the side chains, whereas NMR provides this specifically. Infrared and ultraviolet spectrometry sometimes can add useful information that cannot be obtained by the other methods. Much useful work can be done with NMR plus molecular weight and elemental analysis, however (136). This last combination will be emphasized here.

Part of this section is the unpublished work of R. B. Williams and is presented with his kind permission.

(1) Characterization of Saturates (Olefin- and Aromatic-Free)

A complete determination of the average character of a complex mixture of saturated hydrocarbons can be made from the NMR hydrogen distribu-

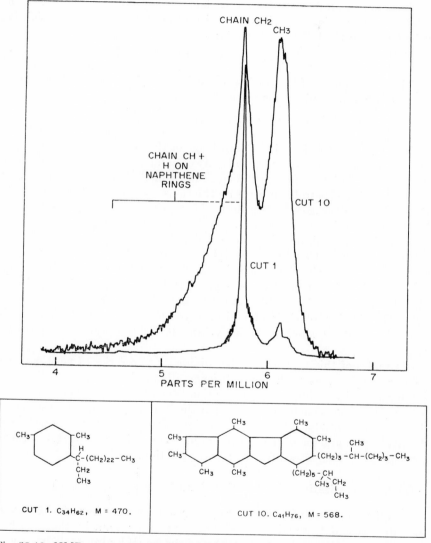

Fig. 39.18. NMR spectra (60 Mc.) and corresponding average molecular structures of two petroleum saturate fractions.

tion (methyl and nonmethyl types), the total hydrogen content, and the average molecular weight. Since both the total hydrogen content and the hydrogen distribution can be determined by NMR, only the molecular weight must be measured by a different method.

The average number of naphthene rings (r) per molecule may be calculated from the weight fraction of total hydrogen (H_t) and the molecular weight (M) by the following formula:

$$r = (1 - 6.957\,H_t)(M/12.01) + 1 \tag{11}$$

Using the fraction of hydrogen present in methyl groups (H_m), the average number of methyl groups per molecule may be calculated from:

$$CH_3/\text{molecule} = MH_tH_m/3.024 \tag{12}$$

From this information plus a knowledge of the general characteristics of such materials that is gained from a study of numbers of similar samples, one can derive a structure for the "average molecule." The NMR spectra of two of a series of petroleum saturate fractions are presented in Fig. 39.18, along with the average structure derived for each of these fractions from the NMR characterizations. Other average structures can be devised to fit the data just as well, but these are reasonable.

The spectrum of Cut *1* resembles closely the spectrum of a normal paraffin of medium molecular weight, indicating that this molecule has a long unbranched chain attached to its ring. Cut *10*, on the other hand, resembles the spectrum of a highly branched paraffin and shows the low-field bulge that is characteristic of hydrogen on naphthene rings. This indicates that Cut *10* consists of highly branched side chains on naphthene rings.

If samples of this type are further divided into a series of very narrow-boiling fractions, as with high-efficiency distillation or preparative gas chromatography, additional information concerning the types of chain terminals present can be deduced from the NMR spectra. Furthermore, the average character of a narrow fraction is much more meaningful than the average character of a wide fraction. The value of MS data also is correspondingly increased for the narrow fraction.

(2) Characterization of Aromatics (Paraffin- and Olefin-Free)

Complex mixtures of aromatic hydrocarbons can be characterized from the same basic data required for saturate fractions: namely, the total hydrogen content, the molecular weight, and the NMR hydrogen distribution. Because of the additional chemical shifts introduced by the magnetic

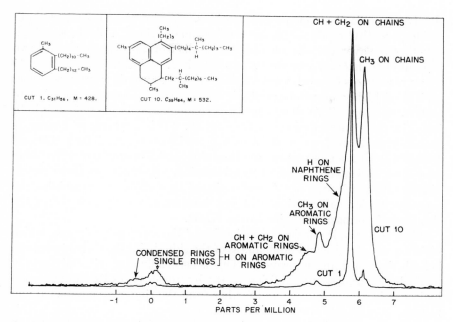

Fig. 39.19. NMR spectra (60 Mc.) and corresponding average molecular structures of two petroleum aromatic fractions.

anisotropy of the aromatic rings, however, the NMR hydrogen distribution for aromatic fractions is much more detailed and informative than it is for saturate fractions. The following hydrogen types are separately detectable and at least approximately separately measurable for aromatics: (1) aromatic ring, (2) CH and CH_2 alpha to the ring, (3) CH_3 alpha to the ring, (4) CH and CH_2 beta and farther from the ring, and (5) CH_3 beta and farther from the ring. The hydrogen on uncondensed aromatic rings is separately detectable from that on condensed aromatic rings, but the two are not usually separately measurable. Proper calculations based on a few reasonable assumptions give (1) the average number of aromatic rings per molecule, (2) the average number, the average size (number of carbons), and the branchiness of the saturate chains, and, for petroleum fractions, (3) the average number of naphthene rings per molecule.

Results of the use of this technique are illustrated in Fig. 39.19. This figure presents the NMR spectra of two of a series of petroleum aromatic fractions, with the structure diagram of the "average molecule" calculated from each. The spectrum of Cut 1 shows no resonances for hydrogen on condensed aromatic rings, and shows aliphatic hydrogen resonances that closely resemble those of normal paraffins. It also gives a positive indication of methyl groups attached to an aromatic ring. Calculations indicate that the average molecule of Cut *1* consists of a benzene ring with two long alkyl chains and a methyl group attached. The spectrum of Cut *10* shows resonances for both single and condensed aromatic rings, resonances typical of highly branched aliphatic chains, and a strong indication of naphthene rings. This all averages to a condensed molecule such as is indicated in the structure diagram for Cut *10*. This average, of course, is probably made up from molecules that are less condensed than this and molecules that are more condensed than this, as well as molecules that may have the indicated degree of condensation. A much more complete picture of the character of this material may be obtained by combining the ring-distribution information obtained from mass spectrometry with the side chain information obtained from NMR.

When the sample consists of molecules of the same general type, which differ only in the size and branchiness of the side chain, the characterization is both simplified and improved. This is especially true with mixtures of monoalkylbenzenes. In addition to the hydrogen types listed above, the hydrogen in groups gamma and farther from the ring can be detected and measured separately from the hydrogen in groups beta to the ring. This leads to an appreciably better picture of the average molecule in such mixtures, and the structure of the average molecule is appreciably more meaningful than it is for more complex materials.

The calculation method used to derive the average structures of complex aromatic mixtures necessarily varies with the band separation obtainable in the spectrum and with the stability of the spectrometer. The complete calculation scheme presented by Williams (136) should be modified to adapt it to the particular spectrum and the particular sample under study. A modified scheme suitable for use with data obtained on petroleum fractions at 60 Mc. is presented in the following paragraphs.

The hydrogen type designations and approximate regions in which the corresponding resonances are located are:

Group	Wt.-% hydrogen	Region, p.p.m.[a]
Aromatic H	H_1	−3.0 to 1.5
Alpha alkyl (ex CH_3)	H_2	1.5 to 4.7
Alpha CH_3 (or ring CH_3)	H_3	4.7 to 5.0
Other alkyl (ex CH_3)	H_4	5.0 to 6.0
Other CH_3 (or chain CH_3)	H_5	6.0 to 7.0

[a] Referenced to tetramethylsilane as 7.0 p.p.m.

In deriving the new calculation scheme, advantage is taken of a correlation between methyls and naphthene rings for petroleum saturate fractions. This correlation indicates that the number of methyls per saturate molecule equals two, plus two additional for each naphthene ring. Assuming that a similar rule applies to the alkyl side chains of the aromatic molecules, it follows that the total methyls per chain is equal to one plus two additional per naphthene ring. (The term "chain" here denotes the total collection of aliphatic chains plus naphthene rings, or portions of naphthene rings, which are attached to an aromatic ring at a single point.) This assumption allows an explicit expression for the C/H ratio of the alkyl groups and also provides an estimate of naphthene rings. The number of aromatic rings per molecule is designated by R, and the number of naphthene rings per alkyl chain by r. For convenience the number of methyls are designated (1) # *ring CH_3* for those directly on aromatic rings, (2) # CH_3 for the other CH_3's, and (3) # *total CH_3* for the sum of (1) and (2). The alkyl chains are thus separated into ring methyls and larger groups. The average carbon number of the larger groups is designated by n. The average alkyl carbon–hydrogen weight ratio, f, is assumed to be the same for nonmethyl groups alpha to the ring as for all other nonmethyl groups.

The following expressions apply to the average chain:

$$\#CH_3 = (12/3)H_5/fH_2 = 4H_5/fH_2 \tag{13}$$

$$n = \frac{f(H_2 + H_4) + 4H_5}{fH_2} = \frac{H_2 + H_4}{H_2} + \#CH_3 \tag{14}$$

$$\#H \ (ex \ CH_3) = 2n + 1 - 2r - 3\#CH_3 \tag{15}$$

$$\#C \ (ex \ CH_3) = n - \#CH_3 \tag{16}$$

$$f = \frac{12\#C \ (ex \ CH_3)}{\#H \ (ex \ CH_3)} = \frac{12(n - \#CH_3)}{2n + 1 - 2r - 3\#CH_3} \tag{17}$$

$$= \frac{6(n - \#CH_3)}{n + 1 - 2\#CH_3}$$

(It is assumed $\#CH_3 = 2r + 1$). Eliminating n and $\#CH_3$:

$$f = (6H_2 + 6H_4 + 4H_5)/(2H_2 + H_4) \tag{18}$$

The weight per cent carbon for various types of groups is now determined:

Peripheral aromatic ring

Unsubstituted $C_1 \ (unsub.) = 12H_1$ (19)

Substituted	$C_1 \text{ (sub.)} = fH_2 + 4H_3$	(20)
Total	$C_1 = C_1 \text{ (unsub.)} + C_1 \text{ (sub.)}$	(21)
Alpha alkyl other than methyl	$C_2 = fH_2$	(22)
Ring methyl	$C_3 = 4H_3$	(23)
Other alkyl except chain methyl	$C_4 = fH_4$	(24)
Chain methyl	$C_5 = 4H_5$	(25)
Total alkyl	$C_s = C_2 + C_3 + C_4 + C_5$	(26)
Number of total peripheral aromatic carbons per molecule	$\#C_1 = C_1 M / 1200$	(27)

The total number of aromatic ring carbons, $\#C_a$, is estimated from the $\#C_1$, assuming kata-condensation of the rings (benzene, naphthalene, anthracene, phenanthrene, etc.). For these structures,

$$\#C_a = 2\#C_1 - 6 \tag{28}$$

If thiophene, benzothiophene, etc., structures are present

$$\#C_a = 2\#C_1 - 6 + 2\#S_t \tag{29}$$

where $\#S_t$ is the number of thiophenic sulfurs. If the sulfur content is known,

$$\#S = (\%S \cdot M)/3200 \tag{30}$$

The fractional $\#S$ occurring in thiophene types has been estimated to lie generally between 0.5 and 1.0 for middle distillate to residual stocks.

Aromatic rings per molecule	$R = \frac{1}{2}(\#C_a - \#C_1) + 1$	(31)
Weight per cent aromatic ring carbon	$C_a = (\#C_a \cdot C_1)/\#C_1$	(32)
Total carbon	$C = C_a + C_s$	(33)
Nonhydrocarbon elements	$\Delta = 100 - C - H$	(34)
Substitution of alkyl groups on aromatic rings	$\% \text{ AS} = \dfrac{100 \cdot C_1(\text{sub.})}{C_1}$	(35)
Number of alkyl chains (other than ring methyls)	$\#\text{Chains} = (\#C_1 \cdot C_2)/C_1$	(36)
Number of ring methyls	$\#\text{Ring CH}_3 = (\#C_1 \cdot C_3)/C_1$	(37)

Total chain methyls

$$\text{Total \#Chain CH}_3 = \text{\#CH}_3 \cdot \text{\#Chains} \tag{38}$$

$$\text{Total methyls} = \text{\#Rings CH}_3 + \text{Total \#Chain CH}_3 \tag{39}$$

Total naphthene rings

$$\text{Total } r = r \cdot \text{\#Chains} \tag{40}$$

$$\text{Total rings} = R + \text{total } r \tag{41}$$

(3) Characterization of Other Hydrocarbons and Nonhydrocarbons

Olefinic hydrocarbons that are known to be aromatic- and paraffin-free can be characterized with the aid of the total hydrogen content, the NMR hydrogen distribution, the bromine number or other measure of total double bonds, and the molecular weight. NMR can separately detect and measure the following hydrogen types: (1) olefinic, (2) CH_2 and CH alpha to double-bonded carbon, (3) CH_3 alpha to double-bonded carbon, (4) CH_2 and CH beta and farther from double-bonded carbon, and (5) CH_3 beta and farther from double-bonded carbon. Terminal and nonterminal olefinic hydrogens are frequently distinguishable but are not always separately measurable. This information leads to a picture of the branchiness and olefinicity of the average molecule.

The characterization of hydrocarbon polymers by high-resolution NMR, without consideration of the molecular weight, leads to a picture of the average repeating group in the polymer. This picture can be interpreted easily in terms of the average monomer of which the polymer is composed, and therefore can be used to characterize polymers of single monomers in terms of the structure of the monomer. This has been useful in identifying the source of undesirable polymer encountered in petroleum processing.

Polymers prepared from known monomers sometimes may be characterized in terms of the ratio of the monomers (in copolymers), the steric arrangement (19), and the bond linkages involved in the polymerization. The migration of double bonds or of carbonium ions during polymerization often can be detected with a high degree of certainty. The rates of propagation of specific steric arrangements sometimes can be studied (20). Each polymer characterization usually requires some techniques and calculation procedures that are peculiar to itself, making it inadvisable to attempt the presentation of a general scheme.

The speed and nondestructiveness of the NMR technique, coupled with the simplicity of the spectra, make NMR a preferred method for making the preliminary observations of an unknown sample. The characterization thus obtained makes it much easier to determine what additional steps should be taken to provide the necessary analysis.

d. KINETIC STUDIES

The ability of NMR to indicate quantitatively and rapidly the changes in key functional groups that occur during chemical reactions makes it adaptable to the study of reaction kinetics. It is preferably applied to those systems that produce unique resonances for key reactants and key products, but conceivably can be applied to some systems for which complete multicomponent analyses can be calculated even though unique resonances are not present. The observation of samples taken periodically from a reacting system will provide the necessary data, but in many cases it is much more desirable to observe the entire reaction within the NMR sample tube. For reactions that require appreciable time to complete, the reactants may be sealed into the sample tube and spectra run periodically at the convenience of the operator until the conclusion of the reaction (33). This eliminates all chance of disturbance to the reacting system by the withdrawing of samples, by the vaporization of materials, or by the introduction of contaminants during the course of the reaction. If necessary, the sample temperature may be controlled. The sample may be sealed under vacuum or under a controlled atmosphere, and light may be excluded. This technique is obviously of considerable value for the study of those reactions that are sensitive to contamination or to sampling upset.

The study of faster reactions can be accomplished in NMR tubes by introducing the last key component (such as a catalyst) while the tube is actually in the spectrometer and the system is being scanned. If the spectrum of the system will permit, scans may be made as rapidly as once every 10 seconds, so that reactions that may be complete in a matter of a very few minutes may still be studied throughout their length by this technique.

Very fast rate processes, such as hydrogen exchange or conformational interchange, may be studied under certain conditions by NMR (References 93, Chapters 13 and 15; 103, Chapter 4; 130, Chapter 9). When hydrogens are changing back and forth from one environment to another, the NMR spectrum they produce depends on the rate of exchange and the chemical shift (frequency separation) between the resonances produced in each of the separate environments. If the rate of exchange is slow compared to the frequency separation, the separate resonance bands produced by the two environments will be observed. As the rate of exchange approaches the frequency separation the bands broaden and coalesce into a single broad band. As the rate of exchange increases further the spectrum sharpens into a single line at a position that is determined by the relative lifetimes of the hydrogen atoms in each of the two environments. Thus, under most conditions, one can deduce that the rate of exchange is slower than, faster than, or comparable to the calculated or measured frequency separation of the resonances produced by the two environments. The actual rate of exchange can be determined from line-width measurements in that region where it is comparable to the frequency separation (41,57,60). Potential barriers and activation energies can be determined from measurements of line width or line separation versus temperature in this intermediate exchange rate region (37,86,119). Both the establishment of intermediate exchange rate and the study of these rates *vs.* temperature require precise temperature control of the sample (Section III-A-6-c). Rates of exchange also may be affected by the concentration of reactants or catalysts (6; 103, Chapter 4).

Changes in the degree of hydrogen bonding and some information concerning the distribution of hydrogen-bonded polymers may be determined by NMR (10,39,66,101,107,111). In general, increased hydrogen bonding causes a downfield shift of the proton resonance and decreased hydrogen bonding causes an upfield shift. In certain sterically hindered molecules, hydrogen bonding within the molecule itself can prevent the exchange of normally labile hydrogens. The existence of this situation is indicated by infrared spectra that exhibit the hydroxyl resonance corresponding to intramolecular hydrogen bonding, with no indication of intermolecular hydrogen bonding or unbonded hydroxyl groups.

B. RESONANCES OF OTHER ISOTOPES

1. Resonances of F^{19}

Fluorine-19 is the second most important isotope for study by high-resolution NMR. Its resonance lines are usually sharp and well resolved and its chemical shifts occupy a range of about 300 p.p.m., 15 times that for hydrogen-1 (24). Intensity measurements should be accurate because of the good band separation, and the recognition of spin-spin multiplets is simpler than for hydrogen resonances. The chemical shifts and the spin-spin couplings do not follow the same pattern as those for H^1, however. The effects of solvents on the fluorine shifts also are considerably greater than they are on hydrogen shifts, so that precise measurements require the extrapolation of all data to zero solvent polarization (42,56) or to infinite dilution in suitable solvents (48). The interpretation of fluorine resonance spectra is therefore more difficult than the interpretation of hydrogen spectra at the present time, but this situation is expected to improve when more comprehensive correlations of fluorine chemical shifts and spin couplings become available in the literature.   Correlations presently available are sparse (24; 93, pp. 317–345).

High-resolution fluorine resonances are now used chiefly to determine the structure of fluorinated compounds, but they are potentially useful for a variety of applications similar to those discussed for hydrogen resonances.

2. Resonances of P[31]

Phosphorus-31 also is suitable for study by high-resolution NMR because it produces lines that are usually sharp and well resolved and it has a chemical shift range of about 700 p.p.m.   The resonances of trisubstituted P[31] appear to behave regularly and predictably with a change in the substituents, the more electronegative groups shifting the resonance to the lower applied field.   The resonances of tetrasubstituted P[31] also appear to behave regularly and predictably with a change in substituents, but the more electronegative groups shift the resonance to the higher applied field (24).   The phosphorus resonances have been used successfully for determination of the structure of phosphorus compounds (24,28,49; 93, pp. 347–356) and for the quantitative determination of various types of phosphorus compounds (1,58).

3. Other Isotopes

A number of other isotopes have been observed successfully by high-resolution NMR, but have not been used extensively for a number of reasons.   Boron-11 has been used for studies of the structure or boranes and their derivatives, and the chemical shift data for these and a number of other boron compounds have been published (83,138).   The usage of this resonance appears to be limited at present by limited interest in boron-containing compounds.

Nitrogen-14 has been useful in some instances, but the quadrupole coupling of its nucleus to electric fields in the sample frequently broadens the spectrum beyond usefulness.   Nitrogen-15, carbon-13, and oxygen-17 have limited application because of the low abundances of these isotopes. Carbon-13 is on the borderline of usefulness (64,74) and will undoubtedly find a number of desirable applications if the instrumental sensitivity to this isotope can be increased adequately.   Silicon-29 is limited by fairly low abundance, but should be useful.   Cobalt-59 has been used for studying cobalt complexes.   Lead-207 has extremely large chemical shifts (up to 1.4%), and has potential value for the study of lead compounds.   The resonances of other interesting isotopes are broadened by quadrupole interactions so that they are observable at high resolution only in special circumstances. Comprehensive surveys of the nuclear magnetic resonance applications of all of these isotopes has been presented by Brownstein (24) and by Pople *et al.* (Reference 93, Chapter 12). A list of all the stable isotopes that are potentially observable by NMR, along with the sensitivities, nuclear and quadrupole moments, and frequency/field ratios is available from Varian Associates (128).

V. APPLICATIONS OF WIDE-LINE NUCLEAR MAGNETIC RESONANCE

Wide-line NMR spectra may be defined as those in which the observed width of the resonance line is as large or larger than the resonance shifts caused by differences in the chemical environment of the observed nucleus. Under this definition, no information concerning the chemical environment of the nucleus is obtained from wide-line spectra. Instead, these spectra provide valuable information concerning the *physical* environment of the observed nucleus. The technique is applicable to gases, liquids, and solids, and to all isotopes observable by NMR (128). In general, only those isotopes that contain odd numbers of protons in their nuclei are observable, but some exceptions, such as beryllium, may have an even number of protons and an odd number of neutrons. Isotopes with even numbers of both protons and neutrons do not have magnetic moments and are not observable by NMR.

Wide-line NMR provides a simple, rapid, and nondestructive method for isotopic and elemental analysis for suitable materials (46,105). The equipment can be made automatic and the procedure can be handled by personnel with little special training (Section III-A-8). With liquid or gaseous samples it can be used with full confidence that the observed isotope is being measured quantitatively in all of its possible forms. In some solid samples, however, the difference in relaxation times of the observed isotope in different environments may be so great that only part of its total resonance can be measured. For this reason it would be wise to calibrate as precisely as possible for all types of solid samples that are to be run by this technique.

The multiplets resulting from direct dipole interactions in solids have been used to determine the arrangement of atoms in solids (Section II-E-1).

Differences in the widths of components of the same spectrum (Fig. 39.13) or differences in the widths of the lines in different spectra indicate different degrees of motional freedom in the samples. Narrow lines indicate a relatively high degree of motional freedom whereas wide lines indicate relatively more restricted motion. Peak heights or areas of the narrow and/or broad components in a wide-line spectrum, when calibrated directly for the system under study, have been used to perform the following analyses (34,110):

1. Water adsorbed on or mixed with (not chemically bound to) solids.

2. Fat or oil content of solids. Moisture content of these samples also can be determined by the use of special drying, freezing, or selective line-broadening techniques.

3. Liquid content of liquid–solid slurries, suspensions, and gels.

4. The "crystallinity" of polymers.

Changes in absorption line width and shape with changes in temperature, pressure, and structure have provided valuable insight into the physical properties of polymers (95,114, and references in both). Since polymerization usually results in a marked change in mobility of the molecules involved, rates of polymerization sometimes can be determined by wide-line spectrometry. Process control by NMR should be feasible in some cases. The variations in transition points and transition ranges determined by this technique provide evidence of the changes produced by irradiation or other modifications of a polymer.

The *second moment* of the spectral band, a parameter that takes into account both line width and shape, has proved valuable in evaluating polymer spectra. The second moment is the mean value of $(H - H_0)^2$, the square of the applied-field deviation from the center value, averaged over the area enclosed by the symmetrical absorption mode signal. It may be expressed as

$$\Delta H_2{}^2 = \int_{-\infty}^{\infty} f(H)(H - H_0)^2 dH \Big/ \int_{-\infty}^{\infty} f(H) dH \qquad (42)$$

where $f(H)$ is the line shape as a function of the applied static magnetic field. $\Delta H_2{}^2$ can be evaluated by numerical methods from the experimental spectrum.

Some of the structural features of complex molecules containing metals can be deduced from the degree of and changes in motion indicated by wide-line NMR studies (81,100). The wide-line technique is used for those samples that do not produce high-resolution spectra.

Although wide-line NMR has not proved nearly as useful as high-resolution NMR, the simplicity of the instrumentation and its applicability to solids as well as to liquids and gases make it a desirable technique for studies of the type listed above.

VI. APPLICATIONS OF ELECTRON MAGNETIC RESONANCE (ELECTRON SPIN RESONANCE)

Because electron magnetic resonance responds uniquely to the presence of unpaired electrons, it is uniquely suited to the detection and study of paramagnetic species. The applications are still in the exploratory stage, but enough work has been done to outline the utility of the technique. The most extensive application has been to the study of free radicals because of the important role these entities are thought to play in many chemical reactions. Many of the more difficult problems of instrumentation and technique have been solved in at least one acceptable manner, so that a rather wide variety of problems involving free radicals can now be brought successfully under the scrutiny of EMR.

A. QUANTITATIVE MEASUREMENT OF FREE-RADICAL CONCENTRATIONS

1. Technique

a. SENSITIVITY

Since free radicals frequently exist only fleetingly and in very low concentrations during the course of a chemical reaction, one of the primary requirements of a method for studying them is the ability to measure them accurately in very low concentrations and sometimes at high speeds. Electron magnetic resonance is far more sensitive and far more rapid than any other available technique sensitive to free radicals, and therefore it is considered the technique of choice for such studies. Ingram (Reference 67, pp. 28–33, 70–71, and 99–100) and Feher (45a) present thorough discussions of the factors that effect the sensitivity of the EMR method. From these discussions, equation (43) for the minimum detectable number of spins may be derived. This equation applies strictly at optimum cavity coupling, the signal falling off (sensitivity decreasing) as coupling deviates from optimum. Since the signal reverses sign at this point, however, it is necessary to operate just far enough from optimum coupling to prevent signal distortion.

$$\frac{N_{\min}}{W} = \frac{5.1 \times 10^{23}(\Delta H)T}{\eta \cdot Q_0 \cdot H_0} \left[\frac{F_n \cdot K \cdot T(\Delta \nu)}{2P_0}\right]^{1/2} \tag{43}$$

Symbol	Definition	Typical values
N_{min}	Minimum detectable number of spins per sample.	10^{11} to 10^{13}
W	Weight of sample. Sample is entirely within the cavity	1 g.
ΔH	Linewidth of signal. See note below.	2 to 50 gauss
H_0	Static magnetic field strength at resonance.	3000 gauss (ν_0 = 9000 Mc.)
P_0	rf power incident on the sample cavity.	0.010 w.
Q_0	Quality factor of cavity containing sample in off-resonance condition (unloaded).	500 to 30,000
η	Filling factor, which depends on field distribution in cavity and sample, and on cavity and sample volumes.	0.01 to 0.3
F_n	Composite noise factor depending on the electronic circuitry.	5 to 10
k	Boltzmann constant.	1.38×10^{-23} watt-sec./deg.
T	Sample (and spin) temperature.	4 to 400°K.
$\Delta\nu$	Bandwidth of detection system.	0.1 to 100 c.p.s.

Note: For absorption signal presentations, ΔH = width at half height. For derivative presentations, ΔH = separation between points of maximum amplitude = width at points of maximum slope of the absorption curve. Since these values are not the same, and since some calculations employ the half width rather than the full width, the exact value used should always be specified. The factor of 2 or so discrepancy is not important in the order-of-magnitude calculation of N_{min}.

The maximum effective sample that can be employed in modern electron resonance spectrometers is about 1 g. For an average molecular weight of 600, the above equation indicates a maximum sensitivity of 10^{-10} to 10^{-8} mole fraction of free radicals.

Free-radical chain reactions in which the chain lengths are very long can proceed with very low concentrations of radicals. The study of the radicals in such reactions may be expected to be limited by the maximum concentration of radicals that can be achieved in a practical system. Even in short chain reactions the lifetimes of the radicals may be so short that the maximum attainable concentration will be very low, and the line widths will be so large as to render detection difficult. Several techniques have been devised to overcome these difficulties (References 67, pp. 222–224 and Chapter 6; 130, pp. 219–223 and Chapter 20). The concentration of photochemically produced free radicals can be raised to a maximum by the direct irradiation of the sample in the microwave cavity (53,87). This direct irradiation is accomplished by means of a window in the side of the cavity or through the end of the sample cell. Radicals with extremely short lifetimes may be stabilized by freezing them at liquid nitrogen or liquid helium temperatures (50,70) or by trapping them in glassy or crystalline solids (27,75,89). The lifetimes of trapped or frozen radicals are extended sufficiently to permit a leisurely study of their properties. Radicals that appear only as short-lived intermediates in chemical reactions have been studied successfully under steady-state conditions by means of a flowing-sample technique (87). The reactants are vigorously mixed at the entrance of the sample cell, and the flow rate is adjusted so that the concentration of free radicals within the cell lies within the detectable limits.

The equation of N_{min} shows that the sensitivity varies directly as the unloaded Q of the sample cavity. Q, in turn, varies inversely with the resistive loss of the sample. The highest Q's (10,000 and above), and therefore the highest sensitivities (lowest N_{min}), may be achieved only with samples of low loss. Aqueous solutions, such as are normally encountered in biochemical work, have very high losses and degrade cavity Q's to the neighborhood of a few hundred. This reduces sensitivity so seriously that the study of such samples requires special technique. Reduction in losses by the use of small samples in flat cells suitably oriented at the node of the electric field in the cavity has been found both necessary and satisfactory for the study of free radicals in aqueous solutions (35,36).

b. STANDARDIZATION

The absolute number of unpaired spins in the effective sample volume, and thus the concentration of free radicals in the sample, is usually determined by comparing the intensity of the resonance from the sample to that from a known standard. The stable free radical 1,1-diphenyl-2-picrylhydrazyl has been a popular intensity standard. It has one unpaired electron per molecule and a molecular weight of 394, giving it 1.53×10^{-21} unpaired spins per gram. Dilution with known amounts of inert material provides standards with lower concentrations of free spins. These standards, in weighed amounts, can be sealed into standard sample tubes under vacuum or inert gas to prevent contamination and deterioration and for convenience in handling.

Preparation of the extremely low concentrations of hydrazyl required for the accurate comparison measurement of very low concentrations of free radicals can lead to some difficulty. It is convenient, under such circumstances, to employ secondary standards consisting of materials that contain low concentrations of stable free radicals and that can be easily ground and diluted to predetermined concentrations. The original material can be standardized against hydrazyl. Materials that have been found suitable for this purpose are coke (the free-radical concentration varying with the

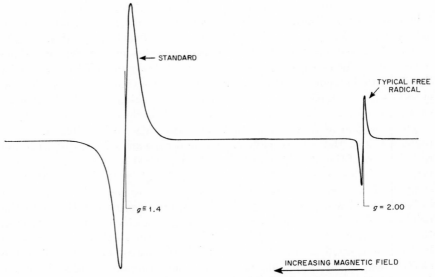

Fig. 39.20. Spectrum of ruby internal standard and free radical.

method of production) and magnesium oxide containing a little paramagnetic impurity.

The g factors of most free radicals are very nearly the same, so that the resonances of the free-radical-type standards are not separated from the resonances of the free radicals they are being used to standardize. It is necessary, therefore, to substitute the standard sample for the observed sample in order to make the necessary measurements. It is more convenient, of course, to employ a standard sample with a resonance well removed from that of the observed sample so that both resonances can be measured during the same scan and recorded on the same chart. The resonances of certain paramagnetic ions trapped in crystal lattices can be used for this purpose. The position and intensity of such resonances depends on the orientation of the crystal in the sample cavity, so that it is necessary to orient such standards properly by trial and error. A very small ruby crystal, which may be a piece broken from a larger crystal, glued to the side of a guide tube into which the sample fits, has been used successfully as a permanent intensity standard (113a). Fig. 39.20 shows the ruby resonance recorded on the same chart with a typical free-radical resonance that does not exhibit hyperfine structure.

The total peak height between the two halves of the derivative presentation may be used as a reasonably accurate measure of signal intensity.

The area under the absorption band, obtained by double integration of the derivative signal, provides a more accurate intensity measurement. Since sensitivity varies directly as the Q of the cavity (see equation for N_{min}), and since Q varies with the characteristics of the sample, difficulty in the measurement of absolute intensities will be experienced unless the standard experiences the same Q factor as the sample. In some cases this may require that the standard be surrounded by or surround the sample symmetrically, so that conditions throughout both the sample and standard materials will be as nearly uniform as possible. The use of a standard intimately mixed with the sample (as internal standard) would provide the ultimate in uniformity. This problem is more serious with high Q cavities than with low Q cavities.

It is possible to determine the absolute number of spins in a sample without the use of standard samples (Reference 139; 67, p. 97), but the numerous factors that must be measured or held constant make the method slower and probably less reliable.

Standardization of the g-factor measurements is accomplished with materials of known g factor. Diphenylpicrylhydrazyl, with a g of 2.0036, also is a favorite for this purpose. The horizontal scale of the spectrum may be calibrated by nuclear resonance or fluxmeter measurements, or by two reference materials with accurately known and well-separated g factors. The calibrated scale then is used to measure line widths and g-factor displacements.

2. Uses

The detection of electron spin resonance in a sample demonstrates unequivocally the presence of unpaired electrons. The g factor and hyperfine structure of the spectrum and the known composition of the sample often indicate strongly that the unpaired electrons are associated with one or more free radicals. Qualitative demonstrations of the appearance and disappearance of free radicals during the course of a reaction indicates the role radicals may play in that reaction. Such observations have provided strong support for the theory that many biochemical reactions proceed via free-radical intermediates (35,36; 130, Chapter 19 and references therein). Qualitative EMR studies also have revealed free radicals that are associated with vinyl polymerization (51) and with the adsorption of aromatic hydrocarbons on cracking catalysts (21,104).

Quantitative measurement of the rates of formation and decay of free radicals as functions of reaction variables provides valuable kinetic data and insight into reaction mechanisms (References 67, Chapter 7; 130, Chapter 17). Flow and nonflow techniques make such measurements applicable to both slow and fast reactions. Typical of kinetics and mechanisms applications are studies of formation and migration of radicals in solid alcohol–hydrogen peroxide mixtures (54), the photodissociation of aryl hydroperoxides (87), the effect of gamma irradiation on polyethylene (75), the action of an aromatic anionic initiator in the polymerization of styrene (76), and the rate of formation of semiquinones in the condensation of diacetyl (References 130, pp. 210–211). Mechanisms studies also are greatly aided by the identification of the number and structures of the radicals involved, as discussed in the next section.

Unpaired electrons can participate in exchange reactions, with a resultant broadening of the hyperfine electron resonances lines and eventual spin decoupling in a manner similar to that already described for protons (Section IV-A-2-d). When the rate of exchange is of the order of the hyperfine line width in frequency units, the lines will be broadened in proportion to the exchange frequency. Variations in line width with concentration, temperature, or other significant parameters lead to values of rate constants and activation energies for such reactions. Exchange of the unpaired electron between the naphthalene negative ion and naphthalene has been studied by this technique (Reference 132; 130, p. 210).

B. DETERMINATION OF MOLECULAR STRUCTURE ASSOCIATED WITH UNPAIRED ELECTRONS

1. Technique

Spin-spin interactions between the unpaired electron and the nuclei around which it circulates produce hyperfine splitting of the EMR signal, which is characteristic of the number and types of nuclei with which the electron is coupled. Observation of this structure may require resolution of lines only a few milligauss wide. To permit this degree of resolution the radicals must be present in low concentrations in an inert liquid of low viscosity (to eliminate exchange and dipole–dipole interactions), the radicals must have relatively long lifetimes, and the magnetic field must have a homogeneity of 1 part in 10^6 or better.

Since the "chemical shift" between an unpaired electron and any of the normally observed nuclei is extremely large, the hyperfine splittings should all follow the simple first-order splitting rules outlined in Section II-E-2; that is, the number of lines will equal $(2nI + 1)$ and the multiplet should be symmetrical about its midpoint. The coupling constant between the unpaired electron and any particular nucleus, and therefore the separation between the multiplet lines produced as a result of this particular coupling, is directly proportional to the unpaired electron density associated with that nucleus (78). This relationship leads to a combination of multiplets for those radicals in which the unpaired electron density varies from point to point. The perinaphthene radical produces a septet of quartets (117), whereas the ethyl radical produces four triplets (47).

This sometimes leads to such a high degree of complexity in a spectrum that its complete interpretation is extremely difficult. In such cases the spectrum can serve as a "fingerprint" of the radical and will be useful in identifying that particular radical in future work.

When the EMR signals are broadened by factors other than applied magnetic field homogeneity, so that hyperfine interactions cannot be observed, a double resonance technique may be used to observe the hyperfine splittings (43–45; 67, pp. 95–97; 77, pp. 67–71). The electron resonance signal is partially saturated (saturated at the center but not in the wings) and is observed continuously. Simultaneously, an rf field in the region of the precession frequency of an appropriate nucleus in the sample is applied. The static magnetic field and microwave frequency are held constant while the lower radio frequency is swept slowly through the proper region. When the radio frequency reaches values corresponding to nuclear transitions the electron resonance will be temporarily desaturated. This desaturation produces an increase in the electron resonance signal during the time that nuclear transitions are induced. The resulting absorptions have the width of the nuclear resonance line instead of the much greater width of the electron resonance line. The electron–nuclear hyperfine coupling constant and the nuclear g factor can be calculated from the line spacings.

2. Uses

Analyses of the hyperfine structure associated with free-radical resonances indicates the number and types of nuclei with which the free electron is associated. This identifies the free radical in many cases, or at least identifies that portion of the molecule with which the unpaired electron is associated. Such identification is extremely important in the study of reactions that proceed via radicals. The identification of the expected dimethyl semiquinone radical confirmed the proposed mechanism for the condensation of biacetyl (Reference 130, p. 208). Identification of the radicals produced by the γ irradiation of amines showed the points of attack of the radiation on the amines or, at least, the final stabilized free radicals that were formed therefrom (27). Identification of the radicals formed at various stages during the polymerization of 2-methyl styrene and methyl methacrylate showed that in each case the benzoyl radical from the benzoyl peroxide initiator abstracts a proton from the monomer to initiate polymerization. In the case of styrene, however, the benzoyl radical added to the styrene in order to initiate polymerization (68). Identification of the perinaphthene radical in a petroleum fraction opens the possibility for the study of the effects of such radicals on the properties of petroleum (118). Changes in the fine structure produced by the isopropyl radical trapped in solid isopropyl alcohol as the temperature was changed indicated a change in the degree of rotational freedom of parts of the radical (53). These are but a few of many examples of the value of free-radical identification through EMR.

C. OTHER APPLICATIONS

Electron magnetic resonance has been applied to the identification of paramagnetic forms of metal atoms and for the study of structures containing them. Vanadyl vanadium in petroleum fractions has been determined quantitatively (40,106). The combined resonances of free radicals and other paramagnetic species present in certain portions of coal and petroleum have made it possible to gain both quantitative and qualitative insight into the character of these materials (22,31,126). Porphyrins, proteins, complex ions, "sandwich" compounds (ferrocenes, etc.), and adsorbed metal atoms have been studied in an effort to obtain information about the structures, but the results have not yet been very promising. Studies of solid or heterogeneous catalyst systems likewise have not been fruitful.

Conduction electrons in metals are normally unpaired, and they can be detected by electron magnetic resonance. Likewise, unpaired electrons associated with "color centers," which are produced by natural or irradiation-induced defects in crystal lattices, can be detected and measured quantitatively by EMR (Reference 130, Chapter 21).

Electron magnetic resonance is still a relatively young technique. Its applicability to the problems of the chemist does not seem to be nearly as general as that of high-resolution NMR, but in the field of free radicals and certain other paramagnetic species it has no rivals for speed and sensitivity. Continued improvements in both instrumentation and technique may be expected to open up a greater number of valuable applications in the future.

REFERENCES

1. Ames, D. P., S. Ohashi, C. F. Callis, and J. R. Van Wazer, *J. Am. Chem. Soc.*, **81**, 6350, 6357, 6360, 6363, 6366 (1959).
2. Anderson, W. A., *Phys. Rev.*, **102**, 151 (1956).
3. Anderson, W. A., and H. M. McConnell, *J. Chem. Phys.*, **26**, 1496 (1957).
4. Andrew, E. R., *Nuclear Magnetic Resonance*, Cambridge University Press, New York, 1955.

5. Arnold, J. T., and M. E. Packard, *J. Chem. Phys.*, **19**, 1608 (1951).
6. Arnold, J. T., *Phys. Rev.*, **102**, 136 (1956).
7. Baker, E. B., and L. W. Burd, *Rev. Sci. Instr.*, **28**, 313 (1957).
8. Banwell, C. N., and N. Sheppard, *Molecular Phys.*, **3**, 351 (1960).
9. Banwell, C. N., N. Sheppard, and J. J. Turner, *Spectrochim. Acta*, **16**, 794 (1960).
10. Becker, E. D., *J. Chem. Phys.*, **31**, 269 (1959).
11. Bennett, L. H., and H. C. Torrey, *Phys. Rev.*, **108**, 499 (1957).
12. Bloch, F., *Phys. Rev.*, **70**, 460 (1946).
13. Bloch, F., W. W. Hansen, and M. Packard, *Phys. Rev.*, **70**, 474 (1946).
14. Borel, J. P., and P. Cornaz, *Compt. rend.*, **247**, 1988 (1958).
15. Bothner-By, A. A., and R. E. Glick, *J. Chem. Phys.*, **26**, 1647 (1957).
16. Bothner-By, A. A., and R. E. Glick, *J. Chem. Phys.*, **26**, 1651 (1957).
17. Bothner-By, A. A., *J. Molecular Spectroscopy*, **5**, 52 (1960).
18. Bovey, F. A., and G. V. D. Tiers, *J. Am. Chem. Soc.*, **81**, 2870 (1959).
19. Bovey, F. A., and G. V. D. Tiers, *J. Polymer Sci.*, **44**, 173 (1960).
20. Bovey, F. A., *J. Polymer Sci.*, **46**, 59 (1960).
21. Brouwer, D. M., *Chem. and Ind. (London)*, **1961**, No. 6, 177.
22. Brown, T. H., H. S. Gutowsky, and K. E. Van Holde, *J. Chem. Eng. Data*, **5**, 181 (1960).
23. Brownstein, S., *Can. J. Chem.*, **37**, 1119 (1959).
24. Brownstein, S., *Chem. Revs.*, **59**, 463 (1959).
25. Buckingham, A. D., *Can. J. Chem.*, **38**, 300 (1960).
26. Buckingham, A. D., T. Schaefer, and W. G. Schneider, *J. Chem. Phys.*, **32**, 1227 (1960).
27. Burrell, E. J., Jr., *J. Chem. Phys.*, **32**, 955 (1960).
28. Callis, C. F., J. R. Van Wazer, J. N. Shoolery, and W. A. Anderson, *J. Am. Chem. Soc.*, **79**, 2719 (1957).
29. Carver, T. R., and C. P. Slichter, *Phys. Rev.*, **92**, 212 (1953).
30. Carver, T. R., and C. P. Slichter, *Phys. Rev.*, **102**, 975 (1956).
31. Cerutti, M., J. Uebersfeld, J. Millet, and J. Parisot, *J. chim. phys.*, **57**, 907 (1960); through *Chem. Abstr.*, **55**, 13815g (1961).
32. Chamberlain, N. F., *Anal. Chem.*, **31**, 56 (1959).
33. Chamberlain, N. F., N. P. Neureiter, R. K. Saunders, and R. B. Williams, *World Petrol. Congr., Proc. 5th Congr., N. Y.*, Section V, Paper 8 (1959).
34. Chamberlain, N. F., "Analytical Applications of Nuclear Magnetic Resonance Spectrometry," in G. L. Clark, Ed., *The Encyclopedia of Spectroscopy*, Reinhold, New York, 1960, pp. 664–670.
35. Commoner, B., J. J. Heise, and J. Townsend, *Proc. Natl. Acad. Sci. U. S.*, **42**, 710 (1956).
36. Commoner, B., B. B. Lippincott, and J. V. Passoneau, *Proc. Natl. Acad. Sci. U. S.*, **44**, 1099 (1958).
37. Connor, T. M., and A. Loewenstein, *J. Am. Chem. Soc.*, **83**, 560 (1961).
38. Corio, P. L., *Chem. Revs.*, **60**, 363 (1960).
39. Drinkard, W., and D. Kivelson, *J. Phys. Chem.*, **62**, 1494 (1958).
40. Dunning, H. N., J. W. Moore, H. Bieber, and R. B. Williams, *J. Chem. Eng. Data*, **5**, 546 (1960).
41. Emerson, M. T., E. Grunwald, M. L. Kaplan, and R. A. Kromhout, *J. Am. Chem. Soc.*, **82**, 6307 (1960).
42. Evans, D. F., *J. Chem. Soc.*, **1960**, 877.

43. Feher, G., *Phys. Rev.*, **103**, 500, 834 (1956); **105**, 1122 (1957).

44. Feher, G., and E. A. Gere, *Phys. Rev.*, **103**, 501 (1956).

45. Feher, G., C. S. Fuller, and E. A. Gere, *Phys. Rev.*, **107**, 1462 (1957).

45a. Feher, G., *Bell System Tech. J.*, **36**, 449 (1957).

46. Ferrett, D. J., *Trans. Soc. Instr. Technol.*, **11**, 66 (1959).

47. Fessenden, R. W., and R. H. Schuler, *J. Chem. Phys.*, **33**, 935 (1960).

48. Filipovich, G. N., and G. V. D. Tiers, *J. Phys. Chem.*, **63**, 761 (1959).

49. Finegold, H., *Ann. N. Y. Acad. Sci.*, **70**, 875 (1958).

50. Foner, S. N., E. L. Cochran, V. A. Bowers, and C. K. Jen, *J. Chem. Phys.*, **32**, 963 (1960).

51. Fraenkel, G. K., J. M. Hirshon, and C. Walling, *J. Am. Chem. Soc.*, **76**, 3606 (1954).

52. Freeman, R., and R. V. Pound, *Rev. Sci. Instr.*, **31**, 103 (1960).

53. Fujimoto, M., and D. J. E. Ingram, *Trans. Faraday Soc.*, **54**, 1304 (1958).

54. Fujimoto, M., and D. J. E. Ingram, *Molecular Phys.*, **2**, 341 (1959).

55. Fujiwara, S., and I. Yamaguchi, *Bull. Chem. Soc. Japan*, **31**, 786 (1958).

56. Glick, R. E., and S. J. Ehrenson, *J. Phys. Chem.*, **62**, 1599 (1958).

57. Grunwald, E., A. Loewenstein, and S. Meiboom, *J. Chem. Phys.*, **27**, 630 (1957).

58. Guffy, J. C., and G. B. Miller, *Anal. Chem.*, **31**, 1895 (1959).

59. Gutowsky, H. S., D. W. McCall, and C. P. Slichter, *J. Chem. Phys.*, **21**, 279 (1953).

60. Gutowsky, H. S., and C. H. Holm, *J. Chem. Phys.*, **25**, 1228 (1956).

61. Gutowsky, H. S., M. Karplus, and D. M. Grant, *J. Chem. Phys.*, **31**, 1278 (1959).

62. Hatton, J. V., and R. E. Richards, *Trans. Faraday Soc.*, **57**, 28 (1961).

63. Hoffman, R. A., C. A. Reilly, and J. D. Swalen, *J. Chem. Phys.*, **33**, 1256 (1960).

64. Holm, C. H., *J. Chem. Phys.*, **26**, 707 (1957).

65. Hotta, K., and R. S. Anderson, Paper in *Fourth International Symposium on Free Radical Stabilization*, Washington, D. C., Aug. 31–Sept. 2, 1959; *Monthly Catalog of U.S. Publications*, Sept., 1959, p. 106, item 13459.

66. Huggins, C. M., G. C. Pimentel, and J. N. Shoolery, *J. Chem. Phys.*, **23**, 1244 (1955).

67. Ingram, D. J. E., *Free Radicals as Studied by Electron Spin Resonance*, Academic Press, New York, 1958, and Butterworths, London, 1958.

68. Ito, K., *J. Am. Chem. Soc.*, **80**, 3502 (1958).

69. Jackman, L. M., *Applications of Nuclear Magnetic Resonance Spectroscopy in Organic Chemistry*, Pergamon Press, New York, 1959.

70. Jen, C. K., S. N. Foner, E. L. Cochran, and V. A. Bowers, *Phys. Rev.*, **112**, 1169 (1958).

71. Johnson, C. E., Jr., and F. A. Bovey, *J. Chem. Phys.*, **29**, 1012 (1958).

72. Karplus, M., *J. Chem. Phys.*, **30**, 11 (1959).

73. Kurita, Y., and K. Ito, *J. Am. Chem. Soc.*, **82**, 296 (1960).

74. Lauterbur, P. C., *Ann. N. Y. Acad. Sci.*, **70**, 841 (1958).

75. Lawton, E. J., J. S. Balwit, and R. S. Powell, *J. Chem. Phys.*, **33**, 395, 405 (1960).

76. Levy, M., and M. Szwarc, *J. Am. Chem. Soc.*, **82**, 521 (1960).

77. Low, W., *Paramagnetic Resonance in Solids*, Academic Press, New York, 1960.

78. McConnell, H. M., *J. Chem. Phys.*, **24**, 764 (1956).

79. McConnell, H. M., *J. Chem. Phys.*, **27**, 226 (1957).

80. Morin, M. G., G. Paulett, and M. E. Hobbs, *J. Phys. Chem.*, **60**, 1594 (1956).

81. Mulay, L. N., E. G. Rochow, E. O. Stejskal, and N. E. Weliky, *J. Inorg. & Nuclear Chem.*, **16**, 23 (1960).

82. Muller, N., and D. E. Pritchard, *J. Chem. Phys.*, **31**, 768 (1959).

83. Onak, T. P., H. Landesman, R. E. Williams, and I. Shapiro, *J. Phys. Chem.*, **63**, 1533 (1959).
84. Overhauser, A. W., *Phys. Rev.*, **92**, 411 (1953).
85. Pajak, Z., and F. Pellan, *Compt. rend.*, **251**, 79 (1960).
86. Piette, L. H., and W. A. Anderson, *J. Chem. Phys.*, **30**, 899 (1959).
87. Piette, L. H., and W. C. Landgraf, *J. Chem. Phys.*, **32**, 1107 (1960).
88. Poindexter, E. H., *J. Chem. Phys.*, **31**, 1477 (1959).
89. Poole, C. P., Jr., and R. S. Anderson, *J. Chem. Phys.*, **31**, 346 (1959).
90. Pople, J. A., *Proc. Roy. Soc. (London)*, **A239**, 541 (1957).
91. Pople, J. A., *Proc. Roy. Soc. (London)*, **A239**, 550 (1957).
92. Pople, J. A., "The Interpretation of Nuclear Magnetic Resonance Shifts in Hydrogen Bonding," in D. Hadzi, Ed., *Hydrogen Bonding*, Pergamon Press, New York, 1959, pp. 71–76.
93. Pople, J. A., W. G. Schneider, and H. J. Bernstein, *High-Resolution Nuclear Magnetic Resonance*, McGraw-Hill, New York, 1959.
94. Pound, R. V., and R. Freeman, *Rev. Sci. Instr.*, **31**, 96 (1960).
95. Powles, J. G., *Polymer*, **1**, 219 (1960).
96. Primas, H., and H. H. Günthard, *Rev. Sci. Instr.*, **28**, 510 (1957).
97. Purcell, E. M., H. C. Torrey, and R. V. Pound, *Phys. Rev.*, **69**, 37 (1946).
98. Ramsey, N. F., *Phys. Rev.*, **77**, 567 (1950); **78**, 699 (1950); **83**, 540 (1951); **86**, 243 (1952).
99. Ramsey, N. F., *Phys. Rev.*, **91**, 303 (1953).
100. Reeves, L. W., *Can. J. Chem.*, **38**, 736 (1960).
101. Reid, C., and T. M. Connor, "A Nuclear Resonance Investigation of Hydrogen Bonding," in D. Hadzi, Ed., *Hydrogen Bonding*, Pergamon Press, New York, 1959, pp. 77–83.
102. Reilly, C. A., *J. Chem. Phys.*, **25**, 604 (1956).
103. Roberts, J. D., *Nuclear Magnetic Resonance—Applications to Organic Chemistry*, McGraw-Hill, New York, 1959.
104. Rooney, J. J., and R. C. Pink, *Proc. Chem. Soc.*, **1961**, 70.
105. Rubin, H., and R. E. Swarbrick, *Anal. Chem.*, **33**, 217 (1961).
106. Saraceno, A. J., D. T. Fanale, and N. D. Coggeshall, *Anal. Chem.*, **33**, 500 (1961).
107. Saunders, M., and J. B. Hyne, *J. Chem. Phys.*, **29**, 1319 (1958).
108. Saunders, R. K., private communication (1961).
109. Schaefer, T., and W. G. Schneider, *J. Chem. Phys.*, **32**, 1218, 1224 (1960).
110. *Schlumberger NMR Analyzer*, Brochure No. 1112, Ridgefield Instrument Group, Schlumberger Corporation, Ridgefield, Conn., 1960.
111. Schneider, W. G., "Proton Magnetic Resonance Measurements of Hydrogen Bonding," in D. Hadzi, Ed., *Hydrogen Bonding*, Pergamon Press, New York, 1959, pp. 55–69.
112. Shoolery, J. N., and J. D. Roberts, *Rev. Sci. Instr.*, **28**, 61 (1957).
113. Silver, A. H., *J. Chem. Phys.*, **32**, 959 (1960).
113a. Singer, L. S., and J. Kommandeur, *J. Chem. Phys.*, **34**, 133 (1961).
114. Slichter, W. P., *Fortschr. Hochpolymer. Forsch.*, **1**, 35 (1958), and *Bell Telephone Systems Technical Publication, Monograph 3049*, Bell Telephone Labs., New York (1958).
115. Slomp, G., *Rev. Sci. Instr.*, **30**, 1024 (1959).
116. Slomp, G., and F. MacKellar, *J. Am. Chem. Soc.*, **82**, 999 (1960).
117. Sogo, P. B., M. Nakazaki, and M. Calvin, *J. Chem. Phys.*, **26**, 1343 (1957).

118. Stehling, F. C., and K. W. Bartz, *J. Chem. Phys.*, **34**, 1076 (1961).

119. Sunners, B., L. H. Piette, and W. G. Schneider, *Can. J. Chem.*, **38**, 681 (1960).

120. Takeda, M., and H. S. Gutowsky, *J. Chem. Phys.*, **26**, 577 (1957).

121. Takeda, M., and O. Jardetzky, *J. Chem. Phys.*, **26**, 1346 (1957)

122. Tiers, G. V. D., *J. Phys. Chem.*, **62**, 1151 (1958).

123. Tiers, G. V. D., and F. A. Bovey, *J. Phys. Chem.*, **63**, 302 (1959).

124. Tiers, G. V. D., "Fluorine Magnetic Resonance," paper presented to Symposium on Analytical Applications of NMR, Pittsburgh Conference on Analytical Chemistry and Applied Spectroscopy, March 2, 1960.

125. Uebersfeld, J., and M. Jacubowicz, "Double Magnetic Resonance of Fluids Adsorbed on Coals," in *Proceedings of the Fourth Conference on Carbon*, Pergamon Press, New York, 1960, pp. 267–270.

126. U. S. Patents 2,909,482 and 2,909,483 (Oct. 20, 1959), R. B. Williams and R. K. Saunders (to Esso Res. and Eng. Co.).

127. U. S. Patent 2,930,966 (March 29, 1960), W. E. Bell and M. E. Packard (to Varian Associates).

128. Varian Staff, *NMR Table*, 3rd Ed., Varian Associates, Instrument Div., Palo Alto, Calif., 1955.

129. *Varian Technical Information Bulletin*, **2**, No. 3, p. 3 (1959).

129a. Varian Staff, *NMR Microcell Data Sheet, Model No. 906733*, Brochure No. INS 1464, Varian Associates, Instrument Division, Palo Alto, Calif., 1962.

130. Varian Staff, *NMR and EPR Spectroscopy*, Pergamon Press, New York, 1960,

131. Varian Staff, *A-60 Analytical NMR Spectrometer System*, Brochure No. INS 1414, Varian Associates, Instrument Division, Palo Alto, Calif., 1961.

132. Ward, R. L., and S. I. Weissman, *J. Am. Chem. Soc.*, **76**, 3612 (1954).

133. Waugh, J. S., *Ann. N.Y. Acad. Sci.*, **70**, 900 (1958).

134. Williams, R. B., *Ann. N.Y. Acad. Sci.*, **70**, 890 (1958).

135. Williams, R. B., "Stabilization of Electromagnet of High Resolution Nuclear Magnetic Resonance Spectrometer," paper presented to National Symposium on Instrumental Methods of Analysis, Instrument Society of America, Houston, Texas, May 12–14, 1958, and to Second Conference on Experimental Aspects of NMR Spectroscopy, Pittsburgh, Pa., Feb. 24–25, 1961.

136. Williams, R. B., *ASTM Spec. Tech. Publ.*, **224**, 168 (1958).

137. Williams, R. B., and N. F. Chamberlain, "Quantitative Analysis by High Resolution NMR," paper presented to Symposium on Analytical Applications of NMR, Pittsburgh Conference on Analytical Chemistry and Applied Spectroscopy, March 2, 1960, and to Symposium on Magnetic Resonance Methods, 138th National Meeting, American Chemical Society, New York, Sept. 13, 1960.

137a. Williams, R. B., "A Study of Nuclear Magnetic Resonance Performance Parameters," paper presented to Third Conference on Molecular Spectroscopy of the Institute of Petroleum Hydrocarbon Research Group, London, March, 1962.

138. Williams, R. E., H. D. Fisher, and C. O. Wilson, *J. Phys. Chem.*, **64**, 1583 (1960).

139. Yariv, A., and J. P. Gordon, *Rev. Sci. Instr.*, **32**, 462 (1961).

140. Zimmerman, J. R., and M. R. Foster, *J. Phys. Chem.*, **61**, 282 (1957).

Chapter 40

MASS SPECTROMETRY

By Frank W. Melpolder and Ralph A. Brown,*
*Research and Development Department, The Atlantic
Refining Company, Glenolden, Pennsylvania*

Contents

* Present address: Esso Research and Engineering Company, Linden, New Jersey.

Contents (*continued*)

Contents (*continued*)

I. INTRODUCTION

In principle, mass spectrometry deals with the successive processes of ion formation, ion separation according to mass, and ion abundance measurement. When applied to analysis, the method is capable of giving vital information on the chemical and structural nature of a molecule. Furthermore, the characteristic mass spectrum offers ample opportunity to determine numerous compounds or types of compounds through systematic interpretation.

The analytical mass spectrometer has been successfully applied to qualitative and quantitative determinations of constituents in a wide variety of mixtures. During its relatively short period of development of about two decades, the method has attained an enviable record in providing accurate and detailed analysis far surpassing the early classic chemical and physical methods. In addition to mixture analysis, mass spectrometry also has made outstanding contributions to the field of chemical physics. Precise determinations have been made of the fundamental constants of atomic weights, isotope abundances, bonds strengths, and nuclear properties. In the immediate future new instrumental designs and greater knowledge of mass spectra undoubtedly will lead to important advances in both analytical and physics research.

The literature relating to mass spectrometry has grown so extensive that no single chapter or monograph can hope to include all phases of the work. It is the aim, therefore, to present in this chapter only a brief description of principles and instrumentation, and to treat in considerable detail the major analytical practices and applications now in use. In particular, interpretive and correlative methods have been given a prominent position because of their importance in forming a basis for mixture analysis. Detailed discussions of specific phases of mass spectrometry and much background information are available elsewhere in a number of monographs (1–13a) and in review articles (80,81,127,215,220a,278).

A. HISTORICAL

Initially, mass spectrometry evolved from a study of the behavior of positive ion rays in both electric and magnetic fields by W. Wein in 1898. J. J. Thomson in 1910 constructed the first parabola mass spectrograph using parallel electrostatic and magnetic fields to separate mass components in the ion beam. With this spectrograph he was able to detect ions of masses 20 and 22 in neon. Later in 1920 Aston, using a more precise instrument (19), found that these ion species were in fact isotopes of neon (20). At about the same time, Dempster (71) introduced a mass spectrometer that employed circular magnetic deflection and electrical rather than photographic measurement of ion intensities. In the following years a marked improvement in instrument design was realized. Other outstanding contributions to the realm of chemical physics were made by Bainbridge, Bleakney, Nier, Mattauch, and their associates. These developments formed a sound basis for the intensive analytical applications that were to follow. The possibility of using the mass spectrometer for chemical analysis was first proposed by Hoover and Washburn (136) in 1940. It was found that mass spectra of simple organic compounds exhibited substantial differences that could be readily adapted to the analysis of multicomponent mixtures. Shortly thereafter, commercial production of mass spectrometers provided industrial laboratories with an opportunity to gain detailed analytical information for the first time. As a result of close cooperation between instrument manufacturers and users, new instrumental developments and applications evolved rapidly. Within a span of eight years analytical techniques had advanced to the point at which lubricating oils and waxes could be handled in addition to gases and volatile liquids. The general utilization of mass spectrometry for the analysis of inorganic solids has been less spectacular, due in part to the fact that commercial instruments for this application have become available only recently.

B. ELECTROMAGNETIC SEPARATION AS AN ANALYTICAL TECHNIQUE

The mass spectrometer is essentially an electromagnetic separator of ions according to their mass, which has gained favorable acceptance as an analytical technique. The mass instrument has been used extensively in clinical practice and research (89). In biological chemistry mass analysis of compounds labeled with stable isotopes has aided in the understanding of metabolic processes (225). Geophysical studies of isotope abundances in various formations have led to dating techniques useful for estimating the age of the earth's crust (220). Another of the important inorganic applications is the determination of isotopes in nuclear research (143).

Perhaps the most widespread application of analytical mass spectrometry is in organic compound analysis. Petroleum and chemical laboratories have put forth a concerted effort to extend the technique to the analysis of mixtures of increasing complexity. The importance of these accurate analytical data to the solution of major research problems cannot be overemphasized. Mass analyses give the research chemist detailed qualitative and quantitative information on both the expected and sometimes unexpected components in the sample. The chemical engineer likewise finds the reliable mass data to be invaluable in studying the many variables associated with process development.

II. PRINCIPLES OF MASS SPECTROMETRY

The major functions of the analytical mass spectrometer include (1) dissociation and ionization of a representative portion of the molecules in the sample, (2) separation of the ions according to their mass or, more strictly, their mass-to-charge ratio (m/e), and (3) measurement of the relative abundance of each ion species for a given m/e value. Since ion formation and separation occur by motion of particles through space, the environment is by necessity a region of high vacuum. A mass spectrometer may be constructed from one of many combinations of ion source, ion separator, and detector designs. Thus far, dozens of diverse types of instruments have been built and undoubtedly many more are yet to be devised. The focal point of this chapter is the organic analytical spectrometer consisting of the electron impact source, magnetic analyzer, and electrometer detector. Other types that have important analytical potentialities also will be mentioned. In order to orient the reader at an early stage, diagrams are shown of a typical analytical instrument in Fig. 40.1 and of a mass spectrum of carbon dioxide in Fig. 40.2. Subsequent sections in the chapter will give additional details on each function.

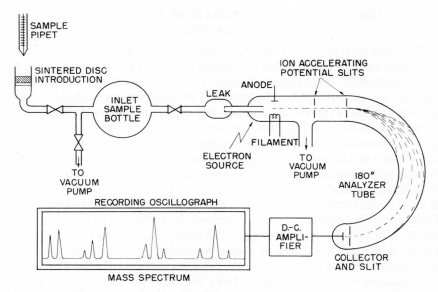

Fig. 40.1. Schematic diagram of an analytical mass spectrometer, showing the primary functions of the sample-introduction system, electron-impact ion source, 180° magnetic-deflection analyzer, ion collector, amplifier, and recorder.

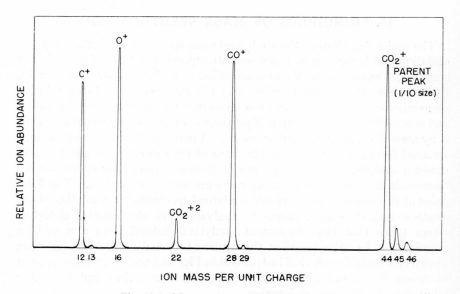

Fig. 40.2. Mass spectrum of carbon dioxide.

A. ION FORMATION

Ionization occurs by interaction of neutral atoms or molecules with a source of energy greater than their ionization potential (203). When the energy source is an electron beam, the probability of ionization becomes substantially greater as the ionizing energy is increased above the minimum or "appearance potential" level. This efficiency of ionization is often referred to as the "ionization cross section" of the ion or molecule (159,212).

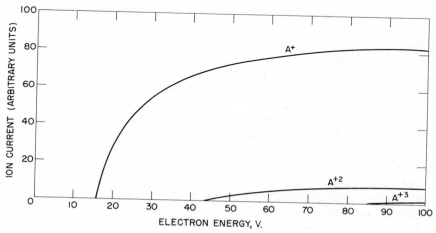

Fig. 40.3. Ionization efficiency curve for argon at various electron energies. Relative efficiencies are seen for production of single, double-, and triple-charged argon ions.

It is seen in Fig. 40.3, for example, that the cross section of argon increases from zero at 15.8 electron volts and rises to a nearly constant value at 80 e.v. Dissociation of the molecule begins at an energy level slightly greater than the ionization potential of the parent molecule. The practical value of ionizing potential usually lies between 50 and 100 e.v. to obtain good reproducibility.

1. Dissociation Processes

Collision between a neutral molecule and an energetic electron can cause the molecule to simply ionize or to decompose by the cleavage of some bond, producing two or more fragments of the molecule, one of which will retain a positive charge. Relative quantities of these ions are an indication of the strength and chemical nature of the bonds uniting them to the rest of the molecule.

The formation of a positive ion resulting from the impact between a molecule R_1—R_2 and an electron, e, is represented by the equation

$$R_1\text{—}R_2 + e \rightarrow R_1 + R_2^+ + 2e$$

where R_1 is a neutral fragment and R_2^+ indicates a positive ion that results from cleavage of the R_1—R_2 valence bond and the loss of an electron. Fragment ions sometimes occur as the result of simple cleavage of a molecule in which one or more bonds are broken. In other instances, ions consist of fragments that are formed by some sort of intramolecular rearrangement. Based on the authors' observations, ion formation appears to occur in the following ways.

1. Ionization with no cleavage—in this case ions of the molecular weight mass are formed. Such ions are normally termed "parent" ions.

2. Single cleavage—refers to ions that are formed as the result of rupturing only one valence bond.

3. Multiple cleavage—fragmentation in which more than one bond is broken. This is the most prevalent type of dissociation.

4. Single cleavage with rearrangement—ion formation is accompanied by migration of one or more atoms. Usually some relocation of hydrogen atoms has occurred.

5. Multiple cleavage with rearrangement—this is similar to *4*, above, but usually involves the transfer of two or more hydrogens.

6. Multiple cleavage with recombination—in this case it appears that a fragment is split out from the interior of the molecule and the end pieces then are recombined to form an ion. This may be a cyclization process, as explained by McLafferty (182).

7. One of the modes *1* to *5*, above, with loss of two or more electrons. This process forms multiple charged ions of apparent mass one-half, or one-third, of the true mass. As a rule these are half masses, i.e., fragments having a double charge.

8. Metastable fragments—these ions are actually whole integer masses that appear at nonintegral locations in the spectrum. They are formed as the result of the disintegration of ions that are traveling in the analyzer tube. The classic example is the diffuse peak of n-butane, which appears at m/e 31.9 as the result of disintegration of mass 58 ions.

One or more of the above processes can occur, according to the nature of the molecule. Aliphatic hydrocarbon spectra show ions that result primarily from single or multiple cleavage of the molecule. Bonds tend to break at the more highly branched points on the carbon chain, and regardless of the branching the most intense ions occur in the C_2 to C_5 mass range. Unsaturation increases the stability of the molecule so that less fragmentation occurs.   Double bonds also favor cleavage of single bonds located in the beta position.   This effect is most noticeable in the case of substituted aromatics, in which relatively few intense ions occur.   These ions consist primarily of the parent molecule or of fragments composed of the aromatic rings and single carbon-atom groups alpha to the ring, as illustrated in this structure:

$$\langle\!\!\!\bigcirc\!\!\!\rangle\!-\!\overset{\overset{\displaystyle H^{+}}{|}}{\underset{\underset{\displaystyle C}{|}}{C}}\!\dashv\!R$$

Oxygenated compounds in general are more predictable than are hydrocarbons because of the influence of the electron-releasing groups that are present.   These groups strongly favor cleavage at the carbon-carbon bond beta to the carbon-oxygen linkage.   This is also true of nitrogen and sulfur groups, particularly in low molecular weight compounds.   All organic molecules show more randomized fragmentation with increasing molecular weights.

2. Types of Positive Ions

a. REARRANGEMENT IONS

Perhaps the most interesting feature of mass spectra are the rearrangement ions, which are prevalent in most spectra.   Very simply these ions occur according to modes *4* and *5* above.   The exact mechanisms of formation have been studied in some detail by a number of investigators.

As early as 1942, Stevenson and Hipple (260) studied the formation of a $C_2H_5{}^+$ ion in isobutane and concluded that isomerization occurred, followed by dissociation:

$$i\text{-}C_4H_{10} \rightarrow n\text{-}C_4H_{10} \rightarrow C_2H_5{}^+ + C_2H_5 + e$$

Langer (160) proposed several possible mechanisms, including (*1*) isomerization, (*2*) a migration of binding electrons, resulting in a shift of hydrogen atoms around the skeleton of the molecule, and (*3*) a more complicated form of regrouping, in which a molecule loses its structural identity in the excited state so that a random recombination into fragments may occur.

McLafferty (184) has done monumental work in this field.   He proposes two types of rearrangements, namely, random and specific.   Random rearrangements are characterized by a general reshuffling and isomerization of the excited molecule.   Langer's mechanisms (*1*) and (*3*) fall into this category.   Rearrangements of this kind occur in molecules in which small energy differences exist between the atomic arrangements taking part in or produced in the dissociation. Saturated hydrocarbons, in particular, fulfill these requirements.

Specific rearrangements occur in molecules possessing functional groups that favor degradation routes of lower energy requirements and that result in stable rearranged products. Ions formed in this manner may be quite intense and, indeed, are frequently the most abundant ions in spectra. Molecules containing oxygen, sulfur, or nitrogen atoms possess polar groups that favor specific rearrangements. Ketones, for example, dissociate to give an intense rearrangement ion in the following manner:

$$\underset{\displaystyle R\overset{\text{O}}{\overset{\|}{C}}CH_2{-}CH_2R'}{} \rightarrow R\overset{\text{O}}{\overset{\|}{C}}CH_3{}^+ + CHR' + e$$

According of McLafferty (184), the structure of the above ion actually is

$$R{-}\underset{}{\overset{\text{OH}}{\overset{|}{C}}}{=}CH_2{}^+$$

A more spectacular but less common type of rearrangement is that of mode *6*. McLafferty (182) postulates that this occurs through a cyclic intermediate. For the compound A—B—C—D, then, the process would be

$$A{-}B{-}C{-}D \rightarrow \underset{\displaystyle D{-}C}{A^+{-}B} \rightarrow AD^+ + BC$$

This rearrangement has been observed in a number of compounds, diphenyl ether being an interesting one. Beynon (34) has noted that CO is split out from the molecule.

$$C_6H_5OC_6H_5 \rightarrow C_6H_5{-}C_5H_5{}^+ + CO$$

$$m/e = 142$$

Beynon *et al.* (34a) have studied various other molecular rearrangements in the spectra of organic compounds involving the loss of carbon monoxide.

In a mass spectrum a preponderance of ions is formed by direct cleavage or by cleavage and rearrangement processes. In addition, other ions exist, as indicated by modes *7* and *8* above, as multiple-charged or metastable fragments.

b. MULTIPLE CHARGED IONS

The most prominent ions measured in a mass spectrometer possess a single positive charge. However, some multiple-charged ions do occur that are primarily particles with a double charge. These are observed in hydrocarbons as well as in other molecules. Fixed gases, such as CO, N_2,

TABLE 40.I. Typical Double-Charged Ions Observed in Some Hydrocarbon Spectra

Compound	m/e	Intensity, %[a]
Paraffins		
n-Butane	19.0	0.04
	19.5	0.01
	20.0	0.02
	25.5	0.36
	26.5	0.08
	27.5	0.05
n-Pentane	25.5	0.04
	31.0	0.33
	31.5	0.08
	32.0	0.13
	32.5	0.05
	33.0	0.07
	33.5	0.02
Mono-olefins		
cis-2-Butene	19.0	0.02
	19.5	0.01
	20.0	0.01
	25.5	1.55
	26.5	0.27
	27.5	0.07
1-Pentene	19.0	0.02
	19.5	0.01
	20.0	0.01
	25.5	0.03
	30.5	0.01
	31.0	1.03
	31.5	0.24
	32.0	0.34
	32.5	0.21
	33.0	0.22
	33.5	0.10
	34.0	0.04
	34.5	0.02
Aromatics		
Benzene	36.5	0.05
	37.5	1.15
	38.5	0.35
	39.0	3.0
Naphthalene	51.5	0.25
	63.5	0.35
	64.5	0.60
Phenanthrene	75.5	0.7
	76.5	1.1
	87.5	0.6
	88.5	1.3
	89.5	1.4

[a] Intensity as relative percentage of base peak.

CO_2, and O_2 have measurable peaks corresponding to CO^{+2}, N^{+2}, CO_2^{+2}, and O^{+2}. Since a mass spectrometer sorts ions according to a mass-to-charge ratio, however, such particles would occur at nominal masses 14, 14, 22, and 16, respectively.

In hydrocarbons the abundance of these ions varies inversely with degree of saturation. Thus, their spectral intensities increase in the order: paraffins, olefins, and aromatics, according to ring number. In hydrocarbons of five or less carbon atoms, the most probable double ionization process involves loss of all but two or three hydrogen atoms without cleavage of carbon–carbon bonds (198). Acyclic molecules of more than five carbon atoms tend to form ions of less intensity with breaking of carbon bonds. In the case of aromatic hydrocarbons, the aromatic nuclei plus adjacent carbon groups are relatively stable and favor the creation of doubly charged ions.

In a mass spectrum, fragments of an even-number mass possibly coincide with the ions of integral masses having a single charge, but an odd-numbered mass fragment will be distinguished by half-integer values. For example, butenes have a noticeable peak at mass 25.5 that is readily identified as $C_4H_3^{+2}$ (mass $= 51$). On the other hand, the ion $C_4H_2^{+2}$ (mass $= 50$) has an apparent mass of 25, which cannot be separately identified from C_2H^+ (mass $= 25$). For this reason the data on doubly charged ions are necessarily incomplete.

The intensity of typical doubly charged ions are shown in Table 40.I for paraffins, olefins, and aromatics. Ions of this kind are of considerable practical value, as will be pointed out subsequently.

c. METASTABLE IONS

Metastable ions are transition fragments that are observed as small, abnormally wide peaks that are, in general, at nonintegral mass positions. These peaks arise from ions that dissociate after passing through the ion-accelerating field (129). Consequently, the transition ions have less than full kinetic energy and an apparent mass, M_a, which is less than the true mass, as represented by the relationship

$$M_a = M_f^2/M_t$$

where M_f is the actual mass after transition and M_t is the mass during passage through the accelerating electric field.

Most organic molecules show metastable ions, and studies of their occurrence have been published by Bloom and his co-workers (40,41). These investigators report that more than 100 different metastable transitions

TABLE 40.II

Portion of Metastable Transition Chart Prepared by Meyer and Earnshaw (193)

Mass-to-charge ratios of ions after dissociation

Mass-to-charge ratios of ions before dissociation

Diagonal column indices (m/e after dissociation): 25, 26, 27, 28, 29, 30, 31, 32, 33, 34, 35, 36, 37, 38, 39, 40, 41, 42, 43, 44, 45, 46, 47, 48, 49, 50, 51, 52, 53, 54, 55, 56, 57, 58, 59, 60, 61

```
(26)  22 40
(27)  13 31 50
(28)  06 23 41 60
(29)  99 16 33 51 70
(30)  92 08 25 43 61 80
(31)  86 02 18 35 53 71 90
(32)  80 95 11 28 45 63 81 00
(33)  75 89 05 21 38 55 73 91 10
(34)  69 84 99 14 31 47 65 83 01 20
(35)  65 79 93 08 24 40 57 75 93 11 30
(36)  60 74 88 03 18 34 50 67 84 03 21 40
(37)  56 69 83 97 12 27 43 60 77 94 12 31 50
(38)  52 64 78 92 06 21 37 53 69 87 04 22 41 60
(39)  48 60 73 87 01 16 31 46 63 79 96 14 32 51 70
(40)  44 56 69 82 96 10 25 40 56 72 89 06 24 42 61 80
(41)  40 52 65 78 91 05 20 34 50 66 82 99 16 34 52 71 90
(42)  37 49 61 74 87 00 14 29 44 59 75 92 09 26 44 62 81 00
(43)  34 45 57 70 82 96 09 23 38 53 69 85 01 18 36 54 72 91 10
(44)  31 42 54 66 78 91 05 18 33 48 63 78 95 11 28 46 64 82 01 20
(45)  28 39 50 62 74 87 00 14 28 42 57 72 88 04 21 38 56 74 92 11 30
(46)  25 36 47 58 70 83 96 09 23 37 51 66 82 98 14 31 48 65 83 02 21 40
(47)  23 33 44 55 67 79 91 04 18 32 46 61 76 91 07 24 40 58 75 93 12 31 50
(48)  20 30 41 52 63 75 88 00 13 27 41 55 70 85 01 17 33 50 68 85 03 22 41 60
(49)  28 38 49 60 72 84 96 09 22 36 50 64 79 95 10 27 43 60 77 95 13 32 51 70
(50)  23 35 46 57 68 80 92 05 18 31 45 59 74 89 04 20 36 53 70 87 05 23 42 61 80
(51)  20 30 43 54 65 76 88 01 14 27 40 54 68 83 98 14 30 46 63 80 97 15 33 52 71 90
(52)  20 30 40 51 62 73 85 97 09 23 36 49 63 76 89 08 23 39 56 72 89 07 25 43 62 81 00
(53)     28 38 48 59 70 81 93 05 18 31 45 58 72 87 02 17 33 49 56 72 89 17 35 53 72 91 10
(54)     25 35 45 56 67 78 90 02 14 27 40 54 67 82 96 11 27 42 59 75 92 09 27 45 63 82 99 17 35 53 72 91 10
(55)     23 33 43 53 64 75 86 98 10 23 36 49 63 77 91 06 21 36 52 68 85 02 19 37 55 73 92 11 30
(56)     21 30 40 50 61 72 83 94 06 19 31 44 58 72 86 00 15 30 46 62 78 94 11 29 46 64 83 02 21 40
(57)        28 38 48 58 69 80 91 03 15 27 40 53 67 81 95 09 24 40 55 71 88 04 21 39 56 74 93 12 31 50
(58)        26 35 45 55 66 77 88 99 11 24 36 49 62 76 90 04 19 34 49 65 81 97 14 48 66 84 03 22 41 60
(59)        24 33 43 53 63 74 85 96 08 20 32 45 58 71 85 99 13 28 43 59 74 91 07 24 41 58 76 94 13 32 51 70
(60)        22 31 40 50 60 71 82 93 04 16 28 41 54 67 80 94 08 23 38 53 68 84 00 17 34 51 68 86 04 23 42 61 80
```

have been observed in hydrocarbons.　These recur in many different hydrocarbons, and more than 1000 different instances of transition are noted in spectral data published by Project 44 of the American Petroleum Institute (API)(15c).

Assignment of the transition that is responsible for a given metastable ion has been, in the past, a rather laborious task.　This was true because only a qualitative rule stated that the height of such a peak depended upon the intensities of M_f and M_i, both to exceed 5% of the maximum peak in a complete spectrum.　In practice, then, trial-and-error calculations were required to select the peaks involved in metastable transitions.　The need for such calculations now has been eliminated through a chart devised by Meyer and Earnshaw (193).　A portion of this chart is shown in Table 40.II.

The numbers on the left of the table (26 to 150—not shown completely in Table 40.II) represent ion masses, M_i, prior to transition, and the numbers across the top (26 to 149—also incomplete) represent the masses, M_f, after transition.　The apparent masses, M_a, are in the body of the table. Only tenths and the first unit of each number are included and the lines between decades have been inserted.　As an example of how to use this table, consider the metastable ion of apparent mass 31.9 ± 0.1 in the spectrum of normal butane.　To be noticeable, metastable ions usually involve the dissociation of relatively abundant ions.　For normal butane, 58, 57, 43, 42, 41, and 39 would then be considered as possible initial ions. Of these, however, only the 43 and 58 could give likely values of 31.8 and 31.9, respectively.　The possible transitions are,

$$(1)\ \ 31.8\ (43^+)\ldots\ldots(37^+) + 6$$

$$(2)\ \ 31.9\ (58^+)\ldots\ldots(43^+) + 15$$

Transition (1) is highly unlikely because it involves a neutral particle of mass 6, whereas the second mechanism includes a reasonable neutral fragment of mass 15.　Logically, then, the latter transition is responsible for the formation of the 31.9 ion.

3. Negative Ions

The formation and behavior of negative ions have been discussed in detail by Massey (10) and Field and Franklin (4).　Only a paucity of experimental data is available on negative ions in mass spectra, and to date no analytical applications have been reported based on such peaks.　This may be attributed to the fact that commercial model spectrometers must be modified extensively to make such measurements.　Furthermore, it has been observed that negative ions generally are present in small intensities. In a survey of negative ion data (222), Reese, Dibeler, and Mohler have reported on CO, O_2, B_5H_9, HCl, CCl_4, ClO_3F, and 12 fluorocarbons. Compounds of this type generally exhibit more intense negative ions than do organics. However, even these spectra show only a few ions of relatively weak intensity as compared with positive ions. Melton and Rudolph (192) have recorded the negative ion spectra of hydrocarbons and alcohols.

4. Isotopic Ions

An ion is uniquely defined by its mass, which, in turn, is dependent upon the combined weights of the atoms constituting that ion. Because atoms may consist of different isotopes, a given molecule or fragment may vary accordingly in mass. A methyl group of formula CH_3 normally is considered to have a mass of 15, as determined by carbon with a mass of 12 and three hydrogens each of mass 1. Actually, however, carbon isotopes of masses 12 and 13 exist, having relative abundances of 98.93 and 1.07%, respectively, and hydrogen isotopes consist of 99.985% of mass 1 and 0.015% of mass 2. For this reason a methyl fragment will vary in mass according to the following distribution:

Isotopic composition	Mass	Relative abundance, %
$C^{12}H^1H^1H^1$	15	98.882
$C^{13}H^1H^1H^1$	16	1.074
$C^{12}H^1H^1H^2$	16	0.040
$C^{13}H^1H^1H^2$	17	0.004

Other combinations are insignificant.

This type of mass proportionation can be both a hindrance and a help in analytical work. It is a hindrance, for example, in that a mass-16 methyl group, $C^{13}H^1H^1H^1$, cannot be separately identified from the normal methane molecule, $C^{12}H^1H^1H^1H^1$. This identification can be done mathematically, however, by taking into consideration natural isotopic abundances. A rather complete set of isotope-abundance factors has been prepared by ASTM Committee E-14 on Mass Spectrometry (16). This manual presents data on hydrocarbons and oxygenated and sulfur compounds in a readily usable form.

Knowledge of isotope abundances can be extremely useful in qualitative analysis. Fragments containing chlorine or bromine atoms, as a rule, can be identified readily. Chlorine has isotopes of masses 35 and 37 with relative abundances of 75.4 and 24.6%, respectively. CH_2Cl ions, accordingly, would occur in pairs at masses 50 and 52 in about the same proportion as Cl^{35} and Cl^{37}. Ions containing more than one chlorine atom would possess an even more unique pattern, having three prominent masses as a result of the combinations, $Cl^{35}Cl^{35}$, $Cl^{35}Cl^{37}$, and $Cl^{37}Cl^{37}$. Bromine atoms are easily identified because of an almost equal distribution of 79 and 81 isotopes. Mass differences are less striking in other cases, but frequently they can be of substantial value to an analyst.

5. Ion Sources

a. ELECTRON IMPACT

The modern ion source for gas instruments has evolved from the electron-impact type developed by Bleakney (37) in 1929. A schematic diagram of a typical ion source is shown in Fig. 40.4. Basically, two functions are performed within the source. First, the hot filament provides a source of electrons to ionize and dissociate a portion of the molecules. Suitable positive potential fields of about 70 e.v. accelerate the electrons across the cavity containing the sample to the anode, as indicated in the illustration.

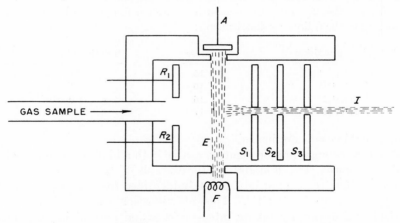

Fig. 40.4. Schematic diagram of an electron-impact ion source. Key: F, filament; A, anode, E, electron beam; R_1 and R_2, positively charged ion-repeller plates; S_1, high positive-potential ion-accelerator slit; S_2, pair of focusing plates; S_3, ground potential slit; and I, ion beam.

Second, the ions thus formed are repelled by two positively charged electrodes, R_1 and R_2, into the ion-accelerating region created by slits S_1 and S_3. The potential difference between S_1 and S_3 may vary from 4000 to 400 v. An intermediate pair of plates, S_2, serves as focusing electrodes to produce a narrow ion beam.

b. CRUCIBLE SOURCE

The electron impact source, normally applicable to gases or vapors from volatile liquids and solids, also can handle materials of extremely low volatility by means of a crucible furnace (54,175). The heater unit is capable of producing vapor from heavy organic residues or inorganic salts and metals at temperatures above 1000°C. It may be located either internally or externally to the ion source. The vapor emitted from the crucible is bombarded with electrons in the usual manner to form ions. This source suffers the disadvantages of low sensitivity and, because the more volatile components in the sample are preferentially vaporized, fractionation occurs.

c. SURFACE IONIZATION SOURCE

Another type of source for analyzing solids is surface ionization by positive-ion emission from a hot filament. This was first employed by Dempster in 1918 (69), who coated a filament with the sample in the form of a salt. The requirements for the surface ionization source are that the filament (tungsten, tantalum, etc.) possess a high work function and high melting point, whereas the element to be ionized must have a low ionization potential (the alkali metals, rare earths, and others). Ions produced in this manner have a low energy spread and may be handled in an instrument with directional focusing only. The efficiency of ionization depends to a great extent on the type of salt placed on the filament. Present-day sources (67,82,128,140,213) usually consist of two or more filaments: one vaporizes the sample at a controlled rate while others operated at a much higher temperature cause the vapor to ionize. Evaporation of samples having components of widely different volatilities results in fractionation, thereby requiring special calibration techniques.

d. VACUUM SPARK SOURCE

The vacuum spark source first used by Dempster (71) has found wide application in the chemical analysis of solids. Of the several kinds of spark sources tried, the high-frequency type (111,241) has proved to be the most successful. Operated intermittently, it does not heat and vaporize the sample, all elements are ionized at nearly the same rate with little isotopic fractionation, and numerous multicharged ions are formed. The source, however, possesses two major disadvantages. The spread in kinetic energy of formation of the ions is very high (76) ($\sim$1000 v.) and the ion beam is so unsteady that photographic detection is required. Despite these formidable obstacles to its use in routine analysis, the spark source is of importance because no special preparation of the sample is required to obtain representative spectra.

e. Ionization Without Dissociation

Sometimes it is desirable in organic mixture analysis to produce "parent" ions with very little fragmentation.   In addition to the low-voltage electron-impact technique, to be described in Section IV-D-2-c-(2), two other methods have been used.   Inghram and Gomer (107,141) adapted the field-emission technique of Müller (202) to mass spectrometry.   Molecular ions are formed in a strong electrostatic field of 7000 to 9000 v. that is created by a very sharp-pointed tungsten electrode.   In another design, Lossing and Tanaka (167) and others (138,201) used a photon source consisting of vacuum ultraviolet rays.   A wavelength of about 1200 A. is capable of ionizing many organic compounds without dissociation.   The chief limitation of the photon-ionization method at present is the lack of a large ultraviolet source needed for adequate ion formation.

B. ION SEPARATION

The separation of ions with different mass-to-charge ratios may be accomplished in several ways.   The objective of the ideal separator is to attain high resolving power along with high transmission of the ions.   Unfortunately, in practice one cannot accomplish both aims simultaneously, and the instrument usually represents the best compromise between selectivity and sensitivity.

1. Magnetic Deflection

Mass spectrometers for organic analysis employ the magnetic-deflection analyzer either in a sector instrument or in the 180° circular type, as illus-

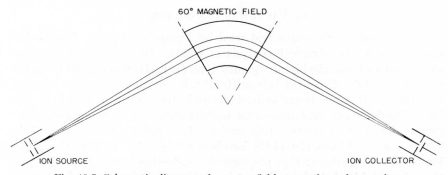

60° MAGNETIC FIELD

ION SOURCE

ION COLLECTOR

Fig. 40.5. Schematic diagram of a sector-field magnetic-analyzer tube.

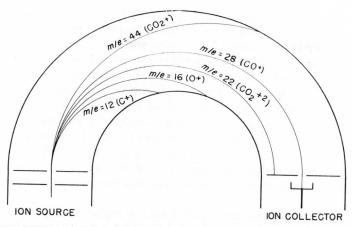

Fig. 40.6. Schematic diagram of a 180° magnetic-analyzer tube, showing the relative dispersion of carbon dioxide ions, with the mass 28 ion in focus at the resolving slit.

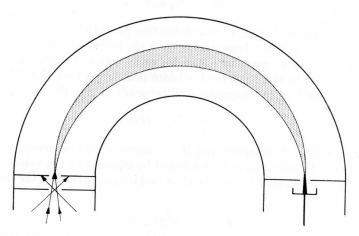

Fig. 40.7. Schematic diagram of spherical abberation occurring in the 180° analyzer as the result of kinetic energy of ions acquired through electron impact. A partial refocusing of the ion beam is observed at the resolving slit.

trated in Figs. 40.5 and 40.6. The ion beam is passed through a magnetic lens system to focus ions of like m/e ratio on the resolving slit. However, the ion beam is subject to aberration from a number of sources (262) not unlike that found in optical lens systems. The initial kinetic energy of ion formation in the ionization source gives rise to spherical aberration for the

Dempster-type apparatus, as shown in Fig. 40.7. The ions tend to refocus to some extent at the resolving slit with a resultant error equal to $2r(1 - \cos \alpha)$, where r is the radius of curvature and α is the angle between the actual direction of the ion as compared to the normal direction through the entrance slit. This kind of focusing error can be minimized by using high ion-accelerating potentials. Another aberration is caused by the space-charge effect. Neighboring ions tend to repel each other and thereby broaden the ion beam during its passage around the analyzer tube. The space charge is a limiting factor in instruments using high ion-transmission currents, such as in the electromagnetic separator or calutron. Other aberration effects include misalignment of the slit system, fringe-field focusing in the sector-type instrument, and inhomogeneities of the magnetic field.

Initially, positive ions are repelled into a region of high electrostatic potential difference and are accelerated to a high velocity, according to the conventional kinetic energy equation:

$$eV = \tfrac{1}{2} mv^2 \tag{1}$$

where e = electron charge, V = accelerating potential, m = mass of ion, and v = velocity of ion. Ions emerge from the ionization source slit into a field-free region and travel in a circular path under the influence of the magnetic field. In this orbit the ion beam possesses a centrifugal force, F, which is balanced by the magnetic field perpendicular to the ion path.

$$F = mv^2/r = Hev \tag{2}$$

where r = radius of curvature and H = magnetic field intensity.

Equations (1) and (2) may be combined by eliminating the velocity term to relate the net effect of ion acceleration and magnetic field on the radius of curvature:

$$r = 1/H\sqrt{2Vm/e} \tag{3}$$

For a given spectrometer, therefore, the ion mass (m/e) is brought into focus through selection of proper values of H and V, as shown below:

$$m/e = 4.8 \times 10^{-5}\,(H^2r^2/V) \tag{4}$$

where H is the magnetic field strength in gauss, r is the radius of curvature of the ion beam in cm., V is the accelerating potential in volts, and m/e is the ion mass in atomic mass units divided by the number of positive charges on the ion.

2. Double Focusing

Spark ionization sources for analysis of solids produce ions having a wide kinetic energy spread in excess of 1000 e.v. The separation of such an ion beam into its component masses cannot be made by magnetic focusing alone. Instead, the ion beam is passed through a double-focusing system consisting of an energy selector followed by a magnetic separator. This method was first used by Aston in his early mass spectrograph (19) to determine atomic masses. Mattauch and Herzog (177) designed an instrument that is double focusing for all masses simultaneously (Fig. 40.8). Dempster (70), Bainbridge and Jordan (21), and Nier and Roberts (208) also have built precise double-focusing instruments for physics research.

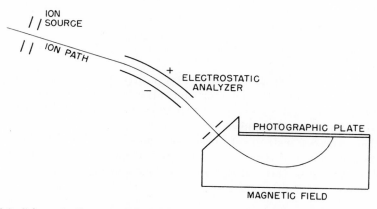

Fig. 40.8. Schematic diagram of the Mattauch double-focusing analyzer tube, comprised of electrostatic and magnetic sections in tandem (177).

In another application the double focusing principle was utilized in analytical research by Beynon (33) for resolving ions having nearly equal but not exactly the same mass. The application of this type of instrument to distinguish such fragment ions will be discussed below in terms of its promising future in component identification.

3. Resonance in Radio-Frequency Fields

A recent nonmagnetic method of mass separation was developed by Bennett (25), as illustrated in Fig. 40.9. The ions are passed through a number of grid structures charged with oscillating potentials at radio frequencies. At a given initial velocity only ions of a specific mass-to-charge ratio become resonant and attain a maximum kinetic energy in passing

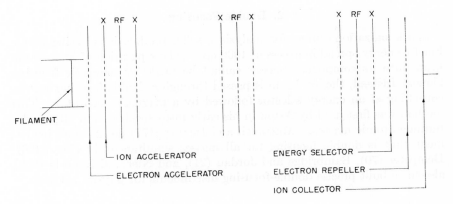

Fig. 40.9. Schematic diagram of the Bennett radio-frequency mass spectrometer (25).

through the tube. At the collector slit a positive grid potential allows the resonant ions to enter the detector while all other ions of lesser energy are repulsed. The great advantage of this type of instrument lies in its small size, since no magnet is required.

Other types of instruments based on the cyclotron principle include: (1) the omegatron of Hipple, Sommer, and Thomas (130), (2) the helical-path instrument of Hays, Richards, and Goudsmit (124), and (3) the mass synchrometer of Smith (249–251).

4. Pulsed Time of Flight

The pulsed "time of flight" nonmagnetic mass spectrometer was first developed by Cameron and Eggers (55), and subsequently other designs were perfected (146,148,302). It differentiates between ion masses by measurement of the time of travel through a drift tube, as seen in Fig. 40.10. In this process the travel time, t, of each ion species of equal energy is directly proportional to the square root of its m/e ratio.

$$t = k\sqrt{m/e}$$

where k is a function of the accelerating potential. Since ion resolution is obtained through differential time measurement, ion bunches must leave the source at essentially the same instant. To accomplish this, the electron beam, the accelerating potential, and the time measurement are pulsed or triggered in proper sequence at a repetitive rate of 10,000 cycles

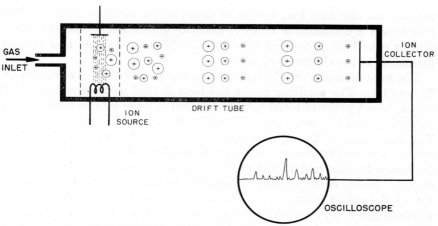

Fig. 40.10. Schematic diagram of a "time-of-flight" mass spectrometer showing the successive separation of ion masses in the drift tube.

per second.   Thus, an entire mass spectrum may be presented every 100 microseconds.   Harrington has compared various time-of-flight and radio-frequency instrument types (122).

C. ION DETECTION

The early method of ion detection through impingement of the beam on a photographic plate has continued to be used with a spark source in inorganic solids analysis.   Since the advent of modern electronics, however, the ion beam current of 10^{-15} to 10^{-9} amp. is nearly always measured by either an electrometer or electron multiplier circuit.   Extreme care in the design of such circuits is required to assure linearity of response over a wide dynamic range of 10^4 to 10^5.   The collector electrode in the spectrometer is carefully shielded to eliminate false currents from secondary electrons and extraneous sources of noise.   The output from the amplifier may be fed into a pen-ink recorder, an oscillograph, or, for fast response, into an oscilloscope.

D. INSTRUMENTAL REQUIREMENTS

A mass spectrometer designed to operate as an analytical instrument must possess certain features of reliability, sensitivity, and mass range. One of its most important requisites is to faithfully reproduce spectra of pure compounds and mixtures according to both the relative dissociation pattern and the peak height per unit of sample pressure.   Variations in the spectrum may cause confusion in the qualitative identification of compounds and also may lead to serious errors in quantitative analysis. For this reason a considerable effort is made to obtain stable operating conditions over long periods of time by incorporating voltage and current regulators in the electronic circuitry.

The resolution of an analytical mass spectrometer has been discussed by Berry (30). The resolving power has been defined as the mass at which two adjacent peaks of equal height, differing in mass by one unit, show a valley between the peaks amounting to 2 to 10% of the height of either. The requirements of resolution vary widely with the application: a resolving power of 60 may suffice for gas analysis, 150 for volatile liquids, 600 for heavy liquids, and 10,000 or more for distinguishing molecular fragments of nearly equal masses. Resolution is determined by the values of three independent parameters. These are (1) the width of the ion beam at the focal point, (2) dispersion, or separation of adjacent beams at the focal plane, and (3) the width of the resolving slit at the collector. A systematic study of high-mass high resolution was made by Voorhies and his coworkers, and experimental data were obtained on three double-focusing instruments (276). Although resolution is a separate problem with each type of instrument, a sharper resolution can be attained at the higher accelerating potentials (285) with the deflection-type analyzer. This occurs because the effect of variations in kinetic energy of ions in the source becomes less pronounced as the acceleration potential is increased.

The range of mass scanning is usually limited by resolution and the strength of the magnetic field or of the accelerating potential. Most instruments have adequate provision for wide scanning and, if necessary, the range can be extended by simple electronic modification.

Ion abundances encountered in even a routine mass spectrum may vary over a range of 10^5. This requires a highly linear amplifier and a method of automatic attenuation of the signal either by multiple simultaneous recording or by predetection of the ion beam. Both methods have provided satisfactory spectra with a precision of 0.1%.

The absolute accuracy of the instrument and method can only be determined by analysis of carefully prepared synthetic mixtures of pure compounds. In most cases an analysis that matches the synthetic mixture within 0.5 mole per cent is considered ample evidence of reliable performance of the instrument.

III. PRACTICE OF MASS SPECTROMETRY

A. COMMERCIAL INSTRUMENTS

Mass spectrometers of diverse and often ingenious designs have been built in university, government, research institute, and industrial laboratories for specific applications in physics research. With the advent of analytical mass spectrometry, however, a partial standardization of the instrument became highly desirable. To meet this need, instrument manufacturers worked diligently to produce reliable apparatus. In the meantime, analytical laboratories were busy developing new applications, spectral correlations, interpretive techniques, and computing methods. As a result the great majority of mass spectrometers employed for analytical work are those obtained from commercial sources.

1. General-Purpose Instruments

The large general-purpose mass spectrometers currently in use incorporate the best features of stability, sensitivity, resolution, and ease of operation. These versatile instruments can perform well on routine organic mixture analysis or, if desired, can be adapted easily to original analytical investigations. One of the most widely used instruments in this country has been the Consolidated Electrodynamics Corp. (subsidiary of Bell and Howell) model 21-103, a 180° magnetic-deflection type with good sensi-

Fig. 40.11. A large analytical mass spectrometer, the Consolidated Electrodynamics Corporation's model 21-103.

tivity, resolution, and range (Fig. 40.11). A medium-sized instrument, model 21-130, has been added recently to the Consolidated series of spectrometers. Sector-type analytical spectrometers were marketed at one time by Westinghouse and General Electric, but the manufacture of these instruments has since been discontinued. In Great Britain the Associated Electrical Industries, has been very active in the field; their model M.S. 2 is a 90° sector-type instrument based on Nier's 1940 design. The Atlas Werke A.G. of Bremen has produced their model CH 4, a large sector-type analytical instrument.

2. High-Temperature Instruments

Because of the individual requirements encountered in high-mass work, no commercial instrument has been produced specifically for this application. The general-pkrpose mass spectrometer is usually modified by adding a "home-made" heated-sample introduction system and by increasing the resolving power. O'Neal and Wier (210) developed the first high-temperature instrument for the analysis of heavy petroleum products. Conversion of a spectrometer to high-mass operation at one time proved to be a formidable task and was attempted only by the larger laboratories (50,210). Recent refinements in design and technique have encouraged many additional laboratories to work in the high-mass region. Use of a dual introduction system has enabled both low- and high-mass work to be performed on the same instrument (50,60,274).

3. Process Monitor

The control of refinery and chemical plant units by continuously monitoring the composition of feed and product streams by mass spectrometry has been highly successful (42,65,82,206,279,293). The monitor is a reliable and precise instrument of limited mass range, fitted with automatic programming of the sampling, scanning, and recording functions. Consolidated Electrodynamics has marketed a magnetic analyzer, model 21-610, and a smaller portable unit, model 21-611 (283) (Fig. 40.12).

4. High Resolution

Beynon pointed out the advantages of extremely high resolution for determination of molecular structures in 1954 (31), and he has since extended this technique (32). Although a number of spectrometers of high resolving power had been built privately for physics research, it was not until 1958 that Associated Electrical Industries developed their Model M.S. 8 for

Fig. 40.12. A small, portable mass spectrometer of limited mass range for process-monitor applications, the Consolidated Electrodynamics model 21-611.

analytical work (62). In this instrument, shown in Fig. 40.13, the double-focusing arrangement of Nier and Roberts (208) was used with 90° electrostatic and 90° magnetic-analyzer sections. A precision of 1 part in 100,000 is attainable in mass measurements with a resolving power of 10,000. This spectrometer was applied to the identification of organic compounds by Beynon (33).

5. Isotope Ratio

Intense interest in determining stable isotopes as tracers in medical and biological research fostered the commercial development of isotope-ratio

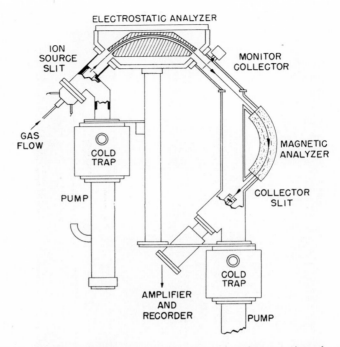

Fig. 40.13. A high-resolution mass spectrometer using electrostatic and magnetic analyzers (62). Courtesy of Associated Electrical Industries.

instruments.   In 1947 Nier designed an isotope-ratio spectrometer (205) that later served as a basis for both the Consolidated and AEI types.   Twin collectors are used for routine determination of isotope-abundance ratios. A dual-purpose mass spectrometer also is manufactured by Consolidated to provide isotope-ratio measurement as well as routine gas analysis over the mass range of 2 to 100.

6. Solids

A Mattauch-type solids mass spectrograph (177) was built by Hannay (117) for analytical applications (118).   Associated Electrical Industries manufactures this type of instrument as their model M.S. 7, consisting of a vacuum spark source, double focusing, and photographic detection (17b). Craig, Errock, and Waldron describe its use for the determination of impurities in solids (63).   Consolidated Electrodynamics has produced a new type mass spectrometer, model 21-110, of the Mattauch-Herzog design (177), with high resolving power, sensitivity, and versatility.   It is adaptable to the analysis of gases, liquids, and solids. Atlas Werke, A. G., has marketed their model 1-S. M. mass spectrometer, of the Mattauch type, which can be equipped with several of the conventional devices for ionization and spectral recording. Stevens and Inghram constructed a surface-emission instrument that was applied mainly to the analysis of uranium samples (257). This spectrometer possesses a 60° sector magnetic analyzer

Fig. 40.14. A time-of-flight mass spectrometer. Courtesy The Bendix Corporation.

on a 12-inch radius and an electronic ratio-recording system. Consolidated has recently announced their production of a similar surface-emission type mass spectrometer for solids analysis. Palmer compared the AEI model M.S. 5 with other instruments for analyses of lead and cadmium (213). Gentry described the line recorder spectrometer as an analytical instrument (102).

7. Radio-Frequency Type

The Bennett radio-frequency mass spectrometer has been used extensively in studies of upper atmosphere composition. Townsend (271), Holmes and Johnson (131), and Meadows (186) have described compact rocket-borne models to detect positive ions, negative ions, and gas composition at altitudes of 150 miles. Donner (74) and Kerr (149) have compared the radio-frequency and magnetic-type mass spectrometers.

8. Pulsed Time of Flight

The Wiley and McLaren pulsed-beam time-of-flight mass spectrometer (299,300), shown in Fig. 40.14, is manufactured by The Bendix Corporation in several models (122). The resolution of 1 in 400 and the high repetitive rate of one spectrum each 100 microseconds makes it particularly adaptable to the analysis of dynamic systems, such as gas effluents from gas chromatographic units (105) and reaction intermediates. For example, high-speed photographs of the oscilloscope trace have been taken by Kistiakowsky and Kydd (155) in flash photochemical reaction studies. Provision for supplemental ion sources and alternate choices for sample introduction, ion acceleration, and ion detection gives this instrument a high degree of versatility. The main advantage of the time-of-flight principle lies in its ability to make high-speed qualitative identification.

9. Other Types

A small cycloidal mass spectrometer based on the principle devised by Bleakney and Hipple (38) was described by Robinson and Hall (227), and is marketed by Consolidated as their model 21-620 (Fig. 40.15).

Hall, Hines, and Slay modified this cycloidal-focusing spectrometer (115) to include high-speed scanning and a line-of-sight inlet system to the ion source. The instrument, with a scanning rate of 10 spectra per second, is well suited for following kinetics of many chemical reactions. Blanchard, Farmer, and Ouellet (35) also constructed a rapid-scan instrument to study the oxidation of acetaldehyde.

A small, inexpensive magnetic mass spectrometer of limited mass range was developed by Consolidated, model 21-611, for the analysis of light gases (283). It is small enough to be easily portable, the heaviest part of the instrument being the mechanical vacuum pump. As mentioned earlier, it also is used as a process monitor.

Fig. 40.15. A cycloidal mass spectrometer, the Consolidated Electrodynamics model 21-620 (227).

10. Leak Detector

The mass spectrometer leak detector is a miniaturized version of the larger analytical types described earlier (209). It has been produced as 60°, 180° deflection, and radio-frequency types (267,273,277), which are set to detect helium. Among those in use are the Consolidated (Fig. 40.16), Beckman radio-frequency, and Associated Electrical Industries models. The use of leak detectors has greatly increased the reliability of both evacuated and pressurized equipment and, furthermore, has decreased substantially the time necessary to locate leaks in process units. In practice the detector is connected to the equipment under test, the system is evacuated, and then helium gas is sprayed from a fine jet over suspected areas. When a leak is

Fig. 40.16. Consolidated Electrodynamics model 24-101A leak detector.

found, an audible alarm sounds immediately. For testing pressurized vessels, a helium-air mixture is pumped into the vessel and a "sniffer" probe from the leak detector is moved around the equipment until the alarm sounds. These methods are extremely sensitive to small leakage rates in the range of 10^{-12} liters per second.

B. BASIC INSTRUMENTAL COMPONENTS

In order to function as an analytical tool, the main sections of the spectrometer are augmented with numerous auxiliary components. Some of these can be obtained commercially, whereas others are designed and built by the individual laboratories to fit their own particular applications.

1. Sample-Introduction System

The sample-introduction system is tailored to meet specific requirements for the types of sample to be analyzed. For gases and volatile liquids boiling below 150°C., the sampling system operates at ambient temperatures. A typical system, shown in Fig. 40.17, consists of a 2-liter reservoir bottle with appropriate lines and valves. A gas sample may be entered

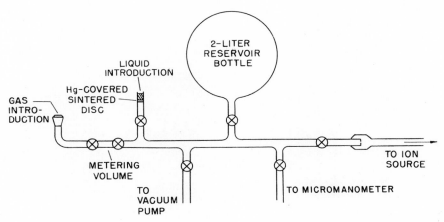

Fig. 40.17. Schematic diagram of an introduction system for the analysis of gases and volatile liquids.

into the spectrometer in the following manner. The sample tube is attached to the manifold with a suitable joint. A small volume of the gas first is trapped in the measuring volume between two valves and then is expanded into the reservoir bottle. A liquid sample is introduced rapidly and reproducibly through a mercury orifice (57) or mercury-covered, sintered-disc device (264) into the bottle. A normal sample pressure of 20 to 40 microns results by introducing 0.1 ml. of gas or 0.0005 ml. of liquid. Sometimes it is necessary to measure this pressure accurately by means of a micromanometer, such as the Consolidated type shown in Fig. 40.18. This electronic device operates on a capacitance change caused by movement of a fragile diaphragm. A vacuum system is connected to the bottle manifold to pump out the sample after analysis.

For the analysis of compounds having normal boiling points between 150 and 500°C. the introduction system is heated to raise the vapor pressure of a sample to at least 1 mm. Hg. The entire system, including the sintered disc, valve, and lines to the ion source, is heated evenly to a maximum of 350°C. Local hot spots may cause thermal decomposition of the sample, and cold spots may condense the heavier portion of the sample. Since the

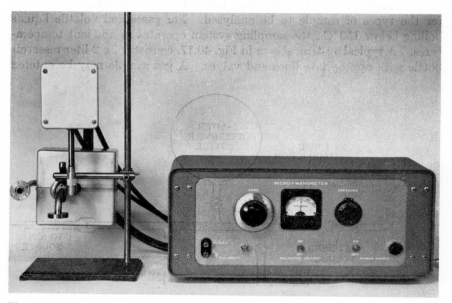

Fig. 40.18. Micromanometer to measure sample pressure in the introduction system (Consolidated Electrodynamics Corporation).

heated system is usually adapted to analysis of high molecular weight compounds, the degree of resolution must be increased to about 600. This is accomplished by reducing the slit width at the collector assembly. The manifold of this system, shown in Fig. 40.19, is not nearly as sophisticated at its low-temperature counterpart. The number of valves is reduced to only one, this being located between the bottle and vacuum pump. The sintered-disc introduction device uses gallium or indium instead of the more volatile mercury (51,101). Rowe described a heated inlet system for either a gas or liquid sample (230), and Peterson built an all-glass heated system (213a). Although a means for measuring sample pressure at ele-

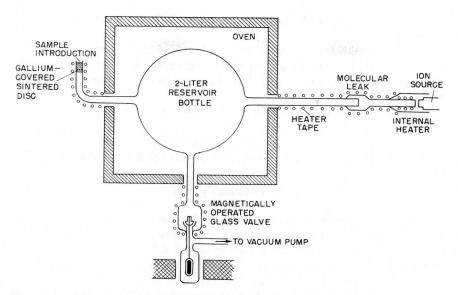

Fig. 40.19. Schematic diagram of a heated introduction system for the analysis of high-boiling samples.

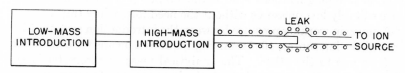

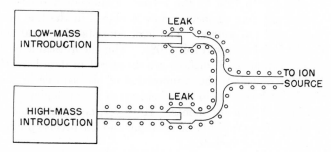

Fig. 40.20. Schematic diagram of dual low- and high-mass introduction systems connected in series (*a*) or in parallel (*b*) arrangements.

vated temperatures is highly desirable, no such device has been perfected as yet.

Separate introduction systems for both low- and high-mass analyses have been combined as a dual unit to connect with a single mass spectrometer. The two systems may be joined either in series (60) or in parallel (51,274), as seen in Fig. 40.20.

The introduction of nonvolatile solid samples requires special devices for placing the sample within the reservoir or ion source. Vacuum port openings with provision for rapidly changing samples have been developed, as for instance the designs of Lumpkin and Taylor (170b) and Stevens (255).

2. Vacuum System

Separate vacuum systems are provided for the introduction system and for the spectrometer tube itself. The former system is a conventional combination of a mechanical and a high-speed oil-diffusion pump to attain a vacuum of about 10^{-4} mm. Hg. The other vacuum arrangement for the spectrometer tube consists of a mechanical pump and two stages of mercury diffusion pumping to reach an ultimate vacuum of 10^{-7} mm. Hg. In addition, liquid nitrogen and dry ice traps are employed in the latter system to remove trace effluents from the analyzer tube as quickly as possible. At present, other pumping methods such as the ion pump (114) are being used to produce suitably low pressures without the need for cooling traps.

The difference in working pressure between the introduction system, 10^{-2} mm. Hg, and the ion source, 10^{-5} mm. Hg, requires a means for controlling gas flow from one to the other. The analytical mass spectrometer is designed for molecular flow of gas through the ion source to the vacuum system. To insure that the composition of a gas mixture in the ion source is identical with that in the introduction-system reservoir, a leak that also allows only free molecular flow is placed in the line between the reservoir bottle and ion source. The leak consists of several small holes in a thin sheet of glass or gold foil (108). The theoretical aspects of molecular gas flow through small orifices are discussed in detail by Honig (133). With the above system the composition of the sample in the reservoir changes slowly with respect to time because of faster depletion rate of the low molecular weight components. However, no error is introduced by this effect because of the rapidity of scanning and the precise programming of manipulations by the operator.

An arrangement that permits viscous gas flow of a sample into the ion source is necessary when sampling directly from atmospheric or higher pressure vessels. It is also employed in measuring isotope ratios (116). Viscous gas flow is controlled satisfactorily by a very small diameter capillary tube several inches long or with an adjustable type of leak (207).

3. Ion Source and Analyzer

An electron-impact source for analytical application is an ingenious arrangement of electrodes and focusing slits possessing outstanding electrical and geometrical properties. One type of ion source is the Consolidated "Isatron" illustrated in Fig. 40.21. Ions generated and accelerated from the source enter the field-free analyzer tube located in a magnetic field

Fig. 40.21. An electron-impact ion source, the Consolidated Electrodynamics Corporation's "Isatron."

The analyzer tube is electrically grounded to allow complete neutralization of all ions not in focus that strike the tube surface. Once neutralized, the molecular fragments combine in various ways and are evacuated through the pumping system. A resolving slit is located at the far end of the analyzer tube to admit ions in focus to the detector. The ion optics of the system, comprised of the entrance slits in the source and the resolving slit, are critically aligned to maximize ion transmission and resolving power.

4. Ion Detection and Recording

The principles of detection and recording of the spectrum have been discussed briefly in an earlier section. Each of these techniques possesses inherent advantages and disadvantages of interest. Photographic detection utilizes the full resolving power provided by the focusing system and integrates a highly variable ion current, such as the one encountered with the spark source (176). However, photographic development is tedious, the range of intensity measurement is limited, and ion-abundance measurement by a densitometer is not highly accurate. Electronic amplification of the ion current is accomplished by direct-coupled or vibrating-reed amplifiers. Nearly all of the analytical instruments for organic analysis employ one or the other of these electronic types. The vibrating-reed amplifier is noted for its low noise level and stable base line. The output from an amplifier may operate a pen-ink recorder or a 4- or 5-channel galvanometer oscillograph. The advantage of the latter system lies in the simultaneous recording of lines representing different degrees of attenuation. A dynamic range of 10^5 with three-digit precision is obtained in this manner. An alternate method of attenuation with a pen-ink recorder requires an anticipation circuit. In this device an ion beam approaching the collector slit strikes a sensing electrode that operates the attenuation controls. Another detector for measurement of very low ion currents, 10^{-12} to 10^{-20} amp., is the electron multiplier (294). Although the response of this type of detector is fast and the gain is extremely high, it is subject to fluctuations that impose limitations for its use as a quantitative device. One convenient way to obtain reliable spectra with this electron multiplier is to use the peak-ratio method (256), wherein all peaks in the spectrum are related to a selected major peak. This procedure tends to cancel out variations in the multiplier gain and thermal background currents.

5. Scanning of Spectrum

Mass spectra may be scanned by varying either the magnetic field or the accelerating potential, although usually the latter method is used. Theoretically, there is little to choose between the two types of scanning and a selection is often based on other design parameters of the instrument. Normally, a scanning rate of one mass peak every 2 to 3 seconds gives creditable records. At this speed a routine gas sample requires a running time of 3 to 4 minutes. A higher speed of one mass peak every 0.5 millisecond was made by Hall *et al.*, using an electron multiplier with a cycloidal mass spectrometer (115). A still higher speed is obtained with the pulsed time-of-flight mass spectrometer, which operates at a rate of 10,000 spectra each second (300), although scanning as such is not required.

C. OPERATING PROCEDURE

From the foregoing discussion it might be expected that operation of a large mass spectrometer would be exceedingly difficult to learn. Actually, the procedures are straightforward and anyone with average laboratory skills can become a proficient operator, regardless of his technical background.

As an example of operating technique, a volatile organic liquid sample would be handled in a Consolidated 21-103 instrument in the following manner. With the previous sample completely pumped out and the ion-accelerating potential returned to its high starting value, the instrument is ready for introduction of this new sample. Liquid sample is drawn into a 0.5-microliter pipet and entered through the introduction device into the reservoir bottle. A short wait of several seconds allows for complete vaporization and equilibration of pressure in the system. The sample pressure of about 30 μ is accurately measured with the micromanometer and the valve to the ion source is then opened. From this moment on the operator follows a prescribed time schedule in starting the scanning of the spectrum. This is required because, as mentioned previously, the low molecular weight compounds pass through the leak slightly faster than the heavier ones. A timed program used for samples and calibration compounds eliminates the need for a correction factor of this type during computation of analysis. The scanning of the spectrum is started simply by turning on the oscillograph and allowing the ion-accelerating potential to slowly decay from about 3800 to 400 v. Scanning is terminated by the operator when it is observed that mass peaks no longer register on the monitor meter. The run is completed by pumping out the remainder of the sample from the reservoir bottle and resetting the high-voltage potential. If a gas sample containing hydrogen or helium is to be analyzed, the magnet current is first reduced substantially in order to bring these light masses into focus. Similarly, heavy samples above mass 100 are focused by raising the magnet current to a higher-than-normal value.

In addition to analyzing samples, the operator also runs pure calibration compounds as required. The frequency and number of calibration runs are dictated by the stability of the instrument, the accuracy sought in an analysis, and the nature and complexity of the samples. Normally only one calibration compound, n-butane, is run regularly once or twice daily to check on spectral variations. Any change in sensitivity for n-butane may be used to correct other selected peaks used in the computation.

D. OPERATING PROBLEMS

Since the analytical mass spectrometer is a combined high-vacuum apparatus and electronic instrument, it is subject to a number of physical operating problems that originate with the sample, operating conditions, and cleanliness of the equipment. The sample itself can be a source of difficulty by virtue of its physical and chemical properties. Polar compounds such as water, ammonia, amines, and alcohols preferentially adsorb on the walls of the introduction system and give low results in the analysis. Those compounds having the strongest affinity for solid surfaces also desorb the lesser polar compounds that had previously collected there. Because of the "hang-up" or memory effects exhibited by polar compounds, several periods of conditioning the introduction system may be needed (147,286). Another solution to this problem is to run troublesome compounds in a heated introduction system, in which sorption is minimized. In the earlier instruments sorption of compounds in stopcock lubricant also caused serious errors. Subsequently, all greased stopcocks were replaced with metal valves or solenoid cut-offs (50) to eliminate this effect.

Spectral patterns and peak sensitivities change appreciably with the temperature of the ion source (28,91,221). Table 40.III shows the variations in hexane isomer patterns as a function of temperature, which were determined by Reese et al. (221). The parent peaks at mass 86 exhibit un-

TABLE 40.III

Change of Peak Sensitivities of Hexane Isomers with Temperature (221)

m/e	Temperature coefficients, %/°C.				
	n-Hexane	2-Methyl-pentane	3-Methyl-pentane	2,2-Dimethyl-butane	2,3-Dimethyl-butane
27	—	+0.02	+0.06	+0.08	+0.07
28	—	−0.03	+0.01	+0.07	+0.07
29	—	+0.01	+0.07	+0.11	+0.03
41	—	+0.01	+0.03	+0.07	+0.02
42	—	−0.06	+0.02	+0.02	−0.06
43	+0.03	−0.06	0	+0.09	−0.01
53	—	—	—	—	+0.02
55	—	—	—	+0.05	+0.02
56	—	—	−0.13	−0.26	—
57	—	—	−0.09	−0.16	—
58	−0.35	—	—	—	—
70	—	−0.25	−0.15	−0.34	0
71	—	−0.13	−0.06	−0.05	−0.14
85	—	—	—	−0.35	0
86 (parent)	−0.51	−0.85	−0.78	−0.94	−0.69

usually large temperature coefficients. Analytical instruments use temperature regulators to hold the source temperature constant to ±0.1°C., thus reducing the pattern fluctuations to a low level.

Interference of one component with another in a mixture has been encountered with all analytical mass spectrometers to some extent (29). The degree of this interference (or "gas sensitivity") may vary from 2 to 15%, depending on the ion-source design and condition of the filament. Blears and Waldron (39) showed that interference could be reduced from 13 to 4% by treatment of the filament with butene for several hours. Sharkey and his co-workers (236) carried out a solid-state study of the tungsten carbide system and concluded that a stable filament in the form of the W_2C phase gives reproducible spectra. On the other hand, a bare metallic tungsten filament or one in the WC phase may be expected to give unpredictable spectra. Various means to achieve a stable filament include (1) conditioning the surface with a light olefin such as butene-2 to form a W_2C phase in a newly-installed filament, or (2) treating with oxygen to oxidize WC back to W_2C in the case of an over-conditioned filament. Experience indicates which treatment or combination of treatments provide the most stable operation. High molecular weight mass spectrometry is particularly susceptible to fluctuating spectra, the effect being severalfold greater than with C_{12} and lighter compounds. In high-mass work filament conditioning is required more often and must be done more precisely. Robinson and Sharkey (228,238) have tested rhenium filaments and found these to yield relatively stable patterns with no conditioning problems.

In the course of routine analysis, sample pressure in the introduction-system reservoir bottle seldom exceeds 40 μ, and linearity of peak height with sample pressure is easily attained. Occasionally for trace analysis it is necessary to charge 200 to 400 μ of sample in order to detect the trace component. At these higher pressures a marked decrease in sensitivity is observed for all components, probably due to secondary ion formation and various aberrations in focusing the ion beam. This relatively high-pressure technique can be applied to analytical problems, however, if calibration data also are obtained under similar conditions.

An ion source under conditions of continuous use gradually acquires deposits on the surfaces of the electrodes and insulators. The deposit may consist of carbon, tungsten carbide, or even oxides, which tend to distort the electrical fields. Deposits eventually cause loss in resolution and alteration of the spectral pattern, and frequently lead to electrical breakdown of the insulators. The latter effect, observed as a high-voltage flashover, may be due to deposits or to a corona phenomenon that is little understood. An ion source used for hydrocarbon gases and volatile liquids may operate very satisfactorily for a year or more without the need for cleaning. By contrast, high molecular weight compounds may lay down enough deposit in 1 to 3 months to cause a shutdown. When this occurs, the very hard surface deposit must be removed by abrasive polishing. This is often done by the manufacturer as a service to the user.

E. HANDLING OF DATA

1. Data Reduction for Mass Spectrum

In conventional mass spectrometry a spectrum is recorded on a strip chart or photographic paper. In the latter case, galvanometer deflections from an oscillograph represent ion intensities along the ordinate with m/e values along the abscissa. A typical spectrum of n-butane is shown in Fig. 40.22, where it is seen that peaks occur at masses ranging from 12 to 59. Normally, markers are available to identify masses at selected intervals so

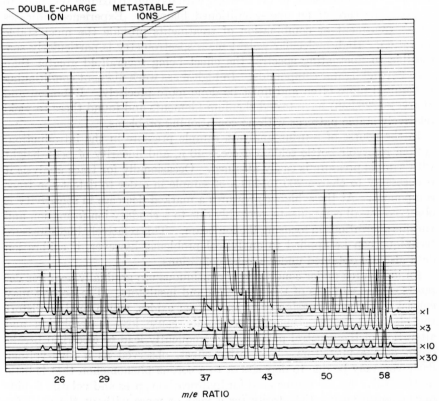

Fig. 40.22. The mass spectrum of n-butane, as recorded by the Consolidated model 21-103 spectrometer. Simultaneous tracings by galvanometers of different sensitivities provide a dynamic range up to 30,000 in this instance.

that all observed peaks can be correctly associated with their true integral mass. In practice, experienced personnel soon learn to recognize characteristic patterns without the need for markers. *n*-Butane, for example, has its most intense ions at odd-numbered masses, and this is generally true of all mass spectra. Other factors of value in assigning mass values are: (*1*) the range covered by a particular scan is fixed by operating variables of the spectrometer and (*2*) regions exist where no ions can possibly occur.

Fig. 40.23. An analog-digital converter to record automatically the peak heights as digital values, the Consolidated Electrodynamics Corporation's "Mascot."

Hydrocarbons, for example, yield no ions in mass regions 18 to 23, 32 to 35, and 46 to 47, other than weak metastable and doubly charged ions.

Galvanometers of variable sensitivity are used to provide a fairly wide dynamic range in the measurement of peak intensities. To obtain ion intensities from a record such as shown for n-butane, peak heights are measured by taking the difference between the top of each peak and its base line. This difference is then multiplied by a sensitivity factor to place each peak height on a common basis. The 58 peak, accordingly, would be equal to $(91.3 - 11.0) \times 3 = 240.9$ units, and the mass 43 ion would be $(64.7 - 2.7) \times 30 = 1860$ units. The galvanometer factors are 3 and 30, respectively.

Manual reading of mass spectral records is a tedious task when a large number of peaks are to be measured. This is a serious problem in laboratories where a large number of analyses are carried out and in the past could only be handled by a sizable computing staff. Some relief has appeared in recent years with the manufacture of analog to digital converters (79,100). These units are connected directly to the output of spectrometers and permit peak heights to be recorded as digital values, which are automatically printed or punched into cards or paper tape (80,151). Equipment of this type, such as the Consolidated Mascot (Fig. 40.23) (78), is in the process of being refined and its application extended to cover wider mass ranges.

2. Calibration-Compound Data Library

In common with the general problem of identifying unknown substances, mass spectrometer workers are dependent upon a ready source of reference spectra. Some laboratories have worked diligently to build up a library of spectra and have been quite successful in providing much of the data they require. Ideally, of course, it is desirable to distribute spectra among laboratories so as to provide data to all the workers in the field. Project 44 of the American Petroleum Institute has taken a major step in this direction by distributing 1500 spectra to industrial, government, and academic laboratories.

Project 44 is primarily concerned with compounds of known purity. As a result, many spectra of potential value are not publishable by this agency. To augment Project 44 in this respect, a catalog of uncertified spectra is being assembled by a working group in Subcommittee 4 of ASTM Committee E-14 on Mass Spectrometry. Within the next few years participating laboratories in this effort undoubtedly will increase their reference libraries by many hundreds of spectra.

3. Methods for Calculation of Analysis

The fundamentals of mass spectral calculations were developed by Washburn and his co-workers (288,289). An additional explanation of the calculation procedure is offered by Brewer and Dibeler (46). The primary requisites for the success of these methods are (1) contributions to each peak are additive for all components present in the mixture, (2) spectra are reproducible within ±1 relative per cent, (3) sensitivities of all components (ion current per unit of partial pressure) are constant relative to one another, and (4) spectra of individual components differ markedly from one another for at least one ion mass. When these conditions are met, ion currents of a given mixture can be expressed mathematically as follows:

$$i_{11}p_1 + i_{12}p_2 + i_{13}p_3 + \ldots + i_{1n}p_n = I_1$$
$$i_{21}p_1 + i_{22}p_2 + i_{23}p_3 + \ldots + i_{2n}p_n = I_2$$
$$i_{31}p_1 + i_{32}p_2 + i_{33}p_3 + \ldots + i_{3n}p_n = I_3$$
$$\vdots$$
$$i_{m1}p_1 + i_{m2}p_2 + i_{m3}p_3 + \ldots + i_{mn}p_n = I_m$$

where i_{mn} is the ion current at mass m due to component n, p_n is the partial pressure of component n, and I is the ion current at mass m in the mixture spectrum. Solution of these simultaneous equations leads to partial-pressure values that are then normalized to 100%.

In practice i_{mn} values are expressed as sensitivities, i.e., peak height per unit pressure of component. Furthermore, I_m's are related directly to peak heights that are used as measured for a given mixture. An alternative procedure is to employ pattern coefficients in place of sensitivities where pattern coefficients are relative peak heights for a given component based on a reference peak being 1. In this case, a solution to the equations yields component peak heights. Prior to normalization these peak values must be converted to partial pressures by calculating the ratio of component peak height to sensitivity.

Mixtures consisting of mass isomers generally can be calculated only by an appropriate set of simultaneous equations. In numerous instances not all of the components are mass isomers and, in such cases, some of the components can be determined from ions that are unique or that can be obtained as residuals. A residual peak is the value of a peak intensity after the contributions of other known compounds have been mathematically subtracted from its original value. The use of this technique and the method of simultaneous equation solution is illustrated by the following calculation of a hydrocarbon sample containing C_4 paraffins, mono-olefins, and a small concentration of propane.

The calibration spectra of the components in this mixture are tabulated in Table 40.IV as fractional pattern coefficients. The mixture spectrum and results of the calculation are shown in Table 40.V.

TABLE 40.IV
Calibration Spectra for Analysis of C_3–C_4 Hydrocarbon Mixture

m/e	Propane	n-Butane	Isobutane	Isobutene	1-Butene	2-Butene (av. cis and trans)
39	0.749	0.171	0.225	0.519	0.405	0.386
40	0.105	0.025	0.034	0.119	0.071	0.068
41	0.494	0.308	0.420	1.00	1.00	1.00
42	0.226	0.126	0.330	0.036	0.035	0.032
43	0.884	1.00	1.00	0.002	0.001	0.001
44	1.00[a]	0.0329	0.0329	0	0	0
55		0.011	0.005	0.164	0.182	0.223
56		0.008	0.004	0.429	0.372	0.463
57		0.025	0.030	0.018	0.017	0.022
58		0.126	0.026	—	—	—
Sensitivity of base peak (underlined)	14.7	67.3	76.3	61.1	58.6	53.1

[a] Monoisotopic peak.

1. Propane is first calculated by using the mass 44 mixture peak. To do this, note that butenes contribute very slightly to ions of this mass so that no correction need be made for their presence. Butanes have essentially the same fractional contribution because, in butanes, mass 44 ions are primarily due to the presence of heavy isotopes of hydrogen or carbon in what are normally mass 43 ions. It will also be observed that propane possesses an ion of mass 43. To allow for this, the propane calibration at mass 44 is precorrected for this same isotopic effect. The propane peak is then calculated according to the equation, m/e 44 − m/e 43 × 0.0329, or 84.6 − 1570 × 0.0329 = 32.9 (propane at mass 44).

2. The contribution of propane at all other peaks is next calculated as shown in column 3, Table 40.V. Normal and isobutane are next solved by using two simultaneous equations based on peaks at masses 43 and 58, as shown below. Prior to using the 43 peak it must first be lowered by the

TABLE 40.V

Calculation of a C_3–C_4 Hydrocarbon Mixture—Contributions of Component

m/e	Mixture spectrum	Propane	n-Butane	Isobutane	Isobutene	1-Butene	2-Butene	Residual spectrum
39	736	24.6	155.6	141.7	173.3	155.9	81.4	+3.5
40	128	3.4	22.7	21.4	39.7	27.3	14.3	−0.8
41	1491	16.2	280.2	264.6	334.0	385.0	211.0	
42	364	7.4	114.6	207.9	12.0	13.5	6.8	+1.8
43	1570	29.1	909.7	629.9	0.7	0.4	0.2	
44	84.6	32.9^a	29.9	20.7	0	0	0	
55	185		10.0	3.1	54.8	70.1	47.0	
56	394		7.3	2.5	143.3	143.2	97.7	
57	58.4		22.7	18.9	6.0	6.5	4.6	−0.3
58	131		114.6	16.4				
P_n		2.24	13.52	8.26	5.47	6.57	3.97	Σ40.03
Mole %		5.6	33.8	20.6	13.7	16.4	9.9	Σ100.0

^{a} Monoisotopic peak.

size of the propane contribution at this location, i.e., $1570 - 29.1 = 1540.9$. (For these calculations butane is abbreviated as B; butene as Bu.)

$$1.00\ n\text{-B} + 1.00\ \text{iso-B} = 1540.9\ (m/e = 43)$$
$$0.126\ n\text{-B} + 0.026\ \text{iso-B} = 131.\ \ (m/e = 58)$$

$$n\text{-B} = 909.7\ (n\text{-butane})$$
$$\text{iso-B} = 629.9\ (\text{isobutane})$$

3. Butane contributions are next determined as shown in columns 4 and 5. Residual peaks at masses 41, 55, and 56 are then combined with the butene calibration coefficients to form three simultaneous equations.

$$1.00\ \text{iso-Bu} + 1.00\ 1\text{-Bu} + 1.00\ 2\text{-Bu} = 930.0\ (m/e = 41)$$
$$0.164\ \text{iso-Bu} + 0.182\ 1\text{-Bu} + 0.223\ 2\text{-Bu} = 171.9\ (m/e = 55)$$
$$0.429\ \text{iso-Bu} + 0.372\ 1\text{-Bu} + 0.463\ 2\text{-Bu} = 384.2\ (m/e = 56)$$

Solution of these equations yields the following values:

$$\text{iso-Bu} = 334.0\ (\text{isobutene})$$
$$1\text{-Bu} = 385.0\ (1\text{-butene})$$
$$2\text{-Bu} = 211.0\ (2\text{-butene})$$

4. As a check on the accuracy of the over-all solution, residual peaks are calculated at masses 39, 40, 42, and 57. The small residuals indicate a satisfactory resolution of the components in the mixture.

5. Partial pressures are next computed by dividing the base peaks by the sensitivities listed in Table 40.IV. These pressures are normalized to 100% to give the composition shown in the bottom row of the table.

4. Solution of Simultaneous Equations

Most mass spectrometric methods involve the solution of matrices containing 6 to 30 simultaneous equations. Determinants or the method of substitition readily used in the case of two or three simultaneous equations become unwieldy for a larger number of equations, and recourse to other methods is therefore necessary. One such procedure that is simple, accurate, and rapid is that of Crout (64), in which a desk calculator is needed. Calculations of this type are fundamental in analytical applications and for that reason are worthy of illustration at this point.

In the Crout method three matrices are dealt with, consisting of the given matrix, an auxiliary matrix, and finally the solution. As an example, consider the problem of resolving butenes as in the previous example. The given matrix is:

X_1 (isobutene)	X_2 (1-butene)	X_3 (2-butene)	M (mixture peaks)
1.00	1.00	1.00	930.0
0.164	0.182	0.223	171.9
0.429	0.372	0.463	384.2

The auxiliary matrix is next determined in the following manner and order:

1. The first column is identical with the first column of the given matrix. All other elements of the first *row* are obtained by dividing corresponding elements of the *given* matrix by the first element, viz.:

X_1	X_2	X_3	M
1.00	$\dfrac{1.00}{1.00} = 1.00$	$\dfrac{1.00}{1.00} = 1.00$	$\dfrac{930.0}{1.00} = 930.0$
0.164	—	—	—
0.429	—	—	—

2. Draw a diagonal through A_{nn} elements as shown above. All other elements *on the diagonal* or *below* are equal to the corresponding element of the *given* matrix minus the sum of those products of elements in corresponding positions of its row and column of the auxiliary matrix, viz.:

X_1	X_2	X_3	M
1.00	1.00	1.00	930.0
0.164	$(0.182 - 1.00 \times 0.164 = 0.01800)$	—	
0.429	$(0.372 - 1.00 \times 0.429 = -0.05700)$	—[a]	

[a] This element cannot be calculated at this point.

3. Each element to the right of the diagonal is calculated in the same manner as in step 2, except that it is finally divided by the diagonal element in the auxiliary matrix, viz.;

X_1	X_2	X_3	M
1.00	1.00	1.00	930.00

$$0.164 \quad 0.01800 \quad \left(\frac{0.223 - 1.00 \times 0.164}{0.01800} \right. \quad \left(\frac{1719 - 930 \times 0.164}{0.01800} \right.$$

$$= 3.27777\Big) \qquad = 1076.66666 \Big)$$

$$0.429 \quad -0.05700 \quad (0.463 - 1.00 \times 0.429 \qquad \left(\begin{array}{c} 384.2 - 930 \times 0.429 - \\ 1076.66666 \times (-0.057) \\ \hline 0.22083 \end{array}\right.$$

$$-3.27777 \times (-0.057)$$

$$= 0.22083)$$

$$= 211.02205 \Big)$$

The auxiliary matrix is now complete as shown below:

X_1	X_2	X_3	M
1.00	1.00	1.00	930.00
0.16400	0.01800	3.27777	1076.66666
0.42900	-0.05700	0.22083	211.02205

The procedure for obtaining the solution as a one-column matrix is contained in the following rules.

1. The last element of the final matrix is equal to the last element in the last column of the auxiliary matrix, viz.:

$$— (X_1)$$

$$— (X_2)$$

$$211.02205 \ (X_3)$$

2. Other elements are equal to the corresponding element of the last column of the *auxiliary* matrix minus the sum of the products obtained by multiplying each element of the *final* matrix by the corresponding element in its row of the *auxiliary* matrix.

$$X_2 = 1076.66666 - 211.02205 \times 3.27777 = 384.98492$$

$$X = 930.0 - 211.02205 \times 1.00 - 384.98492 \times 1.00 = 333.99303$$

It will be noted that the final solution corresponds with that given in the calculation of the preceding C_3–C_4 hydrocarbon mixture. It usually is desirable to check the accuracy of such a calculation, and this can be done by substitution into the given equations. A more desirable check is one in which calculations are checked while in progress. This can be done by a check column written at the right of the given matrix, each element in this column being the sum of the elements in the corresponding row of the matrix. Elements in the check column are calculated in the same manner as the last column of the matrix involved. These columns provide a check because:

1. Any element in the check column of the *auxiliary* matrix is equal to one plus the sum of other elements in the row that lies to the right of the diagonal.

2. Any element in the check column of the *final* matrix is equal to one plus the sum of all other elements in its row.

As examples, consider the calculation of check elements in the first row of the *auxiliary* matrix, viz.:

$$\frac{933.0}{1.00} = 933.0$$

and in the second row of the *final* matrix, viz.:

$$1080.94444 - (212.02206)(3.27777) = 385.98489$$

Matrix solutions of the preceding type are usually used in developing a calculation procedure and in cases in which a limited number of samples is to be analyzed. When a given set of calibrations is to be applied to a large number of samples containing the same components it is expedient to first calculate a *reciprocal* or *inverse* matrix. Such a matrix can be calculated by using a scheme similar to but somewhat more complicated than that already described. Details of this calculation are beyond the scope of the present discussion but are adequately described by Daigle and Young (66).

The advantage of this approach is in the simplicity of solution. The inverse coefficients can be multiplied by appropriate peak heights to yield products that, in turn, are added together to give component peak heights or partial pressures directly. The inverse solution to the butene matrix is:

	M_{41}	M_{55}	M_{56}
X_1 (isobutene) =	0.3294	−22.8927	+10.3146
X_2 (1-butene) =	4.9650	+ 8.5529	−14.8430
X_3 (2-butene) =	−4.2944	+14.3398	+ 4.5284

where X_1, X_2, and X_3 are peak heights due to isobutene, 1-butene, and 2-butene, respectively. M_{41}, M_{55}, and M_{56} refer to mixture peak values at ion masses 41, 55, and 56. Calculation of the respective components is carried out in the following manner:

$$X_1 = (0.3294)(930.0) + (-22.8927)(171.9) +$$
$$(10.3146)(384.2) = 333.9562$$
$$X_2 = (4.9650)(930.0) + (8.5529)(171.9) +$$
$$(-14.8430)(384.2) = 385.0129$$
$$X_3 = (-4.2944)(930.0) + (14.3398)(171.9) +$$
$$(4.5284)(384.2) = 211.0309$$

5. Role of Digital Computers

In the past, mass spectrometric calculations performed on a desk calculator have been time consuming, a situation that has created a serious bottleneck to rapid analysis. For this reason, considerable effort was directed toward building computing devices to do calculations rapidly and accurately. The first computers were analog types that could handle up to 12 simultaneous equations. Such computers were of substantial help but were generally too slow and restricted in use. Subsequently, medium-sized digital computers, such as the IBM 650, were employed by laboratories with large sample loads.

The impact of computers in mass spectrometry has been sensational. These machines are ideally suited to obtain a quick solution to large systems of simultaneous equations (179) or for using previously prepared inverse equations (185). As a result, analyses that formerly required one or more hours of calculation time now can be accomplished in 1 or 2 minutes (51,103a,137,155a,195). In many laboratories computers have taken over the work previously done by several men. Usually this requires a relatively small proportion of available time on a given computer, although in some instances machines are used solely for these calculations.

IV. USES OF MASS SPECTROMETRY

Mass spectrometer analysis of organic mixtures is generally directed toward the determination of either individual compounds or classes of compounds. The method of spectral interpretation distinguishes compounds through an orderly selection of key peaks and, hence, is readily adaptable to the analysis of members of a homologous series. Hydrocarbons of a given class but of varying molecular weight, for example, produce parent peaks in "clusters" that recur every 14 mass units, representing a CH_2 group in the carbon chain. For this reason the hydrocarbon spectra are amenable to systematic treatment and yield reliable quantitative data in most instances. Organic mixtures containing numerous functional groups present more difficulty and require a greater amount of calibration and correlation work as compared to hydrocarbons. Gradually, through the efforts of McLafferty (183), Friedel (93), and others, methods are becoming available to handle a number of classes or organic compounds containing oxygen, sulfur, and nitrogen.

Inorganic mass analysis has been in widespread use on a private basis for many years although it is only recently that commercial instruments have become available. In sharp contrast to organic analysis the determination of the elements and their isotopes is largely an instrumental problem requiring little spectral interpretation. Identification of masses is rendered easy by noting the isotopic abundances or existence of the single, double, and triple charged ions.

A. EVALUATION OF MASS ANALYSIS

The well-balanced laboratory equipped with up-to-date optical and mass spectrometers is faced with the problem of optimum utilization of these instruments. In order to place the mass spectrometer in its correct perspective, a critical appraisal of its performance in relation to the other instruments is highly desirable. An evaluation of the gas-type mass spectrometer devoted to organic mixture analysis points out the following advantages and limitations.

1. Advantages

1. Only a small sample size, of 0.1 ml. of gas or 0.0005 ml. of liquid, is required for a normal analysis. With special techniques, such as temporarily closing off the vacuum system (224), much smaller samples can be placed within the ion source and analyzed satisfactorily.

2. Trace impurities often can be determined directly by increasing the size of the sample by a factor of 10 and using the highest output from a stable vibrating-reed amplifier or electron multiplier.   In another procedure, prior separations can further reduce the limit of detection to the parts per billion range.

3. Qualitative variations resulting from sample impurities or unexpected components can be spotted by the experienced computer operator almost immediately.

4. Although quantitative calculation of unknown complex samples can be laborious, routine analyses are amenable to automatization by data reduction and computing devices.

5. Molecular-weight ranges of compounds and compound types may be calculated.

6. Generally the accuracy of analysis is within a few tenths of 1%.   This is usually better than that obtained with conventional physical and chemical methods.

7. Internal checks to confirm the validity of results may be made by computing values for mixture peaks not included in the matrix solution.

8. Although the initial cost of the large general-purpose instrument is high, the sample output of 1000 to 1500 samples per month provides accurate analyses at low cost.   In addition, there are smaller, inexpensive instruments available of limited applicability, which can accomplish a great deal of work in the low molecular weight range.

9. The mass spectrometer is so versatile that new techniques are being perfected continuously.   In recent years, for example, outstanding work has been done to develop low-voltage ionization, high-resolution measurement, and chemical conversion techniques.

2. Limitations

1. Research chemists are constantly seeking the maximum information concerning important samples.   Because of the complexity of many samples, the mass spectrometer cannot always provide a complete analysis by itself.   Isomeric compounds cannot be resolved as completely as desired in many cases.   Organic mixtures often are too complex for positive interpretation.

2. Sample volatility is a definitely limiting factor with the gas type of spectrometer. Liquid or plastic materials boiling above 600°C. cannot be handled with heated inlet systems presently in use.   Whereas crucible heaters permit running some heavy materials on a nonroutine basis, other techniques such as use of the ion-emission or spark source in a solids-type instrument may be required.

3. High molecular weight organic compounds may be subjected to thermal decomposition at temperatures required for vaporization in the heated inlet system.   Many sulfur, nitrogen, and oxygenated compounds as well as certain hydrocarbons fall in this category.

4. To operate efficiently, the general-purpose instrument requires a sizable central organization.   These functions include operation, maintenance, computation facility, and competent supervision.

3. Combination with Other Methods

In view of the limitations cited above, it is obvious that other means of analysis may be used to great advantage to supplement the mass analysis. The well-integrated laboratory has learned through wide experience that each analytical tool possesses certain inherent strengths and weaknesses. Rather than allowing the various instruments to operate competitively, it was found that each can be used to complement the others through a systematic application to particular tasks.

The infrared spectrometer serves as one of the most effective adjuncts to the mass instrument. In fact, in certain chemical applications, the reverse situation may exist wherein the mass serves as the adjunct to the infrared. Regardless of the role of each instrument in a particular laboratory, however, it was found that each method invariably assists the other in analyzing complex mixtures. The strength of the infrared spectrometer lies in its ability to (1) distinguish functional groups in organic compounds regardless of molecular weight, (2) determine structural isomers such as ortho, meta, and para substituents on aromatic rings and various cis-trans isomers, and (3) help deduce molecular structure by a summation of various absorptions due to CH_2, CH_3, etc.

Similarly the ultraviolet spectrometer has been of value in the examination of polycyclic hydrocarbons and aromatic sulfur compounds. A combination of mass–ultraviolet techniques has been used by Lumpkin and Johnson for the analysis of the aromatic portion of gas oil (170), and Gordon, Moore, and Muller have determined numerous polycyclic aromatic structures in a heavily cracked gas oil (109) by conventional and low-voltage mass and ultraviolet spectrometry. Aczel et al. (13e) and Bartz et al. (22a) characterized the structures of aromatics in light cycle stock by mass and other spectrometric techniques.

Nuclear magnetic resonance spectroscopy is a field of rapidly expanding applications. Its principal use has been in structural studies of relatively pure substances. NMR spectrometers have steadily advanced in quality and capability, and Williams indicates that such instruments can be of much value in determining structure and composition of multicomponent mixtures (301).

Gas chromatography recently has been developed to a high degree as a rapid and simple method of analysis. It possesses a very high efficiency of separation and is capable of yielding accurate results at least as good as those of other methods. Because of the many kinds of column packing and operating conditions employed, each apparatus must be calibrated individually with pure compounds or known mixtures. For this reason, its principal utility is for quantitative analysis of known constituents on a repetitive basis. In this capacity it has taken over much of the work load formerly carried by the mass spectrometer, particularly for routine gas analysis. Higher molecular samples in the liquid range also can be handled if each of the components is known and properly calibrated. However, unknown components cannot be identified qualitatively by gas chromatography alone. The mass spectrometer, infrared, and other methods offer secondary means for analyzing these unknown fractions. The union of the mass spectrometer and gas chromatography (75,105,132) comprises a powerful tool that is unexcelled at the present time for identifying a multitude of components in complex mixtures boiling below about 250°C. Waldron has listed the relative merits of infrared, mass, and gas chromatographic techniques (278).

In addition to gas chromatography, other methods of separation are useful for extending the applications of mass spectrometry through the preparation of pure calibration compounds and for simplifying a gross mixture prior to analysis. Liquid-phase chromatography is particularly effective for separating classes of compounds from each other. Liquid thermal diffusion tends to differentiate the cyclic compounds from the acyclic. Other useful techniques include distillation, extraction, crystallization, and chemical treatment. The advantage of separations lies in simplifying the mass spectrum to enable an unambiguous interpretation to be carried out. For example, a systematic program of separations and mass–infrared–ultraviolet spectrometry has provided an analysis of petroleum catalytic-cracked naphtha in which 92 individual hydrocarbons were identified and determined (190).

B. CORRELATION OF MASS SPECTRA

The value of the mass spectrometer in the qualitative analysis of organic compound mixtures is widely recognized. Unique properties of mass spectra, such as ion masses and intensities as well as the various types of ions, provide information that an experienced analyst can use in deciphering the mass spectrum of an unknown mixture. Successful interpretation thus is closely related to a knowledge of compound behavior. In order to provide workers in the field with this information, a large number of studies has been carried out. These studies pertain to correlations observed in the spectra of compounds according to type, as will be described.

In this discussion ion intensities are represented as relative values compared with the base or most intense peak in a spectrum. The manner in which dissociation occurs in a given molecule is presented as illustrated below.

$$CH_3-CH\!-\!\!\!\!\!+\!\!\!-CH_3^+$$
$$\begin{array}{cc} | & \\ CH_3 & + H \\ \end{array}$$
$$\text{mass} = 16$$

This indicates that isobutane forms a CH_4^+ ion of mass 16. This is a rearrangement process.

$$C_2H_5 \!-\!|\!-\! O\!-\!C_2H_5^+$$
$$mass = 45$$

This indicates that diethyl ether forms an $OC_2H_5^+$ ion of mass 45.

This scheme depicts the valence bonds that apparently are broken, as determined by observing a given class of compounds. Correlation studies usually are empirical in nature, so that on occasion errors may occur in designating the actual valence-bond cleavages. However, the identification of the positive ions would be unaffected in such cases. Because of this uncertainty in the dissociation mechanism, logical atoms in rearrangement processes are generally not shown unless this is justified by labeled molecule studies.

1. Hydrocarbons

a. ALIPHATIC PARAFFINS

No formal study has been published dealing with paraffin spectra as a class. API Project 44 has published spectra of at least 150 different paraffins covering a carbon number range of C_1 to C_{44} (15c). In general, the

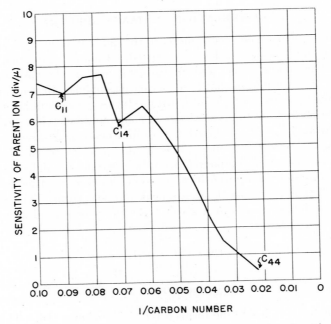

Fig. 40.24. Variation of n-paraffin parent-ion intensities with molecular weight.

most intense ions of all such hydrocarbons occur in the C_2 to C_6 mass range having an empirical formula, C_nH_{2n+1}. These ions would accordingly appear at masses 29, 43, 57, 71, and 85. C_1 to C_5 compounds possess fairly abundant parent ions. Higher molecular weight paraffins, on the other hand, have less intense parent ions and these, in turn, vary inversely with the degree of branching. Normal paraffins all show a peak at the molecular weight mass, whereas monomethyl or more highly branched structures possess weak ions or none at all (210). The graph in Fig. 40.24 shows the gradual decline of parent-ion intensities for n-paraffins over the C_{10} to C_{44} range. Coggeshall (58b) has made a study of the quantitative relationships existing in the normal paraffin spectra. Beynon *et al.* employed isotopically labeled compounds in their investigation of fragmentation in long-chain paraffins (34c).

One general observation has been made that is applicable to C_8 and heavier compounds having one substituent along the carbon chain. This type of compound has the formula,

$$R_1-C-R_3$$
$$|$$
$$R_2$$

Cleavage is favored at the bonds around the substituted carbon atom.

Fragmentation at such bonds in each instance results in a pair of noticeable ions at adjacent masses. Thus, 9-n-butyldocosane dissociates to form the following ions:

$$C_4-C^+ \quad , \text{ also } C_4-C^+ \text{— minus H}$$
$$|\qquad\qquad\qquad |$$
$$C_8 \qquad\qquad\qquad C_8$$
$$\text{mass} = 183 \qquad\qquad \text{mass} = 182$$

$$C_4-C-C_{13} \longrightarrow C_4-C-C_{13}^+, \text{ also } C_4-C-C_{13}^+ \text{ minus H}$$
$$|\qquad\qquad\qquad\qquad |\qquad\qquad\qquad\qquad |$$
$$C_8 \qquad\qquad\qquad\qquad C_8 \qquad\qquad\qquad\qquad$$
$$\text{mass} = 253 \qquad\qquad \text{mass} = 252$$

$$-C-C_{13}^+ \quad , \text{ also } -C-C_{13}^+ \text{ minus H}$$
$$|\qquad\qquad\qquad\quad |$$
$$C_8 \qquad\qquad\qquad C_8$$
$$\text{mass} = 309 \qquad\qquad \text{mass} = 308$$

This mechanism is quite selective and, consequently, fairly intense peaks of this nature are frequently seen in paraffin spectra. In such cases fairly positive structure assignments can be made. Typical behavior of isoparaffins is illustrated by the data in Table 40.VI, in which peak intensities are tabulated for a number of hydrocarbons in the C_{26} region. For comparative purposes sensitivities also are included for the peak summations, Σ 43, 57 and Σ 71, 85, which include the most intense peaks in paraffinic spectra.

TABLE 40.VI. Observed Sensitivities for Some Aliphatic Paraffins of General Formula $R_1\text{—}\underset{R_2}{C}\text{—}R_3$ ($R_3 \geq R_2 \geq R_1$)

Compound	Σ43,57 Sensitivity div./μ	Σ71,85 Sensitivity div./μ	$R_1\text{—}\underset{R_2}{C}\text{—}$ Mass	Sens. div./μ	$R_1\text{—}C\text{—}R_3$ Mass	Sens. div./μ	$\text{—}\underset{R_2}{C}\text{—}R_3$ Mass	Sens. div./μ
$n\text{-}C_{26}$	224	112	—	—	—	—	—	—
$C\text{—}\underset{C}{C}\text{—}C_{21}$	237	102	43	129	323 + 322	6	323 + 322	6
$C\text{—}\underset{C_2}{C}\text{—}C_{17}$ [a]	370	110	57 + 56	248	267 + 266	28	281 + 280	1
$C_2\text{—}\underset{C_2}{C}\text{—}C_{21}$	206	104	71 + 70	113	337 + 336	51	337 + 336	51
$C_4\text{—}\underset{C_4}{C}\text{—}C_{17}$	157	88	127 + 126	29	309 + 308	24	309 + 308	24
$C_6\text{—}\underset{C_6}{C}\text{—}C_{15}$	214	105	183 + 182	36	309 + 308	41	309 + 308	41
$C_4\text{—}\underset{C_8}{C}\text{—}C_{13}$	222	111	183 + 182	30	253 + 252	20	309 + 308	23
$C_4\text{—}\underset{C_{10}}{C}\text{—}C_{11}$	290	144	211 + 210	35	225 + 224	32	309 + 308	31
$C_5\text{—}\underset{C_{10}}{C}\text{—}C_{10}$	269	133	225 + 224	60	225 + 224	60	295 + 294	28

[a] This compound was run under ion-source conditions conducive to greater dissociation than for other compounds listed in the table. Sensitivity of Σ71,85 was arbitrarily reduced from 172 to 110, and all other sensitivities for this compound were reduced by the ratio $110/172 = 0.64$.

b. CYCLOPARAFFINS

Cycloparaffins are similar to aliphatic paraffins in that a relatively large number of abundant ions occur. Fragments are formed as a result of multiple cleavage of the ring along with secondary loss of hydrogen atoms so that ion masses correspond with alkenyl groups. In this respect cycloparaffinic spectra differ from those of aliphatic paraffins, in which intense alkyl group ions are present.

These hydrocarbons also dissociate in a manner related to the branching of the molecule. Thus, rings that have only methyl groups as substituents form fairly intense ions as the result of demethylation. Longer-chain substituents show an even stronger tendency to dealkylate and form a pair of ions, one corresponding in mass with that of the cyclic group and the other being one mass unit lower due to the further loss of a hydrogen atom. This mechanism is as follows:

$$\overset{+}{\boxed{S}} \!\!-\!\!\!\!\mid\!\!-R \qquad \text{and} \qquad \overset{+}{\boxed{S}} \!\!-\!\!\!\!\mid\!\!-R$$
$$\text{mass} = 83 \qquad\qquad\qquad\qquad -H$$
$$\text{mass} = 82$$

Another characteristic behavior observed is that a ternary carbon on a ring results in a major ion originating from the substituent itself. *tert*-Butylcyclohexane, for example, has a major ion of mass 56 not found in the spectrum of other butylcyclohexanes. This ion presumably arises from the dissociation:

$$\boxed{S}\!\!-\!\!\!\!\mid\!\!-\overset{\overset{\displaystyle CH_3}{|}}{\underset{\underset{\displaystyle CH_3}{|}}{C}}\!\!-CH_3$$
$$-H$$
$$\text{mass} = 56$$

c. MONO-OLEFINS

A study of mono-olefinic hydrocarbon spectra has shown the principal ion to be quite predictable (49). As would be anticipated, these compounds tend to rupture at the carbon–carbon bond, which is located beta to the double bond. When this occurs, the fragment containing the double bond usually becomes a positive ion. For example, 1-heptene dissociates to form its base peak at mass 41, as shown:

$$H_2C{=}CHCH_2{}^+\!\!-\!\!\!\!\mid\!\!-C_4H_9$$
$$\text{mass} = 41$$

An exception to this behavior occurs when a branched carbon is located beta to the double bond, such as in 4-methyl-1-pentene:

$$H_2C{=}CHCH_2{-}\!|\!{-}CHCH_3^+$$
$$| $$
$$CH_3$$
$$mass = 43$$

The positive ion originates from the saturate portion of the molecule.

A rearrangement process takes over in the case of molecules of the general structure, $C{=}C{-}C{-}C_n$. Dissociation occurs to form a mass 56 ion, as

$$| $$
$$C$$

indicated below:

$$H_2C{=}C{-}CH_2^+{-}\!|\!{-}C_n$$
$$+H \quad CH_3$$
$$mass = 56$$

By considering these and other observations it was possible to formulate rules for ion formation in olefins. These are:

1. Dissociation will occur at all C—C bonds that are beta to a double bond. As a rule, however, no given carbon is involved in more than one C—C rupture.

a. When dissociation occurs, that part of the molecule containing the double bond usually becomes a positive ion. In these cases hydrogen atoms add to positive ions according to the formula $n - 1$, where n is the number of C—C bonds broken.

b. A linear molecule of the formula $C{=}C{-}C{-}C_n$ normally has its most abundant ion at mass 41. When C_n is a whole number of 5 or 6, however, mass 43 ions are approximately 15% more abundant than 41 ions.

c. When a tertiary or ternary carbon is gamma to the double bond, the positive ion consists of the saturated part of the molecule.

d. An ion of mass 56 will be the most abundant ion for compounds of the structures.

$$C{=}C{-}C{-}C_n \quad \text{and} \quad C{=}C{-}C{-}C{-}C{-}C_n$$
$$| \qquad\qquad\qquad\qquad\qquad\qquad\quad |$$
$$C \qquad\qquad\qquad\qquad\qquad\qquad\quad C$$

2. An exception to these rules occurs for the structure

$$\qquad\qquad\quad H$$
$$H_2C{=}C{-}\!-\!C{-}R$$
$$| \quad\; |$$
$$CH_3 \; CH_3$$

In these cases cleavage occurs at the alpha C—C bond to give a base peak consisting of the fragment containing the double bond. These rules may not apply as rigorously to higher molecular weight olefins because of the decreasing effect of the double bond as the molecule increases in size.

Major ions were predicted for 44 C_6 to C_{15} mono-olefins using these rules and favorable results were obtained. In 29 compounds (66%) the predicted ion was the most abundant one; in 12 cases it was the second most abundant; and in only three cases was the predicted ion of lesser intensity.

d. ALKYLBENZENES

Meyerson (194) has carried out an elegant study of dissociation in 84 alkylbenzenes. He finds that the principal ions result from cleavage of bonds beta to the benzene ring. The only exceptions to this occur in polymethyl and polyethyl benzenes, in which breakage of the alpha bond is generally predominant. In both instances the fragment containing the benzene ring usually becomes the positive ion. Fairly intense parent ions are usually observed in this class of hydrocarbons.

Monoalkylbenzenes of the general structure ΦCH_2R form the two highest peaks in their spectrum by simple cleavage and rearrangement, as:

$$\langle \bigcirc \rangle - CH_2^+ - | - R$$
$$\text{mass} = 91$$

$$\langle \bigcirc \rangle - CH_2^+ - | - R$$
$$+H$$
$$\text{mass} = 92$$

These ions increase in abundance with the length of the side chain. Side chains of seven or less carbon atoms produce a 91 ion that is more intense than the 92, whereas a chain greater than eight carbons results in the 92 peak being higher than the 91. If one of the hydrogens on the alpha carbon is replaced with a methyl group, a base-peak ion at mass 105 is formed. On the other hand, if an alpha carbon has two alkyl groups equal to or greater than ethyl radicals, competition for cleavage of one beta bond occurs. A ternary alpha carbon atom also will favor rupture of one beta bond but, in addition, a rearrangement process of some kind takes place in which an abundant tolyl ion of mass 91 results. Rylander and Meyerson attribute this to a rearrangement through a cationated cyclopropane ring intermediate (232). Dissociation at the alpha bond to form a phenyl-group ion varies directly with the branchiness of the alpha carbon atom, but in all cases the phenyl ion of mass 77 is in the intensity range of 1 to 14% of the base peak. Monoalkylbenzenes also possess weak ions of masses 78 and 79 that apparently result from rearrangement.

Dissociation of poly-substituted benzenes tends to center in the dominant side chain that has the most or longest substituents on the alpha carbon. When all the side chains are as short as methyl, a single alpha-bond cleavage occurs. For polyethylbenzenes alpha and beta bonds break in about equal amounts to form two abundant ions. Otherwise, dissociation follows the rule stated above. Hydrocarbons commonly produce doubly charged ions of relatively weak intensity. Extensive branching on the alpha carbon atom results in greatly magnified doubly charged fragments, which appear at an apparent mass equal to one-half of the molecular weight minus 30 (equal to the loss of two methyl groups). These ions are quite useful in the identification of poly-(2 propyl-) and poly-(*tert*-butyl-) benzenes.

Meyerson (194) discusses other spectral characteristics that are beyond the scope of this text. In addition, a systematic and complete identification scheme is outlined for the benefit of the reader. It is also to be pointed out that the rules governing dissociation of alkylbenzenes apply to other benzene derivatives and nonhydrocarbons.

2. Oxygenated Compounds

a. ALCOHOLS

Friedel, Shultz, and Sharkey studied 67 alcohols in the C_1 to C_{11} molecular weight range (97). They conclude that for correlation purposes it is necessary to subclassify some of the three general alcohol types. According to their classification the primary group consists of (1) normal straight chain and γ, δ, etc. branched, and (2) β-branched structures. Secondary alcohols are as such, with tertiary alcohols subclassified as (1) partly symmetrical (dimethyl, diethyl, etc.), and (2) unsymmetrical. The following sections are based primarily on this work, although some data reported by Brown *et al.* (53) on C_{10} to C_{36} primary alcohols also has been included.

(1) Primary Alcohols

(a) *Normal, Gamma, and Delta Branched*

Base ions in this class of compounds are formed by cleavage of the various carbon–carbon bonds, as shown:

C_1–C_4 R—$\vert$—CH_2OH^+ mass = 31

C_5–C_6 $\begin{array}{c} R^+—\vert—CH_2CH_2OH \\ -H \text{ or } -2H \end{array}$ mass = 41, 42, or 56

C_7–C_{36} $\begin{array}{c} C_3H_7{}^+—\vert—(CH_2)_nOH \\ \text{as is or } -2H \end{array}$ mass = 41 or 43, generally 41

These compounds are not highly specific in their dissociation behavior and, consequently, base-peak intensities are only slightly greater than those of other strong peaks. Exclusive of those that are base peaks, for instance, the 31 ion in other alcohols varies from 20 to 78% of the base peak. Alkenyl ions at 27, 41, 42, 55, and 56 are generally intense, as are the alkyl fragments 29 and 43.

C_4 to C_5 alcohols are rather unique in that they possess ions of 85 to 45% intensities formed by the loss of H_2O. Alcohols of all types also behave in this manner, except that the ion abundances are much less, being of the order <1 to 11% except for 2-methylbutanol, which forms a 36% ion in this manner. Parent ions are fairly abundant for C_1 to C_3 compounds but decrease rapidly in intensity until C_7's and heavier show no detectable parent ions.

(b) Beta Branched

Beta-branched primary alcohols have C_2 to C_4 alkyl fragments as base peaks that occur because of cleavage at the α, β, and β, γ carbon atoms,

$$R_1 \!-\!\!\!|\!-\! CH \!-\!\!\!|\!-\! CH_2OH$$
$$\underset{R_2}{|}$$

where $R_1 \geqslant R_2$. As in the case of other primary alcohols, a number of abundant alkyl and alkenyl ions are present in most spectra. The only prominent alcohol-type peak is at mass 31, whose intensity varies from 20 to 67% of the base. Parent ions are weak or nonexistent.

Almost all alcohols of the various types possess a rearrangement ion of the constitution CH_4OH^+ (mass = 33). In most cases this particle is low in abundance. 2-Methyl-1-propanol is unusual in this respect, showing a 33 peak as 49% of the base peak.

(2) Secondary Alcohols

Secondary alcohols may be subclassified on the basis of location of the hydroxyl on the 2-, 3-, 4-, etc., carbon atom. In contrast to primary alcohols these spectra show a lesser number of prominent peaks. Base peaks can be predicted with considerable certainty according to the dissociation shown:

Type 2	$R\!-\!\!\!|\!-\!\underset{\|}{\overset{OH}{C}}HCH_3^+$	mass = 45
Type 3	$R\!-\!\!\!|\!-\!\underset{\|}{\overset{OH}{C}}HC_2H_5^+$	mass = 59
Types 4 and 5	Alkenyl fragmentation	mass = 55 or 69

The 4- and 5-type alcohols also have a strong tendency to form ions in the same way as base peaks are formed in the 2- and 3-type compounds. Fragments that occur in this way are 51 to 100% of the base in seven compounds studied. Secondary alcohols do possess parent ions of weak intensity as contrasted with primary compounds.

Rearrangement ions generally are of little prominence in these spectra. Among a number of peaks that are rearrangement fragments, one at mass 31 is fairly intense. In a secondary alcohol the 31 ion,

$$\mathrm{R_1-\!\!\!|-\!\!\!\overset{\overset{\displaystyle OH^+}{|}}{CH}-\!\!\!|\!\!\!-R_2}$$
$$+\,H$$

is formed; it differs in abundance systematically with the location of the hydroxyl group, as shown:

Type	No. of compounds	% Base
2-	9	3–8[a]
3-	9	31–60
4-	6	15–34
5-	1	10

[a] An exception is 2-butanol—21%.

(3) Tertiary Alcohols

Tertiary alcohol spectra are characterized by an even smaller number of intense peaks, most of which are readily predicted. For the general case,

$$\mathrm{R_1-\!\!\!|-\!\!\!\overset{\overset{\displaystyle R_2^+}{|}}{\underset{\underset{\displaystyle OH}{|}}{C}}-\!\!\!R_3}$$

dissociation occurs with cleavage of the largest R group. Almost all base peaks are formed in this way. Abundant ions also can result from dissociation between the central carbon atom and smaller R groups. Parent ions are hardly ever detected.

One significant type of rearrangement is observed that is similar to that noted for secondary compounds, namely,

$$\mathrm{R_1-\!\!\!|-\!\!\!\overset{\overset{\displaystyle R_2^+}{|}}{\underset{\underset{\displaystyle OH}{|}}{C}}-\!\!\!|\!\!\!-R_3}$$

$$\mathrm{mass}=45,\,59 \qquad +\,2\,H$$

b. Aldehydes

The most comprehensive study of aldehydes to date was carried out by Gilpin and McLafferty (104), who examined 20 aldehydes—13 straight-chain and seven branched-chain molecules. Aldehyde spectra are more orderly than those of alcohols, which is attributable to the more dominant affect of the polar—CHO group as contrasted with —OH in alcohols.

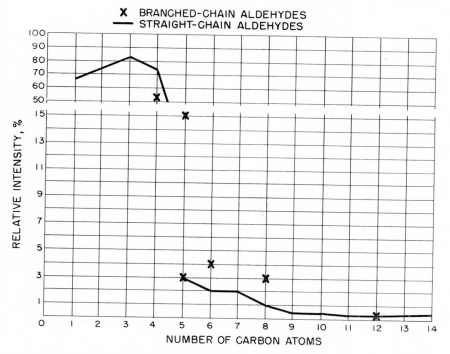

Fig. 40.25. Variation of aldehyde parent-ion intensities with molecular weight.

Parent ions, for example, were found in all aldehydes with intense peaks occurring in the C_1 to C_4 range and weak ones in heavier molecules, as shown in Figure 40.25.

Dissociation of aldehydes is characterized by cleavage of the molecule at either the alpha or beta bond, thus:

$$R \!-\!\!|\!-\! CH_2 \!-\!\!|\!-\! CHO$$

Alpha cleavage predominates only for lower molecular weights, C_1 to C_3, and usually becomes minor where beta cleavage can occur without involving the loss of a methyl group. Fragmentation at the alpha position results in a mass 29 ion of the constitution —CHO. Mass 29 ions of less intensity do appear in the spectra of higher molecular weight aldehydes, but these have been demonstrated to be C_2H_5 groups.

Breakage at the beta bond is accompanied by a rearrangement to yield a mass 44 ion as shown:

$$RCH_2CH_2 \dashv CH_2CHO^+$$
$$+ H$$
$$\text{mass} = 44$$

This mechanism accounts for the highest peak in the spectra of straight chain C_4 to C_7 aldehydes and an appreciable one (30 to 77% of the base peak) in heavier molecules. In the case of C_5 to C_{14} straight-chain compounds, cleavage of the beta bond also results in fragments having a mass equal to its molecular weight minus 44 (6 to 8% of the base peak). Such ions are highly useful in identification work. C_4 to C_{14} aldehydes also possess abundant alkyl groups at masses 43 and 57 that become base peaks for C_8 to C_{14} compounds. It is interesting to note that base peaks occur in an orderly manner as follows, C_1 to C_3 aldehydes —CHO (mass 29), C_4 to C_7 aldehydes —CH₂CHOH (mass 44), and C_8 to C_{14} aldehydes—C_3H_7 (mass 43) or —C_4H_9 (mass 57).

These aldehydes are similar to primary alcohols in forming noticeable ions by loss of water. For C_6's and heavier, these fragments are more intense than their parent peaks.

Branched aldehydes are more random in behavior, although the dominant ions for C_5 and heavier are formed by dissociation at the beta bond. Such ions may however prove to be aldehyde-type structures of mass 58 or 72 and/or alkyl fragments of mass 43 or 57. The branched aldehydes show a greater preponderance of ions from beta-bond cleavage than these straight-chain ones. As shown in Fig. 40.25, these compounds display parent ions of decreasing abundance with molecular weight.

c. KETONES

A correlation of ketone spectra has been carried out by Sharkey, Shultz, and Friedel (239), who studied 35 aliphatic ketones over the range C_3 to C_{13}. Four cyclic and three aromatic ketones also were examined. To simplify their discussion of aliphatic ketones, these investigators note that it is desirable to classify ketones as methyl, ethyl, propyl, etc., on the basis of R_1, the smaller group in R_1—CO—R_2. Prominent peaks result from both direct dissociation and rearrangement; therefore the correlation is divided into two parts according to which of the two processes above are involved.

Direct dissociation with only the loss of an electron to form a parent ion is similar to that observed for aldehydes, in that noticeable parent peaks generally occur. Thirty-three of the 35 ketones possessed such ions, whose intensities varied from 22 to 3% of the base peak in order of decreasing molecular weights. The dominant fragmentation was found to be,

$$R_1-CO^+ \dashv R_2$$

where $R_2 \geqslant R_1$. Methyl ketones all form their base peak (mass 43) in this manner. Ethyl, n-propyl, and butyl types also show intense peaks of the R_1—CO$^+$ structure that vary from base peaks to 40% of the base. For cases in which a base peak is not formed, a rearrangement ion CH$_3$CO (mass 43) generally appears as the base peak. Ketones of the isopropyl and pentyl type also show abundant R_1—CO$^+$ ions of somewhat lesser intensity. As evidence of the importance of a mass 43 ion, it serves as the base peak for 29 of the 39 ketones that were studied.

Other than the CH$_3$CO rearrangement fragment, which sometimes occurs as noted previously, all ketones show rearrangement ions that appear as pairs of even and odd masses. The even ions correspond in mass with that of lower molecular weight ketones. The odd-mass fragment is always one unit heavier than the even one and usually is much less abundant. The intensities of even-mass ions are unpredictable, as they vary from being a base peak to being less than 1% of the base. Rearrangements consist of single or double cleavage accompanied by transfer of one or two hydrogen atoms, as, for example:

$$\begin{array}{c} H \longrightarrow \\ \downarrow \\ R_2C \dashv CH_2CO\ R_1^+ \\ | \\ H \qquad \text{mass} = 58,\ 72,\ \text{or}\ 86 \end{array}$$

The four cyclic ketones behave more like hydrocarbons than aliphatic ketones in that they show strong peaks resulting from the loss of 28, 29, 42, and 43 fragments. A few rearrangement ions also were observed. Aromatic ketones, on the other hand, fragment at the carbonyl group, as do aliphatic ketones, but without rearrangements.

d. Acetals

Experience in the analysis of oxygenated compound mixtures has shown that ions frequently are encountered that obviously contain two oxygen atoms.   Two prospective types of compounds that may account for such peaks are acetals and semiacetals.   In order to provide fundamental information regarding such compounds, Friedel and Sharkey have studied typical spectra and reported on their behavior (95).   In an independent study, LeBlanc has reported some difficulty in obtaining stable acetal spectra (163).   It is concluded in this work that representative spectra can be obtained without thermal decomposition of the sample only with an ion source that has been in constant use for approximately 1 month.

Acetals that have the general formula

$$R_1 - C \begin{array}{c} H \quad OR_2 \\ \diagup \\ \diagdown \\ OR_2 \end{array}$$

where R_1 was H, CH_3, and C_2H_5, and where R_2 varied from methyl to butyl groups, were investigated by Friedel and Sharkey (95).   The R_1 groups represent formals, acetals, and propionals, respectively.   Ten compounds were examined in which preferred cleavage occurred at (1) a C—O bond with loss of —OR_2, and (2) the C—R_1 bond with loss of R_1. In these cases prominent ions are formed in the upper half of the spectrum. —OR_2 produces peaks at masses 59, 73, 87, 101, etc., and loss of —R_1 yields ions of masses 75, 89, 103, etc.   Only in the case of dimethoxy compounds, however, are base peaks formed by one or the other of these two processes.   Of interest is that a single acetal is defined by the equation

$$2 \times \text{(mass of fragment from loss of —}OR_2\text{) —}$$

$$\text{(mass of fragment from loss of —}R_2\text{)} = \text{constant}$$

The constant varies in value, being 15 for a formal, 43 for an acetal, and 71 for a propional.   This relationship can be highly useful in identification work.

Acetal spectra are further characterized either by the absence of parent ions or the presence of extremely weak ones.   They are similar to alcohols in this respect.

During the course of their work, Friedel and Sharkey examined a commercial solution of formaldehyde and observed peaks that were apparently due to the presence of hemiacetal (95).   This was explained by the presence of methanol as an inhibitor that, in solution, reacts with formaldehyde to form hemiformal, H_2C (OH) (OCH_3).   An extended study subsequently was made of several blends of different alcohols with acetaldehyde. Evidence of the presence of hemiacetals was slight, although acetals appeared to be present to approximately 0.3%. These investigators concluded that in the analysis of alcohol–aldehyde mixtures it is important to evaluate possible interference from acetals and hemiacetals. This phenomenon may be discerned by a rise in the reservoir sample pressure, followed by a gradual decline over a period of approximately one hour, corresponding with the decomposition of hemiacetal.

e. ACIDS

Spectra of several monobasic organic acids have been published. These include C_1 to C_8 straight-chain molecules in which spectra of the C_4 to C_8 compounds are similar. These are characterized by weak parent ions and a dominant rearrangement ion of mass 60. The constitution of this fragment has been demonstrated to result from the dissociation (119)

$$R-CH-\!\!\!\!|-CH_2-COOH^+$$
$$H-\!\!\!\!\underline{\qquad\qquad}\!\!\!\!\nearrow$$

mass = 60

This is the base peak in all cases and is associated with an abundant ion at mass 73 and a lesser one at 45. As is frequently the case, lower members of this series do not conform to a general pattern. Formic acid has its base at mass 29, acetic acid at 43, and propionic acid at 28.

Branching introduces the likelihood of more intense alkyl fragments, although where substitution is absent on both the alpha and beta carbon atoms fairly strong peaks also occur at mass 60. Branching on the alpha carbon may result in an intense rearrangement ion at a corresponding higher mass. 2-Ethylbutanoic acid, for example, rearranges to form an intense peak at mass 88:

$$C_2H_5-\!\!\!\!|-CH\ COOH^+$$
$$|$$
$$C_2H_5$$
$$+\ H$$

mass = 88

f. ESTERS

A study in this laboratory of spectra for more than 30 esters over a wide molecular-weight range showed them to be among the most interesting of all substances. Low molecular weight esters having C_1 to C_4 chains in the

TABLE 40.VII

Classification of Esters of C_1 to C_4 Acids and Alcohols

Ester	$R_1-O-C(=O)-R_2^+$		$R_1-O-C(=O)-R_2^+$		$R_1-O-C(=O)-R_2^+ \; +2H$		$^+R_1-O-C(=O)-R_2 \; -H$	
	Mass	Intensity, %	Mass	Intensity, %	Mass	Intensity, %	Mass	Intensity, %
Formates[a]	1	Weak	29	30–70	47[b]	1–8	28, 42, or 56	30–100
Acetates	15	15	43	100	61[b]	10–20	28, 42, or 56	4–35
Propionates	29	46–100	57	64–100	75[b]	7–32	28, 42, or 56	9–35
Butanoates	43	74–100	71	55–100	89[b]	12–51	28, 42, or 56	14–55

[a] Formates are unique in that intense ions occur at mass 31 or 45, apparently due to the rearrangement:

$$R_1 \!-\! CH_2^+ \!-\! O \!-\! C(=O) \!-\! C \!-\! H \; +H \qquad \text{or} \qquad R_1 \!-\! CO^+ \!-\! C(=O) \!-\! CH(CH_3) \; +H$$

$$\text{mass} = 31 \qquad\qquad\qquad\qquad \text{mass} = 45$$

[b] Methyl esters do not rearrange to form 47, 61, 75, or 89 ions.

alcohol and acid groups show a strong tendency to dissociate at the valence bonds:

$$ (1)\ R_1{-}O{-}\overset{\overset{\displaystyle O}{\|}}{C}{-}\!\!\{\!\!{-}R_2{}^+ \qquad (2)\ R_1{-}O{-}\!\!\{\!\!{-}\overset{\overset{\displaystyle O}{\|}}{C}{-}R_2{}^+ \qquad (3)\ R_1{-}\!\!\{\!\!{-}O{-}\overset{\overset{\displaystyle O}{\|}}{C}{-}R_2{}^+ $$

$$ + 2\,H $$

In the third instance, an intense ion also occurs having a mass equal to the alkyl group, R_1 minus one hydrogen.

Methyl to butyl esters may be classified according to the data in Table 40.VII. Inspection of these data shows that these relationships yield a wealth of information for identification purposes. Low molecular weight esters are further characterized by fairly intense parent ions for methyl and ethyl compounds, with higher molecules exhibiting little or extremely weak molecular fragments. These findings generally agree with those of Sharkey, Shultz, and Friedel, who deal with ester spectra in considerably more detail (240). Beynon, Saunders, and Williams examined 27 aliphatic esters under conditions of high resolution and generally have extended the correlation of spectra with molecular structures (34b).

Spectra of high molecular weight esters, such as ethyl tetradecanoate and a series of methyl compounds having acid groups of straight and branched chains varying in length from C_{23} to C_{32}, show a surprisingly similar mode of dissociation (17). The most intense ion observed in these compounds is generally due to the rearrangement:

$$ \underset{H}{\overset{H}{R\ C}}\!\!\{\!\!\underset{H}{\overset{H}{C}}{-}COOCH_3{}^+ \quad \text{and} \quad \underset{H}{\overset{H}{R\ C}}\!\!\{\!\!\underset{H}{\overset{H}{C}}{-}COOC_2H_5{}^+ $$

$$ + H \qquad\qquad\qquad + H $$

$$ \text{mass} = 74 \qquad\qquad\qquad \text{mass} = 88 $$

If hydrogen atoms on the beta carbon are replaced with methyl or ethyl groups, the ion mass is accordingly displaced upward by 14 or 28 units. The second most abundant ion results from simple cleavage of the C—C bond between the gamma and delta carbon atoms. This results in fragments of mass 87, 101, etc. The occurrence of intense 74 and 88 ions in these high molecular weight esters coincides with ions found by Sharkey and his co-workers in methyl and ethyl butanoates (not isobutanoates) and higher molecular weight esters (240). These investigators also report a fairly intense rearrangement ion,

$$ CH_2COO^+ $$
$$ + 2\,H $$

$$ \text{mass} = 60 $$

in the spectra of butanoates (not methyls or isobutanoates) and heavier compounds.

Ester molecules that have long-chain groups in both the acid and alcohol portions also behave in a rather unique manner. These spectra have intense ions consisting of alkyl and alkenyl groups at masses 43, 57, 71, 41, 55, and 69. In addition, an abundant fragment is formed by the same rearrangement mechanism (3) observed in low molecular weight esters. Thus, dodecyl docosanate, $C_{21}H_{43}COOC_{12}H_{25}$, and tetradecyl eicosanate, $C_{19}H_{39}COOC_{14}H_{29}$, possess the ions $C_{21}H_{43}COOH_2$ (mass 341—18% of base peak) and $C_{19}H_{39}COOH_2$ (mass 313—20% of base peak), respectively. Emery (84a) has correlated the mass spectra of seven series of aromatic esters with their molecular structures.

g. ETHERS

Studies of aliphatic ethers in this laboratory and by McLafferty (181) indicate that a regular pattern of dissociation occurs. A summary of the manner in which principal ions are formed is shown in Table 40.VIII. Ethers are classified according to the smaller R group in the general formula, R_1OR_2. Thus, when R_1 is a methyl group, the ether is termed a methyl ether. Similarly, a propyl ether is one in which R_1 is a propyl group and R_2 is a propyl or heavier alkyl group. Based on this classification some general observations seem to be valid.

Methyl ethers in all cases form a base peak according to the mechanism,

$$CH_3O - \overset{\overset{\displaystyle X}{|}}{\underset{\underset{\displaystyle Z}{|}}{C}} - Y^{+}$$

Here R_2 is represented as $\overset{\overset{\displaystyle X}{|}}{\underset{\underset{\displaystyle Z}{|}}{C}} - Y$, where $X \geqslant Y \geqslant Z$. One other prominent ionization is noted in Table 40.VIII as being a simple cleavage accompanied by the loss of two hydrogens:

$$\underset{-2H}{CH_3O} \overset{+}{{\Big|}} \overset{\overset{\displaystyle X}{|}}{\underset{\underset{\displaystyle Z}{|}}{C}} - Y$$

$$mass = 29$$

TABLE 40.VIII

Principal Dissociation Observed in Aliphatic Ethers of the Formula, $ROC-Y$, Where $C-Y \geqslant R$ and $X \geqslant Y \geqslant Z$

No. of compounds	R group	$R-O-\overset{X}{\underset{Z}{C}}-Y^{+}$	$R-O^{+}$ $-2H$	$R-\overset{X}{\underset{Z}{C}}-Y^{+}$ $+H$	$R-O-\overset{X}{\underset{Z}{\overset{+}{C}}}-Y$	Parent ion
				Peak intensity, %		
9	Methyl	100	14–79	0–17	2–57	0–56
7	Ethyl	28–100	0–32	76–100	10–40	0–30
3	n-Propyl	18–24	Low	2–59	84–100	2–7
3	Isopropyl	2–18	Low	59–100	52–100	0–3
1	n-Butyl	16	1	3	100	2
1	n-Pentyl	8	1	4	100	2
1	3-Methylbutyl	1	6	5	90	0

Ethyl ethers behave differently in that their major ion is generally due to the rearrangement

$$C_2H_5 \overset{|}{\underset{+H}{-}} O \overset{X \quad +}{\underset{Z}{-}} C - Y$$

that is, an ion of the agglomeration
$$\begin{bmatrix} H \\ | \\ (OCY) \\ | \\ Z \end{bmatrix}$$

Ethyl ethers do yield ions in the same manner as do methyl ethers, but to a lesser extent, as a rule. Propyl, butyl, and pentyl ethers exhibit an effect that is reflected in a greater preponderance of cleavage at the $-O \overset{|}{-} R_2^+$ valence bond. Typical behavior of this nature is observed in n-propyl isopropyl ether, for example:

$$C-C-C-O \overset{|}{-} \overset{+}{\underset{C}{C}} - C$$

mass = 43 (base peak)

The second most intense ion is due to the rearrangement that is most clearly associated with ethyl ethers:

$$C-C-C \overset{|}{-} O - \overset{+}{\underset{C}{C}} \overset{|}{-} C$$
$$+H \quad C$$

mass = 45

Higher molecular weight ethers are characterized by intense ions at 41, 43, 55, and 57.

Ethers, like most other compounds, have fairly abundant parent ions at low molecular weights. With branching and higher molecular weights, however, weak or undetectable parent ions occur.

McLafferty (181) reports an anomalous ion at one mass unit above the molecular weight for many ethers. Its abundance increases with sample pressure and lowered ion-repeller voltage. These are persistent low-intensity ions of value in molecular-weight determinations.

A study of olefinic ethers consisting of one alkyl and one alkenyl group showed that no rules of behavior could be postulated. This is probably due to highly competitive forces within a molecule consisting of the double bond and the C—O—C structure. An olefinic configuration favors dissociation at a beta-located single bond and C—O—C cleavages at the C—O or adjacent C—C positions.

One example of how a double bond changes the dissociation of an ether is given below by the comparison of diethyl and ethyl, vinyl ethers.

Diethyl ether		Ethyl, vinyl ether	
Peak intensity (% base peak)	Dissociation	Peak intensity (% base peak)	Dissociation
100	C—C⊣O—C⁺⊢C +H mass = 31	100	C—C⊣O—C =C⁺ +H mass = 44
47	C—C—O —C⁺⊢C mass = 59	88	C—C⊣O—C =C⁺ mass = 43
40	C—C⁺⊢O—C—C mass = 29	76	C—C⁺⊢O—C=C mass = 29
38	C—C—O⁺⊢C—C mass = 45	68	C—C—O⊣C =C⁺ mass = 27

It will be observed that ion formation in the two compounds is in extreme contrast. The rearrangement ion of mass 31, the base peak of diethyl ether, is not listed for the vinyl ether (actually mass 31 in vinyl ether amounts to 10% of its base peak). This difference may be attributed to the stability of the double bond and the manner in which it favors cleavage at a beta bond to form the three intense ions at masses 29, 43, and 44. The mass 27 ion in the vinyl ether is formed by rupture of the O—C bond despite being alpha to a double bond. It will be noted that peaks in the ethyl, vinyl ether are relatively more intense compared with its base peak than is the case for diethyl ether. This indicates less selectivity in the dissociation, as might be expected. As a matter of fact, this behavior appears to be the one rule generally applicable to these ethers.

McLafferty (183a) has made a comprehensive survey of the rearrangements occurring with vinyl derivatives.

h. Aromatic Oxygenated Compounds

Aczel and Lumpkin made a thorough study of the mass spectra of benzyl alcohols, phenols, and dihydroxyl benzenes (13b), of aromatic aldehydes and acids (13c), and of benzoate-type esters (13d).

3. Sulfur Compounds

Levy and Stahl have examined spectra of 25 mercaptans and 30 sulfides (165). Some of their findings, along with other observations, are summarized below.

a. MERCAPTANS

The masses of the principal ions are defined according to the four series: $M-14N-1$, $M-14N-6$, $M-14N-5$, and $M-14N-7$. M represents the molecular weight of the compound and N varies in increasing whole numbers, starting at $N = 0, 2, 2$, and 2 for each of the series, respectively.

Primary mercaptans having n-alkyl or branched chains with substitution at γ or higher carbon atoms possess relatively intense parent ions. For C_1 and C_2 mercaptans, parent peaks are 78 to 100% of the base peak, and their intensities diminish regularly until, for undecyl mercaptan, an intensity of 7% is observed. The most intense ions are formed differently, depending upon the molecular weight. C_1 to C_3 compounds have base peaks at 47, 62, and 47, respectively. Heavier molecules, however, are characterized by intense ions consisting of only carbon and hydrogen atoms. The most prevalent base peak occurs at 56 and 41 for low and high molecular weight compounds, respectively. Two ions, each containing a sulfur atom (CH_2SH^+, $m/e = 47$, and $C_2H_4SH^+$, $m/e = 61$), are of particular significance because they occur at an approximately constant ratio of $2:1$ in C_4 and heavier compounds.

Primary β-branched thiols also exhibit fairly abundant parent ions. Base peaks are difficult to predict, and the only generality in this respect is that they consist of alkyl or alkenyl ions. Ions predicted by the $M-14N-1$ rule, and that contain a sulfur atom, vary in intensity from 3 to 50%.

The base peaks of secondary thiols are unpredictable, although they generally consist of alkyl or alkenyl groups. Molecular weight ions are similar in intensity to those of the primary mercaptans. In the $M-14N-1$ series the most intense peak results from cleavage of the larger alkyl group, where $R_2 > R_1$.

$$R_1-\overset{\displaystyle |}{\underset{\displaystyle SH}{C}}\!\!\overset{+}{}\!\!-\!\!\!\mid\!R_2$$

Among mercaptans tertiary structures possess the least intense ions in the $M-14N-1$ series. As in secondary compounds, however, the most predominate cleavage occurs at the heaviest R group. Next in importance for this series are ions formed by splitting of all three groups with rearrangement of two hydrogen atoms. Fragment ions in the M–14N–6 series are weak. Characteristically intense ions occur in the M–14N–5 series which result from the process,

$$
R_1 - \underset{\underset{\text{SH}}{|}}{\overset{\overset{R_2}{|}}{C}} - R_3{}^+
$$

Parent ions of tertiary mercaptans are not quite as intense as in other thiols.

b. SULFIDES

Sulfides are similar to ethers in their behavior. Unlike ethers, however, they have relatively intense molecular ions, as indicated by the fact that an unbranched C_{14} sulfide has a parent-ion abundance of 20%.

Based on a study of 24 sulfide spectra published by API Project 44, an attempt has been made to summarize in Table 40.IX the noteworthy features of the spectra. According to this scheme, sulfides of the formula R_1SR_2 are classified according to the location of the sulfur atom in a chain. Subclassification is then based on the branchiness of the R_1 and R_2 groups.

Several conclusions can be made about the sulfide spectra. Parent ions are intense, and even a highly branched compound such as 2,2,4,4-tetramethyl-3-thiapentane has a noticeable molecular ion of 9%. Secondly, base peaks can be predicted with considerable certainty for some compounds but not for others. Lastly, rearrangement ions are prevalent and help to characterize these compounds.

Straight-chain 2-thia compounds form their base peak according to the dissociation,

$$
CH_3 - S - CH_2 \overset{+}{\big\}} - R
$$

mass = 61

Similarly, for straight-chain 3-thia compounds the base-peak ion is of the constitution $C_2H_5S\text{-}CH_2{}^+$ (mass = 75). No conclusion can be drawn regarding 4- and 5-thia structures because of insufficient data.

Branched-chain sulfides, with the exception of t-butyl compounds, display a random occurrence of base peaks. The t-butyl groups yield a base peak of mass 57 due to the butyl fragment, as observed for each of four compounds in this category.

Cleavage of the carbon–sulfur valence bond yields an abundant ion of the constitution, $R_1\text{—}S^+$, where $R_1 \leqslant R_2$ in the molecule R_1SR_2. The in-

TABLE 40.IX

Mass Spectral Behavior of Aliphatic Sulfides

No. of compounds studied	Structure General formula: R_1SR_2		Type of sulfide	Base peak (m/e)	Parent ion intensity, %	R_1S^+ ion			Rearrangement ions					
	R_1	R_2				m/e	Intensity, %		m/e	Intensity, %	m/e	Intensity, %	m/e	Intensity, %
6	C_1	C_2–C_6 (straight chain)	2-thia	61^a	39–81	47	19–43		35	10–35	48	4–56	49	4–21
2	C_1	C_3–C_4 (branched)	2-thia	41,75, 90	81–100	47	38–50		35	2–18	48	11–78	49	11–42
1	C_1	t-C_4H_9	2-thia	57	36	47	7		35	1	48	3	49	12
3	C_2	C_2–C_4 (straight chain)	3-thia	75	42–69	61	18–56		35	10–18	62	48–51	63	4–22
3	C_2	C_3–C_4 (branched)	3-thia	75,89, etc.	33–71	61	14–49		35	6–12	62	8–67	63	5–17
1	C_2	t-C_4H_9	3-thia	57	23	61	3		35	5	62	4	63	3
3	C_3 (branched)	C_3–C_4 (branched)	3-thia	$43,61^b$	32–38	75	1–14		35	1–3	76	7–28	77	4–7
2	C_3 (branched)	t-C_4H_9	3-thia	57	9–20	75,89	2–16		35	1	76,90	6–10	77,91	2–6
1	n-C_3	n-C_3	4-thia	43	55	75	12		35	1	76	48	77	11
1	$sec.$-C_4	$sec.$-C_4	4-thia	61^b	20	89	4		35	3	90	3	91	4
1	n-C_4	n-C_4	5-thia	61^b	31	89	12		35	2	90	23	91	11

^{a} Base peak of CH_3SCH_3 is at m/e 47.

^{b} Rearrangement ion.

tensity of this ion varies in the range 1 to 50%, with the magnitude varying inversely with degree of branchiness of the R group (Table 40.IX, columns 7 and 8). The abundance also decreases in the order of 2-thia, 3-thia, etc., compounds.

Dissociation at this same location also appears to account for major rearrangement ions according to the processes,

$$R_1—S^+ \cancel{—R_2} \qquad \text{and} \qquad R_1—S^+ \cancel{—R_2}$$
$$+ H \qquad\qquad\qquad\qquad + 2H$$

Depending upon the R_1 group, these ions occur at masses 48, 62, or 76, etc., and at 49, 63, or 77, etc., as shown in columns 11 and 13. Not indicated by the data in Table 40.IX is the interesting observation that relative intensities of the R_1SH and R_1SH_2 ions vary conversely with one another. Thus, in a comparison of similar sulfides, R_1SH may decrease in intensity with molecular weight whereas R_1SH_2 will increase. One other rearrangement ion of particular interest is that of the fragment SH_3 (mass = 35). As shown in column 10, its relative abundance appears to vary inversely with the degree of branching.

These rearrangements stand out in those spectra available for study. It is likely, however, that other ones will manifest themselves as a greater variety of structures are studied. For example, three sulfides characterized by the inner molecular structure

$$\begin{array}{ccc} & C & & C \\ & | & & | \\ —C & —S— & C— \end{array}$$

gave a major ion of mass 61—presumably according to the dissociation,

$$\begin{array}{ccc} CH_3 & & CH_3^+ \\ | & & | \\ —CH \cancel{—} & S—CH \cancel{—} \\ & + H \\ & \text{mass} = 61 \end{array}$$

C. TOTAL IONIZATION

Considerable work has been done to establish relationships between individual ion formation and molecular structure, as reflected in the preceding discussion on correlations. Another property of mass spectra of interest is the total intensity of all ions in a spectrum. This concept, known as total ionization, is evaluated in terms of the total intensity found by summing together all individual ions formed per micron of sample pressure.

Mohler and his co-workers (200) studied the total ionization of C_1 to C_{10} hydrocarbons and found values that were approximately proportional to molecular weight. Within a given class of hydrocarbons, for instance, total ionization increased with molecular weight. It was also found that for a given number of carbon atoms, total ionization varied directly with the number of hydrogen atoms. As might be expected, these values for molecular isomers are essentially constant. Subsequent work indicates that total ionization values behave in a similar manner for compounds having up to 36 carbon atoms (61,134,212).

By placing total ionization on a relative basis as compared with a standard compound, such as n-butane or n-hexadecane, it is now easier to predict how a compound examined in one spectrometer will behave in a different instrument. This is of considerable value to an analyst who frequently must use data measured in a spectrometer other than his own. For comparative purposes, then, spectra of any compound usually include data for n-butane or n-hexadecane. Total ionization also has been utilized to develop methods for determining compound types in unknown mixtures. This application will be dealt with more fully in the discussion on analytical methods.

D. ORGANIC ANALYTICAL APPLICATIONS

Analytical spectrometers are built to handle organic samples of varying volatility levels. In this respect it was found that the great majority of samples can be analyzed successfully in two different instruments, arbitrarily designated as a "low" or a "high" mass spectrometer. Compounds of molecular weight below about 150 have a sufficient vapor pressure to be run in the low-mass instrument without difficulty, whereas heavier compounds in the molecular weight range of 150 to 600 can be analyzed on a routine basis in the high-mass spectrometer at higher temperatures.

The analysis of materials referred to above can be considered as a part of conventional mass spectrometry. Further modified or specialized equipment has been used in other important applications, as for example the analysis of high molecular weight polymers, microcrystalline waxes, and asphalts. Some of these materials up to a molecular weight of 1500 conceivably can be examined by apparatus having an extremely large magnet (242).

Beynon has pioneered significant analytical work based on high-resolution measurements (31). In this and later work (33) it was possible to resolve ions of the same nominal whole mass whose true mass differed according to the packing fraction effect. It was demonstrated, as seen in Fig. 40.26, for instance, that separate peaks could be obtained for each of the ions $C_2H_4{}^+$,

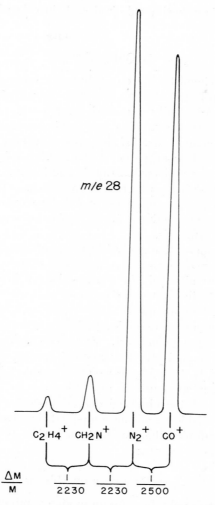

Fig. 40.26. Example of extreme resolution obtained with the AEI double-focusing mass spectrometer (33,62).

CH₂N⁺, N₂⁺, and CO⁺, in which the mass difference is approximately 0.012 units between the ions. This is a powerful research tool that promises to open up an entirely new field for qualitative and quantitative analysis.

Parallel with the diverse instruments used in analytical work are the many basic objectives encountered in sample examination. Thus, qualitative information is sometimes desired and, in other instances, quantitative results are needed.

1. Qualitative

Every analytical chemist will frequently want to identify unknown substances. In an ideal case this may consist of working with a purified fraction comprised principally of a single compound. The first step normally would be to attempt matching the sample spectrum with those of all available reference compounds. If this approach fails, a study of parent ions and principal fragments frequently will suffice to solve the problem. In the event that positive identification is still lacking, a studious examination of the less intense ions becomes mandatory. It is generally desirable to confirm any findings by measuring the spectrum of the postulated compound, if it can be obtained. Sometimes this may require an independent method of synthesis.

A more difficult qualitative analysis consists of identifying an unknown in a mixture of known or suspected compounds. The same basic approach is used in such cases, although the contributions of interfering substances must be mathematically subtracted from the mixture spectrum to finally reduce it to that of the unknown.

The most complex and intangible problem is encountered when two or more compounds must be identified. Situations such as these thoroughly test the mettle of the analyst. Fortunately, even in such cases, any proposed solutions can be tested by calculating a residual spectrum. Theoretically, at least, a spectrum of any mixture can be mathematically matched with that of the observed one. This observation presupposes that spectra are available for all the compounds involved.

The following examples illustrate how an analyst proceeds to deal with the unexpected in mass spectra:

a. Decomposition Products of s-Tetrachloroethane

The partial spectrum obtained for an unknown mixture obtained by the decomposition of s-tetrachloroethane is shown in Table 40.X. The steps involved in unraveling this spectrum are outlined in order below. The role of small but unique peaks is highlighted in this case.

1. Inspection of the spectrum discloses that none of the starting material is present. s-Tetrachloroethane has intense peaks at 131, 133, 166, and 168, which are not observed in the mixture spectrum.

2. Peaks at 117, 119, and 121 are present in abundances very similar to fragments containing three chlorine atoms. A check of reference spectra

m/e	Mixture spectrum	Contribution of Component									Residual spectrum
		CCl_4	$CHCl_3$	HCl	SO_2	COS	CO_2	H_2S	H_2	Air	
2	103								103		0
22	2.1						2.0				+ 0.1
28	79.2					1.3	14.4			60.0	+ 3.5
32	61.0				0.7	9.2		38.6		12.5	0
33	36.0							36.5			− 0.5
34	87.0							87.0			0
35	144	1.6	6.0	131				2.2			+ 3.2
36	640	—	0.8	639				3.7			+ 0.5
37	45	0.5	1.9	41							+ 1.5
38	206	—	0.3	203							+ 2.7
44	130					0.5	129.5				0
45	16						1.5				+ 14.5
46	3.7						0.5				+ 3.2
47	13.0	1.7	11.1								+ 0.9
48	9.4	—	5.0		3.5						0
60	15.7					15.7					+ 2.4
61	2.7					0.3					0
64	7.0				7.0						0
82	2.4	1.1	1.1								+ 0.2
83	30.0	—	30.0								0
84	3.3	0.7	1.1								+ 1.5
85	20.1	—	19.1								+ 1.0
86	1.0	0.1	0.4								+ 0.5
87	4.1	—	3.1								+ 1.0
117	4.0	3.6	0.3								+ 0.1
118	0.8	—	0.6								+ 0.2
119	3.9	3.5	0.3								+ 0.1
120	0.5	—	0.5								0
121	1.2	1.1	0.1								0
Mol. %		0.2	1.2	40	0.5	0.7	6.3	4.0	10.6	3.8	

showed them to coincide with carbon tetrachloride. Weaker ions at 118, 120, and 122 also indicated the presence of fragments constituted by three chlorines, one carbon, and one hydrogen. These were attributed to chloroform. This assignment was easily confirmed by the more intense ions at masses 83, 85, and 87.

3. Contributions of these two compounds to the spectrum were calculated to be as shown in columns 3 and 4 of Table 40.X.

4. Hydrogen chloride was next identified by peaks at 36 and 38. Contributions of hydrogen chloride to the spectrum are in column 5.

5. A small but isolated peak at mass 64 was felt to be sulfur dioxide, which was confirmed by its fit with the residual peak at 48.

6. Another isolated peak at 60 was assigned to carbonyl sulfide. The presence of this compound could not be affirmed with confidence because of the lack of a second abundant peak in its spectrum.

7. A small peak at mass 22 usually can be attributed to carbon dioxide, and there is no exception in this instance. The 44 ion calculated from a 22 ion of carbon dioxide is $2.1/0.0156 = 134.6$ units, which agrees closely with the observed residual value of 129.5.

8. Hydrogen sulfide has distinctive ion abundances at 33 and 34, which agree with the mixture as shown in column 9.

9. Hydrogen was next determined from the ion at mass 2.

10. Residual peaks at 32 and 28 are obviously due to a relatively small concentration of air.

11. As a result of the foregoing analysis, nine components were resolved and a final analysis could be calculated as shown in the bottom row. Residual peaks at 45, 46, and 61 indicate that a small concentration of oxygenated material has not been identified.

b. Analysis of a Deuterated Hydrocarbon

In one study it developed that spectra of two standards could be used to establish that of an intermediate one that was unavailable in the pure state. The compounds of interest in this case consisted of normal and deuterated diphenyl-di-*tert*-butyl ethanes.

$$
\begin{array}{cccc}
t\text{-}C_4H_9 & t\text{-}C_4H_9 & & t\text{-}C_4H_9 \\
| & | & & | \\
(1)\ \Phi CHCH\Phi & (2)\ \Phi CDCH\Phi & \text{and} & (3)\ \Phi CDCD\Phi \\
| & | & & | \\
t\text{-}C_4H_9 & t\text{-}C_4H_9 & & t\text{-}C_4H_9
\end{array}
$$

Infrared data showed the presence of C—D and C—H aliphatic groups in the mixture. It could not be determined, however, whether the mixture consisted of all three species or just (*1*) and (*3*). Mass spectra of pure compounds (*1*) and (*3*) exhibited the following prominent ions, from which it was easy to postulate a spectrum of compound (*2*) as shown.

Compound (*1*)			Compound (*3*)			Compound (*2*)		
ion	m/e	%	ion	m/e	%	ion	m/e	%
ΦCHCHΦ	180	100	ΦCDCDΦ	182	100	ΦCDCHΦ	181	100
ΦCHCHΦ[a]	179	80	ΦCDCDΦ[a]	181	75	ΦCDCHΦ[a]	180	77
ΦCHCHΦ[b]	178	49	ΦCDCDΦ[b]	180	49	ΦCDCHΦ[b]	179	49

[a] Minus one ring hydrogen.
[b] Minus two ring hydrogens.

The mixture spectrum showed fairly intense ions at 178, 179, 180, 181, and 182. Relative intensities were such that only a combination of all three compounds could account for the observed distribution as outlined below.

m/e	Mixture	Compound (*1*)	Compound (*2*)	Compound (*3*)	Residual
178	27	13	10	2	+2
179	60	20	28	9	+3
180	97	27	45	25	0
181	100	4	58	38	0
182	58	0	7	51	0
Approximate mole %	20	43	37		

c. Identification of N_2O in Air

One of the original applications of the mass spectrometer was in the analysis of soil gases. The objective was to establish this as a tool in searching for oil that might be underground. While utilizing a process for concentrating soil gases it became desirable also to study the composition of air. A sample enriched in condensable gases from the atmosphere showed an unexpected ingredient displaying peaks at 44, 30, and 16. A pattern was determined for these peaks and subsequently this was shown to coincide closely with that of pure N_2O.   This was followed by a systematic study of atmospheric samples that established its average concentration to be 0.00005% (248).

2. Quantitative

Most analytical work done with mass spectrometers is quantitative in nature.   Laboratories throughout this country and abroad regularly analyze all types of samples concerned with research, pilot unit, and plant operations.   Much qualitative work, as a matter of fact, is concluded on a quantitative basis.   This is true because once compounds have been identified their concentration usually can be estimated with fair accuracy. Two types of quantitative procedures are prevalent and consist of component or compound type analyses.

a. COMPONENT ANALYSIS

In component analysis an instrument is first calibrated with the pure compounds whose presence is anticipated in a given mixture.   The spectra of these compounds are then studied for peaks that are unique and relatively intense.   By properly selecting one peak to represent each compound, a matrix of calibration coefficients is set up.   Calculation of the matrix and mixture peaks follows one of the procedures previously discussed.

The limit to the number of compounds that can be handled in a single mixture varies with the dissimilarity of their spectra.   Hydrocarbon gases formed by cracking petroleum may contain more than 25 compounds, each of which may be determined.   A less ideal case is the analysis of petroleum fractions having a fairly narrow boiling-point range.   The use of the mass spectrometer to determine C_6 to C_8 saturate hydrocarbons was established several years ago by Brown and his co-workers (52).   This work showed that it was first necessary to obtain five fractions, by high-efficiency distillation, which contained concentrates of C_6's, C_7's, and three different fractions in the C_8 range.   The evaluation of a method to analyze a C_6 fraction is representative of the procedure generally followed in devising component analyses.   This will be described in detail.

Preliminary requirements and tests to be conducted are listed below.

1. All possible compounds on hand must have a purity of 99% for calibration of the instrument.

2. It must be demonstrated that the sample handling equipment is capable of completely vaporizing each compound.   In addition, it must be

possible to readily pump out such samples to leave a memory background of less than 0.1%.

3. Spectra should be reproducible within ±1 relative per cent.

4. It is desirable to have at least one mixture of known composition to serve as a final test of the method.

The next step is to tabulate spectra of the various compounds, as shown in Table 40.XI. These compounds include all possibilities and consist of

TABLE 40.XI
Mass Spectra of Compounds in C_6 Fraction

m/e	Cyclo-pen-tane, %	Meth-yl-cyclo-pen-tane, %	Cyclo-hex-ane, %	2,2-Di-methyl-butane, %	2,3-Di-methyl-butane, %	2-Meth-yl-pen-tane, %	3-Meth-yl-pen-tane, %	n-Hex-ane, %	m/e
41	102	369	90	60.3	32.4	32.5	230	92	41
42	319	162	40.6	5.8	87.9	54.6	21.7	48.9	42
43	12.4	66.4	19.4	100	100	100	100	100	43
55	92.1	148	46.7	14.4	5.9	6.0	29.5	9.2	55
56	4.1	575	134	31.5	1.0	4.5	291	55.6	56
57	0.2	30.5	6.8	105	0.4	10.6	376	128	57
69	3.7	188	29.3	0.8	0.6	0.6	2.2	0.5	69
70	100	10.5	1.6	3.6	0.7	7.0	5.6	0.9	70
71	5.5	0.3	0.0	80.0	17.1	29.4	20.6	6.7	71
84		100	100	0.0	0.0	0.0	0.1	0.1	84
85		6.8	6.5	0.2	0.8	0.8	2.5	0.6	85
86		0.2	0.2	0.0	4.3	3.8	13.8	21.1	86
Sens. (peak/μ press.)	27.8	12.2	43.8	56.5	100	94.7	18.9	47.1	

cyclopentane, two C_6 cycloparaffins, and the five hexane isomers. To facilitate a visual comparison of these spectra, they are presented as pattern coefficients based on selected peaks, which will accentuate spectral differences. Thus, cyclopentane is based on mass 70, the C_6 cycloparaffins on mass 84, and hexanes on mass 43.

The process of selecting analytical peaks is empirical, and final judgment should be based on results obtained with a known mixture(s). After considerable experience in this work, however, it is frequently satisfactory to use residual peaks as a final test. Residual peaks of 1 relative per cent or less indicate that an accurate resolution of components has been obtained.

In this example an inspection of the spectra in Table 40.XI readily leads to the choice of mass 70 for cyclopentane, mass 69 for methylcyclopentane, and mass 84 for cyclohexane. These peaks are virtually free of interference from hexanes, and the relative peak intensities of the three compounds involved are markedly different from one another. Prior to selecting analytical peaks for the hexanes it is first desirable to rule out such possibilities as masses 41 and 55. These are eliminated because neither one is highly selective for any one hexane and because methylcyclopentane also contributes to these peaks to considerable extent. This leaves the following probable assignments.

2,2-Dimethylbutane	43, 57, 71
2,3-Dimethylbutane	42, 43
2-Methylpentane	43
3-Methylpentane	43, 56, 57
n-Hexane	43, 57, 86

Upon inspection of the array above it is noted that some peaks appear only once and these can, therefore, be assigned directly. On this basis masses 71, 42, and 86 may be chosen to determine 2,2-dimethylbutane, 2,3-dimethylbutane, and n-hexane, respectively. Only one possible peak, mass 43, has been listed for 2-methylpentane, so that this selection follows forthwith. This then leaves 3-methylpentane to be mated either with the peak at mass 56 or 57. In this case mass 56 is desirable because it is interfered with less by other hexanes. On the other hand, mass 57 has a markedly lower contribution from cycloparaffins. The conclusion is then reached that mass 56 should be used in the absence of cycloparaffins and that 57 would be preferred in their presence. Any method would finally be adjudged on the basis of residual peaks and the accuracy with which a known mixture can be analyzed. The analytical peaks that were finally selected for each component are underlined in Table 40.XI.

A large number of quantitative methods have been described in the literature. Many unpublished ones are undoubtedly in use. These applications are not confined to hydrocarbons by any means and, in fact, almost any type of organic material has been found susceptible to mass spectrometry. It is beyond the scope of this chapter to discuss the many analytical methods individually. However, a partial summary of published methods in Table 40.XII vividly demonstrates the versatility of this tool for both low and high molecular weight samples.

TABLE 40.XII

A Partial Summary of Mass Spectrometric Methods for Compounds in Multicomponent Mixtures

Type of mixture	Author	Year	Reference
Room-Temperature Mass Spectrometer			
H_2, HD, D_2	Alfin-Slater, Rock, Swislocki	1950	15
	Roth	1954	229
D_2O	Washburn, Berry, Hall	1953	287
H_2–C_5 hydrocarbons	Washburn, Wiley, Rock	1943	288
	Washburn, Wiley, Rock, Berry	1945	289
	Brewer, Dibeler	1945	46
Synthesis gas (carburetted)	Shepherd	1950	244
Natural gas	Shepherd	1947	243
C_3–C_5 hydrocarbons	Dibeler, Mohler	1947	73
C_6–C_7 saturate hydrocarbons	Sobcov	1952	253
C_6–C_8 saturate hydrocarbons	Brown, Taylor, Melpolder, Young	1948	52
C_6–C_8 saturate hydrocarbons	Friedel, Logar, Shultz	1952	94
C_6–C_9 alkylbenzenes in gasoline	Lumpkin, Thomas	1951	171
C_1–C_4 alcohols	Gifford, Rock, Comaford	1949	103
C_1–C_4 alcohols	Kelley	1951	147
C_7 alcohols	Yarborough	1953	303
C_1–C_5 alcohols, aldehydes, ketones	Gifford, Rock, Comaford	1949	103
	Thomas, Seyfried	1949	266
C_1 alcohol, aldehyde, acid, ester	Langer, Fox	1949	161
C_2–C_6 alcohol, ether, water	Taylor, Brown, Young, Headington	1948	263
C_1–C_4 acids	Kelley	1951	147
Fluoride gases	Bentley, Hamer, Evans	1958	26
C_1–C_2 chlorides	Bernstein, Semeluk, Arends	1953	27
C_1–C_4 chlorides, iodides	Taylor, Brown, Young, Headington	1948	263
Fluorocarbons	Mohler, Bloom, Lengel, Wise	1949	197
Amines	Collin	1953	59
Thiophenes	Kinney, Cook	1952	152
	Amberg	1959	15a
Oxides of nitrogen	Friedel, Sharkey, Shultz, Humbert	1953	96

(*Table continued*)

TABLE 40. XII (*continued*)

Type of mixture	Author	Year	Reference
Atmospheric pollutants	Harp, Stewart, Brockmyre	1950	120
	Shepherd, Rock, Howard,		
	Stormes	1951	245
	Quiram, Metro, Lewis	1954	218
	Friedel	1956	93
	Weaver, Hughs, Guntler,		
	Schuhmann, Redearn,		
	Gorden	1957	290
	Quiram, Biller	1958	217
	Mohler, Bradt, Dibeler	1958	199
Exhaust gas	Walker, O'Hara	1955	280
Water contaminants	Melpolder, Warfield,		
	Headington	1953	191
	Happ, Stewart, Cooper	1957	121

High-Temperature Mass Spectrometer

Polyisopropylbenzenes	McLafferty	1956	180
C_{16}–C_{27} alcohols	Brown, Young,		
	Nicolaides	1954	53
Aromatic acids and esters	Gohlke, McLafferty	1955	106
Vinyl ethers of diethylene			
glycol	McLafferty	1957	182
Steroids	Friedland, Lane, Longman,		
	Train, O'Neal	1959	99
Halogenated hydrocarbons	McLafferty	1956	180
Fluorinated polyphenyls	Bradt, Mohler	1955	45
Phosphate additives in gasoline	Quayle	1958	216
Products of ethyl sorbate	Kourey, Tuffly,		
	Yarborough	1959	157a
Methyl esters of resin acids	Genge	1959	101a
Aliphatic amides	Gilpin	1959	104a
o-Xylene oxidation products	Lumpkin, Nicholson	1960	170a
Condensed aromatic	Ardenne, Steinfelder,		
hydrocarbons	Tuemmler	1961	16b
Aliphatic amines	Gohlke, McLafferty	1962	106a
Aliphatic halogenated			
compounds	McLafferty	1962	184a
Aromatic halogenated			
compounds	McLafferty	1962	184b
Aliphatic nitriles	McLafferty	1962	184c

b. Compound-Type Analysis

(1) Low Mass

Compound-type analysis has been of particular importance in the petroleum industry for many years. Petroleum products are complex mixtures of many different types of hydrocarbons that normally cannot be determined individually. In evaluating gasoline, heating oil distillate, and other such materials, chemists therefore have had to depend upon less definitive compositional information such as compound-type analyses. For many years these analyses could be obtained only by correlative analysis of physical property measurements such as density, refractive index, and molecular weight. These methods are still used extensively and continue to be extremely valuable in petroleum research, but they have been augmented by chromatographic and spectrometric methods. Such methods based on mass spectrometry have been found to be fast, reliable, and more informative than other procedures. The entire range of petroleum fractions, with the exception of asphalt, is now analyzed on a routine basis in many laboratories.

In a chronological sense, the development of hydrocarbon type-analysis methods came several years after spectrometers had been in routine use for gas analysis. Brown (47) found that the principal compounds in gasoline possessed characteristic ions. A study of C_4 to C_{16} compounds showed that ions at masses 43, 57, 71, 85, and 99 generally were most abundant in paraffins. Similarly, relative large peaks at 41, 55, 69, 83, and 97 appeared to characterize cycloparaffins and mono-olefins. Ions at masses 67, 68, 81, 82, 95, and 96 were contributed generally by cyclo-olefins, diolefins, and acetylenes. Alkylbenzene fragments were found at masses 77, 78, 79, 91, 92, 105, 106, 119, 120, 133, and 134.

When the peaks in each group listed above are mathematically combined and treated as one, it was found that pattern coefficients of combined peaks were similar for compounds of the same type but showed marked differences for dissimilar compound types. This made it possible to consider gasoline as consisting of only four components that could be resolved with four simultaneous equations. Cycloparaffins and olefins were considered as one component that was subsequently resolved by a chemical determination of olefins.

As an example of the similarity noted for compounds of the same type, data for the nine heptane isomers are tabulated in Table 40.XIII. Reference to this table shows that spectral data are presented in terms of ratios for different Σ values. Σ's represent each particular group of peaks used in the calculation, i.e., $\Sigma 43$ denotes the sum of peaks at 43, 57, 71, and 85.

TABLE 40.XIII

Calibration Coefficients of Heptane Isomers as Used in Hydrocarbon Type Analysis

	Ratio				$\Sigma F_{43}{}^a$ (peak height div./μ
Compound	$\Sigma43/\Sigma43$	$\Sigma41/\Sigma43$	$\Sigma67/\Sigma43$	$\Sigma77/\Sigma43$	press.)
n-Heptane	1.00	0.363	0.003	0.001	131
2-Methylhexane	1.00	0.306	0.003	0.001	156
3-Methylhexane	1.00	0.362	0.004	0.001	134
3-Ethylpentane	1.00	0.273	0.003	0.001	142
2,2-Dimethylpentane	1.00	0.284	0.005	0.001	192
2,3-Dimethylpentane	1.00	0.431	0.005	0.001	119
2,4-Dimethylpentane	1.00	0.304	0.005	0.001	169
3,3-Dimethylpentane	1.00	0.193	0.003	0.001	192
2,2,3-Trimethylbutane	1.00	0.327	0.004	0.001	153

^{a} ΣF_{43} denotes the sensitivity of the summation peak, which is the sum of the individual peaks that comprise $\Sigma43$. The other ratio values are:

$\Sigma43 = 43 + 57 + 71 + 85;$
$\Sigma41 = 41 + 55 + 69 + 83;$
$\Sigma67 = 67 + 68 + 81 + 82 + 95 + 96;$ and
$\Sigma77 = 77 + 78 + 79 + 91 + 92 + 105 + 106 + 119 + 120 + 133 + 134.$

All sigma values are defined in Table 40.XIII. To illustrate the dissimilarity between different types of compounds, a typical calibration matrix is shown in Table 40.XIV.

TABLE 40.XIV

A Typical Calibration Matrix in Gasoline Analysis

	$\Sigma43$	$\Sigma41$	$\Sigma67$	$\Sigma77$	Sensitivity (div./μ)
Paraffins	1.00	0.266	0.005	0.002	180
Cycloparaffins	0.15	1.00	0.153	0.012	121
Mono-olefins	0.37	1.00	0.058	0.017	108
Cyclo-olefins, etc.	0.13	0.75	1.00	0.08	133
Alkylbenzenes	0.004	0.012	0	1.00	156

The analysis of gasoline has received considerable attention from workers in the petroleum field, and a number of improvements and extensions in the procedure have occurred. At the present time seven different hydrocarbon types can be determined in a nonolefinic gasoline. In the presence of olefins a saturated portion of the sample is prepared by acid treatment.

The original and olefin-free samples are then analyzed on the mass spectrometer and the data are combined to obtain a final composition. In this case a total of 10 different hydrocarbon types can be determined. An analysis of a typical gasoline is shown in Table 40.XV (based on a method published for information only by ASTM Committee D-2 on Petroleum Products and Lubricants (18)).

TABLE 40.XV

Analysis of an Olefinic Gasoline Based on a Combination Mass Spectrometer–Acid Absorption Method (18)

Hydrocarbon type	Volume %
Paraffins	20.9
Monocycloparaffins	14.9
Dicycloparaffins	1.9
Tricycloparaffins	0.4
Mono-olefins	13.4
Coda[a]	9.5
Cyclodiolefins	1.4
Alkylbenzenes	33.2
Indanes and/or tetralins	3.6
Naphthalenes	0.8
Total	100.0

[a] Coda refers to cyclo-olefins, diolefins, and/or acetylenes.

Type methods such as those described here require considerable effort to develop and to establish the rather complex calculations on a firm basis. Once this has been done, however, analyses can be accomplished in one or two hours. Indeed, the calculations may be programmed for a digital computer so as to materially shorten the time needed for one analysis.

More recently, compound-type methods have been based on total ionization measurements (61). This offers the advantage of being independent of sensitivity variations that occur between instruments. That is, total ionization has been found to be relatively constant and, consequently, calibrations based on such values provide the basis for methods of more universal application.

The status of compound type analysis is indicated by the list of low-mass methods shown in Table 40.XVI.

(2) High Mass

The determination of high molecular weight (M.W. 250 to 500) compounds in petroleum wax was first reported in 1951 by O'Neal and Wier

TABLE 40.XVI

A Partial Summary of Mass Spectrometric Methods for Compound-Type Analysis

Type of mixture	Author	Year	Reference
Room-Temperature Mass Spectrometer			
Low olefinic gasoline	Lumpkin, Thomas, Elliott	1952	172
	Crable, Coggeshall	1958	61
	Franke	1960	91a
	ASTM D-2 Committee,		
	Res. Div. IV	1958	18
Olefinic gasoline	Brown	1951	47
	Mikkelsen, Hopkins, Yee	1958	196
	Frisque, Grubb, Ehrhardt,		
	Vander Haar	1961	99a
	Klaas, McSweeney	1962	155a
	Lawry, Paulson	1962	162a
Isoparaffins and *n*-paraffins			
in gasoline	Sobcov	1952	254
	Ferguson, Howard	1958	85
Alcohols	Friedel, Shultz, Sharkey	1956	97
Nonolefinic naphtha	Cirillo, Skahan, Hollis,		
	Morgan	1962	57b
Cyclopentanes and			
cyclohexanes in gasoline	Howard, Ferguson	1961	137b
High-Temperature Mass Spectrometer			
Kerosene, furnace oil	Brown, Doherty, Spontak	1950	48
	Fitzgerald, Cirillo,		
	Galbraith	1962	87a
C_{12}–C_{20} petroleum products	Kearns, Maranowski, Crable	1959	146a
Gas oil–saturate hydrocarbons	Melpolder, Brown, Washall,		
	Doherty, Young	1954	189
	Lumpkin	1956	168
	Hood, O'Neal	1958	135
Gas oil–aromatic hydrocarbons	Lumpkin, Johnson	1954	170
	Melpolder, Brown, Washall,		
	Doherty, Young	1954	189

(210). Except for *n*-paraffins, practically all work done in the high-mass region is of the type-analysis variety because of the intricate nature of molecular structures. The computational procedure developed for high-mass analysis is similar to but less certain than that described in the previous section for lighter compounds.

Progress in the high-mass region has been gratifying in view of the complex heavy hydrocarbon structures and a lack of sufficient calibration compounds. Fortunately, a large number of pure heavy hydrocarbons have

TABLE 40. XVI (*continued*)

Type of mixture	Author	Year	Reference
	King, McSweeney, Kant, Priestley	1955	150
	Hastings, Johnson, Lumpkin	1956	123
	Gordon, Moore, Muller	1958	109
Lube oil–saturate hydrocarbons	Clerc, Hood, O'Neal	1955	58
	Melpolder, Brown, Washall, Doherty, Headington	1956	188
	Hood, O'Neal	1958	135
	Carlson, O'Neal	1958	56
Lube oil–aromatic hydrocarbons	King, McSweeney, Kant, Priestley	1955	150
	Orkin, Benderaitis, Brown, Williams	1958	211
Lubricating oils	Carlson, O'Neal	1958	56
Paraffin wax	Andre, O'Neal	1959	16a
	O'Neal, Wier	1951	210
	Brown, Skahan, Cirillo, Melpolder	1959	51
Heavy petroleum compounds	Hood, Clerc, O'Neal	1959	134a
Propylene polymer	Brown, Skahan, Cirillo, Melpolder	1959	51
Asphalt	Clerc, O'Neal	1960	58a
Alkylated benzenes	Brown, Cirillo, Melpolder	1959	51
Liquid products from coal hydrogenation	Sharkey, Wood, Shultz, Wender, Friedel	1959	240a
Paraffins, olefins, alcohols, ketones	Friedel, Wood, Shultz, Sharkey	1957	98
Cyclic nitrogen compounds	Sauer, Melpolder, Brown	1952	233
Nitrogen compounds in petroleum	LaLau	1959	158

been prepared by API Project 42 (15b) and submitted to several laboratories for mass spectral determination. Data from these compounds have been extremely valuable in developing applicable methods for heavy petroleum fractions. Despite this progress, however, more pure hydrocarbons with structures similar to those actually present in petroleum are needed to refine existing methods. This is a herculean task on which API Project 42 is currently expending considerable effort.

Persistent effort in this field has resulted in the publication of a number of compound-type analysis methods for petroleum fractions. These are applicable to kerosene, heating oil distillate, gas oil, and lubricating oil. The petroleum wax method referred to previously has been used by numerous laboratories to relate composition with properties. Also, an impressive number of applications have occurred in the analysis of petrochemicals, coal products, and other nitrogen or oxygenated compounds. Illustrative of many such applications are the methods listed in Tables 40.XII and 40.XVI.

The value of mass spectral data in structural studies already has been stressed. It is not surprising then to report that work in high-mass spectrometry has considerably extended the horizon of knowledge relative to the structure of heavy petroleum molecules. Based on a modest amount of work, it now appears that petroleum hydrocarbons are perhaps not as complex or as diverse in structure as has usually been imagined. Preliminary studies have depicted predominant structures for isoparaffins, monocycloparaffins, alkylbenzenes, and polycycloparaffins (135,188). These postulated structures may vary to some degree according to the investigator, but this may be attributed in part to differences between waxy and viscous petroleum fractions. Carlson et al. (56a) recently applied a high-resolution instrument (276) to the interpretation of petroleum-products spectra.

Future progress in both the structural and analytical aspects of high-mass spectrometry will depend to a great extent of the availability of additional pure compounds. In the absence of sufficient precise calibration data, each laboratory will continue to develop its own correlations based on previous experience, machine calculations, and sometimes intuition. No general agreement for selecting the "best" matrix coefficients can be expected although there is little evidence that any one method of computation is subject to gross error. In view of this situation, further improvement most probably will be the result of a cooperative program directed toward (1) the synthesis and purification of additional heavy hydrocarbons having particular structures of interest, (2) adoption of stringent operating procedures based on the best practices of different laboratories, (3) selection of standard instrumental parameters and operating conditions, and (4) cooperative testing of both known mixtures and commercial products. It may be anticipated that such a program will eventually reach fruition as more laboratories become active in the high-mass field.

c. SPECIALIZED TECHNIQUES

(1) Chemical Treatment

A number of analytical problems have been encountered in which the component(s) could not be directly determined by using mass spectral data.

This may happen in instances in which a given component(s) lacks a distinctive or characterizing peak. Occasionally, chemical treatment may alter the mixture spectrum sufficiently to allow identification and analysis.

(a) Isobutene Analysis

An early example of this type occurred in regard to the determination of isobutene in the presence of other butenes. In this case a very satisfactory method was developed based on the prior conversion of isobutene to *tert*-butyl chloride, which has a unique peak of mass 77. This was accomplished by first reacting a mixture with anhydrous hydrogen chloride and then using the mass spectrometer to determine isobutene as *tert*-butyl chloride (187).

(b) Alcohol–Water Analysis

Alcohols of intermediate molecular weight or alcohols mixed with hydrocarbons cannot be directly analyzed. Langer and his co-workers (162) encountered this problem in Fischer-Tropsch synthesis studies and solved it by quantitatively converting alcohols to their trimethylsilyl derivatives. These derivatives can then be analyzed by mass spectrometry because of their characteristic spectra. Hexamethyldisilazane (I) is used as a converting reagent to react with alcohols or water to give trimethylsilyl ethers (II) or hexamethyldisiloxane (III), as shown below.

$$(CH_3)_3SiNHSi(CH_3)_3 \quad \begin{array}{l} \xrightarrow{\text{2 ROH}} 2ROSi(CH_3)_3 + NH_3 \\ \qquad\qquad\quad (II) \\ \\ \xrightarrow{\text{H}_2\text{O}} (CH_3)_3SiOSi(CH_3)_3 + NH_3 \\ \qquad\qquad\quad (III) \end{array}$$

(I)

Compounds II and III give intense ions corresponding in mass with their molecular weight minus 15, due to the loss of a methyl group caused by cleavage at the silicon–carbon valence bond,

$$RO \overset{\displaystyle CH_3}{\underset{\displaystyle |}{Si}}(CH_3)_2{}^+$$

This method was demonstrated to be applicable to C_1 to C_{11} alcohol mixtures. Sharkey *et al.* (237) also pointed out the applicability of this principle to phenols, amines, and thiols.

(c) Ketone Analysis

Siegel and Schissler have successfully used another organic reaction to aid them in the analysis of C_7 and C_8 aliphatic ketones (247). They were faced with the problem of identifying such compounds in the absence of the essential reference materials. A special procedure was devised to convert ketones to aliphatic hydrocarbons using the Wolff-Kishner reduction. In general it was found possible to identify rather easily the hydrocarbons that possessed the same carbon skeletal structure as the corresponding ketone. This method does not, however, establish the location of the carbonyl group.

A typical example of this reaction is shown below for 4-methyl-2 hexanone.

$$\underset{\underset{\displaystyle CH_3}{|}}{CH_3\overset{\overset{\displaystyle O}{\|}}{C}CH_2CHCH_2CH_3} + \underset{\text{(hydrazine)}}{H_2NNH_2} \rightarrow \underset{\underset{\displaystyle CH_3}{|}}{CH_3\overset{\overset{\displaystyle NNH_2}{\|}}{C}CH_2CHCH_2CH_3}\ \text{(hydrazone)}$$

$$\downarrow \text{(alkaline catalyst)}$$

$$\underset{\underset{\displaystyle CH_3}{|}}{CH_3CH_2CH_2CHCH_2CH_3}$$
$$\text{(3-methylhexane)}$$

The product, 3-methylhexane, has a characteristic spectrum that enables its identification in the presence of other heptanes and some octanes.

(2) Low-Voltage Mass Spectrometry

The conventional mass spectrum of a polyatomic molecule is complex, consisting of parent and fragment ions at many masses. It is possible, however, to adjust ionization voltages so that they are larger than the ionization potential of the molecule but smaller than the lowest appearance potential. Such a spectrum would then consist simply of parent ions that could be identified directly as to empirical formula.

Field and Hastings (87) have utilized this fact to enhance the determination of olefinic and aromatic hydrocarbons. These compounds have appearance potentials at least one or two volts lower than those of aliphatic and cycloparaffins. By using a voltage of 6.9 v. between the filament and the ionization chamber, Field and Hastings found measurable parent ions for olefins and aromatics to the exclusion of ions from aliphatic paraffins. Cycloparaffins were found to give some ions, but of much lower intensity than those of the olefins. A study of this source of error indicated that olefins might be erroneously high by about 5% of the paraffin–cycloparaffin concentration. Because of this it is desirable to apply this technique to fractions that are relatively rich in olefins and/or aromatics. Crable et al. (61a) tabulated the sensitivities of aromatic compounds at low ionization potentials.

Multicomponent mixtures (275), gasoline (87), propylene polymer (169), and aromatic fractions from gas oil (109,169) have all been analyzed by low-voltage mass spectrometry. These applications indicate that widespread use of this technique will follow.

(3) Isotope-Dilution Methods

Both radioactive and stable isotopes have been used extensively in isotope-dilution methods (291). Researchers have employed this technique, which is based on the addition of heavy isotopes of oxygen, carbon, sulfur, and nitrogen, to organic mixtures (43,113,145,153,225). A mass spectrometer is then used to measure isotopic abundances.

To determine oxygen, for instance, a known amount of sample is equilibrated with a known weight of oxygen rich in O^{18}. This is done by combustion in a platinum tube at 800°C. The carbon dioxide formed is analyzed by mass spectrometry to determine the excess O^{18}. From this value and the O^{18} content of the oxygen used in combustion, the weight per cent of oxygen in the sample can be calculated readily. Carbon is determined by adding a known amount of $C^{13}O_2$ to the oxygen used in combustion and then measuring the relative quantities of $C^{13}O_2$ and $C^{12}O_2$. Nitrogen analysis depends upon converting nitrogen in the sample to N_2^{14} and a known amount of $N^{15}H_3$ to N_2^{15}.

(4) Pyrolysis Methods

All of the applications dealt with in previous sections generally pertain to the analysis of materials that can be vaporized and directly measured on a mass spectrometer. Heavy polymers do not fall in this category. Yet, analytical procedures have been developed for such materials that depend ultimately upon mass spectrometric measurements.

Certain classes of organic polymers, upon pyrolysis, are known to give volatile products characteristic of the original material. Various different experimental procedures consequently have been developed (173,281,282, 305) whereby these volatile products are introduced to a mass spectrometer for analysis. A wide variety of synthetics have been examined; of particular interest are those that yield essentially a single compound or compound class. These include natural rubber–isoprene, neoprene–chloroprene, polystyrene–styrene, polyethylene–C_nH_{2n}, Teflon–C_nF_{2n}, Kel-F–$CF_2{=}CFCl$, and polyvinyl chloride–HCl + benzene. Other typical samples that were studied gave a variety of decomposition products. This was found to be true for polyisobutylene, polyisoprene, polybutadiene, polyethylene, GR-S rubber, and polyfluorocarbons (174). Bua and Manaresi (53a) have analyzed the pyrolyzates obtained from the copolymer of ethylene and propylene.

An interesting variation of polymer analysis has been described by Bradt, Dibeler, and Mohler (44). Samples are pyrolyzed inside the spectrometer tube, with the degradation products evaporated directly into the ion source after comparatively few collisions. These workers identified ions corresponding to monomer, dimer, trimer, tetramer, and pentamer in a study of polystyrene.

(5) Molecular Weight Measurement by Rate of Effusion

The role of parent ions in the determination of molecular weights has been covered rather thoroughly in this chapter. It is interesting to note that a different type of mass spectrometric measurement also can be used for molecular weight determinations. This arises from the fact that while a sample is going from its reservoir bottle to the ion source it is under molecular flow conditions. This means then that the rate of flow is inversely proportional to the square root of its molecular weight. This rate can be measured in terms of the drop in sample pressure, as indicated by peak-height decay per unit of time.

In practice a calibration curve is determined that relates molecular weight with leak rates. Any peak in a mass spectrum can be used for molecular weight analysis. This technique is particularly useful in dealing with compounds that possess an indistinguishable parent ion. It also can be of value in the assignment of peaks in mixture spectra or in dissociation studies of pure compounds in which possible impurities must be checked upon.

Zemany (304) has been eminently successful in determining molecular weights of a large variety of organic compounds up to values as high as 200. Mixture components were determined by Eden, Burr, and Pratt (83).

E. INORGANIC ANALYTICAL APPLICATIONS

Relatively few methods for the determination of inorganic solids by mass spectrometry have been reported to date (63,111,118). The situation may soon change, however, since the recent availability of commercial solid mass spectrometers should accelerate the development of inorganic analytical methods. Fortunately there is much pertinent information to be found in the current literature in the closely related fields of physical and geological research.

Basically, an inorganic analysis requires a quantitative determination of the elements or of the isotopes in a sample. Very often, constituents pres-

TABLE 40.XVII

A Partial Summary of Mass Spectrometer Determinations of Inorganic Compounds and Isotopes

Application	Author(s)	Year	Reference
Heavy isotope analysis	Grosse, Hinden, Kirshenbaum	1949	112
Analysis of stainless steels	Gorman, Jones, Hipple	1951	111
Analysis of uranium and lead	Hess, Brown, Inghram, Patterson, Tilton	1953	126
Impurities in semiconductors	Hannay, Ahearn	1954	118
Analysis for U, Th, Pb	Tilton, Aldrich, Inghram	1954	268
Air-borne lead particulate analysis	Tilton, Patterson, Brown, Inghram, Hayden, Hess, Larsen	1955	270
Isotope analysis	Stevens	1957	258
Inorganic solids analysis	Associated Electrical Industries	1957	17a
Lead isotope analysis	Bate, Miller, Kulp	1957	23
Determination of uranium	Goris, Duffy, Tingey	1957	110
Analysis of enriched stable isotopes	Walton	1957	284
Analysis of nonconducting solids	James, Williams	1958	144
Analysis of impurities in solids	Craig, Errock, Waldron	1958	63
Analysis of uranium and other elements	Shields, Dibeler	1959	246
Age study of minerals	Aldrich, Davis, Tilton, Wetherill	1956	14
Lead age determination of minerals	Tilton, Davis, Wetherill, Aldrich	1957	269
Isotope geology applications	Russell	1958	231

ent in very low concentrations may be of greater interest than the major ones. In order to provide the most reliable analysis of trace components, the isotope-dilution method has been developed to a high degree (291). It is specific, sensitive, and accurate, as compared to other methods of trace analysis. The method is based on adding to the sample a known quantity of an element having an isotopic composition different from that in the natural element. A mass spectrometer then determines the change in isotopic composition. The tracer used in this work is usually a stable isotope enriched through electromagnetic separation (22).

Mass spectrometric studies have materially promoted the technology associated with geological research. Typical applications include the dating of minerals, rocks, and geological formations, and a study of variations in the isotopic abundances as a result of natural fractionation processes. Russell has described the use of the mass spectrometer as a geological instrument (231), and additional background information is provided by Rankama (220) and Duckworth (3).

A partial list for a variety of mass spectrometric applications to the determination of inorganic solids is given in Table 40.XVII.

F. APPLICATIONS IN THE FIELD OF CHEMICAL PHYSICS

The utilization of the mass spectrometer in research investigations, beginning with the early studies of Aston in 1920 (20), has continued through the years to be a dominant factor in determining the fundamental properties of matter. Work in the field of chemical physics has been accomplished largely with privately designed, specialized instruments having extraordinary capabilities, such as high resolving power or sensitivity. In many respects these "home-made" spectrometers are greatly superior to the commercially produced analytical types, although other features desirable for routine operation may be lacking. Some of the recent research applications briefly reviewed below point out the wide scope of mass spectrometry in chemical physics.

1. Physical Constants

a. Isotope Abundances

Abundances have been measured for practically all the naturally occurring isotopes with an uncertainty of about 1 relative per cent. The limit of detection of the rare isotopes has been reduced to about 10^{-8} through the use of a two-stage magnetic analyzer first designed by Inghram and Hess (142). A highly sensitive apparatus using this technique with a 20-stage multiplier detector (294) was used by White, Collins, and Rourke for measuring isotopic abundances of a large number of elements (295). More recently White, Rourke, and Sheffield have built a three-stage mass spectrometer (296). The stages are comprised of two magnetic analyzers in tandem and one electrostatic analyzer. The sensitivity of this instrument as measured with sodium isotopes was one part in 10^{10}. It was disclosed recently (16c) that a 100-inch radius double-focusing spectrometer is under construction at Argonne National Laboratory. It will be used for the precise determination of constants of the transuranium elements.

The determination of isotope abundances is of widespread interest in establishing average atomic weights of the naturally occurring elements. The mass spectrometer also has proved to be valuable for studying absolute isotopic abundances in widely separated areas of the earth's crust.

b. Mass Assignments

The determination of isotopic masses by the peak-matching technique can be made with a precision of about one part in 10^8. Quisenberry, Scolman, and Nier (219) have combined a high-resolving power, double-focusing instrument with a sensitive detector to ascertain the relative position of a doublet consisting of two peaks having similar mass. By a successive comparison of numerous doublets, an unambiguous and precise assignment may be made for most isotopes. Smith and Damm determined atomic masses by matching peaks with a frequency measurement (251). Duckworth (77) has compiled lists of doublets used to determine many isotopic masses. Kerr, Bainbridge, Dewdney, and Duckworth have determined some atomic masses with a precision of 2×10^{-8}, using a large single-stage magnetic analyzer (148).

The mass spectrometric data give values representing the physical scale of atomic masses based on the atomic mass of the oxygen isotope, $O^{16} = 16$. The difference between this scale and the chemical scale, based on naturally occurring oxygen (O^{16}, O^{17}, O^{18}) = 16, has been a source of controversy between the physicist and chemist for many years. Efforts that were underway (157,297,298) to adopt a more suitable primary standard, carbon-12, which can be compared with working standards such as silver, chlorine, and bromine by mass spectrometry and nuclear-reaction data, eventually reached fruition (57a).

c. Appearance Potentials and Bond Strengths

The appearance potential is the minimum energy required to dissociate a molecule to form a fragment ion and neutral fragment in the ground state. Because of a variety of inhomogeneities existing within an ion source, the theoretical ionization potential seldom is observed directly. Fox *et al.* were able to produce an equivalent monoenergetic electron beam by modulation techniques (90). Values that approximate the appearance potential can be determined from a conventional instrument by graphical extrapolation of corrected data. The theoretical aspects of appearance-potential measurement has been discussed thoroughly by Field and Franklin (4).

Bond-dissociation energies may be calculated from the appearance potential of an ion and a knowledge of the ionization potential of its parent free radical (4,11). For example, the dissociation energy of the carbon–hydrogen bond in methane may be determined from the equations:

$$CH_4 + e \rightarrow CH_3{}^+ + H + 2e$$

Then

$$A(CH_3^+) = I(CH_3) + D(CH_3\!-\!H)$$

where $A(CH_3^+)$ is the appearance potential of the methyl ion (14.3 e.v.), $I(CH_3)$ is the ionization potential of the methyl radical (10.1 e.v.), and $D(CH_3\!-\!H)$ is the dissociation energy of the carbon–hydrogen bond. Therefore:

$$D(CH_3\!-\!H) = A(CH_3^+) - I(CH_3)$$
$$D(CH_3\!-\!H) = 14.3 \text{ e.v.} - 10.1 \text{ e.v.} = 4.2 \text{ e.v.}$$

d. Nuclear Properties

The precise mass spectrometric determination of isotope abundances has been of tremendous importance in nuclear physics research. A large number of applications have been described by Inghram (139,143) and by Mayne (178), and were summarized by Duckworth (3). Although a detailed account of these investigations is not feasible in this chapter, a few interesting applications will be presented as typical examples.

The determination of half lives of long-lived radioisotopes has been measured by at least three different mass spectrometric methods. Thode and Graham measured the half life of Kr^{85} by its rate of disappearance from stable Kr isotopes (265). Nier determined the half life of U^{235} by measuring the growth rate of its daughter Pb^{207} (204). Sellers, Stevens, and Studier determined the half life of U^{232} by an isotope-dilution method using the addition of a known quantity of natural uranium (235).

In other applications, Lewis and Hayden used a mass spectrograph to collect and measure small quantities of radioisotopes having very short half lives (166). Dempster first showed the change in the isotopic constitution of cadmium under long exposure to neutrons (72). This served as a basis for the determination of isotopic absorption cross sections for neutrons. Reynolds (223) utilized the mass spectrometer abundance measurements to determine the branching ratio of the disintegration of Cu^{64}. Two daughters were formed, Ni^{64} from either the emission of a positron or a K capture branch, and Zn^{64} from electron radiation. Using the isotope-dilution technique he accurately determined the branching ratio Ni^{64}/Zn^{64}. Petruska, Thode, and Tomlinson made a mass analysis of the yields from light and heavy fragments in the thermal neutron fission of U^{235} (214).

2. Reaction Studies

a. Ion-Molecule Reactions

A reaction between ions and molecules in a mass spectrometer ion source, at pressures somewhat greater than are commonly used today, was first reported by Smyth in 1931 (252). Little interest was shown in these reactions until recently. Stevenson and Schissler (261) determined the rate constants of several gas reactions of the type

$$X^+ + YH = XH^+ + Y$$

and found these to be bimolecular. Schissler and Stevenson reported many more gaseous reactions (234), as for example

$$CH_3^+ + CH_4 \rightarrow C_2H_5^+ + H_2$$

The significance of ion-molecule reaction rates in relation to reaction mechanisms was discussed by Stevenson (259). Field, Franklin, and Lampe published a series of papers on reactions of gaseous ions, the first of these being on methane and ethylene (86). Franklin, Field and Lampe also reviewed the status of ion-molecule reactions (92). Wells and Melton constructed a mass spectrometer to study the ion-molecule collision processes (292). A comprehensive review of these secondary processes in the mass spectrometer is given by Field and Franklin (4). In these studies it was apparent that a marked similarity existed between ion-molecule reactions and those found in radiation-induced chemical reactions.

b. REACTION MECHANISMS

Mass spectrometric studies of fast gas reactions have shed considerable light on the role played by free radicals, ions, and other short-lived elementary species. Numerous investigators, using molecular beams in special ion source arrangements, have detected and identified free radicals, measured velocity constants, and calculated various activation energies (84,88,125,155,272). A comprehensive survey by Beckey (24) covers reaction properties of free radicals and atoms as described in the literature prior to 1958.

Eltenton, in his monumental experiments (84), attached a reaction chamber to the ion source with a line-of-sight opening between the reactor and source. Free radicals formed in the reaction could pass directly into the ionizing reaction without suffering collision with surfaces. Qualitatively, the free radicals were detected by selecting an electron energy slightly lower than the appearance potential of a similar ion produced from a stable molecule. Eltenton studied the thermal decomposition of the light hydrocarbons in addition to low-pressure combustion flame reactions. Foner and Hudson (88) also investigated flame reactions at high pressures, using an improved molecular-beam inlet system and a rapid-scanning mass spectrometer. The relation between the chemical properties of a catalyst surface and the products formed in the heterogeneous reaction is discussed by LeGoff (164). Blanchard and LeGoff investigated the disappearance of iodine atoms and free radicals during collision with the walls of a low-temperature ion source (36). A high-speed camera and time-of-flight spectrometer were used by Kistiakowsky and Kydd to observe the role of free radicals in flash photochemical reactions (155). Robertson has discussed low-pressure reactions of polyatomic molecules on hot metal filaments (226).

3. Electromagnetic Separation

The electromagnetic principle has been applied to the separation of stable isotopes by means of large mass spectrographs (13). The first machines designed at the University of California for this purpose were given the name Calutron. A facility in operation at the Oak Ridge National Laboratory has collected usable, enriched amounts of all naturally occurring isotopes (22, 103a). The Isotopes Division processes routinely the 55 elements that have naturally occurring stable isotopes. Other isotope separators in operation abroad have been described (68,154,156).

The Oak Ridge equipment utilizes a large 180° magnetic analyzer tube and a number of isotope reception pockets, in which the separated isotopes are collected. In some cases all the isotopes of an element can be collected simultaneously, whereas in other instances insufficient resolution limits the number of isotopes that can be separated; for example, the isotopes of mercury cannot all be separated at one time.

ACKNOWLEDGMENTS

The authors wish to express their gratitude to the management of the Research and Development Department, The Atlantic Refining Company, for the encouragement and help offered during the writing of this chapter. Sincere thanks also are extended to those directly responsible for the preparation of the manuscript and illustrations. Members of the mass spectrometer group, likewise, were of material help in collecting data and performing sample calculations.

REFERENCES

1. Aston, F. W., *Mass Spectra and Isotopes*, Longmans, Green, New York, 1942.
2. Barnard, G. P., Ed., *Modern Mass Spectrometry*, The Institute of Physics, London, 1953.
2a. Beynon, J. H., *Mass Spectrometry and Its Applications to Organic Chemistry*, D. Van Nostrand, Princeton, N. J., 1960.
2b. Biemann, K., *Mass Spectrometry, Organic Chemical Applications*, McGraw-Hill, New York, 1962.
3. Duckworth, H. E., *Mass Spectroscopy*, Cambridge University Press, New York, 1958.
3a. Elliot, R. M., Ed., *Advances in Mass Spectrometry*, Pergamon, New York 1963 Vol. 2.

4. Field, F. H., and J. L. Franklin, *Electron Impact Phenomena*, Academic Press, Inc., New York, 1957.

5. Hintenberger, H., Ed., *Nuclear Masses and Their Determination*, Pergamon, New York, 1957.

6. Inghram, M. G., and R. J. Hayden, Eds., *A Handbook on Mass Spectroscopy, Nuclear Sci. Ser., Rept. No.* **14,** National Research Council, Washington, 1954.

7. *Mass Spectrometry,* Conference of Mass Spectrometer Panel, The Institute of Petroleum, London, 1952.

8. *Applied Mass Spectrometry,* Conference of Mass Spectrometer Panel, The Institute of Petroleum, London, 1954.

9. *Mass Spectroscopy in Physics Research, Natl. Bur. Standards Circ. No.* **522,** (1953).

10. Massey, H. S. W., *Negative Ions,* Cambridge University Press, London, 1950.

11. Massey, H. S. W., and E. H. S. Burhop, *Electronic and Ionic Impact Phenomena,* Oxford University Press, New York, 1952.

12. Robertson, A. J. B., *Mass Spectrometry,* Wiley, New York, 1954.

13. Smith, M. L., Ed., *Electromagnetically Enriched Isotopes and Mass Spectrometry,* Academic, New York, 1956.

13a. Waldron, J. D., Ed., *Advances in Mass Spectrometry,* Pergamon, New York, 1959.

13b. Aczel, T., and H. E. Lumpkin, *Anal. Chem.,* **32,** 1819 (1960).

13c. Aczel, T., and H. E. Lumpkin, *Anal. Chem.,* **33,** 386 (1961).

13d. Aczel, T., and H. E. Lumpkin, *Anal. Chem.,* **34,** 33 (1962).

13e. Aczel, T., K. W. Bartz, H. E. Lumpkin, and F. C. Stehling, *Anal. Chem.,* **34,** 1821 (1962).

14. Aldrich, L. T., G. L. Davis, G. R. Tilton, and G. W. Wetherill, *J. Geophys. Research,* **61,** 215 (1956).

15a. Amberg, C. H., *J. Inst. Petrol.,* **45,** 1 (1959).

15b. American Petroleum Institute, New York, Research Project 42.

15c. American Petroleum Institute, New York, Research Project 44.

16. American Society for Testing and Materials, Committee E-14 on Mass Spectrometry, Philadelphia,

16b. Ardenne, M. von, K. Steinfelder, and R. Tuemmler, *Angew. Chem.,* **73,** 136 (1961).

16c. Argonne National Laboratory, *Chem. Eng. News* (Jan. 25), **38,** 49 (1960).

17. Asselineau, J., R. Ryhage, and E. Stenhagen, *Acta Chem. Scand.,* **11,** 196 (1957).

17a. Associated Electrical Industries, "Mass Spectrometry of Inorganic Solids," *Atomics and Nuclear Energy,* **8,** No. 10 (1957).

17b. Associated Electrical Industries, *Chem. Eng. News* (Feb. 13), **39,** 54 (1961).

18. "ASTM Proposed Method of Test for Hydrocarbon Types in Low Olefinic Gasoline by Mass Spectrometry," *ASTM Standards on Petroleum Products*—**1958,** Appendix VII, American Society for Testing Materials, Philadelphia, 1958.

19. Aston, F. W., *Phil. Mag.,* **38,** 709 (1919).

20. Aston, F. W., *Phil. Mag.,* **39,** 449 (1920).

21. Bainbridge, K. T., and E. B. Jordan, *Phys. Rev.,* **50,** 282 (1936).

22. Baker, P. S., *Chem. Eng. News* (Feb. 2), **37,** 60 (1959).

22a. Bartz, K. W., T. Aczel, H. E. Lumpkin, and F. C. Stehling, *Anal. Chem.,* **34,** 1814 (1962).

23. Bate, G. L., D. S. Miller, and J. L. Kulp, *Anal. Chem.,* **29,** 84 (1957).

24. Beckey, H. D., *Angew. Chem.,* **70,** 327 (1958).

25. Bennett, W. H., *J. Appl. Phys.,* **21,** 143, 723 (1950).

26. Bentley, P. G., A. N. Hamer, and P. B. F. Evans, "The Analysis of Corrosive

Gases with a Mass Spectrometer," in J. D. Waldron, Ed., *Advances in Mass Spectrometry*, Pergamon, New York, 1959.

27. Bernstein, R. B., G. P. Semeluk, and C. B. Arends, *Anal. Chem.*, **25**, 139 (1953).

28. Berry, C. E., *J. Chem. Phys.*, **17**, 1164 (1949).

29. Berry, C. E., *Phys. Rev.*, **78**, 597 (1950).

30. Berry, C. E., *Mass Spectroscopy in Physics Research, Natl. Bur. Standards Circ. No. **522**, 99 (1953).

30a. Betts, J. F., E. H. Paufe, and W. C. Wiley, *Appl. Spectroscopy*, **14**, 119 (1960).

31. Beynon, J. H., *Nature*, **174**, 735 (1954).

32. Beynon, J. H., *Mikrochim. Acta*, **1**, 437 (1956).

33. Beynon, J. H., "High Resolution Mass Spectrometry of Organic Materials," in J. D. Waldron, Ed., *Advances in Mass Spectrometry*, Pergamon, New York, 1959.

34. Beynon, J. H., personal communication (1959).

34a. Beynon, J. H., G. R. Lester, and A. E. Williams, *J. Phys. Chem.*, **63**, 1861 (1959).

34b. Beynon, J. H., R. A. Saunders, and A. E. Williams, *Anal. Chem.*, **33**, 221 (1961).

34c. Beynon, J. H., R. A. Saunders, A. Topham, and A. E. Williams, *J. Phys. Chem.*, **65**, 114 (1961).

35. Blanchard, L. P., J. B. Farmer, and C. Ouellet, *Can. J. Chem.*, **35**, 115 (1957).

36. Blanchard, L. P., and P. LeGoff, "A Mass Spectrometer with a Low Temperature Ionization Chamber to Study Heterogeneous Reactions of Atoms and Free Radicals," in J. D. Waldron, Ed., *Advances in Mass Spectrometry*, Pergamon, New York, 1959.

37. Bleakney, W., *Phys. Rev.*, **34**, 157 (1929).

38. Bleakney, W., and J. A. Hipple, *Phys. Rev.*, **53**, 521 (1938).

39. Blears, J., and J. D. Waldron, in G. P. Barnard, Ed., *Modern Mass Spectrometry*, The Institute of Physics, London, 1953, p. 209.

40. Bloom, E. G., F. L. Mohler, J. H. Lengel, and C. E. Wise, *J. Research Natl. Bur. Standards*, **40**, 437 (1948).

41. Bloom, E. G., F. L. Mohler, C. E. Wise, and E. J. Wells, *J. Research Natl. Bur. Standards*, **43**, 65 (1949).

42. Bogardus, B. J., and J. R. Mahoney, *Mass Spectrometer as a Process Monitoring Instrument*, Union Carbide Nuclear Co., Oak Ridge, Tenn., 1958.

43. Boos, R. N., S. L. Jones, and N. R. Trenner, *Anal. Chem.*, **28**, 390 (1956).

44. Bradt, P., V. H. Dibeler, and F. L. Mohler, *J. Research Natl. Bur. Standards*, **50**, 201 (1953).

45. Bradt, P., and F. L. Mohler, *Anal. Chem.*, **27**, 875 (1955).

46. Brewer, A. K., and V. H. Dibeler, *J. Research Natl. Bur. Standards*, **35**, 125 (1945).

47. Brown, R. A., *Anal. Chem.*, **23**, 430 (1951).

48. Brown, R. A., W. Doherty, and J. Spontak, *Consolidated Electrodynamics, Group Rept. No.* **84** (1950).

49. Brown, R. A., and E. Gilliams, "Mass Spectra of Monoolefins," paper presented to Meeting of ASTM Committee E-14 on Mass Spectrometry, New Orleans, La., May, 1954.

50. Brown, R. A., F. W. Melpolder, and W. S. Young, *Petroleum Processing*, **7**, 204 (1952).

51. Brown, R. A., D. J. Skahan, V. A. Cirillo, and F. W. Melpolder, *Anal. Chem.*, **31**, 1531 (1959).

52. Brown, R. A., R. C. Taylor, F. W. Melpolder, and W. S. Young, *Anal. Chem.*, **20**, 5 (1948).

53. Brown, R. A., W. S. Young, and N. Nicolaides, *Anal. Chem.*, **26**, 1653 (1954).

53a. Bua, E., and P. Manaresi, *Anal. Chem.*, **31**, 2022 (1959).

54. Cameron, A. E., *Rev. Sci. Instr.*, **25**, 1154 (1954).

55. Cameron, A. E., and D. F. Eggers, Jr., *Rev. Sci. Instr.*, **19**, 605 (1948).

56. Carlson, E. G., and M. J. O'Neal, Jr., *Am. Soc. Testing Materials. Spec. Tech. Rept. No. 224*, 151 (1958).

56a. Carlson, E. G., G. T. Paulissen, R. H. Hunt, and M. J. O'Neal, Jr., *Anal. Chem.*, **32**, 1489 (1960).

57. Charlet, E. M., *Group Rept. No. 74*, Consolidated Engineering Corp., Pasadena, Calif., 1948.

57a. *Chem. Eng. News* (Aug. 21), **39**, 22 (1961).

57b. Cirillo, V. A., D. J. Skahan. B. Hollis, and H. Morgan, *Anal. Chem.*, **34**, 1353 (1962).

58. Clerc, R. J., A. Hood, and M. J. O'Neal, Jr., *Anal. Chem.*, **27**, 868 (1955).

58a. Clerc, R. J., and M. J. O'Neal, Jr., paper presented to Petroleum Division, American Chemical Society, New York, Sept. 11–16, 1960.

58b. Coggeshall, N. D., *J. Chem. Phys.*, **33**, 1247 (1960).

59. Collin, J., *Bull. soc. roy. sci.*, Liège, **21**, 446 (1953).

60. Cook, G. L., R. A. Meyer, and D. G. Earnshaw, "A Dual-Purpose Inlet System for a Mass Spectrometer," paper presented to Meeting of ASTM Committee E-14 on Mass Spectrometry, New Orleans, June, 1958.

60a. Coulson, D. M., *Anal. Chem.*, **31**, 906 (1959).

61. Crable, G. F., and N. D. Coggeshall, *Anal. Chem.*, **30**, 310 (1958).

61a. Crable, G. F., G. L. Kearns, and M. S. Norris, *Anal. Chem.*, **32**, 13 (1960).

62. Craig, R. D., and G. A. Errock, "Design and Performance of a Double Focusing Mass Spectrometer for Analytical Work," in J. D. Waldron, Ed., *Advances in Mass Spectrometry*, Pergamon, New York, 1959.

63. Craig, R. D., G. A. Errock, and J. D. Waldron, "Determination of Impurities in Solids by Spark Source Mass Spectrometry," in J. D. Waldron, Ed., *Advances in Mass Spectrometry*, Pergamon, New York, 1959.

64. Crout, P. D., *Am. Inst. Elec. Engrs. Trans.*, **60**, 1235 (1941).

65. Crowe, D., *Inst. Petrol. Rev.*, **9**, 29 (1955).

65a. Cuthbert, J., *Quart. Revs. (London)*, **13**, 215 (1959).

66. Daigle, E. C., and H. A. Young, *Anal. Chem.*, **24**, 1190 (1952).

67. Datz, S., and E. H. Taylor, *J. Chem. Phys.*, **25**, 389 (1956).

68. Dawton, R. H. V. M., and M. L. Smith, *Quart. Revs. (London)*, **9**, 1 (1955).

69. Dempster, A. J., *Phys. Rev.*, **11**, 316 (1918).

70. Dempster, A. J., *Proc. Am. Phil. Soc.*, **75**, 755 (1935).

71. Dempster, A. J., *Rev. Sci. Instr.*, **7**, 46 (1936).

72. Dempster, A. J., *Phys. Rev.*, **71**, 829 (1947).

73. Dibeler, V. H., and F. L. Mohler, *J. Research Natl. Bur. Standards*, **39**, 149 (1947).

74. Donner, W., *ISA Journal*, **3**, 89 (1956).

75. Drew, C. M., J. R. McNesby, S. R. Smith, and A. S. Gordon, *Anal. Chem.*, **28**, 979 (1956).

76. Duckworth, H. E., *Rev. Sci. Instr.*, **21**, 54 (1949).

77. Duckworth, H. E., *Rev. Mod. Phys.*, **29**, 767 (1957).

78. Dudenbostel, B. F., Jr., and P. J. Klass, "Digitization of Mass Spectra," in J. D. Waldron, Ed., *Advances in Mass Spectrometry*, Pergamon, New York, 1959.

79. Dudenbostel, B. F., Jr., and W. Priestley, Jr., *Anal. Chem.*, **26**, 1275 (1954).

80. Dudenbostel, B. F., Jr., and W. Priestley, Jr., *Chem. Eng. News* (Nov. 29), **32**, 4736 (1954).

81. Dunning, W. J., *Quart. Revs. (London)*, **9**, 23 (1955).

82. Echo, M. W., and T. D. Morgan, *Anal. Chem.*, **29**, 1593 (1957).

83. Eden, M., B. E. Burr, and A. W. Pratt, *Anal. Chem.*, **23**, 1735 (1951).

84. Eltenton, G. C., *J. Chem. Phys.*, **15**, 455 (1947).

84a. Emery, E. M., *Anal. Chem.*, **32**, 1495 (1960).

85. Ferguson, W. C., and H. E. Howard, *Anal. Chem.*, **30**, 314 (1958).

86. Field, F. H., J. L. Franklin, and F. W. Lampe, *J. Am. Chem. Soc.*, **79**, 2419 (1957).

87. Field, F. H., and S. H. Hastings, *Anal. Chem.*, **28**, 1248 (1956).

87a. Fitzgerald, M. E., V. A. Cirillo, and F. J. Galbraith, *Anal. Chem.*, **34**, 1276 (1962).

88. Foner, S. N., and R. L. Hudson, *J. Chem. Phys.*, **21**, 1374 (1953).

89. Fowler, K. T., and P. Hugh-Jones, *Brit. Med. J.*, **5029**, 1205 (1957).

90. Fox, R. E., W. M. Hickam, D. J. Grove, and T. Kjeldaas, Jr., *Rev. Sci. Instr.*, **26**, 1101 (1955).

91. Fox, R. E., and J. A. Hipple, *J. Chem. Phys.*, **15**, 208 (1947).

91a. Franke, G., *Erdöl u. Kohle*, **13**, 263 (1960).

92. Franklin, J. L., F. H. Field, and F. W. Lampe, "Ion Molecule Reactions in the Gas Phase," in J. D. Waldron, Ed., *Advances in Mass Spectrometry*, Pergamon, New York, 1959.

93. Friedel, R. A., *Anal. Chem.*, **28**, 1806 (1956).

94. Friedel, R. A., A. F. Logar, Jr., and J. L. Shultz, *Appl. Spectroscopy*, **6**, No. 5, 24 (1952).

95. Friedel, R. A., and A. G. Sharkey, Jr., *Anal. Chem.*, **28**, 940 (1956).

96. Friedel, R. A., A. G. Sharkey, Jr., J. L. Shultz, and C. R. Humbert, *Anal. Chem.*, **25**, 1314 (1953).

97. Friedel, R. A., J. L. Shultz, and A. G. Sharkey, Jr., *Anal. Chem.*, **28**, 926 (1956).

98. Friedel, R. A., G. Wood, J. L. Shultz, and A. G. Sharkey, Jr., "Carbon Number Distribution of Some Hydrocarbons and Oxygenates in Fischer-Tropsch Products," paper presented to Meeting of ASTM Committee E-14 on Mass Spectrometry, New York, May, 1957.

99. Friedland, S. S., G. H. Lane, Jr., R. T. Longman, K. E. Train, and M. J. O'Neal, Jr., *Anal. Chem.*, **31**, 169 (1959).

99a. Frisque, A. J.. H. M. Grubb, C. H. Ehrhardt, and R. W. Vander Haar, *Anal. Chem.*, **33**, 389 (1961).

100. Fritts, B. K., and G. Peattie, *Anal. Chem.*, **28**, 10 (1956).

101. Genge, C. A., *Anal. Chem.*, **31**, 1747 (1959).

101a. Genge, C. A., *Anal. Chem.*, **31**, 1750 (1959).

102. Gentry, W. O., "The Line Recorder Mass Spectrometer as an Analytical Instrument," *Rept.* **PNW-12–58**, Instrument Society of America, 13th Annual Conference, Philadelphia, Sept., 1958.

103. Gifford, A. P., S. M. Rock, and D. J. Comaford, *Anal. Chem.*, **21**, 1026 (1949).

103a. Gillette, J. H., *Chem. Eng. News* (Feb. 20), **39**, 46 (1961).

103b. Gillette, J. M., *Anal. Chem.*, **31**, 1518 (1959).

104. Gilpin, J. A., and F. W. McLafferty, *Anal. Chem.*, **29**, 990 (1957).

104a. Gilpin, J. A., *Anal. Chem.*, **31**, 935 (1959).

105. Gohlke, R. S., *Anal. Chem.*, **31**, 535 (1959).

106. Gohlke, R. S., and F. W. McLafferty, "Mass Spectrometer Analysis of Aromatic Acids and Esters," paper presented to Meeting of ASTM Committee E-14 on Mass Spectrometry, San Francisco, Calif., May, 1955.

106a. Gohlke, R. S., and F. W. McLafferty, *Anal. Chem.*, **34**, 1281 (1962).

107. Gomer, R., and M. G. Inghram, *J. Am. Chem. Soc.*, **77**, 500 (1955).

108. Gordon, S. A., *Rev. Sci. Instr.*, **29**, 501 (1958).

109. Gordon, R. J., R. J. Moore, and C. E. Muller, *Anal. Chem.*, **30**, 1221 (1958).

110. Goris, P., W. E. Duffy, and F. H. Tingey, *Anal. Chem.*, **29**, 1590 (1957).

111. Gorman, J. G., E. J. Jones, and J. A. Hipple, *Anal. Chem.*, **23**, 438 (1951).

112. Grosse, A. V., S. G. Hinden, and A. D. Kirshenbaum, *Anal. Chem.*, **21**, 386 (1949).

113. Grosse, A. V., and A. D. Kirshenbaum, *Anal. Chem.*, **24**, 584 (1952).

114. Hall, L. D., *Rev. Sci. Instr.*, **29**, 367 (1958).

115. Hall, L. G., C. K. Hines, and J. E. Slay, "A High Speed Cycloidal Mass Spectrometer," in J. D. Waldron, Ed., *Advances in Mass Spectrometry*, Pergamon, New York, 1959.

116. Halstead, R. E., and A. O. Nier, *Rev. Sci. Instr.*, **21**, 1019 (1950).

117. Hannay, N. B., *Rev. Sci. Instr.*, **25**, 644 (1954).

118. Hannay, N. B., and A. J. Ahearn, *Anal. Chem.*, **26**, 1056 (1954).

119. Happ, G. P., and D. W. Stewart, *J. Am. Chem. Soc.*, **74**, 4404 (1952).

120. Happ, G. P., D. W. Stewart, and H. F. Brockmyre, *Anal. Chem.*, **22**, 1224 (1950).

121. Happ, G. P., D. W. Stewart, and H. C. Cooper, *Anal. Chem.*, **29**, 68 (1957).

122. Harrington, D. B., "The Time-of-Flight Mass Spectrometer," in J. D. Waldron, Ed., *Advances in Mass Spectrometry*, Pergamon, New York, 1959.

123. Hastings, S. H., B. H. Johnson, and H. E. Lumpkin, *Anal. Chem.*, **28**, 1243 (1956).

124. Hays, E. E., P. I. Richards, and S. A. Goudsmit, *Phys. Rev.*, **84**, 824 (1951).

125. Herzog, R. F., and F. F. Marmo, *J. Chem. Phys.*, **27**, 1202 (1957).

126. Hess, D. C., H. Brown, M. G. Inghram, C. Patterson, and G. Tilton, *Mass Spectroscopy in Physics Research*, *Natl. Bur. Standards Circ. No.* **522**, 183 (1953).

127. Hintenberger, H., *Mikrochim Acta*, **1956**, 71.

128. Hintenberger, H., and C. Lang, *Z. Naturforsch.*, **11a**, 167 (1956).

129. Hipple, J. A., and E. U. Condon, *Phys. Rev.*, **68**, 54 (1945).

130. Hipple, J. A., H. Sommer, and H. A. Thomas, *Phys. Rev.*, **78**, 332 (1950).

131. Holmes, J. C., and C. Y. Johnson, *Anal. Chem.*, **30**, No. 9, 19A (1958).

132. Holmes, J. C., and F. A. Morrell, *Appl. Spectroscopy*, **11**, 86 (1957).

133. Honig, R. E., *J. Appl. Phys.*, **16**, 646 (1945).

134. Hood, A., *Anal. Chem.*, **30**, 1218 (1958).

134a. Hood, A., R. J. Clerc, and M. J. O'Neal, *J. Inst. Petrol.*, **45**, 168 (1959).

135. Hood, A., and M. J. O'Neal, "Status of Application of Mass Spectrometry to Heavy Oil Analysis," in J. D. Waldron, Ed., *Advances in Mass Spectrometry*, Pergamon, New York, 1959.

135a. Hoogendonk, W. P., and F. W. Porsche, *Anal. Chem.*, **32**, 941 (1960).

136. Hoover, H., Jr., and H. W. Washburn, *Am. Inst. Mining Met. Engrs.*, *Tech. Publ. No.* **1205** (1940).

137. Hopp, H. F., and R. Wertzler, *Anal. Chem.*, **30**, 877 (1958).

137a. Howard, H. E., W. C. Ferguson, and L. R. Snyder, *Anal. Chem.*, **32**, 1814 (1960).

137b. Howard, H. E., and W. C. Ferguson, *Anal. Chem.*, **33**, 1870 (1961).

138. Hurzeler, H., M. G. Inghram, and J. D. Morrison, *J. Chem. Phys.*, **28**, 76 (1958).

139. Inghram, M. G., in *Mass Spectroscopy in Physics Research*, *Natl. Bur. Standards (U.S.) Circ. No.* **522**, 151 (1953).

140. Inghram, M. G., and W. A. Chupka, *Rev. Sci. Instr.*, **24**, 518 (1953).

141. Inghram, M. G., and R. Gomer, *J. Chem. Phys.*, **22**, 1279 (1954).

142. Inghram, M. G., and D. C. Hess, in M. G. Inghram and R. H. Hayden, Eds., *A*

Handbook on Mass Spectroscopy, Nuclear Sci. Ser. Rept. No. **14**, National Research Council, Washington, 1954, p. 24.

143. Inghram, M. G., et al., *Proc. Intern. Conf. Peaceful Uses At. Energy, Geneva, 1955*, **4**, 105 (1956).

144. James, J. A., and J. L. Williams, "The Analysis of Nonconducting Solids by the Mass Spectrometer," in J. D. Waldron, Ed., *Advances in Mass Spectrometry*, Pergamon, New York, 1959.

145. Jones, S. L., and N. R. Trenner, *Anal. Chem.*, **28**, 387 (1956).

146. Katzenstein, H. S., and S. S. Friedland, *Rev. Sci. Instr.*, **26**, 324 (1955).

146a. Kearns, G. L., N. C. Maranowski, and G. F. Crable, *Anal. Chem.*, **31**, 1646 (1959).

147. Kelley, H. M., *Anal. Chem.*, **23**, 1081 (1951).

148. Kerr, J. T., G. R. Bainbridge, J. W. Dewdney, and H. E. Duckworth, "Some New Atomic Mass Determinations Made with a Large Single-Focusing Mass Spectrometer," in J. D. Waldron, Ed., *Advances in Mass Spectrometry*, Pergamon, New York, 1959.

149. Kerr, L. W. J., *Electronics*, **2**, 179 (1956).

150. King, W. H., Jr., W. P. McSweeney, F. H. Kant, and W. Priestley, Jr., "An Approach to Mass Spectrometer Analysis of High Molecular Weight Petroleum Fractions," paper presented to Meeting of ASTM Committee E-14 on Mass Spectrometry, San Francisco, May, 1955.

151. King, W. H., and W. Priestley, Jr., *Anal. Chem.*, **23**, 1418 (1951).

152. Kinney, I. W., and G. L. Cook, *Anal. Chem.*, **24**, 1391 (1952).

153. Kirshenbaum, A. D., and A. V. Grosse, *Anal. Chem.*, **22**, 613 (1950).

154. Kistemaker, J., and C. J. Zilverschoon, in *Mass Spectroscopy in Physics Research*, *Natl. Bur. Standards (U.S.)* Circ. *No.* **522**, 179 (1953).

155. Kistiakowsky, G. B., and P. H. Kydd, *J. Am. Chem. Soc.*, **79**, 4825 (1957).

155a. Klaas, P. J., and W. P. McSweeney, *Anal. Chem.*, **34**, 30 (1962).

156. Koch, J., in *Mass Spectroscopy in Physics Research*, *Natl. Bur. Standards (U.S.)* Circ. *No.* **522**, 165 (1953).

157. Kohman, T. P., J. H. E. Mattauch, and A. H. Wapstra, *Physics Today*, **12**, 31 (1959).

157a. Kourey, R. E., B. F. Tuffly, and V. A. Yarborough, *Anal. Chem.*, **31**, 1760 (1959).

158. LaLau, C., *Anal. Chim. Acta*, **22**, 239 (1960).

159. Lampe, F. W., J. L. Franklin, and F. W. Field, *J. Am. Chem. Soc.*, **79**, 6129 (1957).

160. Langer, A., *J. Phys. & Colloid Chem.*, **54**, 618 (1950).

161. Langer, A., and R. E. Fox, *Anal. Chem.*, **21**, 1032 (1949).

162. Langer, S. H., R. A. Friedel, I. Wender, and A. G. Sharkey, *Anal. Chem.*, **30**, 1353 (1958).

162a. Lawrey, D. M. G., and J. F. Paulson, *Anal. Chem.*, **34**, 538 (1962).

163. LeBlanc, R. B., *Anal. Chem.*, **30**, 1797 (1958).

164. LeGoff, P., *J. Chem. Phys.*, **53**, 369 (1956).

164a. Levy, E. J., R. R. Doyle, R. A. Brown, and F. W. Melpolder, *Anal. Chem.*, **33**, 698 (1961).

165. Levy, E. J., and W. H. Stahl, *Anal. Chem.*, **33**, 707 (1961).

166. Lewis, L. G., and R. J. Hayden, *Rev. Sci. Instr.*, **19**, 599, 922 (1948).

167. Lossing, F. P., and Tanaka, I., *J. Chem. Phys.*, **25**, 1031 (1956).

168. Lumpkin, H. E., *Anal. Chem.*, **28**, 1946 (1956).

169. Lumpkin, H. E., *Anal. Chem.*, **30**, 321 (1958).

169a. Lumpkin, H. E., and J. O. Beauxis, *Anal. Chem.*, **32**, 1815 (1960).

170. Lumpkin, H. E., and B. H. Johnson, *Anal. Chem.*, **26**, 1719 (1954).

170a. Lumpkin, H. E., and D. E. Nicholson, *Anal. Chem.*, **32**, 74 (1960).

170b. Lumpkin, H. E., and G. R. Taylor, *Anal. Chem.*, **33**, 476 (1961).

171. Lumpkin, H. E., and B. W. Thomas, *Anal. Chem.*, **23**, 1738 (1951).

172. Lumpkin, H. E., B. W. Thomas, and A. Elliott, *Anal. Chem.*, **24**, 1389 (1952).

173. Madorsky, S. L., and S. Straus, *J. Research Natl. Bur. Standards*, **40**, 417 (1948).

174. Madorsky, S. L., S. Straus, D. I. Thompson, and L. Williamson, *J. Research Natl. Bur. Standards*, **42**, 499 (1949).

175. Matheson, R. M., L. S. Nergaard, and R. H. Plumlee, *RCA Rev.*, **18**, 385 (1957).

176. Mattauch, J., and H. Ewald, *Z. Physik.*, **122**, 314 (1944).

177. Mattauch, J., and R. Herzog, *Z. Physik.*, **89**, 786 (1934).

178. Mayne, K. I., "The Study of Nuclear Reactions by Mass Spectrometry," in J. D. Waldron, Ed., *Advances in Mass Spectrometry*, Pergamon, New York, 1959.

179. McAdams, D. R., *Anal. Chem.*, **30**, 881 (1958).

180. McLafferty, F. W., *Anal. Chem.*, **28**, 306 (1956).

181. McLafferty, F. W., *Anal. Chem.*, **29**, 1782 (1957).

182. McLafferty, F. W., *Appl. Spectroscopy*, **11**, *No.* 4, 148 (1957).

183. McLafferty, F. W., "Interpretation of Mass Spectra of Organic Molecules," in J. D. Waldron, Ed., *Advances in Mass Spectrometry, Pergamon, New York,* 1959.

183a. McLafferty, F. W., *Anal. Chem.*, **31**, 2072 (1959).

184. McLafferty, F. W., *Anal. Chem.*, **31**, 82 (1959).

184a. McLafferty, F. W., *Anal. Chem.*, **34**, 2 (1962).

184b. McLafferty, F. W., *Anala. Chem.*, **34**, 16 (1962).

184c. McLafferty, F. W., *Anal. Chem.*, **34**, 26 (1962).

184d. McLafferty, F. W., and R. S. Gohlke, *Anal. Chem.*, **31**, 2076 (1959).

185. McTeer, M. L., and G. S. Morgan, Quality Control Lab., Carbide and Carbon Chemicals Co., South Charleston, W. Va., 1958.

186. Meadows, E. B., "A Progress Report on Upper Atmospheric Research with Mass Spectrometers," paper presented to Meeting of ASTM Committee E-14 on Mass Spectrometry, New Orleans, June, 1958.

187. Melpolder, F. W., and R. A. Brown, *Anal. Chem.*, **20**, 139 (1948).

188. Melpolder, F. W., R. A. Brown, T. A. Washall, W. Doherty, and C. E. Headington, *Anal. Chem.*, **28**, 1936 (1956).

189. Melpolder, F. W., R. A. Brown, T. A. Washall, W. Doherty, and W. S. Young, *Anal. Chem.*, **26**, 1904 (1954).

190. Melpolder, F. W., R. A. Brown, W. S. Young, and C. E. Headington, *Ind. Eng. Chem.*, **44**, 1142 (1952).

191. Melpolder, F. W., C. W. Warfield, and C. E. Headington, *Anal. Chem.*, **25**, 1453 (1953).

192. Melton, C. E., and P. S. Rudolph, *J. Chem. Phys.*, **31**, 1485 (1959).

193. Meyer, R. A., and D. G. Earnshaw, *U.S. Bur. Mines Rept. Invest. No.* **5329** (1957).

194. Meyerson, S., *Appl. Spectroscopy*, **9**, 120 (1955).

195. Mihm, C. H., L. W. Pollock, and R. O. Shelton, *Anal. Chem.*, **30**, 874 (1958).

196. Mikkelsen, L., R. L. Hopkins, and D. Y. Yee, *Anal. Chem.*, **30**, 317 (1958).

197. Mohler, F. L., E. G. Bloom, J. H. Lengel, and C. E. Wise, *J. Am. Chem. Soc.*, **71**, 337 (1949).

198. Mohler, F. L., E. G. Bloom, E. J. Wells, J. H. Lengel, and C. E. Wise, *J. Research Natl. Bur. Standards*, **42**, 369 (1949).

199. Mohler, F. L., P. Bradt, and V. H. Dibeler, *J. Research Natl. Bur. Standards*, **60**, 615 (1958).

200. Mohler, F. L., L. Williamson, and H. M. Dean, *J. Research Natl. Bur. Standards*, **45**, 235 (1950).

201. Morrison, J. D., *J. Appl. Phys.*, **28**, 1409 (1957).

202. Müller, E. W., *Ergeb. exakt Naturw*, **27**, 290 (1953).

203. Nicholson, A. J. C., *J. Chem. Phys.*, **29**, 1312 (1958).

204. Nier, A. O., *Phys. Rev.*, **55**, 153 (1939).

205. Nier, A. O., *Rev. Sci. Instr.*, **18**, 398 (1947).

206. Nier, A. O., T. A. Abbott, J. K. Pickard, W. T. Leland, T. I. Taylor, C. M. Stevens, D. L. Dukey, and G. Goertzel, *Anal. Chem.*, **20**, 188 (1948).

207. Nier, A. O., E. P. Ney, and M. G. Inghram, *Rev. Sci. Instr.*, **18**, 191 (1947).

208. Nier, A. O., and T. R. Roberts, *Phys. Rev.*, **81**, 507 (1951).

209. Nier, A. O., C. M. Stevens, A. Hustrulid, and T. A. Abbott, *J. Appl. Phys.*, **18**, 30 (1947).

210. O'Neal, M. J., Jr., and T. P. Wier, *Anal. Chem.*, **23**, 830 (1951).

211. Orkin, B. A., J. G. Bendoraitis, B. Brown, and R. H. Williams, *Am. Soc. Testing Materials, Spec. Tech. Publ. No.* **224**, 59 (1958).

212. Otvos, J. W., and D. P. Stevenson, *J. Am. Chem. Soc.*, **78**, 546 (1956).

213. Palmer, G. H., "High-Sensitivity Solid-Source Mass Spectrometry," in J. D. Waldron, Ed., *Advances in Mass Spectrometry*, Pergamon, New York, 1959.

213a. Peterson, L., *Anal. Chem.*. **34**, 1850 (1962).

214. Petruska, J. A., H. G. Thode, and R. H. Tomlinson, *Can. J. Phys.*, **33**, 693 (1955).

215. Priestley, W., and B. F. Dudenbostel, *Ind. Eng. Chem.*, **48**, No. 2, 81A (1956).

216. Quayle, A., "The Mass Spectra of Some Organic Phosphates," in J. D. Waldron, Ed., *Advances in Mass Spectrometry*, Pergamon, New York, 1959.

217. Quiram, E. R., and W. B. Biller, *Anal. Chem.*, **30**, 1166 (1958).

218. Quiram, E. R., S. J. Metro, and J. B. Lewis, *Anal. Chem.*, **26**, 352 (1954).

219. Quisenberry, K. S., T. T. Scolman, and A. O. Nier, *Phys. Rev.*, **102**, 1071 (1956).

220. Rankama, K. *Isotope Geology*, McGraw-Hill, New York, 1954, Chapter 4.

220a. Reese, R. M., *Anal. Chem. (Review Ed.)*, **34**, 243R (1962).

221. Reese, R. M., V. H. Dibeler, and F. L. Mohler, *J. Research Natl. Bur. Standards*, **46**, 79 (1951).

222. Reese, R. M., V. H. Dibeler, and F. L. Mohler, *J. Research Natl. Bur. Standards*, **57**, 367 (1956).

223. Reynolds, J. H., *Phys. Rev.*, **79**, 789 (1950).

224. Reynolds, J. H., *Rev. Sci. Instr.*, **27**, 928 (1956).

225. Rittenberg, D., and T. D. Price, *Ann. Rev. Nuclear Sci.*, **1**, 569 (1952).

226. Robertson, A. J. B., "The Investigation of Certain Surface Processes by Mass Spectrometry," in J. D. Waldron, Ed., *Advances in Mass Spectrometry*, Pergamon, New York, 1959.

227. Robinson, C. F., and L. G. Hall, *Rev. Sci. Instr.*, **27**, 504 (1956).

228. Robinson, C. F., and A. G. Sharkey, Jr., *Rev. Sci. Instr.*, **29**, 250 (1958).

229. Roth, E., in *Applied Mass Spectrometry*, Conference of Mass Spectrometer Panel, The Institute of Petroleum, London, 1954, p. 81.

230. Rowe, E. H., *Rev. Sci. Instr.*, **28**, 1094 (1957).

231. Russell, R. D., "The Mass Spectrometer as a Geological Instrument," in J. D. Waldron, Ed., *Advances in Mass Spectrometry*, Pergamon, New York, 1959.

232. Rylander, P. N., and S. Meyerson, *J. Am. Chem. Soc.*, **78**, 5799 (1956).

233. Sauer, R. W., F. W. Melpolder, and R. A. Brown, *Ind. Eng. Chem.*, **44**, 2606 (1952).
234. Schissler, D. O., and D. P. Stevenson, *J. Chem. Phys.*, **24**, 926 (1956).
235. Sellers, P. A., C. M. Stevens, and M. H. Studier, *Phys. Rev.*, **94**, 952 (1954).
236. Sharkey, A. G., Jr., E. H. Bean, R. A. Friedel, and L. J. E. Hofer, "Conditioning of Mass Spectrometer Filaments; Formation of Tungsten Carbides," paper presented to Meeting of ASTM Committee E-14 on Mass Spectrometry, New York, May, 1957.
237. Sharkey, A. G., Jr., R. A. Friedel, and S. H. Langer, *Anal. Chem.*, **29**, 770 (1957).
238. Sharkey, A. G., Jr., C. F. Robinson, and R. A. Friedel, "Use of Rhenium Filaments and Low Ionizing Voltages for Analyzing Liquid Products from Coal Hydrogenation by Mass Spectrometry," in J. D. Waldron, Ed., Advances in Mass Spectrometry, Pergamon, New York, 1959.
239. Sharkey, A. G., Jr., J. L. Shultz, and R. A. Friedel, *Anal. Chem.*, **28**, 934 (1956).
240. Sharkey, A. G., Jr., J. L. Shultz, and R. A. Friedel, *Anal. Chem.*, **31**, 87 (1959).
240a. Sharkey, A. G., Jr., G. Wood, J. L. Shultz, I. Wender, and R. A. Friedel, *Fuel*, **38**, 315 (1959).
241. Shaw, A. E., and W. Rall, *Rev. Sci. Instr.*, **18**, 278 (1947).
242. Shell Oil Co., *Chem. Eng. News* (Sept. 19), **33**, 3988 (1955).
243. Shepherd, M. *J. Research Natl. Bur. Standards*, **38**, 491 (1947).
244. Shepherd, M., *J. Research Natl. Bur. Standards*, **44**, 509 (1950).
245. Shepherd, M., S. M. Rock, R. Howard, and J. Stormes, *Anal. Chem.*, **23**, 1431 (1951)
246. Shields, W. R., and V. H. Dibeler, paper presented to Meeting of ASTM Committee E-14 on Mass Spectrometry, Los Angeles, May, 1959.
247. Siegel, H., and D. O. Schissler, *Anal. Chem.*, **28**, 1646 (1956).
248. Slobod, R. L., and M. E. Krogh, *J. Am. Chem. Soc.*, **72**, 1175 (1950).
249. Smith, L. G., *Phys. Rev.*, **81**, 295 (1951).
250. Smith, L. G., and C. C. Damm, *Phys. Rev.*, **90**, 324 (1953).
251. Smith, L. G., and C. C. Damm, *Rev. Sci. Instr.*, **27**, 638 (1956).
252. Smyth, H. D., *Rev. Mod. Phys.*, **3**, 347 (1931).
253. Sobcov, H., *Anal. Chem.*, **24**, 1386 (1952).
254. Sobcov, H., *Anal. Chem.*, **24**, 1908 (1952).
255. Stevens, C. M., *Rev. Sci. Instr.*, **24**, 148 (1953).
256. Stevens, C. M., and M. G. Inghram, *Rev. Sci. Instr.*, **24**, 987 (1953).
257. Stevens, C. M., and M. G. Inghram, "A Mass Spectrometer for Routine Solid Analysis," *U. S. At. Energy Comm. Rept.*, **ANL-5251** (1954).
258. Stevens, R. H., *U.S. At. Energy Comm. Rept.*, **K-1334** (1957).
259. Stevenson, D. P., *J. Phys. Chem.*, **61**, 1453 (1957).
260. Stevenson, D. P., and J. A. Hipple, *J. Am. Chem. Soc.*, **64**, 1588 (1942).
261. Stevenson, D. P., and D. O. Schissler, *J. Chem. Phys.*, **23**, 1353 (1955).
262. Svartholm, N., in *Mass Spectroscopy in Physics Research, Natl. Bur. Standards* (*U.S.*) *Circ. No.* **522**, 75 (1953).
263. Taylor, R. C., R. A. Brown, W. S. Young, and C. E. Headington, *Anal. Chem.*, **20**, 396 (1948).
264. Taylor, R. C., and W. S. Young, *Anal. Chem.*, **17**, 811 (1945).
265. Thode, H. G., and R. L. Graham, *Can. J. Research*, **A 25**, 1 (1947).
266. Thomas, B. W., and W. D. Seyfried, *Anal. Chem.*, **21**, 1022 (1949).
267. Thomas, H. A., T. W. Williams, and J. A. Hipple, *Rev. Sci. Instr.*, **17**, 368 (1946).
268. Tilton, G. R., L. T. Aldrich, and M. G. Inghram, *Anal. Chem.*, **26**, 894 (1954).
269. Tilton, G. R., G. L. Davis, G. W. Wetherill, and L. T. Aldrich, *Trans. Am. Geophys. Union*, **38**, 360 (1957).

270. Tilton, G. R., C. Patterson, H. Brown, M. G. Inghram, R. J. Hayden, D. C. Hess, and E. Larsen, *Bull. Geol. Soc. Am.*, **66**, 1131 (1955).
271. Townsend, J. W., Jr., *Rev. Sci. Instr.*, **23**, 538 (1952).
272. Vanreusel, L., and J. M. Delfosse, *Ann. soc. sci. Bruxelles, Ser. I*, **70**, 67 (1956).
273. Varadi, P. F., and L. G. Sebestyen, *J. Sci. Instr.*, **33**, 392 (1956).
274. Varsel, C. J., personal communication (1958).
275. Varsel, C. J., F. A. Morrell, F. E. Resnik, and W. A. Powell, *Anal. Chem.*, **32**, 182 (1960).
276. Voorhies, H. G., C. F. Robinson, L. G. Hall, W. M. Brubaker, and C. E. Berry, "Theoretical and Experimental Study of High-Resolution High-Mass Spectrometers," in J. D. Waldron, Ed., *Advances in Mass Spectrometry*, Pergamon, New York, 1959.
277. Wagener, J. S., and P. T. Marth, *J. Appl. Phys.*, **28**, 1027 (1957).
278. Waldron, J. D., *Research (London)*, **9**, 306 (1956).
279. Walker, J. K., A. P. Gifford, and R. Nelson, *Ind. Eng. Chem.*, **46**, 1400 (1954).
280. Walker, J. K., and C. L. O'Hara, *Anal. Chem.*, **27**, 825 (1955).
281. Wall, L. A., *J. Research Natl. Bur. Standards*, **41**, 315 (1948).
282. Wall, L. A., "Polymer Degradation Mechanisms," *Natl. Bur. Standards (U.S.) Circ. No.* **525**, 239 (1953).
283. Wall, R. F., *Ind. Eng. Chem.*, **49**, 59A (1957).
284. Walton, J. R., *U.S. At. Energy Comm. Rept.*, **ORNL-2315** (1957).
285. Washburn, H. W., and C. E. Berry, *Phys. Rev.*, **70**, 559 (1946).
286. Washburn, H. W., C. E. Berry, and L. G. Hall, in *Mass Spectroscopy in Physics Research, Natl. Bur. Standards (U.S.) Circ. No.* **522**, 141 (1953).
287. Washburn, H. W., C. E. Berry, and L. G. Hall, *Anal. Chem.*, **25**, 130 (1953).
288. Washburn, H. W., H. F. Wiley, and S. M. Rock, *Ind. Eng. Chem., Anal. Ed.*, **15**, 541 (1943).
289. Washburn, H. W., H. F. Wiley, S. M. Rock, and C. E. Berry, *Ind. Eng. Chem., Anal. Ed.*, **17**, 74 (1945).
290. Weaver, E. R., E. E. Hughs, S. M. Guntler, S. Schuhmann, N. T. Redfearn, and R. Gorden, Jr., *J. Research Natl. Bur. Standards*, **59**, 383 (1957).
291. Webster, R. K., "Isotope Dilution Analysis," in J. D. Waldron, Ed., *Advances in Mass Spectrometry*, Pergamon, New York, 1959.
292. Wells, G. F., and C. E. Melton, *Rev. Sci. Instr.*, **28**, 1065 (1957).
293. Wherry, T. C., and F. W. Karasek, *J. Appl. Phys.*, **26**, 682 (1955).
294. White, F. A., and T. L. Collins, *Appl. Spectroscopy*, **8**, 169 (1954).
295. White, F. A., T. L. Collins, and F. M. Rourke, *Phys. Rev.*, **101**, 1786 (1956).
296. White, F. A., F. M. Rourke, and J. C. Sheffield, "A Three-Stage Research Mass Spectrometer," *U. S. At. Energy Comm. Rept.*, **KAPL-1843** (1958).
297. Wichers, E., *Chem. Eng. News* (Sept. 8), **36**, 76 (1958).
298. Wichers, E., *Physics Today*, **12**, 28 (1959).
299. Willey, W. C., *Science*, **124**, 817 (1956).
300. Wiley, W. C., and I. H. McLaren, *Rev. Sci. Instr.*, **26**, 1150 (1955).
301. Williams, R. B., *Am. Soc. Testing Materials Spec. Tech. Publ. No.* **224**, 168 (1958).
301a. Wilson, C. O., and I. Shapiro, *Anal. Chem.*, **32**, 78 (1960).
302. Wolff, M. M., and W. E. Stephens, *Rev. Sci. Instr.*, **24**, 616 (1953).
303. Yarborough, V. A., *Anal. Chem.*, **25**, 914 (1953).
304. Zemany, P. D., *J. Appl. Phys.*, **23**, 924 (1952).
305. Zemany, P. D., *Anal. Chem.*, **24**, 1709 (1952).

ION-SCATTERING METHODS

By Sylvan Rubin, *Stanford Research Institute,
Menlo Park, California*

Contents

Notation

M_0 = atomic mass of stationary scattering element
M_1 = mass of incident and scattered ions
V = ion velocity
E = ion energy
k = ratio of ion velocity immediately after scattering to velocity immediately before
      scattering
z = atomic number of scattered ion
Z = atomic number of scattering element
t = target thickness, in cm.
n = atomic concentration per unit volume
c = atomic concentration per unit area
N = number of ions incident on target
q = electric charge incident on target
Y = number of particles detected by spectrometer
I = integral of Y with respect to particle momentum

R_c = collector resolution factor of spectrometer
r = spectrometer radius
D = dispersion factor of spectrometer
P = particle momentum
p = proton
d = deuteron
γ = gamma-ray quantum
δ = difference between scattering angles in laboratory and center-of-mass coordinate
ϵ = stopping power per atom, in e.v. $cm.^2$
Ω = solid angle (Ω' in C.M. coordinate)
Ω_s = solid angle of spectrometer
ϕ = angle through which incident particles are scattered (ϕ' in C.M. coordinate)
σ = scattering cross section per atom
$\dfrac{d\sigma}{d\Omega}$ = differential scattering cross section per unit solid angle
θ = angle between ion direction of motion and normal to surface of target

Subscripts

i refers sequentially to all the chemical elements or isotopes in the sample
j refers to the specific element for which calculation is being made
1 specifies quantities before scattering occurs
2 specifies quantities after scattering occurs

I. INTRODUCTION

The use of ion scattering as a means of chemical analysis arose from techniques developed in the field of nuclear physics for the study of nuclear reactions and nuclear scattering. In this work, targets of various elements are bombarded by beams of accelerated charged particles, such as protons or alpha particles from such well-known machines as Van de Graaff accelerators and cyclotrons. The particles or radiation emitted as a result of the nuclear encounters thus produced are observed in various ways.

When high-resolution magnetic spectrometers were developed for examining the products of such nuclear reactions, it was found that the presence of contaminant elements in the target materials often could be detected, especially in scattering experiments. In fact, the nuclear physicists could check the analyses of their target materials against the compositions given by the chemists who prepared them.

For example, in studies of the nuclear reactions of protons with beryllium, using beryllium foil targets, surface films of carbon and oxygen on the beryllium foils were detected and their thickness was measured from the observation on the scattered protons (21).

The first use of this method for the specific purpose of analyzing an unknown sample occurred in August, 1949, when smoggy air in Pasadena and Los Angeles was sampled by means of a jet impactor, and the microgram-sized samples of particulate smog were analyzed in the nuclear physics laboratory at California Institute of Technology, using a proton beam from the 2-M.e.v. electrostatic accelerator and the 12-inch magnetic spectrometer (18).

The samples were deposited on beryllium, aquadag, and aluminum backings; the best results were obtained using aluminum foil. The analyses of smog particles showed that carbon, oxygen, sulfur, and lead were principal constituents. It is a very cumbersome matter to collect a large enough sample of smog aerosol for any conventional method of chemical analysis, but a small impactor passing about 1 cubic foot of air in a few minutes collected a large enough sample to be analyzed by nuclear scattering. This demonstrates one of the merits of this technique—its capability for analyzing extremely small quantities of material.

Among other types of problems for which this method provides special facility are: (1) detection of contaminants on surfaces, (2) analysis of the composition and thickness of surface films, and (3) study of diffusion into solids. One useful feature of the method is that the sample is not generally changed either physically or chemically by the analytical procedure, except for heating by the bombardment.

However, there also are severe limitations on the applicability of this method. The heating effects of the beam are not severe on good heat conductors, such as metallic samples, but they cause rather high temperatures at the point of bombardment in thermal insulators. Insulating samples are thus limited to refractory substances. This eliminates essentially all organic materials as possible subjects for analysis. Furthermore, the samples must be capable of exposure to a vacuum of about 1 μ Hg, so that volatile materials cannot be analyzed.

The particle beam is stopped by a small thickness of matter, usually of a few microns, so that only the surface of any sample is analyzed. In a sense this is also an important merit of the technique, because it makes it a specialized method for the analysis of surface layers as such, which are frequently significantly different in composition from the underlying matter.

The use of particles in the energy range of 1 M.e.v. leads to the very high sensitivity obtainable, because each individual scattered particle can be detected and counted. Consequently, since we are dealing with very large numbers of atoms per second in the beam, the small nuclear scattering cross sections and the small aperture of a high-resolution spectrometer still give many counts per second in the detector for scattering from a target layer averaging 1 atom in thickness.

The particle energy is very large compared to any chemical or crystalline binding energies, which are generally in the range of 1 e.v. or smaller. Therefore this method is not influenced by the chemical or crystalline properties of the substances under analysis. It distinguishes only between different elements or isotopes by virtue of their differing nuclear masses and does not distinguish among the different chemical states of a given element.

II. THEORY OF METHOD

A. VELOCITY CHANGE ON SCATTERING

The dynamics of elastic scattering of nuclear particles is essentially the same as that of billiard balls with different masses. The conservation of energy and momentum leads to the following equation for the ratio of final to initial velocity of a particle of mass M_1, scattered by an initially stationary nucleus of mass M_0, into the angle ϕ with its initial direction:

$$\frac{V_2}{V_1} = \frac{1}{M_0 + M_1}\left[M_1 \cos \phi + (M_0{}^2 - M_1{}^2 \sin^2 \phi)^{1/2}\right] \qquad (1)$$

When M_0 is large compared to M_1, this is approximated by a much simpler equation entirely adequate for our purposes. We will denote the change in velocity of the M_1 particle by ΔV:

$$\Delta V/V_1 \cong - [M_1/(M_0 + M_1)](1 - \cos \phi) \qquad (2)$$

From this equation, it is clear that the fractional change in velocity will be much greater for scattering from light elements (with small M_0) than from heavy elements. Also, it is evident that the largest practicable scattering angle should be used to maximize the difference in velocity changes for different elements. Below, in the section on Computation and Results, a table of values of $k = 1 - (\Delta V/V_1)$ is given for protons scattered at 90° and 150° from nearly all nuclides. The approximation is not useful for scattering of protons from hydrogen (or alpha particles from hydrogen and helium). Protons will be scattered from hydrogen only at angles less than 90°, since their masses are identical. For the resolution of the heavier elements, it is clearly advantageous to scatter heavier particles, such as alpha particles, since $\Delta V/V_1$ is proportional to M_1.

B. SCATTERING CROSS SECTION

The concept of cross section is commonly used in nuclear physics. It means exactly that—it is the effective area of each nucleus for interception of an incident particle leading to some particular reaction or observation.

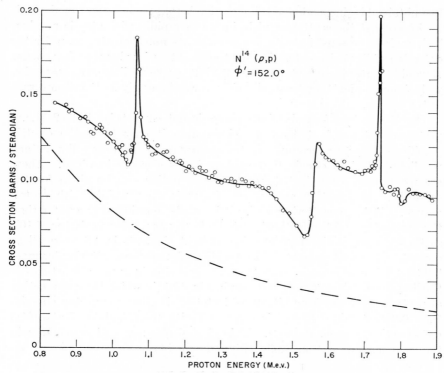

Fig. 41.1. Scattering cross section of N^{14} for proton scattering at 150°.

For example, the number of protons scattered at a particular angle into each unit of solid angle is given by multiplying together the number of incident protons, the numerical density of scattering nuclei, the thickness of the scattering layer, and the differential elastic scattering cross section. The scattering cross section is a function of several variables: the particular scattering nucleus, the kind of incident particle, the energy of the incident particle, and the scattering angle.

The Rutherford formula for the differential elastic scattering cross section is

$$\frac{d\sigma}{d\Omega} = \frac{1.3 \times 10^{-27}(zZ)^2}{E^2} \sin^{-4}\frac{\phi}{2} \tag{3}$$

where z is the atomic number of the incident particle, Z that of the scattering nucleus, E the energy (in M.e.v.) of the incident particle, and ϕ the scattering angle, in center-of-mass coordinates. The most significant fact obtained by inspection of this equation is that the cross section depends on Z^2, so that the scattering yield increases rapidly with atomic number. This makes the sensitivity to heavy elements much greater than for the detection of light elements. It might appear that low bombarding energy E would greatly increase the sensitivity but, as we shall see, the scattering yield from a thick target actually only varies inversely as the square root of the energy.

The Rutherford formula given above is not correct for 1- to 2-M.e.v. protons scattered from light nuclei, because it only takes the electric repelling forces into account. In this energy range, protons will approach the light nuclei so closely that nuclear forces also are involved. These are much more complicated, so that no equation can be given for the scattering cross section and it actually may vary rapidly with proton energy. At large scattering angles it is usually considerably greater than the value given by the Rutherford formula (by as much as a factor of 10), so that the sensitivity for detection of light elements is not as small as equation (3) would suggest. Cross sections for proton scattering by most light nuclei have been measured and are reported in numerous articles in the literature. An example is shown in Fig. 41.1, in which the cross section of protons scattered from nitrogen-14 at 150° is given for proton energies from 0.8 to 1.9 M.e.v., and is compared with the calculated Rutherford cross section (shown dashed). This also displays several resonances in the cross section, at 1.06, 1.55, 1.74, and 1.80 M.e.v.

C. STOPPING POWER

Before going on to give the equation relating the atomic concentrations in the sample to the observed counting yield, it is necessary to discuss briefly the way in which the particles are stopped in matter. Putting aside the relatively infrequent scattering collisions with nuclei, which do not contribute significantly to the *mean* energy loss, the fast-moving charged particle causes ionization of the atoms along its path and continuously loses its energy by this process. Without describing the process in any detail, we can state that each increment in distance traveled through a given substance will cause an increment in energy loss that is proportional to the numerical density, n, of atoms along the path and to the distance, Δt.

$$\Delta E = \epsilon n \Delta t \qquad (4)$$

The constant of proportionality, ϵ, is called the "stopping cross section," and is in units of energy times area. Fig. 41.2 shows how ϵ for protons depends on the energy of the proton and on the atomic number of the atoms being ionized. In a material composed of more than one element,

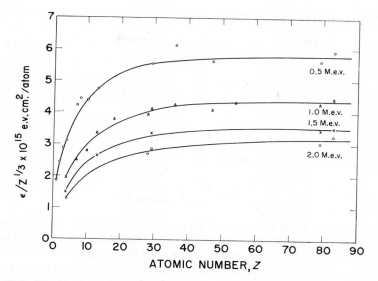

Fig. 41.2. Stopping power, ϵ, of various elements for protons of energy at 0.5, 1.0, 1.5, and 2.0 M.e.v. Calculated from stopping power data compiled by R. Fuchs and W. Whaling of the California Institute of Technology (unpublished).

the effective ϵ is simply the average of the ϵ's for each kind of atom in the material, each weighted by its relative atomic concentration.

D. SCATTERING YIELD

In developing the equations for the number of scattered particles that are detected by a particle spectrograph (referred to as *yield*), it is convenient to consider first the case of thin targets and then to extend the results to thick targets, which are those of principal interest.

If a sample or a scattering layer is so thin that the momentum loss of the scattered particles in penetrating through it is smaller than the momentum resolution of the spectrometer, it is called a *thin target*. This frequently may be true for surface films. The width of the thin-target peak will be that of the over-all momentum resolution of the system, and the height of each peak will be inversely proportional to resolution, for a given scattering yield, so that the integral under each such peak must be measured to determine the surface concentration of the atoms producing the peak.

The yield from a thin film is given by

$$Y_j = N \left(\frac{d\sigma}{d\Omega}\right)_j \Omega_s n_j t \tag{5}$$

and the integral of this for a single peak is

$$I_j = N \left(\frac{d\sigma}{d\Omega}\right)_j \frac{\Omega_s n_j t S_j}{R_c}$$

where S_j is the spectrometer reading at the peak. Since t is measured parallel to the direction of the incident beam, if t_0 is the actual film thickness,

$$t_0 = t \cos \theta_1$$

But $n_j t_0$ is the surface concentration c_j of the element j; therefore

$$\frac{I_j}{c_j} = N \left(\frac{d\sigma}{d\Omega}\right)_j \frac{\Omega_s S_j}{R_c \cos \theta_1} \tag{6}$$

Now we consider a thick target to be one in which the momentum loss of the scattered particles in penetrating any homogeneous or nearly homogeneous stratum of the material is larger than the momentum resolution of the spectrometer. Most samples to be analyzed will fall into this category. In this case, there is an effective target or lamina whose thickness is defined by the momentum interval admitted by the spectrometer.

This effective target thickness t, as shown in Fig. 41.3, again measured parallel to the direction of the incident beam, is given by

$$t = \frac{2E_2'}{R_c \Sigma_i n_i [\epsilon_{i1}(\partial E_2/\partial E_1) + \epsilon_{i2} (\cos \theta_1/\cos \theta_2)]} \tag{7}$$

(The derivation of equation (7) is discussed in an appendix of the paper by Brown *et al.* (3).)

For elastic scattering, $\partial E_2/\partial E_1 = E_2/E_1 = k^2$ and also, if the scattering lamina is sufficiently close to the surface of the sample, $E_2' \cong E_2$.

With these modifications, equation (7) is substituted into the generalized yield formula of equation (5), giving the result

$$\frac{Y_j}{n_j} = N \left(\frac{d\sigma}{d\Omega}\right)_j \frac{2 \, \Omega_s E_1}{R_c \Sigma_i n_i \left[\epsilon_{i1} + \dfrac{1}{k_j^2} \epsilon_{i2} \dfrac{\cos \theta_1}{\cos \theta_2}\right]} \tag{8}$$

In making precise calculations, it is necessary, in principle, to convert the scattering angle and the spectrometer solid angle from their measured values in the laboratory coordinate system to their values in the center-of-mass system, in which they appear in the equations given above. The change depends on the mass of the scattering nucleus. Whereas the conversion usually can be omitted for scattering from heavy elements, the

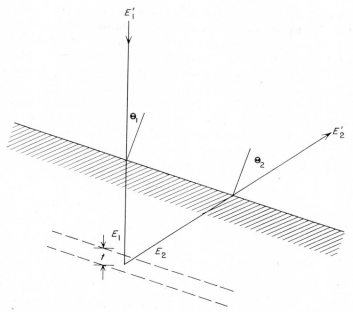

Fig. 41.3. Geometry of "thin target," t, defined within thick target by particle spectrometer.

error in angle may amount to several degrees, and the error in solid angle may be as much as 20% for 150° scattering from some light elements.

Let unprimed quantities be those measured in laboratory coordinates, and primed quantities be the same ones in center-of-mass coordinates. The following equations for converting between the two systems apply *only to the case of elastic particle scattering* (the general case of nuclear reactions with nonzero excitation energies requires more complicated functions of particle mass and energies).

Let $\phi' = \phi + \delta$. Then,

$$\sin \delta = \frac{M_1}{M_0} \sin \phi \qquad (9)$$

and

$$\frac{\Omega'}{\Omega} = \frac{\left[1 + \dfrac{2M_1}{M_0} \cos \phi' + \left(\dfrac{M_1}{M_0} \right)^2 \right]^{3/2}}{1 + \dfrac{M_1}{M_0} \cos \phi'} \qquad (10)$$

We see that equation (8), the thick-target case, differs from the thin-target case in two important respects. In the case of thick targets, we must know the average stopping power of the sample, which does not enter into the thin-target problem. Secondly, for thick targets we measure the concentration of each component as atoms per unit volume; for thin targets we measure concentrations as atoms per unit area.

The approximate dependence of the thick target yield on the beam energy can be calculated readily. As we have seen, the scattering cross section varies as E^{-2}. The stopping cross section, ϵ, has a rather complicated theoretical equation, but for nuclear particles of sufficiently high energy it can be approximated by the simple expression

$$\epsilon \simeq CZ^2 \sqrt{M_1/E}.$$

(For protons, this is true down to about 0.2 M.e.v.)

Substituting these relations into equation (8), we see that Y_j/n_j is proportional to $E^{-1/2}$, assuming that R_c is independent of energy. This means that there is no major advantage in increased sensitivity by use of very low-energy particles.

Actually, for scattering from the light elements, where maximum yield is most urgent, the cross sections for large-angle proton scattering at energies above 1 M.e.v. generally vary less rapidly than E^{-2} and, in some cases, are approximately constant. This results in greater values of Y with increasing energy, in contrast to the behavior of the yield from heavier elements.

III. APPLICATION OF METHOD

A. APPARATUS

1. Accelerator

For this application we require a homogeneous ion beam that is uniform in composition, direction, and energy. Of these, the most important requirement is homogeneity of energy, since the changes due to scattering of light ions, such as protons, from heavy nuclei, are very small. The most highly developed source of such an ion beam, in the M.e.v. energy region, is the Van de Graaff, or electrostatic, accelerator. Many of these machines are now in operation, producing charged-particle beams of from 0.2 to 12 M.e.v. Detailed descriptions are readily obtainable from texts on experimental nuclear physics (17) or from manufacturers (10).

It is generally possible to obtain a proton (ionized hydrogen), deuteron, or alpha-particle (ionized helium) beam of several microamperes, with an energy spread as small as 0.1%, from a modern electrostatic accelerator when it is used in conjunction with a beam analyzer.

The beam analyzer is a magnetic or electrostatic deflection device, with suitable entrance and exit slits arranged so that the analyzer field intensity and the radius of curvature define the mean energy of the beam and the slit widths define its spread in energy. The beam energy may then be stabilized by electronically amplifying the signal from insulated exit slit jaws and by controlling the accelerator voltage by this signal so that the beam is "locked" in position. Since the magnetic or electric field of the analyzer can be independently regulated with very high precision, this provides a stable reference for the beam energy. Furthermore, the beam energy can be determined from measurements of the analyzer field and the radius of curvature, or, alternatively, the field measuring device can be calibrated against known reference energies of the ion beam, such as nuclear resonances.

2. Spectrometer

The spectrometer is required to measure the momentum or the energy distribution of the scattered particles with very high resolution. It does this by deflecting the particles and focusing them on an image plane so that the position of the image is a function of the particle momentum or energy. This is analogous to the mode of operation of a mass spectrometer, except that in this case all the scattered particles have the same mass. It is essentially a high-dispersion lens system and, in analogy with a lens, the focal length, the magnification, the aperture, and the focusing aberrations can be specified. The relation of image plane to object plane and the dispersion can all be defined in terms of its fixed parameters.

For high resolution it must have very small focusing aberrations and must also have a relatively large solid angle, so that adequate counting rates are obtainable even when the exit slit is reduced to dimensions comparable to the focal errors, that is, when the resolution factor, R_c, is about equal to the ultimate resolving power. In general, the magnification of a spectrometer is of the order of unity, so that the effective source width must be comparable to the exit slit width. The final resolving power will be determined by the combination of all sources of momentum spread, i.e. the beam momentum, source width, focusing aberrations, exit slit width, and angular spreads in beam collimation and scattering angle.

Several instruments have been designed for nuclear research to meet the above requirements (4,15,19,20). Most of them have used magnetic deflection and focusing, although at least one electrostatic spectrometer also exists (5). With the magnetic instruments, ultimate resolving powers of

1000 to 3000 are obtainable. This momentum spread is comparable to that introduced by the accelerator—0.1% energy spread is 0.05% momentum spread.

There are two general methods for recording the particles passed by the spectrometer. A narrow exit slit can be used with an electronic particle detector of some kind, such as a proportional counter or a scintillation device operating a counting circuit. The other approach, which is described by Browne and Buechner (4), uses a photographic emulsion instead of an exit slit. This permits data to be collected simultaneously over a wide momentum range, which has advantages in minimizing the accelerator operating time although it requires subsequent counting of microscopic grain tracks in the emulsion to obtain quantitative data.

The dispersion of a spectrometer is defined as the ratio of the fractional change in radial position of the image to the fractional change in momentum:

$$D = \frac{\Delta r}{r_0} \Big/ \frac{\Delta P}{P_0} \tag{11}$$

For a magnetic spectrometer

$$D = \frac{1 + m}{1 - \nu}$$

where m = radial magnification (image/source) and ν = exponent in the equation for the magnetic field at the median plane.

$$H = H_0(r_0/r)^\nu$$

For a uniform field instrument (4), $\nu = 0$, so that D is approximately 2. For a point-focusing spectrometer (15,19,20), $\nu = \frac{1}{2}$, so that D is about 4. With the larger value of D, larger sources and slits can be used for a given resolution.

The collector resolution factor, R_c, which appears in the yield equation, is given theoretically by

$$R_c = \frac{P_0}{\Delta P_c} = \frac{D r_0}{\Delta r_c} \tag{12}$$

Consider, for example, a point-focusing spectrometer ($D = 4$) with a radius of 12 inches. An exit slit width of 0.048 inch will make $R_c = 1000$. This, of course, is not the momentum resolving power, because the beam momentum spread and source size also contribute to loss of resolving power. It is useful to be able to vary the exit slit width to trade resolution for counting rate.

For a detailed discussion of the general theory of magnetic spectrometers, see the article by Judd (14). The value of R_c for a given instrument is difficult to determine by direct measurement, except in the case of a uniform field spectrometer, because of the difficulty of measuring ν. However, in practice, the ratio, Ω_s/R_c, which appears in the yield equation, can be determined by measurement of the scattering yield from a sample of known cross section and known stopping power, such as pure copper or gold. The aperture, Ω_s, can be measured by comparison with a smaller reference aperture that can be interposed between the target and the spectrometer, using relative yields determined with and without the reference aperture.

3. Auxiliary Equipment

Under this heading we include the essential but minor items of equipment whose functions and performance are not as critical to the success of the method as are the accelerator, the analyzer, and the spectrometer. This group includes the ion beam lens, the target chamber, the charge integrator, and the particle detector.

The function of the beam lens is to focus the total beam current into the small area on the sample defined by the resolution requirements. A beam collimator using defining slits can be used, but generally at the cost of a large factor in available counting rate; consequently, a collimator increases the elapsed time necessary to achieve a particular precision in yield measurements by a large factor. Therefore, the lens is desirable as a means of time and cost reduction. A number of lens systems suitable for charged particles are known, using various kinds of magnetic or electric field configurations. One of the most convenient systems is the quadrupole (or "strong-focusing") lens, using either magnetic or electric fields, for which the theory has been given by Courant, Livingston, and Snyder (8). Magnetic quadrupole lenses can now be purchased commercially (16). However, it is not difficult to construct a compact electrostatic lens to focus 2-M.e.v. protons, as described by Bullock (6), using a few thousand volts obtained from very simple low-current, high-voltage supplies.

The target chamber provides the mechanical means for supporting the sample in the vacuum system so that its surface is accurately located at the object plane of the spectrometer, and it provides for measurement of the total beam current striking the target. The area of the sample that is bombarded by the beam constitutes the source to the spectrometer. Its position with respect to the spectrometer affects the location of the image, the values of Ω_s and R_c, and, most important, the calibration constant of the spectrometer relating its field intensity to the particle momentum. Consequently, it is important that this source position be on the central

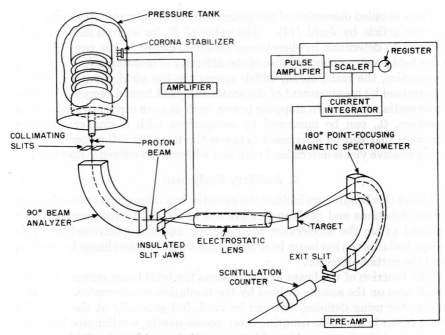

Fig. 41.4. Schematic diagram of ion-scattering apparatus.

"optical axis" of the spectrometer and at a fixed position on that axis. The target chamber is, therefore, mounted rigidly with respect to the spectrometer, and the devices for actually holding the sample are designed so that the beam intersects the sample surface at the specified source position. It is useful to analyze different positions on a particular sample, or to be able to adjust it so that the beam strikes some spot of particular interest. To do this, positioning controls should be available.

The sample and its holder must be electrically insulated so that the beam current can be collected in an integrating circuit. In order to make accurate measurements of positive-ion current, the emission of secondary electrons from the surface must be suppressed. This can be done either by maintaining the sample at a sufficient positive potential with respect to its surroundings or, preferably, by providing a negative potential region completely surrounding the sample. Most of the secondary electrons emitted at a large angle to the incident beam direction have very low energy and are blocked by a potential barrier of 100 v.

For convenience, it is also helpful to be able to transfer samples in and out of the vacuum system easily. The target chamber can include an air

Fig. 41.5. A 2-mv. Van de Graaff accelerator, shown with pressure tank removed.

lock for this purpose, separated from the target chamber by a gate valve of sufficient dimensions to admit the sample in its mounting. Many target chambers have been designed and are described in the literature. In general, anyone familiar with vacuum technology can design a satisfactory one.

Fig. 41.6. View of analyzer magnet, spectrometer magnet, and control console. Accelerator is supported above analyzer magnet by steel frame structure.

The number of particles incident on the sample is measured with a charge-integrating circuit. The simplest version of this circuit is a condenser and high-resistance voltmeter. More elaborate automatic circuits have been designed that operate relays when some preset value of charge has been collected (2). These are especially convenient for scattering analysis, since one is primarily concerned with comparing scattering yields for a constant number of incident particles. Such an automatic integrator can turn off counting circuits, intercept the beam, wake up the operator, etc. The only important requirement is a high degree of reproducibility, so that small changes in yield can be measured reliably. The circuit described by Bouricius and Shoemaker (2) is one of the best available for high-precision measurements.

Finally, a brief mention will be made of the detecting device for the scattered particles. In addition to photographic emulsions (several types of nuclear track emulsions are supplied by Eastman and by Ilford), there are many kinds of electronic particle detectors, ranging from Geiger tubes to scintillation counters. Any of these can be used, depending on the

Fig. 41.7. Magnetic spectrometer and target chamber.

preference of the designer. Geiger and proportional counters are gas-filled
and therefore require a vacuum window to the spectrometer. Scintillation
counters can be mounted directly in the vacuum, but are more expensive.
Except for the photographic emulsions (located at the image plane of the
spectrometer, and which, by virtue of their positional discrimination, eliminate the need for an exit slit) the electronic detectors are mounted behind
the exit slit of the spectrometer.

The ion-scattering method requires a rather complex apparatus. The
reader's visualization of it may be facilitated by pictures and diagrams of a
specific installation—which has been in use at Stanford Research Institute

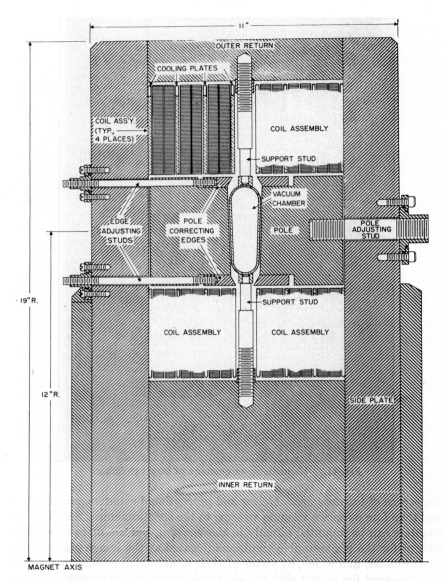

Fig. 41.8. Radial section through magnetic spectrometer, showing mechanical design features.

since 1953. This was the first such apparatus assembled specifically for the purpose of surface analysis by proton scattering.

Figure 41.4 shows a schematic of the basic system. Figs. 41.5, 41.6, and 41.7 are photographs of the principal components. Fig. 41.8 is a cross-section drawing of the spectrometer magnet to show those features not observable in the photograph. A detailed description of this spectrometer is given by Rubin and Sachs (19).

B. SAMPLE PREPARATION AND RESTRICTIONS

1. Materials

The trajectory of the ion beam must be in a fairly good vacuum, otherwise it will be badly scattered and slowed down. The pressure should be below 1 μ (Hg); therefore the materials analyzed must be sufficiently nonvolatile to be placed in such a vacuum without significant loss or deterioration.

Heat will be produced in the surface being analyzed by the dissipation of the energy of the ion beam. If the beam current is 1 μamp., its energy 1 M.e.v., and it is focused on an area of 1 mm.^{2}, then the power dissipated in the surface is 100 w./cm.^{2} This heat will be removed by radiation and conduction. If the sample is a good heat conductor and is mounted on a conducting bar coupled to a cooling system, it will not get very hot. If it is a poor conductor, however, it could reach temperatures as high as 1000 to 2000°K.

An obvious way to reduce the temperature is by reduction of the beam current. However, the time required for an analysis becomes inconveniently long if the beam current is less than the range of 0.01 μamp., especially if very low-concentration contaminants are to be detected.

Consequently, this is not a suitable method for analysis of materials of low heat conductivity unless they are sufficiently refractory to withstand temperatures of at least 500°K. without damage or the volatilization of any components.

2. Sample Geometry

As indicated by equation (8), the scattering yield from a given substance depends on the orientation of its surface to the beam. Therefore it is desirable for samples to have plane surfaces that are fairly smooth so that the portion of the surface to be analyzed has a definable and uniform angle to the ion beam. If the sample is very rough the yield will not be the same as that from a smooth sample of the same composition. An extreme case, that of deep cracks in the surface, will cause reduction of the yield in proportion to the surface area occupied by these cracks, because ions entering the cracks may go too deep to be able to return to the surface after being scattered.

Very large objects must have pieces cut from them that can fit into a target chamber. Cutting oils from machine tools generally can be removed adequately by vapor degreasing.

C. MEASUREMENT PROBLEMS AND LIMITATIONS

1. Identification of Elements

In order to identify an element positively, it must be distinguishable from elements of adjacent atomic numbers. Table 41.I gives values of the scattering factor, k (ratio of final to initial momentum), for protons scattered by elements from helium to bismuth. Elements are identified by comparison of the observed momentum distribution of scattered protons with these factors. This task is relatively easy for the light elements because the fractional change in momentum of a scattered particle is quite large, and thus the differences in scattering factor for adjacent light elements are large compared to the momentum resolution.

For example, the factors for carbon and nitrogen (at 150°) are 0.8548 and 0.8741, so that they differ by about 2% of the initial momentum. On the other hand, the differences between many of the very heavy elements, such as barium and lanthanum, or gold and mercury, are only 0.0001, which is smaller than either the beam homogeneity or the spectrometer resolution, so that it is not possible to resolve adjacent heavy elements using present techniques.

In practice, of course, one usually has other information indicating what elements are likely to be present, and the elements of particular interest are not necessarily adjacent in mass. However, this restriction does impose a real limitation on this method of analysis.

In order to relate the calculated scattering factors to an observed momentum distribution, the number of scattered particles must be plotted or recorded as a function of relative momentum. If magnetic analyzers and spectrometers are used, the particle momenta are proportional to the magnetic fields in the apparatus, and thus the counting data can be plotted as a function of relative magnetic-field intensities in the spectrometer and the analyzer. If electric-field deflection is used, its magnitude is proportional to the energy or to the square of the particle momentum. In this case it is more convenient to use a different table of computed factors, corresponding to the instrumental quantity actually measured.

The scale of relative momentum can be determined on an absolute basis, but this requires very high accuracy of field measurement and accurate measurement of the radius of curvature of the instruments. This is only feasible with analyzers especially constructed to have uniform fields. A more practical approach is to calibrate a relative scale by scattering from known elements. If several elements are used, ranging from very light to very heavy, even some nonlinearity of the scale can be allowed for.

In any case, high precision and sensitivity of field measurement are necessary. For uniform magnetic fields, nuclear magnetic resonance devices will give very high precision of field measurement. However, if the field is nonuniform, as in a point-focusing magnetic spectrometer, the resonance may be too broad for high precision and other types of fluxmeters are required. Most of these fluxmeters require extremely careful construction to be used to a sensitivity of 10^{-4}; their stability with time is generally not good, so that frequent recalibration is required. Measuring the voltage applied to the deflecting plates of an electrostatic analyzer is relatively simple by using a precision potentiometer and stable resistors.

2. Measurement of Concentrations and Film Thickness

The concentrations of any element may be determined from the observed scattering yield by application of equation (8). However, this requires that the energy of the incident beam, and also the average composition of the sample, be known.

It is generally more convenient to measure concentrations by comparison with samples of known composition. If the beam energy and scattering angle are held constant, one can then write an equation for the ratio between the unknown and the known concentration that involves only the relative yields and the average stopping powers of the two samples. This procedure is especially helpful in analysis for the light elements, because the scattering cross sections for these elements are not accurately calculable and the measured data may not be available at exactly the scattering angle required, or these data may not be sufficiently accurate.

The principal source of error in the data reduction is the separation of the observed yield for each element from the total observed yield at each momentum. This, of course, is because the particles lose momentum both by scattering and by slowing down with depth, as described above. Consequently, protons scattered from a light element at the surface may have the same momentum as those scattered from a heavier element at a greater depth. The spectrometer can only record the total yield at each momentum level, regardless of how it was produced.

TABLE 41.I
Ratio, k, of Final to Initial Velocity of Protons Elastically Scattered from the Principal Stable Nuclei, at 90° and 150°, in Laboratory Coordinates

Element	Atomic No.	Mass No.	Abundance (%)	$k_{90°}$	$k_{150°}$
Helium	2	4	100	0.7731	0.6184
Lithium	3	6	92.6	0.8445	0.7292
		7	7.4	0.8654	0.7634
Beryllium	4	9	100	0.8938	0.8109
Boron	5	10	18.8	0.9043	0.8289
		11	81.2	0.9123	0.8427
Carbon	6	12	98.9	0.9193	0.8548
Nitrogen	7	14	99.6	0.9305	0.8741
Oxygen	8	16	99.8	0.9389	0.8890
Fluorine	9	19	100	0.9484	0.9059
Neon	10	20	90.5	0.9508	0.9104
		22	9.2	0.9552	0.9193
Sodium	11	23	100	0.9572	0.9215
Magnesium	12	24	78.6	0.9589	0.9245
		25	10.1	0.9605	0.9275
		26	11.3	0.9620	0.9303
Aluminum	13	27	100	0.9634	0.9327
Silicon	14	28	92.2	0.9645	0.9350
Phosphorus	15	31	100	0.9679	0.9412
Sulfur	16	32	95.1	0.9690	0.9429
		34	4.2	0.9708	0.9462
Chlorine	17	35	75.4	0.9716	0.9477
		37	24.6	0.9731	0.9504
Argon	18	40	99.6	0.9751	0.9541
Potassium	19	39	93.2	0.9744	0.9530
Calcium	20	40	96.9	0.9751	0.9541
Scandium	21	45	100	0.9778	0.9590
Titanium	22	48ᵃ	73.4	0.9792	0.9616
Vanadium	23	51	100	0.9805	0.9638
Chromium	24	50	4.4	0.9801	0.9631
		52	83.7	0.9809	0.9645
		53	9.5	0.9813	0.9652
Manganese	25	55	100	0.9820	0.9664
Iron	26	54	5.9	0.9817	0.9658
		56	91.6	0.9824	0.9670
Cobalt	27	59	100	0.9833	0.9686
Nickel	28	58	67.9	0.9830	0.9681
		60	26.2	0.9836	0.9692
Copper	29	63	69.0	0.9844	0.9707
		65	31.0	0.9849	0.9715
Zinc	30	64	48.9	0.9846	0.9711
		66	27.8	0.9850	0.9719
		68	18.6	0.9855	0.9727

TABLE 41.I (*continued*)

Element	Atomic No.	Mass No.	Abundance (%)	$k_{90°}$	$k_{150°}$
Gallium	31	69	60.2	0.9857	0.9731
		71	39.8	0.9861	0.9739
Germanium	32	70	20.6	0.9859	0.9735
		72	27.4	0.9863	0.9742
		74	36.6	0.9867	0.9749
Arsenic	33	75	100	0.9869	0.9753
Selenium	34	78	23.5	0.9873	0.9762
		80	49.8	0.9877	0.9768
Bromine	35	79	50.6	0.9875	0.9765
		81	49.4	0.9879	0.9771
Krypton	36	84^a	57.0	0.9882	0.9779
Rubidium	37	85	72.8	0.9884	0.9781
		87	27.2	0.9887	0.9786
Strontium	38	88	82.7	0.9888	0.9788
Yttrium	39	89	100	0.9889	0.9791
Zirconium	40	90	51.5	0.9890	0.9793
		92	17.1	0.9892	0.9797
		94	17.4	0.9895	0.9801
Columbium	41	93	100	0.9894	0.9799
Molybdenum	42	92	15.7	0.9892	0.9797
		95	15.7	0.9896	0.9804
		96^a	16.5	0.9897	0.9806
		98	23.9	0.9899	0.9810
Ruthenium	44	101	17.0	0.9902	0.9816
		102^a	31.3	0.9903	0.9818
		104	18.3	0.9905	0.9821
Rhodium	45	103	100	0.9904	0.9819
Palladium	46	105	22.6	0.9906	0.9823
		106	27.1	0.9907	0.9825
		108	26.7	0.9908	0.9828
Silver	47	107	51.4	0.9908	0.9826
		109	48.6	0.9909	0.9829
Cadmium	48	112^a	24.0	0.9912	0.9834
		114	28.8	0.9913	0.9837
Indium	49	115	95.8	0.9914	0.9839
Tin	50	116	14.2	0.9914	0.9840
		118	24.0	0.9916	0.9843
		120	33.0	0.9917	0.9846
Antimony	51	121	57.2	0.9918	0.9847
		123	42.8	0.9919	0.9850
Tellurium	52	128	31.8	0.9922	0.9855
		130	34.4	0.9924	0.9858
Iodine	53	127	100	0.9922	0.9854
Xenon	54	129	26.2	0.9923	0.9856
		132	26.9	0.9925	0.9860

(*Table continued*)

TABLE 41.I (*continued*)

Element	Atomic No.	Mass No.	Abundance (%)	$k_{90°}$	$k_{150°}$
Cesium	55	133	100	0.9925	0.9861
Barium	56	138	71.7	0.9928	0.9866
Lanthanum	57	139	99.9		0.9867
Cerium	58	140[a]	88.5		0.9868
Praseodymium	59	141	100	0.9930	0.9869
Neodymium	60	144[a]			0.9871
Samarium	62	150[a]			0.9876
Europium	63	152[a]		0.9935	0.9878
Gadolinium	64	157[a]			0.9982
Terbium	65	159	100		0.9883
Dysprosium	66	163[a]			0.9886
Holmium	67	165	100	0.9940	0.9888
Erbium	68	167[a]			0.9889
Thulium	69	169	100		0.9890
Ytterbium	70	173[a]			0.9893
Lutecium	71	175	97.4		0.9894
Hafnium	72	179[a]			0.9896
Tantalum	73	181	100	0.9945	0.9898
Tungsten	74	184[a]			0.9899
Rhenium	75	186[a]			0.9900
Osmium	76	191[a]			0.9903
Iridium	77	193[a]	61.5		0.9904
Platinum	78	195[a]			0.9905
Gold	79	197	100	0.9950	0.9906
Mercury	80	201[a]			0.9907
Thallium	81	205	70.5		0.9909
Lead	82	207[a]			0.9910
Bismuth	83	209	100	0.9952	0.9911

[a] Nearest integral to the average mass number of the element.

In order to obtain the yield for each element from the observed yield curves, a certain amount of judgment is required. Usually one makes the simplest possible assumptions in making the analysis. Fig. 41.9 is a typical example of such a yield spectrum. It is an analysis of a piece of steel containing products of gun propellant. Note particularly the peaks at carbon and oxygen. The scattering yields from both are added to a much larger scattering yield from iron. In subtracting to determine the carbon and oxygen concentrations, one makes the reasonable assumption that the iron concentration is constant and therefore that the actual carbon and oxygen yields are those lying above the straight-line extension of the iron curve. However, it is easy to imagine more complex situations. For example, the oxygen concentration could extend more than 0.5 μ deep

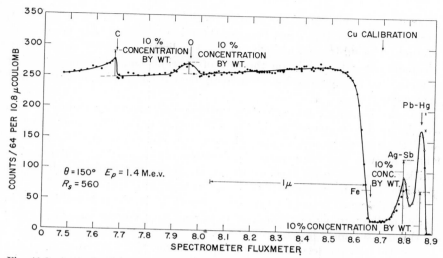

Fig. 41.9. Analysis of a steel sample that had been exposed to gun propellant combustion.

into the sample, and so it would overlap the carbon curve just as the two heavy-element peaks overlap, with a possible but indeterminate tail of the heavier element peak at 8.85 extending under the lighter of the two, at 8.79. Measurement of the separate yields in the overlapping regions is somewhat uncertain. It is this kind of problem that primarily limits the accuracy of concentration measurement.

However, in favorable cases, such as those in which there is no background or a well-defined background (as in Fig. 41.9) to be subtracted, the precision of a concentration measurement will depend on statistical errors. Whether the scattered particles are detected by an electronic counter or by photographic plates, the final data is in the form of a finite number of particles counted at each point. Consequently, there is an irreducible statistical uncertainty associated with each such datum. For reasonable values of current, spectrometer aperture, and resolution it is rarely possible to obtain a sufficient number of counts at each point to make the statistical error much smaller than 1% without spending an inconveniently long time in data collection or in track counting.

This means that the precision of concentration measurements will be 1% or poorer, depending on the relative magnitude of the yield due to each element and the total scattering yield in that momentum region. It also means that the sensitivity for detection of light elements in the presence of a large concentration of heavy elements will not be much better than around 1%. Of course, the sensitivity for heavy elements is generally very much better than this, because there is not usually any large background to be subtracted in such cases. The limiting sensitivity for heavy elements depends mainly on the rate of spurious counts in the detecting system, due to causes such as cosmic ray background, noisy amplifiers, and bad connections.

In addition to measuring concentrations, this scattering technique also can be used to measure the thickness of surface films. For our purposes, surface films can be put into two classes; (1) films so thin that they satisfy the definition of a "thin target" (discussed in Section II): and (2) films thick enough to be resolved by the spectrometer but thin enough so that particles scattered from their back surfaces are detected.

The thickness of the first type, the very thin film, is measurable only in terms of the number of atoms per unit area that comprise it. The theory of this measurement is discussed above. •

For the thicker second type of surface layer, the scattering data give a direct measurement of the momentum loss of particles penetrating twice through it. From a knowledge of the stopping power of the film substance, one can then compute its actual thickness in a straightforward way. The same procedure is used to obtain the depth scale of the concentration of contaminants diffused into a substrate material. In this case, however, the stopping power used must be that of the average composition of the sample.

The depth scale shown in Fig. 41.9 is an example of this latter procedure; the stopping power of iron for protons of 1.4 M.e.v. was used to compute the fractional momentum loss per micron. The depth scale is then calculated, taking into account the angle between the paths of the protons and the line normal to the surface of the sample, as well as the fact that the protons must travel the path in both directions. The geometrical considerations are obvious from Fig. 41.3.

3. Beam Energy and Resonant Scattering

It is useful to know the beam energy because it enters into yield calculations and because of the problem of resonant scattering. The deflecting field of the beam analyzer usually provides a method of energy measurement with adequate precision. The simplest method for calibrating this scale is by means of known sharp resonances in light-element nuclear reactions. Several of the reactions of protons in light elements produce a copious yield of gamma rays at very narrow and well-defined proton energies, or produce neutrons starting at a sharply defined threshold energy. Some of these have been measured on an absolute-energy scale for use as

TABLE 41.II
Data Sources for Proton Scattering Cross Sections of Light Elements

Element	Proton energy range, M.e.v.	Reference to scattering cross section
Li^7	0.36–1.4	Warters, W. D., W. A. Fowler, and C. C. Lauritsen, *Phys. Rev.*, **91**, 917 (1953).
Be^9	0.8–2.6	Dearnaley, G., *Phil. Mag.*, Ser. 8, **1**, 821 (1956).
Be^9	0.25–1.3	Thomas, R. G., S. Rubin, W. A. Fowler, and C. C. Lauritsen, *Phys. Rev.*, **75**, 1612 (1949).
B^{11}	0.6–2.0	Tautfest, G. W., and S. Rubin, *Phys. Rev.*, **103**, 196 (1956).
C^{12}	0.4–4.3	Jackson, H. L., A. L. Galonsky, F. J. Eppling, R. W. Hill, E. Goldberg, and J. R. Cameron. *Phys. Rev.*, **89**, 365 (1953).
C^{12}	0.3–0.55	Milne, E. A., *Phys. Rev.*, **93**, 762 (1954).
C^{13}	0.45–1.6	Milne, E. A., *Phys. Rev.*, **93**, 762 (1954).
N^{14}	0.85–1.9	Tautfest, G. W., and S. Rubin, *Phys. Rev.*, **103**, 196 (1956).
O^{16}	0.6–4.5	Laubenstein, R. A., M. J. W. Laubenstein, L. J. Koester, and R. C. Mobley, *Phys. Rev.*, **84**, 12 (1951).
F^{19}	0.5–2.1	Dearnaley, G., *Phil. Mag.*, Ser. 8, **1**, 821 (1956).
F^{19}	0.6–1.8	Webb, T. S., F. B. Hagedorn, W. A. Fowler, and C. C. Lauritsen, *Phys. Rev.*, **99**, 138 (1955).
Ne^{20}	0.2–4.4	Haeberli, W., *Phys. Rev.*, **99**, 640A (1955).
Na^{23}	0.4–1.0	Dearnaley, G., *Phil. Mag.*, Ser. 8, **1**, 821 (1956).
Na^{23}	0.6–1.5	Baumann, N. P., F. W. Prosser, W. G. Read, and R. W. Krone, *Phys. Rev.*, **104**, 376 (1956).
Mg^{24}	0.4–4.0	Mooring, F. P., L. J. Koester, E. Goldberg, D. Saxon, and S. G. Kaufmann, *Phys. Rev.*, **84**, 703 (1951).
Al^{27}	1.35–3.2	Shoemaker, F. C., J. E. Faulkner, G. M. B. Bouricious, S. G. Kaufmann, and F. P. Mooring, *Phys. Rev.*, **83**, 1011 (1951).
S^{32}	1.0–2.8	Ferguson, A. J., and H. E. Gove, *Phys. Rev.*, **91**, 439 (1953).

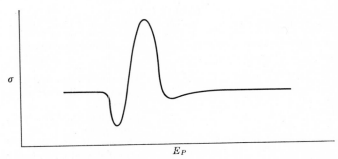

Fig. 41.10.   Possible behavior of the scattering cross section at a resonance (not to scale).

energy-calibration points.   For example, the reaction Li^7 (p, γ) Be^8 produces energetic gamma rays at a proton energy of 0.441 M.e.v., with a
width of 0.012 M.e.v. (11).   Other absolute proton energies are available
up to 1.8 M.e.v. for gamma-emission reactions and up to 3.2 M.e.v. for
neutron emission (7,12,13).   (These references cover only a few of the
absolute measurements of (p, γ) resonances on Li^7, B^{11}, F^{19}, Mg^{26}, Al^{27},
and Ni^{58}, giving an energy scale from 0.16 to 1.8 M.e.v.   For more nuclear
reaction data and references, see the major review articles on nuclear
data (1,9).)

Of course, once the energy scale of an analyzer is known for protons, it
is easily converted for other ions, since their relative masses and charges
are known.

At those proton energies at which there are resonances for a particular
nuclear reaction, there usually are also resonances in the elastic-scattering
cross section.   These scattering resonances are particularly strong in the
light elements.   If one attempts a scattering analysis of a particular element with protons at a resonance energy (or slightly higher energy), the
rapid variation of yield with proton energy will give an apparent change of
concentration with depth.   Consequently, if information on the concentration as a function of depth is desired, it is well to avoid proton energies
corresponding to a strong, sharp resonance.   Data are available on the
elastic proton-scattering cross sections as a function of energy for most of
the light elements, as indicated in Table 41.II.

Most of the data in the references listed in the table were obtained at
scattering angles of 90° or greater.   In most cases, data are given in the
range of 140 to 165°.   At these large scattering angles, resonance effects
are relatively stronger, compared to the Rutherford scattering cross section,
than at smaller angles.   Usually the cross section increases at a resonance,
but, in a few cases, it decreases.

In carbon-12, for example, there are two strong resonances, at 0.46 and 1.7 M.e.v. Both of these resonances show a typical "diffraction" interference effect between the nuclear potential and the electric potential. In a narrow energy range at each resonance, as the proton energy increases, the scattering cross section first decreases almost to zero, then increases to several times the "normal" value, then decreases to a relatively constant value again, as indicated by Fig. 41.10. The widths of the scattering resonances vary widely, from less than 1 k.e.v. to several hundred k.e.v. However, it is only the narrow resonances (in which the cross section changes rapidly with proton energy) that interfere with concentration measurements.

4. Computation and Results

In computing concentrations from the measured scattering-yield data, it is rarely necessary, or even useful, to use the full complexity of equation (8). In most cases one can determine a concentration of one element by comparison of its scattering yield with that of some other element of known concentration. If the unknown and the reference element are in different substances, then stopping-power calculations are necessary. However, it is frequently possible to use one of the major constituents of a sample as the reference element and to determine concentrations of contaminants by comparison with it.

There may, of course, be cases in which the sample composition is entirely unknown. In that case, one can proceed by successive approximations to obtain a consistent value of the composition, using earlier approximations in computing the stopping power.

For example, consider a sample containing aluminum and oxygen in unknown proportions. We can write an equation for the ratio of the atomic concentrations, based on equation (8), as follows:

$$\frac{n_O}{n_{Al}} = \frac{Y_O \sigma_{Al} \Omega_{Al}}{Y_{Al} \sigma_O \Omega_O} \left[\frac{a n_O + b n_{Al}}{c n_O + d n_{Al}} \right]$$

Assume that the target is oriented so that $\theta_1 = \theta_2$, and therefore that $\cos \theta_1 / \cos \theta_2 = 1$.

$$a = \epsilon_{Al_1} + \frac{1}{k_O{}^2} \epsilon_{Al_3}$$

$$b = \epsilon_{O_1} + \frac{1}{k_O{}^2} \epsilon_{O_3}$$

$$c = \epsilon_{Al_1} + \frac{1}{k_{Al}^2} \epsilon_{Al_2}$$

$$d = \epsilon_{O_1} + \frac{1}{k_{Al}^2} \epsilon_{O_2}$$

The subscripts O and Al refer to oxygen and aluminum; the subscripts 1, 2, and 3 refer to the three proton energies: E_1 = initial proton energy; E_2 = energy after scattering from the aluminum nucleus; and E_3 = energy after scattering from the oxygen nucleus.

The primary data are: E_1 = 1.40 M.e.v.; ϕ = 150°; Y_{Al} = 50 (arbitrary units); and Y_O = 55 (arbitrary units).

From Table 41.I we know that k_{Al} = 0.933, k_{Al}^2 = 0.870, k_O = 0.889, and k_O^2 = 0.790. Now the k's are ratios of velocity, so that

$$E_2 = (k_{Al})^2 E_1 \qquad E_3 = (k_O)^2 E_1$$

$$E_2 = 1.22 \text{ M.e.v.} \qquad E_3 = 1.11 \text{ M.e.v.}$$

The scattering cross sections for 1.4 M.e.v. protons scattered at 150° are

$$\sigma_{Al} = 0.44 \times 10^{-24} \text{ cm.}^2$$

$$\sigma_O = 0.12 \times 10^{-24} \text{ cm.}^2$$

From Fig. 41.3 we obtain values for ϵ for protons of energies of 1.4, 1.2, and 1.1 M.e.v.:

ϵ_{Al_1} = 6.5 $\times$ 10^{-15} e.v.cm.^{2}/atom $\qquad$ ϵ_{O_1} = 4.4 $\times$ 10^{-15} e.v.cm.^{2}/atom

ϵ_{Al_2} = 7.1 $\times$ 10^{-15} e.v.cm.^{2}/atom $\qquad$ ϵ_{O_2} = 4.8 $\times$ 10^{-15} e.v.cm.^{2}/atom

ϵ_{Al_3} = 7.45 $\times$ 10^{-15} e.v.cm.^{2}/atom $\qquad$ ϵ_{O_3} = 5.1 $\times$ 10^{-15} e.v.cm.^{2}/atom

Then a = 1.59 $\times$ 10^{-14}; b = 1.09 $\times$ 10^{-14}; c = 1.47 $\times$ 10^{-14}; and d = 0.99 $\times$ 10^{-14}.

From equation (10) we compute the ratio of the spectrometer solid angle in center-of-mass (C.M.) coordinates to that in laboratory coordinates. In laboratory coordinates the solid angle is a fixed constant of the apparatus, the same for all elements. Therefore, the ratio of the two solid angles in C.M. coordinates is simply the ratio of the conversion factor given by the equation. If much computing is to be done, it is convenient to make a curve of this equation as a function of M_0. Using such a curve for M_1 = 1, we obtain the factors

for Al^{27}: Ω'/Ω = 0.935

for O^{16}: Ω'/Ω = 0.890

Therefore

$$\frac{\Omega_{Al}}{\Omega_o} = \frac{0.935}{0.890}$$

Now we can write the numerical equation:

$$\frac{n_o}{n_{Al}} = \frac{55}{50} \cdot \frac{0.44}{0.12} \cdot \frac{0.935}{0.890} \left[\frac{1.59 + 1.09 \dfrac{n_o}{n_{Al}}}{1.47 + 0.99 \dfrac{n_o}{n_{Al}}} \right]$$

giving the result $n_o/n_{Al} = 1.36$.

The above calculation depends only on ratios of equivalent quantities, and therefore there is no problem of units. The only measured quantities required are the counting data and the beam energy, which is needed to obtain the cross sections.

Although the previous example is typical of the usual type of computation, it is of pedagogical value to give another example taken from an experiment to measure the scattering cross section of nitrogen. This example gives a better idea of the magnitude and the significance of the factors in the yield formula.

The target was powdered melamine $N_6C_3H_6$ compressed into a solid cake with a smooth surface. The proton-beam energy was determined to be 1.43 M.e.v. from the calibration curve for the analyzer magnet fluxmeter. The scattering angle was $150°$ and the face of the target was oriented at $15°$ to the beam, so that $\theta_1 = \theta_2$.

The intermediate exit slit of the spectrometer was used, giving a resolution factor $R_e = 1165$. The spectrometer solid angle is 2.52×10^{-3} steradians, and the solid angle conversion factor for scattering protons from N^{14} at $150°$ is 0.8735, giving a center-of-mass solid angle of 2.21×10^{-3} steradians.

The charge collected on the target for each run was 10.77 μcoulombs, obtained by charging a 1.00 μf. condenser to 10.77 v. (supplied by reference cells). The number of incident protons is obtained by dividing the collected charge by the electronic charge, giving 6.74×10^{13} incident protons. The number of scattered protons counted was 1912.

The scattering factor of N^{14} at $150°$ is 0.874 (from Table 41.I). From this we calculated the proton energy after scattering to be 1.10 M.e.v.

Knowing the two values of proton energy, we next computed the stopping cross sections of N, C, and H for each energy, using the values of $\epsilon/Z^{1/3}$ from Fig. 41.2, and interpolating for the appropriate proton energy.

$$\epsilon_{N_1} = 3.98 \times 10^{-15} \text{ e.v.cm.}^2/\text{atom} \qquad \epsilon_{N_2} = 4.74 \times 10^{-15} \text{ e.v.cm.}^2/\text{atom}$$

$$\epsilon_{C_1} = 3.38 \times 10^{-15} \text{ e.v.cm.}^2/\text{atom} \qquad \epsilon_{C_2} = 4.21 \times 10^{-15} \text{ e.v.cm.}^2/\text{atom}$$

$$\epsilon_{H_1} = 0.65 \times 10^{-15} \text{ e.v.cm.}^2/\text{atom} \qquad \epsilon_{H_2} = 1.34 \times 10^{-15} \text{ e.v.cm.}^2/\text{atom}$$

One can now substitute these values into the equation

$$\frac{d\sigma}{d\Omega} = \frac{1.6 \times 10^{-13} Y_N R}{2 \, E_1 \, q \, \Omega} \left[\left(\epsilon_{N_1} + \frac{\epsilon_{N_2}}{k_N^2} \right) + \right.$$
$$\left. \frac{n_C}{n_N} \left(\epsilon_{C_1} + \frac{\epsilon_{C_2}}{k_N^2} \right) + \frac{n_H}{n_N} \left(\epsilon_{H_1} + \frac{\epsilon_{H_2}}{k_N^2} \right) \right]$$

For melamine, therefore,

$$\frac{n_C}{n_N} = \frac{1}{2}; \; \frac{n_H}{n_N} = 1$$

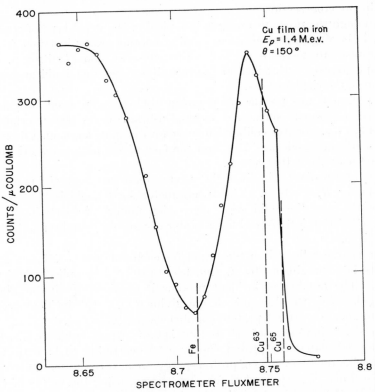

Fig. 41.11. Proton-scattering spectrum from copper film on iron base.

For this calculation, units are significant. Since ϵ is in e.v.cm.², E_1 must be in units of e.v.; q is given in microcoulombs and Ω in steradians, giving $d\sigma/d\Omega = 0.89 \times 10^{-24}$ cm.² steradian.

One generally computes the scattering angle in center-of-mass coordinates to facilitate comparison of the measured with a theoretical cross section. Using equation (9), $\delta = 2.0°$, so that the C.M. angle of scattering is 152°.

Figure 41.11 shows the scattering spectrum obtained from a thin film of copper on a piece of iron. This is a good example with which to illustrate a film-thickness measurement.

The front edge of the copper-scattering distribution is at 8.757 on the relative momentum scale and the mean rear edge is at 8.728, although it varies from about 8.71 to 8.74. However, for illustration, it will serve to compute the mean thickness. The arithmetic difference is then 0.029, or a fractional momentum change of $0.029/8.74 = 0.0033$ for two passages through the copper film. Since the fractional energy change is twice the momentum change, the energy loss for one passage is 0.0033×1.4 M.e.v. = 4.6 k.e.v. We obtain the number of atoms/cm.² by dividing the energy loss by the stopping cross section, which is 10.6×10^{-15} e.v.cm.²/atom giving 4.3×10^{17} atoms/cm.².

The beam was incident at an angle of 15°, so this must be multiplied by cos 15° to get the normal thickness. Converting to mass, we get an average copper film thickness of 4.4×10^{-5} g./cm.².

As may be seen from the figure, this thickness is much greater than the resolution limit of the apparatus, so that one can obtain quite detailed information on the structure of films from about one-tenth of this thickness upward, and thus detect and identify very much thinner films.

REFERENCES

1. Ajzenberg, F., and T. Lauritsen, "Energy levels of light nuclei. V.," *Revs. Modern Phys.*, **27**, 77 (1955).
2. Bouricius, G. M. B., and F. C. Shoemaker, *Rev. Sci. Instr.*, **22**, 183 (1951).
3. Brown, A. B., C. W. Snyder, W. A. Fowler, and C. C. Lauritsen, *Phys. Rev.*, **82**, 159 (1951).
4. Browne, C. P., and W. W. Buechner, *Rev. Sci. Instr.*, **27**, 899 (1956).
5. Browne, C. P., D. S. Craig, and R. M. Williamson, *Rev. Sci. Instr.*, **22**, 952 (1951).
6. Bullock, M., *Am. J. Phys.*, **23**, 264 (1955).
7. Butler, J. W., K. L. Dunning, and R. O. Bondelid, *Phys. Rev.*, **106**, 1224 (1957).
8. Courant, E. D., M. S. Livingston, and H. S. Snyder, *Phys. Rev.*, **88**, 1190 (1952).
9. Endt, P. M., and J. C. Kluyver, "Energy Levels of Light Nuclei (Z-11 to Z-20)," *Revs. Modern Phys.*, **26**, 95–166 (1954).
10. High Voltage Engineering Corp., Burlington, Mass.
11. Hunt, S. E., *Proc. Phys. Soc. (London)*, **A65**, 982 (1952).
12. Hunt, S. E., and K. Firth, *Phys. Rev.*, **99**, 786 (1955).

13. Hunt, S. E., and W. M. Jones, *Phys. Rev.*, **89**, 1283 (1953).
14. Judd, D., *Rev. Sci. Instr.*, **21**, 213 (1950).
15. Mileikowsky, C., *Ark. Phys.*, **7**, 33, 57 (1953).
16. Pacific Electric Motor Co., Oakland, Calif.
17. Pollard, E., and W. L. Davidson, *Applied Nuclear Physics*, Wiley, New York, 1942.
18. Rubin, S., and V. K. Rasmussen, *Phys. Rev.*, **78**, 83 (1950).
19. Rubin, S., and D. S. Sachs, *Rev. Sci. Instr.*, **26**, 1029 (1955).
20. Snyder, C. W., S. Rubin, W. A. Fowler, and C. C. Lauritsen, *Rev. Sci. Instr.*, **21**, 852 (1950).
21. Tollestrup, A. V., W. A. Fowler, and C. C. Lauritsen, *Phys. Rev.*, **76**, 428 (1949).

SECTION D-2: Electrical Methods

Part I
Section D-2

Chapter 42

FUNDAMENTALS OF ELECTRODE PROCESSES

By CHARLES N. REILLEY, *University of North Carolina, Chapel Hill, North Carolina*

Contents

I. HISTORICAL DEVELOPMENT

There is little question but that hindsight is better than foresight. This is apparent in any historical review of scientific developments, and electrochemical methods are no exception. Many instances can be seen of new techniques stemming rapidly from fundamental studies while other techniques await development for as long as 50 years, although the fundamental principles necessary for their fruition were widely recognized. Occasionally, a technique was discovered accidentally and its use became widespread even before a rational approach was forthcoming. In contrast there are cases in which a technique, well based fundamentally, was developed but lay dormant for several decades until the time was ripe and it was "rediscovered." Although the logic of these developments often may appear mysterious, there is little doubt that the absence of appropriate instrumentation and the primary interest in determining only the major constituents in samples at the time of original development had much to do with the lack of progress in many areas.

A. ELECTROANALYSIS AND COULOMETRY

In the earliest stages of development of electrochemistry, primary interest was devoted to the study of the chemical transformations resulting from the flow of current through electrical cells. Emphasis in this stage was given to the qualitative observation of the various products obtained. As early as 1801, Cruikshank (11) noted that copper and silver metals could be obtained by electrolysis of their respective salt solutions, and he pointed out that such electrolysis could be used as a qualitative test for these metals. Quantitative studies were pursued by Faraday, and in 1834 he demonstrated his famous law of electrochemical equivalence. As his experiments were not performed under conditions that would exhaustively deplete a given metal ion from a solution, little attention was paid to his coulometric studies from the viewpoint of quantitative analysis. The first application of electrolysis to quantitative analysis stems from the work of Wolcott Gibbs (19) and C. Luckow (39), who weighed deposits of metals formed on platinum electrodes by extensive electrolysis of samples. By the turn of the century *electrogravimetry* had become a useful analytical method for the determination of many metals.

When samples contained more than one electrolyzable material, methods for selective reduction or oxidation were necessary and often were achieved by the empirical addition of various reagents and by an approximate control of current density. Sand (45) and Fischer (16) recognized that a judicious choice of electrode potential would permit selective deposition in most cases. However, their principle was not widely applied in these years because, due to the lack of appropriate instrumentation, such potential control could be effected only by manually monitoring the potential and adjusting the current flow accordingly. Hence, only recently has there been any real interest in *controlled-potential electrolysis*. Although the role of potential in governing the products of electrolysis was recognized by Haber (25), his ideas were of primary interest in preparative electrolysis. Despite the principle of electrochemical equivalence demonstrated by Faraday in 1834—the determination of substances from the quantity of electricity consumed—*coulometry* was not employed until 1917, when Grower (22) estimated the thickness of corrosion layers, a situation in which 100% current efficiency was simple to achieve. Even then Grower did not employ the simple technique of constant current but measured the quantity of electricity by a water coulometer. In order to achieve 100% current efficiency in other types of reactions, Lingane (38) employed electrolysis at controlled potential and determined the number of coulombs by a water coulometer. The principle of coulometric titrations was advanced by Szebelledy and Somogyi in 1938 (49), but undoubtedly interest in this technique became serious with the advent of the papers by Briglio, Brockman, and Shaffer (8,48), who used controlled current to monitor mustard gas; the current, and hence the rate of generation of bromine titrant required to titrate the inflow of mustard gas, was automatically adjusted and the number of equivalents was determined by a simple electronic integrator. The use of constant current by Swift and his co-workers (47) greatly simplified the experimental technique and focused wide attention on the area of coulometric titrations.

B. ELECTROCHEMICAL METHODS OF END-POINT DETECTION

The early work in quantitative analysis, with its prime interest on accurate determination of major constituents, was based on gravimetric and volumetric procedures. The electrochemical methods mentioned previously were employed primarily for quantitative separation, and the nature of the analysis was essentially gravimetric. With the increasing application of volumetric methods, electrochemical techniques eventually found use as methods of end-point detection.

The classic work of Hittorf on transference processes, which eventually led to separations (electromigration and electrophoresis), enhanced the investigations of Kohlrausch on the conductance of electrolytes. Dutoit in 1910 (13) recognized the usefulness of *conductometric* measurements for end-point detection. Shortly thereafter, extensive applications of this technique were proposed by Kolthoff, Britton, Jander, Pfundt, and others.

Because of the lack of specificity of conductance, the value of which depends on the total salt content, other more selective methods became preferred. Whereas the fundamental basis of conductometric measurements was well established, a seemingly different technique was proposed by Blake (4) in 1933, in which the end point in titrations was detected at high frequencies (*high-frequency titrations*) and in which the electrodes were not in direct contact with the sample solution. In 1946 this method was rediscovered in somewhat different form by Jensen and Parrack (33). It was soon recognized that this technique was essentially based upon conductance changes within the solution, and a satisfactory interpretation of the experimental results was then possible.

Although the quantitative treatment of electrochemical equilibria was set forth by J. Willard Gibbs between 1875 and 1878, it was really Nernst (40) who, in deriving his well-known equation, laid the foundations for *potentiometry* in 1889. The application of potential measurement to end-point detection was soon proposed by Behrend (1), and Hildebrand's pioneering work (30) on the use of the hydrogen electrode in teaching and research (particularly for analytical purposes) did much to stimulate interest in this area. The potentiometric technique, because of its simplicity and greater degree of specificity than conductometric methods, encouraged many to apply this method. As a result of the work of Bottger, Müller, Kolthoff, Furman, Willard, and numerous other investigators, this versatile method of end-point detection became well established. Today there are numerous instruments for performing volumetric titrations with automatic potentiometric end-point detection, and the scope of the method permits end-point detection in acid-base (aqueous and nonaqueous), oxidation-reduction, precipitation, and complexation titrations.

As a result of the work of Arrhenius, Ostwald, and Debye and Hückel, it was recognized that potentiometric measurements could not yield in a simple way highly accurate values for concentrations of ions, but that there were many cases in which a rough measurement was sufficient. For example, *direct potentiometry* is of immense value in pH measurements, a development that, in its present form, stems from the work of Haber and Klemenciewicz (26), who discovered the usefulness of the glass electrode. By careful control of ionic strength and temperature it is now possible to estimate the content of other ionic species such as chloride; the results are frequently secured by the use of concentration-cell measurements.

The advent of end-point detection using *polarized* electrodes occurred fairly early with the work of Nernst and Merriam (42). Van Name and Fenwich (51) studied and applied the method, using potentiometry with controlled current even though the basis of the technique was little understood. Much the same can be said for the amperometric titration made popular by the work of Foulk and Bawden (17); because of its practical importance, this method came into widespread use despite the lack of a fundamental basis for its interpretation. It was only after the principles of voltammetry and polarography had become widely appreciated that the basis for these polarized end-point techniques became obvious.

C. QUANTITATIVE METHODS BASED UPON MASS-TRANSFER PROCESSES

The work of Faraday in 1834 and the laws of diffusion proposed by A. Fick in 1855 (15) really laid the foundations for voltammetry and polarography. In 1879 Weber (53) and in 1901 Sand (46) interpreted properly the increasing polarization of electrode systems through the use of Fick's laws and established the first principles of *chronopotentiometry*. However, this technique lay idle until it was revived by Gierst and Juliard in 1950 (20). The first method based on mass transfer processes that gained widespread attention was that of Heyrovský (28), who in 1922 discovered empirically the technique of *polarography*. Soon thereafter, in 1934, Ilkovic (31) laid the theoretical groundwork of this technique, from which many novel and important uses were forthcoming. It is interesting to note that the first amperometric titration with a dropping mercury electrode was performed in 1929 by Heyrovský and Berezicky (29), although the method was still in an empirical state. The advent of polarography coincided with the change in outlook of the analytical chemist, whose attention was being turned more and more to the estimation of trace constituents in samples. This undoubtedly accounts for the rapid evolution of this technique since its proposal. Aside from its prime application in analytical chemistry, the polarographic technique also encouraged further studies into the nature of electrode processes, including the study of rapid reactions by Brdicka, Koutecky, and Weisner (6,36,54) and studies of irreversible reactions stemming from the absolute rate theory of electrochemical processes, promoted by Eyring, Glasstone, and Laidler in 1939 (14). Since then the interpretation of electrode processes has received widespread attention, and many studies using stationary electrodes as well as dropping mercury electrodes have been forthcoming. For this work a wide assortment of electrochemical techniques was developed, in which transient electrode processes are investigated under the influence of applied current and potential functions (square-wave, a.c., etc.). As a result of these studies, new methods have been proposed and reinterpretation of older methods, first established empirically, has been made. Undoubtedly the appearance of the book by Delahay (12) did much to focus attention on these newer electrochemical techniques and principles. Because of the increasing awareness of the close connection between theory and practice, today's analytical chemist stands ready to contribute to the fundamental theory and to make rapid application of developed theories.

II. THERMODYNAMIC CONSIDERATIONS

The fundamental measurements in electroanalytical chemistry include *potential, current,* and *time.* The precise relationship among these three measurements and the composition of the sample depends in largest measure on the exact manner in which the measurement is made. In this section, we shall consider the relationship between potential and the composition of the sample when the system is at equilibrium. In the next section the various kinetic considerations will be discussed.

A. ELECTRON FREE-ENERGY LEVELS: INTENSIVE FACTOR

Consider a suitable metal electrode in equilibrium with a sample solution in which it is immersed. The electrode will exhibit a potential that is invariant with time and is related thermodynamically to the composition of the solution. The potential measured is a function of the free energy of the electrons in the metal electrode, and this potential can be said to be an *intensive* factor, i.e., it is independent of the quantity of the sample solution.

The concept of electron free-energy levels is similar in principle to that advanced by Gurney (23,24) for protons, and it also can be applied to complexes. This concept of free-energy levels is valuable in illustrating the reaction tendency of chemical and electrochemical systems toward limiting concentrations of reactants such as protons, ligands, and electrons.

Consider the equilibrium that exists between protonated and unprotonated substances, that is, in conjugate acid and base forms:

		Conjugate base		*Conjugate acid*
H^+	+	Ac^-	$\rightleftharpoons$	HAc
H^+	+	HCO_3^-	$\rightleftharpoons$	H_2CO_3
H^+	+	NH_3	$\rightleftharpoons$	NH_4^+
H^+	+	CO_3^{-2}	$\rightleftharpoons$	HCO_3^-

Notice that the difference between the conjugate base and the conjugate acid forms is *one* hydrogen ion. Systems that contain high concentrations of the conjugate base and conjugate acid are well buffered with respect to the hydrogen ion concentration, whereas systems containing only the conjugate base or conjugate acid are poorly buffered. For such chemical systems one usually writes the equilibrium relations (ignoring activity co-efficients):

$$K_a = \frac{[H_3O^+][B^-]}{[HB]\,[H_2O]}$$

$$pH = pK_a + \log \frac{[B^-]}{[HB]}$$

In Fig. 42.1 is illustrated a proton free-energy scale, expressed either in terms of electron volts per proton (G^0) or as pH. The energy associated with a process in which a proton is raised from the lower occupied proton level of a water molecule, H_2O, to the vacant proton level of ammonia, NH_3, is given by the separation in the respective proton free-energy levels, 0.28 e.v. Conversely, the energy associated with the transfer of a proton from the occupied level, NH_4^+, to the unoccupied level, OH^-, is -0.28 e.v. In an assemblage of occupied and unoccupied proton free-energy levels, the pH is a measure of the *average* proton free energy per proton and depends on the relative population and energy values of the levels present. When the population of occupied and unoccupied proton levels of a system is equal, i.e., when $[NH_3] = [NH_4^+]$, pH $= pK_a$, the pH is given on the left-hand scale in Fig. 42.1 at a value corresponding to the horizontal line for this system. When the energy corresponding to the separation between the proton free-energy levels of two systems approaches that of thermal energy, kT (equals 0.0257 e.v.), protonation of the upper unoccupied level occurs through thermal excitation of a proton from the lower occupied level. It is obvious that to populate any lower level with protons without simul-taneous population of any adjacent higher level the separation between the proton-energy levels must be several times kT.

The values of G^0 in Fig. 42.1 are obtained by the following considerations. The free energy, ΔG^0, of the proton transfer reaction

$$H_2O + B^- \rightarrow OH^- + HB$$

is given by

$$\Delta G^0_h = -kT \ln K_w/K_a$$

where the units of ΔG^0 are electron volts per proton and k is 8.615×10^{-5} e.v. per degree-proton. The energy of the above transformation is com-posed of the energy difference between the reactions

$$H^+ + B^- \rightarrow HB \qquad G^0_{HB}$$

$$H^+ + OH^- \rightarrow H_2O \qquad G^0_{H_2O}$$

$$G^0_{HB} - G^0_{H_2O} = \Delta G^0_h$$

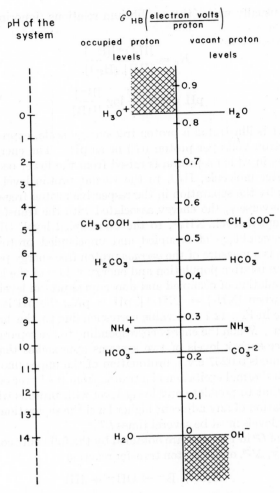

Fig. 42.1. Proton free-energy levels. The standard free-energy level, G_0, of the H_2O, OH^- system has been chosen arbitrarily to be zero.

By arbitrarily assigning $G^0_{H_2O}$ a value of zero, we establish a scale of relative proton-free energies that, at 25°C., is

$$G^0_{HB} = -0.0591 \log K_w/K_a \qquad (1)$$

In the above, the standard state of solutes is in moles/liter and water is assumed to have unit concentration.

To illustrate further, consider a system containing OH^-, NH_3, and CH_3-COO^-. If protons, H^+, are added to the system, they tend to populate the lowest free-energy state, which in this case (aqueous solution) is that of the hydroxide ion. As soon as the hydroxide ion level is more or less completely populated, continued addition of protons will then lead to population of the next highest level, i.e., that of NH_3, and a change in pH will be noted, since the presence of a larger number of protons in the higher-energy level increases markedly the average proton energy. Similarly, upon nearly complete population of the ammonia level, population of the acetate level commences to be rapid. This stepwise process continues until the proton level is very high and the population of the H_2O level is extensive. Here the solvent, because of its relatively large concentration, exerts a *leveling* influence on the system, and pH values much lower than zero cannot be achieved in dilute aqueous solutions. When filled energy levels are depopulated, the reverse scheme holds. That is, as protons are removed, they are lost from the highest energy level first, i.e., from H_3O^+, until that level is essentially depopulated. Then depopulation of the acetic acid level commences, etc., and eventually depopulation of the H_2O level, forming OH^-, becomes extensive. In this case of proton removal, the solvent again exerts a leveling influence, but this time on the lowest free-energy level. When a species of a populated high-energy level is added to a species in an unpopulated lower level (for example, the addition of H_3O^+ to OH^-), the proton will transfer from the former to the latter (from H_3O^+ to the OH^-). The extent of this reaction depends upon the separation in the free-energy levels indicated on the diagram.

In a similar manner, an electron free-energy scale may be established for oxidation-reduction reactions. The free energy, ΔG^0, of the electron transfer reaction

$$O_1 + n/2\ H_2 \rightarrow R_1 + nH^+$$

is given by

$$\Delta G^0 = -kT \ln K = -kT \ln \frac{[R_1]}{[O_1][e]^n} - kT \ln \frac{[H^+][e]}{[H_2]^{1/2}}$$

where K corresponds to the equilibrium constant for the electron-transfer reaction given. The units for ΔG^0 are electron volts per electron and k is 8.615×10^{-5} e.v. per degree-electron. The free energy of the above transformation is composed of the free-energy difference between the reactions

$$O_1 + ne \rightarrow R_1 \qquad G^0_1$$
$$H^+ + e \rightarrow 1/2\ H_2 \qquad G^0_H$$
$$\Delta G^0 = G^0_1 - G^0_H$$

By arbitrarily assigning G_H^0 a value of zero $(G_H^0 = -kT \ln \{[H_2]^{1/2}/ [H^+][e]\} = 0)$, we establish a scale of relative electron free energies, which at 25°C. is

$$G_1^0 = -kT \ln \frac{[R_1]}{[O_1][e]^n} = -kT \ln K \tag{2}$$

In the above, the standard state of solutes is in moles per liter except for gases, which are expressed in atmospheres, and water is assumed to have unit concentration.

From equation (2), the electron free-energy scale in terms of G^0 values may be established as in Fig. 42.2. To relate this scale to potential, a rearrangement of equation (2) yields

$$-kT \ln [e] = \frac{kT}{n} \ln K - \frac{kT}{n} \ln \frac{[R_1]}{[O_1]}$$

or

$$E = E_1^0 - \frac{kT}{n} \ln \frac{[R_1]}{[O_1]}$$

where $-nE_1^0 = G_1^0$.

This form of the Nernst equation has been used rather than the more familiar form containing the Faraday, F, because free energy, G^0, has been expressed in electron volts per electron rather than in joules per mole. The potential, E (left-hand scale), constitutes a measure of the *average* electron free energy per electron of an assemblage of occupied and unoccupied electron free-energy levels and depends on the relative population and energy values of the levels present. When the population of occupied and unoccupied levels of a given system correspond to their standard states (or equal in the case of simple redox pairs, i.e., $[R_1] = [O_1]$), then $E = E_1^0$.

From Fig. 42.2, the energy associated with a process in which an electron is raised from the lower occupied electron level of a solvated hydrogen molecule to the vacant electron level of a solvated vanadium(III) ion is given by the separation in the respective electron free-energy levels, which in this case equals 0.255 e.v. per electron transfer. Similarly, the energy associated with raising an electron from the bromide level to the vanadium(III) level is given by the energy-level separation, which equals 1.265 e.v. per electron transfer.

Next consider an aqueous system containing Cl_2 and $Fe(CN)_6^{-3}$. If electrons are added to the system they tend to populate the lowest free-energy state first, which in this case is that of Cl_2. As soon as this level is nearly completely populated, continued addition of electrons will then lead

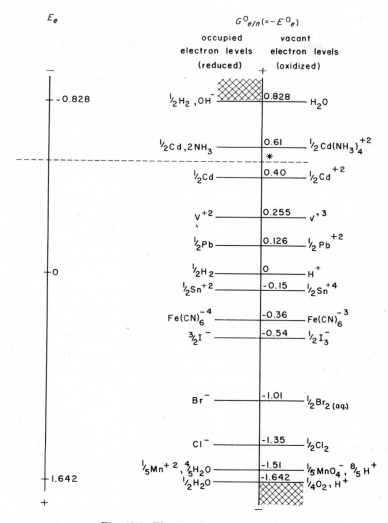

Fig. 42.2. Electron free-energy levels.

to population of the next highest level, i.e., that of $Fe(CN)_6^{-3}$, and a change in E will occur, since the presence of a larger number of electrons in the higher energy level increases markedly the average electron energy. The sharpness of such a potential change depends upon the separation of the respective electron free-energy levels and, because of the effect of thermal agitation, upon the value of kT. For practical work, the separation between adjacent levels must be several times kT. Upon nearly complete population of the $Fe(CN)_6^{-3}$ level, the electrons then commence to populate the water level (forming H_2 and OH^-), and another change in E occurs. Henceforth, the solvent, because of its relatively large concentration, exerts a leveling influence on the system and a potential, E, corresponding to true equilibrium cannot achieve values much more negative than -0.828 v. in dilute aqueous solution. Conversely, when filled electron-energy levels are depopulated, the reverse scheme is operative. In this case, electron removal from the solvent (to form H^+ and O_2) results in a leveling effect at the low end of the free-energy scale, and true equilibrium potentials much more positive than 1.642 v. are difficult to achieve in dilute aqueous solutions.

When a species in a populated high-energy level is added, as in a titration, to a species in a lower unpopulated level (for example, the addition of vanadium(II) to chlorine), electrons will transfer from the former to the latter. The extent of this reaction, as measured by the equilibrium constant K_e, depends upon the separation of their free-energy levels ($G_1^0 - G_2^0 = -kT \ln K_e$).

Previously, it was pointed out that in an assemblage of occupied and unoccupied electron free-energy levels the average electron free energy depended on the relative populations and energy values of the levels present. This average electron energy would determine the potential, E, of an electrode inserted into the system. If, however, a different potential is imposed upon this electrode, the relative population of the electron energy levels would be modified through electron transfer at the surface of this electrode, and this electron-transfer process will continue until the new population distribution conforms to this potential. For example, if the imposed electrode potential is that denoted by the asterisk in Fig. 42.2, the populations of the energy levels of all systems present will adjust to this potential. For systems whose electron free-energy levels lie above that of the electrode, the population distribution will be shifted toward that of the unpopulated state, whereas for systems below the electrode's electron free-energy level the distribution will lie in favor of the occupied state. The distribution ratio for any given level will depend upon the separation of its free-energy level from that of the electrode.

It is obvious that the addition of a complexing agent to a system, i.e., cadmium in Fig. 42.2, shifts the electron free-energy level since a different species $(Cd(NH_3)_4^{+2})$ now constitutes the unoccupied level. It is also important to note that such systems $(Cd(NH_3)_4^{+2}, MnO_4^-)$ have a composite nature in that the average electron free energy is governed in part by the ligand or proton concentration. In multicomponent systems in which the electron free-energy levels are insufficiently separated, they often may be spread apart by the addition of ligands or protons, and this principle is widely employed in polarography and redox titrations.

B. ELECTRON FREE-ENERGY LEVELS: CAPACITY FACTOR

Once a sufficient spread in the electron free-energy levels is achieved, we are in a position to consider a selective and quantitative conversion of one species to another. This conversion, which is the basis of an analytical determination, is based on the *capacity* factor of the system: the number of electrons required in bringing the system from one potential to another (i.e., in altering the intensive factor from one value to another). In order to effect this change in the average electron free-energy level, the ratio of the oxidized to reduced form necessarily must be altered. Hence at $E = +1.00$ v., the system $Fe(CN)_6^{-4}$, $Fe(CN)_6^{-3}$ is nearly depleted of electrons and can be said to be composed quantitatively of $Fe(CN)_6^{-3}$. If the potential is then altered to -0.7 v., almost complete depopulation of $Fe(CN)_6^{-3}$ occurs, yielding $Fe(CN)_6^{-3}$. The number of electrons involved in this conversion is equivalent to the quantity of $Fe(CN)_6^{-3}$ present. This measure of the capacity factor may be accomplished by adding known quantities of electrons electrochemically, as in coulometric titrations, or via reagents of higher electron free energy, that is, by strong reducing agents such as V^{+2} ion. It is clear that the extent to which the system can be converted from one form to another depends upon the values of the initial and final potentials (the *intensive* factors, which are independent of the quantity of solution). On the other hand, the number of electrons required for the conversion, the *capacity* factor, is obviously directly proportional to the quantity of a given sample solution.

For a given change in the intensive factor, a given degree of change in the capacity factor is achieved. A change from a $1:100$ ratio of R to O to a ratio of $100:1$ is achieved by proceeding from a potential value equal to $2.3(2kT/n)$ v. less than E^0 to a value of $2.3(2kT/n)$ v. greater than the E^0 value. This represents an acceptable quantitative conversion. In a mixture containing equal amounts of two different redox systems, a selective analysis for each may be secured if their electron free-energy levels differ by at least $2.3(2kT/n_1 + 2kT/n_2)$ v.

III. KINETIC CONSIDERATIONS

As discussed above, an electrode in equilibrium with a solution in which it is immersed will exhibit a potential thermodynamically related to the composition of the solution. If, by some external means, the potential of the electrode is forced to assume a different value, current will then flow in the electrode circuit until the composition of the electrode and/or solution is altered sufficiently to exhibit this new potential under equilibrium conditions. Although the direction of the current and the number of coulombs (current × time) can be predicted a priori from the thermodynamic considerations above, the *rate* of this process, and thus the magnitude of current at any particular time, is a *kinetic* phenomenon and, in the last analysis, must be determined experimentally.

Current flow through an electrochemical system must take place through a series network of individual elements, each having a characteristic influence on the current flow. In any given system, the magnitude of the current flow usually is limited by a single rate process occurring in one particular element. The more familiar elements in the current-path network are metal conductors, metal-metal contacts, electrode-solution interfaces, and the bulk solution itself. Processes occurring in the latter two elements most frequently limit the current.

Within the solution phase, charge (current) may be carried by one or both of two paths. One of these paths involves migration of charged species, *electrical ionic mobility,* and the other involves *polarization of the dielectric.* The latter, being a transient process, contributes significantly only in carrying alternating current. At electrode–solution interfaces, the processes important in current flow are electron-transfer reactions (*Faradaic current*) and charging of the electrical double layer (*non-Faradaic current*). Because the current in an electrochemical cell is governed by the slowest of the above processes, for an effective understanding of the system as a whole it is necessary to consider in detail the characteristics of each of the individual processes. The success of any electroanalytical measurement is dependent upon the degree to which one can achieve experimental control over the rate of each and all of these processes.

A. PROCESSES OCCURRING AT ELECTRODE–SOLUTION INTERFACES

1. Faradaic Currents

Obviously, electrolysis involves reactions occurring at the surface of an electrode. The rate of each reaction, and hence the current, is controlled in part by the rate of an electron-transfer reaction and in part by the rate of transport of a solution species into the near vicinity of the electrode surface. In this section, only the case in which the electron-transfer step is much slower than the mass-transport step will be considered. Under this assumption, the solution is homogeneous and the surface concentration of the electroactive species is equal to its concentration in the bulk solution.

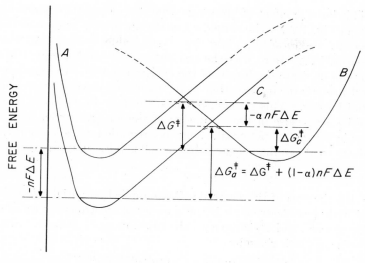

Fig. 42.3. Reaction coordinate diagram for an electron-transfer reaction at an electrode.

The rate of electron transfer depends on the nature and concentration of the electroactive species and on the nature and potential of the electrode. In order to cause passage of a net Faradaic current at an electrode, it is necessary to shift the potential from its equilibrium value. For purposes of discussion, consider Fig. 42.3; here curve A represents the potential-energy curve (44) for the species in one form (in the reduced form), and curve B represents the potential-energy curve for the species in its oxidized form and at the equilibrium potential of the couple. For an electron to transfer from one form to the other, i.e., from the reduced to oxidized form or vice versa, an energy barrier of height $\Delta G^{\ddagger}$ must be surmounted. $\Delta G^{\ddagger}$ is the free energy of activation; that is, the free energy necessary to convert a mole of reactant to the activated state in the reaction. It is clear that the rate of passage of electrons is equal in both directions under these equilibrium conditions. Although the net rate of passage of electrons, and thus the current, is zero, in this dynamic equilibrium the passage of current in a single direction is not zero and is called the *exchange current*, i_0. Because this is an activated kinetic process, this exchange current will be proportional to the surface concentration, C^0, and $\exp(-\Delta G^{\ddagger}/RT)$, and the latter term is strongly dependent upon the height of the energy barrier, $\Delta G^{\ddagger}$. If the electrode potential is changed by an amount, ΔE, so as to favor the cathodic reaction, the free energy of the system is changed by an amount $-n_a F \Delta E$, where n_a is the number of electrons required in the kinetic process.   This has the effect of lowering curve A to a position represented by curve C in Fig. 42.3.   The cathodic free energy of activation now becomes $\Delta G^{\ddagger}_{c} = \Delta G^{\ddagger} - \alpha n_a F \Delta E$, while the anodic value becomes $\Delta G^{\ddagger}_{a} = \Delta G^{\ddagger} + (1-\alpha)n_a F \Delta E$.   Here α is the fraction of the total energy, $-n_a F \Delta E$, that acts to decrease the height of the energy barrier for the cathodic reaction and $1 - \alpha$ is the fraction that tends to increase the height of the anodic potential barrier.   This symbol, α, called the *transfer coefficient*, is clearly seen to be a measure of the symmetry of the energy barrier and, over a reasonable range of potential, may be regarded as a constant.   The cathodic current can then be given by the following equation:

$$i_c = nFk_sAC^0_{ox}.e^{-\alpha n_a F(E-E^0)/RT} \tag{3a}$$

where A is the area of the electrode, E the applied potential referred to the normal hydrogen electrode, n is the number of electrons for the electrode reaction process, and k^0_f is the cathodic reaction rate constant.   Similarly, the anodic current is given by

$$i_a = -nFk_sAC^0_{red}.e^{(1-\alpha)n_a F(E-E^0)/RT} \tag{3b}$$

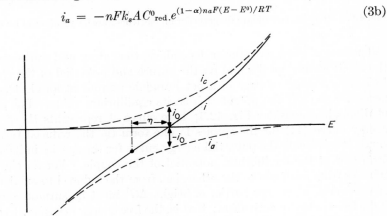

Fig. 42.4. Current-potential relationship for an electrode process controlled by activation polarization.

The behavior of each of these currents as a function of potential is shown in Fig. 42.4.   The net current at an electrode, i, is then equal to the sum of the two opposing currents, i_a and i_c.   At the equilibrium potential the magnitudes of the anodic and cathodic currents are equal to each other and to the exchange current, i_0.   At any potential, the net current, i, is given by the arithmetic sum

$$i = i_c + i_a = nF_skA \,|C^0_{ox}.e^{-\alpha n_a F(E-E^0(/RT} - C_{0red}.e^{(1-\alpha)n_a F(E-E^0)/RT} \tag{4}$$

At the equilibrium potential, $E = E_{eq.}$, no net current flows and equations (3a) and (3b) yield:

$$\frac{C^0_{ox.}}{C^0_{red.}} = \frac{k^0_b}{k^0_f} e^{(nF/RT)E_{eq.}}$$

(5a)

Because $E_{eq.} = E^0$ when $C^0_{ox.}/C^0_{red.} = 1$,

$$\frac{C^0_{ox.}}{C^0_{red.}} = e^{(nF/RT)(E_{eq.} - E^0)}$$

(5b)

This shows that the Nernst equation does not involve the transfer coefficient, α. Since the exchange current, i_0, is given either by i_c or i_a at equilibrium, it follows readily that

$$i_0 = nFA(k_f^0)^{1-\alpha}(k_b^0)^{\alpha}(C^0_{ox.})^{1-\alpha}(C^0_{red.})^{\alpha}$$

(6)

The net current, $i_c + i_a$, at any potential may be given by combining equations (3, 5, and 6) to yield

$$i = i_0 e^{-(\alpha n_a F/RT)(E - E_{eq.})} - i_0 e^{(1-\alpha)(n_a F/RT)(E - E_{eq.})}$$

(7)

Thus, the passage of a net current causes the potential to deviate from its equilibrium value by an amount $E - E_{eq.}$, which is called the *activation overpotential*, symbolized by η. This overpotential is caused by a slow kinetic process in the electron-transfer reaction and must be distinguished from *concentration polarization*, which arises from depletion of the surface concentrations of oxidized and reduced species. In practical measurements of activation overpotential, care must be taken to avoid any surface concentration depletion, i.e., by stirring and by obtaining potential measurements almost immediately after current flow commences.

When η is small (in comparison to $0.0257/\alpha n_a$ and $0.0257/(1-\alpha)n_a$ at 25°C.), the exponential terms in equation (7) can be expanded in the form $e^{-x} \approx 1 - x$. In this case, equation (7) becomes

$$i = -i_0 n_a F\eta/RT$$

(8)

For $\alpha = 0.5$ and η small compared with 51 mv. ($n_a = 1$) or with 25.7 mv. ($n_a = 2$), this equation indicates a direct proportionality between η and current, i, under these conditions. The value of $(di/d\eta)_{t=0}$ equals $-i_0 n_a F/RT$, and the reciprocal of this value, having the dimensions of resistance, is usually termed the *polarization resistance*. This is the effective resistance imposed at the electrode surface by the finite rate of the electron-transfer process.

For large values of η the back-reaction can be neglected. Thus, for cathodic polarization greater than $-25.7/\alpha n_a$ mv., equation (7) becomes

$$i_c = i_0 e^{-\alpha n_a F \eta / RT}$$

or, in log form,

$$\eta = \frac{2.3RT}{\alpha n_a F} \log i_0 - \frac{2.3RT}{\alpha n_a F} \log i_c$$

This equation has the form, $\eta = a + b \log i_c$, which is the well-known *Tafel equation* (50), expressing overpotential as a linear function of the logarithm of current. Tafel plots have long been known to fit experimental data obtained in studies of activation overpotential (such as the evolution of hydrogen and oxygen at various electrodes).

As seen from Fig. 42.4, the activation overpotential is a function of current. This diagram and the principles related previously were all under the assumption that the concentrations of the electroactive species at the electrode surface were constant; obviously, this cannot remain true for very long after a current or potential is applied, since the progress of the electrolysis depletes or increases the concentration of the species present at the electrode surface. The alteration of these concentrations in turn establishes a polarization of the electrode, that is, a potential at the electrode surface different from its equilibrium value calculated from the bulk concentrations of the species. Hence, it often is difficult to measure with any precision the activation overpotential without the other side effects. In fact, electrode processes are classified to be *"reversible"* if the activation overpotential is immeasurably small and *"irreversible"* if the activation overpotential is measurable. Clearly, the distinction between "reversible" and "irreversible" electrode processes is somewhat artificial since it is highly dependent upon the conditions of the electrolysis. Whereas the activation overpotential is readily measured when large, very special techniques must be employed to measure its value when small. In the latter case the overpotential is measured under conditions in which the electrochemical process is virtually completely controlled by the rate of electrochemical reaction, i.e., where the rate of mass transfer toward or away from the electrode is effectively infinite. One method (18), for example, is to apply a constant potential suddenly and to extrapolate the current obtained back to zero time, the time when the concentrations of the oxidized and reduced forms are the same at the electrode surface as they are in the bulk of the solution (before concentration polarization has proceeded to any degree).

2. Non-Faradaic Currents: The Electrical Double Layer

In the absence of an oxidizable or reducible substance, it has been found experimentally that a finite current passes when the potential of an electrode of fixed area is altered. This current is referred to as "non-Faradaic," since it does not arise from an electron-transfer reaction. Similarly, when a new electrode area is being created at constant potential (such as is the case with a dropping mercury electrode), non-Faradaic current also results even in the absence of electroactive species.

These effects may be explained (9) on the basis of formation of an *electrical double layer* at the electrode surface. Imagine, for example, a positively polarized mercury surface immersed in a solution of sodium chloride. In this case, the positive electrode surface attracts the negative chloride ions because of electrostatic action, van der Waals' forces, and specific chemical effects. As a result, a layer of essentially nonhydrated chloride ions will accumulate very close to the electrode surface, forming what is known as the *inner Helmholtz layer*. Because of the presence of this negatively charged layer of chloride ions, a double layer is said to exist. Just beyond this layer is a second layer of tightly held but hydrated chloride ions, a layer that marks the boundary of the *outer Helmholtz layer*. Beyond this extends a *diffuse layer*, with a net charge whose ionic atmosphere contains ions of one sign in excess of their normal concentration and those of the other sign in defect. This assemblage of charged layers is commonly referred to as simply the *double layer* (see Fig. 42.5). Upon decreasing the potential of the electrode, the positive charge on the layer just within the mercury surface is decreased, the force holding the nonhydrated chloride ions to the positive charge decreases, and the chloride ions are to a large extent desorbed, although the hydrated chloride ions in the outer Helmholtz layer still remain. This redistribution of the ions decreases the original ionic charge separation in a way that is equivalent to discharging the double layer. This process leads to a net flow of current that persists as long as the redistribution is in progress and, in this sense, has the properties of capacitance. The capacitance of the double layer is large (often between 20 to 50 μf. per square centimeter of electrode surface), and it varies markedly with potential and with the nature of the electrode (composition and surface state) and electrolyte solution. For example, the less readily hydrated ions (CNS^-, I^-, NO_3^-, Cl^-, R_4N^+, Cs^+) seek positions on the surface to a larger extent than easily hydrated ions (OH^-, F^-, Li^+, Na^+). In addition to ionic double layers, molecular double layers exist because of an energy of interaction between the electrode surface and polar molecules. The net interaction depends upon the dipoles' relative at-

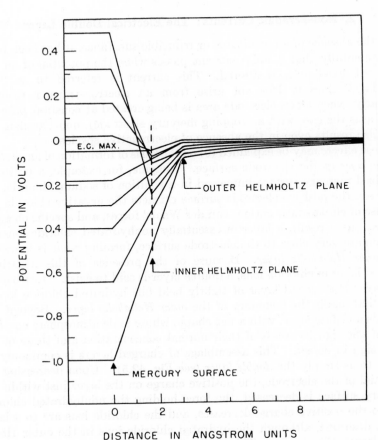

Fig. 42.5. Potentials in the electrical double layer between mercury and aqueous 0.3M sodium chloride at various polarizing potentials (according to Graham (21)). The potentials are relative to the value of the electrocapillary maximum in the absence of adsorption.

traction toward and repulsion from the two phases. In the case of surface-active materials, which tend to collect at interfaces partially because of their poor ability to be hydrated by the solvent, a double layer is formed except at very negative and positive potentials. In these extreme potential regions, ions tend to displace them because of the more powerful forces of electrostatic attraction.

It is commonly felt that the electroactive species, when undergoing an electron-transfer reaction, approaches the electrode no closer than the outer Helmholtz plane; hence, the potential that governs the rate of electron transfer is determined by the potential difference between the outer Helm-holtz plane and the mercury surface (7). Thus, in detailed studies of electron-transfer processes, it is necessary to employ the potential dif-ference between the outer Helmholtz plane and that of the mercury surface for η and the concentration of the species in the outer Helmholtz layer for C^0. The kinetics of the electron-transfer process also are strongly depend-ent upon the composition and structure of the electrical double layer. For example, the presence of adsorbed layers of surface-active materials, oxide coatings, etc., may have a drastic influence on the rate and mecha-nism of the electrode reaction. Although such fundamental effects are the subject of many current investigations, there are many aspects of this area that are as yet unexplored.

B. MASS TRANSFER OF SPECIES TO THE ELECTRODE–SOLUTION INTERFACE

It is clear that a species can be oxidized or reduced electrochemically only if and when the species is brought to the immediate vicinity of the electrode surface. At certain potentials the rate of electron transfer may be much larger than the rate of the mass-transfer process. Under these conditions the current is controlled by the latter process. Three methods for ac-complishing mass transport are through *migration, diffusion,* and *convection.*

1. Migration

In migration, the driving force that operates to move the species to (or away from) the electrode surface is the force exerted on a charged particle by a potential gradient existing in the body of the solution. Thus, for example, a potential gradient in an electrolytic solution will cause a current

TABLE 42.I
Equivalent Ionic Conductances at Infinite Dilution in Aqueous Solutions at 25°C.

Cations	Conductance mho-cm.^{2}/g. equivalent	Anions	Conductance mho-cm.^{2}/g. equivalent
H$^+$	349.82	OH$^-$	197.6
K$^+$	73.52	SO$_4^{-2}$	79.8
NH$_4^+$	73.4	Br$^-$	78.4
Ba^{+2}	63.64	Cl$^-$	76.34
Ca^{+2}	59.50	NO$_3^-$	71.44
Mg^{+2}	53.06	F$^-$	55
Na$^+$	50.11	B(C$_6$H$_5$)$_4^-$	21
Li$^+$	38.69		

to flow within the body of the solution such that negative species will move one way, positive the other, and neutral species will remain unaffected. The rate of movement of a charged particle depends upon the magnitude of its charge, size, degree of hydration, etc. Some typical values are given in Table 42.I for comparison. In conductometric measurements, migration is the sole factor that limits the current. In other cases, such as polarography, it is desirable to eliminate the contribution of migration, and this end is accomplished by addition of an excess (about 100-fold) of an inert electrolyte that, in turn, decreases the potential gradient to a value sufficiently small so that diffusion and/or convection processes become current-limiting.

2. Diffusion

This transport mechanism has its origin in a gradient of chemical potential or, more simply, in a concentration gradient. Thus, if the concentration of the species in the bulk of the solution is greater than its concentration at the electrode surface (because of the electrode reaction), the species will tend to diffuse from the bulk of the solution toward the electrode surface. Whereas the direction of diffusion is from regions of larger to smaller concentrations, its rate is proportional to the magnitude of the concentration differences and to certain characteristic properties of the diffusing species and medium.

Diffusion that takes place in a single direction (diffusion to a plane sur-

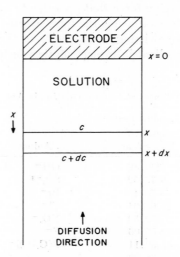

Fig. 42.6. Semi-infinite linear diffusion to a plane electrode.

face) is termed *linear diffusion* and is mathematically and experimentally the simplest case. Consider the linear diffusion to a plane electrode shown in Fig. 42.6. Here the concentration increases as one proceeds from the electrode downward. Hence the diffusion proceeds upward. The number of moles, N, of the diffusing substance that diffuse across a cross-sectional plane of unit area ($A = 1$ cm.^{2}) in the infinitesimal interval of time, dt, is the *flux*. It is proportional to the concentration gradient, $\partial C/\partial x$, at the plane in question and is given by

$$f_{(x,t)} = \frac{1}{A}\frac{dN_{(x,t)}}{dt} = D\left(\frac{\partial C_{(x,t)}}{\partial x}\right)$$

where D is the diffusion coefficient (expressed usually in cm.^{2}/second) and $C_{(x,t)}$ refers to the concentration at distance x from the electrode surface and at time t. This equation was first proposed by Fick (15) and is usually referred to as *Fick's First Law*. Note that $dN_{(x,t)}/dt$ and $\partial C_{(x,t)}/\partial x$ are written as functions of the variables x and t. At a distance $x + dx$ from the electrode, the flux is given by

$$\frac{1}{A}\frac{dN_{(x+dx,t)}}{dt} = D\left[\frac{\partial C_{(x,t)}}{\partial x}\right] + \frac{\partial\{D[\partial C_{(x,t)}/\partial x]\}}{\partial x}\,dx$$

From the values of flux at x and $x + dx$ one deduces that the rate of change of concentration ($\partial C_{(x,t)}/\partial t$) between two planes parallel to the electrode at distances x and $x + dx$, respectively, is

$$\frac{\partial C_{(x,t)}}{\partial t} = \frac{\partial\{D[\partial C_{(x,t)}/\partial x]\}}{\partial x}$$

and as D is assumed to be independent of x and t,

$$\frac{\partial C_{(x,t)}}{\partial t} = D\frac{\partial^2 C_{(x,t)}}{\partial x^2}$$

This is the fundamental differential equation for *linear* diffusion and is referred to as *Fick's Second Law*. Other forms of this equation may be developed for other types of diffusion, such as cylindrical and spherical diffusion. These laws are the fundamental starting points for deriving the various relationships for the different electrochemical methods subsequently discussed in this book.

To solve the differential equations given by Fick's laws, one must define certain *initial* and *boundary* conditions in order to obtain an explicit solution for concentration as a function of time, t, and distance from the electrode surface, x. In any experiment, the initial distribution of concentrations (i.e., before application of any current or potential) is ordinarily well known and can be set down in definite terms: this establishes what are called the "initial conditions." Upon commencement of the experiment (such as application of a current or potential), the distribution of concentrations of course will be changed in a way dependent upon the geometry of the experimental system and upon the nature of the current or potential function used. These parameters and any subsequent implications may then be written in mathematical terms that constitute what are called the "boundary conditions" of the experiment. One then has the information needed to obtain an explicit solution for $C_{(x,t)}$. This procedure will be illustrated by obtaining solutions for the electroanalytical techniques known as (1) *chronoamperometry* and (2) *chronopotentiometry*.

a. CHRONOAMPEROMETRY

This technique involves the sudden application of a potential of sufficient magnitude to cause an electrode reaction and the measurement of the resulting current as a function of time.

Let us consider the case of a plane electrode situated in a homogeneous solution containing an electroactive species at concentration C. This solution is unstirred (to eliminate convection as a means of mass transport) and in addition contains a large concentration of inert supporting electrolyte (to eliminate migration as a means of mass transport). Hence the electroactive species has the diffusion process as its sole mode of transport. Fick's Second Law as stated above for linear diffusion therefore will apply to this situation. As stated previously, the first step in obtaining the explicit solution (for a particular experimental case such as that above) is accomplished by setting down the necessary initial and boundary conditions.

Initial Condition

Initially $(t = 0)$ the concentration at any value of x is given to be C. Thus the initial condition is

$$C_{(x,0)} = C$$

Boundary Conditions

As stated above, the experiment commences upon the application of a potential that causes an electrode reaction to occur. For our case, we will assume that the potential is chosen so as to cause the immediate depletion of the electroactive species at the electrode surface ($x = 0$). This gives the boundary condition:

$$C_{(0,t)} = 0 \text{ at } t > 0$$

Furthermore, the solution is of sufficient thickness such that, in the time for which the experiment is performed, there is negligible change in the concentration of the electroactive species in areas remote ($x = \infty$) from the electrode. This yields the boundary condition:

$$C_{(\infty,t)} = C \text{ at } t > 0$$

This is therefore a case of linear *semi-infinite* diffusion.

By the use of appropriate mathematical techniques, the solution of Fick's Second Law for these initial and boundary conditions is:

$$C_{(x,t)} = C \ \mathrm{erf}(x/2D^{1/2}t^{1/2}) \tag{9}$$

The error function (erf) is defined as

$$\mathrm{erf}\,(\lambda) = \frac{2}{\pi^{1/2}} \int_0^\lambda \exp\,(-z^2)\,dz$$

Tables of numerical values of the error function for various values of λ are readily available (34) and permit calculation of the concentration-distance profile at any time during the electrolysis.

Of primary interest, however, is the variation of the measured current with time. Because the diffusing material is electrolyzed as soon as it reaches the electrode surface, one can obtain the value of the current from Fick's First Law:

$$i_t = nF \left[\frac{dN_{(0,t)}}{dt} \right] = nFAD \left[\frac{\partial C_{(0,t)}}{\partial x} \right]$$

where n is the number of electrons, F is the Faraday, and $\partial C_{0,t}/\partial x$ is the concentration gradient at the electrode surface. By differentiating equation (9) and setting $x = 0$, substitution into this expression yields the desired relationship:

$$i_t = nFAC\,(D/\pi t)^{1/2}$$

Further discussion of the use and significance of this equation is given in the chapter on chronoamperometry.

Derivation of the Cottrell Equation

Above it was mentioned that the differential equation expressed by Fick's Second Law could be solved by appropriate mathematical means using the initial and boundary conditions. One of the most powerful tools for doing this is the Laplace transformation (32). Just as it is convenient to perform certain mathematical operations such as multiplication and division by transforming the original numbers into logarithms, thereby simplifying the mathematics greatly (multiplication becomes addition, division becomes subtraction), the use of Laplace transforms permits algebraic solutions to ordinary linear differential equations and frequently converts partial differential equations into ordinary differential equations. For this purpose, the differential equation, $f(t)$, is transformed according to

$$f(P) = \int_0^\infty f(t) \exp{(-Pt)}\, dt$$

The next step consists of algebraically solving the resulting equation and evaluating the constants by use of the initial and boundary conditions. The last step consists of taking the inverse Laplace transform, yielding the explicit solution. This latter step is analogous to taking the antilogarithm when solving a simple numerical calculation. Just as a logarithm table contains transform pairs, i.e., the number and its logarithm, tables of Laplace transform pairs have been tabulated and are readily available (27).

The present problem involves the solution of the partial differential equation given by

$$\frac{\partial C_{(x,t)}}{\partial t} = D\frac{\partial^2 C_{(x,t)}}{\partial x^2}$$

The first step is to take the Laplace transformation of each side of this equation, yielding

$$\frac{d^2 \bar{C}_{(x,P)}}{dx^2} - \frac{P}{D}\bar{C}_{(x,P)} = -\frac{C_{(x,0)}}{D}$$

The next step is to solve this ordinary differential equation by conventional means, whereby one obtains:

$$\bar{C}_{(x,P)} = \alpha \exp\left[\frac{P^{1/2}}{D^{1/2}}x\right] + \beta \exp\left[-\frac{P^{1/2}}{D^{1/2}}x\right] + \frac{C_{(x,0)}}{P}$$

There are three constants, α, β, and $C_{(x,0)}$, in this equation whose values must now be established. One makes use of the initial and boundary conditions for this purpose. From the initial condition, $C_{(x,0)} = C$, one immediately obtains:

$$\bar{C}_{(x,P)} = \alpha \exp\left[\frac{P^{1/2}}{D^{1/2}}x\right] + \beta \exp\left[-\frac{P^{1/2}}{D^{1/2}}x\right] + \frac{\acute{C}}{P} \tag{10}$$

To evaluate α, one looks for the boundary condition in which the second term in equation (10) becomes zero, i.e., the boundary condition in which x goes to infinity. The appropriate boundary condition is $C_{(\infty,t)} = C$. The Laplace transform of this boundary condition is

$$L\{C_{(\infty,t)} = C\} \qquad \text{is} \qquad \bar{C}_{(\infty,P)} = \frac{C}{P}$$

Hence $\alpha = 0$ and equation (10) becomes

$$\bar{C}_{(x,P)} = \beta \exp\left[-\frac{P^{1/2}}{D^{1/2}}x\right] + \frac{C}{P} \tag{11}$$

The last constant, β, is evaluated from the remaining boundary condition, $C_{(0,t)} = 0$. The Laplace of this boundary condition is

$$L\{C_{(0,t)} = 0\} \qquad \text{is} \qquad \bar{C}_{(0,P)} = 0$$

The application of this boundary condition in equation (11) yields the value for β:

$$\beta = -\frac{C}{P}$$

Hence the complete solution in the Laplace plane is

$$\bar{C}_{(x,P)} = \frac{C}{P} - \frac{C}{P} \exp\left[-\frac{P^{1/2}}{D^{1/2}}x\right] \tag{12}$$

The final step is taking the inverse Laplace transform of equation (12) by consulting the tables. One obtains

$$C_{(x,t)} = C - C \operatorname{erfc} \frac{x}{2D^{1/2}t^{1/2}}$$

where $\operatorname{erfc}(\lambda) = 1 - \operatorname{erf}(\lambda)$; hence this equation may also be written

$$C_{(x,t)} = C \operatorname{erf} \frac{x}{2D^{1/2}t^{1/2}} \tag{13}$$

As mentioned in the above general discussion, the current was evaluated by determining $dC_{(0,t)}/dx$. The differential of an error function is

$$\frac{d(\operatorname{erf}\lambda)}{dx} = \left[\frac{2}{\pi^{1/2}}\exp\left(-z^2\right)\frac{dz}{dx}\right]_{z=0}^{z=\lambda} = \frac{2}{\pi^{1/2}}\exp\left(-\lambda^2\right)\frac{d\lambda}{dx}$$

Differentiation of equation (13) hence yields

$$\left(\frac{\partial C}{\partial x}\right)_{x=0} = \frac{C}{\pi^{1/2}D^{1/2}t^{1/2}}$$

Thus the Cottrell equation (10) is

$$i = nFAD\left(\frac{\partial C_{(0,t)}}{\partial x}\right) = \frac{nFAC\,D^{1/2}}{\pi^{1/2}t^{1/2}}$$

b. CHRONOPOTENTIOMETRY WITH CONSTANT CURRENT

Chronopotentiometry with constant current involves the application of a constant current to an electrode and subsequent measurement of its potential against some reference electrode as a function of time.

Initial Condition

The initial experimental conditions and hence the "initial conditions" are the same for this case as for the case cited above for chronoamperometry. Hence

$$C_{(x,0)} = C \qquad (t = 0)$$

Boundary Conditions

Again the solution is of sufficient thickness such that, in the time for which the experiment is performed, there is negligible change in the concentration of the electroactive species in areas remote ($x = \infty$) from the electrode. This yields

$$C_{(\infty,t)} = C \qquad (t > 0)$$

This experiment commences upon the application of a constant current that causes an electrode reaction to occur. In order to write a boundary condition for the concentration of the electroactive species at the electrode surface at $t > 0$, one must make use of Fick's First Law, written in the form

$$\left(\frac{\partial C_{(x,t)}}{\partial x}\right)_{x=0} = \frac{i}{nFAD} \qquad (14)$$

Again by the use of appropriate mathematical techniques, the solution of Fick's Second Law for these initial and boundary conditions is

$$C_{(x,t)} = C - \frac{2it^{1/2}}{nFAD^{1/2}\pi^{1/2}}\exp\left(-\frac{x^2}{4Dt}\right) + \frac{ix}{nFAD}\,\text{erfc}\left(\frac{x}{2D^{1/2}t^{1/2}}\right) \qquad (15)$$

where erfc $\lambda = 1 - $ erf λ. Because the experimentally measured potential is a function of the concentration at the electrode surface, $C_{(0,t)}$, equation (15) is then rewritten for this condition:

$$C_{(0,t)} = C - \frac{2it^{1/2}}{nFAD^{1/2}\pi^{1/2}}$$

It is obvious that during the course of electrolysis the concentration, $C_{(0,t)}$, falls to zero at some time, τ. At this time, called the *transition time*, the potential suddenly changes to a value corresponding to the reaction of some other species because the diffusion of the initial species no longer can support the impressed current. It may be noted that this transition time is related to the concentration of the electroactive species in the bulk of the solution by the following equation (known as the *Sand* equation (46,53)):

$$\tau^{1/2} = \frac{nFAD^{1/2}\pi^{1/2}C}{2i}$$

A more complete discussion of the chronopotentiometric method is given in the chapter on chronoamperometry and chronopotentiometry.

Solution for the Sand Equation

As seen under the derivation of the Cottrell equation, the Laplace transform of Fick's Second Law and solution of the resulting differential equation yielded:

$$\bar{C}_{(x,P)} = \alpha \exp\left(\frac{P^{1/2}}{D^{1/2}}x\right) + \beta \exp\left(-\frac{P^{1/2}}{D^{1/2}}x\right) + \frac{C_{(x,0)}}{P}$$

The initial condition and one of the boundary conditions are identical to that for chronoamperometry; hence, as above, we obtain through application of these two conditions:

$$\bar{C}_{(x,P)} = \beta \exp\left(-\frac{P^{1/2}}{D^{1/2}}x\right) + \frac{C}{P} \tag{16}$$

The second boundary condition in chronopotentiometry was given above as equation (14).

$$\left(\frac{\partial C_{(0,t)}}{\partial x}\right)_{x=0} = \frac{i}{nFAD}$$

The Laplace transform of this equation is

$$\frac{\partial \bar{C}_{(0,P)}}{\partial x} = \frac{1}{P}\left(\frac{i}{nFAD}\right) \tag{17}$$

To evaluate β, one differentiates equation (16) in respect to x and equates the result at $x = 0$ to that given in equation (17). This yields

$$\beta = -\frac{i}{nFAD^{1/2}P^{3/2}}$$

Therefore the solution in the transform plane is

$$\bar{C}_{(x,P)} = \frac{C}{P} - \frac{i}{nFAD^{1/2}P^{3/2}}\exp\left(-\frac{P^{1/2}}{D^{1/2}}x\right) \qquad (18)$$

Finally, taking the inverse Laplace transform of equation (18), we obtain the explicit solution for the concentration as a function of x and t

$$C_{(x,t)} = C - \frac{2it^{1/2}}{nFAD^{1/2}\pi^{1/2}}\exp\left(-\frac{x^2}{4Dt}\right) + \frac{ix}{nFAD}\operatorname{erfc}\frac{x}{2D^{1/2}t^{1/2}}$$

As seen from the above general discussion, this equation yields the Sand equation when $C_{(0,t)} = 0$.

c. Chronopotentiometry with Other Controlled Currents

The derivation given above for chronopotentiometry represented the solution of the case of semi-infinite linear diffusion with application of a constant or *step* current, $i(t) = \theta$. Obviously a number of other current excitations can be applied, such as current *impulses;* currents that increase linearly with time, or *ramp currents* $[i(t) = \theta t]$; square-root-of-time currents $[i(t) = \theta t^{1/2}]$; general power of time current $[i(t) = \theta t^r]$; and exponential currents $[i(t) = \theta e^t]$; as well as combinations of simple current functions such as constant current reversal and constant current with superimposed alternating current $[i(t) = \theta_1 + \theta_2 \sin \omega t]$. The surface concentrations of the oxidized and reduced species that are present at various times during the application of these applied currents often can be readily calculated.

For this purpose equation (18) may be rearranged to yield the surface concentrations of the oxidized and of the reduced species:

$$\bar{C}_{ox.} - \bar{C}_{ox.(0,P)} = \frac{i}{nFAD^{1/2}P^{3/2}} = \left(\frac{i}{P}\right) \times \left(\frac{1}{nFAD_{ox.}^{1/2}P^{1/2}}\right)$$

$$\bar{C}_{red.} - \bar{C}_{red.(0,P)} = \frac{-i}{nFAD_{red.}^{1/2}P^{3/2}} = \left(\frac{i}{P}\right) \times \left(\frac{-1}{nFAD_{red.}^{1/2}P^{1/2}}\right)$$

Notice that in these equations the Laplace transformation of the excitation current, i/P, may be factored from the net expression to yield an expression of the general form:

Response transform = current excitation transform $\times$ system transform

or

$$\bar{R}_{(P)} = \bar{\Psi}_{(P)} \times \bar{S}_{(P)}$$

The *response transform*, $\bar{R}_{(P)}$, corresponds to the Laplace transform of the change in the surface concentration of the oxidized or of the reduced form as the result of applying a given excitation current to the system. The *excitation transform*, $\bar{\Psi}_{(P)}$, corresponds to the Laplace transformation of the excitation current that was applied. In the case of constant current the excitation current is given by $i(t) = i t^0$; hence its Laplace transformation is $\bar{i}_{(P)} = i/P$. The *system transform*, $\bar{S}_{(P)}$, represents the transform operative in the case of a single species under semi-infinite diffusion conditions.

Application of this product principle makes it easy to determine the variation of surface concentration with time when a given excitation current is applied. One simply takes the Laplace transformation of the particular excitation current employed and inserts this expression in place of i/P in the two equations given above; upon taking the inverse Laplace transformation, an expression for the time dependence of surface concentrations is obtained. In some cases the inverse transformation may be more easily accomplished by evaluating the convolution integral:

$$C - C_{(0,t)} = \int_0^t i(\tau) \times \frac{\pm 1}{nFAD^{1/2}\pi^{1/2}(t - \tau)^{1/2}} \, d\tau$$

$$= \int_0^t i(t - \tau) \times \frac{\pm 1}{nFAD^{1/2}\pi^{1/2}\tau^{1/2}} \, d\tau$$

where the plus and minus signs in the integral are employed for the oxidized and the reduced species respectively. The first method will now be illustrated by examples.

Ramp Current $[i(t) = \theta t]$

The Laplace transformation of this current excitation function is given by $\bar{i} = \theta/P^2$; thus the appropriate response transforms are:

$$\bar{C}_{ox.} - \bar{C}_{ox.(0,P)} = \frac{\theta}{P^2} \times \frac{1}{nFAD_{ox.}^{1/2}P^{1/2}} = \frac{\theta}{nFAD_{ox.}^{1/2}P^{5/2}}$$

$$\bar{C}_{red.} - \bar{C}_{red.(0,P)} = \frac{\theta}{P^2} \times \frac{-1}{nFAD_{red.}^{1/2}P^{1/2}} = \frac{-\theta}{nFAD_{red.}^{1/2}P^{5/2}}$$

The inverse transforms, readily found in standard tables, are:

$$C_{\mathrm{ox.}} - C_{\mathrm{ox.}(0,t)} = \frac{4\theta t^{3/2}}{3\pi^{1/2}nFAD_{\mathrm{ox.}}{}^{1/2}}$$

$$C_{\mathrm{red.}} - C_{\mathrm{red.}(0,t)} = \frac{-4\theta t^{3/2}}{3\pi^{1/2}nFAD_{\mathrm{red.}}{}^{1/2}}$$

The surface concentrations of oxidized, $C_{\mathrm{ox.}(0,t)}$, and reduced, $C_{\mathrm{red.}(0,t)}$, forms obtained from the above equations may be inserted into equation (4) (or into equation (5b) if the system is reversible) in order to determine the potential–time response. The *transition time* may be calculated simply by determining the value of t when the appropriate value of $C_{(0,t)}$ becomes zero.

Square-Root-of-Time Case $[i(t) = \theta t^{1/2}]$

The Laplace transformation of this current-excitation function is $\bar{\imath} = \pi^{1/2}\theta/2P^{3/2}$. Thus the surface concentration of the oxidized form, in the Laplace plane, is given by

$$\bar{C}_{\mathrm{ox.}} - \bar{C}_{\mathrm{ox.}(0,P)} = \frac{\theta}{\pi^{1/2}P^{3/2}} \times \frac{1}{nFAD^{1/2}P^{1/2}} = \frac{\pi^{1/2}\theta}{2nFAD_{\mathrm{ox.}}{}^{1/2}P^2}$$

The inverse Laplace transformation is:

$$C_{\mathrm{ox.}} - C_{\mathrm{ox.}(0,t)} = \frac{\pi^{1/2}\theta}{2nFAD_{\mathrm{ox.}}{}^{1/2}}$$

The value for the *transition time*, τ, in this case is directly proportional to the initial bulk concentration of the oxidized species.

$$\tau = 2nFAD_{\mathrm{ox.}}{}^{1/2}C_{\mathrm{ox.}}/\pi^{1/2}\theta$$

For reversible systems, the potential–time behavior exhibits the same *shape* as obtained in polarography; this can be seen by inserting the values for $C_{\mathrm{ox.}(0,t)}$ and $C_{\mathrm{red.}(0,t)}$ into the Nernst equation.

General Power-of-Time $[i(t) = \theta t^r]$

The Laplace transformation of this current excitation function is $\bar{\imath} = \theta\Gamma(r + 1)/P^{(r + 1)}$. Thus the response transform for this excitation is given by

$$\bar{C}_{\mathrm{ox.}} - \bar{C}_{\mathrm{ox.}(0,P)} = \frac{\theta\Gamma(r + 1)}{nFAD_{\mathrm{ox.}}{}^{1/2}P^{(r + 3/2)}}$$

Taking the inverse transformation gives:

$$C_{\mathrm{ox.}} - C_{\mathrm{ox.}(0,t)} = \frac{\theta\Gamma(r + 1)t^{(r + 1/2)}}{nFAD_{\mathrm{ox.}}{}^{1/2}\Gamma(r + 3/2)}$$

This equation is valid for any value of r equal to or greater than $-1/2$. The term $\Gamma(r + 1)$ is the gamma function, and its value for integral values of r is identical to the factorial $r!$.

Exponential Currents $[i = \gamma e^{\theta t}]$

The Laplace transformation of this current function is $\bar{\imath} = \gamma/(P - \theta)$. Thus, the concentration response in the Laplace plane is given by

$$\bar{C}_{\text{ox.}} - \bar{C}_{\text{ox.}(0,P)} = \frac{\gamma}{nFAD_{\text{ox.}}^{1/2}P^{1/2}(P - \theta)}$$

whose inverse transformation is given by

$$C_{\text{ox.}} - C_{\text{ox.}(0,t)} = \frac{\gamma e^{\theta t}\text{erf}(\theta t)^{1/2}}{nFAD_{\text{ox.}}^{1/2}\theta^{1/2}}$$

Impulse Current

In this case, an impulse of current is applied. Ideally the impulse passes a given number of coulombs in an infinitely short time. In practice the duration of the current must simply be short compared to the time during which the response is measured. The Laplace transformation of this type of excitation current is given by $i = Q$, where Q corresponds to the number of coulombs passed in the impulse and, within the limitations described above, is independent of the manner in which the current varies with time. The response transform is given by

$$\bar{C}_{\text{ox.}} - \bar{C}_{\text{ox.}(0,P)} = \frac{Q}{nFAD_{\text{ox.}}^{1/2}P^{1/2}}$$

Note that the response transform in the case of a *unit* impulse is simply the system transform. The response in the time plane (often called the *impulsive response*) is given by

$$C_{\text{ox.}} - C_{\text{ox.}(0,t)} = \frac{Q}{nFAD_{\text{ox.}}^{1/2}\pi^{1/2}t^{1/2}}$$

Composite Excitation: Constant Current with Current Reversal

If, at some time, t_1, after the application of a step excitation current, $i(t) = \theta t^0$, another step in excitation current is applied, $i(t) = \theta_1(t^0 - t_1^0)$, the over-all current program may be written as

$$i(t) = \theta t^0 + \theta_1(t^0 - t_1^0)$$

If θ and θ_1 are both positive the effect would be to increase the current from θ to $\theta + \theta_1$ after time t_1. On the other hand, if θ is positive but θ_1 is negative and twice the magnitude of θ, the current flowing after t_1 will be negative in direction and equal in magnitude to the positive current flowing prior to that time; this is the case of constant current with current reversal. The Laplace transform of this composite current excitation function is given by

$$\bar{\imath} = \frac{\theta}{P} + \frac{\theta_1 e^{-t_1 P}}{P}$$

Note that for excitation functions initiated at time t_1 the corresponding transform is $\bar{\psi}_{(0,P)}$ $\times e^{-t_1 P}$ where $\bar{\psi}_{(0,P)}$ is the excitation transform when the excitation is initiated at zero time. This is the *zero shifting* theorem.

For the case of current reversal, a transition time for the reduced species will be an important result; hence the response transform of interest is:

$$\bar{C}_{\text{red.}} - \bar{C}_{\text{red.}(0,P)} = -\left(\frac{\theta}{P} + \frac{\theta_1 e^{-t_1 P}}{P}\right) \frac{1}{nFAD_{\text{red.}}^{1/2} P^{1/2}}$$

and the surface concentration response in the time plane is given by

$$C_{\text{red.}} - C_{\text{red}(0,t)} = \frac{-2\theta t^{1/2}}{nFAD_{\text{red.}}^{1/2} \pi^{1/2}} - \frac{2\theta_1 (t - t_1)^{1/2}}{nFAD_{\text{red.}}^{1/2} \pi^{1/2}}$$

The last right-hand term exists only at times where $t > t_1$.

For the case in which the initial concentration of the reduced species, $C_{\text{red.}}$, is zero and $2\theta = -\theta_1$, the resulting transition time relation for the reduced species is

$$\frac{\tau_r}{t_1} = \frac{4}{3}$$

where τ_r is measured from zero time. Thus the ratio of the *reverse* transition time, $t_r - t_1$, to the *forward* time, t_1, is 1:3.

Composite Excitation Current: Constant Current with Superimposed Alternating Current

In this case, a constant current of value θ and a constant alternating current of value $\theta_1 \sin(\omega t)$ is applied. The response transform for the oxidized species is given by

$$\bar{C}_{\text{ox.}} - \bar{C}_{\text{ox.}(0,P)} = \frac{\theta}{nFAD_{\text{ox.}}^{1/2} P^{3/2}} + \frac{\theta_1 \omega}{nFAD_{\text{ox.}}^{1/2} P^{1/2}(\omega^2 + P^2)}$$

and its inverse transform at pseudosteady state is given by

$$C_{\text{ox.}} - C_{\text{ox.}(0,t)} = \frac{2\theta t^{1/2}}{nFAD_{\text{ox.}}^{1/2} \pi^{1/2}} + \frac{\theta_1}{nFAD_{\text{ox.}}^{1/2} \omega^{1/2}} \sin(\omega t - \pi/4)$$

This case has been considered in detail by Takemori, Kambara, Senda, and Tachi (50a).

d. SPHERICAL DIFFUSION

The cases above have been concerned with the problem of semi-infinite linear diffusion, and Fick's Second Law was defined above only for this case. Other analytical techniques make use of electrodes with other geometry, and important cases are those of diffusion to a sphere of constant radius and to an expanding sphere. These are the geometries that correspond to the hanging mercury drop (and spherical microplatinum electrode) and to the dropping mercury electrode (*polarography*), respectively. For theoretical treatment of these new geometries, one applies the new geometrical considerations to Fick's First Law so as to gain an expression analogous to

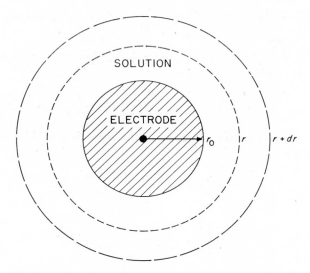

Fig. 42.7. Semi-infinite diffusion to a spherical electrode.

Fick's Second Law for these cases.   For example, consider the case of diffusion in an unstirred solution to a stationary sphere of constant radius. Consider Fig. 42.7, which illustrates the diffusion problem.   The expression for Fick's First Law for this case is

$$f_{(r,t)} = \frac{1}{A_r}\frac{dN_{(r,t)}}{dt} = D\frac{\partial C_{(r,t)}}{\partial r}$$

By a procedure analogous to that described above, one may formulate an expression for the change in concentration as a function of time at some value of r to give the differential equation for symmetrical spherical diffusion:

$$D\left[\frac{\partial^2 C_{(r,t)}}{\partial r^2} + \frac{2}{r}\frac{\partial C_{(r,t)}}{\partial r}\right] = \frac{\partial C_{(r,t)}}{\partial t}$$

The flux at $r + dr$ is given as

$$f_{(r+dr,t)} = f_{(r,t)} + \left[\frac{\partial f_{(r,t)}}{\partial r}\right]dr \tag{19}$$

One may note that the difference in total flux entering and leaving this layer, dr, divided by the volume of this layer, $4\pi r^2\ dr$, gives the change in concentration in this infinitesimal volume in time, dt.   In this way

$$\frac{4\pi(r+dr)^2 f_{(r+dr,t)} - 4\pi r^2 f_{(r,t)}}{4\pi r^2 dr} = \frac{\partial C_{(r,t)}}{\partial t} \qquad (20)$$

Substituting the value for the flux at $r + dr$, given by equation (19), into equation (20) yields

$$\frac{(r+dr)^2}{r^2 dr} f_{(r,t)} + \frac{(r+dr)^2}{r^2 dr} \left[\frac{\partial f_{(r,t)}}{\partial r} \right] dr - \frac{r^2}{r^2 dr} f_{(r,t)} = \frac{\partial C_{(r,t)}}{\partial t}$$

Expansion of this equation, neglecting the second- and third-order infinitesimals, yields

$$\frac{2}{r} f_{(r,t)} + \frac{\partial f_{(r,t)}}{\partial r} = \frac{\partial C_{(r,t)}}{\partial t}$$

which is

$$D \left[\frac{\partial^2 C_{(r,t)}}{\partial r^2} + \frac{2}{r} \frac{\partial C_{(r,t)}}{\partial r} \right] = \frac{\partial C_{(r,t)}}{\partial t}$$

Equations for chronoamperometry, chronopotentiometry, and other techniques using a stationary spherical electrode can then be derived from the differential equation, using mathematical methods analogous to those described under chronoamperometry and chronopotentiometry. For this purpose one merely substitutes r for the previously used term x. For example, in the case of chronoamperometry, the initial and boundary conditions would be

$$C_{(r_0,t)} = C \qquad t = 0$$

$$C_{(r_0,t)} = 0 \qquad t > 0$$

$$C_{(\infty,t)} = C \qquad t > 0$$

where r_0 is the radius of the spherical electrode. The solution obtained is

$$C_{(r,t)} = C \left[1 - \frac{r_0}{r} \, \mathrm{erfc} \left(\frac{r - r_0}{2 D^{1/2} t^{1/2}} \right) \right]$$

and, in terms of current,

$$i = \frac{nFAD^{1/2}C}{\pi^{1/2}t^{1/2}} + \frac{nFADC}{r_0}$$

This equation is identical to the Cottrell equation except for the presence of the last term.

In the case of an expanding spherical drop, such as is encountered in polarography, the treatment is analogous but is a few orders of magnitude more complicated. The original equation for this latter case was solved by Ilkovic (31), who assumed semi-infinite linear diffusion rather than spherical diffusion.

This was accomplished by taking the Cottrell equation, $i = nFACD^{1/2}\pi^{-1/2}t^{-1/2}$, substituting in the time dependence of the surface area $A\ [= 4\pi(3mt/4\pi d)^{2/3}]$ of a growing sphere, and multiplying the result by the "correction" term $(7/3)^{1/2}$ to account for the expansion of the drop into bulk media. The result obtained was

$$i_d = 7.082 \times 10^4 nm^{2/3}t^{1/6}D^{1/2}C$$

where m is the rate of flow of mercury in grams per second, i_d is the instantaneous current in amperes, and C is moles cm.$^{-3}$.

The surface area A was expressed in terms of m and t as follows. The volume of the growing sphere is given by $V = (4/3)\pi r^2 = (m/d)t$, where d is the density of mercury; and, therefore, the radius of the drop is given by $r = [(3/4\pi)(mt/d)]^{1/3}$. The surface area is then given by $A = 4\pi r^2 = 4\pi[(3/4\pi)(mt/d)]^{2/3}$.

As mentioned, this equation was based on linear rather than spherical diffusion laws. When the latter is taken into account, a multiplying term $(1 + KD^{1/2}t^{1/6}m^{-1/3})$ appears; this expression usually has a value between 1.05 and 1.15 and is often neglected except in very accurate work.

3. Convection

This mode of mass transport of a species is accomplished whenever the solution bearing the species is stirred into the path of the electrode. This is often called hydrodynamic transport. This stirring action obviously increases the rate of transport of the species to the electrode. Quantitative treatment (37) of this mode of mass transport is exceedingly difficult. Because of increased sensitivity, convection is frequently employed in electroanalytical techniques. Some examples include the rotating platinum electrode, the rotating mercury electrode, vibrating electrodes, and even the stirring action employed at the working electrode in coulometric titrations, etc. Frequently one must resort to the use of empirical expressions in the interpretation of these techniques.

a. Nernst Diffusion Layer

A concept that has been of considerable importance in the less rigorous treatment of mass transfer in stirred solutions is that proposed by Nernst (41). In his model, a stagnant layer of a definite thickness, δ, is assumed to exist at any solid–liquid interface. Furthermore, it was assumed that the solution in contact with this stagnant film was kept homogeneous by the stirring action. In an experiment such as chronoamperometry at a rotating electrode, the current rapidly decreases at $t > 0$ but eventually levels off at a finite value, which is called the *steady-state* current value. According to the Nernst diffusion-layer model, this steady-state current implies

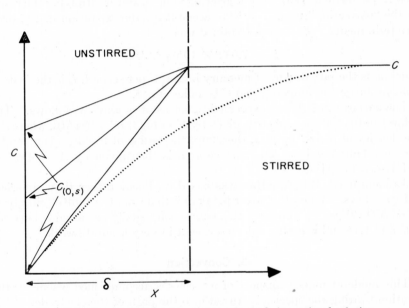

Fig. 42.8. Nernst diffusion layer at an electrode in a stirred solution.

a linear concentration gradient within the stagnant layer (see Fig. 42.8). The concentration gradient at the electrode surface at steady state may be given by

$$\frac{\partial C_{(0,s)}}{\partial x} = \frac{C}{\delta}$$

where $C_{(0,s)}$ corresponds to the concentration at the electrode surface at a time, s, when the steady-state situation has been reached. In cases in which the potential applied to the electrode is not sufficient to reduce the concentration of the diffusing species to zero at the electrode surface, the expression is then

$$\frac{\partial C_{(0,s)}}{\partial x} = \frac{C - C_{(0,s)}}{\delta}$$

In terms of current, this equation may be written in the form

$$i = nFAD \frac{C - C_{(0,s)}}{\delta}$$

Consider an experiment in which a rotating electrode is immersed in a solution containing a concentration, C, of a reducible material. If one applies a potential to this electrode that does not cause appreciable reduction of the species, then $C - C_{(0,s)}$ is zero. As the potential is made progressively more negative, a potential region eventually will be reached in which the concentration, $C_{(0,s)}$, commences to be decreased and, at sufficiently negative potentials, will become virtually zero. Thus, the steady-state currents will be found to increase when the potential has reached a value negative enough to cause an appreciable electrode reaction, and the current will reach a maximum value of sufficiently negative potentials. The current is then said to be a *limiting* current, i_l, and is given by

$$i_l = \frac{nFADC}{\delta}$$

Early workers measured values of δ for various species and for various degrees of stirring and found that δ apparently approached a limiting value at high stirring rates. Because of the existence of this limiting value, many early workers were led to believe that this technique could be employed for measuring stagnant-film thicknesses. However, later work (3,43) on the detailed theory of hydrodynamics showed that stagnant films do indeed exist, but that they are not of definite thickness. In actuality the solution immediately adjacent to the electrode is indeed unstirred, but as one proceeds away from the electrode surface the degree of stirring increases continuously. Thus, more realistically, the diffusion profile is that shown by the dotted line in Fig. 42.8.

Although the Nernst concept of a diffusion layer of definite thickness is most helpful in any empirical formalism, it is by no means a rigorous approach.

b. Turbulent and Laminar Flow

The considerable work in the field of hydrodynamics has permitted a classification of fluid flow into three categories: stagnant regions, laminar flow, and turbulent flow. Laminar flow occurs in parallel planes caused by the sheer action on the fluid, whereas turbulent flow is without appreciable order or direction. Depending upon the geometry, all three of these may occur simultaneously. In the flow of fluid through a cylindrical pipe, a stagnant layer occurs at the solid–liquid interface; just beyond the interface there is laminar flow while, in the bulk of the liquid, turbulent flow is present. Further discussion of hydrodynamic transport may be found in the chapter on voltammetry at fixed electrodes, by Adams.

C. CONVERSION OF SPECIES TO AN ACTIVE FORM

Thus far we have discussed two factors that may control the rate of an electrochemical reaction: (1) the electron transfer process and (2) mass transfer of the chemical species to the electrode surface. There are cases, however, in which neither of these two processes constitutes the rate-limiting step.

1. Kinetic Currents

In some cases the rate-limiting step is the conversion of some bulk species (inert electrochemically) into an "active" form. The electron-transfer process may be considered to occur between the electrode and this active form. The active form may be a particular one of several species in equilibrium with one another, the equilibrium being shifted toward the active form as it is consumed by electrolysis. If the shift in equilibrium occurs at a rate comparable to or much slower than the rate of mass transfer, the magnitude of the current will depend strongly on this rate of conversion (called "kinetic" currents). A classic example (5) of a kinetic current is that found upon the reduction of pyruvic acid, CH_3COCO_2H, which we will abbreviate, HA. The scheme of the reduction may be outlined as follows:

$$HA \underset{k_b}{\overset{k_f}{\rightleftharpoons}} A^- + H^+ \qquad (21)$$
$$\downarrow ne \qquad \downarrow ne$$

products   products

In acid solution, as the potential of the electrode is made progressively more negative, reduction of the species HA commences. In alkaline solution the potential must be made much more negative to obtain a reduction corresponding to species A^-. At a pH equal to the pK_a of the acid, the bulk solution contains equal concentrations of HA and A^-; however, as the potential is scanned in the negative direction for this solution, a reduction is obtained that corresponds only to that of HA, which is indicated by the reduction occurring at the earlier potential. At pH values somewhat higher than pK_a, the form present in solution will be that of A^-; it was found in these cases that a small amount of current would still flow at the more positive potential corresponding to the reduction of HA. This latter reduction process can be accounted for only by the shift of equilibrium from right to left in the above equation, this shift being caused by the decrease in the concentration of HA by electrolysis. As the potential is made more negative, a limiting current value is attained for the reduction of HA, and at even more negative potentials a further increasing current occurs (due to A^-), which eventually becomes limiting at sufficiently negative potentials. There is no direct relationship between the magnitude of these two limiting currents and the relative quantities of HA and A^- present in the bulk of the solution. The first limiting current is larger than would be expected from the equilibrium concentration of HA in the bulk of the solution, but in addition it is not so large as to be that which would have been obtained had the equilibrium shifted completely to the left. Hence it is concluded that this first limiting current is not controlled solely by diffusion, but also by the rate with which H^+ recombines with A^- to form HA. For this reason such limiting currents are said to be in part kinetically controlled.

A number of weak acids exhibit this type of behavior. Some examples include maleic, citraconic, fumaric, azobenzenemonocarbonic acid, and cupferron. Formaldehyde can exist in the hydrated form, $H_2C(OH)_2$, and as the free aldehyde, HCHO, with the equilibrium greatly in favor of the hydrated form. However, the hydrated form is not reducible, whereas the free aldehyde is readily reduced. Again, limiting currents are obtained whose magnitudes are much greater than could be explained by the concentration of free aldehyde in the bulk of the solution. The interpretation is based upon the kinetic conversion of the hydrated form to the free aldehyde form as the latter is consumed by the electrode process (2,52). The kinetics of the interconversion may be studied by measurement of this type of current. In order to study such kinetic phenomena electrochemically, the experiment must be carried out under conditions such that the rate of mass transfer is comparable to the kinetic rate of the conversion under study.

In order to derive equations appropriate for the experimental method, Fick's differential equation for the given experimental method must be modified to take into account the change in concentration resulting from the chemical reaction. Consider the reaction of weak acids given in equation (21). For this reaction we may write the following expressions for the kinetic steps

$$\frac{\partial [HA]_{(x,t)}}{\partial t} = k_b [A^-]_{(x,t)} [H^+]_{(x,t)} - k_f [HA]_{(x,t)}$$

and

$$\frac{\partial [A^-]_{(x,t)}}{\partial t} = k_f[\mathrm{HA}]_{(x,t)} - k_b[A^-]_{(x,t)}[H^+]_{(x,t)}$$

Hence Fick's Second Law may be modified to yield

$$\frac{\partial [\mathrm{HA}]_{(x,t)}}{\partial t} = D_{\mathrm{HA}}\frac{\partial^2 [\mathrm{HA}]_{(x,t)}}{\partial x^2} + k_b[A^-]_{(x,t)}[H^+]_{(x,t)} - k_f[\mathrm{HA}_{(x,t)}]$$

$$\frac{\partial [A^-]_{(x,t)}}{\partial t} = D_{A^-}\frac{\partial^2 [A^-]_{(x,t)}}{\partial x^2} + k_f[\mathrm{HA}]_{(x,t)} - k_b[A^-]_{x,t}[H^+]_{(x,t)}$$

For the case of semi-infinite linear diffusion, the initial conditions will then be

$$[\mathrm{HA}]_{(x,0)} + [A^-]_{(x,0)} = C$$

where C is the total stoichiometric concentration of the weak acid.

Because the ionization constant for the weak acid may be written as a ratio of rates, we have the second initial condition

$$\frac{[A^-]_{(x,0)}}{[\mathrm{HA}]_{(x,0)}} = \frac{k_f}{k_b[H^+]_{(x,0)}} = \frac{K_a}{[H^+]_{(x,0)}}$$

By buffering the solution, the term $K_a/[H^+]$ will be a constant.

For experimental situations in which only the electrode reaction involving HA is important and in which its concentration becomes zero by the application of a suitable potential (chronoamperometry), we obtain the first boundary condition

$$[\mathrm{HA}]_{(0,t)} = 0 \qquad t > 0$$

For chronopotentiometry the first boundary condition would be

$$\left(\frac{\partial [\mathrm{HA}]}{\partial x}\right)_{(0,t)} = \frac{i(t)}{nFAD}$$

Because, in these experiments, we operate at potentials where the species A^- is not reduced, we can write another boundary condition:

$$D_{A^-}\frac{\partial [A^-]_{(0,t)}}{\partial x} = 0 \qquad t > 0$$

TABLE 42.II. System Transforms for Kinetic and Catalytic Cases

Mechanism	System transform equation[a]
Prekinetics	
1. $\quad A \underset{k_2}{\overset{k_1}{\rightleftharpoons}} Ox. \overset{ne}{\to} Red.$	$\bar{C}_{ox.} - \bar{C}_{ox.(0,P)} = \bar{\psi}_{(P)} \times \left\{ \dfrac{D^{1/2}k_1}{P^{1/2}(k_1 + k_2)} + \dfrac{D^{1/2}k_2}{(P + k_1 + k_2)^{1/2}(k_1 + k_2)} \right\} / \lambda_n$
Catalytic	
2. $\quad Ox. \overset{ne}{\to} Red. \overset{k_1}{\to} Ox.$	$\bar{C}_{ox.} - \bar{C}_{ox.(0,P)} = \bar{\psi}_P \times \left\{ \dfrac{D^{1/2}}{(P + k_1)^{1/2}} \right\} / \lambda_n$
3. $\quad Ox. \overset{ne}{\to} Red. \underset{k_2\,A}{\overset{k_1}{\rightleftarrows}} Ox.$	$\bar{C}_{ox.} - \bar{C}_{ox.(0,P)} = \bar{\psi}_{(P)} \times \left\{ \dfrac{D^{1/2}k_2}{P^{1/2}(k_1 + k_2)} + \dfrac{D^{1/2}k_1}{(P + k_1 + k_2)^{1/2}(k_1 + k_2)} \right\} / \lambda_n$
4. $\quad Ox. \overset{ne}{\to} Red. \overset{k_1}{\to} A \overset{k_2}{\to} Ox.$	$\bar{C}_{ox.} - \bar{C}_{ox.(0,P)} = \bar{\psi}_{(P)} \times \left\{ \dfrac{D^{1/2}k_1}{(P + k_2)^{1/2}(k_2 - k_1)} - \dfrac{D^{1/2}k_2}{(P + k_1)^{1/2}(k_2 - k_1)} \right\} / \lambda_n$
Postkinetics	
5. a. $Ox._1 \overset{ne}{\to} Red. \overset{k_1}{\to} A$ b. $Ox._2 \overset{-me}{\leftarrow} Red. \overset{k_1}{\to} A$	$\bar{C}_{red.(0,P)} = \bar{\psi}_n \left\{ \dfrac{D^{1/2}}{(P + k_1)^{1/2}} \right\} / \lambda_n$ $\qquad\qquad + \bar{\psi}_m \left\{ \dfrac{D^{1/2}}{(P + k_1)^{1/2}} \right\} / \lambda_m$
6. $\begin{array}{c} Ox._1 \overset{ne}{\to} Red. \overset{k_1}{\to} A \\ {\scriptstyle -me}\downarrow \quad \downarrow{\scriptstyle k_2} \\ Ox._2 \leftarrow \quad \longrightarrow B \end{array}$	$\bar{C}_{red.(0,P)} = \bar{\psi}_n \left\{ \dfrac{D^{1/2}}{(P + k_1 + k_2)^{1/2}} \right\} / \lambda_n$ $\qquad\qquad + \bar{\psi}_m \left\{ \dfrac{D^{1/2}}{(P + k_1 + k_2)^{1/2}} \right\} / \lambda_m$
7. $\begin{array}{c} Ox._1 \overset{ne}{\to} Red. \overset{k_1}{\rightleftharpoons} A \\ \quad\quad \downarrow{\scriptstyle k_2} \\ {\scriptstyle -me}\downarrow \\ Ox._2 \leftarrow \end{array}$	$\bar{C}_{red.(0,P)} = \{\bar{\psi}_n/\lambda_n + \bar{\psi}_m/\lambda_m\}$ $\left\{ \dfrac{k_1 D^{1/2}}{(k_1 + k_2)(P + k_1 + k_2)^{1/2}} + \dfrac{k_2 D^{1/2}}{(k_1 + k_2)P^{1/2}} \right\}$
8. $\begin{array}{c} Ox. \overset{ne}{\to} Red. \overset{k_1}{\rightleftharpoons} A \\ \quad\quad {\scriptstyle k_2}\downarrow {\scriptstyle -me} \\ B \leftarrow \end{array}$	$\bar{C}_{A(0,P)} = \bar{\psi}_n \left\{ \dfrac{k_1}{k_1 + k_2} \right\} \left\{ \dfrac{D^{1/2}}{P^{1/2}} \right.$ $\left. - \dfrac{D^{1/2}}{(P + k_1 + k_2)^{1/2}} \right\} / \lambda_n + \bar{\psi}_m \left\{ \dfrac{k_1 D^{1/2}}{(k_1 + k_2)P^{1/2}} \right.$ $\left. + \dfrac{k_2 D^{1/2}}{(k_1 + k_2)(P + k_1 + k_2)^{1/2}} \right\} / \lambda_m$

[a] $\bar{\psi}_n$ or $\bar{\psi}_m$ = Excitation current transform for current responsible for process denoted by ne or me, respectively.

$\lambda_n = nFAD$; $\lambda_m = mFAD$.

The conditions existing remote from the electrode then give the remaining two boundary conditions required.

$$[HA]_{(\infty,t)} + [A^-]_{(\infty,t)} = C \qquad t > 0$$

$$\frac{[A^-]_{(\infty,t)}}{[HA]_{(\infty,t)}} = \frac{K_a}{[H^+]_{(\infty,t)}} \qquad t > 0$$

The above represents a typical starting point for the rigorous solution of electrochemical processes involving kinetic contributions.

The system transforms for a number of kinetic and catalytic cases are summarized in Table 42.II. For chronopotentiometry the Laplace transform, $\bar{\psi}$, of the current function employed is obtained and is inserted into the appropriate equation; the inverse transform is then taken.

In the case of postkinetic mechanisms the influence of the kinetic steps is usually studied best by applying first a cathodic current, ψ_n, which causes only the electrode reaction denoted by ne to occur; this cathodic current is then removed and a new anodic current function, ψ_m, is applied that causes only the reaction denoted by me to occur. The appropriate transforms, $\bar{\psi}_n$ and $\bar{\psi}_m$, are obtained, inserted into the equations, and the inverse transform is then taken. The transition time that occurs during application of the second current function is readily found as that value of t at which $C_{red.~(0,t)}$ or $C_{A~(0,t)}$ become zero.

From the experimentally observed variation of this transition time with different current magnitudes or functions, the type of mechanism and the value of the rate constants can be elucidated.

In examples 1 to 4 of the table, the current–time response in the case of chronoamperometry can be found by setting $\bar{C}_{ox.} - C_{ox.(0,P)} = C_{ox.}/P$, and finding the inverse transform of $\bar{\psi}_n$ in terms of the remaining parameters.

2. Catalytic Currents

For illustrative purposes consider the well-known case of the reduction of molybdate in hydrogen peroxide solutions (35). The molybdate ion is oxidized by the hydrogen peroxide to a peroxy-molybdate, which is reduced at less cathodic (negative) potentials than hydrogen peroxide. Hence, if a potential suitable for the reduction of the peroxy-molybdate is applied, the following scheme holds:

$$MoO_5^{-2} + 2H^+ + 2e \rightarrow MoO_4^{-2} + H_2O$$
$$+ \qquad\qquad\qquad\qquad +$$
$$H_2O \qquad\qquad\qquad\qquad H_2O_2$$

Hence it is seen that upon the reduction of the peroxy-molybdate the resulting product, molybdate, is reoxidized by the hydrogen peroxide to reform the peroxy-molybdate. In this way the hydrogen peroxide is indirectly reduced through the catalytic medium of the molybdate, peroxy-molybdate couple. If the rate constant, k_f, is small (the rate of the peroxide reaction is small with respect to the rate of mass transfer), a limiting current will be obtained whose magnitude is governed solely by the rate of diffusion of the peroxy-molybdate content in the bulk of the solution. On the other hand, if k_f is very large the reaction of molybdate with peroxide will take place at a rate sufficient to deplete eventually the hydrogen peroxide; in this case the limiting current obtained will be proportional to the hydrogen peroxide content and independent of the molybdenum content originally present. In this particular instance, k_f actually has an intermediate value. In the presence of swamping excesses of hydrogen peroxide, the current obtained is related to the molybdenum content of the sample (as well as to the bulk concentration of the hydrogen peroxide), but the current obtained is much larger than that expected for a simple diffusion-controlled process. Hence the method is extremely sensitive and can be used to detect concentrations of molybdate as low as 5γ (of molybdenum) per liter. Similar schemes can be employed for the analysis of vanadates and tungstates.

In order to derive equations for electrochemical methods involving catalytic currents, such as in the case above, one first writes the expressions for the rate constant

$$\frac{\partial [\text{MoO}_5{}^{-2}]_{(x,t)}}{\partial t} = k_f [\text{H}_2\text{O}_2]_{(x,t)} [\text{MoO}_4{}^{-2}]_{(x,t)}$$

which can then be inserted into the appropriate form of Fick's Second Law to obtain (in the case of linear diffusion)

$$\frac{\partial [\text{MoO}_5{}^{-2}]_{(x,t)}}{\partial t} = D_{\text{MoO}_5{}^{-2}} \frac{\partial^2 [\text{MoO}_5{}^{-2}]_{(x,t)}}{\partial x^2} + k_f [\text{H}_2\text{O}_2]_{(x,t)} [\text{MoO}_4{}^{-2}]_{(x,t)}$$

Then by setting down the appropriate and initial boundary conditions, rigorous equations can be derived for this case of catalytic currents.

D. POTENTIAL GRADIENTS AND CURRENT FLOW IN SOLUTIONS

Previously we have discussed three major factors that control current flow in electrochemical experiments: electron transfer and the establishment of the electrical double layer at electrode–solution interfaces, mass transfer of a species to the electrode surface, and conversion of a predominant species to an active species. When these Faradaic and non-Faradaic electrode processes are extremely rapid, the application of potential will give rise to a current limited only by processes taking place within the bulk of the solution. This is the situation encountered in *conductometric* and *dielectric constant* measurement. In these cases we focus our attention primarily on the potential gradient within the bulk of the solution and its effect on the current flow.

1. Current Flow by Ion Movement and Dielectric Polarization

Experimentally the simplest way to achieve nonpolarization at the electrode surface is to employ alternating currents at fairly high frequencies. In this way the double-layer capacitance will permit the flow of large non-Faradaic currents and hence there would be no necessity to rely on the rapidity of other electrode processes to maintain nonpolarization of the electrode.

Under these conditions, the limiting factor in current–voltage relationships is attributed not to a surface electrode process but to the rate of migration of ions and the displacement of charge in the bulk of the solution. When a sinusoidal voltage gradient is applied across a solution, the resulting current, called the *admittance* current, will also have a sinusoidal shape with the same frequency, as illustrated in Fig. 42.9. A complete description of the current-voltage relationship requires not only the values of the current and voltage amplitudes but also their phase relation. This arises from the fact that the charge is carried through the bulk solution by two separate processes: the migration of ions and the electrical polarization of the dielectric.

Under the influence of a voltage gradient, an ion is caused to move at a rate depending upon its charge, size, and the microscopic viscosity of the medium as well as upon the magnitude of the voltage gradient. Because the rate of ionic movement is directly proportional to the voltage gradient, the current (which is a direct result of this ionic flow) is *in phase* with the applied voltage. This is illustrated in Fig. 42.9, where E is the applied voltage and i' is the current resulting from the migration of ions. Because of the sinusoidal form of the applied voltage, we can write

$$E = E_{max} \sin(\omega t)$$

where ω is the radial frequency and is equal to $2\pi f$, f being the frequency in cycles per second. Because the current and voltage are in phase, the former also must vary sinusoidally according to

$$i' = i'_{max} \sin(\omega t)$$

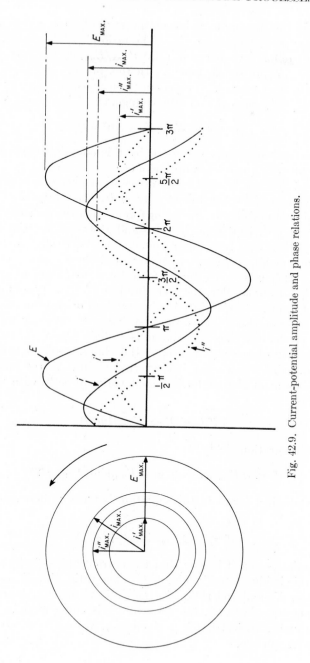

Fig. 42.9. Current-potential amplitude and phase relations.

where i'_{max} is the maximum value of the current that occurs, as shown in Fig. 42.9, at a time equal to $\pi/2$. The ratio E_{max}/i'_{max} is the *resistance* of a solution (ohms), whereas the ratio i'_{max}/E_{max} is the *conductance*, K, of the solution (expressed in mhos). In this process electrical energy is converted into heat energy. The energy consumed at any time is equal to the product of the current times the voltage, which is seen to be

$$energy = E_{max} \, i'_{max} \, \sin^2 (\omega t)$$

Because the value of energy expressed by this equation is positive at all times, there must be a net consumption of electrical energy.

The current flow, i'', in a dielectric arises from electrochemical behavior in which a charge is displaced elastically under the influence of a voltage gradient and in opposition to a restoring force. The displacement of charge stems from the polarization of electrons and atoms within a molecule (*induced polarization*) and from the alignment of electrically unsymmetrical molecules (*orientation polarization*) under the influence of an external electrical field. Although the restoring force for a displacement of electrons and atoms is intramolecular, the restoring force for the polar molecules is the effect of temperature in introducing random orientation of the molecules. Because of the presence of these inherent restoring mechanisms, the energy used to displace the charge is stored on one part of the cycle and returned on the next; hence, if the charging–discharging cycle is perfectly reversible, no energy is converted to heat in the process. Because the amount of charge displacement varies directly with the voltage gradient, then

$$\int i'' dt \, \propto \, E = E_{max}\sin(\omega t)$$

which upon integration yields

$$i'' \, \propto \, \omega E_{max} \cos(\omega t) = \omega E_{max}\sin(\omega t + \pi/2)$$

The proportionality factor in this equation is termed the capacitance, C, and hence

$$i'' = \omega C E_{max}\sin(\omega t + \pi/2) \tag{22}$$

From this relationship it is seen that the current and voltage are 90° out of phase; this is illustrated in Fig. 42.9. The ratio, E_{max}/i''_{max}, is termed the *reactance*, X, and the ratio i''_{max}/E_{max} is termed the *susceptance*, B. As seen from equation (22), the susceptance is equal to ωC. Hence the current through a dielectric for a given a.-c. voltage is directly proportional to the frequency.

In any ionic solution the current produced by an alternating voltage is equal to the sum of the two types of current:

$$i = KE_{max} \sin(\omega t) + \omega C E_{max} \sin(\omega t + \pi/2)$$

As the frequency of the applied voltage is increased, the contribution to the total current, i, attributed to ionic mobility remains constant while the contribution arising from the dielectric effects increases proportionately. At a frequency of zero, the current, i, is in phase with the applied voltage, E, but a phase shift is noted as the frequency is increased and in the limit this shift attains a value of $\pi/2$. It is instructive to calculate the frequency at which the current contribution from both mechanisms is equal in magnitude, i.e., $i'_{max} = i''_{max}$. The conductance, K, and the capacitance, C, for a given cell geometry are

$$K = \frac{\kappa A}{l}$$

$$C = \frac{AD}{(1.13 \times 10^{13}l)}$$

where κ is the specific conductance (mho cm.$^{-1}$); A, the area of one of the parallel electrodes (cm.^{2}); l, the distance between the two electrodes (cm.); and D, the dielectric constant of the medium relative to air ($D = 1$). The specific conductance of a $0.1 M$ aqueous KCl solution is 0.0128 mho cm.$^{-1}$. Taking the dielectric constant of the solution as equal to that of water ($D = 80$), the calculated frequency for equal contributions is 2.88×10^8 cycles per second. For the usual conductance measurements performed for analytical purposes at 60 and 1000 c.p.s., the effect of the dielectric properties of water on the measurement is quite negligible. Although the above considerations may point to the use of low frequencies in conductivity measurements, the extent to which frequency may be decreased is limited by the onset of electrode polarization. Polarization commences when the voltage drop across the double layer (which is acting like a capacitor) becomes appreciable and in the extreme may lead to the onset of an electron-transfer process. It is interesting in this connection to note that the large microscopic area of a platinized platinum electrode provides the large double-layer capacitance desirable for conductometric measurements at reasonable frequencies.

Above, the proportionality constants, K and C, were assumed to be independent of frequency, but this is not actually the case because of the phenomenon of *relaxation*. The existence of relaxation, the lag in response of a system to the change in the electrical force to which it is subjected, becomes noticeable when the response occurs at a rate near the frequency of the alternating voltage. For example, if the dielectric contains molecules that are permanent dipoles, the electric field tends to align these dipoles along its own direction. However, if the frequency is very high or the viscosity of the material great, the molecules may not have time to take up the orientation in the electric field. Thus at lower freuuencies the value of the capacitance will be larger than at higher frequencies, at which the contributions of the permanent dipoles become very small. Solutions of average viscosity at room temperature have relaxation times that are very much shorter in duration than the period corresponding to the frequency range usually employed. In these cases relaxation effects may be considered negligible.

2. Effect of Electrode Capacitance

Analytical measurements based upon the conductance and dielectric properties of solutions have been performed in two seemingly different ways. In the first, two metal electrodes are placed in direct contact with the solution; in the second method, the electrodes are not in direct contact with the solution but are separated from it by the glass walls of the containing vessel. Measurements using the first technique often are classified as "low-frequency" methods, whereas the second group are classified as "high-frequency" or "oscillometric" methods (12). As pointed out below, considerations of the *electrode capacitance* form a more fundamental basis for comparison of the two techniques than do the frequencies employed. The former is characterized by a "high electrode-to-solution capacitance" and the latter by a "low electrode-to-solution capacitance."

The case in which the metal electrodes are in direct contact with the solution can be depicted by:

metal contact	double-layer capacitance	solution capacitance and resistance	double-layer capacitance	metal contact

At each phase boundary a double layer exists within each phase in close proximity to the interface. The capacitance associated with each double layer is determined primarily by the nature of the particular phase, and its magnitude may vary within wide limits. In general the double-layer capacitance decreases in the order: metals, electrolytic solutions, nonconductors. Consider this and the fact that the *lowest* double-layer capacitance in the system virtually determines the net capacitance of all the double layers since they are effectively connected in series. In the case under consideration, the double-layer capacitance in the solution phase immediately

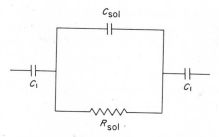

Fig. 42.10. Equivalent circuit.

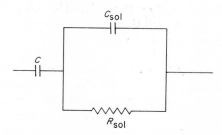

Fig. 42.11. Equivalent circuit.

adjacent to the metal, denoted as C_1, is of primary interest. The whole cell assembly can be considered as two series double-layer capacitances connected in series with a parallel combination of a solution resistance and a capacitance (R_{sol}, C_{sol}), as shown in Fig. 42.10.

In the case in which the metal contact is separated from the solution by the glass walls of the containing vessel, the capacitance attributed to the glass walls is much smaller than the double-layer capacitance existing at the various interfaces. Because the net capacitance resulting from a series combination of large and small capacitances is determined essentially by the smallest capacitance, one need only consider the capacitance of the glass walls and the conductance and capacitance of the solution.

From the foregoing it is seen that in both types of cell design the parallel combination of the solution resistance and capacitance is connected in series with a second capacitance, the value of the second capacitance being determined by the magnitude of the double-layer capacitance in the case of directly immersed electrodes and by the capacitance of the glass walls in the case in which the electrodes are placed on the outer walls of the containing vessel. This is illustrated in Fig. 42.11, where C is the capacitance attributed to the double layers or the glass walls, C_{sol} is the capacitance of the sample solution, and R_{sol} is the resistance of the sample solution. Because most instruments in use today for determining conductance or capacitance yield numerical values for a parallel combination of capacitance and resistance (hence yielding the correct value for C_{sol} and R_{sol} if C were not present), it is instructive to consider the effect of C on the accuracy of these measurements.

In the presence of C, the experimental value for the conductance is given by

$$K^* = \frac{\omega^2 C^2 K}{K^2 + \omega^2 (C + C_{sol})^2} \tag{23}$$

where K^* is the experimentally measured conductance and K is the actual conductivity of the sample solution. From the equation it can be seen that the experimentally obtained value, K^*, more closely approaches the true conductivity of the sample solution, K, (1) when the solution conductance is small, (2) when C is much greater than C_{sol}, and (3) when high frequencies are employed in the measurement. It is important to realize that no *one* of these changes will necessarily lead to a one-to-one correspondence between K and K^*. For example, at high frequencies a linear relation may exist between K^* and K, but the proportionality constant is not unity but

$$C^2/(C + C_{sol})^2$$

Hence one-to-one correspondence can be obtained only when ωC is much larger than ωC_{sol} *and* K. This again points to the necessity for platinizing electrodes in conductivity measurements. While these and many other valuable conclusions can be drawn from inspection of equation (23), of particular interest is the fact that the fundamental difference between the so-called "low-frequency" and "high-frequency" methods arises from the fact that the "electrode capacitance" of the former is great compared to the sample solution, whereas in the latter case it is small. The frequency employed is simply a by-product resulting from this fundamental dissimilarity.

REFERENCES

1. Behrend, R., *Z. physik. Chem.*, **11**, 466 (1893).
2. Bieber, R., and G. Trümpler, *Helv. Chim. Acta*, **30**, 607 (1947).
3. Bircumshaw, L. L., and A. C. Riddiford, *Quart. Revs. (London)*, 6, 157 (1952).
4. Blake, G. G., *J. Roy. Soc. Arts London*, **82**, 154 (1933).
5. Brdicka, R., *Chem. listy*, **40**, 232 (1946).
6. Brdicka, R., and K. Wiesner, *Collection Czechoslov. Chem. Communs.*, **12**, 138 (1947).
7. Breiter, M., M. Kleinerman, and P. Delahay, *J. Am. Chem. Soc.*, **80**, 5111 (1958).

8. Briglio, A., Jr., J. A. Brockman, Jr., and P. A. Shaffer, Jr., *OSRD Rept.* 6047, *PB 5925*, U. S. Dept. Commerce Office of Publication Board, 1945.
9. Butler, J. A. V., *Electrical Phenomena at Interfaces*, Methuen, London, 1951.
10. Cottrell, F. G., *Z. physik. Chem.*, **42**, 385 (1902).
11. Cruikshank, W., *Ann. Physik*, **7**, 105 (1801).
12. Delahay, P., *New Instrumental Methods In Electrochemistry*, Interscience, New York–London, 1954.
13. Dutoit, P., *J. chim. phys.*, **8**, 12 (1910).
14. Eyring, H., S. Glasstone, and K. J. Laidler, *J. Chem. Phys.*, **7**, 1053 (1939).
15. Fick, A., *Pogg. Ann.*, **94**, 59 (1855).
16. Fischer, A., *Z. angew. Chem.*, **20**, 134 (1907).
17. Foulk, C. W., and A. T. Bawden, *J. Am. Chem. Soc.*, **48**, 2045 (1926).
18. Gerischer, H., *Anal. Chem.*, **31**, 33 (1959).
19. Gibbs, W., *Z. anal. Chem.*, **3**, 327 (1864).
20. Gierst, L., and A. Juliard, *Proc. Intern. Comm. Electrochem. Thermodynam. and Kinet., 2nd Meeting*, Jamburini, Milan, 1950, pp. 117, 279.
21. Graham, D. C., *Chem. Revs.*, **41**, 441 (1947).
22. Grower, G. G., *Proc. Am. Soc. Testing Materials*, **17**, 129 (1917).
23. Gurney, R. W., *Introduction to Statistical Mechanics*, McGraw-Hill, New York, 1949.
24. Gurney, R. W., *Ionic Processes in Solution*, McGraw-Hill, New York, 1953.
25. Haber, F., *Z. Elektrochem.*, **4**, 506 (1898).
26. Haber, F., and Z. Klemenciewicz, *Z. physik. chem.*, **67**, 385 (1919).
27. *Handbook of Chemistry and Physics*, Chemical Rubber Publishing Co., Cleveland, Ohio, 1961.
28. Heyrovský, J., *Chem. listy*, **16**, 256 (1922).
29. Heyrovský, J., and S. Berezicky, *Collection Czechoslov. Chem. Communs.*, **1**, 19 (1929).
30. Hildebrand, J. H., *J. Am. Chem. Soc.*, **35**, 847 (1913).
31. Ilkovic, D., *Collection Czechoslov. Chem. Communs.*, **6**, 498 (1934).
32. Jaeger, J. C., *An Introduction to the Laplace Transformation*, Methuen, London, 1949.
33. Jensen, F. W., and A. L. Parrack, *Ind. Eng. Chem., Anal. Ed.*, **18**, 595 (1946).
34. Kolthoff, I. M., and J. J. Lingane, *Polarography*, 2nd ed., Interscience, New York–London, 1952.
35. Kolthoff, I. M., and E. P. Parry, *J. Am. Chem. Soc.*, **73**, 5315 (1951).
36. Koutecky, J., and R. Brdicka, *Collection Czechoslov. Chem. Communs.*, **12**, 337 (1947).
37. Levich, B., *Disc. Faraday Soc.*, **1**, 26 (1947).
38. Lingane, J. J., *J. Am. Chem. Soc.*, **67**, 1916 (1945).
39. Luckow, C., *Dinglers Polytech. J.*, **177**, 231 (1865); *Chem. Zentr.*, 735 (1865).
40. Nernst, W., *Z. physik. chem.*, **4**, 129 (1889).
41. Nernst, W., *Z. physik. chem.*, **47**, 52 (1904).
42. Nernst, W., and E. S. Merriam, *Z. physik. chem.*, **52**, 235 (1905).
43. Page, A., and H. C. H. Townsend, *Proc. Roy. Soc. (London)*, **A135**, 656 (1932).
44. Randles, J. E. B., *Trans. Faraday Soc.*, **48**, 828 (1952).
45. Sand, H. J. S., *J. Chem. Soc.*, **91**, 373 (1907).
46. Sand, H. J. S., *Phil. Mag.*, **1**, 45 (1901).
47. Sease, J. W., C. Niemann, and E. H. Swift, *Anal. Chem.* **19**, 197 (1947).
48. Shaffer, P. A., Jr., A. Briglio, Jr., and J. A. Brockman, Jr., *Anal. Chem.*, **20**, 1008 (1948).
49. Szebelledy, L., and Z. Somogyi, *Z. anal. Chem.*, **112**, 313 (1938).

50. Tafel, J., *Z. physik. Chem.*, *Leipzig*, **A50**, 641 (1905).
50a. Takemori, Y., T. Kambara, M. Senda, and I. Tachi, *J. Phys. Chem.*, **61**, 968 (1957).
51. Van Name, R. G., and F. Fenwick, *J. Am. Chem. Soc.*, **47**, 19 (1925).
52. Vesely, K., and R. Brdicka, *Coll. Czech. Chem. Communs.*, **12**, 313 (1947).
53. Weber, H. F., *Wied. Ann.*, **7**, 536 (1879).
54. Wiesner, K., *Z. elektrochem.*, **49**, 164 (1943).

Chapter 43

INTRODUCTION TO ELECTROCHEMICAL TECHNIQUES

By CHARLES N. REILLEY AND ROYCE W. MURRAY, *University of North Carolina, Chapel Hill, North Carolina*

Contents

Contents (*continued*)

I. INTRODUCTION

The purpose of this chapter is to present a brief introduction to and comparison of the better-known electrochemical techniques. The fundamental thermodynamic and kinetic principles of electrochemistry, discussed in Chapter 42, form a rational basis for this comparison. Although the variety of electrochemical methods may seem to be large, all of them are based on a rather limited number of fundamental precepts, the particular combination of which determines the nature of the technique. It is important to recognize that the most fruitful approach to successful electrochemical investigation lies in the deliberate manipulation and control of the pertinent electrochemical parameters so as to yield the desired experimental behavior. In this way one literally designs into the system those response characteristics that best suit the purpose of the investigation.

The manner in which the methods discussed in this chapter are classified is based on the parameters controlled: (*1*) mode of mass transport, and (*2*) potential and current. Mass transport, as noted in Chapter 42, may occur through migration, convection, or diffusion. In cases in which convection and diffusion predominate, it is implicit that an electron-transfer reaction occurs; in the case of migration as the sole means of mass transport, electron-transfer processes do not occur to any appreciable extent or their effects are relatively minor. Thus we have an obvious breakdown into electrochemical methods that utilize electron-transfer reactions and those in which electron-transfer reactions are per se unimportant. In the cases in which electron transfer is important, a distinction may be made according to whether the behavior of the electrochemical system will be governed by the principles of thermodynamics or by those of kinetics. By control of the current flowing, the net Faradaic current can be made to be zero and, in the ideal case, true equilibrium exists; under these circumstances thermodynamic considerations govern the potential of the electrochemical cell. Also, since the net current is zero, the mode of mass transport in this equilibrium system is rendered superfluous.

In the case of kinetic control, the over-all rate of a simple electrolysis process may be governed by the rate of mass transport (convection or diffusion) and/or by the inherent rate of the electron-transfer process itself. The desired degree of control in a given experiment by one or both of these factors may be obtained through proper control of the potential or current. Thus either potential or current may be fixed so as to cause a rate-determining step via mass transport, electron transfer, or some combination of the two.

Electrochemical nomenclature itself is based in part on the variables controlled in the experiment (potential, current, or coulombs), in part on those measured (potential, current, coulombs, or time), and in part upon the mode of mass transport. At least one technique is named on the basis of the electrode employed (polarography). Precise use of electroanalytical nomenclature is, as in any other field, important in that much can be said about how an investigation was carried out simply by naming the technique employed in the investigation. Thus, if the potential of an electrode in a stirred solution is maintained at a constant value and the resulting steady-state current is measured, the technique is called *voltammetry*. If this solution were unstirred and a similar experiment were performed, the resulting current would have a *transient* character and the technique would be called *chronoamperometry*. If the electrode used in this unstirred solution were a dropping mercury electrode, this would be a special case of chronoamperometry and the technique would be called *polarography*.

It is important to note that in steady-state measurements the variable controlled (i.e., potential) and the variable measured (i.e., current) can be reversed to yield identical results. Hence in the above example of voltammetry it is immaterial whether the current or potential is controlled. On the other hand, methods that yield transient responses may differ according to whether potential or current is controlled. For example, if a constant current is applied in the case of an unstirred solution, the resulting potential transient is different from the current transient in chronoamperometry and the technique bears the different name, *chronopotentiometry*.

II. METHODS INVOLVING ELECTRON-TRANSFER REACTIONS AT ZERO FARADAIC CURRENT

As pointed out above, thermodynamic considerations will apply to the equilibrium situation when an electron-transfer reaction occurs at zero Faradaic current. This is the technique known as *potentiometry at zero current* or, more commonly, simply as *potentiometry*. Because the electrode reactions are at equilibrium, their forward rates equal their backward rates. Analytical use is made of this case by means of thermodynamic relations between cell potentials and concentrations.

A. DIRECT POTENTIOMETRY

Direct potentiometry utilizes a single measurement of cell potential for the analysis, concentration being related to potential through the well-known *Nernst equation*. In order to effect a measurement of the concentration of a single species by this method, all other variables in the experiment must be maintained at constant and known values. Consider the following electrochemical cell employed for measuring the concentration of Ag^+:

$$\text{Hg}; \ \text{Hg}_2\text{Cl}_2; \ \text{KCl(satd.)} \| Ag^+(x\text{M}); \ \text{Ag} \qquad (1)$$

in which the reaction occurring spontaneously (if current were allowed to flow) is

$$2Ag^+ + 2\text{Hg} + 2\text{Cl}^- \rightarrow 2\text{Ag} + \text{Hg}_2\text{Cl}_2$$

If the concentration of KCl is maintained at a constant value, then the half cell on the left has a constant relative potential. This then is a *reference electrode*, as its potential is independent of the concentration of unknown species. The above reference electrode is referred to as the *saturated calomel electrode* (S.C.E.); the potential of the half cell containing the unknown silver ion concentration is measured versus this reference. The cell potential may be written as

$$E_{\text{cell}} = E^{\circ}_{Ag^+,Ag} - E_{\text{ref.}} + \frac{RT}{nF} \ln [Ag^+] \qquad (2)$$

where $E^{\circ}_{Ag^+,Ag}$ is a standard electrode potential and $E_{\text{ref.}}$ is the electrode potential of the S.C.E. (accurately known to have a value of 0.2415 v.

vs. the N.H.E.). Metallic silver is assumed to have unit activity. A measurement of the potential of this cell would yield the unknown concentration by direct calculation from equation (2). The reference electrode chosen for this cell could also have been the N.H.E.; however, convenience of experimental operation often rules otherwise.

The species whose concentration is to be measured is not necessarily a direct participant in the electrode reaction. For example, consider the following cell:

$$\text{Hg; Hg}_2\text{Cl}_2; \text{ KCl(satd.)} \| \text{Cl}^-(x\text{M}); \text{ AgCl; Ag}$$

The concentration of silver ion is governed by the concentration of chloride ion. Although the silver ion does not necessarily participate directly in the electrode reaction, the potential of this cell nevertheless may be expressed by equation (2). The cell potential also may be written in terms of the chloride ion concentration. For this purpose the concentration of silver ion in equation (2) is replaced by $Ksp/[\text{Cl}^-]$, yielding

$$E_{\text{cell}} = E^{\circ}_{\text{Ag}^+,\text{Ag}} - E_{\text{ref.}} + \frac{RT}{nF} \ln Ksp - \frac{RT}{nF} \ln [\text{Cl}^-]$$

or

$$E_{\text{cell}} = E^{\circ}_{\text{AgCl,Ag}} - E_{\text{ref.}} - \frac{RT}{nF} \ln [\text{Cl}^-] \tag{3}$$

where the Ksp term has been combined with the E° value for silver. The above equation shows that a one-unit change in pCl will produce a 59mv. change in the cell potential.

Two disadvantages of the use of this method for a direct concentration measurement exist. Often a junction potential occurs at the interface between the two half cells. This small potential arises from differences in concentration and mobility of ions diffusing across the interface and is, except in the most simple cases, an unknown quantity adding to the cell potential. Unfortunately, estimation of its value cannot be made with certainty. Also, the potentials measured are determined by activities rather than concentrations; thus a knowledge of activity coefficients (a rare event) may become in some cases a necessity in order to obtain a measurement of the true concentration.

Some of the above difficulties of direct potentiometry may be eliminated if the cell in equation (1) is replaced by

$$\text{Ag; Ag}^+ \text{ (known)} \| \text{Ag}^+ (x); \text{ Ag}$$

The potential of this cell is determined by the difference in the silver ion concentrations in the two half cells. Such a cell is known as a *concentration cell*, and its potential is given by

$$E_{cell} = \frac{RT}{nF} \ln \frac{[x]}{[known]}$$

An unknown concentration can be evaluated by a knowledge of the silver ion concentration in one half cell and by a measurement of the cell potential. If the two solutions have similar silver ion concentrations and contain similar concentrations of the same salts, junction potentials will be negligible and activity coefficients will cancel. The technique of adjusting the known silver ion concentration to exactly equal that in the unknown solution (as evidenced when the measured potential equals zero) has been termed *null-point potentiometry* (16).

A frequent analytical determination is that of pH by means of a potentiometric measurement using the glass electrode. This determination actually makes use of a concentration cell of a somewhat different type. A typical cell containing a glass electrode may be shown as

$$\text{Ag; AgCl; HCl} \; \underset{\text{glass membrane}}{\underline{\parallel \text{H}^+(x\ M)}} \parallel \text{S.C.E.}$$

The potential of this cell is dependent upon the difference between the Ag–AgCl and S.C.E. reference electrode potentials (which is constant) and upon the difference of the hydronium ion concentrations (or average proton free energies) on the two sides of the glass membrane. The potential arising at the glass membrane may be interpreted as a junction potential that is selectively sensitive to differences in hydronium ion concentrations. Because of the variable characteristics of different glass membranes, the potential response to this cell is calibrated with a solution of known pH. The equation relating potential to hydronium ion concentration may be written as

$$E_{cell} = \epsilon - \frac{RT}{nF} \ln [\text{H}_3\text{O}^+]$$

or

$$E_{cell} = \epsilon + 0.05915\ \text{pH} \qquad \text{at } 25° \text{ C.}$$

where ϵ is a constant.

The glass used for the membrane must be of a special composition that yields a selective response to hydronium ion concentration. Other glass compositions also have been prepared that exhibit a selective response to other ions. For example, special glass membranes have been fabricated that possess a selective response toward sodium ion concentration (7,20); such electrodes permit measurement of pNa in a manner analogous to that for pH.

B. POTENTIOMETRIC TITRATIONS

Because of junction potentials and activity effects, direct potentiometry may not yield values for concentrations as accurate as might be desired. Furthermore, concentration is related logarithmically to potential and, for $n = 1$, a relative error of 1% is achieved only if the potential is measured accurately to 0.25 mv.   Higher accuracy is obtained if measured potentials are used to detect the changes in concentration that occur at the equivalence point of a titration, i.e., a *potentiometric titration*. By way of illustration, consider the cell in equation (3) above. The unknown chloride concentration can be determined by titration with silver ion, following the variation in the chloride ion concentration by measurement of the potential of the Ag–AgCl indicator electrode. The most rapid change in pCl will occur at the equivalence point; this is reflected in a corresponding rapid change in the measured cell potential, as shown in Fig. 43.1. As this is a 1:1 reaction, the titration curve is symmetrical and the equivalence point is taken at the midpoint of the potential break.

Obviously in a potentiometric titration the *change* in potential rather than its absolute value is of interest and the influences of junction potentials and

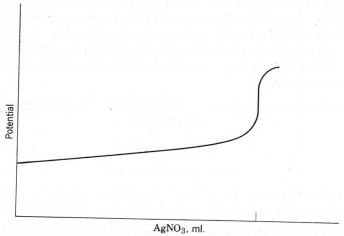

Fig. 43.1. Potentiometric titration curve for the titration of chloride ion with silver ion.

activity coefficients may be ignored. The accuracy of this method is determined primarily by the accuracy of measurement of the titrant volume and by the sharpness of the potential break at the equivalence point. The latter factor is determined by the size of the equilibrium constant for the reaction.

The potentiometric titration technique is applicable to a wide variety of types of titration reactions: acid-base, redox, precipitation, and complexation. It also is a very useful tool in nonaqueous systems, in which, because of unknown activities, direct potentiometric measurements are not feasible.

The discussion above has been based upon the assumption that the electrode reaction is at equilibrium. If this condition is not met, the Nernst equation is not rigorously applicable. Direct potentiometry fails in such cases and potentiometric titrations at zero current may not be satisfactory because of the slow response of the electrode potential to concentration changes. Other potentiometric titration techniques may then be desirable (see Section III-A-2).

A more complete discussion is given in the chapter on potentiometry and in References 12R and 17R to 23R.*

III. METHODS UTILIZING ELECTRON-TRANSFER REACTIONS AT NET FARADAIC CURRENT

For an electrochemical process in which a net Faradaic current flows, the over-all rate of the electrode reaction is governed by the kinetic characteristics of the various processes in the electrochemical cell. The processes most commonly governing this rate are those of mass transport and of electron transfer. The relative importance of these two depends on the choice of experimental conditions and on the mode of application of potential or current. In the techniques considered in this section, mass transport occurs through either diffusion or convection-diffusion, and the discussion is divided accordingly.

A. METHODS USING MASS TRANSPORT BY CONVECTION-DIFFUSION

1. Voltammetry

a. Limiting Currents

The study of current-potential relationships of electrode reactions in stirred solutions is the electrochemical technique known as *voltammetry*.

* References marked with the letter "R" appear in the General References, immediately following the list of specific references at the end of this chapter.

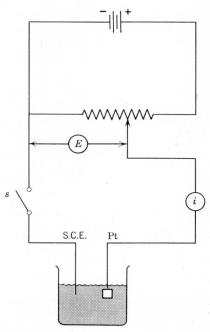

Fig. 43.2. Schematic circuit for voltammetry with two electrodes.

Because voltammetry involves steady-state processes only, it is immaterial whether the potential is controlled and the resulting current is measured, or vice versa. Both modes of operation yield the same current–potential relationship.

Consider an electrochemical cell consisting of an S.C.E. reference electrode and a platinum electrode immersed in a stirred solution of Fe^{+3} containing a supporting electrolyte to eliminate migration transport. The S.C.E. reference electrode should be designed so as to be nonpolarizable, i.e., it must be well-poised with a large supply of reactant and product and the electron transfer process must be rapid. If potential control is desired, a potential of known value is impressed across these electrodes, as shown in Fig. 43.2, and the current is measured. Application of a potential of 0.8 v. (*vs.* the S.C.E.) to the platinum electrode results in virtually no current flow. If now the applied potential is gradually shifted to more negative values, initiation of a steady cathodic current will be observed in the vicinity of 0.6 v. This arises from the reduction of Fe^{+3}. With increasingly negative applied potentials the current increases but eventually levels off at a maximum value, as shown in Fig. 43.3. No further

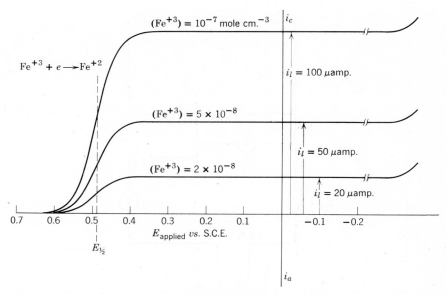

Fig. 43.3. Voltammetric current-potential curves for Fe^{+3} in $1M$ $HClO_4$. $E^{\circ}{}_{Fe^{+3}, Fe^{+2}}$ = 0.732, $E_{1/2}$ = 0.490 ($vs.$ S. C. E.), curves calculated for A = 1.04 cm.², D = 1×10^{-5} cm.² sec.⁻¹, and δ = 10^{-3} cm.

increase in current is observed until at very negative potentials the reduction of solvent or of supporting electrolyte occurs. The maximum current for the reduction of Fe^{+3} on this *current-potential wave* (or *voltammetric wave*) is termed the *limiting current, i_l*. The magnitude of i_l is governed by the rate of mass transport of Fe^{+3} from the solution to the electrode surface and is proportional to the bulk concentration of Fe^{+3}, as shown in Fig. 43.3.

In order to obtain the equation expressing the proportionality between concentration and limiting current, the concentration gradient at the electrode must be found. It was pointed out in Chapter 42 that a thin unstirred layer of solution exists at the electrode–solution interface, and diffusion across this interface is the true transport-limiting step. The concentration-distance profile for the electrode, when a limiting current is flowing, is shown in Fig. 43.4 by curve a. Quantitative treatment of this type of transport is difficult, but a useful approximation may be readily applied: the *Nernst diffusion-layer* concept. This approximation assumes that the unstirred film has a definite thickness, an abrupt transition from stirred to unstirred solution. The resulting limiting-current profile is shown by curve b in Fig. 43.4 for a film thickness of δ. This picture yields

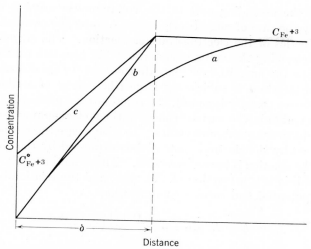

Fig. 43.4. Concentration-distance profiles for a polarized electrode in stirred solution.

a concentration gradient at the electrode surface, $C_{Fe^{+3}}/\delta$, which may be inserted into Fick's First Law to yield an expression for the limiting current:

$$i_l = \frac{nFAD_{Fe^{+3}}C_{Fe^{+3}}}{\delta} \tag{4}$$

where $C_{Fe^{+3}}$ is the bulk concentration of Fe^{+3} in moles cm.$^{-3}$, A is the area of the electrode in cm.^{2}, and $D_{Fe^{+3}}$ is the diffusion coefficient of Fe^{+3} in cm.^{2} second^{-1}. It must be remembered that equation (4) is based on the Nernst approximation and is thus not rigorous in all respects. It has been shown experimentally (3,13) that the limiting current is actually proportional to a *fractional* power of $D_{Fe^{+3}}$. Also, the value of δ is an *effective* film thickness (22). The limiting current is dependent on the rate of stirring (δ decreases with increased stirring) and is directly proportional to the bulk concentration. This latter fact has been found experimentally to be exact (17) and is the basis of the use of voltammetry for analysis. Measurement of an unknown concentration may be effected by a measurement of i_l, having established the proportional relationship between i_l and C using standard solutions and identical experimental conditions.

b. CURRENT-POTENTIAL RELATIONS FOR REVERSIBLE REACTIONS

It is of interest to consider the portion of the current-potential wave before the limiting current is attained. The magnitude of the current flowing on the ascending part of the voltammetric wave is determined not only by the rate of mass transport but also by the electrode potential and the kinetics of the electron-transfer reaction. The current-potential relations describing the voltammetric wave fall into two extreme classes, depending on the magnitude of the rate constant for the electron transfer. If this rate constant is sufficiently large (the energy of activation, $\Delta G^{\ddagger}$, for the electron transfer is small), the reaction may proceed at a rate fast enough to maintain the surface concentrations of reactants and products very close to their equilibrium values. In such a case these concentrations are governed by the electrode potential as expressed by the Nernst equation, and the reaction is termed *reversible*. The reduction of Fe^{+3} under the proper conditions is a reaction of this type, and the relation between the electrode potential and surface concentrations is

$$E = E^{\circ}{}_{Fe^{+2}, Fe^{+3}} - \frac{0.059}{n} \log \frac{C'^{\circ}{}_{Fe^{+2}}}{C^{\circ}{}_{Fe^{+3}}} \tag{5}$$

The absolute magnitude of the current flowing at a given potential is now governed by the rate of mass transport. Assuming the existence of the Nernst diffusion layer, a linear drop in the concentration of Fe^{+3} occurs across the film thickness, δ, as shown in curve c of Fig. 43.4. The concentration gradient is determined by the value of δ and by the difference between the bulk concentration, $C_{Fe^{+3}}$, and the surface concentration, $C^{\circ}{}_{Fe^{+3}}$. The latter concentration is governed at any given electrode potential by equation (5). Thus by Fick's First Law the current is given by

$$i = nFAD_{Fe^{+3}} \frac{C_{Fe^{+3}} - C^{\circ}{}_{Fe^{+3}}}{\delta}$$

By combining this equation with equation (4), the surface concentration of Fe^{+3} is

$$C^{\circ}{}_{Fe^{+3}} = \frac{\delta(i_l - i)}{nFAD_{Fe^{+3}}} \tag{6}$$

Noting that the concentration gradient of the reaction product, Fe^{+2}, at the electrode surface is $-C^{\circ}{}_{Fe^{+2}}/\delta$, an equation analogous to equation (6) may be written for its surface concentration

$$C^{\circ}{}_{Fe^{+2}} = \frac{\delta(i)}{nFAD_{Fe^{+2}}} \tag{7}$$

Equations (6) and (7) may now be inserted into equation (5), yielding

$$E = E_{1/2} + \frac{0.059}{n} \log \frac{i_l - i}{i} \tag{8}$$

where

$$E_{1/2} = E°_{Fe^{+3},\ Fe^{+2}} + \frac{0.059}{n} \log \frac{D_{Fe^{+2}}}{D_{Fe^{+3}}} \tag{9}$$

This equation represents the current-potential relation for a reversible voltammetric wave. $E_{1/2}$ is termed the *half-wave potential* and is equal to the electrode potential, E, at $i = 0.5i_l$. The half-wave potential is a quantity characteristic of a given electroactive species in a given medium, often being very close to the value of the standard potential of the couple. Although the Nernst layer concept was used to obtain equation (8), the approximate features of this treatment do not greatly distort the exactness of this equation because the inexact δ and D terms tend to cancel.

The form of the log (current) term in equation (8) varies according to the type of electrode reaction taking place. For example, if Fe^{+2} were also present in the bulk of the solution, equation (8) would assume the form

$$E = E_{1/2} + \frac{0.059}{n} \log \frac{(i_l)_c - i}{i - (i_l)_a}$$

where $(i_l)_c$ and $(i_l)_a$ correspond to the cathodic and anodic limiting currents for the Fe^{+3} and Fe^{+2} waves, respectively, and $E = E_{1/2}$ at $i = 0.5[(i_l)_c - (i_l)_a]$, the sign of the anodic current being negative. Current-potential waves for Fe^{+2}, Fe^{+3}, and mixtures of the two are shown in Fig. 43.5.

Another important example is the case of a reversible reaction that yields an insoluble product on the electrode surface, such as the deposition of silver on a platinum electrode. If the activity of the silver metal on the electrode surface is taken as unity, which would be true after the platinum electrode had been coated with at least a monolayer of silver atoms, the current-potential equation is

$$E = E°_{Ag^+,Ag} + \frac{0.059}{n} \log \frac{\delta}{D_{Ag^+}} + \frac{0.059}{n} \log (i_l - i) \tag{10}$$

There is no characteristic half-wave potential in a case such as this because the potential at $i = 0.5i_l$ is dependent on the bulk concentration of metal ion and the stirring rate. The current flowing at the foot of the wave is experimentally somewhat different from that predicted from equation (10), as shown in Fig. 43.6, because initially no silver is present on the electrode and the activity of the metal deposit is less than unity (10,26).

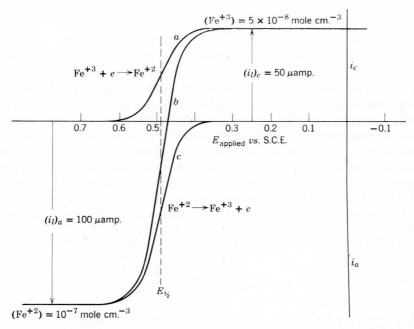

Fig. 43.5. Voltammetric current-potential curves for Fe^{+3} and Fe^{+2} in $1M$ $HClO_4$. $E°_{Fe^{+3},Fe^{+2}} = 0.732$, $E_{1/2} = 0.490$ ($vs.$ S. C. E.), curves calculated for $A = 1.04$ cm.^{2}, $D = 1 \times 10^{-5}$ cm.^{2} sec.$^{-1}$, and $\delta = 10^{-3}$ cm. Curve a, Fe^{+3} present; curve b, Fe^{+2} present; and curve c, Fe^{+3} and Fe^{+2} present.

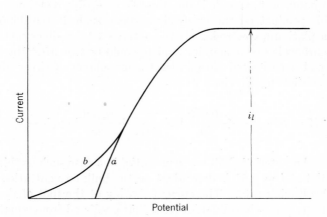

Fig. 43.6. Voltammetric current-potential curves for a deposition reaction. Curve a, unit activity of deposit; curve b, activity of deposit varies.

c. CURRENT-POTENTIAL RELATIONS FOR IRREVERSIBLE REACTIONS

If the energy of activation for the electron-transfer reaction is large, and the rate of electron transfer correspondingly slow, the concentrations at the electrode surface will not be equilibrium values and the Nernst equation is not applicable. Electrode reactions of this type are termed *irreversible*. The magnitude of the current at a given potential is a composite function of the rate of the electron transfer and the rate of mass transport. The expression for current in this case was given in Chapter 42 as

$$i = nFAk_f^\circ(C^\circ_{ox.})e^{-\alpha n_a FE/RT} - nFAk_b^\circ(C_{red.}^\circ)e^{(1-\alpha)n_a FE/RT} \quad (11)$$

where

$$k_f^\circ/k_b^\circ = e^{n_a FE^\circ/RT} \quad (12)$$

$C^\circ_{ox.}$ and $C^\circ_{red.}$ are the surface concentrations of oxidized and reduced species respectively, k_f° and k_b° are the heterogeneous reaction rate constants for the cathodic and anodic reactions respectively, n_a is the number of electrons involved in the rate-controlling step of the electron-transfer process, and α is the transfer coefficient.

Equation (11) shows the relation of i at a given potential, E, to the electron transfer rate characteristics (expressed by k_f°, k_b°, and α) and to the rate of mass transport (which determines $C^\circ_{ox.}$ and $C^\circ_{red.}$). The surface concentrations may be obtained in forms identical to those of equations (6) and (7) by use of the Nernst diffusion-layer approximation. If these values of $C^\circ_{ox.}$ and $C^\circ_{red.}$ are inserted into equation (11) and the resulting equation is solved for i, the result is

$$i = \frac{\dfrac{k_f^\circ}{D_{ox.}}(i_l)_c e^{-\alpha n_a FE/RT} + \dfrac{k_b^\circ}{D_{red.}}(i_l)_a e^{(1-\alpha)n_a FE/RT}}{\dfrac{1}{\delta} + \dfrac{k_f^\circ}{D_{ox.}}e^{-\alpha n_a FE/RT} + \dfrac{k_b^\circ}{D_{red.}}e^{(1-\alpha)n_a FE/RT}} \quad (13)$$

where $(i_l)_c$ and $(i_l)_a$ are the cathodic and anodic limiting currents, respectively (7R). The form of this equation is somewhat complex and it is instructive to consider the simpler case when $k_f^\circ \gg k_b^\circ$, i.e., the relative rate of the anodic process is so small as to be negligible. This is termed a *totally irreversible* reaction. From equation (13) this yields in terms of potential

$$E = E_{1/2} + \frac{RT}{\alpha n_a F} \ln \frac{(i_l)_c - i}{i} \quad (14)$$

where the half-wave potential (E at $i = 0.5(i_l)_c$) is given by

$$E_{1/2} = \frac{RT}{\alpha n_a F} \ln \frac{k_f{}^\circ \delta}{D_{\mathrm{ox.}}} \qquad (15)$$

Equations (14) and (15) show that the shape of the current-potential curve for a totally irreversible electrode reaction is determined by the value of αn_a, whereas the position of the wave on the potential scale is determined

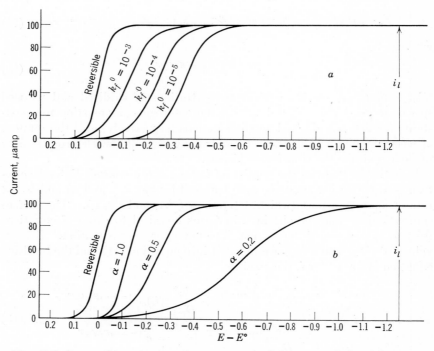

Fig. 43.7. Irreversible voltammetric current-potential curves calculated for $D_{\mathrm{ox.}} = 10^{-5}$ cm.^{2} sec.$^{-1}$, $n_a = 1$, $\delta = 10^{-3}$ cm., $i_l = 100$ μamp. Key: a shows the position of the curve as a function of $k_f{}^\circ$ when $\alpha = 0.5$, and b is the shape of the curve as a function of α when $k_f{}^\circ = 10^{-4}$ cm. sec.$^{-1}$.

by the value of the rate constant, $k_f{}^\circ$. These effects are shown in the curves of Fig. 43.7. The difference, for a given value of i, between the experimentally obtained E and the E that would have been obtained had the wave been reversible is termed the *overpotential*, η. This quantity is a *qualitative* measure of the degree of irreversibility, as its value is obviously dependent on the current. The values of δ and D_{ox}. have less tendency to cancel in equation (15) than in equation (9) (treatment of a reversible reaction); the approximate nature of these irreversible current-potential equations therefore must be kept in mind.

At sufficiently negative potentials the rate of mass transport becomes much slower than the rate of the electron-transfer process, and the current flowing, i_l, is independent of the rate of the electron-transfer reaction and directly proportional to the bulk concentration (see equation (4)). Thus *the limiting current can be used for the analysis of an unknown concentration whether the voltammetric wave is reversible or irreversible.*

Comparison of equations (8) and (14) shows that the current-potential equations for reversible and irreversible waves differ only by the presence of n as opposed to αn_a in the log (current) term. In order to evaluate the reversibility of a voltammetric wave, a plot of E *vs.* the logarithm of the current term corresponding to the particular type of reaction is employed. Such a plot yields a straight line in either case, but the slope is $0.059/n$ in the reversible case and $0.059/\alpha n_a$ in the irreversible case. Since α always has values less than one, comparison with the known value of n provides a criterion for reversibility.

The above classification of electrode reactions into reversible and irreversible types is based upon experimental obedience to one or the other of two types of theoretical relations. In absolute rigor, however, it must be realized that there is no such thing as a perfectly reversible electrode reaction. In a practical sense, a reaction is termed reversible if, within the limits of error of experimental measurement, its behavior follows the Nernst equation under the given experimental conditions. Moreover, because no reaction has an infinite rate constant, a reaction that appears to be reversible under one set of experimental conditions may not behave reversibly under a different set of experimental conditions in which the reaction is required to proceed at a much faster pace. This is caused by the fact that the reaction may no longer be able to maintain equilibrium concentrations under these new conditions. Thus, a reaction that appears reversible under typical conditions of voltammetry may have an irreversible character in a chronopotentiometric or a.-c. polarographic experiment (*vide infra*). In addition, reversibility of an electrode reaction may be destroyed by changing the nature of the electrode surface at which the electron-transfer reaction must occur, or by complexing the electroactive species to form a complex with unfavorable electron-transfer reaction-rate characteristics. Further discussion of the nature and relationships of reversible and irreversible reactions is given in Chapters 44, 46, 47, and 48 and in References 7R and 14R.

d. Effects of Complexation

Selective shifting of electron free-energy levels by complexation, as stated in Chapter 42, is a useful means of separating otherwise coincident energy levels of two electron-transfer reactions so that they may be made to proceed at different potentials. This principle is indeed useful in instances in which the potential regions in which two voltammetric waves occur is too narrow for sufficient individual observation of each wave. To show the effect of complexation on the potential of a voltammetric wave, consider the reversible reaction

$$M^{n+1} + ne \rightarrow M^+$$

The current-potential relation for this type of reaction is given by equation (8). Addition of a ligand, L^-, forms with M^{n+1} a complex, ML_p^{n+1-p}, which has an instability constant, K_c. The concentration of M^{n+1} is governed by the concentration of free ligand and the complex species. Thus equation (8) may modified to yield

$$E = E_{1/2} + \frac{0.059}{n} \log \frac{i_l - i}{i} - \frac{0.059\,p}{n} \log [L^-]^{\circ} \tag{16}$$

where

$$E_{1/2} = E^{\circ}{}_{M^{n+1},M^+} + \frac{0.059}{n} \log \frac{D_{M^+}}{D_{ML_p}} + \frac{0.059}{n} \log K_c$$

and i_l is the limiting current for the reduction of the complex species, ML_p^{n+1-p}. It can be seen that the $E_{1/2}$ of the wave may be continuously shifted by varying the concentration of the ligand, L^-. An example of this shifting of waves and of the effect of the value of K_c is shown in Fig. 43.8. By observation of the value of $E_{1/2}$ as a function of $[L^-]$ and by comparison with the value of $E_{1/2}$ obtained for the simple ion, evaluation of p and K_c is possible. Two criteria are necessary for this determination. The value of $E_{1/2}$ is determined by the concentration of ligand at the electrode surface (equation (16)). A greatly simplifying assumption may be made if $[L^-] \gg [ML_p^{n+1-p}]$, in which case $[L^-]^{\circ} = [L^-]$ at all values of current since the concentration change arising from the reduction of ML_p^{n+1-p} is then negligible. Also, the above treatment is based upon the hypothesis that the simple and the complex species both yield reversible waves. Because complexation may change the reversibility of the electrode reaction, it is necessary to verify the existence of reversibility.

In the case of reactions that involve protons, the current-potential waves also are affected by the pH at the electrode surface; this is true because the

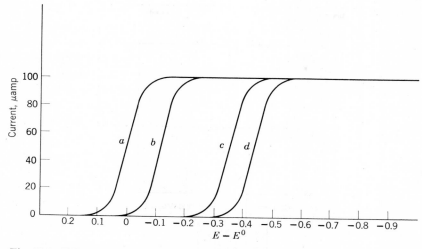

Fig. 43.8. Shifting of voltammetric current-potential curves by complexation. Assume $n = 1$, $D_{M^+} = D_{Mn^{+1}}$; $= D_{MLp}$, $[L^-] \gg [M^{n+1}]$, and the concentration of reducible species is such as to give $i_l = 100$ μamp. Curve a: reduction of the simple ion, M^{n+1}; curve b: $[L^-] = 10^{-1}M$, $p = 2$, $K_c = 10^{-4}$; curve c: $[L^-] = 10^{-1}M$, $p = 2$, $K_c = 10^{-8}$; and curve d: $[L^-] = 0.5$ M, $p = 2$, $K_c = 10^{-8}$.

surface concentration of protons appears in the current-potential expression for the wave. Therefore a buffer system of sufficient capacity must be present in the solution. Addition of buffer is a frequent necessity in studies of electrode reactions of organic compounds, since protons are very commonly participants in such reactions.

2. Potentiometric Titrations with Polarized Electrodes

The potentiometric titrations previously discussed were performed under conditions of zero Faradaic current. Such titrations also may be carried out when a small, constant current is passed through the cell. In this case, one or both of the electrodes of the cell is polarized and the method is termed a *potentiometric titration with polarized electrodes*.

a. With One Polarized Electrode

The experimental arrangement in this method (9) consists of a polarizable indicator electrode and a nonpolarizable reference electrode immersed in the stirred solution of the titration cell. Consider a redox titration in which both couples yield reversible voltammetric current-potential waves, such as the titration of Fe^{+2} with Ce^{+4}. By means of the circuit shown in

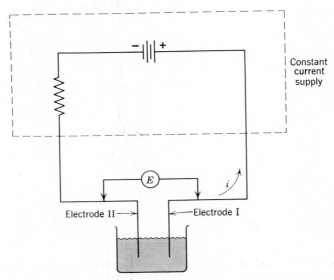

Fig. 43.9. Schematic circuit for potentiometry with polarized electrodes. Electrode I: Pt (polarized); electrode II: (*a*), S.C.E. (titration with one polarized electrode), and (*b*) Pt (titration with two polarized electrodes).

Fig. 43.9, a small, constant current is passed through the cell in a direction such that the anodic reaction occurs at the indicator electrode (electrode I in case (*a*) in Fig. 43.9). If the indicator electrode is "inert," such as platinum, the anodic process is the oxidation of Fe^{+2}. In order to explain the variation of the cell potential, it is instructive to use current-potential curves to describe the concentrations of reactants and products at various stages of the titration (see Fig. 43.10). The potential of the indicator electrode is determined by the particular electrode reaction occurring as a result of the impressed current. Before the equivalence point, the anodic reaction at the electrode is the oxidation of Fe^{+2}, and the electrode potential is given by the intersection of the impressed current line with the voltammetric wave of Fe^{+2} in Fig. 43.10. Because of the removal of Fe^{+2} throughout the titration, the limiting current for the Fe^{+2} wave will decrease eventually to a value less than that of the impressed current (curve *c*). Some other electrode reaction also must occur at this point to support the current, and the electrode potential thus shifts to the potential at which Ce^{+3} is oxidized. This potential break is sudden and serves to indicate the titration end point. The resulting potentiometric titration curve is shown in Fig. 43.11 by curve *a*. The end point observed is slightly premature, but if the impressed current is very small in comparison to the

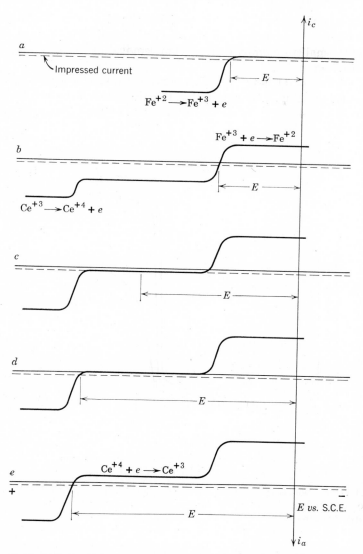

Fig. 43.10. Voltammetric current-potential curves describing concentrations during a potentiometric titration (with one polarized electrode) of Fe^{+2} with Ce^{+4}. Key: a, original solution; b, midpoint of titration; c, just before equivalence point; d, equivalence point; and e, excess Ce^{+4}.

initial limiting current for Fe^{+2}, the resulting titration error is negligibly small.   The impressed current and the size of the indicator electrode also must be kept small to eliminate error from removal of Fe^{+2} through the electrode reaction.

Curve b in Fig. 43.11 is the titration curve obtained for a zero-current potentiometric titration.   By noting that this titration curve could be constructed from Fig. 43.10 by using the intersection of the current-potential

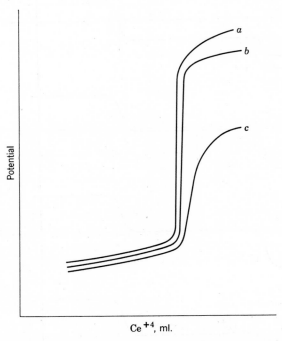

Fig. 43.11. Potentiometric titration curves for Fe^{+2} titrated with Ce^{+4}. Key: a, with one (anodically) polarized electrode; b, at zero current; and c, with one (cathodically) polarized electrode.

curves with the zero-current axis, the reason for the similarity of curves a and b becomes obvious.   Curve c corresponds to the titration curve obtained when the impressed current is cathodic at the indicator electrode. This latter case differs somewhat from the previous two because the cerium wave is actually slightly irreversible and the potential break is thus not quite as large as in the zero-current case.

b. With Two Polarized Electrodes

If a small, constant current is imposed on two identical polarizable electrodes, a cathodic reaction occurs at one (electrode II in Fig. 43.9, case (b)) and an anodic reaction at the other (electrode I in Fig. 43.9).   The

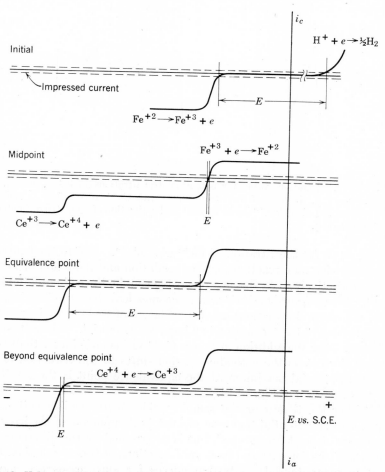

Fig. 43.12. Voltammetric current-potential curves describing concentrations during a potentiometric titration (with two polarized electrodes) of Fe^{+2} with Ce^{+4}.

potential difference between these two electrodes is given by the distance along the potential axis between the points of intersection of the impressed current lines and the voltammetric waves describing the system, as seen

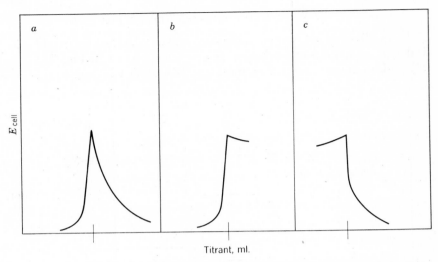

Fig. 43.13. Titration curves for potentiometric titrations with two polarized electrodes. Key: a, titration of Fe^{+2} (reversible) with Ce^{+4} (reversible); b, titration of Fe^{+2} (reversible) with CrO_4^{-2} (irreversible); and c, titration of $S_2O_3^{-2}$ (irreversible) with Ce^{+4} (reversible).

in Fig. 43.12 for the titration of Fe^{+2} with Ce^{+4}. Before the equivalence point, the electrode reactions are the oxidation and reduction of Fe^{+2} and Fe^{+3}, respectively. As this is a reversible couple, the cell potential is very small. When i_l for the Fe^{+2} wave becomes less than the impressed current, the electrode reactions are the oxidation of Ce^{+3} as well as Fe^{+2} and the reduction of Fe^{+3}, resulting in a large cell potential. The cell potential decreases after the addition of excess Ce^{+4} yields an i_l larger than the impressed current as the cathodic reaction shifts to the reduction of Ce^{+4}. A sharp potential maximum at the equivalence point is the result, as is shown by curve a of Fig. 43.13.

If either the titrant or the sample yields an irreversible voltammetric wave, the cell potential that results when both members of the irreversible couple are present is not small, but is determined by the difference in the kinetics of the forward and backward reactions of this couple, i.e., the activation overpotential. Titration curves for such cases are shown as b and c of Fig. 43.13.

The sharpness of the peaked potentials obtained in the two-polarized-electrodes technique (25,30,31) is less in very dilute solutions, because the original limiting currents for the species present may not be sufficiently large in comparison to the impressed current.

The advantages of the use of polarized electrodes in potentiometric titrations are primarily in titration reactions involving irreversible couples. In such cases, because of the slow kinetics of the irreversible reactions, electrode potentials reach equilibrium values very slowly when the titration is performed at zero current. The use of polarized electrodes results in a much faster attainment of a steady potential, making possible some titrations that would be difficult to perform at zero current.

3. Amperometric Titrations

A titration in which measurement of the current flowing at an electrode is used for detection of the equivalence point is termed an *amperometric titration*. The measurement may be of the limiting current of the product, reactant, and/or titrant, depending upon the selection of the applied potential. For this purpose either one or both of the electrodes of the cell are concentration polarized; the following discussion is divided accordingly.

a. WITH ONE POLARIZED ELECTRODE

A suitable indicator electrode and a nonpolarizable electrode are immersed in the stirred solution of the titration cell. By means of a circuit such as that illustrated in Fig. 43.2, a potential sufficient to secure the limiting current of the desired species is applied to the cell. The resulting current is measured throughout the titration. By way of illustration, consider the titration of silver ion with chloride ion. The potential impressed on the indicator electrode, in this case a silver metal electrode, yields the limiting cathodic current for silver ion. The removal of silver ion by precipitation with chloride ion results in a decrease in this limiting current, as shown in Fig. 43.14a. Because i_l is proportional to C_{Ag^+}, the decrease in i_l with added volume of chloride solution ($\Delta i_l / \Delta V$) is linear. This is true both before and after the equivalence point. The current-volume curve is somewhat rounded in the vicinity of the equivalence point, the extent of the rounding being determined by the equilibrium constant for the titration reaction. This rounding is not necessarily serious since the equivalence point may be readily determined by extrapolation of the linear portions of the current-volume curves, as shown in Fig. 43.14a.

Consider now the reverse case, namely the titration of chloride ion with silver ion. A potential is selected so as to yield a current limited by the transport of chloride ion, as shown in Fig. 43.14b. The removal of chloride ion by titrant silver ion results in a linear decrease in the magnitude of the current. However, because the applied potential also is sufficient to reduce silver ion, the presence of excess silver ion beyond the equivalence point

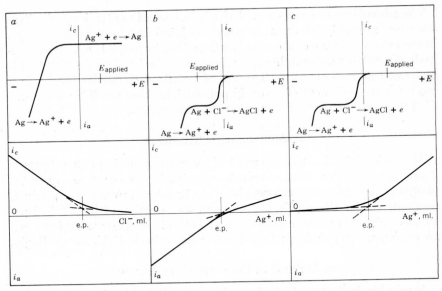

Fig. 43.14. Amperometric titration curves for the silver ion–chloride ion system. Key: *a*, titration of Ag^+ with Cl^-, measure $[Ag^+]$; *b*, titration of Cl^- with Ag^+, measure $[Cl^-]$ and $[Ag^+]$; and *c*, titration of Cl^- with Ag^+, measure $[Ag^+]$.

causes an increasing current in the cathodic direction. As before, some rounding of the titration curve occurs at the equivalence point because of the incompleteness of the titration reaction; the equivalence point is therefore determined by extrapolation.   The difference in the slopes of the current-volume curves before and after the equivalence point arises from differences in the diffusion coefficients of silver and chloride ions.

The alternative procedure of titrating to zero current would cause an error unless the applied potential is identical to that found at the equivalence point in a normal zero-current potentiometric titration.

A second choice of potential for the amperometric titration of silver ion with chloride ion is shown in Fig. 43.14*c*. The potential chosen in this case is sufficient to reduce excess silver ion but insufficient to oxidize silver metal to form AgCl. The shape of the resulting current-volume curve demonstrates that the selection of the applied potential is important to accurate detection of the equivalence point, as curve *c* obviously permits a more accurate evaluation of the equivalence point than does curve *b*.   The AgCl precipitate is assumed to be nonelectroactive.

Amperometric titrations with one polarized electrode (14,15) have been particularly useful in titrations of the precipitation and complexation type.

Applications to redox titrations also have been successful; generally these employ titration to zero current since changes in the slope of the current-volume curves at the equivalence points are usually too small for accurate end-point detection.

b. WITH TWO POLARIZED ELECTRODES

In this technique, a potential is impressed across two identical indicator electrodes immersed in the stirred sample solution and the resultant cur-

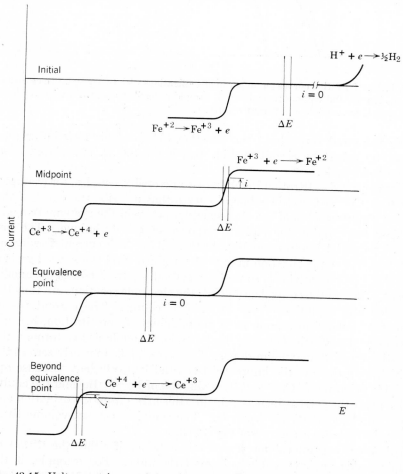

Fig. 43.15. Voltammetric current-potential curves describing concentrations during an amperometric titration with two polarized electrodes.

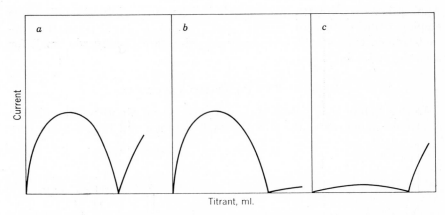

Fig. 43.16. Titration curves for amperometric titrations with two polarized electrodes. Key: *a*, titrant and sample reversible; *b*, sample reversible and titrant irreversible; and *c*, sample irreversible and titrant reversible.

rent is measured throughout the titration (8,25). This may be accomplished by using the circuit of Fig. 43.2 if the S.C.E. is replaced by a platinum electrode.

Consider a redox titration involving two reversible couples, for example, Fe^{+2} with Ce^{+4}. Current-potential curves that describe the effect of the varying concentrations of the electroactive species in the system are again useful in interpreting the current response of this technique. The impressed potential is shown in Fig. 43.15 as ΔE. The current flowing at various stages of the titration may be determined from the figure by placing ΔE on the potential axis so that the cathodic current equals the anodic current. Before the equivalence point, the electrode reactions are thus the reduction and oxidation of the Fe^{+3}, Fe^{+2} couple. The current passes through a rounded maximum near the midpoint of the titration, because here the voltammetric wave for the Fe^{+3}, Fe^{+2} couple passes through the potential axis with maximum slope. The current falls to nearly zero at the equivalence point, as the impressed potential is insufficient to cause appreciable oxidation of Ce^{+3} and the reduction of Fe^{+3}. Beyond the equivalence point the current increases again; this arises from the oxidation and reduction of the Ce^{+4}, Ce^{+3} couple. The complete current-volume titration curve is shown as curve *a* of Fig. 43.16.

A different current-volume response is obtained if either the titrant or sample yields an irreversible voltammetric wave. For example, if the titrant is irreversible, the impressed potential may not be sufficient to cause both oxidation and reduction of the titrant couple beyond the equivalence point.   The current-volume curve is unaffected before the equivalence point, where both members of the reversible sample couple are present, but no increase in current occurs past the equivalence point. The titration curve for this case is shown as curve *b* of Fig. 43.16.   Because accurate detection of the equivalence point may be accomplished by titration until the current falls to zero, this type of titration curve is commonly termed a "dead-stop" titration.   Curve *c* shows the reverse case, in which the sample is irreversible and the titrant is reversible.

Like potentiometric titrations, amperometric titrations are limited in accuracy only by the errors involved in measurement of titrant volume and by the abruptness of the signal response at the equivalence point.   These two techniques are both very useful in that they are applicable to a wide variety of titration reactions.   The sensitivity of amperometric techniques is, for a given reaction, generally felt to be somewhat greater than that of potentiometric titrations.

4. Electrolysis Methods

In the previously discussed electrochemical techniques that involved the passage of a net Faradaic current, it was implicit in the method that no appreciable depletion of the concentration of the bulk solution occurred as a result of the electrode reaction.   *Electrolysis methods*, on the other hand, aim at an exhaustive conversion of the electroactive species.   (Some exceptions are found in the method of stripping analysis.)   Because the electrolysis process should ideally consume only a short time for the completion of the reaction, the mode of mass transport picked generally is that which is most efficient, i.e., convection-diffusion transport.

a. ELECTRODEPOSITION

As the name implies, an *electrodeposition* process results in the formation of an insoluble deposit on an electrode.   It is a technique in which the electrode reaction is ordinarily carried to completion.   The purpose of an electrodeposition may be varied: (1) the deposit may be used for analysis of the electrolyzed species by weighing of the pure deposit; (2) the deposition may be carried out in order to secure a separation of a mixture of species, and an analysis may be performed simultaneously with the separation or during some later step; and (3) the electrolysis may be carried out for preparative purposes, and in this case the product of the electrolysis is not necessarily an insoluble species.   The first two of these purposes will be discussed below; (3) is beyond the scope of this chapter but its principles have much in common with those discussed below.

(1) Electrolytic Separations

When an electrolytic separation of two or more electroactive species is to be performed, it is necessary to consider all aspects of the electrolysis technique used that may influence the time required for completion of the separation and the possibility of codeposition (the simultaneous deposition of two or more substances). Factors that must be considered in this respect are the choice of the electrochemical variable to be controlled and the value at which this variable is controlled. Three choices exist as to the manner of control: electrolysis at constant current, electrolysis with a fixed potential applied to the cell, and electrolysis with controlled potential.

Electrolysis at constant current involves the application of an approximately constant current to the cell for a period of time sufficient to cause complete reaction of the desired species. This technique may be quite suitable when only one electroactive species present yields an insoluble deposit, but it possesses disadvantages when several such species are present. Take, by way of illustration, the separation of copper and lead. If a constant cathodic current is applied to an electrode immersed in a hydrochloric acid solution of these two ions, initially the only electrode reaction that occurs is the deposition of copper metal. Eventually, however, the concentration of copper ion is depleted to such an extent that its limiting current becomes less than the impressed current. Codeposition of lead then occurs to support the impressed current and the separation is unsuccessful. Two approaches may be employed to avoid this: use of a lower current or of a cathodic depolarizer.

Although the use of sufficiently low current in the constant-current electrolysis of copper and lead ions can secure a satisfactory separation, a much longer electrolysis time is required. For example, if the impressed current in the above example was 0.01 amp. and the limiting current for copper ion was 0.1 amp., codeposition of lead would commence after only 90% deposition of the copper. Lowering the impressed current to a value of 0.0001 amp. would yield 99.9% completion of copper deposition before any lead codeposition occurred, but now the time for the separation is 100 times longer. This approach, obviously, would not be satisfactory.

Codeposition of lead with copper also may be circumvented by the addition in large excess of some material giving a soluble, noninterfering electrolysis product and reacting in the potential region between that for deposition of copper and that for lead. Such a substance is termed a *depolarizer;* nitrate ion is suitable in this case. Whereas this procedure results in satisfactory speed of electrolysis and separation of the copper ion, it is now difficult to secure a cathodic reaction for more negatively reduced ions unless the nitrate depolarizer is removed. Thus, if electrolysis of more than one component of a mixture is desired, it is disadvantageous to use a depolarizer unless it is easily rendered innocuous.

Electrolysis at constant applied potential involves the application of a fixed potential to the cell until reaction is complete. In this technique, as in electrolysis at constant current, it is not possible to satisfy simultaneously the objectives of a rapid completion of the electrolysis and an effective separation. This is true primarily because the potential of the working electrode shifts continuously during the electrolysis as the bulk concentration of the reacting species is depleted. In the electrolysis of a solution containing copper and lead ions, as the bulk concentration (and thus the electrode surface concentration) of copper ion decreases, the cathode potential gradually shifts to more negative values. If a rapid electrolysis of the copper is desired it is necessary to apply a large potential to the cell. However, in the presence of another electroactive species, i.e., lead ion, this would then result in codeposition before the copper separation was complete. To obtain a complete separation, the applied potential must be sufficiently small so that the cathode potential does not drift to potentials so negative as to yield reaction of lead ion prior to 100% deposition of the copper. This may be successfully accomplished (making this technique more selective than electrolysis at controlled current), but at the cost of a greatly increased electrolysis time. Thus the objectives of a rapid electrolysis and a complete separation are incompatible in this method. A cathodic depolarizer (nitrate ion) could be used to limit the cathodic potential drift of the working electrode and thus achieve a rapid and complete separation, but this would yield no advantage over constant-current electrolysis using depolarizers.

The most desirable electrolysis technique is obviously one requiring only a short time for completion and in which the potential of the working electrode is maintained at a constant and known value. This is accomplished in the method known as *electrolysis at controlled potential*. The potential of the working electrode is continuously monitored *vs.* a third reference electrode. The total potential applied to the working and auxiliary electrodes comprising the cell is automatically and continuously adjusted by an error signal from the potential-measuring device so as to maintain the working electrode potential at precisely the desired value *vs.* the reference electrode. The instrument used for this type of potential control is called a *potentiostat,* and a schematic circuit is shown in Fig. 43.17. Electrolysis at controlled potential possesses the ultimate in selectivity of the various electrolysis methods known at this date.

Consider again the separation of copper and lead ions. The selected

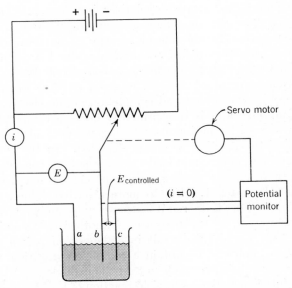

Fig. 43.17. Potentiostat for controlled-potential electrolysis. Key: a is the auxiliary electrode, b is the working electrode, and c is the reference electrode.

value of potential at which the cathode is controlled is one sufficiently negative to yield the copper reaction but not quite so negative as to bring about the deposition of lead. Initially the value of the total applied potential necessary to yield the fastest copper reaction is quite large but, as the copper ion is depleted, the applied potential is automatically lowered to smaller values to prevent drift of the working electrode potential. This process yields the maximum efficiency in time and selectivity of the separation.

If the controlled potential produces a single electrode reaction, the value of the resulting current flowing through the cell as a function of time often obeys the following relationship:

$$i_t = i_i \, 10^{-kt} \tag{17}$$

where i_t is the instantaneous current, k is a constant, and i_i is the initial electrolysis current. If the electrode potential is sufficient to yield the limiting current of the desired species, the rate of decrease of concentration in the solution is given by the relationship

$$-\frac{dC}{dt} = \frac{DA}{V}\frac{dC}{dx} = \frac{DA}{V\delta}C$$

where V is the solution volume in cm.^{3}. Integration of this expression yields

$$C = C_i \, 10^{-0.43(DA/V\delta)t}$$

where C_i is the initial concentration in moles cm.$^{-3}$. Because concentration at any time is proportional to current, the value of the constant, k, in equation (17) is

$$k = 0.43 \, \frac{DA}{V\delta} \tag{18}$$

Equations (17) and (18) provide a basis for the optimum choice of experimental conditions of stirring, etc., so as to obtain a rapid electrolysis.

In the selection of the appropriate value at which to control the potential, some knowledge of the current-potential characteristics of the sample is necessary. Although some information as to the choice of potential may be obtained from polarographic half-wave potentials (*vide infra*), because of the often wide variation in $E_{1/2}$ with the electrode material and solvent medium, such data may be unusable or not available at all. The best recourse in such a case is to carry out a separate determination of the current-potential curve for the solution under investigation (using a microelectrode of the same material) and to select the electrolysis potential on this basis. If the waves obtained for the various species overlap to an extent that renders a perfect separation impossible, they often may be spread sufficiently through varying the supporting electrolyte and/or solvent, the addition of complexing agents (see equation (16)), or the addition of other materials such as surface-active agents to change the reversibilities of the electrode reactions. These and other aspects of electrolytic separations are discussed in Chapter 48 of this volume and in References 12R, 36R, and 37R.

(2) Analysis by Electrogravimetry

If a potential for selective electrodeposition of a given species in a mixture can be chosen, and if the deposit obtained is adherent to the electrode, sufficiently insoluble, and chemically stable, an analysis of the species deposited may be achieved by determining the weight of the deposit. This technique of analysis is termed *electrogravimetry* and is the oldest quantitative electroanalytical method known. By using the controlled-potential electrolysis method, a series of analyses often may be performed on a single sample via electrogravimetry. The method is limited in its sensitivity by the requirement that a weighable amount of deposit must be obtained. The reader may refer to Chapter 48 for details concerning the factors affecting the physical nature of the deposit obtained and for a list of established electrogravimetric determinations.

b. Coulometry

A *coulometric technique* is one in which the quantity of electricity required for a quantitative electrode reaction of a species is measured and related to the amount of the species present via Faraday's law. Use of this technique is restricted to cases in which the current efficiency for the over-all electrode reaction is 100%, or effectively so. There are two useful techniques for which this requirement can be met: coulometry at controlled potential and coulometry at constant current (coulometric titrations).

(1) Coulometry at Controlled Potential

The application of a controlled potential to an electrode under conditions resulting in depletion of a solute species yields a current that decays to a small value upon complete reaction of the species (see equation (17)). If the current efficiency for the reaction is 100%, i.e., if no other reaction takes place, integration of the total current flowing permits calculation of the solution concentration. The selectivity of controlled-potential coulometry, as can be inferred from the above discussion of electrolytic separations, is very good. The sensitivity is primarily determined by two factors: the accuracy of integration of the current-time curve and the accuracy of correction for residual and non-Faradaic currents.

A large variety of integrating devices (*coulometers*) may be used for evaluation of the current-time integral. They may be classified, according to their mode of operation, into the following types: chemical coulometers, electromechanical coulometers, and electronic coulometers. Chemical coulometers can be quite accurate for measurements of relatively large integrals. Electromechanical devices vary considerably in the accuracy obtainable and in limits of sensitivity. Electronic integrators possess good accuracy over a considerable range of integrals; a schematic circuit of an integrator based on operational amplifiers (53R) is shown in Fig. 43.18.

Particularly in measurements of small quantities of sample, it is necessary to correct the integral of the current-time curve for the presence of non-Faradaic and residual currents. Non-Faradaic currents arise from charging of the electrical double layer when a potential is suddenly applied to an electrode. Residual currents arise from the presence of trace electroactive impurities and generally may be reduced to small values by preelectrolysis of the reagents used. The sensitivity of controlled-potential

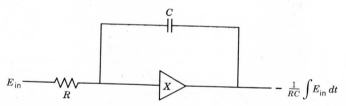

Fig. 43.18. Schematic diagram of electronic coulometer. X is an operational amplifier such as that described as the K_2-X in Reference 53R.

coulometry is far greater than that of electrogravimetry because of the greater accuracy with which small quantities of electricity can be measured. Also, determinations are not limited to those species giving insoluble deposits.

(2) Coulometric Titrations at Constant Current

This electrochemical technique is in essence a titration in which the titrant is a constant flow of electrons. Consider a cell composed of a silver working electrode and an inert auxiliary electrode immersed in a solution containing chloride ions. If a constant anodic current is applied to the silver electrode, the reaction $Ag + Cl^- \rightarrow AgCl + e$ will occur. Eventually, beyond the end point of this "titration," an excess of silver ions will appear in the solution. The detection of excess silver ion may be accomplished by means of any of the potentiometric or amperometric methods discussed above, using a separate pair of electrodes. The only difference between this method and the corresponding volumetric techniques is that the addition of the silver is accomplished electrochemically. The above determination would be called a coulometric titration of chloride with electrogenerated silver and potentiometric (or amperometric) end point.

The product of the current flowing and the time required for the indication of the equivalence point in the above example, $i \times t$, yields the total coulombs corresponding to the sample. As before, the current flow must be of 100% efficiency for the oxidation of silver. This requirement is very simply met in this example by using a silver electrode of sufficient area, and the only limitation on the size of the current employed—and thus the brevity of the time required to complete the analysis—is the time required for the measuring system used to detect the presence of an excess of silver ion. This response time includes as a major factor the time required for thorough mixing of the solution.

A somewhat different case is the coulometric titration of Fe^{+2} with electrogenerated Ce^{+4}. An anodic current is applied to an inert (platinum)

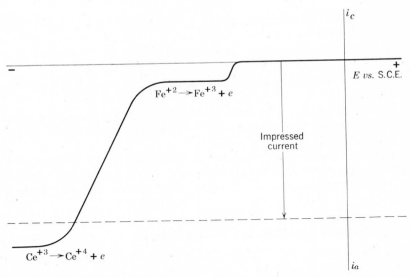

Fig. 43.19. Coulometric titration of Fe^{+2} with electrogenerated Ce^{+4}. The reaction scheme is:

$$Fe^{+2} \xrightarrow{\text{(electrode)}} Fe^{+3} + e$$
$$Ce^{+3} \xrightarrow{\text{(electrode)}} Ce^{+4} + e$$

$$Fe^{+2} \downarrow \text{(solution)}$$

$$Ce^{+3} + Fe^{+3}$$

electrode in contact with the Fe^{+2} solution. This solution also contains a large excess of Ce^{+3}. The size of the impressed current is much larger than the limiting current of Fe^{+2} in this system, but cannot be larger than the limiting current for the Ce^{+3} (see Fig. 43.19). Two electrode reactions will occur, the oxidation of Fe^{+2} and the oxidation of Ce^{+3} to yield Fe^{+3} and Ce^{+4}, respectively. The *over-all* current efficiency for the oxidation of Fe^{+2} is nevertheless 100%, as the Ce^{+4} generated will, upon being stirred into the solution, immediately oxidize the Fe^{+2} remaining in the bulk solution. The equivalence point of the titration may be detected potentiometrically by using a separate pair of electrodes.

The advantages of coulometric titrations are summarized as follows.

1. No standard solutions are required.

2. Reagents that are too unstable to be stored as standard solutions often may be coulometrically generated with ease. Some examples are Cl_2, Ag^{+2}, and Cr^{+2}.

3. Very small quantities of reagent (i.e., electrons) may be added with ease and accurately measured.

4. Impurities in the reagent may be pretitrated before addition of the sample.

5. Remote operation is possible, an advantage in studies of radioactive species.

6. The titration can be performed entirely automatically; for example, the equivalence-point detection system can operate the cutoff of the generating current.

Coulometric methods are discussed in more detail in Chapter 49 and in References 7R, 12R, and 30R.

c. STRIPPING ANALYSIS

Stripping analysis, a very powerful tool for trace analysis, consists of two separate and distinct operations: electrolysis to form a concentrated deposit on the working electrode, and subsequent dissolution (stripping) of this deposit. The method of deposition and stripping need not be the same; in practical stripping analysis the two electrochemical techniques are combined in an appropriate manner so as to display the best qualities of each in performing its required function.

The deposition step ordinarily is performed in a uniformly stirred solution and may involve the reaction of all of the electroactive sample or only a known and reproducible fraction thereof. No quantitative measurements are made during this step, although the variables governing the quantity of deposit are carefully controlled. The selection of the deposition method may be from any of the three electrolysis techniques discussed above; the most commonly used is controlled-potential electrolysis. The choice of complete or partial deposition is dictated by a number of factors; the shorter analysis time involved in the partial-deposition procedure often makes it the more desirable one. If a partial deposition is used the system must be calibrated with known samples to determine the fraction deposited. Reproducible fractional deposition is accomplished by electrolysis for a fixed time with carefully controlled stirring.

A variety of techniques are suitable for the stripping step; the most appropriate selection is made on the basis of the particular experimental situation. Unstirred solutions are generally used. The methods using potential control are:

1. Application of a constant potential of sufficient size to cause the stripping reaction. Complete stripping is used in this case and the quantity of the deposit is obtained from the integral of the current-time curve, i.e., by coulometry.

2. Application of a potential varying linearly with time; a current-potential curve is obtained that has a peaked current (because of depletion of the deposit). If the deposit is insoluble in the electrode material and is thus concentrated at its surface, the stripping is complete and the quantity of deposit may be evaluated from the peak current (chronoamperometry with potential sweep) or by integration of the current-potential curve (coulometry). If the deposit is soluble in the electrode material, stripping may or may not be quantitative, depending on the rate of potential scan; measurement of the peak current is preferable.

In the case of current control a constant current is imposed on the working and auxiliary electrodes and the potential of the working electrode is measured *vs.* a third reference electrode. The name given to the method depends on the solubility or insolubility of the deposit in the electrode material. If the deposit is insoluble, stripping is complete. The time at which completion of the stripping reaction occurs is determined by observing the potential of the working electrode; a change in potential occurs upon complete stripping of the deposit due to a shift to some other electrode reaction. If the current efficiency for stripping is 100% up to this point, the product $i \times t$ yields the coulombs corresponding to the deposit. This is a coulometric method. If the deposit is soluble in the electrode material and thus must diffuse to the electrode surface to react, stripping is incomplete and diffusion laws must be used to evaluate the time required for the potential break. This method is termed chronopotentiometry, and the product of the impressed current and the square root of the time for the potential break is proportional to the concentration of deposit dissolved in the electrode (assuming semi-infinite linear difussion).

The advantages of the use of stripping analysis are primarily in the area of trace analysis. The difficulty in the determination of a very low concentration of an electroactive species by a current measurement is that the sample current may be very small in comparison to the Faradaic current arising from the presence of higher concentrations of other electroactive species, i.e., the residual current. A natural feature of the deposition-stripping procedure used in stripping analysis is the elimination of these interfering residual currents. In a reduction reaction, imyurities that are reduced during the deposition step at more positive potentials than the sample might yield currents totally obscuring the current arising from the sample. During the stripping step, however, if the sample is reversibly oxidized it is stripped before the more noble impurities, and the resulting Faradaic current is due to sample alone. This, however, can be true only if no appreciable quantities of more noble impurity remain in the solution, as some sample deposit would then be regenerated through reaction with the impurity at the electrode surface.

In any electrochemical technique during which the electrode potential is varied (either suddenly at $t = 0$ or continuously), a non-Faradaic current will flow because of charging or discharging of the electrical double layer. This is another source of interfering current in the measurement of a sample current and correction for it is generally unavoidable.   The magnitude of the charging-current correction may be minimized by proper choice of stripping technique, i.e., the charging correction for stripping with chrono-amperometry with potential sweep is less than that required for stripping with constant applied potential.   Concentrations as low as $10^{-9}M$ may be thus determined for electroactive species that will form an insoluble deposit and undergo a reversible electrode reaction.   Further discussion of the field of stripping analysis is given in Chapter 50 of this volume.

B. METHODS USING MASS TRANSPORT BY DIFFUSION

In contrast to the use of the approximate Nernst layer concept for convective mass transport, treatment of the rate of mass transport by diffusion can be accomplished quantitatively via the use of Fick's laws of diffusion. Electrochemical methods in which the measurements made are based on the rate of diffusion transport thus generally have a more solid theoretical foundation than corresponding methods using convection-diffusion transport.   The following discussion will be divided, as before, into consideration of various types of control of potential or current so as to achieve the desired degrees of control over the rate of the electrode reaction by the processes of diffusion and electron transfer.   Because the potential or current response obtained in an unstirred solution is transient in nature, different theoretical relations must be used for potential and current control.

1. Potential Controlled at a Constant Value

a. CHRONOAMPEROMETRY

If a potential sufficient to cause an electrode reaction is applied suddenly to an electrode in an unstirred solution containing a supporting electrolyte, the resulting current may be governed by the rate of diffusion, the rate of the electron-transfer reaction, or by some combination of the two.   Observation of the current flowing as a function of time is termed *chronoamperometry*.   The circuit used for chronoamperometric experiments is that shown in Fig. 43.2.

If the energy of activation for the electron-transfer process is low, and the rate of electron transfer is correspondingly rapid, the current flowing may, in a given experimental situation, be controlled by the rate of mass transport of electroactive species to the electrode surface.   This is then a reversible reaction, and the ratio of concentrations of reactants and products at the electrode surface are governed by the applied potential according to the Nernst equation. The relation of the current flowing to time and the applied potential may be obtained, as was shown in Chapter 42, by solution of Fick's Second Law under the appropriate boundary conditions, and the relation for the reaction, ox. $+ ne \rightarrow$ red., is given by the general form of the Cottrell equation:

$$i_t = \frac{nFAD_{ox.}^{1/2}C_{ox.}}{\pi^{1/2}\,t^{1/2}}\left\{1 + \frac{D_{ox.}^{1/2}}{D_{red.}^{1/2}}\,e^{\frac{nE}{RT}(E-E^\circ)}\right\}^{-1} \qquad (19)$$

where i_t is the instantaneous current at time t, $C_{ox.}$ is the bulk concentration of the oxidized species, and the type of diffusion is linear semi-infinite. Equation (19) shows that the current decays with time because of the progressive depletion of the electroactive species around the electrode. At any given time the value of the current is determined by the applied potential, E. The maximum limiting value of current for any given time is obtained when E is much more negative than E°. The proportionality between current and concentration at a given time may be utilized for the determination of $C_{ox.}$, but this technique is rarely used for analysis.

If the activation energy for the electron-transfer process is high, the current is given by the equation for an irreversible reaction (see equation (11)). Changes in the surface concentrations, $C^\circ_{ox.}$ and $C^\circ_{red.}$, arising from the electrode reaction make it necessary to effect a solution of Fick's law for a description of the current flowing as a function of time (see Chapter 44). Observations of current-time curves obtained with the chronoamperometric technique are useful mainly in studies of electron-transfer kinetics.

b. POLAROGRAPHY

The polarographic technique is a special case of chronoamperometry using an electrode (the *dropping mercury electrode*, D.M.E.) which endows this variation of chronoamperometry with very special and useful characteristics. Apply to a D.M.E. a constant potential of such a size that $C^\circ_{ox.} = 0$. The diffusion problem is now complicated by the fact that the area of the electrode is increasing, the type of diffusion is spherical semi-infinite, and the electrode is growing into the depleted layer of solution. The net effect is a growth of the current during the life of the mercury drop, as shown in Fig. 43.20. If the type of diffusion is approximated to be linear rather than spherical, the solution for the current-time relation for the expanding mercury sphere is

$$i_d(t) = 708.2\,nm^{2/3}\,D_{ox.}^{1/2}\,t^{1/6}\,C_{ox.} \qquad (20)$$

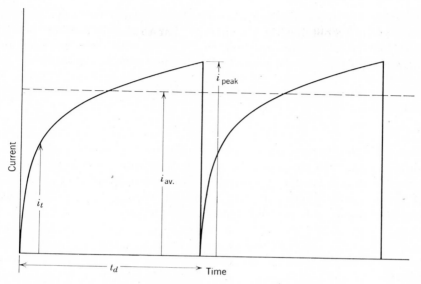

Fig. 43.20. Current-time characteristics at the dropping mercury electrode.

where m is expressed in mg. second^{-1}, t is time in seconds, and $i_d(t)$ is now expressed in microamperes and C_{ox} in millimoles cm.$^{-3}$. Because the fall of the mercury drop destroys the diffusion layer and the next drop starts its growth in a homogeneous solution,* the current-time relation for each drop is the same. If equation (20) is averaged over the life of a drop, an equation for the average current is obtained:

$$i_d(\text{av.}) = 607.0 \ nm^{2/3} \ D_{ox.}^{1/2} \ t_d^{1/6} \ C_{ox.} \tag{21}$$

where t_d is the drop time and $i_d(\text{av.})$ is the *diffusion current* (since $C^{\circ}_{ox.} = 0$, this current is solely diffusion controlled). Thus, although the current flowing at the D.M.E. is not a steady current, by use of equation (21) it may be treated as such. Equation (21) may be recognized as the well-known Ilkovic equation (12).

If the average current flowing is determined as a function of potential, a current-potential wave (a *polarogram*) is obtained that is analogous to that in a uniformly stirred solution (see Fig. 43.3). If the reaction is

* This statement is an approximation to the truth. Actually only the "first drop" obeys the $i-t^{1/6}$ relation exactly owing to a small residual concentration polarization remaining after the drop falls (Reference 51R, Vol. I, Chap. 3). The extent of this residual polarization is the same for all successive drops, however, and thus a common $i-t$ behavior for successive drops results.

reversible, the concentrations of reactants and products at the electrode surface may be obtained in a manner similar to that in Section II-A-1-b of this chapter. For the reaction, ox. + $ne \rightarrow$ red., where both *ox.* and *red.* are soluble species and where $C_{red.} = 0$, these surface concentrations are

$$C^{\circ}_{ox.} = (i_d - i)/k$$

and

$$C^{\circ}_{red.} = i/k$$

where k is the current-concentration proportionality constant of the Ilkovic equation. (In this case, the surface concentrations also may be obtained in an identical form by an entirely rigorous approach.) Substitution of these concentrations into the Nernst equation yields the current-potential equation for a reversible polarographic wave:

$$E = E_{1/2} + \frac{RT}{nF} \ln \frac{i_d - i}{i} \tag{22}$$

where

$$E_{1/2} = E^{\circ}_{ox.,red.} + \frac{RT}{nF} \ln \frac{D_{red.}^{1/2}}{D_{ox.}^{1/2}}$$

As before, the form of the current term in equation (22) is dependent upon the type of the electrode reaction.

If the rate of the electrode reaction is governed by the rate of the electron-transfer process, the Nernst equation cannot be used for the expression of the irreversible current-potential wave and equation (11) must be employed. This may be accomplished in a manner similar to that for equation (13). The reader is referred to Chapter 46 of this volume for further details on irreversible polarographic waves.

The advantages and complexities of the polarographic technique are many and varied. The constantly renewed mercury surface is a decided advantage in many studies because the effects of accumulation of soluble electrode reaction products in the mercury and of adsorption of undesirable materials on the electrode surface are minimized. The polarographic method has been extensively employed for analysis (via the $i_d - C$ relation), for studies of the kinetics of electron-transfer reactions and other reactions in the solution that may influence the flow of current (kinetic and catalytic currents) and as an amperometric indicator electrode for titrations. Further discussion of these is beyond the scope of this chapter and the reader is referred to Chapter 46 and to other comprehensive works (7R, 12R, 39R to 51R).

2. Potential Varying Linearly with Time

a. Chronoamperometry with Potential Sweep

If the potential of an electrode in an unstirred solution containing a reducible species is varied rapidly from positive to negative potentials, a current-potential wave of the type shown in Fig. 43.21 is obtained. Initially

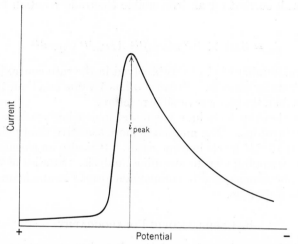

Fig. 43.21. Reversible current-potential curve for chronoamperometry with potential sweep.

the rate of the electrode reaction is very low and virtually no current flows through the cell. When a sufficiently negative potential is reached, the reaction commences and the current rapidly increases. However, opposing this increase in current is the depletion of the electroactive species near the electrode surface. Eventually this depletion will become controlling and the current-potential curve will show a maximum. For a reversible electrode reaction involving soluble reactants and products, the value of this peak current is given by the Randles-Sevcik equation (24,27):

$$i_p = 2.72 \times 10^5 \, n^{3/2} \, A D^{1/2} \, C_{\text{ox}} . v^{1/2} \qquad \text{at } 25°\text{C}. \qquad (23)$$

where i_p is the peak current in amperes, A is the area of the electrode in cm.^{2}, and v is the rate of voltage scan in volts second^{-1}. The potential at which the peak occurs is related to the polarographic half-wave potential by

$$E_{\text{peak}} = E_{1/2} - 1.1RT/nF$$

and is a constant potential, $0.028/n$ v. more cathodic than $E_{1/2}$ at 25°C. If the reversible electrode reaction leads to the deposition of an insoluble substance, the numerical coefficient of equation (23) becomes 3.67×10^5 and the value of E_{peak} is dependent on the concentration of reducible species (2).

The value of the peak current, as might be expected, varies with the reversibility of the reaction, as does the potential at which the peak occurs. The peak current for an irreversible electrode reaction (4) is given by

$$i_p = 3.01 \times 10^5\, n(\alpha n_a)^{1/2}\, A D_{ox.}^{1/2}\, C_{ox.}\, v^{1/2}$$

where n_a is the number of electrons involved in the rate-controlling step of the electron-transfer process. Because α has a value less than 1, this peak current is less than that for a reversible reaction.

The potential-sweep technique has found increasing use in a number of analytical applications. The method is more sensitive than polarography, being useful at $10^{-7}M$ levels in some cases. It is also an excellent method for use in the stripping step in stripping analysis. Studies of kinetics, of double-layer phenomena, and of compounds formed in amalgams also have employed this technique.

b. OSCILLOSCOPIC POLAROGRAPHY

If a potential sweep is performed at a dropping mercury electrode at a rate such that the area of the electrode does not change appreciably during the recording of the current-potential curve, the technique is then a special case of chronoamperometry with potential sweep and is termed *oscilloscopic polarography* (43R). (The name of this method originated from the use of oscilloscopic equipment to record the current-potential curve; however, recording apparatus is now available that renders the use of an oscilloscope unnecessary.) The great advantage of the D.M.E.—the availability of a clean and reproducible electrode surface—undoubtedly explains its use in many of the potential-sweep studies reported.

3. Potential Varying Periodically with Time

a. ALTERNATING-CURRENT POLAROGRAPHY

Consider the application of a steady potential to a D.M.E. immersed in a solution containing the oxidized form of a reversible, soluble couple. Superimpose on this d.-c. potential an a.-c. potential (sine wave) of a few millivolts magnitude. If the d.-c. potential is now varied from positive to negative values, a d.-c. potential wave is obtained, and superimposed on the direct current is an a.-c. component arising from the presence of the applied a.-c. signal. Measurement of the magnitude of the alternating current flowing as a function of the value of the applied d.-c. potential is the technique called *a.-c. polarography*.

The magnitude of the alternating current flowing during the negative and positive halves of the a.-c. cycle is dependent on the values of the surface concentrations of oxidizable and reducible species, respectively. The total alternating current will be greatest when these surface concentrations

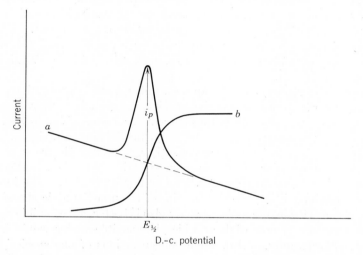

Fig. 43.22. Relationship between direct-current and alternating-current polarograms
Key: *a*, a.-c. polarogram; *b*, d.-c. polarogram.

are of equal magnitude, i.e., at the d.-c. half-wave potential, $E_{1/2}$. The alternating current arising from the electrode reaction will thus go through a maximum at $E_{1/2}$ and will have its lowest values on the flat portions of the d.-c. potential wave. The alternating and direct currents are compared in Fig. 43.22; the shape of the a.-c. polarogram is similar to the derivative of the d.-c. polarogram.

The above discussion presumed that the rate of the electron-transfer process did not limit the size of the alternating current. If, however, an activation overpotential for the electron-transfer reaction is present, a smaller increase in current results from the addition of a small potential increment during each portion of the a.-c. cycle and the alternating current is smaller. In the limiting case (totally irreversible) no a.-c. wave is observed. The appearance of reversibility of the electrode reaction may depend on the frequency of the applied a.-c. potential. If the frequency is high, the rate of the electron-transfer reaction may become controlling, and a reaction that appeared reversible under d.-c. conditions or at low a.-c. frequencies may now appear irreversible.

Some alternating current will flow even in the absence of an electron-transfer reaction; this current arises from the charging and discharging of the electrical double layer at the electrode surface during each part of the a.-c. potential cycle. Because the double-layer structure changes with the electrode potential, the value of this charging current also varies with the value of the d.-c. component of the applied potential. Thus the "base line" of the a.-c. polarogram is not zero, nor is it flat. However, this non-Faradaic current is usually linear over a narrow range of potential and may be extrapolated under an a.-c. peak arising from a Faradaic reaction (see Fig. 43.22).

Because the peak current in an a.-c. polarogram is proportional to the bulk concentration of electroactive species, the technique may be used for analysis. As the peak alternating current for a reversible reaction is proportional to the square root of the frequency of the a.-c. signal, the frequency must be carefully controlled. For reversible electrode reactions, analysis by a.-c. polarography is more sensitive than d.-c. polarography, and may be applied to concentrations as low as $10^{-6}M$. The limitation on the sensitivity is imposed by the size of the non-Faradaic charging current. Selectivity in a.-c. polarography also is better, as reversible reactions can be observed at potentials at which irreversible waves would interfere in d.-c. polarography. Also, small concentrations of one species may be measured more readily in the presence of a large concentration of another species.

Because the magnitude of the alternating current may be dependent on the rate of the electron-transfer reaction, a.-c. polarography has proven useful in evaluating the kinetics of electron-transfer reactions that are too rapid to be studied by normal d.-c. polarography. The theoretical treatments used in such studies, however, are complicated by the presence of non-Faradaic charging current.

Although the D.M.E. is commonly used in a.-c. techniques, other electrodes have also been employed. Alternating-current polarography is discussed in Chapter 46 of this volume and elsewhere (7R, 15R).

b. SQUARE-WAVE POLAROGRAPHY

The square-wave polarographic technique (1) involves the same principles as a.-c. polarography, except that a *square-wave* potential of small amplitude is superimposed on the applied d.-c. potential.   This method has one distinct advantage over the use of a sine wave—the current required to charge the double layer occurs only at the start of each half cycle rather than existing over the entire half cycle.   Thus measurement of the current flowing during the latter portion of the square-wave current on each half cycle minimizes the effect of the non-Faradaic current and hence enhances the sensitivity markedly.   Because of the necessity for exact timing, this advantage is gained only at the cost of greater instrumental complexity.

4. Application of a Controlled Current: Chronopotentiometry

If a constant cathodic current is suddenly caused to flow at an electrode in an unstirred solution (using the circuit of Fig. 43.23), the surface concentration of the most readily reducible electroactive species present will

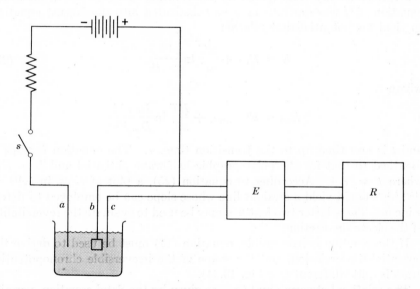

Fig. 43.23. Schematic circuit for chronopotentiometry with constant current.   Key: *a*, auxiliary electrode; *b*, working electrode; *c*, reference electrode; *E*, measures potential between *b* and *c* at zero current, *R*, recorder, and *s*, switch.

decrease and eventually will reach zero.   At this time some other electrode reaction also must occur to support the impressed current, and the electrode potential will shift to that of this new reaction.   Measurement of the potential of this working electrode as a function of time is the electrochemical technique known as *chronopotentiometry*.   The time at which the potential shifts is called the *transition time*, τ, and is given by the Sand equation:

$$\tau^{1/2} = \frac{\pi^{1/2} \, nFAD_{ox.}{}^{1/2}C_{ox.}}{2i} \tag{24}$$

where i is the impressed current in amperes and $C_{ox.}$ is the bulk concentration in moles cm.$^{-3}$ (see also Chapter 42).

The value of the transition time is controlled by the rate of diffusion mass transport and is independent of the rate of electron transfer. Thus two species identical in all respects except that one is reversible and the other irreversible yield the same τ. The shape of the potential-time curve (the *chronopotentiogram*) is, however, dependent on the reversibility of the electrode reaction. For a reversible reaction, the values of the surface concentrations at any time (given by the solution of Fick's law from which equation (24) was derived) may be substituted into the Nernst equation to yield the potential-time relation

$$E = E_{1/2} + \frac{RT}{nF} \ln \frac{\tau^{1/2} - t^{1/2}}{t^{1/2}} \tag{25}$$

where

$$E_{1/2} = E^{\circ}{}_{ox.,red.} + \frac{RT}{nF} \ln \frac{D_{red.}{}^{1/2}}{D_{ox.}{}^{1/2}}$$

and t is any time up to the transition time, τ. The equation for $E_{1/2}$ is identical to that for the polarographic half-wave potential and $E = E_{1/2}$ where $t = \tau/4$. According to equation (25), a plot of E *vs.* $\ln (\tau^{1/2} - t^{1/2})/t^{1/2}$ should yield a straight line whose slope can be employed to determine n. These latter two features may be used to evaluate the reversibility of the electrode reaction.

If the reaction is irreversible, equation (11) must be used to derive the potential-time relation, and the shape of the irreversible chronopotentiogram is quite different (see Fig. 43.24).

The relation between τ and $C_{ox.}$, as given by the Sand equation, permits use of the chronopotentiometric technique for analysis. The most promising applications are in the analysis of electroactive species in media in which the use of the D.M.E. or rotated solid electrodes is impossible or cumbersome, e.g., in molten salts (16).

Chronopotentiometry also has proven to be a most useful tool in fundamental studies of electron-transfer kinetics, surface phenomena at electrodes (adsorbed layers, oxide films, etc.), and kinetics of solution reactions (7R,14R). Studies in the latter area are enhanced by the use of the tech-

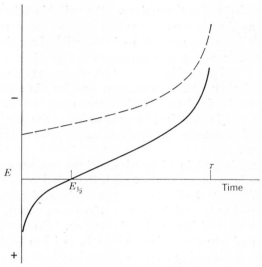

Fig. 43.24. Comparison of reversible and irreversible chronopotentiograms: ————, reversible; - - - - -, irreversible.

nique of current reversal.   For example, if an electroactive species is reduced at an electrode and the product of this reduction undergoes an irreversible decomposition to yield a nonelectroactive species, the kinetics of this decomposition may be evaluated by reversing the current and noting the fraction of the reduced form that has not decomposed (29).   This technique appears to be applicable to rather fast solution reactions.

The chronopotentiometric technique generally has been used with a constant applied current because of the simplicity of the instrumentation and the mathematical treatments for this case.   It is, however, not limited in the type of current function employed.   For example, if the current is varied according to powers of time $(i = kt^r)$, the general relation (21) between concentration and transition time shows that $\tau^{r+1/2}$ is proportional to $C_{ox.}$.

The chronopotentiometric technique is discussed further in Chapters 42 and 44 of this volume and elsewhere (7R,12R,14R,15R).

IV. METHODS IN WHICH ELECTRON-TRANSFER REACTIONS ARE UNIMPORTANT: CHARGE TRANSPORT BY MIGRATION AND DIELECTRIC POLARIZATION

The methods described in Sections II and III were based upon electrochemical phenomena arising from processes occurring at, and in the near vicinity of, the electrodes themselves. By suitable selection of experimental conditions the electrode processes may be made relatively rapid, with the result that the application of potential gives rise to a current limited only by charge-transport processes taking place within the bulk of the solution. As discussed in Chapter 42, charge may be carried through the bulk of a solution by ion movement and by dielectric polarization. The former process is of primary significance in conductometry, conducto-metric titrations, and in high-frequency titrations, whereas the latter property is of practical significance in methods based upon the measurement of dielectric constant.

In conductometric and in dielectric-constant measurements, the electrodes are placed in intimate contact with the solution and an alternating potential is applied. Polarization at the surface of these electrodes is avoided by increasing the microscopic surface area through platinization and/or operation at sufficiently high frequency. Under these conditions the contribution of non-Faradaic currents is so large that the electrode process itself is not governing and the potential drops across the electrode solution interfaces are constant. A linear potential drop equal in magnitude to that applied to the solution is then assumed for the bulk solution. In the so-called high-frequency methods the electrodes are separated from the solution by a dielectric material. Polarization of such electrodes is dependent upon the thickness and dielectric properties of the film, upon the frequency employed, and (of primary interest) upon the properties of the bulk solution itself.

A. CONDUCTOMETRY AND CONDUCTOMETRIC TITRATIONS

Under the influence of a potential gradient, the ions in the bulk of the solution move at a rate dependent upon their charge and size, upon the microscopic viscosity of the medium, and upon the magnitude of the potential gradient. In addition, the net current resulting from the movement of these ions will depend upon the number of the ions present. Hence the electrical conductance of the solution is not a specific property of any particular ionic species, but is a summation of contributions from all of the ions present. For this reason, conductometry will permit the determination of the concentration of an ion (e.g., Na^+) only if the type of its oppositely charged ion ($Cl^-, SO_4^{-2}, \ldots$) is known and the contributions due to other electrolytes are known or are zero. More specifically, the conductance, K, may be represented by the expression

$$K = b \sum^{i} C_i \lambda_i z_i$$

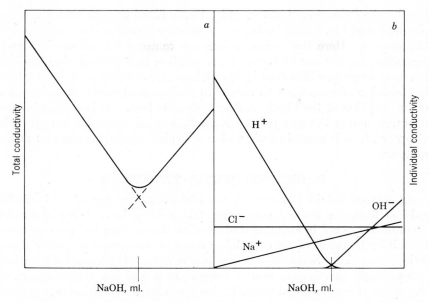

Fig. 43.25. Conductometric titration of HCl with NaOH. Dilution of the solution during the titration is assumed to be negligible. Key: *a*, change in total conductivity; *b*, change in individual contributions to the conductivity.

where b is a constant characteristic of the geometry and the size of the conductance cell, C is the molar concentration of the individual ions in the solution, λ is the equivalent ionic conductance of the individual ions, and z is the ionic charge of the individual ions. Some values for λ are given in Table 42.I of Chapter 42. Despite the lack of specificity in conductance measurements, the technique is useful in giving a measure of the over-all ionic content of a solution, such as in the determinination of the purity of distilled water, and in monitoring solutions containing only a given electrolyte type.

Specificity, however, can be achieved by replacing a given ion with a second one, such as in the process of a *conductometric titration*. The titration is devised so that the ionic species to be determined can be replaced by another ionic species of significantly different conductance. Hence, by following the *change* in conductance of the solution as the replacing species is added, the volume of titrant required to achieve complete replacement may be determined. This volume, of course, will correspond to the end point. This may be illustrated by the titration of HCl with NaOH, the addition of the latter decreasing the hydrogen ion concentration by the formation of water.   Fig. 43.25a illustrates the titration curve obtained and Fig. 43.25b indicates the relative contribution of each ion in the process.   Here the hydrogen ions are replaced by sodium ions and, consequently, the conductance of the solution is decreased since sodium ion has a lower mobility than hydrogen ion.   Once this process is complete, the addition of excess NaOH results in an increased conductance because of the addition of the highly mobile hydroxide ions.   This change in conductance marks the end point.   Numerous other examples are given in Chapter 51, as is a detailed discussion of typical electrodes and measuring systems.

B. HIGH-FREQUENCY TITRATIONS

As pointed out in Chapter 42, the high-frequency technique is distinguished from the normal conductometric method in that the electrodes themselves are not in intimate contact with the solution but are separated from it by the walls of the containing vessel or some other dielectric (insulating) material.   Some advantages accrue from this physical separation. For example, particulate matter present in a solution might adhere to electrodes placed in direct contact with the solution, resulting in a marked change in the conductance value measured.   In high-frequency titrations the effects resulting from this deposit will be much less noticeable.   Hence the high-frequency method does offer some advantages in precipitation titrations and in measuring the conductance of nonhomogeneous solutions. Furthermore, the use of platinized platinum, common in normal conductometric work, may catalyze certain reactions within the solution.   In high-frequency cells, this disturbing feature is avoided.   Another instance in which advantage may be taken of the electrode-solution separation is in the monitoring of the bands appearing within a chromatographic column. Here the electrodes may be placed conveniently on the outside wall of the chromatographic column; this is, of course, much simpler than making direct contact with the solution.

As discussed in Chapters 42 and 51, the presence of the insulating dielectric separating the electrodes from the solution complicates the response characteristics of the cell.   The cell as a whole is now a composite of two "lumped" capacitors and one resistor.   More specifically, the cell may be represented as a series combination of a capacitance (representing the dielectric material separating the electrodes from the solution) and a parallel-connected capacitance and resistance (representing the solution capacitance and resistance, respectively).   The response of the cell will therefore depend upon the frequency employed, the electrical property measured (high-frequency conductance or capacitance), the cell geometry, and the dielectric and conducting properties of the sample solution itself.   Because of the somewhat complex nature of this composite, the response of the cell is not necessarily a linear function of either the conductivity or the capacitance of the sample solution.   Despite these disadvantages, the response of a high-frequency cell can be given in a rational manner in terms of the variables described here.   These are considered in further detail in Chapters 42 and 51.

C. METHODS BASED ON DIELECTRIC-CONSTANT MEASUREMENTS

The current flow in a dielectric arises from electrochemical behavior in which a charge is displaced elastically under the influence of a potential gradient and in opposition to a restoring force.   This displacement of charge stems in part from the polarization of electrons and nuclei within a molecule (induced polarization) and hence is a property of the molecule itself.   The restoring force for a displacement of electrons in atoms is intramolecular and depends upon the number and "looseness" of electrons, the strength of the bonds, the type of bonding forces between atoms, etc. The second mechanism for displacement of charge stems from alignment of electrically unsymmetrical molecules (orientation polarization) under the influence of an externally applied electrical field.   The contribution to this term depends primarily on the geometry of the molecule in question and its resulting electrical asymmetry, these factors being expressed by the dipole moment of the molecule.   The dielectric constant is a measure of the sum of the effects of orientation polarization and induced polarization. Because two different molecules may have different dielectric constants, it is clear that measurements based upon dielectric polarization may be used for analytical purposes.   At the same time, it is also clear that the property itself is not specific for any given molecule in the presence of others, but is dependent upon the sum of contributions from each species present.

The principles and applications of such measurements are further discussed in Chapter 52.

V. DIFFERENTIAL METHODS

If a measurement is made of the difference between the signals obtained from two electrochemical systems, the resultant technique is termed a *differential method*.   It is, in principle, possible to apply such a method to any of the above basic electrochemical techniques.   If two electrochemical systems are identical in all respects except one, and the signals obtained from the systems using a given electrochemical method are sensitive to the presence of this factor, then a measurement of the difference between the response of the two systems yields a measure of the response of this factor alone, the signal arising from other components of the systems having been canceled out. Use of a differential method in analysis is primarily of advantage in the determination of the quantity of a certain component in the presence of a much larger quantity of another. The difficulties associated with its use obviously arise from the necessity of precisely matching the two systems.

By way of illustration, consider two identical polarographic cells, each with its associated potential-applying and current-measuring circuitry. The two dropping mercury electrodes are identical and their drop times coincide. If the solutions in the two cells contain no electroactive species and the same solvent and supporting electrolyte, separate polarograms run on each are identical. If the current signal from each is now inserted into a circuit that measures the difference between the two currents, the resulting difference would be zero, i.e., the residual current has canceled. If now a sample solution containing lead ion is added to one cell (the sample cell), the difference current would be due to the reduction of the lead ion alone. By thus compensating for the residual current, concentrations of lead ion can be determined by *differential polarography* (11) that are more dilute than those possible using ordinary polarography. Moreover, if a large concentration of, for example, copper ion is also present in the sample solution and in larger concentration than the lead ion, it is possible to compensate for the interfering copper wave by adding an equal amount of copper ion to the reference cell.

The difficulty with the above technique lies primarily in the synchronization of the falling mercury drops. If a hanging mercury drop electrode is substituted for the D.M.E., and a rapid potential sweep in unstirred solution is used (19), the instrumentation required for a differential method is simplified, although it is still more complex than with the ordinary method of chronoamperometry with potential sweep.

As stated, differential methods can, in principle, be applied to any electrochemical technique; this statement might be further applied to many other areas of analysis, for example, differential spectrophotometry. In general, because of the ordinarily greater complexity of the experimental apparatus required, practical use of differential techniques is limited to cases in which other more sensitive and less complex methods are lacking.

VI. OPERATIONAL ASPECTS OF ELECTROCHEMISTRY

The motives behind the initiation of an electrochemical investigation may be many and varied: the objective may be the use of electrochemistry as a tool for the measurement of some property of a system, or the development of a new experimental technique and/or the theory thereof. In any of these situations, the experimenter is faced with the choice of *modus operandi*, i.e., which technique is best suited to measure a certain quantity, what experimental conditions should be used, what instrumentation is adequate for the study, etc. The above discussion of a number of well-established electrochemical methods has briefly noted the experimental operation of each and some of the resulting limitations and advantages. The purpose of the following discussion is to provide, in an *operational* manner, a rational basis for the characterization and comparison of existing techniques and to provide, to some extent, further insight into new areas of study.

An electrochemical method has the following operational aspects: (*1*) the experimental conditions (which govern the system function), (*2*) the *excitation signal* (which initiates and sustains the experiment), (*3*) the resulting over-all behavior of the electrochemical system (the *response function*), and (*4*) the measurement of some aspect of the response function.

A. EXPERIMENTAL CONDITIONS

The experimental conditions selected for an electrochemical experiment will determine the response of the system to a given excitation signal. These initial conditions are established by the physical and chemical design and arrangement of the cell and are thus fixed by operations prior to the initiation of the experiment. The primary factors involved in the selection of experimental conditions are the following.

1. The mode of *mass transport*. The choice of stirred or unstirred solutions is important when electrode polarization may occur. As far as rate of mass transport is concerned, diffusion transport is less efficient, and hence less sensitive, than convection-diffusion; however, the theoretical treatment of diffusion processes is generally more rigorous. In addition, it must be remembered that the time of experimentation for which diffusion can be relied upon to be the sole mode of mass transport is limited by the onset of natural convection (through density or thermal gradients), which disturbs the diffusion layer. Electrodes may be shielded to extend the useful time for diffusion experiments.

2. The nature of the electrode(s) used. The *electrode material* may drastically affect the reversibility and/or mechanism of an electrode reaction. For example, the reversibility of hydrogen evolution on platinum metal is much greater than that on mercury; this allows study of other electrode processes at more cathodic potentials on the latter metal. The *surface conditions* of a given metal also may be important. For example, the reversibility of a reaction at a platinum electrode may be determined by the presence of oxide films, catalytically active surface sites (such as exist on platinized platinum), or adsorbed layers of surface-active materials. Much recent research has been stimulated by the realization that valuable fundamental information may be obtained by studying the behavior of an electrode reaction as a function of surface conditions. However, if the effects of variable surface conditions are harmful to the particular investigation, it is desirable to select an electrode whose surface characteristics may be made reproducible by pretreatment, constant replenishment of the surface (as with the D.M.E. and streaming mercury electrode), etc. The *shape* of a polarized electrode in an unstirred solution determines the type of diffusion (linear, spherical, or cylindrical) and thus the form of Fick's diffusion law to be used in the theoretical treatment. Because linear diffusion is mathematically the simplest form, the theoretical treatment of complex electrochemical systems is generally facilitated by the use of planar geometry. The projected *surface area* of the electrode is directly proportional to current in most polarized systems and is of importance when the bulk concentration of reactant is to be depleted or when a measurement is based on the current flowing. Electrodes may have time-dependent size, shape, or surface properties, for example, the D.M.E. Deposition, adsorption, etc., on an electrode may produce time-variant surface conditions.

3. The nature of the medium. The *solvent* and *supporting electrolyte* (where needed) are selected on the basis of solubility of reactants and products, the accessible potential range (limited by solvent or electrolyte oxidation and reduction), and the effects on the electrode reaction (through complexation, buffering capabilities, the structure of the electrical double layer, specific adsorption on the electrode, etc.). The concentration of electroactive species is established at a level compatible with the other experimental conditions, the excitation signal, and the time of measurement of response. Obviously the most readily obtainable form of concentration distribution is that of a homogeneous solution, although there are cases in which a nonhomogeneous distribution can be obtained and is usable (as in the current-reversal step in chronopotentiometry).

4. Physical design of the cell. In a high-resistance medium, the electrodes should be close together to minimize IR drop. Proper means must be taken to eliminate the introduction of undesirable ions from reference electrodes, etc.

5. Temperature. Because of the 1 to 2% degree^{-1} temperature dependence of diffusion coefficients, and the much larger temperature dependency of rate of electron transfer in irreversible reactions, the temperature must often be carefully controlled to $\pm 0.1°C.$, or better.

B. EXCITATION

An action that disturbs an electrochemical system from its initial state (equilibrium or otherwise) is termed an *excitation*. The excitation may

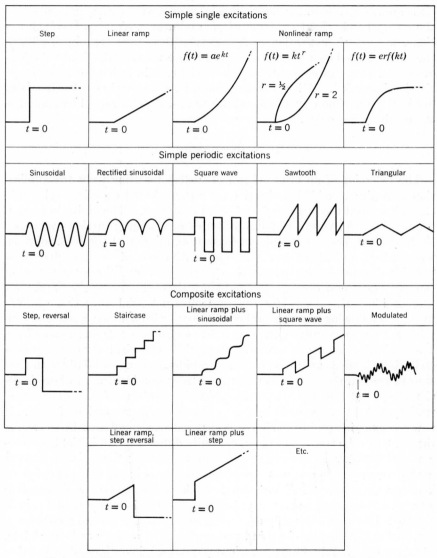

Fig. 43.26. Shapes of various types of potential or current excitations.

take the form of an impressed current or potential or the addition of a titrant. A titrant excitation may consist of a more-or-less constant inflow of reactant (as in an automatic titration), or of a series of additions (the response of the system being noted after each). Potential or current excitations applied to a working electrode may have a wide variety of shapes and these may be classified as *simple single* excitations, *simple periodic* excitations, or *composite* excitations. A variety of these are shown in Fig. 43.26; the excitations shown may be either current or potential. The technique of potentiometry at zero current is a special case in which no electrical excitation is applied. A large area of potential advances in electrochemistry lies in the use of new types of excitations and the theoretical treatment of the resulting responses.

C. RESPONSE

The behavior of an electrochemical system resulting from the application of a given excitation signal (under the selected experimental conditions) is termed the *response function* of the system. The excitation will of course yield an over-all response in terms of changing surface concentrations, current, potential, bulk concentration, density of the bulk solution, temperature, optical density, etc. The relative magnitudes of each of these individual responses depends on the experimental conditions, the nature of the excitation, and the time elapsed since the excitation was applied. By way of illustration, consider the controlled-potential reduction of Fe^{+3} under the following experimental conditions: stirred aqueous solution containing $HClO_4$ electrolyte, large-area Pt electrode, small solution volume. The excitation itself is a potential step. The electrical response found is an initially large current that decreases rapidly and exponentially with time toward zero current. The concentration response is an immediate depletion of Fe^{+3} at the electrode surface, a rapid depletion of the bulk concentration of Fe^{+3}, and a rapid increase of the bulk concentration of Fe^{+2}. If now the experimental conditions are changed to a small-area Pt electrode, the nature of the response will appear quite different. An initial large current and a depleted surface concentration results, as before, but the current rapidly decreases to a steady value and then remains at this value over a long period of time (until appreciable depletion of the bulk concentration occurs). This latter, apparently constant, current is termed a *steady-state* current; its value is actually decreasing exponentially toward zero current but during the time involved in the experiment its decay rate is negligible. Thus the time required for the various responses is in a different proportion than in the above case.

All of the individual responses are, of course, not measured nor are they, in many cases, all directly measurable. The operational nature of any electrochemical technique (and hence its ultimate usefulness) is determined by the choice of measurement of one or several of these responses. In order to extract the desired information from the system under study, certain criteria should be applied to the choice of the measured response. The requisite characteristics of the response are *sensitivity* to the value of the quantity under study, *selectivity* of response to the desired quantity (minimum interference from the response characteristics of other properties of the system), adequacy of the available *theoretical treatment* of the response (so as to allow a rigorous interpretation of the results to yield the desired quantity), and the *time* required to obtain the response. Of no small consequence in the selection of a measured response is also the instrumentation required to measure the response as well as that to produce the excitation signal. For each given excitation and set of experimental conditions one may thus select for measurement the response yielding maximum sensitivity and selectivity consistent with the minimum time and instrumentation required for measurement of that response. It must be recognized that not often are these four factors perfectly harmonious with one another, and a happy medium must be struck in any practical situation.

An interesting feature of electrochemical techniques is a frequent *reciprocity* of current and potential excitations. This is invariably true if the response is measured at the electrode to which the signal is applied. It was stated earlier that in stirred solutions the same theory and experimental results could be obtained by using either as a step excitation. In unstirred solutions, step potentials and currents yield different results (i.e., chrono-amperometry and chronopotentiometry). A step potential yields a current inversely proportional to $t^{1/2}$. However, if in "chronopotentiometry" the excitation is a current inversely proportional to $t^{1/2}$, a constant potential ("chronoamperometry") is the response (21). Thus the methods are reciprocal in this case. See Chapter 42 for further discussion.

D. INSTRUMENTATION FOR EXCITATION AND MEASUREMENT OF RESPONSE

The feasibility of the use of a given excitation or the measurement of a given response often is determined by the instrumentation required. The development of new electrochemical instrumentation is a prime factor in many of the current advances in this field, particularly in the area of study of very rapid phenomena such as fast electron-transfer processes. The utility of operational amplifiers in providing electrochemical excitations and response measurements has become highly apparent in recent years, and this type of apparatus has become an integral part of the serious electrochemist's laboratory (3a,3b,12a,24a,51Ra,51Rb,52Ra,53R).

1. Instrumentation for Excitation Signals

As pointed out earlier, the excitation signal may take the form of a titrant, current, or potential. Current and potential signals may have various shapes, as shown in Fig. 43.26. In general, any electrical network that will furnish either a given current or a potential excitation may be readily rearranged to furnish the other. Thus, the instrumentation for applying a potential excitation of the desired shape to an electrode also may be used to yield a current excitation of the same shape by inserting a fixed resistor of appropriate size between the signal output and the cell. The adequacy of this procedure in producing a current excitation of precisely the same shape is dependent on the potential response of the cell being negligible in comparison to the voltage drop across this resistor; in general this is not difficult to achieve. The simplest type of excitation to supply is that of a step. Linear ramp and sinusoidal excitations also are commonplace. Differentiation or integration of certain simple functions also may yield useful excitation functions. For example, a linear ramp signal may be generated quite simply by integrating a step function. Often more complex signals may be achieved simply by the addition or multiplication (modulation) of two or more simple forms, i.e., composite excitations.

Titrant excitations in the form of reactive solutions may be delivered manually or automatically. If the titrant is a constant flow of electrons (as in coulometric titrations, this is actually a current excitation), "automatic" delivery is used. In any case, it is desirable that the magnitude of the excitation (rate of flow of solution or electrons) be large from the standpoint of the time required for the titration. The usable magnitude of the excitation may be limited by a number of factors; of primary importance are the response times of the electrochemical system and of the response-measuring apparatus (*vide infra*). In automatic titrations, to overcome a slow response time of the electrochemical system but still use minimum time for the titration, it is desirable that the response-measuring system furnish "anticipation" of the end point. Thus an initially large excitation is supplied and near the end point feedback from the response-measuring system causes the size of the excitation to be reduced.

2. Measurement of Response

The nature of the response-measuring apparatus is obviously dependent on the choice of the particular response function chosen for measurement and the nature of the excitation. Because of the frequent interdependence of all of the various responses resulting from an excitation, it is not always necessary, nor sometimes possible, to measure directly the response of most interest; a different response that has a sensitive and selective relation to the desired one may be measured. The present discussion will be limited to the measurement of selected responses that may be observed through the potential or current of an electrode (thus excluding optical density, weight of a deposit, etc.). The measurement then always will be indirect, the potential or current response of the electrode being related in some fashion to a response in the solution.

Consider first the application of a current excitation to an electrode that yields in the solution the responses: (1) charging of the electrical double layer and the movement of charged particles throughout the solution until the electrode assumes a potential sufficient to cause an electron transfer reaction; (2) depletion of the surface concentration of reactant; (3) eventual depletion of the bulk concentration of reactant, in the order given, and (4) simultaneously with (2) and (3), the concentration of product increases. As pointed out earlier, the relative magnitude of responses (2) and (3) at any given time is dependent on the experimental conditions and the magnitude of the excitation signal. Measurement of responses (1) and (2) is best accomplished by observation of the potential of the electrode to which the excitation was applied. Measurement of response (3) might be carried out in the same manner, but measurement of (3) and (4) also could be accomplished by using a different electrode(s) situated in the bulk solution. The response of the separate electrode(s) to changes in the bulk concentration might be potentiometric with zero current, potentiometric with applied current, amperometric, conductometric, etc. In all but the first technique, the measurement of (3) is actually dependent on the application of an auxiliary excitation to the *separate* electrode(s). Thus an excitation is used in the response-measuring system to detect response (3) resulting from the primary current excitation. Obviously, the effects of the auxiliary excitation on the bulk concentration must be negligible in comparison to those of the primary current excitation.

If the applied current signal has an average value of zero over a relatively short time interval (i.e., it is periodic, such as sinusoidal or square wave), only responses (1) and (2) above are obtained. Thus the response-measuring system in this case would most logically be one that measures the varying potential of the electrode to which the periodic current excitation is applied.

Similar considerations may be applied when a potential excitation is used. The responses in the solution are charging of the electrical double layer and the movement of charge in the solution and, if the potential excitation is of sufficient size, the above responses (2), (3), and (4) then occur. The measurement of these responses may be accomplished by observation of the current flowing at the electrode to which the potential excitation was applied and, as before, responses (3) and (4) might be measured by a separate electrode system.

The primary response to a titrant excitation is a change in bulk concentration of reactant and product. The response-measuring system in this case would be any of the separate electrode systems noted above to measure responses (3) and (4). Again, an excitation used in the response-measuring system must have an effect on the bulk concentration negligible in comparison with the effect of the titrant excitation.

It can be seen that, after the selection of the most desirable response to measure as outlined in Section VI-B, certain criteria must be applied to the response-measuring system:

1. If the response measurement is indirect, the value of the response actually measured must be sensitive and selective toward the value of the desired response.

2. If any of the responses are rapid transients, the response time of the measuring system must be a few orders of magnitude more rapid.

3. The response-measuring system must not disturb the state of the system which it is measuring.

4. In some areas, particularly those in which periodic current or potential excitations are applied, the response-measuring system used may result in the overlooking of valuable information about the system studied. Consider, for example, Fig. 42.9 in Chapter 42. Here, an alternating-potential signal applied across two platinum electrodes in a solution is seen to yield a response current that is a composite of two individual response currents. The first, denoted by i', is in phase with the applied potential excitation, whereas the second, denoted by i'', is 90° out of phase. The response current i' is related to the migration of ions within the solution, and the current i'' to the electrical polarization of the dielectric. If information is desired concerning the number of ions in the solution, i' is the obvious choice of response to be measured, and the response-measuring instrumentation must be selective to this current. In this system, application of a sinusoidal excitation resulted in a sinusoidal response of the same frequency but not necessarily in phase with the excitation signal. This is true for any system

that behaves as a network of resistances and capacitances.   As pointed out previously, in measuring the response of a system involving an electron-transfer reaction, the non-Faradaic response current arising from charging of the electrical double layer contributes to the over-all response and may, for dilute solutions, obscure the desired response.   Hence it is desirable to employ some procedure that gives a selective measure of the response current of the electron-transfer reaction.   Because of the capacitative nature of the electrical double layer, application of a sinusoidal potential excitation will yield a non-Faradaic sinusoidal response current of the *same* frequency. In Chapter 42 it was noted that the relationship between Faradaic current and overpotential, η, was linear for small values of η.   On the other hand, a *nonlinear* relationship is obtained if η is large.   As is well known in electronic circuit theory, application of a sine-wave excitation signal ($\sin \omega t$) to a nonlinear element will give a response composed of sine waves of the same frequency as the impulse ($\sin \omega t$) and of multiple frequencies ($\sin 2\omega t$, $\sin 3\omega t$, . . .), i.e., harmonics.   Thus Faradaic response currents of harmonic frequencies are expected when η is large.   Hence by measurement of one or more of the harmonic response currents rather than the total response current, interference from non-Faradaic response can be circumvented (28).   Similarly, other techniques employed in the electronics trade for measuring non-linearity may be used, i.e., the intermodulation distortion test, in which sine waves of two different frequencies are simultaneously applied as an excitation and the resulting sum and difference frequencies in the response signal are measured (23).

VII. OPERATIONAL CLASSIFICATION OF ELECTROANALYTICAL METHODS

In Table 43.I the various types of electroanalytical methods are listed according to an operational classification based on the discussion given in

TABLE 43.I
Operational Classification of Electroanalytical Methods

Experimental conditions	Excitation	Response measured	Bulk concentration-response relation	Name
A. *Methods using potential excitation*				
Unstirred	Step E	$i = f(t)$	$i_t \propto C$	Chronoamperometry
Unstirred, D.M.E.	Step E	i_{av} or $i = f(t)$	$i_d \propto C$	Polarography

(*continued*)

TABLE 43.I (*continued*)

Experimental conditions	Excitation	Response measured	Bulk concentration-response relation	Name
Unstirred	Linear ramp E	$i = f(E)$	$i_p \propto C$	Chronoamperometry with potential sweep
Unstirred	Triangular E	$i = f(E)$	$i_p \propto C$	Cyclic voltammetry
Unstirred, D.M.E.	Linear ramp E	$i = f(E)$	$i_p \propto C$	Oscilloscopic polarography
Unstirred, D.M.E.	Linear ramp E + sinusoidal E (small amplitude)	i (a.c.) $= f$(ramp E)	$i_p \propto C$	A.C. polarography
Unstirred, D.M.E.	Linear ramp E + square-wave E (small amplitude)	i (square wave) $= f$ ramp E)	$i_p \propto C$	Square-wave polarography
Stirred	Step E	i (steady state)	$i_l \propto C$	Voltammetry[a]
Stirred, large-area electrode	Step E	Weight of deposit	Weight $\propto C$	Electrogravimetry
Stirred, large-area electrode	Step E	$\int i\,dt = q$	$q \propto C$	Coulometry at controlled potential (polarographic coulometry when electrode is D.M.E.)
Stirred, electrode polarization negligible	Sinusoidal E	i (a.c.)	i (a.c.) $\propto C$ (total salt)	Direct conductometry

B. Methods using current excitations

Unstirred	Step i	$E = f(t)$	$\tau^{1/2} \propto C$	Chronopotentiometry
Unstirred, D.M.E.	Step i	$E = f(t)$	Complex	Controlled-current polarography
Stirred	Step i	E (steady state)	$i \propto C$ (in certain range of E)	Voltammetry[a]
Stirred, large-area electrode	Step i	Weight of deposit	Weight $\propto C$	Constant-current electrogravimetry

TABLE 43.I (*continued*)

Experimental conditions	Excitation	Response measured	Bulk concentration-response relation	Name
Unstirred	Step i + sinusoidal i (small amplitude)	E (a.c.) $= f(t)$	$\tau^{1/2} \propto C$	Chronopotentiometry with superimposed alternating current, or a.c. chronopotentiometry
Unstirred, D.M.E.	Sinusoidal i (large amplitude)	E (d.c.) $+ E$ a.c. $= f(t)$	Complex	A.C. oscilloscopic polarography
Stirred	Zero i (special case)	E	$E = k + k' \log C$	Direct potentiometry

			Response-measuring system			
Experimental conditions	Excitation	Response	Experimental conditions[b]	Excitation	Response measured	Name

C. *Methods using titrant excitations*

Stirred	Titrant solution	ΔC	Stirred	Zero i (special case)	$E = f$ (volume)	Potentiometric titration (at zero current)
Stirred	Titrant solution	ΔC	Stirred, one indicating electrode	Step i	$E = f$ (volume)	Controlled-current potentiometric titration (with one polarized electrode)
Stirred	Titrant solution	ΔC	Stirred, two indicating electrodes	Step i	$E = f$ (volume)	Controlled-current bipotentiometric titration (with two polarized electrodes)
Stirred	Titrant solution	ΔC	Stirred, one indicating electrode	Step E	$i = f$ (volume)	Amperometric titration (with one polarized electrode)
Stirred	Titrant solution	ΔC	Stirred, two indicating electrodes	Step E	$i = f$ (volume)	Biamperometric titration (with two polarized electrodes)

(*continued*)

TABLE 43.I (*continued*)

Experimental conditions	Excitation	Response	Response-measuring system			
			Experimental conditions[b]	Excitation	Response measured	Name
Stirred	Titrant solution	ΔC	Stirred, electrode polarization negligible	Sinusoidal E	i (a.c.) $= f$ (volume)	Conductometric titration and high-frequency titration
Stirred	Titrant solution	ΔC	Unstirred, D.M.E.	Step E	$i = f$ (volume)	Amperometric titration (polarographic titration)
Stirred	Titrant solution	ΔC	Unstirred, two D.M.E.'s	Step E	$i = f$ (volume)	Biamperometric titration (bipolarographic titration)
Stirred	Titrant solution	ΔC	Unstirred	Step i	$E = f(t,C)$	Chronopotentiometric titration
Stirred, species to produce titrant ion	Step i_g[c]	ΔC	Stirred	Zero i	$E = f(i_g t)$	Coulometric titration with potentiometric end point
Stirred, species to produce titrant ion	Step i_g	ΔC	Stirred, one indicating electrode	Step i	$E = f(i_g t)$	Coulometric titration with controlled-current potentiometric end point
Stirred, species to produce titrant ion	Step i_g	ΔC	Stirred, two indicating electrodes	Step i	$E = f(i_g t)$	Coulometric titration with controlled-current bipotentiometric end point
Stirred, species to produce titrant ion	Step i_g	ΔC	Stirred, one indicating electrode	Step E	$i = f(i_g t)$	Coulometric titration with amperometric end point
Stirred, species to produce titrant ion	Step i_g	ΔC	Stirred, two indicating electrodes	Step E	$i = f(i_g t)$	Coulometric titration with biamperometric end point

[a] The voltammetric technique is reciprocal for step E and step i and is thus included in both sections A and B.

[b] The experimental conditions of the system are not necessarily the same at the time when the titrant excitation is applied and when the response is measured.

[c] The term i_g refers to the coulometric generating current.

Section VI. A similar table, but one based on a different theoretical classification, has been given by Delahay, Charlot, and Laitinen (5,6).

REFERENCES

1. Barker, G. C., and I. L. Jenkins, *Analyst*, **77**, 685 (1952).
2. Berzins, T., and P. Delahay, *J. Am. Chem. Soc.*, **75**, 555 (1953).
3. Bircumshaw, L. L., and A. C. Riddiford, *Quart. Revs. (London)*, **6**, 157 (1952).
3a. Booman, G. L., *Anal. Chem.*, **29**, 213 (1957).
3b. DeFord, D. D., mimeographed notes, Northwestern Univ., Evanston, Ill.
4. Delahay, P., *J. Am. Chem. Soc.*, **75**, 1190 (1953).
5. Delahay, P., G. Charlot, and H. A. Laitinen, *Anal. Chem.*, **32**, 103A (1960).
6. Delahay, P., G. Charlot, and H. A. Laitinen, *J. Electroanal. Chem.*, **1**, 425 (1960).
7. Eisenman, G., D. O. Rudin, and J. U. Casby, *Science*, **126**, 831 (1957).
8. Foulk, C. W., and A. T. Bawden, *J. Am. Chem. Soc.*, **48**, 2045 (1926).
9. Gaugin, R., G. Charlot, C. Bertin, and J. Badoz, *Anal. Chim. Acta*, **7**, 360 (1952).
10. Herzfeld, K. F., *Physik. Z.*, **14**, 29 (1913).
11. Heyrovský, J., *Anal. Chim. Acta*, **2**, 533 (1948).
12. Ilkovic, D., *Collection Czechoslov. Chem. Communs.*, **6**, 498 (1934).
12a. Kelley, M. T., E. J. Fisher, and H. C. Jones, *Anal. Chem.*, **31**, 1475 (1959); **32**, 1262 (1960).
13. King, C. V., and W. H. Cathcart, *J. Am. Chem. Soc.*, **59**, 63 (1937).
14. Kolthoff, I. M., *Anal. Chim. Acta*, **2**, 606 (1948).
15. Laitinen, H. A., *Anal. Chem.*, **21**, 66 (1949); **24**, 46 (1952).
16. Laitinen, H. A., and W. S. Ferguson, *Anal. Chem.*, **29**, 4 (1957).
17. Laitinen, H. A., and I. M. Kolthoff, *J. Phys. Chem.*, **45**, 1061 (1941).
18. Malmstadt, H. V., and J. D. Winefordner, *Anal. Chim. Acta*, **20**, 283 (1959).
19. Martin, K. J., and J. Shain, *Anal. Chem.*, **30**, 1808 (1958).
20. Mattock, G., "Glass Electrodes Responsive to Sodium Ions," in *Proceedings of the International Symposium on Microchemistry*, Pergamon, London, 1959.
21. Murray, R. W., and C. N. Reilley, *J. Electroanal. Chem.*, **3**, 64 (1962).
22. Page, A., and H. C. H. Townend, *Proc. Roy. Soc. (London)*, **A135**, 656 (1932).
23. Paynter, J., and W. H. Reinmuth, paper presented to 140th National Meeting, American Chemical Society, Chicago, 1961.
24. Randles, J. E. B., *Trans. Faraday Soc.*, **44**, 327 (1948).
24a. Reilley, C. N., *J. Chem. Ed.*, **39**, A853, A933 (1962).
25. Reilley, C. N., W. D. Cooke, and N. H. Furman, *Anal. Chem.*, **23**, 1223, 1226 (1951).
26. Rogers, L. B., and A. H. Stehney, *J. Electrochem. Soc.*, **95**, 25 (1949).
27. Sevcik, A., *Collection Czechoslov. Chem. Communs.*, **13**, 349 (1948).
28. Smith, D. E., and W. H. Reinmuth, *Anal. Chem.*, **33**, 482 (1961).
29. Testa, A. C., and W. H. Reinmuth, *Anal. Chem.*, **32**, 1512 (1960).
30. Van Name, R. G., and F. Fenwick, *J. Am. Chem. Soc.*, **47**, 19 (1925).
31. Willard, H. H., and F. Fenwick, *J. Am. Chem. Soc.*, **44**, 2516 (1922).

GENERAL REFERENCES

A. General Electrochemistry

1R. Allen, M. J., *Organic Electrode Processes*, Reinhold, New York, 1958.
2R. Bockris, J. O'M., *Modern Aspects of Electrochemistry*, 2 vols., Butterworths, London; Academic Press, New York, 1954 and 1959.
3R. Bi-Annual Reviews, *Anal. Chem.*, April issues, even-numbered years.
3Ra. Butler, J. A. V., *Electrical Phenomena at Interfaces*, Methuen, London, 1951.
4R. Charlot, G., "Modern Electroanalytical Methods," in *Proceedings of the International Symposium on Modern Electrochemical Methods of Analysis, Paris, 1957*, Elsevier, New York, 1958.
5R. Charlot, G., and D. Bezier, *Methodes Electrochémiques d'Analyse*, Masson et Cie, Paris, 1954.
6R. Conway, B. E., *Electrochemical Data*, Elsevier, New York–Houston, 1951.
7R. Delahay, P., *New Instrumental Methods in Electrochemistry*, Interscience, New York–London, 1954.
8R. Delahay, P., *Advances in Electrochemistry and Electrochemical Engineering*, Interscience, New York–London, 1961.
9R. Gurney, R. W., *Ionic Processes in Solution*, McGraw-Hill, New York, 1953.
10R. Kortum, G., and J. O'M. Bockris, *Textbook of Electrochemistry*, Elsevier, Houston, 1951.
11R. Latimer, W. M., *Oxidation States of the Elements and Their Potentials in Aqueous Solution*, 2nd ed., Prentice-Hall, Englewood, N. J., 1952.
12R. Lingane, J. J., *Electroanalytical Chemistry*, 2nd ed., Interscience, New York–London, 1958.
13R. MacInnes, D. A., *The Principles of Electrochemistry*, Reinhold, New York, 1939.
14R. Reinmuth, W. H., "Theory of Electrode Processes," in C. N. Reilley, Ed., *Advances in Analytical Chemistry and Instrumentation*, Interscience, New York–London, 1960.
15R. Vetter, K. J., *Elektrochemische kinetik*, Springer-Verlag, Berlin, 1961.
16R. Weissberger, A., Ed., *Technique of Organic Chemistry*, 3rd ed., Vol. I, Interscience, New York–London, 1960.

B. Potentiometric Methods (see also Part A)

17R. Bates, R. G., *Electrometric pH Determinations*, Wiley, New York, 1954.
18R. Clark, W. M., *Determination of Hydrogen Ions*, Williams and Wilkins, Baltimore, 1922.
19R. Clark, W. M., *Oxidation-Reduction Potentials of Organic Systems*, Williams and Wilkins, Baltimore, 1960.
20R. Dole, M., *The Glass Electrode*, Wiley, New York, 1941.
21R. Fritz, J. S., *Acid-Base Titrations in Nonaqueous Solvents*, G. F. Smith Chemical Company, Columbus, Ohio, 1952.
22R. Kolthoff, I. M., and N. H. Furman, *Potentiometric Titrations*, 2nd ed., Wiley, New York, 1932.
23R. Kolthoff, I. M., and H. A. Laitinen, *pH and Electro-titrations*, Wiley, New York, 1941.

C. Conductometric Methods (see also Part A)

24R. Britton, H. T. S., *Conductometric Analysis*, Van Nostrand, Princeton, N. J., 1934.
25R. Britton, H. T. S., "Conductometric Analysis," in W. G. Berl, Ed., *Physical Methods in Chemical Analysis*, Academic Press, New York, 1951, pp. 51–104.
26R. Fuoss, R. M., and F. Accascina, *Electrolytic Conductance*, Interscience, New York–London, 1959.
27R. Reilley, C. N., "High-Frequency Methods," in P. Delahay, Ed., *New Instrumental Methods in Electrochemistry*, Interscience, New York–London, 1954.
28R. Robinson, R. A., and R. H. Stokes, *Electrolyte Solutions*, Academic Press, New York, 1955.
29R. Shedlovsky, T., "Conductometry," in A. Weissberger, Ed., *Technique of Organic Chemistry*, 3rd ed., Vol. I, Interscience, New York–London, 1960.

D. Electrolysis Methods (see also Part A)

30R. Cooke, W. D., "Coulometric Methods," in J. Mitchell, Jr., Ed., *Organic Analysis*, Vol. II, Interscience, New York–London, 1954.
31R. Diehl, H., *Electrochemical Analysis with Graded Cathode-Potential Control*, G. F. Smith Chemical Company, Columbus, Ohio, 1948.
32R. Dole, M., *Experimental and Theoretical Electrochemistry*, McGraw-Hill, New York, 1935.
33R. Gatos, H. C., J. W. Faust, Jr., and W. J. LaFleur, Eds., *Surface Chemistry of Metals and Semiconductors*, Wiley, New York, 1960.
34R. Glasstone, S., *Introduction to Electrochemistry*, Van Nostrand, Princeton, N. J., 1944.
35R. Haissinsky, M., *Electrochimie des Substances Radioactives et des Solution Extrémement Dilueés*, Hermann, Paris, 1946.
36R. Meites, L., "Electrolytic and Coulometric Methods," in A. Weissberger, Ed., *Technique of Organic Chemistry*, 3rd ed., Vol. I, Interscience, New York–London, 1960.
37R. Sand, H. J. S., *Electrochemistry and Electrochemical Analysis*, Vol. II, Blackie and Son, Ltd., Glasgow, 1940.
38R. Yeager, E., "Electrode Processes," in *Transactions of the Symposium on Electrode Processes, Philadelphia, 1959*, Wiley, New York, 1961.

E. Voltammetric Methods (including Polarography; see also Part A)

39R. *Bibliography of Polarographic Literature: 1922–1955*, E. H. Sargent and Company, Chicago, 1956.
40R. Brezina, M., and P. Zuman, *Polarography in Medicine, Biochemistry, and Pharmacy*, Interscience, New York–London, 1958.
41R. Elving, P. J., "Application of Polarography to Organic Analysis," in J. Mitchell, Jr., Ed., *Organic Analysis*, Vol. II, Interscience, New York–London, 1954.
42R. Heyrovský, J., *Polarographie*, Springer-Verlag, Berlin, 1941.
43R. Heyrovský, J., and R. Kalvoda, *Oszillographische Polarographie mit Wechselstrom*, Akademie-Verlag, Berlin, 1960.
44R. Kolthoff, I. M., and J. J. Lingane, *Polarography*, 2nd ed., Interscience, New York–London, 1952.
45R. Meites, L., *Polarographic Techniques*, Interscience, New York–London, 1955.

46R. Milner, G. W. C., *The Principles and Applications of Polarography and Other Elec-troanalytical Processes*, Longmans, Green, New York, 1957.
47R. Müller, O. H., "Polarography," in A. Weissberger, Ed., *Techniques of Organic Chemistry*, 3rd ed., Vol. I, Interscience, New York–London, 1960.
48R. Müller, O. H., *Polarographic Methods of Analysis*, 2nd ed., Journal of Chemical Education, Easton, Pa., 1951.
49R. Schwabe, K., *Polarographie Und Chemische Konstitution Organischer Verbindungen*, Akademie-Verlag, Berlin, 1957.
50R. Von Stackelberg, M., *Polarographische Arbeitsmethoden*, de Gruyter, Berlin, 1950.
51R. Zuman, P., Ed., *Advances in Polarography*, 2 Vols., Interscience, New York–London, in preparation.

F. Instrumentation

51Ra. Bair, E. J., *Introduction to Chemical Instrumentation*, McGraw-Hill, New York, 1962.
51Rb. DeFord, D. D., "Analytical Instrumentation Using Operational Amplifiers," in C. N. Reilley, Ed., *Advances in Analytical Chemistry and Instrumentation*, Interscience, New York, in preparation.
52R. Landee, R. W., D. C. Davis, and A. P. Albrecht, *Electronic Designers' Handbook*, McGraw-Hill, New York, 1957.
52Ra. Malmstadt, H. V., C. G. Enke, and E. C. Toren, Jr., *Electronics for Scientists*, W. A. Benjamin, New York, 1962.
53R. Philbrick, G. A., *Application Manual for Octal Plug-In Computing Amplifiers*, and other literature on analog computors, Researches, Inc., Boston, Mass.
54R. Phillips, J. P., *Automatic Titrators*, Academic Press, New York, 1959.
55R. Strobel, H. A., *Chemical Instrumentation*, Addison-Wesley, Reading, Mass., 1960.

G. Mathematical Treatment of Diffusion

56R. Carslaw, H. S., and J. C. Jaeger, *Conduction of Heat in Solids*, Oxford University Press, London, 1947.
57R. Churchill, R. V., *Modern Operational Mathematics in Engineering*, McGraw-Hill, New York, 1944.
58R. Crank, J., *The Mathematics of Diffusion*, Oxford University Press, London, 1956.
59R. Day, W. D., *Introduction to Laplace Transforms for Radio and Electronic Engineers*, Interscience, New York–London, 1960.
60R. Doetsch, G., *Theorie und Anwendung der Laplace-Transformation*, Dover Publications, New York, 1943.
61R. Doetsch, G., *Tabellen zur Laplace-Transformation*, Springer-Verlag, Berlin, 1947.
62R. Jaeger, J. C., *An Introduction to the Laplace Transformation*, Wiley, New York, 1947.
63R. Sneddon, I. N., *Fourier Transforms*, McGraw-Hill, New York, 1951.

Chapter 44

CHRONOAMPEROMETRY AND CHRONOPOTENTIOMETRY

By Paul Delahay, *Louisiana State University, Baton Rouge, Louisiana*

Contents

I. INTRODUCTION

A. CONTROL OF POTENTIAL *vs.* CONTROL OF CURRENT

Electroanalytical methods based on current–potential–time characteristics of electrode processes can be divided into two groups according to whether an electrode potential or the cell current is controlled. This chapter is limited to methods in which *stationary* electrodes are immersed in an unstirred solution, i.e., reactants and soluble electrolysis products are transported to and from the electrode by diffusion. Convection and migration are negligible. The electrode area remains constant during electrolysis.

Measurements depend on the electrical quantity being controlled. Thus, current–time variations are determined at controlled potential (*chronoamperometry*); potential–time variations are determined at controlled current (*chronopotentiometry*). (For a classification and nomenclature of electroanalytical methods, see Reference 25.) Only methods at constant potential or constant current will be discussed, with the exception of one method at variable current. Fundamental ideas will be emphasized rather than details of theory, but experimental methods and applications to analytical chemistry will be covered at some length.

Interpretation is simplified when the electrode being studied (*working electrode*) is coupled with an electrode of known behavior. The latter is generally an *unpolarized electrode*, e.g., an electrode whose potential is practically independent of current density over the current range in which it is used. (Any electrode becomes quite polarized at sufficiently high current densities.) Since the potential of the unpolarized electrode is constant and known during electrolysis, the potential of the working electrode is readily computed from the cell voltage, allowance being made for the ohmic drop in the cell and cell circuit if necessary.

The apparatus is very simple in principle. In chronoamperometry, the cell is connected to a power supply of adjustable output voltage; a recorder or an oscilloscope and a switch are inserted in the cell circuit. In chronopotentiometry, the cell is connected to a current power supply, and a voltmeter, a recorder, or an oscilloscope is connected across the cell.

B. HISTORICAL

Electrolysis had been studied for many years before Nernst, in 1889, introduced the concept of the electrode potential. Early investigations were carried out at controlled current, since this was thought to be the electrical quantity of significance. Weber in 1879 and, especially, Sand (98) in 1901 applied electrolysis at constant current to the determination of diffusion coefficients. The cell voltage was not recorded but the "end" of electrolysis was determined by the formation of hydrogen bubbles on the working electrode. In 1906 Karaoglanoff (62) derived equations for processes obeying the Nernst equation. These early investigations were soon forgotten, and it was only in 1951 that Gierst and Juliard (49) showed the potentialities of chronopotentiometry as an analytical tool. Application to electrode kinetics soon followed: this has remained to this day the most important use of the method.

Chronoamperometry was discovered (see Brdicka's account (11)) as polarography by Heyrovský (1922), and it is in connection with the polarographic method that the fundamentals of chronoamperometry were established. Ilkovic (59) in 1934 derived current–time characteristics for the plane and the dropping mercury electrode. Circumstances surrounding Ilkovic's work have been recounted by Heyrovský (52). Current–potential–time characteristics were derived the next year (53) for processes obeying the Nernst equation and, about 1950, for processes not obeying this equation. No significant analytical application of chronoamperometry has been reported thus far (although some will be indicated), but discussion of this method is essential for the understanding of some of the fundamental ideas of electroanalytical chemistry. Less emphasis will be placed in this chapter on chronoamperometry than on chronopotentiometry because of the close relationship between the former method and polarography.

Since about 1945 there has been a greatly increased activity in electro-analytical chemistry and in electrode kinetics in general: better understanding of fundamentals, development of new methods, application of new techniques, etc. The first systematic discussion of these ideas appeared in 1954 (19).

II. FUNDAMENTALS OF CHRONOAMPEROMETRY

A. CURRENT–POTENTIAL–TIME CHARACTERISTICS FOR REVERSIBLE PROCESSES—DIFFUSION CURRENT

We shall consider a chronoamperometric electrolysis at constant potential in unstirred solution for conditions in which diffusion is the sole mode of mass transfer. Current–time variations are followed during electrolysis at different potentials. Our fundamental problem is to account for these variations.

Two different cases are encountered: (1) the electrode reaction is so rapid in comparison with the diffusion process that electrochemical equilibrium is achieved at the electrode and the Nernst equation can be applied (*reversible* electrode processes); and (2) the kinetics of the electrode reaction must be considered, and the electrode process is said to be *irreversible*. The first case is considered here. The second case and the reversibility of electrode processes are examined in Section II-B.

We consider the electrode reaction, $O + ne = R$, involving the soluble substances O and R. Substance R is soluble either in solution or in the electrode (amalgam). The current–potential–time characteristic for this reaction will be established on the assumption that each diffusing particle is a point, there being no interaction between particles in solution. The concentrations of substances O and R are obtained by solution of Fick's equation for diffusion. It will be assumed here that the form of this equation for linear diffusion holds.

In this calculation we must know the concentrations of O and R before electrolysis as functions of the distance from the electrode, and we must prescribe some correlation between these concentrations at the electrode surface during electrolysis. In other words, we must know conditions before electrolysis and we must characterize the electrolysis in some fashion. We shall assume that the solution has a uniform composition before electrolysis, i.e., that there is no gradient of concentration before electrolysis. Conditions during electrolysis are characterized as follows.

The Nernst equation is supposed to be valid, and consequently the ratio of the concentrations of O and R *at the electrode surface* at a given potential is constant. Furthermore, there is conservation of mass at the electrode surface during electrolysis, and the sum of the fluxes of substances O and R at the electrode surface is equal to zero.

The solution of Fick's equation is not needed for our purpose (see Reference 19 for details), but the above-mentioned conditions for which the solution is derived are important. The essential points can be made from Fig. 44.1, which was constructed for the following data: $n = 2$; the bulk concentration of substance O is $C = 10^{-6}$ mole cm.$^{-3}$; no substance R is initially present; the diffusion coefficient of substance O is $D_O = 10^{-5}$ cm.$^{-2}$ seconds^{-1} and $D_R = 2 \times 10^{-5}$ cm.^{2} seconds^{-1}; the potential E is equal to the half-wave potential defined by equation (4) below; and the activity coefficients of O and R are equal to unity. Note that, during electrolysis, (*1*) there is progressive depletion of O and enrichment of R near the electrode, and (*2*) the concentrations of O and R at the electrode surface remain constant. The condition stated by the Nernst equation, that the ratio of these concentrations is constant, is thus fulfilled. The curves of Fig. 44.1 have as asymptotes the abscissa axis and the horizontal line C.

Mathematically, depletion and enrichment extend to infinity, but it is convenient to characterize concentration profiles by their *diffusion layer thickness*, δ. The concentration profile is replaced by the tangent to the C vs. x curve at $x = 0$ (Fig. 44.1). It is assumed in this *simplified* model that C remains constant for $x > \delta$. The idea of the diffusion layer was introduced by Nernst to interpret processes with convection. For further details see, for instance, Reference 19.

We now return to our basic problem, namely the derivation of the cur-

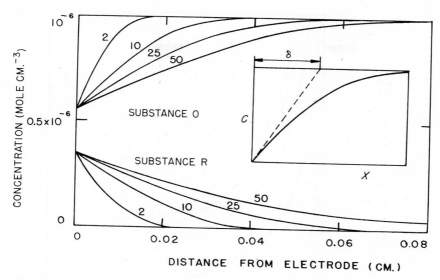

Fig. 44.1. Variations of concentrations of substances O and R with the distance from the electrode for different times (in seconds) in electrolysis at constant potential in unstirred solution. See data in text. The diagram in the box pertains to the definition of the diffusion-layer thickness.

rent–potential–time characteristic. It was necessary to consider first the variations of concentrations to obtain some idea of the phenomena occurring at the electrode. Once the concentrations are known, the current is readily deduced from the flux of substance O at the electrode. Thus, the current i at potential E when no substance R is initially present in solution is (see, for instance, Reference 19):

$$i = i_d \frac{1}{1 + (D_R/D_O)^{1/2} (f_O/f_R) \exp [(nF/RT)(E - E^\circ)]} \qquad (1)$$

with

$$i_d = [(nFAD_O^{1/2})/(\pi^{1/2}t^{1/2})]C \qquad (2)$$

The notations and units in equations (1) and (2) not previously defined are as follows: i and i_d are in units of amperes; R is the gas constant; T is the absolute temperature; F is the faraday (96,494 coulombs); A is the electrode area in cm.²; the f's are the activity coefficients; C is the bulk concentration of O in units of mole cm.$^{-3}$; E is the potential of the working electrode in volts; E° is the standard potential for the reaction $O + ne = R$; and t is the time elapsed since the beginning of electrolysis in seconds

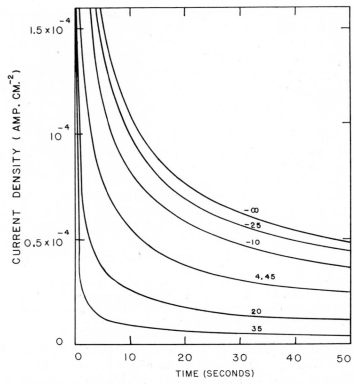

Fig. 44.2. Variations of current density with time for a reversible electrode process and different potentials. Same data as in Fig. 44.1. The numbers on the curves are the values of $E - E^\circ$ in millivolts. The curve for 4.45 mv. corresponds to the half-wave potential of equation (4).

Note that i and i_d are total currents and that the current density for an electrode having an area different from unity is simply the ratio of the total current to the electrode area, i/A.

Variations of i/A with t for different values of $E - E^\circ$ are shown in Fig. 44.2 for the same data as in Fig. 44.1. When the potential is made increasingly cathodic, i.e., E becomes more negative in the European convention, the current approaches at any time the value i_d/A. Since the ratio C_O/C_R of concentrations at the electrode surface approaches zero as E approaches $-\infty$ (Nernst equation), molecules or ions of substance O are reduced as soon as they reach the electrode. The electrode process is entirely controlled by the rate of diffusion of substance O toward the electrode, and i_d/A is therefore called the *diffusion current density*.

Some of the factors in equation (2) can be understood from simple considerations. Thus, the proportionality between i_d and C, which is at the basis of possible analytical applications, can be expected from intuition: if the bulk concentration substance O is doubled, the rate at which O is supplied at the electrode is also doubled. The product nF results from the following relationship: the current is equal to the product of the electrode reaction rate, in mole seconds^{-1}, and the charge involved in this reaction for one mole of substance, e.g., nF coulombs, according to the Faraday law. The factors $D_O^{1/2}$ and $1/\pi^{1/2}t^{1/2}$ cannot be understood without mathematical analysis. Only a decrease of current during electrolysis can be explained qualitatively as a result of the progressive depletion of reactant at the electrode as the electrolysis proceeds (Fig. 44.1).

The current-potential characteristics can now be constructed from values of i/i_d at different potentials but always for the same time. The corresponding equation is derived by rearrangement of terms in equation (1), and the familiar equation for reversible polarographic characteristics is obtained (53):

$$E = E_{1/2} + \frac{RT}{nF} \ln\left[\frac{i_d}{i} - 1\right]$$

(3)

with the half-wave potential $E_{1/2}$ being given by

$$E_{1/2} = E^\circ + \frac{RT}{nF} \ln\frac{f_O}{f_R}\left[\frac{D_R}{D_O}\right]^{1/2}$$

(4)

The variable time t does not appear in equation (3) because i_d/i is independent of t but, of course, i and i_d do depend on t (see equations (1) and (2)). Implications of equations (3) and (4) need not be discussed here since they are known to anyone familiar with polarography.

Extension of the foregoing treatment to other cases in which the Nernst equation is applicable is immediate: deposition of an insoluble species, electrode reaction involving hydrogen ions in a well-buffered solution, reduction of metallic complex ions, etc. The reasoning is always the same. Extension to the case in which both substances O and R are present before electrolysis is also straightforward.

Nonplanar electrodes lend themselves to the same type of analysis. Spherical and cylindrical electrodes have been treated (19). Equation (2) holds for these electrodes when the electrolysis is so short that the diffusion-layer thickness is very small in comparison with the radius of curvature r of the electrode, i.e., when the condition $Dt/r^2 \ll 1$ is satisfied. For instance, for $D = 10^{-5}$ cm.^{2} seconds^{-1} and $r = 2 \times 10^{-2}$ cm., one should have $t < 1$ second to allow application of equation (2) to spherical and cylindrical electrodes.

B. CURRENT-POTENTIAL-TIME CHARACTERISTICS FOR IRREVERSIBLE PROCESSES

Numerous electrode processes involving organic substances are not reversible at the current densities generally prevailing in chronoamperometry and polarography. Electrochemical equilibrium is not achieved, i.e., the Nernst equation cannot be applied to correlate the electrode potential with the concentrations of reactants. The kinetics of the electrode reaction must be considered. The introduction of such kinetic considerations by several investigators around 1950 is one of the significant steps in the theoretical development of chronoamperometry and polarography. See, e.g., Reference 19 for details.

The current–potential–time characteristic is obtained by consideration of the electrode process as a heterogeneous reaction with two steps in series: the electrode reaction proper and diffusion of the reactant and the product of electrolysis. Only the kinetics of first-order processes will be considered here to simplify matters, but more complicated reactions are not infrequent, particularly with organic substances (consecutive steps or side chemical reactions).

If the species involved in the reaction $O + ne = R$ are soluble, one can reasonably assume that the net rate is of the form $k_f C_O - k_b C_R$, where the C's are the concentrations at the electrode surface and the k's are rate constants for the forward and backward electrode reactions in units of cm. seconds^{-1}. The rate is written in such a form that a net reduction rate is positive. The rate constants are functions of potential, but the dependence of k_f and k_b on E is not needed at this stage. Since the potential is constant during electrolysis and there is a large excess of supporting electrolyte, it suffices to know that k_f and k_b have given values at a constant potential and that the k's are not affected during electrolysis by variations of C_O and C_R.

We shall first consider the case in which the backward reaction can be neglected. Because of conservation of mass, the rate of the forward reaction, $k_f C_O$, is equal to the flux of substance O at the electrode. The solution of Fick's equation for a thick solution (extending to infinity in principle) having initially a uniform composition (no gradient of concentration) is, for a plane electrode,

$$i/i_d = \pi^{1/2} \lambda \exp (\lambda^2) \operatorname{erfc} (\lambda) \tag{5}$$

with

$$\lambda = k_f t^{1/2} / D_O^{1/2} \tag{6}$$

The error function complement is defined by

$$\text{erfc}(\lambda) = 1 - (2/\pi^{1/2}) \int_0^\lambda e^{-z^2} dz \qquad (7)$$

The relationship between the current and the rate constant k_f is fully determined by equation (5). A plot of i/i_d against λ (see such a diagram in Reference 19) shows that i/i_d increases with λ, i.e., with k_f for a given

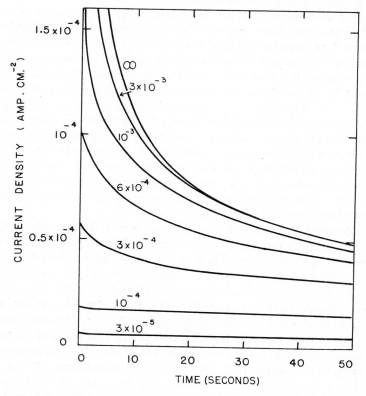

Fig. 44.3. Variations of current density with time for an irreversible electrode process and different rate constants (in cm. second^{-1}). Same data as in Fig. 44.1.

time t. One has $i/i_d = 0$ for $\lambda = 0$, and the current density is equal to zero since the electrode reaction is infinitely slow. Conversely $(i/i_d) \to 1$ for $\lambda \to \infty$, and the current tends to be solely diffusion controlled when the rate constant is sufficiently large. The effect of k_f on the current density–time curves is shown in Fig. 44.3. The $i - t$ curve for $k_f > 3 \times 10^{-3}$ cm. seconds^{-1} tends to coincide with the $i_d - t$ curve at least for $t > 20$ seconds, and the process is then diffusion controlled for all practical purposes. Conversely, $i \ll i_d$ for $k_f < 3 \times 10^{-5}$ cm. seconds^{-1}. The *approximate* limits $10^{-5} < k_f < 10^{-2}$ cm. seconds^{-1} represent the range of rate constants that can be determined by polarography. Somewhat higher values of k_f (<1 cm. seconds^{-1}) can be determined by chronoamperometry from current–time curves recorded for shorter times ($t > 10^{-4}$ seconds) than in polarography (see equation (6)).

The current–time curves for reversible (Fig. 44.2) and irreversible (Fig. 44.3) processes have the same general shape, but they differ in one major aspect, namely the value of the current at time $t = 0$. The calculated current for a reversible process is infinite for $t = 0$ (see equations (1) and (2)), whereas the current for an irreversible process is finite at $t = 0$. This result is consistent with the hypotheses that were made in the derivation. Thus, we assume in the foregoing for reversible processes that diffusion is the sole rate-determining factor. In the time $t = 0$ to $t = \Delta t$ the concentration C_0 at the electrode surface must vary from C to another value prescribed by the Nernst equation. This change in concentration corresponds to an infinite current as Δt approaches zero. Conversely, the current density at time $t = 0$ for irreversible processes is simply nFk_fC, where C is the bulk concentration of substance O. The concentration C is used here since there is no depletion of O at $t = 0$.

Current-potential characteristics can be obtained from plots of i/i_d against potential for any given time. The resulting curves have the same shape as reversible polarographic waves but are flatter along the axis of potential. The shape of irreversible current-potential curves depends on the relationship between the rate constant k_f and the electrode potential. The rate constant k_f at any potential along the ascending segment of the current-potential curve can be computed from the experimental value of i/i_d at a given time (see equations (5) and (6)). The value of D_0 needed in the calculation of k_f from λ is computed from the diffusion current density by application of equation (2). The same method can be applied to irreversible polarographic waves (19,66), but the correlation between i/i_d and λ is not given by equation (5).

As a *first approximation* one has $k_f = k_f^\circ \exp(-\beta FE/RT)$, where k_f° is the value of k_f at $E = 0$ (*vs.* N.H.E., for instance) and β is a factor depending on the electrode reaction and the electrolysis conditions. The rate constant k_f also can be expressed in terms of the exchange-current density and the overvoltage, but this approach is not needed here. The foregoing expression for k_f is only approximate because *the structure of the double layer must be considered*. Details can be found in reviews (12,36,88). Over a narrow interval of potential (perhaps 0.1 v.), k_f is represented with a fair approximation by a simple exponential function of potential. Consideration of the structure of the double layer, however, is essential in the interpretation of the salt effect on current-potential characteristics for irreversible processes.

It was pointed out in the foregoing that current-potential curves for irreversible processes have the same general shape as reversible polarographic waves. In fact, current-potential curves for irreversible processes can be represented *approximately* by equation (3), in which the factor β is substituted for n (66). The half-wave potential $E^{1/2}$ for irreversible current-potential curves, however, is *not* given by equation (4), since kinetic considerations were not introduced in the derivation of this equation. The potential $E^{1/2}$ for an irreversible process depends on t, whereas $E_{1/2}$ for a reversible process does not (see equation (4)). Thus, by definition $i/i_d = 0.5$ at $E_{1/2}$ and, according to equation (5), this condition determines λ at $E_{1/2}$. Since $\lambda = k_f t^{1/2}/D_O^{1/2}$, $k_f t^{1/2}$ must be constant at $E_{1/2}$, and consequently k_f is inversely proportional to $t^{1/2}$. The potential $E_{1/2}$ varies accordingly with $\ln t^{1/2}$, since k_f is an exponential function of E.

Extension of the foregoing analysis by consideration of the forward and backward reactions is quite simple. It can be shown that reversible behavior is approached more and more closely as the rate constants k_f and k_b, at a given potential, increase. Such a *criterion of reversibility* can be expressed quantitatively (19). It can be stated qualitatively that reversible behavior is observed for inherently fast electrode reactions with high exchange current densities and irreversible behavior for slow electrode reactions. A reversible process is thus so fast that the potential can be correlated with the concentrations of reactants solely by thermodynamics. Conversely, nothing can be learned about the kinetics of the electrode reaction from reversible current-potential curves. *Relaxation methods* are then applied, in which the response of an electrode is studied after a sudden or periodic perturbation from equilibrium. (See Reference 23 for a review.) For a detailed review and further discussion of irreversible polarographic processes, see References 19 and 21. A sample discussion is also available (22).

C. ELECTRODE REACTIONS WITH COUPLED CHEMICAL REACTIONS

In some electrode processes the electrochemical reaction proper, i.e., the charge-transfer process, is preceded by a purely chemical reaction. Three steps in series can now be distinguished: diffusion, chemical reaction, and charge transfer. If the charge transfer is sufficiently rapid, the resulting *limiting current* depends on the rates of diffusion and of the chemical reaction. Such *kinetic currents* are of interest from a physicochemical point of view, but they are not observed for most substances in electroanalytical studies. The opposite case also is encountered infrequently, in which the substance consumed in the charge-transfer process is regenerated in part by a purely chemical reaction. A *catalytic current* is thus observed.

For a systematic and detailed discussion of kinetic and catalytic currents see Reference 19, for instance. The paper by Koutecky and Koryta (66) gives a comprehensive view of the corresponding studies in polarography as of 1960.

D. CHARGING OF THE DOUBLE LAYER

The cell current is the algebraic sum of two components, the *faradaic current* for the electrode reaction and the *nonfaradaic current* (capacity current) for the charging or discharging of the double layer. The capacity current in chronoamperometry results from the change of potential at the beginning of electrolysis. In presence of a large excess of supporting electrolyte, the capacity current i_{cap} is essentially independent of the bulk concentration C of reducible or oxidizable species (except for certain adsorbed organic substances). Conversely, the diffusion current is proportional to C, and the existence of a capacity current possibly limits the application of chronoamperometry to low concentrations, since measurements of i_d are meaningful only when i_d is not small in comparison with i_{cap}.

III. FUNDAMENTALS OF CHRONOPOTENTIOMETRY

A. CURRENT-POTENTIAL-TIME CHARACTERISTICS FOR REVERSIBLE PROCESSES—TRANSITION TIME

The working electrode in chronopotentiometry generally operates at a constant current density in unstirred solution, diffusion being the sole mode of mass transfer. The potential of the working electrode is recorded and a potential–time curve is thus obtained. Reactions of the type O + ne = R, in which O and R are soluble, will be considered first. Substance O is reduced at a constant rate and R is produced at a constant rate. Consequently, the flux of these substances at the electrode surface is constant. Furthermore, the sum of these two fluxes must be equal to zero because of conservation of mass. Fick's equation can be solved for such conditions, and the concentrations of O and R are obtained as functions of time and the distance from the electrode. Typical concentration profiles are shown in Fig. 44.4 for the following data: $i/A = 7.64 \times 10^{-5}$ amp. cm.$^{-2}$, $n = 2$, $D_O = 10^{-5}$ cm.^{2} seconds^{-1}, $D_R = 2 \times 10^{-5}$ cm.^{2} seconds^{-1}, and $C = 10^{-6}$

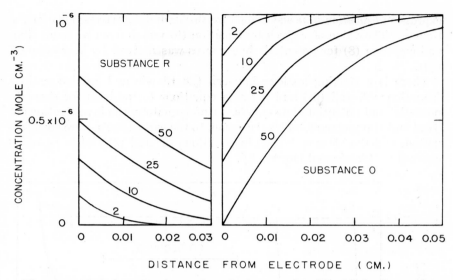

Fig. 44.4. Variations of concentrations of substances O and R with the distance from the electrode for different times (in seconds) in electrolysis at constant current in unstirred solution. See data in text.

mole cm.$^{-3}$ for O; no R is initially present. [Compare this diagram with Fig. 44.1 for chronoamperometry.]

Because of variations of the concentrations at the electrode surface, the potential changes continuously during electrolysis. The potential–time characteristic for a reversible process is obtained by introduction of C_O and C_R at the electrode surface into the Nernst equation. For a plane electrode in a thick layer of solution (extending to infinity mathematically), one has

$$E = E_{1/2} + (RT/nF) \ln [(\tau^{1/2}/t^{1/2}) - 1] \tag{8}$$

$$\tau^{1/2} = \frac{\pi^{1/2} nFA C^0 D_O^{1/2}}{2i} \tag{9}$$

$E_{1/2}$ being defined by equation (4).

It follows from equation (8) that $E \to -\infty$ for a reduction process when $t = \tau$. The concentration C_O at the electrode surface drops to zero at $t = \tau$ (see Fig. 44.4), and the reduction of substance O no longer suffices to maintain the constant-current density i/A. The potential varies rapidly as t approaches τ, and another electrode reaction—for instance the reduction of the supporting electrolyte—contributes to the current. The expression *transition time* was coined by Butler and Armstrong (14) for the time τ. The value of τ given by equation (9) was derived by Sand (98), and equation (8) for potential–time curves was derived by Karaoglanoff (62).

There is a striking analogy between the Ilkovic and Sand equations (equations (2) and (9)) and between equations (3) and (8) for current–potential and potential–time curves. Unfortunately, the investigations of Sand and Karaoglanoff, which date back to the early 1900's, were soon forgotten, and the ideas embodied in equations (2) and (3) had to be rediscovered by Ilkovic and Heyrovský.

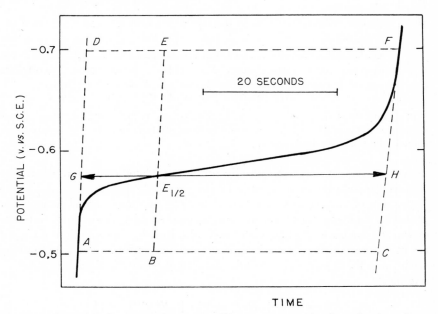

Fig. 44.5. Potential–time curve for a reversible process, namely the reduction of 4 × $10^{-3}M$ cadmium(II) in $1M$ potassium nitrate on a mercury pool.

The properties of potential–time curves can be deduced readily from equations (8) and (9) as follows.

1. The square root of the transition time is proportional to the bulk concentration C and inversely proportional to the current density.

2. The factor $i\tau^{1/2}/A$ is independent of current density (for a plane electrode).

3. A plot of $t^{1/2}$ against E is similar to a reversible current–potential curve in chronoamperometry. Either E is plotted against t (not $t^{1/2}$), which is perhaps the most logical way of presenting these data, or t is plotted against E to obtain diagrams similar to those of chronoamperometry and polarography.

4. The potential $E_{1/2}$ corresponds to the time $t = \tau/4$ (Fig. 44.5), whereas $E_{1/2}$ corresponds to $i = i_a/2$ in chronoamperometry.

5. A plot of $\ln [(\tau/t)^{1/2} - 1]$ against E yields a straight line whose reciprocal slope is RT/nF, just as for a plot of $\ln [(i_a/i) - 1]$ against E in chronoamperometry.

These different properties are verified experimentally for aqueous solutions (27,49,92) and molten salts (70,71,112). For details see Reference 19 and, for a review without mathematical emphasis, see Reference 26.

The foregoing treatment can be transposed to spherical and cylindrical electrodes (13,65,74,77,89). The condition for the use of equation (9) for nonplane electrodes, discussed at the end of Section II-A, also is applicable to transition times. Transposition of the above treatment to reversible processes with formation of an insoluble species is immediate (28).

B. CURRENT-POTENTIAL-TIME CHARACTERISTICS FOR IRREVERSIBLE PROCESSES

The equation for the transition time, just as for the diffusion current, is the same for reversible and irreversible processes. The potential–time characteristic, however, depends on the kinetics of the electrode reaction, as we shall now see. Discussion will be limited to processes for which the backward reaction can be neglected at the current densities being considered. [See Reference 94 for the more general case.]

The potential–time characteristic is obtained as follows: (*1*) the rate $k_f C_O$ is equated to i/nFA; (*2*) the explicit form of C_O at the electrode surface as a function of time is introduced; and (*3*) the rate constant k_f is written as a function of E. There results (24)

$$E = E_i + \frac{RT}{nF} \ln \left[1 - \left(\frac{t}{\tau}\right)^{1/2} \right] \tag{10}$$

with

$$E_i = (RT/\beta F) \ln (nFAC \, k_f^\circ/i) \tag{11}$$

where β and k_f° have the values assigned to them in Section II-B.

It follows from equation (10) that $E = E_i$ at $t = 0$ (Fig. 44.6), and that a plot of $\ln [1 - (t/\tau)^{1/2}]$ against E yields a straight line having the reciprocal slope $RT/\beta F$. These conclusions are verified experimentally (19,26,27). The potential $E_{1/2}$ at $t = \tau/4$ has no particular significance in this case.

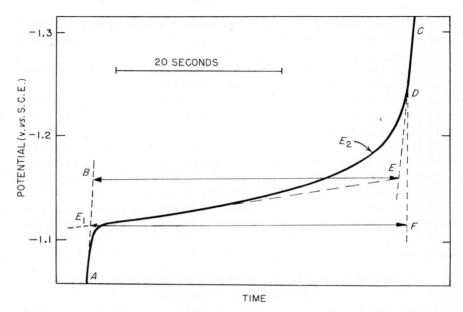

Fig. 44.6. Potential–time curve for an irreversible process, namely the reduction of $4 \times 10^{-3}M$ potassium iodate in $1M$ sodium hydroxide on a mercury pool.

C. CONSECUTIVE AND STEPWISE ELECTRODE PROCESSES

Consecutive and stepwise electrode processes were not discussed under chronoamperometry because diffusion currents are simply additive, except in the very rare instance in which a chemical reaction occurs between species involved in two different electrode reactions. Interpretation is more complex in chronopotentiometry. Consider, for instance, the reduction of two substances O_1 and O_2, which are such that O_1 is reduced at less cathodic (negative) potentials than O_2. The potential–time curve exhibits two distinct steps characterized by the transition times τ_1 and τ_2. The Sand equation (equation (9)) is obeyed for τ_1 but not for τ_2. Thus, after the time τ_1, substance O_1 continues to diffuse to the electrode where it is reduced, and there is simultaneous reduction of O_1 and O_2. The contribution of O_1 decreases because of progressive depletion of O_1 near the electrode (Fig. 44.7), and the fraction of the cell current corresponding to the reduction of O_2 increases continuously. It was shown by Berzins and Delahay (8) that

$$(\tau_1 + \tau_2)^{1/2} - \tau_1^{1/2} = \frac{\pi^{1/2} n_2 F A D_2^{1/2} C_2'}{2i} \qquad (12)$$

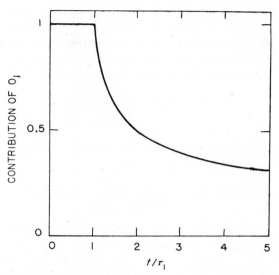

Fig. 44.7. Contribution of the reduction of O_1 to the total current in the reduction of two substances, O_1 and O_2. Substance O_1 is reduced at less-cathodic potentials than O_2.

where the subscript 2 refers to substance O_2. Note that equation (12) is of the same form as the Sand equation (equation (9)), except that $(\tau_1 + \tau_2)^{1/2} - \tau_1^{1/2}$ is substituted for the square root of the transition time. For $n_1 = n_2$, $C_1 = C_2$, and $D_1 = D_2$, one has $\tau_2 = 3\tau_1$, and the contribution of O_1 during the second step triples the second transition time that would be observed if only O_2 were present. This "exaltation" effect can be applied in analytical determinations, but its usefulness seems quite limited. The validity of equation (12) is verified by experiment for aqueous solutions (8) and for molten salts (70,71).

It was suggested by Reilley and his co-workers (92) and shown mathematically by Kambara and Tachi (61) that equation (12) can be generalized for the case of more than two substances. The sum $(\tau_1 + \tau_2 \ldots \tau_p^{1/2} - (\tau_1 + \tau_2 \ldots \tau_{p-1})^{1/2}$ is equated to the right-hand member of equation (12) as written for the pth substance. This general equation was verified for three substances (92). Application of chronopotentiometry to the reduction (or oxidation) of more than two substances, however, is not practical because of accumulation of errors in the determination of the least reducible (oxidizable) substance.

The stepwise chronopotentiometric reduction or oxidation of a single substance is also more complicated than in chronoamperometry. Consider the stepwise reduction $O_1 + n_1 e = O_2$ and $O_2 + n_2 e = R$. For times longer than τ_1, some of the molecules or ions of O_2 that were produced during the first step diffuse back to the electrode and are reduced. Furthermore, O_1 continues to diffuse to the electrode, where it is reduced directly to R. One then has, according to Berzins and Delahay (8),

$$\frac{\tau_1 + \tau_2}{\tau_1} = \left[\frac{n_1 + n_2}{n_1}\right]^2 \tag{13}$$

For $n_2 = n_1$ one has $\tau_2 = 3\tau_1$; and for $n_2 = 2n_1$, one has $\tau_2 = 8\tau_1$. Equation (13) is verified experimentally (8).

D. ELECTRODE REACTIONS WITH COUPLED CHEMICAL REACTIONS

Theoretical equations have been derived for the transition time and the potential–time curves for a number of electrode processes with coupled chemical reactions, and they have been tested in certain instances. The process initially analyzed involved a first-order, or pseudo first-order, chemical reaction that preceded the charge transfer reaction, i.e., $X = O + ne = R$, where X is not reduced directly. Since a chemical reaction, in addition to diffusion, now controls the supply of O at the electrode, the transition time τ_k for the above process is smaller than the transition τ_d which would be observed if X were reduced directly. Further, one expects the influence of the chemical reaction to decrease with current density. At the limit, $i \to 0$, one expects $\tau_k \to \tau_d$.

This type of process was analyzed by Gierst and Juliard (49) on the basis of a reaction-layer model. A more rigorous approach was followed by Delahay and Berzins (24), who showed that

$$i\tau_k^{1/2} = i\tau_d^{1/2} - \frac{\pi^{1/2}}{2K(k_f + k_b)^{1/2}} i \tag{14}$$

where $K = C_O/C_X$ is the equilibrium constant for the reaction $X = O$, and the k's are the corresponding rate constants. Equation (14) is the approximate form of a more general equation, which need not be discussed here. Furthermore, equation (14) was derived on the assumption that the diffusion coefficients for X and O are equal. (An equation for τ_k for which this restriction is removed was derived by Matsuda (80).) It follows from equation (14) that $i\tau_k^{1/2}$ decreases linearly with i (except when $(\tau_k/\tau_d)^{1/2}$ approaches zero, i.e., when equation (14) does not apply), and the rate constants k_f and k_b thus can be evaluated, provided K is known. These conclusions are borne out by experiment, and a few applications have been made (16,20,26,29,40,44).

A complication may arise in some electrode processes because of the influence of the double-layer structure on the *apparent* values of k_f and k_b obtained by application of equation (14). A very large salt effect is thus observed, i.e., experimental values of k_f and k_b depend strongly on the concentration of foreign electrolyte. This matter was elucidated by Gierst (46a) and Delahay and his co-workers (12), and quantitative interpretations of this double-layer effect have been advanced by Matsuda (81) and Hurwitz (48,56). Strong influence of the supporting electrolyte on the transition time is a good warning to the analytical chemist of a possible complication by double-layer effects.

More complex schemes than the reaction for which equation (14) applies have been considered by a number of authors (28,30,34,35,65,75,94,95,103a, 105). The compendium of equations and mechanisms criteria by Reinmuth should be consulted (94).

It should be noted that the effect of a coupled chemical reaction is not frequently observed with inorganic substances under usual chronopotentiometric conditions. The chemical reaction, if there is one, is often too rapid to be detected. Detection may be possible in some instances by relaxation methods, and particularly by faradaic rectification, in which conditions are far more stringent than in chronopotentiometry (23).

E. INFLUENCE OF CURRENT REVERSAL

Current reversal at some stage of electrolysis—usually at the transition time—may prove useful in the elucidation of reaction mechanisms. The method was initially developed by Berzins and Delahay (8) for a simple reaction $O + ne = R$, O and R being soluble. The transition time τ_r for the potential–time curve obtained by current reversal at the transition time τ is such that $\tau_r = \tau/3$, the current density being the same in both cases. (See Reference 8 for the case of different current densities.) This relationship is verified by experiment (8,27). Reversibility of the electrode reaction can be ascertained by comparison of the $E - t$ curves before and after current reversal (8). Current reversal, as noted by Reinmuth (94), also is useful in the detection of an insoluble electrolysis product for a reaction $O + ne = R$, since $\tau_r = \tau$ when R is insoluble.

Current reversal also gives supporting evidence in the analysis of electrode processes in which the reaction paths are not the same for the forward and backward reactions (Geske (43)). The problem was treated mathematically by King and Reilley (63). Other reaction schemes have been analyzed (31,37,105).

F. CHARGING OF THE DOUBLE LAYER

The effect of double-layer charging can be discussed conveniently by comparison of the quantity of electricity for the faradaic (q_f) and non-faradaic (q_c) processes, respectively (19,26,49). Thus, $q_f = \int_0^\tau i_f dt$ and $q_c = \int_0^\tau c_d dE$. If one assumes that $i_f \approx i$ (the cell current) and that c_d is independent of E, one has $q_f = i\tau$ and $q_c = c_d \Delta E$, ΔE being the variation of potential from $t = 0$ to $t = \tau$. Now, according to equation (9), τ is of the form $k(C/i)^2$, where k is a constant for a given substance and given conditions of electrolysis. There follows

$$q_c/q_f = (c_d \Delta E)/k \; (i/C^2) \tag{15}$$

Two important conclusions can be drawn from this approximate treatment. The double-layer effect, and consequently the distortion of potential–time curves, becomes more pronounced when the current density increases and the concentration C decreases. The influence of the concentration is particularly pronounced (term in C in equation (15)). Distortion of potential–time curves at low concentrations can be minimized by adjustment of i at a sufficiently low value. Convection begins to interfere when τ is too long, and in practice *chronopotentiometry is limited to concentrations above 10^{-5} to 10^{-4} molar.*

Graphical methods, inspired from polarography, are applied in the determination of transition times to minimize the distortion of potential–time curves. The procedure of Fig. 44.5, which may be applied to reversible E-t curves when distortion is not very pronounced, is as follows (24): trace the lines AD and CF, which are not necessarily parallel; trace the horizontal lines AC and DF, and mark the points B and E for which $AB = AC/4$ and $DE = DF/4$; and trace BE and mark the intersection $E_{1/2}$ with the potential–time curve. Trace the horizontal segment GH, which represents the transition time.

One of the following two procedures of Fig. 44.6 can be applied to any type of E-t curves (including reversible processes): (1) trace AB and CD; determine the points E_1 by extrapolation (the curvature in the initial segment of the E-t curves is due to charging of the double layer); determine the point D where the potential–time curve departs from a straight line; construct the vertical line DF; the segment E_1F represents the transition time (24). (2) Determine E_2 by extrapolation and construct BE_2, which represents the transition time (96). No theoretical justification can be offered for these methods, and a method is selected that gives in the absence of convection a constant value of $i\tau^{1/2}$ for a given concentration and a plane electrode. Reinmuth (96) noted that determination of BE_2 gives better results than the other two methods. It should be noted, however, that the determination of E_2 is somewhat more uncertain than E_1 because of the greater curvature (especially for irreversible E-t curves) of E-t curves in the transition-time region than in the initial region (cf. Fig. 44.6).

G. METHOD WITH CURRENT INCREASING WITH THE SQUARE ROOT OF TIME

According to equation (9) the square root of the transition time is proportional to C. Direct proportionality between τ and C is obtained, as was shown by Senda (100), when the current increases in direct proportion to the square root of time during electrolysis, i.e., $i = pt^{1/2}$. The derivation is the same as for equation (9), except that the flux of substance O at the electrode surface is now assumed to increase with $t^{1/2}$ instead of being constant. Thus

$$\tau = \frac{2nFACD_O^{1/2}}{\pi^{1/2}p} \tag{16}$$

This result was confirmed by Kambara and Tachi (61) and was put to experimental test by Hurwitz and Gierst (58). The latter authors also pointed out (details to be given in a subsequent publication) that transition times for consecutive or stepwise reactions are additive. Extension of equation (16) to spherical and cylindrical electrodes was made by Hurwitz (57).

Equations for potential–time curves for reversible and irreversible processes of the type $O + ne = R$ were also given by Hurwitz and Gierst (58). For example, one has for a reversible process, O and R being soluble,

$$E = E_{1/2} + \frac{RT}{nF} \ln\left[\frac{\tau}{t} - 1\right] \tag{17}$$

where τ is given by equation (16) and $E_{1/2}$ is the polarographic half-wave potential of equation (4). Equation (16) is of the same form as equation (3) for reversible E-i curves, and E-t curves in this method are identical to conventional polarographic curves.

Charging of the double layer causes a distortion of E-t curves much in the same way as in chronopotentiometry at constant current. The initial segment of the E-t curve should cover a time interval very short in comparison with τ if equation (16) is to hold reasonably well. This equation, indeed, was derived on the assumption that the current is purely faradaic.

The advantages of this method over the method at constant current—linearity of τ with C and additivity of transition times—are offset at least in part by the necessity of equipment for the generation of a current increasing with $t^{1/2}$. If chronopotentiometry is ever to be used as a routine tool, even on a limited scale (which is not the case at the present), it seems likely that the method with linear dependence of τ on C will be preferred by many of the analytically minded users. Advantages of this method over the conventional method in the study of electrode reactions do not seem apparent at the present.

IV. EXPERIMENTAL METHODS

A. CELLS

Cells with two or three electrodes are utilized: the working electrode, the auxiliary electrode that completes the electrolysis circuit, and the reference electrode. The functions of the auxiliary and reference electrodes can be combined in a single electrode when current densities are not too large, as in polarography, for instance. The ohmic drop in solution can then be neglected (or corrected for), and the reference electrode remains unpolarized. The reference electrode is fitted with a small tip (Luggin-Haber capillary) placed within 1 or 2 mm. from the working electrode to decrease the ohmic drop component in the voltage between the working and reference electrodes. Luggin-Haber capillaries are less effective with spherical or cylindric electrodes of small diameter because an important fraction of the ohmic drop in cells with such electrodes is localized in a thin shell near the spherical or cylindric electrode. For improvements in capillary design see Reference 19.

The ideal geometry for a plane electrode is achieved in a cell in which circular working and auxiliary electrodes are in a cylindrical cell having the electrode diameter as the inner diameter. The electrodes are perpendicular to the axis of the cell. Good geometry is achieved for spherical electrodes by means of two concentric spheres, the auxiliary electrode being a hollow sphere. A cylinder having a large diameter (perhaps ten times) in comparison with the spherical working electrode can also serve as the auxiliary electrode. Two concentric cylinders of equal length as working and auxiliary electrodes also provide good current distribution. The design of cells for analytical applications often departs, for ease of handling and construction, from ideal geometry.

Electrodes of platinum, gold, or graphite are generally utilized for anodic processes. Mercury is used in general for cathodic processes because of the high overvoltage for hydrogen evolution on this metal. Mercury is of limited application in anodic processes because it is easily oxidized, especially in electrolytes forming insoluble mercurous salts. Kuwana and Adams (67,68) reported the use of mercury electrodes passivated by a thin layer of mercurous halide in anodic oxidations at highly anodic potentials.

This passivated electrode was tested for slow recording conditions, and difficulties might possibly be encountered in the rapid recording of current–time and potential–time curves.

Metallic solid electrodes generally have the form of foil, wire, or small (1-mm. diameter) spheres. Conditions for semi-infinite linear diffusion are nearly achieved with plane electrodes in which a metal disk is sealed in a glass tube perpendicularly to the axis of the tube (72). The tube should extend at least a few millimeters on the side of the disk in contact with solution. If electrolysis is of sufficiently short duration, the geometry of the electrode is unimportant (see end of Section II-A).

Platinum and gold electrodes become coated with a thin oxide film at sufficiently anodic potentials, as was shown by Hickling (54) and by Kolthoff and Tanaka (64). Correction for oxide formation in anodic chronopotentiometry can be made, as was shown by Anson and Ligane (4). Pronounced distortion of E-t curves and strong perturbation of electrode kinetics may result from such oxide films (5,51,73). The oxide film can be removed by reduction with an acid solution of a ferrous salt.

Graphite electrodes can be used at potentials more anodic than platinum or gold electrodes. They are utilized in the form of a graphite rod impregnated with ceresin to decrease porosity (32,33,38,84). The section perpendicular to the electrode axis is the electrode surface. This surface can be renewed under reproducible conditions with a simple cutting machine based on the same principle as the lathe.

Impregnation can be avoided, according to Adams (1), by preparation of the electrode from a paste of graphite (1 g.) in bromoform (7 g.). A small Teflon cup with a platinum wire contact in the bottom is filled with the paste, which is tamped into the cup until the graphite surface is smooth and flush with the edge of the cup. The excess of paste is trimmed with a small spatula. The cup is immersed in the solution to be analyzed in an inverted position, the platinum wire being not in contact with the solution. Adams cites the following advantages of this electrode: (1) the rather long impregnation is avoided; (2) a paste solvent can be used in which the electrolysis product is soluble, much in the same way as an amalgam is formed at mercury electrodes; and (3) the possibility of using a dropping graphite electrode (not described in Adams's note) with continuously renewed surface. The graphite paste electrode was used with good results in the determination of current–potential curves under slow recording conditions. The electrode behavior for rapid variations of current or potential should be tested.

Three types of mercury working electrodes are used: the mercury pool electrode, the hanging drop, and the dropping mercury electrode. A

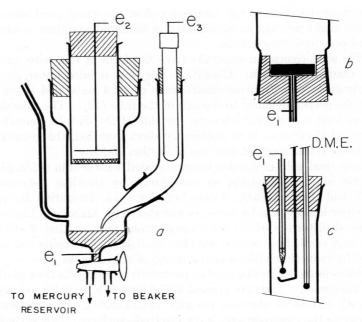

Fig. 44.8. Cell (a) with mercury pool: e_1 is the working electrode, e_2 is the auxiliary electrode, and e_3 is the calomel reference electrode; b is a plastic cup for the mercury pool; and c is a hanging mercury drop.

typical cell with mercury pool is shown in Fig. 44.8a (27). The auxiliary electrode e_2 has approximately the same diameter as the mercury pool to achieve fairly uniform current-density distribution. Electrodes e_1 and e_2 are in two different compartments, separated by a fritted glass disk to avoid diffusion of the products formed at e_2 toward the mercury pool. The two compartments are filled with the solution being analyzed. The reference electrode e_3, which is generally a calomel or silver–silver chloride electrode, is inserted in a glass sleeve fitted at its end with a Luggin-Haber capillary. The sleeve of electrode e_3 is filled with the analyzed solution. The cross section of the cell in the pool region should be uniform to achieve a reproducible electrode area without critical adjustment of the mercury level. Creeping of solution between mercury and the cell wall is minimized by silicone coating of the cell. Wetting is also avoided with mercury pools in plastic (Lucite, Teflon) cups (Fig. 44.8b). Areas are reproducible within 1 to 2% with good technique.

The design of cells with mercury pools can be greatly varied. For instance, H cells of the polarographic type can be readily adapted to the mercury pool electrode. The mercury pool is in one arm of the cell (without or with plastic cup) and the auxiliary electrode is in the other arm. The reference electrode is inserted in a vertical sleeve with a Luggin-Haber capillary that is fitted in the stopper of the arm with the mercury pool. Current distribution at the working electrode is not uniform, but the cell is very robust and well adapted to analytical determinations.

Mercury pools of small diameter (1 mm.) in capillary have been designed (87), but they have one disadvantage, namely that the electrode area changes appreciably with potential because of variations of the mercury-solution surface tension with potential.

The hanging mercury drop was introduced in electrochemical studies, to the writer's knowledge, by Frumkin and his school for measurements of the double-layer capacity (see, for instance, Reference 82). A mercury drop hanging at the tip of a capillary was utilized by these investigators. Gerischer (39) developed a particularly simple device in which the drop falling from a dropping mercury (or amalgam) electrode is collected in a small scoop and hung at a fine platinum tip (Fig. 44.8c). Two or three drops can be collected and hung on the platinum tip if a larger area is desired. The drop is removed from the tip by bringing it in contact with a small globule of mercury (a few drops) in the scoop. Manipulations are very simple with a well-machined plastic stopper or with a ground-glass stopper.

The tip of the dropping mercury electrode either is immersed in solution or is kept above the solution. The latter method is advantageous when a very small volume of solution is available. The drop is hung in the air on its tip, which is then lowered into the bottom of the cell. When the dropping mercury electrode is immersed in solution, the reproducibility of area is improved by polarization of the electrode at a constant potential (78). Variations of drop size resulting from change of potential are thus avoided. If this precaution is not taken, the dropping mercury electrode has the mixed potential corresponding to compensation of the capacity current by the faradaic current. Variations of potential and consequently of electrode area might result with an electrode in open circuit. The applied potential should be such that there is practically no reduction or oxidation. Areas are reproducible within 0.2% with good technique. Preparation of the electrode is described in detail by Shain (97,101).

Another type of hanging mercury drop was devised by Randles and White (91), in which a reproducible volume of mercury is expelled from a microsyringe fitted with a micrometer. Areas are reproducible within 2%.

The dropping mercury electrode can be utilized as an electrode of constant and known area, provided that measurements are made at a known stage of the drop life in a short time in comparison with the drop life.

Three methods have been developed for synchronization of the measurements with the drop formation.

1. The transient in the measuring circuit caused by dislodging of each drop triggers a timing circuit (Randles (90)).

2. The fall of the drop is detected with a photocell connected to the timing circuit (Corbusier and Gierst (15)).

3. Drops are regularly dislodged by a magnetic hammer connected to the timing circuit (Airey and Smales (3)).

The last method is most frequently applied because of its simplicity. Drops are dislodged toward the end of drop life because the rate of drop growth decreases with time, and variations of area are thus minimized. Ordinary polarographic capillaries are generally satisfactory, but capillaries with a drop time of 1 to 2 minutes can be made, if necessary, by drawing out a constricted section in the middle of an ordinary polarographic capillary. The rather fragile drawn-out capillary is inserted into another glass tube for protection.

The foregoing considerations can be transposed readily to the design of cells for solvents other than water. However, Luggin-Haber capillaries cannot be utilized with electrolyte solutions of very low conductivity, e.g., with certain organic solvents. The ohmic drop between the capillary tip and the working electrode is then too large and the control of potential is unsatisfactory. For cells for molten salts see, for example, References 70, 71, and 91.

Little need be said here about the preparation of solutions, since the polarographic technique generally can be followed in analytical applications (supporting electrolyte, removal of oxygen, etc.). However, much greater care about purification of solutions than in polarography is generally required in kinetic studies, because of the great sensitivity of kinetic parameters to adsorbed impurities (cf. Reference 23, e.g., for a discussion). Maximum suppressors are generally not needed in analytical applications and they should be excluded in kinetic studies (7).

B. CHRONOAMPEROMETRY

The determination of diffusion currents with a stationary electrode requires only simple apparatus similar to a manual polarograph. The cell composed of the working electrode and an unpolarized auxiliary electrode is connected to a potentiometer of low internal resistance (perhaps 100 ohms). This potentiometer is fed by a 3-v. dry cell with resistance in series. The voltage across the cell is read on a voltmeter connected across the terminals of the potentiometer (not across the cell because of the current consumption by the voltmeter). A calibrated adjustable resistance and a switch are inserted in series with the cell. The resistance is connected to a cathode-ray oscilloscope or to a pen-and-ink recorder with sufficiently fast response. In recordings of short duration (less than 0.1 second), a blade switch in the cell circuit is preferable to a toggle switch, which produces transients due to vibrations. Transients can be greatly minimized by the use of relays, particularly mercury-wetted relays. The oscilloscope or recorder can be replaced by a combination of galvanometer and timer if measurements are of sufficient duration.

Current–time curves should not be recorded beyond 1 minute at room temperature and beyond a few seconds in molten salts (70,71,112) for plane electrodes. Convection interferes with diffusion for longer electrolysis times. Interference by convection becomes quite pronounced after a few seconds for spherical and cylindric electrodes of small diameter, even at room temperature.

Proper conditions must be selected to minimize the capacity current. A correction can be made from current–time curves recorded with the supporting electrolyte alone.

The recording of current–time curves outside the range of potentials of the diffusion current, with the simple instrument described in the foregoing, involves a difficulty: the current for a given cell voltage varies continuously and the potential of the working electrode changes continuously because of the variable ohmic drop in the cell and cell circuit. This difficulty does not arise in the determination of diffusion currents because that current is practically independent of potential, whereas an error of potential of only a few millivolts in the ascending part of current–potential curves is quite serious. The resistance of the cell circuit can be reduced to a minimum, but it is more practical to compensate automatically for variations in ohmic drop by means of an electronic *potentiostat* with fast response. Hodgkin, Huxley, and Katz (55) were the first to design such an instrument with fast response (which they use in a study of nervous impulses) and their work was soon followed by that of Schön and Staubach (99) on a potentiostat for electrochemical studies. Gerischer and Vielstich (107) introduced the use of such instruments in electrode kinetics. Much specialized development work has been done (9,9a,13,41,42,111), and only principles will be covered here.

A potentiostat (Fig. 44.9) is composed of a high-gain (at least 1000) amplifier A_1, whose input is connected in series with the potential–time generator $E = f(t)$ to the working electrode e_1 and the reference electrode e_2 (with Luggin-Haber capillary). The output of A_1 is applied to the power amplifier A_2, which supplies the electrolysis current. The time lag in the variation of potential does not exceed a few microseconds in instruments

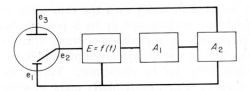

Fig. 44.9. Schematic diagram of an electronic potentiostat with fast response.

with optimum characteristics. This time lag increases with the resistance of the reference electrode, which must thus be kept at a minimum. Current–time curves are recorded by conventional techniques.

Operation of the potentiostat can by synchronized easily with a dropping mercury electrode by coupling of the $E = f(t)$ generator with the magnetic hammer dislodging the drop. Manual operation also is possible with drop times of at least 10 seconds.

Concentrations also can be determined by integration of current–time curves, as was shown by Crittenden and his co-workers (10). The integral is proportional to the bulk concentration of analyzed substance, as can be ascertained readily from equation (2). The capacity current, as obtained for the supporting electrolyte alone, is also integrated for the same conditions as the diffusion current, and correction for the capacity current can thus be made. Electronic integration is applied, and the result is directly read on a counter. The method fails at low concentrations because the correction for the capacity current becomes too large.

C. CHRONOPOTENTIOMETRY

Apparatus for the recording of potential–time curves with stationary electrodes is essentially composed of a constant-current power supply and a recorder with high input resistance (Fig. 44.10). The simplest constant-current generator is composed of a constant-voltage source (dry cells, power supply with electronic regulation) with a large resistance in series. The cell voltage (perhaps 1 v.) is quite negligible in comparison with the power-supply voltage (100 to 300 v.), and consequently the current is practically determined by the ohmic drop in the resistances R_1 and R_2 in series with the cell. Variations of cell voltage during electrolysis affect the current by a few tenths of 1% at the most. Better control of the current is achieved by electronic regulation of the current. Such power supplies are described in the literature on coulometric titrations and also in the discussion that follows.

The cell current is determined by potentiometric measurement of the ohmic drop in the calibrated resistance R_2. The recorder is connected

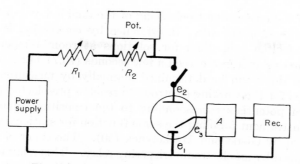

Fig. 44.10. Apparatus for chronopotentiometry.

directly to the cell, or an amplifier A with high input resistance (for instance, a line-operated pH meter) is inserted between cell and recorder. A preamplifier is needed when the current in the recorder exceeds more than a few tenths of 1% of the cell current. A cathode-ray oscilloscope is used whenever pen-and-ink recorders are too slow. Detailed circuits have been described (8,19,27,86,92).

It is essential that the cell circuit remain open before the recording of potential–time curves to avoid formation of the electrolysis product at the working electrode. If electrodes e_1 and e_2 of Fig. 44.10 are connected by a high resistance (perhaps 1 megohm), e_1 becomes quite anodic if e_2 has an anodic potential. Electrode e_1, mercury for instance, is then oxidized, and the resulting reducible product of electrolysis interferes during the subsequent recording of the potential–time curve. The same remark is applicable to the circuit of electrodes e_1e_3. This point should be kept in mind in the design of constant-current power supplies.

Mercury-wetted relays also can cause a similar difficulty because their resistance at open circuit may not exceed a few hundred megohms. Thus, with an applied voltage of 200 to 300 v. there is a continuous cell current of perhaps 1 μamp. Progressive depletion of reactants at a stationary working electrode results, and the transition time is too small.

The remark made in Section V-B about interference by convection also applies here. Optimum conditions have been studied by most investigators who reported transition-time measurements. Bard's study (6) of solid electrodes is particularly meticulous and extensive since his determinations of τ covered the range from 0.001 to 300 seconds for different substances and several electrode geometries. He concluded that the transition time constant $i\tau^{1/2}/AC$ was constant to $\pm0.2\%$ for $7 < \tau < 145$ seconds for a horizontal electrode with glass sleeve. Convection and the possible effect of sphericity interfered for longer transition times, whereas distortion of E-t curves due to charging of the double layer decreased the precision for $\tau < 7$ seconds. Interference by convection is more pronounced in molten salts than for solutions at room temperature, and transition times should not exceed a few seconds (70,71,112).

Transition times can be determined manually by measurement of the time required for the working electrode to reach a preselected potential in the range of potentials corresponding to the transition time (92). An automatic instrument fulfilling the same function for stationary electrodes was described by Gierst and Mechelynck (50). The timer of this instrument is stopped by an electronic triggering relay. This relay is connected as a balance indicator between the cell composed of the working and reference electrodes and a potentiometer. The latter is adjusted at the voltage corresponding to the preselected potential of the working electrode. A complete potential–time curve is determined by repetition of the measurements for a series of potentials.

Automatic determination of transition times was extended to the dropping mercury electrode by Gierst (45). Transition times do not exceed a few tenths of a second to minimize variations of the electrode area. The timer is a combination of an oscillator operating at 10,000 cycles per second and a pulse counter with Dekatron tubes of the type used in nuclear counters. (Commercial counters of this type are available.) The oscillator is stabilized with a thermostated quartz, and frequency is constant within 0.005%. The error on time does not exceed 0.1 milliseconds. The current is stabilized within 0.1%, and the sensitivity of the triggering circuit of the timer is ±0.5 mv. Because of these remarkable characteristics, errors in concentration do not exceed ±0.2% in favorable cases.

Differentiation of potential–time curves can be applied to the determination of transition times. Potential–time curves exhibit in the transition-time region a point of inflection that can be taken as corresponding to the transition time in comparative measurements. At this point, dE/dt is maximum, and $d^2E/dt^2 = 0$ and changes sign. Double differentiation was performed by Iwamoto (60) with the Malmstadt automatic titrator (76), based on differentiation with resistance-capacitor circuits studied in detail by Delahay (18). I also investigated this use of the Malmstadt titrator, but found it sufficiently sensitive only for steep potential–time curves in the transition–time region. The addition of an amplification stage would improve the sensitivity.

Superimposition of a small sinusoidal component to the constant current through the cell also provides differentiation of the potential–time curve. The magnitude of the sinusoidal component of the working electrode potential is proportional to the derivative dE/dt. Theory and instrumentation were developed by Tachi and his co-workers (104). (See also Reference 103.)

Instrumentation for chronopotentiometry with current proportional to $t^{1/2}$ is briefly surveyed by Hurwitz and Gierst (58). Several methods are outlined for slow and fast increase of current. One method, which was the only one actually applied by these authors, is based on the use of a potentiometer whose coil is wound as to supply a voltage varying linearly with $t^{1/2}$. This voltage was applied to a resistance that was connected to the input amplifier of an electronic potentiostat. The output amplifier was connected to the cell. The voltage between the working electrode and a reference electrode was recorded with a pen-and-ink recorder.

The reader is referred for further details on instrumentation in chronopotentiometry to the original papers and to a review by Gierst (46) on electrolysis with various current pulses.

V. APPLICATIONS

Chronoamperometry and chronopotentiometry cannot compete in general with polarography, but there are instances in which these methods are useful. Chronoamperometry appears primarily useful in the determination of concentrations below $10^{-5}M$, at which value classic polarography fails. Other methods, however, such as square-wave polarography, chronoamperometry with linearly varying potential, faradaic rectification, and, particularly, anodic stripping may prove more advantageous.

Chronopotentiometry cannot be applied to concentrations below 10^{-4} to $10^{-5}M$ (see Section III-F). However, three types of useful analytical applications of chronopotentiometry are apparent from the limited number of papers published so far: high precision determinations, anodic oxidation, and analysis of molten salts.

Precision instruments for chronopotentiometry might compete with polarography in cases in which high accuracy is desired. A comparative study of the two methods should be made to determine whether chronopotentiometry is really superior to polarography in this respect.

Few analytical applications of chronopotentiometry have been made at room temperature in inorganic chemistry (e.g., References 17, 83, and 85). Anodic oxidation of organic substances has been explored somewhat: phenols and aromatic amines (2,32), sulfanilamide and sulfa drugs (108), anthracene (109), mercaptans (110), and ferrocene and similar compounds of various metals (69).

Chronopotentiometry was applied to molten salts by Laitinen and his co-workers (70,71) and by Wood (112). Laitinen *et al.* studied the reduction of cadmium, cobalt, lead, and thallium ions on a platinum electrode in the eutectic mixture of potassium and lithium chlorides at 450°C. Wood investigated several reactions in mixtures of sodium and calcium chlorides at 550°C. The analytical use of the anodic oxidation of zinc and lithium in liquid bismuth in the potassium–lithium chlorides eutectic by Van Norman (106) is noteworthy.

Chronopotentiometry was applied by Reilley and Scribner (93) to the determination of the equivalence point of titrations. Titration curves are of the same types as for classic amperometric titrations.

Electrode-reaction mechanisms also have been studied by chronopotentiometry: anodic oxidation of mercury with formation of an insoluble product, by Gierst and Bourgeois (47) and Khalafalla and his co-workers (102); and the anodic oxidation of iodide on platinum electrode by Anson and Lingane (4).

The study of electrode kinetics by chronoamperometry and chronopotentiometry is of considerable significance but outside the realm of this discussion. Reviews are available (19,21–23,41).

REFERENCES

1. Adams, R. N., *Anal. Chem.*, **30**, 1576 (1958).
2. Adams, R. N., J. B. McClure, and J. H. Morris, *Anal. Chem.*, **30**, 471 (1958).
3. Airey, L., and A. A. Smales, *Analyst*, **75**, 287 (1950).
4. Anson, F. C., and J. J. Lingane, *J. Am. Chem. Soc.*, **79**, 1015, 4901 (1957).
5. Anson, F. C., *Anal. Chem.*, **33**, 934, 939 (1961).
6. Bard, A. J., *Anal. Chem.*, **33**, 11 (1961).
7. Bermane, D., dissertation, University of Brussels, 1955.
8. Berzins, T., and P. Delahay, *J. Am. Chem. Soc.*, **75**, 4205 (1953).
9. Bewick, A., A. Bewick, M. Fleischmann, and M. Liller, *Electrochem. Acta*, **1**, 83 (1959).
9a. Booman, G. L., *Anal. Chem.*, **29**, 213 (1957).
10. Booman, G. L., E. Morgan, and A. L. Crittenden, *J. Am. Chem. Soc.*, **78**, 5533 (1956).
11. Brdicka, R., *Collection Czechoslov. Chem. Communs.*, **15**, 691 (1950).
12. Breiter, M., M. Kleinerman, and P. Delahay, *J. Am. Chem. Soc.*, **80**, 5111 (1958).
13. Breiter, M., and F. G. Will, *Z. Elektrochem.*, **61**, 1177 (1957).
14. Butler, J. A. V., and G. Armstrong, *Proc. Roy. Soc. (London)*, **A139**, 406 (1933).
15. Corbusier, P., and L. Gierst, *Anal. Chim. Acta*, **15**, 254 (1956).
16. Dandoy, J., and L. Gierst, *J. Electroanal. Chem.*, **2**, 116 (1961).
17. Davis, D. G., and J. Ganchoff, *J. Electroanal. Chem.*, **1**, 248 (1960).
18. Delahay, P., *Anal. Chem.*, **20**, 1212, 1215 (1948).
19. Delahay, P., *New Instrumental Methods in Electrochemistry*, Interscience, New York–London, 1954.
20. Delahay, P., *Disc. Faraday Soc.*, **17**, 205 (1954).
21. Delahay, P., *Ann. Rev. Phys. Chem.*, **8**, 229 (1957).
22. Delahay, P., *Rec. Chem. Progress*, **19**, 83 (1958).

23. Delahay, P., in *Advances in Electrochemistry and Electrochemical Engineering*, P. Delahay and C. Tobias, Eds., Interscience, New York–London, 1961, Vol. I.
24. Delahay, P., and T. Berzins, *J. Am. Chem. Soc.*, **75**, 2486 (1953).
25. Delahay, P., G. Charlot, and H. A. Laitinen, *Anal. Chem.*, **32**, No. 6, 103A (1960).
26. Delahay, P., and G. Mamantov, *Anal. Chem.*, **27**, 478 (1955).
27. Delahay, P., and C. C. Mattax, *J. Am. Chem. Soc.*, **76**, 874 (1954).
28. Delahay, P., C. C. Mattax, and T. Berzins, *J. Am. Chem. Soc.*, **76**, 5319 (1954).
29. Delahay, P., and W. Vielstich, *J. Am. Chem. Soc.*, **77**, 4955 (1955).
30. Dracka, O., *Collection Czechoslov. Chem. Communs.*, **24**, 3523 (1959).
31. Dracka, O., *Collection Czechoslov. Chem. Communs.*, **25**, 338 (1960).
32. Elving, P. J., and A. F. Krivis, *Anal. Chem.*, **30**, 1648 (1958).
33. Elving, P. J., and D. L. Smith, *Anal. Chem.*, **32**, 1849 (1960).
34. Fischer, O., and O. Dracka, *Collection Czechoslov. Chem. Communs.*, **24**, 3046 (1959).
35. Fischer, O., O. Dracka, and E. Fischerova, *Collection Czechoslov. Chem. Communs.*, **25**, 323 (1960).
36. Frumkin, A. N., in *Advances in Electrochemistry and Electrochemical Engineering*, P. Delahay and C. Tobias, Eds., Interscience, New York–London, 1961, Vol. I, pp. 65–121.
37. Furlani, C., and G. Morpurgo, *J. Electroanal. Chem.*, **1**, 351 (1960).
38. Gaylor, V. F., A. L. Conrad, and J. H. Landerl, *Anal. Chem.*, **29**, 224 (1957).
39. Gerischer, H., *Z. physik. Chem.*, **202**, 302 (1953).
40. Gerischer, H., *Z. physik. Chem. (Frankfurt)*, **2**, 79 (1954).
41. Gerischer, H., *Z. Elektrochem.*, **59**, 604 (1955).
42. Gerischer, H., and K. E. Staubach, *Z. Electrochem.*, **61**, 789 (1957).
43. Geske, D. H., *J. Am. Chem. Soc.*, **81**, 4145 (1959).
44. Gierst, L., *Z. Elektrochem.*, **59**, 784 (1955).
45. Gierst, L., *Anal. Chim. Acta*, **15**, 262 (1956).
46. Gierst, L., *Intern. Comm. Electrochem. Therm. Kin.*, 7th Meeting, Butterworths, London, 1957, pp. 49–68.
46a. Gierst, L., *Agrégation*, Thesis, University of Brussels, 1958.
47. Gierst, L., and L. Bourgeois, *Intern. Comm. Electrochem. Therm. Kin.*, 6th Meeting, Butterworths, London, 1955, pp. 273–279.
48. Gierst, L., and H. Hurwitz, *Z. Elektrochem.*, **64**, 36 (1960).
49. Gierst, L., and A. Juliard, *Intern. Comm. Electrochem. Therm. Kin.*, 2nd Meeting, Tamburini, Milan, 1951, pp. 117, 279.
50. Gierst, L., and P. Mechelynck, *Anal. Chim. Acta*, **12**, 79 (1955).
51. Giner, J., *Electrochim. Acta*, **4**, 42 (1961).
52. Heyrovský, J., *Radiometer Polarographics*, **1**, 97 (1952).
53. Heyrovský, J., and D. Ilkovic, *Collection Czechoslov. Chem. Communs.*, **7**, 198 (1935).
54. Hickling, A., *Trans. Faraday Soc.*, **41**, 333 (1945).
55. Hodgkin, A. L., A. F. Huxley, and B. Katz, *J. Physiology*, **116**, 424 (1952).
56. Hurwitz, H., *Z. Elektrochem.*, **65**, 178 (1961).
57. Hurwitz, H., *J. Electroanal. Chem.*, **2**, 142 (1961).
58. Hurwitz, H., and L. Gierst, *J. Electroanal. Chem.*, **2**, 128 (1961).
59. Ilkovic, D., *Collection Czechoslov. Chem. Communs.*, **6**, 498 (1934).
60. Iwamoto, R. T., *Anal. Chem.*, **31**, 1062 (1959).
61. Kambara, T., and I. Tachi, *J. Phys. Chem.*, **61**, 1405 (1957); see also *Z. physik. Chem. (Leipzig)*, special issue **89** (1959).

62. Karaoglanoff, Z., *Z. Elektrochem.*, **12,** 5 (1906).
63. King, R. M., and C. N. Reilley, *J. Electroanal. Chem.*, **1,** 434 (1960).
64. Kolthoff, I. M., and N. Tanaka, *Anal. Chem.*, **26,** 632 (1954).
65. Koutecky, J., and J. Cizek, *Collection Czechoslov. Chem. Communs.*, **22,** 914 (1957).
66. Koutecky, J., and J. Koryta, *Electrochim. Acta*, **3,** 318 (1961).
67. Kuwana, T., and R. N. Adams, *J. Am. Chem. Soc.*, **79,** 3609 (1957).
68. Kuwana, T., and R. N. Adams, *Anal. Chim. Acta*, **20,** 51 (1959).
69. Kuwana, T., D. E. Bublitz, and G. Hoh, *J. Am. Chem. Soc.*, **82,** 5811 (1960).
70. Laitinen, H. A., and W. S. Ferguson, *Anal. Chem.*, **29,** 4 (1957).
71. Laitinen, H. A., and H. C. Gaur, *Anal. Chim. Acta*, **18,** 1 (1958).
72. Laitinen, H. A., and I. M. Kolthoff, *J. Am. Chem. Soc.*, **61,** 3344 (1939).
73. Lingane, J. J., *J. Electroanal. Chem.*, **1,** 379 (1960).
74. Lingane, J. J., *J. Electroanal. Chem.*, **2,** 46 (1961).
75. Lorenz, W., *Z. Elektrochem.*, **59,** 730 (1955).
76. Malmstadt, H. V., and E. R. Fett, *Anal. Chem.*, **26,** 1348 (1954).
77. Mamantov, G., and P. Delahay, *J. Am. Chem. Soc.*, **76,** 5323 (1954).
78. Mamantov, G., P. Papoff, and P. Delahay, *J. Am. Chem. Soc.*, **79,** 4034 (1957).
79. Martin, K. J., and I. Shain, *Anal. Chem.*, **30,** 1808 (1958).
80. Matsuda, H., *J. Am. Chem. Soc.*, **82,** 331 (1960).
81. Matsuda, H., *J. Phys. Chem.*, **64,** 336 (1960).
82. Melik-Gaikazyan, V. I., *Zhur. Fiz. Khim.*, **26,** 560 (1952).
83. Moorhead, E. D., and N. H. Furman, *Anal. Chem.*, **32,** 1507 (1960).
84. Morris, J. B., Ph.D. thesis, Pennsylvania State University, 1956.
85. Morris, J. B., unpublished investigation from Howard University, 1958.
86. Nicholson, M. M., and J. H. Karchmer, *Anal. Chem.*, **27,** 1095 (1955).
87. Nikelly, J. G., and W. D. Cooke, *Anal. Chem.*, **29,** 933 (1957).
88. Parsons, R., in *Advances in Electrochemistry and Electrochemical Engineering*, P. Delahay and C. Tobias, Eds., Interscience, New York–London, 1961, Vol. I, pp. 1–64.
89. Peters, D. G., and J. J. Lingane, *J. Electroanal. Chem.*, **2,** 1 (1961).
90. Randles, J. E. B., *Trans. Faraday Soc.*, **44,** 322 (1948).
91. Randles, J. E. B., and W. White, *Z. Elektrochem.*, **59,** 666 (1955).
92. Reilley, C. N., G. W. Everett, and R. H. Johns, *Anal. Chem.*, **27,** 483 (1955).
93. Reilley, C. N., and W. G. Scribner, *Anal. Chem.*, **27,** 1211 (1955).
94. Reinmuth, W. H., *Anal. Chem.*, **32,** 1514 (1960).
95. Reinmuth, W. H., *Anal. Chem.*, **33,** 322 (1961).
96. Reinmuth, W. H., *Anal. Chem.*, **33,** 485 (1961).
97. Ross, J. W., R. D. DeMars, and I. Shain, *Anal. Chem.*, **28,** 1768 (1956).
98. Sand, H. J. S., *Phil. Mag.*, **1,** 45 (1901).
99. Schön, J., and K. E. Staubach, *Regelungstechnik*, **2,** 157 (1954).
100. Senda, M., *Rev. Polarography (Japan)*, **4,** 89 (1956).
101. Shain, I., this volume.
102. Shams, El Din, A. M., S. E. Khalafalla, and Y. A. El Tantawy, *J. Phys. Chem.*, **62,** 1307 (1958).
103. Shinagawa, M., and F. Nakashima, *J. Sci. Hiroshima Univ.*, **24,** 445 (1960).
103a. Snead, W. K., and A. E. Remick, *J. Am. Chem. Soc.*, **79,** 6121 (1957).
104. Takemori, Y., T. Kambara, M. Senda, and I. Tachi, *J. Phys. Chem.*, **61,** 968 (1957).
105. Testa, A. C., and W. H. Reinmuth, *Anal. Chem.*, **32,** 1512, 1518 (1960).
106. Van Norman, J. D., *Anal. Chem.*, **33,** 946 (1961).
107. Vielstich, W., and H. Gerischer, *Z. physik. Chem. (Frankfurt)*, **4,** 10 (1955).

108. Voorhies, J. D., and N. H. Furman, *Anal. Chem.*, **30**, 1656 (1958).
109. Voorhies, J. D., and N. H. Furman, *Anal. Chem.*, **31**, 381 (1959).
110. Voorhies, J. D., and J. S. Parsons, *Anal. Chem.*, **31**, 516 (1959).
111. Will, F., *Z. Elektrochem.*, **63**, 484 (1959).
112. Wood, J. M., paper presented at the 111th Meeting of the Electrochemical Society, Washington, 1957.

Chapter 45

POTENTIOMETRY

By N. H. Furman, *Department of Chemistry,*
*Princeton University, Princeton, New Jersey**

Contents

* Present address: Department of Chemistry, Wake Forest College, Winston-Salem,
North Carolina.

I. INTRODUCTION

Potential measurements of galvanic cells have a multitude of applications in analytical chemistry. The various potentiometric techniques may be classified operationally under (1) potentiometry at zero current, and (2) potentiometry at constant current.

The former, potentiometry at zero current, includes classic potentiometric titrations and direct potentiometry (the measurement of ion concentrations or activities, e.g. pH, pM, etc., and measurements made on concentration cells). Potential measurements at zero current are ordinarily made with sensitive electrometers, including most of the well-designed pH meters. Such measurements actually involve a small continuous current drain on the cell of the order of 10^{-12} to 10^{-15} amp. Because of its small magnitude, this current drain does not appreciably disturb the equilibrium conditions at the electrodes in most cases. However, critical studies reveal that there are sometimes appreciable differences in potentials measured by different instruments when solutions contain microgram or submicrogram amounts of substances (56), indicating that the current drain may in such cases distort the response of the system. Many other factors also may enter into the uncertainty of potential measurements at very low concentrations.

The second major class of potentiometric measurements, (2), consists in measuring potential changes while a nearly constant current, generally the order of a few microamperes, is passed through the cell. In this technique polarization occurs at the electrodes and the interpretation of the potential response involves a knowledge of actual current–potential curves of the various chemical systems at one or both electrodes during the progress of the titration. The sharp potential change near the end point may exceed that in a zero-current potentiometric titration under certain conditions of concentration of reagent and solution titrated. To minimize duplication, the reader is referred to Chapter 43 for a systematic discussion of the general operations and interpretations of the above basic potentiometric techniques.

II. FUNDAMENTAL RELATIONS

Analytical applications of potentiometry have evolved in very large measure from the Nernst concept of the variations of electrode potentials with concentrations of potential-determining ions. The potential of an electrode at which the reaction, $M^{+n} + ne^- \rightarrow M^0$, occurs is expressed by

$$E = E^0 - (0.0001987 \ T/n) \log C^0_{M^{+n}} \tag{1}$$

where E^0 represents the standard potential of the M^{+n}, M^0 couple, T is the absolute temperature, and C^0_{M+n} is the surface concentration of the metallic ion.

A. ELECTRODE PROCESSES AND THE E.M.F. OF CELLS

In accord with modern thermodynamic conventions, if the free-energy expression $\Delta G^0 = -nFE$ is negative, a spontaneous electrode reaction is indicated when E for the cell is positive. The E for the cell is thought of as the sum of the potential for the oxidation reaction and the potential for the reduction reaction, both of which values are referred to the N.H.E. If the cell has a liquid-junction potential, its magnitude and sign must be taken into account in a detailed equation for E. By way of illustration, consider the cell:

$$\ominus Zn^0; \ Zn^{+2} \qquad Pb^{+2}; \ Pb^0 \oplus$$

with perchlorate as the anion. The potential of this cell may be calculated in the following manner.

The half-cell potential for the oxidation of zinc, $Zn \rightarrow Zn^{+2} + 2e^-$, is given, at 25°C., by

$$E = 0.76 - (0.0591/2) \log C^0_{Zn^{+2}}$$

The half-cell potential for the reduction of lead, $Pb^{+2} + 2e^- \rightarrow Pb^0$, is given by

$$E = -0.126 + (0.0591/2) \log C^0_{Pb^{+2}}$$

If the liquid-junction potential for the cell may be ignored and if $C^0_{Zn^{+2}} = C^0_{Pb^{+2}} = 1$ mole liter^{-1},

$$E_{cell} = 0.634 \text{ v.}$$

The spontaneous reaction, $Zn^0 + Pb^{+2} \rightarrow Zn^{+2} + Pb^0$, is indicated. For the cell as written the lead electrode is positive relative to the zinc.

In actuality, the potential of the cell is determined by the *activity* of a compound rather than by its concentration. In a titration process, potential measurements indicate the change in the activity of a compound as the titration progresses. However, near the end points of titrations in which the total ionic strength is nearly constant, the activities of small increments of potential-determining ions are usually closely proportional to concentration, and liquid-junction potential effects change very little in this region.

In direct potentiometry, the effects of activity and junction potentials are more serious and sometimes make measurement of true concentration difficult.

To illustrate the effects of junction potentials in direct potentiometry, consider the cell:

$$Hg^0 \mid Hg_2Cl_2,\ H^+,\ Fe^{+2},\ Fe^{+3},\ Cl^- \mid Pt$$

Knowing the potential of the saturated calomel reference electrode to be 0.2458 v. *vs.* N.H.E. and the standard potential of the Fe^{+3}, Fe^{+2} couple to be 0.771 v. *vs.* N.H.E., a measurement of the potential of this cell yields the ratio of the activities of Fe^{+3} and Fe^{+2}. If the Fe^{+3} and Fe^{+2} ions are assumed to have identical activity coefficients and identical concentrations, the cell e.m.f. should be 0.525 v. It is known that the liquid-junction potential of the system, KCl (sat'd.) $+\|-$ 0.1M HCl is about 0.0047 v. at room temperature. If this latter information was unknown or ignored, the activity ratio of Fe^{+2} to Fe^{+3} would have to have a value of 0.83 to give the above cell e.m.f.

B. FORMAL POTENTIALS

Since there is rarely enough information in practical analytical operations to make more than a rough appraisal of activity effects, it has been found to be useful to measure the potentials of a number of practical systems with equimolar concentrations of oxidant and reductant at various known molarities of the common acids. The potentials measured in this way are *formal potentials*, E^0. The activity coefficients of the given system are thus included in this "standard" potential.

Figure 45.9 presents some formal potentials. A constant may be calculated from the formal potentials of two systems at a particular acidity by the relationship $-nFE_c^0 = RT \ln K$. If m is the number of electrons exchanged, $\log K = [m(E_{c(1)}^0 - E_{c(2)}^0)]/0.0591$ at 25°C., where $E_{c(1)}^0$ is the formal potential of the more strongly oxidizing system and $E_{c(2)}^0$ is that of the other system.

Formal potentials are useful since they give practical and usable information as to the relative oxidizing power of various systems in the presence of various complexing agents, acids, etc.

III. ELECTRODE SYSTEMS

The following is a brief survey of the chief types of electrode systems that are used for measuring changes in concentration of ions or for measurement of ionic activities.

A. CLASSIFICATION OF ELECTRODE SYSTEMS

Electrode systems used for the measurement of potentials may be classified on the basis of the species that primarily determines the electrode potential. The following are the three most common types.

1. First-Class Electrodes

A metal in contact with a solution of its ions, for example silver in contact with a solution of a soluble silver salt, has a potential that is dependent upon the activity of the metal ion and the temperature. In general, the potential for such systems is given by:

$$E_M = E^0 + [0.0591/n] \log a_{M^{+n}} \qquad \text{at } 25°C.$$

The hydrogen electrode has been the most important electrode of this class. Since hydrogen gas participates in the electrode reaction and the hydrogen is supplied at the prevailing atmospheric pressure, the activity of hydrogen gas is variable. By definition, E^0 for the hydrogen electrode is taken as 0.0000 v. If the hydrogen gas is not at atmospheric pressure, there is a correction term, $\Delta E = (0.0591/2) \log (760/pH_2)$, applied to the equation $E_H = 0.0000 - 0.0591 \log a_{H^+}$.

Few nonmetallic elements are available in solid form. Hence, in such cases an "inert" electrode is used as the site for the electron-transfer reaction. Pt; I_3^-, I^- represents an iodine electrode. The saturated or unsaturated oxygen electrode has been much used as an indicator in acid–base titrations. In general *Element* $+ ne^- \rightarrow Anion^{-n}$ is a typical reduction process for a nonmetallic element.

2. Second-Class Electrodes

In this case a metallic electrode in contact with one of its very slightly soluble salts may respond reversibly to changes in *anion* activity:

Metal, insoluble salt of the metal, anion

The two most important examples are: Ag, AgCl, Cl⁻, and Hg, Hg_2Cl_2, Cl⁻. At a fixed concentration of chloride ion, either of these electrodes may serve as a reference electrode. Alternatively, the electrode may be used to respond reversibly to changes in chloride concentration. A silver electrode coated with any one of a number of its insoluble salts will respond to changes in activity of the anion of that salt. Such electrodes may be thought of as responding to changes in metal-ion concentration governed by the common-ion effect.   For example, the potential of the silver–silver chloride electrode may be given as

$$E_{Ag} = E^0 + 0.0591 \log a_{Ag^+} = E^0 + 0.0591 \log K_{s.p.} - 0.0591 \log a_{Cl}$$

where $K_{s.p.}$ is the solubility product of silver chloride.   Although silver and mercury electrodes have found the most general application, certain other electrodes are of considerable interest.   For example, the $Bi, BiF_3; F^-$ electrode responds to changes in fluoride-ion concentration.

3. Third-Class Electrodes

These electrodes consist of a metal in contact with one of its own slightly soluble salts or slightly ionized complexes and with the slightly more soluble salt of a second metal or the slightly more ionized complex of the second metal.   The slightly soluble or the slightly ionized compounds must have a common ion.   Such electrode systems may be used to obtain a potential response for an ion that is nonelectroactive in the usable potential range.   Some examples are:

$$Ag \mid Ag_2C_2O_4; \; CaC_2O_4; \; Ca^{+2}$$

$$Hg \mid Hg_2C_2O_4; \; CaC_2O_4; \; Ca^{+2}$$

$$Hg \mid HgY^{-2}; \; MY^{-2}; \; M^{+2}$$

where Y^{-2} is an abbreviation for the anionic part of ethylenediamine-tetraacetic acid (EDTA).   The last electrode may be used for titrations of individual ions or their mixtures in, for example, the series Zn^{+2}, Cu^{+2}, Pb^{+2}, Ca^{+2}.

Electrodes of this type are often referred to as pMetal electrodes since they respond to changes in concentration of metallic ions by $0.0591/n$ v. per tenfold change in activity at 25°C.

B. OXIDATION-REDUCTION ELECTRODES

Whereas every electrode of the type $M^{+n} + ne^- \rightarrow M^0$ that is in equilibrium with M^{+n} represents a redox process, electrodes that are only slightly attackable have a special significance in indicating the course of reactions between *soluble* oxidants and reductants.   The range of potentials that can be indicated by any one metal such as platinum, iridium, gold, etc., is limited at the cathodic end of the potential scale by the tendency of the metal to catalyze electrode reactions, producing hydrogen gas.   The platinum then acts as an unsaturated hydrogen electrode.   In solutions of oxidants such as cobaltic, permanganic, ceric, bichromate, and other powerfully oxidizing ions, the noble metal is covered with an oxide film, the presence of which can be determined by coulometric and other methods. For this reason different noble metals may show rather large differences in potential, as much as 0.2 v. for cobaltic systems, at Pt and Au electrodes respectively. The extent of film formation and its removal by reduction becomes of significance in attempting to titrate microgram and submicrogram amounts of oxidants or reductants. The state of the electrode surface is of importance near the equivalence points of titration reactions because of its effects on the reversibilities of the potential-determining couples. Sometimes accurate analytical resutls may be obtained with zero-current potentiometry in spite of slow drifts of the electrode response, resulting when an irreversible couple is potential-determining. This may be done by taking e.m.f. readings at arbitrary times after each increment of reagent has been added.

C. MEMBRANE ELECTRODES

These electrodes find use either as reference electrodes or as indicator electrodes. A suitable reference half cell is separated from the solution upon which a measurement is to be made by a suitable membrane. The membrane must respond to the activity of one species of ion. The glass electrode commonly used for pH measurement is of this type and has the construction shown in Fig. 45.1. The potential of the glass electrode, except in very alkaline regions, changes 59 mv. per unit change in pH. Because of an "asymmetry" potential of the glass membrane, the glass electrode must be calibrated in order to use it for pH measurement. The glass electrode is immersed in a buffer solution of known pH and the potential for the cell

$$\text{Ref}_1, \underset{C_1}{\text{HCl}} \Big\| \underset{C_2}{\text{H}^+, \text{X}^-}, \text{Ref}_2$$

is set on the potential-measuring device to give a value corresponding to the pH of the standard buffer. Since glass membranes have a resistance of many megohms, a sensitive line-operated vacuum-tube voltmeter is used for the potential measurement. Generally a series potentiometer is provided so that one pH unit on the meter scale may be set to correspond to a change of $0.0001985\ T$ v. in the measured potential.

The glass membranes used are of special compositions. Soft glass membranes have a high sodium ion error in alkaline media and an error attributed to water transport in highly acidic solutions. Modern glass electrodes contain lithium, cesium, barium, and rare earth oxides. A typical composition is: silica 63 to 67, lithia 24 to 26, 1 to 4 each of lan-

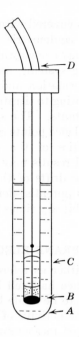

Fig. 45.1. A typical glass electrode for pH measurements. *A* is a special glass membrane, *B* is the reference electrode, *C* is the solution of HCl of concentration c_1, and *D* is a shielded wire.

thanum, calcium, and barium oxides, and 2 of cesium oxide, all numbers being in mole per cent. The glass membrane, perhaps by proton exchange, takes up a potential that responds logarithmically to proton activity. Hence by having a fixed proton activity in the inner compartment (C_1), the over-all response of the cell depends on the activity of protons in the solution that is being measured (C_2).

Other membranes, such as fused silver halides, calcium fluoride films, etc., have been studied but not extensively used. Ion-exchange membranes have found some use for indication in titrations. Thus far, however, no practical way has been found to make ion-exchange membranes as specific for given ions as is the case for glass membranes.

D. OTHER pH-RESPONSIVE ELECTRODES

In principle, any redox process involving production or consumption of hydrogen or hydroxide ions might serve as a potentiometric indicator of pH or [H$^+$]. Actually, in very few systems is it possible to control the oxidant–reductant ratio so that the response of the electrode is due solely to pH changes. The best-studied reaction of this type is:

$$C_6H_4O_2 + 2H^+ + 2e^- \rightarrow C_6H_4(OH_2)$$

Quinone $\qquad\qquad\qquad$ Hydroquinone

An equimolar mixture (quinhydrone) of quinone and hydroquinone is slightly soluble in various slightly acidic media (4), and the potential response of this couple is closely proportional to pH. The effect of activities of various salts on the quinhydrone system has been studied and corrections can be made (66). As a first approximation in very dilute solutions, we may state that

$$E_{QH} = E^0 + 0.0591 \log [H^+] + (0.0591/2) \log [quinone/hydroquinone]$$

vs. the S.C.E. When $E_{obs.}$ is the reading on the platinum electrode vs. the S.C.E.,

$$pH = (0.4554 - E_{obs.}/0.0591) \qquad \text{at } 25°C.$$

on the assumption that [quinone] = [hydroquinone] and that activity effects either are negligible or are corrected for by an appropriate term (E_c^0). The electrode is suitable only from about pH zero to pH 8 or 9, and hence only in the measurement of acidic media or in titrations of acids. Oxidation by atmospheric components and the acid functions of hydroquinone upset the equilibria above pH 9. The presence of powerful reductants or oxidants also will upset the ratio of quinone to hydroquinone and thus interfere with either pH measurements or titration experiments.

The analogous "chloranil" electrode has been found useful in anhydrous hydrogen acetate for acid–base titrations (24). Free acetic anhydride has a disturbing action:

$$C_6Cl_4O_2 + 2H^+ + 2e^- \rightarrow C_6Cl_4(OH)_2$$

Chloranil $\qquad\qquad\qquad$ Tetrachlor

$\qquad\qquad\qquad\qquad\qquad$ hydroquinone

In general, a metal that is in contact with one or with a mixture of its oxides will show a response of RT/F volt per unit pH change, provided the oxide is sufficiently insoluble and the metal is relatively unattackable. There have been numerous studies of such metal–metal oxide electrodes for pH measurements or for acid–base titrations. Platinum, either surrounded by oxygen or air or coated with an oxide film by immersion in bichromate or ceric solutions, is useful in acid–base titrations (19) and in pH measurements (62). The antimony–antimonous oxide electrode has long been used in titrations and in pH measurements (34). The potential of the electrode is disturbed by many complexing agents (citrates, tartrates, etc.), by dissolved oxygen, and by some powerful oxidants and reductants. Small amounts of cupric ion cause errors in pH measurements.

Among the other electrodes that are useful as indicators in acid–base titrations are tungsten (7), molybdenum (6), germanium (51), and tellurium (13).

E. BIMETALLIC ELECTRODE PAIRS

If the electrode system consists of two wires of similar or dissimilar metals, the experimental apparatus may be greatly simplified (Fig. 45.2). Efforts in this field may be classified as follows:

1. One metal, usually coated by design or by chance with a thin film of its oxide, serves as an indicator and the other wire as a reference. In

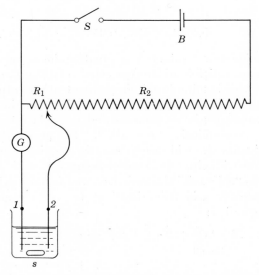

Fig. 45.2. The dead-stop circuit of Foulk and Bawden. When switch S is closed the fall in potential along R_1, R_2 is approximately 1.5 v. from the battery, B. R_1 is very small relative to R_2, so that the drop across R_1 is equivalent to about 10 mv. G is a sensitive lamp and scale galvanometer and *1* and *2* are platinum electrodes dipping into the solution; s represents a stirrer bar.

acid–base titrations, one of the metals Pt, Sb, W, Mo, etc., serves as an indicator and silver (with chloride present or added) as a reference (33).

2. For redox reactions, Hostetter and Roberts first proposed the Pt–Pd pair, the latter acting as a reference electrode of a sort (29). A detailed study of numerous bimetallic pairs for redox reactions was first made by Willard and Fenwick (69).   They found the Pt–W system to be one of the best pairs.   This writer and E. B. Wilson, Jr. (unpublished) found that the system works well for the standard reduction potential range of 1.5 down to 0.5 or 0.6 v., but was not satisfactory below this range.   A large break in potential occurs near, but not at, the equivalence point, presumably because of kinetic effects in the formation or removal of superficial layers of oxides on the two metals.

3. For precipitations, the Pt–Ni, Pt–graphite, and Pt–SiC pairs are among the best (3).

In general, bimetallic systems have fallen into disfavor except for well-studied situations in which simplification of apparatus is a chief requirement (cf., I. M. Kolthoff, *Anal. Chem.*, **26**, 1685 (1954)).

F. DIFFERENTIAL TITRATIONS, "RETARDED" OR SHELTERED ELECTRODES

If, in a potentiometric titration, the cell is comprised of two identical indicator electrodes, and the effective volume of titrant that has been added to the solution around these two electrodes differs by a small amount, the end-point response of one electrode will "lag" behind that of the other and a differential potential–volume titration curve is obtained.   Cox (10) first demonstrated this principle by using two burets, two identical electrodes, and two equal portions of solution in two beakers connected by a salt bridge.   Reagent was added to each beaker, but one buret was started 0.05 ml. ahead of the other.   Each solution was stirred mechanically.

E. Müller (50) used a retarded (*gebremste*) electrode prepared by surrounding one electrode inside a porous cylinder with a reagent that would keep this electrode short of the end point (because of the slow diffusion through the cylinder) while a similar electrode was exposed to the solution. The apparatus was designed for industrial applications.   It did not, however, give a true differential response.

If a retarded electrode is produced at intervals by withdrawing a portion of the solution to a compartment containing this electrode before each addition of reagent to the solution containing the other electrode (see Fig. 45.3), a differential response is obtained at the end point.   This method is capable of great precision and accuracy (43,44).

G. BURET REFERENCE ELECTRODES

Instead of a conventional reference electrode, it is often convenient in a titration to use a wire sealed below the stopcock of the buret (70) or otherwise inserted (49).   The tip of the buret dips into the solution that is

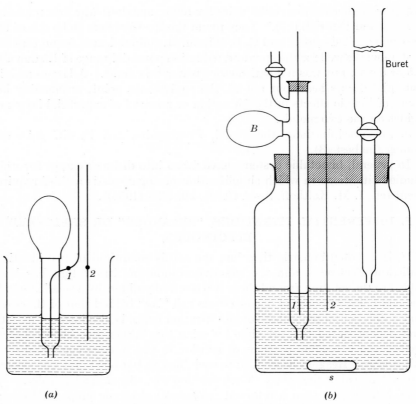

Fig. 45.3. Diagram *a* represents a simple medicine-dropper arrangement for shielding electrode *1* from the solution.   Electrodes *1* and *2* are made of the same material (Hall, Jensen, and Backstrom, *J. Am. Chem. Soc.* **50,** 2217 (1928)).

Diagram *b* represents a differential arrangement that permits the use of an inert gas. *B* is a rubber bulb for mixing the liquid around electrode *1* with the bulk of the solution; *s* is a stirrer bar (Clarke and Wooten, *J. Phys. Chem.*, **23,** 1468 (1929)).

titrated, and diffusion is not a serious problem.   The potential–volume response is of conventional form.

IV. APPARATUS FOR POTENTIOMETRY

The most reliable reference potential for the calibration of potentiometric devices is that of a standard cell, such as the Weston saturated cell:

$$\text{Cd–Hg;} \quad \text{CdSO}_4\cdot 8/3 \text{ H}_2\text{O;} \quad \text{Hg}_2\text{SO}_4; \quad \text{Hg}$$
$$12\% \text{ Cd} \quad \text{sat'd.} \quad\quad\quad \text{sat'd.}$$

Its value in absolute volts is 1.018646 at 20°C. and 1.01842 v. at 25°C., and its temperature coefficient is small, between −20 and 43°C. The unsaturated Weston cell is filled with cadmium sulfate solution saturated at 4°C. and unsaturated at higher temperatures. The temperature coefficient is very small. The cells are certified by manufacturers—the Weston Electric Instrument Co. of Newark, N. J., or the Eppley Laboratory, Inc. of Newport, R. I.—by comparison with saturated Weston cells. The National Bureau of Standards maintains ultimate standards.

A. POTENTIOMETERS

The principle of opposing the potential to be measured by an equal and opposite potential was introduced by Poggendorff. With a sufficiently sensitive and accurate null-sensing device, for example a good voltmeter,

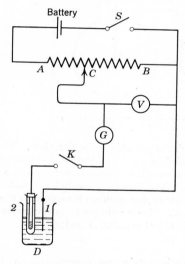

Fig. 45.4. Simple apparatus for potentiometric titrations. With the aid of the battery, the switch (S), the uniform slide wire (AB), and the voltmeter (V), the fall from A to B is set at some convenient value, such as 2 v. During a titration the slide wire junction, C, is set at a point at which the galvanometer reads zero when the key, K, is depressed. The solution and electrodes *1* and *2* are in the beaker, D.

it is possible to make measurements adequate for titration purposes without a standard cell and with a slide wire that is not strictly linear, as shown in Fig. 45.4. The sliding contact, C, is moved until no deflection of the galvanometer is shown. The voltage read at this point is equal to that of the cell.

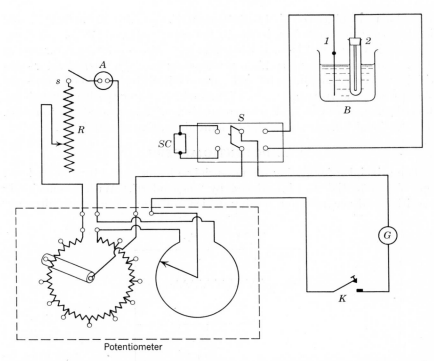

Fig. 45.5. Classic circuit for potentiometric titrations. The uniform resistance wire of the potentiometer consists of a series of coils and a slide wire, each coil and the slide wire being of equal resistance. The potentiometer is set to read volts directly with the aid of a standard cell (SC), a battery (A), a switch (s), and a resistance (R). Balance during adjustment and later during readings is made with the aid of the galvanometer, G, and the tapping key, K. The circuit from the electrodes 1 and 2 and the solution in the beaker, B, is connected by the D.P.D.T. switch, S.

Fundamental potentiometric measurements are made with a suitable potentiometer consisting of a uniform resistance wire, commonly constructed in a series of coils of equal resistance and a slide wire of resistance equal to that of each coil. The instrument is set to read volts directly with the aid of a standard cell, resistances, and a galvanometer, as shown schematically in Fig. 45.5. The potential of the titration cell or of other cells may then be read with the aid of the slide, C, tapping key, K, and sensitive galvanometer, G.

Even with available galvanometers of high sensitivity, it is impractical to measure cells of resistance much greater than one million ohms (1 megohm). Glass-membrane cells have resistances of 30 to 100 megohms.

The early development of pH measurement using glass electrodes was hampered by the frail nature of the early membranes of soft glass and by the fact that a quadrant electrometer, with elaborate shielding, was then the only instrument sensitive enough to detect the point of balance. The advent of modern electrometer tubes and electronic amplifying devices has boosted tremendously the use of glass-membrane electrodes and others of high resistance, for both indication or reference purposes. A modern pH meter may have the chief components shown in Fig. 45.6.

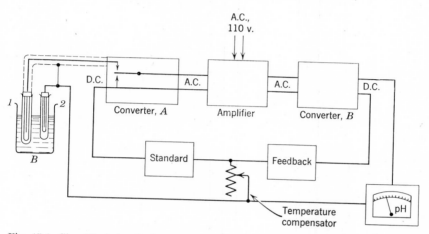

Fig. 45.6. Simplified circuit diagram of a modern pH meter. The chopper may be a vibrating condenser. The a.-c. response is amplified and then rectified, and then is read on a d.-c. microammeter; or, if desired, the response may be recorded with a chart recorder of suitable impedance.

The advent of magnetic stirrer bars has made it possible to operate conveniently either in open or closed vessels. Commercially available electrodes, e.g., glass, calomel, platinum, silver, etc., are available in various sizes. The writer has for many years used home-made platinum electrodes of the simple design shown in Fig. 45.7.

The majority of modern titration studies are made with the aid of line-operated pH meter instruments and professionally produced electrodes.

B. AUTOMATIC POTENTIOMETRIC TITRATION

Three major approaches may be recognized in this area:

1. The flow of the titrant is automatically stopped at the end point.

2. The graph of e.m.f., or of derivative readings, *vs.* the amount of reagent is plotted automatically.

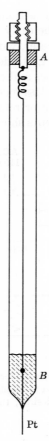

Fig. 45.7. Simple, home-made platinum electrode design used by the author. A short piece of platinum is welded to a copper wire (*B*) by short heating in a small blow-pipe (gas-air) reducing tip. The platinum wire is then sealed in the glass tube, paraffin is poured in, and the copper wire is soldered or otherwise connected to a suitable binding post that is held in place by a sealing wax or a high-resistance plastic (*A*).

3. Routine measurements of sample, titration, and record of the result are made automatically.

1. Automatic Titration to an End Point

This goal has been achieved by allowing the potential signal, amplified if necessary, to turn off a stopcock (72) or to operate a magnetic valve (54). The flow of titrant must be very slow or, alternatively, anticipation must be provided to slow down the addition of titrant or to stop and resume titration until a predetermined end-point region is reached. The traditional arrangement of buret, electrodes, and stirrer to cause some of the titrant to reach the indicator electrode before being thoroughly mixed with the solution has been used for half a century or longer to give a good measure of anticipation in manual titrations. Lingane (39) demonstrated that this principle also is effective in automatic titrations. In general, modern automatic titrators utilize the difference between a reference potential and that given by the indicator system to speed up the addition of reagent until the rate of change of electrode response increases. The buret valve can then be opened and closed automatically until the electrical indication proves that the region of the equivalence potential has been reached.

Malmstadt (45) devised a circuit with resistance–capacity differentiation to close the buret valve when the second derivative of potential vs. ml. is zero.

The Beckman Model K titrator uses the principle of comparison of the amplified electrode signal with a preset reference voltage in the region of the potential at the end point. Resistance–capacitance changes are used in connection with the anticipation circuit (26). The circuit is well adapted to coulometric end points (40).

H. A. Frediani (16) devised an instrument, based on the use of time-delay switches and a sensitive relay, for the Karl Fischer titration method for water, as based on the "dead-stop" end point. The instrument may stop titrating temporarily before the end point, but titration is resumed if the signal drifts back within a preset time interval. The original model, somewhat modified, has been marketed by Beckman, as has a model involving vacuum-tube amplification. The end-point phenomena in this titration are amperometric rather than potentiometric.

2. Automatic Plotting of E.M.F. vs. Titrant Added

The titrator of Robinson (63) became the Precision-Dow instrument. A description of a modification of this equipment is available (14). The Robinson titrator and that of Lingane (41) include most of the principles that are common to many of the commercially available automatic recording titrators, and others, that have been devised. A motor-driven syringe buret adds the titrant, and the motor drive is synchronized with the chart travel. An amplifier is used to transform the electrode response into terms that are adapted to the conventional recorder characteristics. The sensing, or anticipation, feature is generally based on the changing signal and a preset potential reference.

A detailed description of a typical assembly built from standard sub-assemblies is given by Irving and Pettit (31). They adopted the principle of driving the syringe buret and the recorder by a single motor.

3. Measurement of Sample, Stopping the Titration, and Recording the Result

There have been numerous approaches to the problem of taking samples at intervals, titrating, and recording the result automatically. One such automatic titrator has been described by Brown and Weir (9).

4. Analysis and Control of Flowing Streams

Coulometric titration to a preset potential has been applied to the analysis of gaseous streams in the "Titrolog" device, built by the Consolidated Engineering Corp. Gases that are titratable by electrolytically generated bromine are estimated by the amount of current necessary to complete the reaction in a sample by-passed from the stream and measured (65).

The Leeds and Northrup analyzer for residual chlorine in water admixes the water and the reagent, ferric sulfate, in fixed proportions by suitable pumps. The current necessary to titrate the chlorine by electrolytically generated ferrous ion to a predetermined index potential may be calibrated in terms of parts per million of chlorine (53).

The foregoing section has presented only a few of the many ideas in automatic titration devices. A comprehensive review of the subject is given by Phillips (54).

V. APPLICATIONS OF POTENTIOMETRY

Different methods used for the determination of the end point in a potentiometric titration are discussed by Kolthoff and Furman (1931, as referred to in Chapter VI). A more critical discussion of the location of the end point in various types of titration will be given in a chapter in the volume of this Treatise dealing with titrimetry.

A. ACID–BASE REACTIONS

In general any acidic or basic function can be titrated with a "strong" base or acid, provided the weakly acidic or basic function has an ionization constant that exceeds K_w by a number of powers of ten, depending upon the concentration of the original solution and the reagent. For a practical limit of 1% accuracy, the following conditions apply:

Normality of salt produced at the equivalence point	0.001	0.01	0.1	1.0
Minimum K_a value	10^{-6}	10^{-6}	10^{-8}	10^{-10}

Similar conditions apply for weak bases. These conclusions are based upon experience in the temperature range 18 to 25°C.

If two weakly acidic functions in the range pK_a 3 to 10, or two weakly basic functions from pK_b 3 to 10, are titrated with a highly ionized base or acid, respectively, two well-defined electrometric end points will be found if the two pK values differ by 4 units. The two functions may be on the same molecule or in a roughly equimolar mixture of acids or bases. In the case of mixtures of weak reagents, if the concentration ratios are extreme, e.g., 100 to 1 or 1000 to 1, a greater spread than 10^4 in K values will be needed.

Theoretically, the potentiometric method can give greater accuracy than indicator methods in critical cases, provided the pH at the equivalence point is known theoretically. One then titrates to a reference potential, which can be accomplished to a high degree of precision.

Weak bases can be titrated more effectively and with sharper end points in concentrated neutral salt solutions, e.g., 6 to $8M$ sodium iodide, $6M$ sodium chloride, $8M$ lithium chloride, and $4.5M$ calcium chloride, than in water. Aniline gives a very sharp break at the end point when titrated with $0.5M$ hydrochloric acid, the medium being $7M$ aqueous sodium iodide. Usually several of the basic functions can be differentiated, as for example the first two of diethylenetetramine or the first three of triethylenetetramine. Certain mixtures can be analyzed, such as pyridine and triethylamine. The concentrated salt solution lowers the pH at the end point for a single amine, without affecting the course of pH until the equivalence point is approached (11). A small amount of methanol may be added, if needed, to solubilize the amine. Conditions must be arranged so that the acid needed in the titration does not increase the volume more than 10 to 15%.

Readings of pH during the formation of basic salts or hydrous oxides, or during the dissolution of precipitates, have revealed that there are relatively few such processes that are useful for direct analytical determinations. It has long been known that the titration of the solution of a limestone or a dolomite gives one large change in pH after the completion of the neutralization of the excess acid and the precipitation of ferric iron, and a second fairly well-defined break at the end of the precipitation of magnesium hydroxide. The alkali must be quite concentrated, preferably $1.000N$ (27). Potentiometric titration has long been an excellent technique in detailed studies of the precipitation of basic salts (8).

B. ACID–BASE TITRATIONS IN NONAQUEOUS MEDIA

A rather extensive treatment of acid–base relationships in nonaqueous media has been given by Kolthoff and Bruckenstein in Chapter 13 of this Treatise (Part I, Vol. 1, pp. 475–541). Table 13.XVIII of that chapter gives a summary of titration possibilities in various solvents and information as to electrode systems that may be used for indication.

An appreciation of the potentialities of nonaqueous systems as media for acid–base titrations has evolved gradually, due to the pioneering work of E. C. Franklin (15) on the liquid ammonia system, Hall, Conant, and others (25) on anhydrous acetic acid, and the theoretical views of Brønsted on the nature of acids and bases and the somewhat broader views of G. N. Lewis (1923). The study of alcohols as solvents developed early, as exemplified by potentiometric studies by Hildebrand and others (28). The titration of acids by standard bases in alcoholic medium has been standard practice for many decades. The physical chemistry of a number of solvent systems is still to be investigated. Only in the case of anhydrous hydrogen acetate is there a fairly complete interpretation of the dissociation and ionization equilibria (35).

For the present, most of the approximate rationalization has been made on the basis of apparent pH values read at half-neutralization points. It is well known that these values are variable with dilution for many reagents in various solvents. Nonetheless, these "formal" constants may be used somewhat similarly to formal redox potentials in order to decide whether differentiation of acids or bases is possible by a succession of end points.

An acidic solvent such as glacial acetic acid enables one to find measurable differences in the acid strengths of the strong acids that are "leveled" in water due to the completeness of the reaction:

$$HB + H_2O \rightarrow H_3O^+ + B^-$$

In hydrogen acetate the relative order is: perchloric acid (strongest) > hydrobromic > sulfuric > hydrochloric > nitric acid. The apparent strength of weak bases is enhanced due to the equilibrium

$$RNH_2 + HC_2H_3O_2 \rightleftharpoons RNH_3^+ + C_2H_3O_2^-$$

the acetate ion being the typical strong base of the hydrogen acetate system.

In practical work any water in the glacial acetic acid used is removed by allowing it to react with the proper amount of acetic anhydride, being careful to avoid an excess of the latter since it will destroy amino functions by acetylation. The amino function of amino acids can be readily titrated in the medium, as can many other bases that are too weak in aqueous

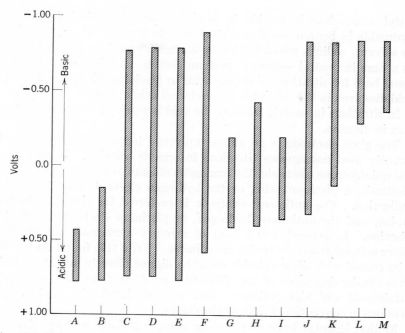

Fig. 45.8. Voltage range realizable in acid–base titrations in various solvents. In most cases the glass electrode–calomel electrode arrangement was used. Key to solvents: *A*, hydrogen acetate (anhydrous acetic acid); *B*, acetic anhydride; *C*, chlorbenzene; *D*, acetone; *E*, methyl isobutyl ketone; *F*, acetonitrile; *G*, methanol; *H*, isopropanol; *I*, water; *J*, dimethylformamide; *K*, pyridine; *L*, *n*-butylamine; and *M*, ethylenediamine. After H. B. Van der Heijde and E. A. M. F. Dahmen (68); acetic anhydride (*B*) and methyl isobutyl ketone (*E*) were added.

medium for a practical titration. The preferred acidic titrant is perchloric acid, prepared by dissolving the proper amount of 72% perchloric acid in 250 ml. of glacial acetic acid; for a $0.1N$ solution, 20 ml. of acetic anhydride is added and the solution is diluted to 1 liter with glacial acetic acid. The perchloric acid solution is standardized against potassium acid phthalate, which is a base in anhydrous hydrogen acetate. The preferred base for titration of acids is either sodium acetate or guanidine acetate dissolved in glacial acetic acid.

The general range of apparent pH, as indicated by the lengths of the accessible potential scale, is shown in Fig. 45.8. This presentation was derived by van der Heijde and Dahmen (68), with some additional solvents listed (acetic anhydride and methyl isobutyl ketone). In general, the standard base is hydroxide in the form of potassium hydroxide, tetra-*n*-

butyl ammonium hydroxide in methanol or other alcohol, or sodium hydroxide in benzene methanol mixture. In the case of ethylenediamine as solvent, sodium ethanolamine is the base. Sodium methoxide serves as a base in neutral solvents. Sodium acetate, as has been stated, is the usual base for titrations of strong acids in glacial acetic acid. Perchloric acid dissolved in the solvent is the preferred acidic reagent.

In titrations in neutral solvents the acid is made up as a standard solution in dioxane.

The glass electrode is an almost universal indicator for the more frequently used nonaqueous titrations in organic solvents. In many cases the quinhydrone electrode, the analogous chloranil electrode, an antimony electrode, a platinum wire, or the hydrogen electrode may be used for indication. The antimony electrode is preferred for titrations in butyl amine, and the antimony, hydrogen, or platinum electrode in ethylenediamine. In general, some form of mercury–mercurous salt or silver–silver salt reference electrodes are suitable. Fritz (17) found that a silver wire coated with silver chloride could be dipped directly into the solution, thus eliminating some of the difficulties resulting from slow equilibrium attainment and high resistance that are associated with capillary connections in conventional calomel electrodes.

Methyl isobutyl ketone or acetone serve especially well as solvents in which mixtures of strong and weak acids give a succession of sharp breaks. For example, perchloric acid and the two stages of sulfuric acid are resolved. Successive breaks are obtained in the titration of perchloric, hydrochloric, salicylic, and acetic acids and phenol (see Figs. 13.2 and 13.3 on pages 479 and 480 of Vol. 1).

Palit (52) pointed out the advantages of mixed glycol–hydrocarbon solvents, as for example 15 to 70% by volume of isopropyl alcohol, the remainder being ethylene or propylene glycol, for solubilizing salts of fatty acids prior to titration with acid or for titrating weak bases such as ammonia, aniline, or alkaloids. Pifer *et al.* (55) have pointed out that the addition of a miscible solvent with a low dielectric constant to a non aqueous solution may permit accurate titrations at 0.01 or $0.001N$ concentrations. Due to the enhanced resistance, the calomel reference and glass indicator electrodes must be positioned to be almost touching each other.

Typical procedural details are given for nonaqueous acid–base titrations by Fritz (18).

C. PRECIPITATION AND COMPLEX FORMATIONS

The majority of useful precipitation reactions involve standard silver nitrate as titrant and the use of a silver wire as indicator and a nitrate salt bridge in contact with a calomel half cell. The silver wire becomes coated with the slightly soluble silver salt that is precipitated and hence responds to changes in the anion concentration when it is present in excess. Individual titrations of any one of Br^-, Cl^-, I^-, CNS^-, SH^-, S^{-2}, N_3^-, $(C_6H_5)_4B^-$, ferri- and ferrocyanides, phosphates, etc., may be made. Application of the method to mixtures is governed by proper difference in solubility products and by adsorptive or mix-crystal tendencies of the precipitates. Cyanide ion forms first the very stable complex ion, $Ag(CN)_2^-$, and then upon addition of another equivalent of silver ion, silver cyanide, $Ag_2(CN)_2$, is precipitated. If silver iodide is dissolved in excess potassium cyanide solution the mixture, when titrated with silver, shows a sharp break in e.m.f. at the end of the formation of the silver cyanide complex ion, a second sharp break at the end of the precipitation of silver iodide, and a final inflection at the completion of the precipitation of silver cyanide. Cyanide complexation also is useful in the determination of nickel since the silver cyanide complex formation may be used to determine how much excess standard cyanide has been added over that needed to form $Ni(CN)_4^{-2}$.

The titration of silver with chloride or other halides is a precise method for determining silver.

The electrode system consists of a silver wire, a nitrate salt bridge, e.g., 3% potassium nitrate in agar, and a calomel half cell. The half cell and salt bridge may be dispensed with by using the differential technique, p. 2279, or by using a glass electrode as a reference half cell.

A mercury electrode of small area serves to indicate the equivalence points in the titration of halides and other ions with a standard solution of mercurous perchlorate or mercurous nitrate. Conversely, mercurous ion may be titrated with a standard halide solution. Iodide gives accurate results in extremely dilute solutions. A review of the classical methods involving the mercury electrode is given in the treatise of Kolthoff and Furman (34).

The mercury electrode has been shown by Reilley and his associates to be very useful as an indicator in connection with the titration of many metallic ions with various chelating agents, and also in fundamental studies of the constants of metal chelates. The addition of one drop of 0.01 or 0.001M mercuric chelonate, e.g., Hg–EDTA, establishes the indicating action. For each chelate there is a range of pH that is useful; below a given pH there is a limiting potential for each metal chelate, and the upper pH limit for each metal chelate is limited by the process $HgO + H_2O + 2e^- \rightarrow Hg + 2OH^-$.

The potentiometric and equilibrium relations for salts of metallic ions with the ions of ethylenediaminetetraacetic acid, EDTA, are given in detail by Reilley and Schmid (57); similar studies have been published for tetraethylenepentamine as a titrant (58). Quantitative results were obtained in the titration of the ions of Ca, Sr, Ba, Mg, Zn, Cd, Hg(II), Cu, Pb, Mn, Co, Ni, V(IV), Al, Ga, In, Tl, Cr(III), rare earths, Zr, Hf, Th, and Bi with standard EDTA solution. Tetraethylenepentamine is especially useful for the titration of Hg, Cu, Cd, Ni, and Zn ions, alone or in certain mixtures. The alkaline earths, rare earths, aluminum, bismuth, and lead do not interfere.

D. OXIDATION–REDUCTION PROCESSES

The potentiometric method is very useful in the study, development, and application of redox titrations. If all reactions and electrode equilibria were reversible and rapid, the potentials at the equivalence points, E_E, could be calculated as the weighted averages of the standard potentials of the two half reactions:

$$E_E = (aE_1^0 + bE_2^0)/(a + b)$$

for the reaction

$$a_{Ox_1} + b_{Red_2} \rightarrow a_{Red_1} + b_{Ox_2}$$

Here Ox_1 is the more powerful oxidant. For example, in the titration of stannous tin with ferric ion, E_1^0 is 0.77 for the ferric–ferrous system and E_2^0 is 0.15 for the stannic–stannous system, and $a = 2$ and $b = 1$. Hence $E_E = [0.77 + (2 \times 0.15)]/(1 + 2) = 0.35$ v. E_E is always weighted toward the side of the reactant that yields or accepts the greater number of electrons per molecule or ion. In titrations with permanganate, for example, the theoretical equivalence point is high and toward the E^0 for the permanganate system when uni- or bivalent ions are titrated with the loss of one or two electrons per ion.

The completeness of the reaction is deducible from

$$\log K_{eq.} = [m(E_1^0 - E_2^0)]/0.0591 \qquad \text{at } 25°\text{C.}$$

where m is the number of electrons exchanged in the balanced ionic reaction.

The magnitude of $\Delta E/\Delta$ ml. near the equivalence point depends upon the difference between E_1^0 and E_2^0, that is, upon $K_{eq.}$.

The mechanism and kinetics of the redox processes are quite involved since a succession of one-electron exchanges in one-to-one encounters of ions or molecules is involved. In many cases a slow, or rate-determining step, is involved. Very frequently such reactions may be catalyzed by adding a substance that has multivalent states, e.g., Mn, Co, Os ions, etc. Presumably a succession of one-electron exchanges becomes possible. Heating often speeds up the reactions. Sometimes it is necessary to add excess reagent, heat, and titrate back the excess reagent.

Electrode equilibria are sometimes established sluggishly in zero-current potentiometric titrations. Platinum and gold indicator electrodes become coated with oxide layers in solutions of powerful oxidants. Strong reductants, e.g., Cr^{+2}, may cause the indicator electrode to act like an unsaturated hydrogen electrode.

For the foregoing reasons, theoretical relations are rarely realized in the course of titrations. Temperatures are rarely controlled precisely and it is not feasible to wait for equilibrium to be established at the electrode surface.

There is sometimes a notably different character or hysteresis in the potential–volume curve, depending upon which reagent is used as titrant. The classic case, observed in 1914–1915 by Kelley and others, is that ferrous ion when titrated in dilute sulfuric acid medium with standard bichromate solution gives a normal S-shaped graph near the end point. On the contrary, bichromate when titrated with ferrous sulfate solution shows an anomalous *rise* in apparent reduction potential, then a practically horizontal or slightly rising curve until shortly before the end point, where the curve rounds down somewhat and then plunges sharply as the end point is passed. This anomalous behavior has been attributed to various causes, of which one of the more plausible is the formation of Cr^{+5} of higher reduction potential than the Cr^{+6} system. Similar cases of an anomalous rise in reduction potential upon addition of reductants are known.

Much information can be summarized in graphs of formal potentials as a function of pH or the gross molarity of acid or base. In Fig. 45.9 are values of formal potentials for a number of common systems as a function of molar acid concentrations.

The data enable one to calculate "formal" equilibrium constants at any particular acidity. It was deduced by Murray that the reduction of vanadic acid solutions by shaking with mercury in 1 to $2N$ hydrochloric acid solutions could lead to reduction partially beyond the vanadyl stage. The V^{+3} thus formed is reoxidized to vanadyl ion in ordinary filtrations prior to titration. When preparing large amounts of vanadyl solution by this method it was observed that the reducing power was greater than for a one-stage reduction and that the trivalent vanadium slowly disappeared, after which the quadrivalent vanadium was stable for long periods.

The chief merits of the potentiometric technique in oxidation-reduction titrations are applicability to highly colored solutions, ability to realize a

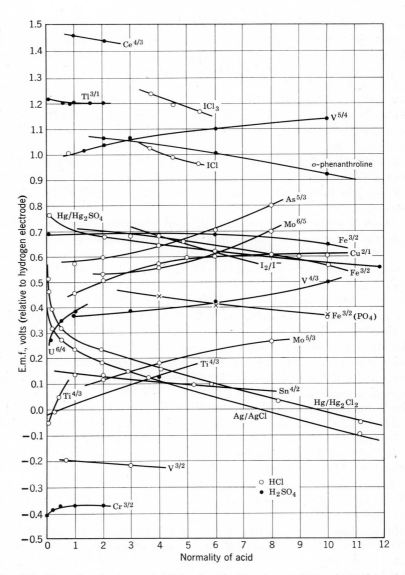

Fig. 45.9. Formal reduction potentials of various systems relative to the standard hydrogen electrode. Compiled by W. M. Murray, Jr., and N. H. Furman from data in the literature. Key: open circles, O, denote chloride solutions; closed circles, ●, denote sulfate media.

succession of end points for numerous mixtures of oxidants or reductants, and ability to interpolate the end points between readings, recording, or control applications.

In order to realize a succession of end points in processes, e.g., $Mo^{+3} \rightarrow Mo^{+5} \rightarrow MoO_4^{-2}$; $V^{+2} \rightarrow V^{+3} \rightarrow VO^{+2} \rightarrow V(OH)_4^+$; $U^{+3} \rightarrow U^{+4} \rightarrow UO_2^{+2}$, the effective potentials and rates must be such that if, for example, during the titration of V^{+2} some of the V^{+3} that is being formed is momentarily oxidized to VO^{+2}, the remaining V^{+2} will immediately reduce this VO^{+2} back to V^{+3}.

A point of view that is often feasible is to select an oxidant of reduction potential adequate to titrate the reductant in a solution and yet not great enough to titrate other reductants present. An example is that standard ferric solutions are often used to titrate U^{+4} solutions that contain iron, chromium, nickel, etc. Suppose the reduction has been performed with a reagent that yields U^{+4} and Fe^{+2}. Titration with Fe^{+3} will then be selective for the process $U^{+4} \rightarrow UO^{+2}$, regardless of the presence of the Fe^{+2}.

E. CONCENTRATION-CELL METHODS

Concentration cells are used chiefly in two ways in chemical analysis: (1) the actual reading of the cell is translated into concentration of substance sought with the aid of a prior calibration, and (2) an adjustment of the concentration of one-half of the cell is made by titration with standard solution until at the null, or balance, point its concentration is the same as that in the unknown side.

1. Direct Measurement

In connection with standard cell work, G. A. Hulett (30) made critical studies of the purification of mercury by distillation. Distillates were tested by placing the purest obtainable mercury in one arm of an H-shaped cell and the other mercury in the other arm. Upon covering to a point above the cross tube with a suitable solution it was possible to detect very minute amounts of cadmium or other metals in the impure mercury.

Johnson and Low (32) developed a concentration-cell technique comparable in precision with the usual equal-opalescence method in atomic weight determinations. Furman and Low (20) developed several techniques for using the concentration cell to determine minute amounts of chloride in various nitrates. Empirically determined activity coefficients were necessary since rather concentrated solutions were used. In one modification the unknown was precisely matched by a synthetic solution after a preliminary estimate by testing the unknown *vs.* a like portion of the unknown with a small amount of added chloride. Significant results could be obtained down to 0.00036 g. $(10^{-5}M)$ chloride per liter. Low and Pryde (42) measured concentrations of fluoride in the range 27 to 125 γ per 5 ml. by the complexing effect on ferric ion. The cell consisted of identical platinum wire electrodes in a mixture of 0.0005 molar ferric salt and $0.0002M$ in ferrous ion. The sides of the cell were as nearly as possible identical in ionic strength and in nature of all the components except fluoride.

Blaedel *et al.* (5) extended the concentration-cell principle to the determination of small amounts of chloride in various sulfate mixtures.

Gaseous mixtures containing hydrogen or oxygen have been compared with pure reference gases by passing the two gases through hydrogen electrodes dipping into the solution of an electrolyte.

Various quinhydrone preparations have been compared with standard material by saturating portions of a buffer solution with each sample and comparing the mixtures with two similar platinum electrodes and a salt bridge.*

2. Titration Methods

Mlle. de Brouchère (12) long ago proposed the titration of one side of a concentration cell until two similar electrodes showed no difference in potential. Copper electrodes dipped into a solution of unknown copper content and a standard solution of copper more concentrated than the unknown, respectively, were used. A salt bridge connection was made and the known solution was titrated with water until zero potential difference was found.

Swain and Ross (67) used a similar principle to study reaction kinetics in the hydrolysis of *t*-butyl chloride in water–5% acetone. Two silver wires in separate beakers connected by a salt bridge were provided with the same amount of sodium perchlorate solution that was $0.144M$ in 5% acetone–water, but one beaker contained $0.001M$ concentration of *t*-butyl chloride. The other cell was treated at known time intervals with standard chloride solution to restore the null of a galvanometer connecting the two electrodes. Both solutions were stirred. The kinetics of the reaction between ceric sulfate and oxalate was studied in a similar manner (64).

The titration technique has been revived in a more precise way by Malmstadt and Winefordner (46) by making provision to maintain the ionic strength constant. If the concentration of chloride is greater in an

* Private communication from the late G. A. Perley (*ca.* 1936).

unknown than in the reference sample, dilution to a null point between two silver chloride electrodes is made with a rather concentrated solution ($2N$ sulfuric acid), this medium being the main electrolyte in the standard. If the chloride solution is more dilute than the standard, a solution of chloride in $1M$ sulfuric acid that is twice as concentrated as the reference standard is added to a point of balance. The same general principle has been applied to the indirect determination of oxidants through iodine liberation, or of reductants by their reaction with iodine solution. Iodine is then generated electrolytically until two similar electrodes in the respective solutions show zero difference in e.m.f. (47). A similar application to the chloride case has been made for silver in alloys (48).

The technique is referred to by its authors as "precision null-point potentiometry." It is obvious that knowledge must be obtained as to the nature and amounts of electrolytes in the unknown solution in order to eliminate ionic strength effects.

VI. POTENTIOMETRY WITH POLARIZED ELECTRODES

If a small and nearly constant current of 2 to 10 μamp. is passed between an indicator electrode and a reference electrode (one polarized electrode), or between similar indicator electrodes (two polarized electrodes), a useful potential response can be obtained from the cell, using for measurement a vacuum-tube voltmeter or a line-operated pH meter of high impedance. The small regulated current is obtained by using a high-voltage source such as a 45-v. "B" battery and a swamping resistance from 10 to 20 megohms to keep the small current through the indicating system approximately constant in spite of resistance changes or back-e.m.f. from the electrodes. The indicating meter is connected to the two electrode terminals of the indicating system.

The general principles of this technique were applied first by H. H. Willard and F. Fenwick (71), who found that the swamping resistance was so small, less than 0.1 megohm, that the current could vary appreciably during the course of the titration. This writer and his associates (59) applied the principle to a number of titrations with ceric sulfate. They explained the general principles from the standpoint of current–voltage curves (60). Gauguin (22) and others (23) related various electrometric end points to polarization curves and gave a mathematical analysis of various reversible and irreversible cases. The relation between amperometric titrations and potentiometry also has been reviewed by Kolthoff (37). Reinmuth (61) has extended the treatment to include chronopotentiometry and chronopotentiometric titration theory.

The nature of the response when a small controlled-current input is applied to two similar electrodes during the titration of the reductant, Red_2, of a reversible redox system with the oxidant, Ox_1, of a second reversible redox system is explained in Figs. 45.10 and 45.11. In cases in which

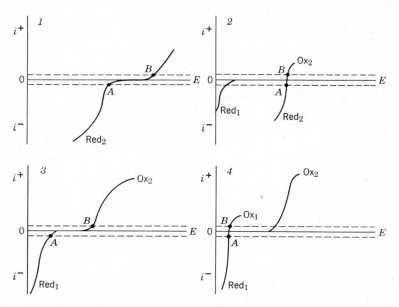

Fig. 45.10. Polarization curves during the titration of a reductant, Red_2, with an oxidant, Ox_1. Both systems are reversible. The ordinates of the current, i, are as in polarographic conventions. E is the e.m.f. between the two platinum electrodes, and AB represents the $E_{obs.}$ value. There is about 4 μamp. of steady current between the dotted lines.

Curve 1: the anodic curve for Red_2 and the reduction of a component of the solvent determine the magnitude of $E_{obs.}$.

Curve 2: as soon as both components Red_2 and Ox_2 of a reversible system are present because of the addition of reagent Ox_1 at AB, $E_{obs.}$ drops almost to zero.

Curve 3: at the equivalence point the small current can only be passed by the operation of the current on Red_1 at the anode and on Ox_2 at the cathode. $E_{obs.}$, therefore, increases sharply near this point.

Curve 4: after the end point is passed the current can flow again because of the reaction between Red_1 and Ox_1, and $E_{obs.}$ (at AB) once more is almost zero.

one process is irreversible, the $E_{obs.}$ will not fall nearly to zero on one side or the other of the equivalence point. At extreme dilutions of reactants the maximum of $E_{obs.}$ may be on a very flat rounded curve. The method will then be found less satisfactory than other electrometric methods of equiv-

alance-point indication. A systematic study of this and other electrometric titration techniques has been given in Chapter 43.

Detailed information as to types of phenomena in titrations with ceric
sulfate (2,59), bromate (1), electrolytically generated bromine (38), or
cerous sulfate in alkaline media (21) has been published.

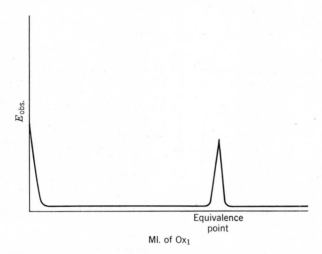

Fig. 45.11. The value of $E_{obs.}$ *vs.* milliliters of oxidant in the titration of a reductant.
For the type of process represented in Fig. 45.10 the course of $E_{obs.}$, initially rather
large, will drop as oxidant is added until the equivalence point is approached. A
maximum coincides with the equivalence point.

In certain concentration ranges the change in millivolts per 0.01 ml. of
$0.1N$ reagent near the end point may be greater than by the classic potentiometric method. A good example is found in work of Adams (2) on the
titration of arsenite using a platinum indicator electrode made negative to
a calomel half cell. The addition of one small drop (0.01 ml.) gave abrupt
potential changes near the end point of 0.4 to 0.5 v. Similar results were
found in the titration of dilute iodide solutions with ceric sulfate (59).

GENERAL REFERENCES

Most of the literature of potentiometry can be traced through the following monographs and reviews:

Kolthoff, I. M., and N. H. Furman, *Potentiometric Titrations*, 2nd ed., Wiley, New
    York, 1931.
Müller, E., *Elektrometrische (potentiometrische) Massanalyse*, 4th ed., Steinkopf, Dresden,
    1926.

Böttger, W., "Potentiometrische Massanalyse," in *Physikalische Methode der analytischen Chemie*, Akad. Verlagsgesellschaft, Leipzig, 1939, Part III, pp. 478–760.

Charlot, G., Ed., *Modern Electroanalytical Methods*, Elsevier, New York, 1958.

Reviews by N. H. Furman: *J. Chem. Educ.*, **3**, 932 (1926); *Ind. Eng. Chem., Anal. Ed.*, **2**, 213 (1930); **14**, 367 (1942); *Anal. Chem.*, **22**, 33 (1950); **23**, 21 (1951); **26**, 84 (1954).

Reviews by C. N. Reilley: *Anal. Chem.*, **28**, 671 (1956); **30**, 765 (1958); **32**, 185R (1960).

REFERENCES

1. Adams, R. N., *Anal. Chem.*, **26**, 1933 (1954).
2. Adams, R. N., C. N. Reilley, and N. H. Furman, *Anal. Chem.*, **24**, 1200 (1952).
3. Atanasiu, I. A., *Z. Anal. Chem.*, **85**, 120 (1931); K. Takagi and Y. Shimizu, *J. Electrochem. Soc. (Japan)*, **18**, 150 (1950).
4. Biilman, E., *Ann. Chim.*, **15**, 109 (1921); F. Hovorka and W. C. Dearing, *J. Am. Chem. Soc.*, **57**, 446 (1935); J. L. R. Morgan *et al.*, *J. Electrochem. Soc.*, **61**, 409 (1932); H. S. Harned and D. D. Wright, *J. Am. Chem. Soc.*, **55**, 4849 (1933).
5. Blaedel, W. J., W. B. Lewis, and J. N. Thomas, *Anal. Chem.*, **24**, 509 (1952).
6. Brintzinger, H., and B. Rost, *Z. Anal. Chem.*, **115**, 241 (1939).
7. Britton, H. T. S., and E. N. Dodd, *J. Chem. Soc.*, **1931**, 829.
8. Britton, H. T. S., *The Determination of Hydrogen Ions*, D. Van Nostrand, Princeton, N. J., 1934.
9. Brown, J. F., and R. J. Weir, *Analyst*, **83**, 491 (1958); J. F. Brown and A. G. Stanley, *Trans. Soc. Instr., Technol.*, **8**, 156 (1956).
10. Cox, D. C., *J. Am. Chem. Soc.*, **47**, 2138 (1925).
11. Critchfield, F. E., and J. B. Johnson, *Anal. Chem.*, **30**, 1247 (1958).
12. de Brouchère, L., *Bull. Soc. Chim. Belg.*, **7**, 103 (1928).
13. de Brouwer, S., *Bull. Soc. Chim. Belg.*, **48**, 158 (1939); O. Tomiček and J. Feldmann, *Casopis Ceskoslov. lekarnictva*, **15**, 127 (1935).
14. Dunn, E. B., F. W. Melpolder, R. C. Taylor, and W. S. Young, *Proc. Mid-Year Meeting, Am. Petrol. Inst.*, **30** (MIII), 45 (1950).
15. Franklin, E. C., *J. Am. Chem. Soc.*, **27**, 820 (1905).
16. Frediani, H. A., *Anal. Chem.*, **24**, 1126 (1952).
17. Fritz, J. S., *Anal. Chem.*, **22**, 1028 (1950).
18. Fritz, J. S., *Acid-Base Titrations in Nonaqueous Solvents*, G. Frederick Smith Chemical Co., Columbus, Ohio, 1952.
19. Furman, N. H., *J. Am. Chem. Soc.*, **44**, 2685 (1922).
20. Furman, N. H., and G. W. Low, Jr., *J. Am. Chem. Soc.*, **57**, 1585, 1588 (1935).
21. Furman, N. H., and A. J. Fenton, Jr., *Anal. Chem.*, **32**, 745 (1960).
22. Gauguin, R., *Anal. Chim. Acta*, **7**, 172 (1952).
23. Gauguin, R., G. Charlot, and J. Coursier, *Anal. Chim. Acta*, **7**, 184 (1952).
24. Hall, N. F., and J. B. Conant, *J. Am. Chem. Soc.*, **49**, 3047 (1927).
25. Hall, N. F., and J. B. Conant, *J. Am. Chem. Soc.*, **49**, 3062 (1927); N. F. Hall and T. H. Werner, *J. Am. Chem. Soc.*, **50**, 2367 (1928); N. F. Hall, *J. Am. Chem. Soc.*, **52**, 5115 (1930).
26. Hawes, R. C., and A. Strickler, U. S. Patent 2,770,531 (1956); R. C. Hawes, A. Strickler, and T. H. Petterson, *Elec. Mfg.*, **47**, 76 (1951).
27. Hildebrand, J. H., *J. Am. Chem. Soc.*, **35**, 849 (1913); J. H. Hildebrand and H. S. Harned, *Intern. Congr. Pure and Appl. Chem., 8th Congr.*, **1**, 217 (1912).

28. Hildebrand, J. H., E. R. Bishop, and E. B. Kittredge, *J. Am. Chem. Soc.*, **44**, 135 (1922).
29. Hostetter, J. C., and H. S. Rogerts, *J. Am. Chem. Soc.*, **41**, 1337 (1919).
30. Hulett, G. A., *Phys. Rev.*, **21**, 288 (1899); **33**, 307 (1911).
31. Irving, H., and L. D. Pettit, *Analyst*, **84**, 641 (1959).
32. Johnson, C. R., and G. W. Low, Jr., *J. Phys. Chem.*, **36**, 2392 (1932).
33. Kahlenberg, L., and A. C. Krueger, *Trans. Am. Electrochem. Soc.*, **56**, 201 (1929); M. L. Holt and L. Kahlenberg, *Trans. Am. Electrochem. Soc.*, **57**, 361 (1930).
34. Kolthoff, I. M., and N. H. Furman, *Potentiometric Titrations*, Wiley, New York, 1931; G. A. Perley, *Ind. Eng. Chem., Anal. Ed.*, **11**, 316, 319 (1939); F. Hovorka and G. H. Chapman, *J. Am. Chem. Soc.*, **63**, 955, 2024 (1941).
35. Kolthoff, I. M., and S. Bruckenstein, *J. Am. Chem. Soc.*, **78**, 1, 10, 2914 (1956).
36. Kolthoff, I. M., and N. H. Furman, *Potentiometric Titrations*, 2nd ed., Wiley, New York, 1931.
37. Kolthoff, I. M., *Anal. Chem.*, **26**, 1685 (1954).
38. Lee, J. K., and R. N. Adams, *Anal. Chem.*, **30**, 240 (1958).
39. Lingane, J. J., *Anal. Chem.*, **20**, 285, 797 (1948); **31**, 497 (1949).
40. Lingane, J. J., *Anal. Chem.*, **26**, 622 (1954); G. E. Gerhardt, H. C. Lawrence, and J. S. Parsons, *Anal. Chem.*, **27**, 1752 (1955).
41. Lingane, J. J., *Anal. Chem.*, **20**, 285 (1948).
42. Low, G. W., Jr., and E. H. Pryde, *J. Am. Chem. Soc.*, **61**, 2237 (1939).
43. MacInnes, D. A., and P. T. Jones, *J. Am. Chem. Soc.*, **48**, 2831 (1926).
44. MacInnes, D. A., and I. A. Cowperthwaite, *J. Am. Chem. Soc.*, **53**, 555 (1931).
45. Malmstadt, H. V., and E. R. Fett, *Anal. Chem.*, **26**, 1348 (1954); **27**, 1757 (1955); **29**, 1901 (1957).
46. Malmstadt, H. V., and J. D. Winefordner, *Anal. Chim. Acta*, **20**, 283 (1959).
47. Malmstadt, H. V., and H. L. Pardue, *Anal. Chem.*, **32**, 1034 (1960).
48. Malmstadt, H. V., T. P. Hadjiioannou, and H. L. Pardue, *Anal. Chem.*, **32**, 1039 (1960).
49. Moss, M. L., J. H. Elliott, and R. T. Hall, *Anal. Chem.*, **20**, 784 (1948).
50. Müller, E., *Z. Physik. Chem.*, **135**, 102 (1928).
51. Nichols, M. L., and S. R. Cooper, *Ind. Eng. Chem., Anal. Ed.*, **7**, 353 (1935).
52. Palit, S. R., *Ind. Eng. Chem.*, **18**, 246 (1946).
53. U. S. Patents 2,758,079 and 2,832,734, E. L. Eckfeldt (1958).
54. Phillips, J. P., *Automatic Titrators*, Academic Press, New York, 1959.
55. Pifer, C. W., E. G. Wollish, and M. Schmall, *Anal. Chem.*, **25**, 310 (1953).
56. Purdy, W. C., E. A. Burns, and L. B. Rogers, *Anal. Chem.*, **27**, 1988 (1955).
57. Reilley, C. N., and R. W. Schmid, *Anal. Chem.*, **30**, 947, 953 (1958).
58. Reilley, C. N., and A. Vavoulis, *Anal. Chem.*, **31**, 243 (1959).
59. Reilley, C. N., W. D. Cooke, and N. H. Furman, *Anal. Chem.*, **23**, 1223 (1951).
60. Reilley, C. N., W. D. Cooke, and N. H. Furman, *Anal. Chem.*, **23**, 1226 (1951).
61. Reinmuth, W. H., *Anal. Chem.*, **32**, 1509, 1514, 1518 (1960).
62. Richards, W. T., *J. Phys. Chem.*, **32**, 990 (1928).
63. Robinson, H. A., *Trans. Am. Electrochem. Soc.*, **92**, 445 (1947).
64. Ross, S. D., and C. G. Swain, *J. Am. Chem. Soc.*, **69**, 1325 (1947).
65. Shaffer, P. A., Jr., A. Briglio, Jr., and J. A. Brockman, Jr., *Anal. Chem.*, **20**, 1008 (1948).
66. Stonehill, H. I., *Trans. Faraday Soc.*, **39**, 67 (1943).
67. Swain, C. G., and S. D. Ross, *J. Am. Chem. Soc.*, **68**, 658 (1946).

68. Van der Heijde, H. B., and E. A. M. F. Dahmen, *Anal. Chim. Acta,* **16,** 378 (1957); E. A. M. F. Dahmen *et al., Anal. Chim. Acta,* **19,** 64 (1958); **21,** 193 (1959).

69. Willard, H. H., and F. Fenwick, *J. Am. Chem. Soc.,* **44,** 2504 (1922); G. VanName and F. Fenwick, *J. Am. Chem. Soc.,* **47,** 8 (1925).

70. Willard, H. H., and A. W. Boldyreff, *J. Am. Chem. Soc.,* **51,** 471 (1929).

71. Willard, H. H., and F. Fenwick, *J. Am. Chem. Soc.,* **44,** 2516 (1922).

72. Ziegel, H., *Trans. Am. Electrochem. Soc.,* **26,** 91 (1914); E. Müller, *Elektrometrische Massanalyse,* 4th ed., Steinkopf, Dresden, 1926.

VOLTAMMETRY AT THE DROPPING MERCURY ELECTRODE (POLAROGRAPHY)

By Louis Meites, *Department of Chemistry, Polytechnic Institute of Brooklyn, Brooklyn, New York*

Contents

Contents (*continued*)

I. INTRODUCTION

A. NATURE AND SCOPE

Polarography is the name generally applied to the branch of voltammetry in which a dropping mercury electrode is used as the indicator or "polarized" electrode. It deals with the relationships among three fundamental variables: the composition of the solution in which the dropping electrode is immersed, the potential applied to the dropping electrode, and the current flowing through the cell.

Figure 46.1a is a typical polarogram or current–potential curve obtained with a dropping mercury electrode in a hydrochloric acid solution containing cadmium ion; Fig. 46.1b was obtained under otherwise identical conditions in a cadmium-free solution. The sigmoid-shaped "wave" in curve a is due to the reduction of cadmium ion to cadmium amalgam; its level portion or "plateau," which begins at about -0.75 v., reflects the practically complete reduction of all of the cadmium ions reaching the surface of the electrode. This results in the establishment of a concentration gradient in the solution around the electrode, and this in turn causes cadmium ions to diffuse up to the electrode surface at a rate that is proportional to the concentration of cadmium ion in the solution. Hence the "diffusion current" indicated on the figure, which is the increase in current at a potential (on the plateau) resulting from the addition of the cadmium, is proportional to the cadmium concentration. The constant of proportionality involved depends on a number of experimental variables, but it can be evaluated for any combination of experimental conditions by measurements with solutions of known concentrations. This is the basis of quantitative polarographic analysis.

The location of the wave with reference to the potential axis is governed by the formal potential of the half reaction responsible for the wave, and by the kinetic parameters characteristic of that half reaction. The half reactions

$$Pb(II) + xHg + 2e = Pb(Hg)_x$$

$$Cd(II) + xHg + 2e = Cd(Hg)_x$$

in $1F$ hydrochloric acid attain equilibrium in the sense of the Nernst equation very rapidly at potentials near their respective formal potentials. However, the formal potential of the lead ion–lead amalgam half reaction is appreciably less negative than that of the cadmium ion–cadmium amalgam half reaction. On a polarogram of a $1F$ hydrochloric acid solution containing both lead and cadmium ions, the lead wave therefore occurs at a considerably less negative potential than the cadmium wave.

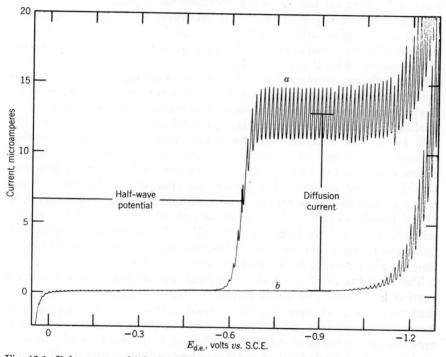

Fig. 46.1. Polarograms of (a) $1F$ hydrochloric acid containing 0.5mM cadmium ion, and (b) $1F$ hydrochloric acid alone.

The formal potential of the half reaction that occurs when nickel(II) is reduced from $1F$ hydrochloric acid is also somewhat more positive than the formal potential of the cadmium ion–cadmium amalgam couple. At its formal potential, however, the reduction of nickel ion proceeds so slowly as to give rise to only an immeasurably small current. The rate of this reduction increases with increasingly negative potential and a nickel wave does eventually appear, but only at a potential considerably more negative than the range of potentials in which the cadmium wave occurs.

For one or the other of these reasons, the waves corresponding to different half reactions occur at different potentials. It is customary to denote the position of a wave along the potential axis by means of its "half-wave potential." This is the potential at which, after appropriate correction for the residual current, the current is exactly half the diffusion current. The half-wave potential is indicated on Fig. 46.1. For a so-called "reversible" wave, such as the lead and cadmium waves in the above discussion, the half-wave potential has an exact thermodynamic significance; but for "irreversible" waves, such as the nickel wave, the half-wave potential serves merely as an arbitrary, though convenient, way of specifying the position of a wave, and is appreciably dependent on the experimental conditions under which it is measured.

Since different substances give rise to waves having different half-wave potentials, it is possible to identify the substance responsible for a wave by the judicious use of tables of half-wave potentials. This is the principle of qualitative polarographic analysis. Of fundamental importance in this field is the fact that the thermodynamic and kinetic parameters that characterize different half reactions are often affected in different ways by changes in the pH or ionic strength of the environment or by the introduction of a complexing ion. This permits the analyst to decide among alternative possibilities or to resolve two overlapping waves. For example, in $1F$ nitric acid a wave with a half-wave potential of ± 0.00 v. vs. S.C.E. might be due to either iodate or copper(II). But in an acetate buffer the half-wave potentials of these two substances differ by more than 0.4 v., so that their differentiation in such a medium would be a simple matter.

The magnitudes of the residual current and of the constant of proportionality relating diffusion current to concentration are usually such that the necessity of correcting for the residual current introduces a rapidly increasing uncertainty as the concentration of the substance being determined decreases below about $10^{-5}M$. In certain favorable cases, however, analyses can be carried out at concentrations as low as $10^{-6}M$ with errors not exceeding a few per cent; by the exercise of meticulous attention to experimental details, and with the aid of special electrical circuitry, it is occasionally possible to obtain useful results with solutions as dilute as $10^{-7}M$. On the whole, a concentration of about 2 to $3 \times 10^{-6}M$ may fairly be regarded as the lowest that may be satisfactorily determined by conventional techniques in the routine laboratory. At the other extreme, the migration current and the appearance of maxima often cause difficulties in dealing with concentrations above about $2 \times 10^{-2}M$; there is no indication that these difficulties are insuperable, but there is little reason to suppose that their solution would lead to the widespread adoption of polarographic analysis in preference to the numerous simple and accurate methods already available for use in this range.

Accuracy and precision of the order of $\pm 0.2\%$ have occasionally been achieved in the polarographic analysis of technical materials, but a figure approximating $\pm 2\%$ is much more nearly representative of what may be expected in the routine laboratory. Although the factors responsible for this difference are fairly well understood, the exigencies of time in industrial practice generally restrict the use of polarography to those analyses in which the required accuracy is between 1 and 5%.

Polarographic analysis is directly applicable to the determination of any substance—molecular or ionic, organic or inorganic—that can be reduced or oxidized at a mercury electrode in any solvent whose dielectric constant is sufficiently high to permit a reasonable (0.05 to $1M$) ionic strength to be attained by the addition of some indifferent electrolyte. In addition, many substances that cannot be reduced or oxidized at the dropping electrode can be determined by indirect methods, by which one measures the diffusion current of a second substance that is reducible or oxidizable and that is formed by some chemical reaction in an amount stoichiometrically equivalent to the amount of the substance sought.

Amperometric titration is a technique in which diffusion-current measurements are employed to locate the end point of a titration with a standard solution of a suitable reagent. Provided that such sources of error as coprecipitation, competing reactions, and the like can be eliminated, amperometric titrations can give results considerably more accurate and precise than ordinary polarographic analysis, an accuracy of $\pm 0.2\%$ being by no means uncommon. Like the indirect methods just mentioned, amperometric titrations can be used for the determination of substances that cannot themselves be reduced or oxidized; this is possible if a reaction can be found that results in either the stoichiometric consumption of an electroactive reagent or the stoichiometric formation of an electroactive product

B. HISTORY

Polarographic measurements were first made by Heyrovský at the Charles University in Prague, and were first described in 1922 (96). During the next 15 years, much work was carried out in Heyrovský's laboratory on the theory, methodology, instrumentation, and applications of the method. The steadily growing proof of the versatility of polarography, which received its first systematic exposition in 1936 (100), then led to a rapid growth of interest on the part of analytical chemists in many other countries. An important stimulus to this growth of interest was the publication in 1941 of the monograph by Kolthoff and Lingane (156). Polarography has since become one of the most widely used techniques of analytical chemistry. It may fairly be regarded as the precursor of a number of other electroanalytical methods that have been developed during the last decade and that are described elsewhere in this Treatise.

For the convenience of the reader desiring a more complete treatment of polarography than is possible in the space available here, a group of monographs and other references are listed under "General References" at the end of this chapter.

II. POLAROGRAPHIC THEORY

A. NATURE AND PROPERTIES OF THE DROPPING MERCURY ELECTRODE

A conventional dropping mercury electrode consists essentially of a length of capillary tubing having a very small inside diameter (about 0.06 to 0.08 mm.). The upper end of the capillary is attached to a tube containing a column of mercury that is electrically connected to the external circuit, and the tip of the capillary is immersed in the solution being studied.

Under these conditions, mercury flows through the capillary and forms a droplet at the tip. The droplet grows until it reaches an accurately reproducible size, which depends on the geometry of the capillary tip and on the interfacial tension between mercury and the solution; then it falls, stirring the solution to some extent, and another drop is born to start the cycle again.

The periodic nature of this process is peculiar to the dropping electrode alone among the indicator electrodes that have been employed in voltammetric measurements. Under fixed experimental conditions, the current varies during the life of each drop in a manner that reflects the increase of drop area and the depletion of the reducible or oxidizable species in the diffusion layer surrounding the drop. But each drop repeats the history of the one that preceded it, and so the average current is the same from one drop to the next. No long-term accumulation of solid products (e.g., adsorbed materials, deposited metals, or noble-metal oxides) is possible, which greatly improves the reproducibility and facilitates the interpretation of the data obtained, in contrast to what is true of solid metal indicator electrodes. At the same time, the very small area of the dropping electrode renders concentration changes during an experiment negligibly small (except when, for certain special purposes, only a very small volume of solution is taken for study), and hence the bulk depletion of the solution and the accumulation of soluble products of the electrode reaction may be neglected; this is in marked contrast to voltammetry with stationary electrodes (mercury pool, hanging drop, etc.), in which the phenomena involved are intrinsically transient and time-dependent.

Unlike most other voltammetric methods, therefore, polarography ordinarily does not involve time as a significant variable. This consequence of the integrating property of the dropping mercury electrode is largely responsible for the relative simplicity, both instrumentally and manipulatively, and for the widespread use of polarographic methods.

B. THEORY OF THE LIMITING CURRENT

The limiting current is the total current measured at a potential on the plateau of a polarographic wave. It is the sum of three components:

1. The residual current, which is observed with the supporting electrolyte alone;

2. The migration current, which is due to the reduction or oxidation of ions of the substance responsible for the wave that are brought to the electrode surface by electrical transference; and

3. The diffusion current, which reflects the reduction or oxidation of material reaching the electrode surface under the influence of diffusive forces alone.

Practical methods of quantitative polarographic analysis are generally directed toward the measurement of the diffusion current. To this end the migration current is suppressed by the addition of a large excess of some electrolyte, which serves to conduct the current through the solution and eliminate transference by the reducible or oxidizable ions, and the residual current is corrected for in some suitable fashion.

1. The Residual Current

A residual current curve, as shown in Fig. 46.1b, consists of three portions. These are the initial current rise, in which the current rises rapidly from large negative values, an intermediate portion, and a final current rise, in which the current increases rapidly to large positive values. The initial current rise reflects the virtual cessation of an anodic process that is usually the oxidation of mercury, and its location depends on the composition of the solution, varying from about +0.3 v. *vs.* S.C.E. in neutral or acidic perchlorate solutions to about −0.7 v. *vs.* S.C.E. in 1*M* cyanide. The final current rise similarly reflects the apparent onset of the reduction of some substance present at high concentration; its location also varies with solution composition from about −1.0 v. *vs*. S.C.E. in fairly concentrated acids to about −2.7 v. *vs*. S.C.E. in neutral or alkaline solutions of certain tetraalkylammonium salts (110,329). Except, in some marginal cases, by the use of differential or derivative polarography (Sections III-B and III-C), useful information can be secured only in the intermediate range, where the rates of both of these limiting processes are extremely small.

In this intermediate range, the residual current may be regarded as the sum of two components: a "condenser" current, which is consumed in charging the drop and the electrical double layer around its surface, and a "faradaic" current, which is consumed by the oxidation or reduction of traces of impurities.

A number of studies of the condenser current (28,30,121,156,217,338) have confirmed the theoretical relationship

$$i_c = 0.0085 \; \kappa(E_m - E) \; m^{2/3}t^{-1/3} \tag{1}$$

where i_c is the average condenser current during the life of a drop at a potential E, E_m is the potential of the electrocapillary maximum (65,73,85) in the solution under investigation, κ is the capacity of the electrical double layer, and m and t are the capillary characteristics defined below. No similarly general equation can be given for the faradaic current; this is best eliminated as completely as possible by the use of the purest available reagents (further purification, which may conveniently be effected by controlled-potential electrolysis (222), is often necessary in trace analysis) and the exertion of scrupulous care in freeing the solution from dissolved oxygen (97,152,158,231) before obtaining a polarogram.

The ultimate sensitivity of polarographic analysis depends largely on the magnitude of the residual current and on the accuracy with which the necessary correction for it can be made (51). One may either measure the residual current separately and correct for it arithmetically (321) or instrumentally (124,135), or find the diffusion current by extrapolation on the recorded polarogram, as described in Section V-B-3. The latter procedure is simpler, but since κ is not independent of potential it is not always satisfactory in trace analysis (36).

2. The Migration Current

In addition to the diffusive force due to the concentration gradient around the electrode, there is also an electrical force that affects the rate at which the reducible or oxidizable ions reach the electrode surface. The portion of the total current that is due to the existence of this electrical force is known as the migration current (98,119,188,202,299). This increases as the transference number of the ion responsible for the wave increases, and it also depends on the charge carried by that ion. Cations are attracted to a negatively charged electrode, and thus the electrical force under these conditions leads to an increase of the limiting current, so that the migration current is positive. Exactly the opposite is true when the electroactive species is anionic. In either case, the transference number is considerably affected by the addition of a trace of a foreign electrolyte, whose ions assist in conducting electricity through the solution.

Hence it is customary to carry out all polarographic measurements in the presence of a fairly high concentration of a supporting electrolyte, which decreases the transference number of the electroactive ion virtually to zero and thus practically eliminates the migration current. The supporting electrolyte serves the additional purpose of decreasing the cell resistance to a value so low that the iR drop through the solution becomes negligible; this permits equating the voltage applied from the external circuit to the potential difference between the two electrodes. For these two reasons, polarograms are rarely secured at ionic strengths less than about 0.1; when the dielectric constant of the solvent is so low that this cannot be attained, distorted polarograms result unless special measures are taken (252,261).

3. The Diffusion Current

Although the diffusion current is so pre-eminently important in quantitative analysis that it has been the subject of extensive theoretical and experimental study, there remain a number of important questions on which no general agreement has yet been reached.

a. Equations for the Diffusion Current

According to the equation first derived by Ilkovič (119,122), and more rigorously by MacGillavry and Rideal (203),

$$i_d = 607 \ nD^{1/2}Cm^{2/3}t^{1/6} \tag{2}$$

where i_d is the average diffusion current (microamperes), n is the number of electrons consumed by each ion or molecule of the electroactive species (both n and i_d are negative for anodic processes), D is the diffusion coefficient of the electroactive species (cm.²/second) and C is its concentration (millimoles/liter), m is the average rate of flow of mercury through the capillary (mg./second), and t is the drop time (seconds), i.e., the length of time that elapses between the instants of fall of two successive drops.

The quantities m and t are known as the "capillary characteristics"; the factors by which they are affected are discussed in a subsequent section.

In accordance with a suggestion made by Walkley (339) and Lingane (180), the Ilkovič equation is often written in the form

$$i_d/Cm^{2/3}t^{1/6} \;=\; 607 \; nD^{1/2} \;=\; I \tag{3}$$

Under fixed experimental conditions (supporting electrolyte composition, temperature, etc.), D is constant for any particular electroactive species;

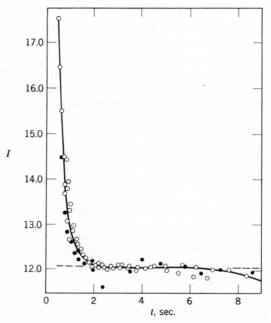

Fig. 46.2. Diffusion-current constant of iodate in $0.1F$ potassium chloride and $0.1F$ hydrochloric acid (*open circles* (216)), and in $0.2F$ sodium phosphate at pH 7.0 (*solid circles* (197)). Reproduced by permission from the *Journal of the American Chemical Society.*

although n may assume different values if the original species is reduced or oxidized stepwise, giving multiple waves, it is constant for any one wave. Hence the quantity I, the "diffusion current constant," should be a constant for any particular wave, and once its value has been measured in one laboratory, equation (3) can be used to calculate the concentration of the same species from data on i_d and $m^{2/3}t^{1/6}$ obtained in other laboratories or with different capillaries.

The validity of this "absolute" method of analysis depends on the constancy of I as m and t are varied. Some typical data bearing on this question are shown in Figs. 46.2 and 46.3. It is evident that I increases rapidly at low drop times; this is because of convection around the rapidly forming drops and is the reason that drop times shorter than about 2 seconds should never be used in practical measurements. Although at higher drop times equation (3) appears to be closely obeyed in the absence of a maximum suppressor (Fig. 46.2), this is not true in the presence of a maximum suppressor (Fig. 46.3). Similar behavior has been reported for a number of other reducible substances (190,197,216,218,234), but other

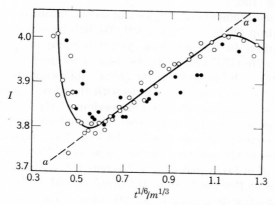

Fig. 46.3. Diffusion-current constant of lead in 0.1F potassium chloride and 0.1F hydrochloric acid (*open circles* (218)) and in 1F potassium chloride (*solid circles* (197)); both contain 0.01% gelatin. Reproduced by permission from the *Journal of the American Chemical Society*.

workers have asserted (92,312,313) that the behavior typified by Fig. 46.3 is displayed regardless of whether a maximum suppressor is present.

There is, however, general agreement that, at least in the presence of a maximum suppressor, the diffusion current is more accurately described by the equation

$$i_d = 607 \ nD^{1/2}Cm^{2/3}t^{1/6}(1 + kD^{1/2}t^{1/6}/m^{1/3}) \qquad (4)$$

than by equation (3). Equation (4) was originally derived by Strehlow and von Stackelberg (313), who gave $k = 17$, and by Lingane and Loveridge (191), who gave $k = 39$. Koutecký's still more recent derivation (164) led to the equation

$$i_d = 607 \ nD^{1/2}Cm^{2/3}t^{1/6}(1 + 34 \ D^{1/2}t^{1/6}/m^{1/3} + 100 \ Dt^{1/3}/m^{2/3}) \qquad (5)$$

in which the third term within the parentheses is so small as to be virtually undetectable by present techniques. The data of Lingane and Loveridge (191) and of Meites and Meites (216,218,234) seem to indicate that k in equation (4) is about 31, a figure whose difference from that in equation (5) is commensurate with the experimental errors involved in the measurements. On the other hand, the data of von Stackelberg and his co-workers (92,312,313) are in equally good agreement with $k = 17$: the discrepancy between this value and that of equation (5) has been ascribed to a "depletion effect" (307). Even more recently, a detailed derivation leading, in effect, to equation (4) with $k = 34.6$ has been given by Koutecký and von Stackelberg (166a).

Numerous measurements of the instantaneous diffusion current during the life of the drop (29,86,91,120,185,191,204,322) have failed to provide a conclusive solution to the problem, partly because of variations of m during the drop life (185) and partly because of incomplete stirring by the falling drop (91). Kůta and Smoler (168a), following Hans and Henne (91), have obtained current–time curves with the "first" drop (i.e., a drop growing into a solution not subjected to previous electrolysis and therefore perfectly homogeneous); they assert that these conform closely to equation (4) and that deviations therefrom with the second and following drops are due to depletion of the solution around them when they are young. According to equation (4), a plot of $i_\tau/\tau^{1/6}$ versus $\tau^{1/6}$ (i_τ being the diffusion current τ seconds after the birth of the drop) should be linear, but for the second and following drops this is not the case. When the drop falls the mercury thread breaks inside the capillary, and for some milliseconds thereafter i_τ amounts to only a few per cent of the expected value (86); presumably the mercury surface is still above the capillary orifice during this interval. Later the value of $i_\tau/\tau^{1/6}$ increases, but it approaches the slope predicted by equation (4) only as a limit at the end of the drop life (168a,232a), and the integrated average diffusion current is smaller (typically by 20% or so) than that predicted by the theory or observed for the first drop.

It is thus impossible at the present time to give any detailed rigorous treatment of the theory of the diffusion current. One consequence of this fact is that most practical analyses are still carried out by "comparative" methods, in which the constant of proportionality relating diffusion current and concentration is measured for each substance being determined with the aid of the particular capillary being used. The specific techniques by which this is done are discussed in Section V-B-4. In general, the user of the "absolute" method described above must be prepared to tolerate an uncertainty of perhaps $\pm 3\%$ due to the variation of I with capillary characteristics.

b. Factors Affecting the Diffusion Current

Notwithstanding our inability to give an exact mathematical description of the diffusion current, the factors that affect it are fairly well understood. As some understanding of these is essential if meaningful and useful data are to be obtained, a brief discussion of the principal factors is presented in the following sections.

(1) Concentration of the Electroactive Species

In the absence of such disturbing factors as adsorption on the drop surface (13,26,221,245) or on the walls of the cell (135), dissociation (156), precipitation (156,158,194), and other side reactions (5,158) in the diffusion layer, and after appropriate correction for the residual current, the diffusion current has been repeatedly found to be exactly proportional to the concentration of the substance responsible for the wave (156,187,192, 232). It has sometimes been asserted (36,89) that this rule fails at low concentrations of the electroactive species even in some quite simple cases, but this is because the graphical estimation of the diffusion current in the manner illustrated by Fig. 46.2 yields erroneous results when applied to the distorted waves often obtained at low concentrations (156,232).

Since the proportionality between diffusion current and concentration is tacitly assumed in most polarographic methods of analysis, it is important to be able to recognize the conditions under which such a proportionality may not be observed. The proportionality between the diffusion current and concentration must be carefully checked if:

1. The wave exhibits the characteristics of an adsorption or kinetic wave (cf. Sections II-B-4 and II-B-5 below);

2. The electroactive species can dissociate or undergo any chemical side reaction with some constituent of the diffusion layer (e.g., the product of the electrode reaction occurring on its own or any preceding wave);

3. The variation in the concentration of the electroactive species is accompanied by a substantial variation in the concentration of any major constituent of the solution (e.g., if successive aliquots of a strongly acidic solution of the sample are added to a neutral supporting electrolyte, or if successive aliquots of a solution of an organic compound in 95% ethanol are added to a supporting electrolyte containing 50% ethanol);

4. The wave exhibits a maximum; or if

5. The diffusion current is estimated by any graphical procedure.

If the proportionality is found to fail, analyses can be carried out by only the standard solution method (cf. Section V-B-4).

(2) The Capillary Characteristics

The drop weight, mt, obtained with a capillary such as is normally employed in polarographic measurements is very nearly proportional to the interfacial tension, σ, between mercury and solution:

$$mt = k\sigma \tag{6}$$

where k depends on the radius of the capillary orifice (93). Meanwhile m may be described by the Poiseuille equation (156,225):

$$m = \frac{125\pi r_c^4 d_{Hg}}{l\eta}\left(h_{Hg}d_{Hg}g - h_{soln.}d_{soln.}g - 43.1\frac{d_{Hg}\sigma^{1/3}}{m^{1/3}t^{1/3}}\right) \tag{7}$$

where r_c and l are the radius and length of the capillary (cm.), d_{Hg} and η are the density and viscosity of mercury, h_{Hg} and $h_{soln.}$ are the heights of the mercury column and the solution, respectively, above the tip of the capillary, g is the gravitational constant, and $d_{soln.}$ is the density of the solution. The first term in the parentheses expresses the pressure of the column of mercury above the capillary; the second gives the hydrostatic back pressure of the column of solution above the capillary tip; and the third gives the average back pressure due to interfacial tension. Equation (7) is usually written

$$m = 4.64 \times 10^9 \frac{r_c^4}{l}h_{corr.} \tag{8}$$

where

$$h_{corr.} = h_{Hg} - (3.1/m^{1/3}t^{1/3}) \tag{9}$$

These equations are secured from equation (7) by neglecting the small hydrostatic back pressure, introducing numerical values of the various constants, and taking an average value of 400 dynes/cm. for σ. Actually, σ is considerably affected by electrode potential and also by traces of surface-active materials (maximum suppressors), but since the back-pressure term is usually only a few per cent of $h_{corr.}$ the use of the average value introduces no significant error.

From equations (2), (6), and (8) it follows that, under fixed experimental conditions (119,199),

$$i_d/h_{corr.}^{1/2} = \text{constant} \tag{9}$$

if the wave height is controlled solely by the rate of diffusion of the electroactive species to the electrode surface. This criterion is useful in the identification of adsorption and kinetic waves, and it also indicates the

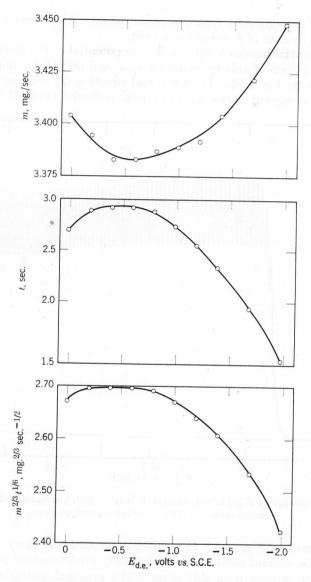

Fig. 46.4. Effects of applied potential on m, t, and $m^{2/3}t^{1/6}$ in 0.1F potassium chloride (217).

necessity of exerting close control over the height of the mercury column if reproducible values of i_d are to be secured.

The interfacial tension σ varies with the potential of the dropping electrode; the effects of this variation on m, t, and $m^{2/3}t^{1/6}$ are shown for a typical case by Fig. 46.4. From this and equation (2) it is apparent that the diffusion current varies with electrode potential (119,187,199), as is

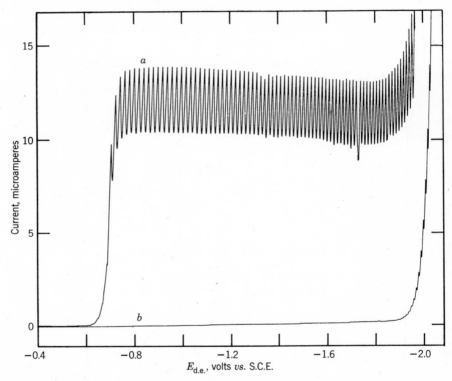

Fig. 46.5. Polarogram of (a) 1.0mM lead(II) in 0.1F sodium hydroxide and (b) residual-current curve for the supporting electrolyte alone.

clearly shown by Fig. 46.5. It is evidently necessary to carry out analytical diffusion-current measurements at exactly predetermined potentials to avoid errors arising from this effect. The principal methods of accomplishing this are discussed in Section V-B-3.

The change of interfacial tension resulting from the addition of a maximum suppressor is one source of the effects of such substances on the diffusion current (156,217,232).

(3) Solution Composition

The diffusion current depends on the diffusion coefficient of the electro-active species, and the latter is in turn affected by variations in the viscosity of the solution or in the size of the diffusing species.

According to the Stokes-Einstein relation, the diffusion coefficient of a spherical particle much larger than a solvent molecule is inversely proportional to the viscosity η of the solution; on this basis, from equation (2), the product $i_d \eta^{1/2}$ should be constant. This is often found to be the case even for the relatively small ions and molecules involved in many polarographic electrode processes (24,241), and the consequences of this effect in practical analysis have been examined by Taylor (320). Changes of viscosity accompanied by changes in hydration or ion-pair formation produce more complicated effects (211). In any case, the solvent composition and salt concentration must be fairly closely controlled in preparing samples for polarographic analysis. It is usually stated that the concentration of each constituent of the supporting electrolyte should be controlled to about $\pm 10\%$, but this is only a very rough guide. The viscosity of a dilute potassium chloride solution is so nearly independent of its concentration that a considerably wider variation could be tolerated. But much closer control would be needed if concentrated phosphoric acid were used as the supporting electrolyte, because the viscosity would then be quite sensitive to variations in the phosphoric acid concentration. Evidently each case must be judged on its own merits.

Complex ions formed by the substitution of small ligands for water molecules in the coordination sphere of a metal ion generally have diffusion coefficients about equal to those of the corresponding aquo complexes. Although exceptions are sufficiently numerous to warrant considerable caution in its application, the rule

$$I \cong 1.5n \tag{10}$$

has been suggested (225) as a guide to what may usually be expected in dealing with such substances.

Coordination with large ligands such as tartrate, citrate, and ethylenediaminetetraacetate, however, does markedly increase the size of the diffusing species. It is therefore not uncommon for the diffusion-current constant of a metal chelonate to be only half, or even less than half, the value for the same metal ion in a noncomplexing medium. In this connection it also must be remembered that the addition of a complexing agent can alter the value of n for an electrode reaction. Thus, in perchlorate and similar weakly complexing media manganese(II) can be reduced only to the metal, but in cyanide solutions a manganese(I) cyanide complex is produced instead (33,241,241a,296).

(4) Temperature

The temperature coefficient of the diffusion current constant is usually about $+1.3\%$/degree when equation (9) is obeyed. This includes the effects of temperature on D, m, t, C, and the numerical constant in the Ilkovič equation (123,156,217,225). Temperature control, preferably to $\pm 0.25°C.$ or better, is therefore essential in practically all polarographic work, although variations of a few degrees can be tolerated when the pilot-ion method is used. When dealing with kinetic and catalytic waves, much higher temperature coefficients may be encountered (55,113,219,343), ranging in some cases up to $+80\%$/degree (219).

(5) Maxima and Maximum Suppressors

Polarograms are often distorted by maxima such as are shown in Fig. 46.6; these are due to streaming of the solution past the drop surface over a certain range of potentials (4,306,308). An excellent review of the theories of maximum formation has been given by Kolthoff and Lingane (156).

It is evident from Fig. 46.6*b* that the diffusion current of a wave showing a maximum can be measured only at potentials considerably more negative than the half-wave potential, whereas Fig. 46.6*a* illustrates the difficulty that arises when another wave follows closely upon the one whose height is of interest. In this situation it is convenient to add a surface-active material whose adsorption on the drop surface suppresses the maximum; gelatin (115,156), methyl red (156), and Triton X-100 (233) appear to be the most useful of the many substances that have been recommended (225).

As was mentioned above, maximum suppressors alter the drop time, and hence the diffusion current, even when they are present at quite low concentrations. This, however, is a relatively small effect, amounting to perhaps 1 or 2% in i_d, and is quite another thing from the effects frequently resulting from the addition of too high a concentration of a maximum suppressor. These include gross changes of the diffusion current (275), shifts of a volt or more in the position of the wave (214), and various other undesirable phenomena (39,233) whose causes have been discussed by Schmid and Reilley (289) and by Delahay and Trachtenberg (56). Unless it has been definitely established for any particular case that no harm results from the use of a larger concentration, no more than 0.005%

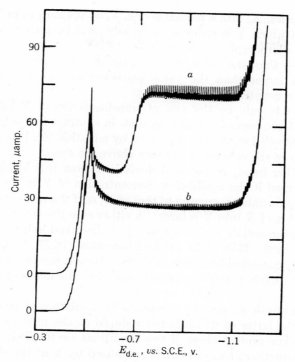

Fig. 46.6. Polarogram of $1F$ potassium chloride–$0.1F$ hydrochloric acid containing (a) 4mM lead and 4mM cadmium, and (b) 4mM lead alone (225). Reproduced from Meites, *Polarographic Techniques.*

gelatin, 0.002% Triton X-100, or 0.0004% methyl red should ever be employed in polarographic analysis (225). In investigative work there is no excuse for adding a maximum suppressor until it has been found to be necessary. Directions for the preparation and storage of stock solutions of maximum suppressors can be found elsewhere (225).

The suppression by surface-active materials of the pronounced maximum on a polarogram of oxygen under carefully controlled conditions has been used as the basis of a method for the evaluation of refined sugars (330). Similar techniques may prove useful in other applications to quality control.

4. Kinetic Currents

The theory of kinetic and catalytic currents has been outlined in Chapter 44. The pure kinetic current that arises from the transformation of a non-reducible species, X, into a reducible one, Y, at the surface of the drop, at potentials at which Y is reduced as rapidly as it is formed, has two distinguishing polarographic characteristics:

1. It is less than the value predicted for the reduction of all of the X present, but larger than the value predicted for the reduction of the equilibrium concentration of Y; and

2. It depends only on the rate of transformation of X into Y and is therefore independent of m and t, so that, in contrast to the behavior of a diffusion-controlled current as described by equation (9), it is independent of the height of the column of mercury above the drop.

On the other hand, pronounced deviations from this idealized pattern will be observed if the equilibrium concentration of Y in the bulk of the solution is appreciable compared to that of X, or if the rate constant for the transformation of X into Y is large; in either case the current will display properties intermediate between those just described and those of a true diffusion current (225). The original literature (18,27,46,47,141,176,331, 332) must be consulted for further details. Here it need only be remarked that kinetic currents are rather poorly suited to the needs of the practical analyst.

A pure catalytic current is obtained with a mixture of two substances, X and Y, the latter of which is not reduced at the potential under consideration when present alone, if two conditions are fulfilled:

1. The reduction product of X is reoxidized by Y at the surface of the drop; and

2. The quantity of X thus regenerated is large compared to the amount that reaches the drop surface by diffusion from the bulk of the solution. One then has the reaction scheme

$$X + e \rightarrow X' \hspace{4cm} (a)$$

$$Y + X' \rightarrow X + Y' \hspace{3.5cm} (b)$$

$$X + e \rightarrow X', \text{ etc.} \hspace{3.8cm} (c)$$

in which the diffusion current originally obtained from reaction (a) is only a small fraction of the total current obtained from the cyclic process represented by equations (b) and (c). Again various intermediate patterns of behavior may be observed.

There are two analytical applications of catalytic currents; in both, the ratio of concentrations $[X]/[Y]$ should be as low as possible. In one, the conditions are such that reaction (b) is very rapid, so that practically all of the Y reaching the drop surface is reduced; the current then secured is a measure of the concentration of Y. This is the basis of an excellent method for the determination of nitrate (= Y) in the presence of a trace of uranium or molybdenum (= X) (128,147). In the other application, the conditions are so arranged that reaction (b) is relatively slow, so that most of the Y at the drop surface remains unreduced; then the rate of reduction of Y, and hence the current, can be related to the concentration of the primary depolarizer, X. Since each X ion or molecule may be regenerated many times by reaction (b), this leads to currents much larger than the diffusion current observed in the absence of Y, and the situation is therefore very well adapted to the determination of minute concentrations of X (25,94, 99,107,147,161,259,272,300).

5. Adsorption Currents

Adsorption waves may be due either to the reduction of ions or molecules of the electroactive species adsorbed on the surface of the electrode ("post-wave") or to the adsorption of the product of the electrode reaction ("pre-wave") (26,245). At low concentrations only the adsorption wave is obtained, but at higher concentrations a second wave may appear that represents the corresponding "normal" electrode reaction in which neither species is adsorbed. When both waves appear, the sum of their heights obeys equation (9), but the height of the adsorption wave is then independent of the concentration of the electroactive species and proportional to the height of the column of mercury above the capillary.

Adsorption waves occur fairly frequently (7,13,221,243,337), but have very little analytical utility.

C. THEORY OF THE CURRENT–POTENTIAL CURVE

1. Polarographic Reversibility

The notion of polarographic reversibility is an empirical but useful concept, related to the rates of the electrochemical reactions occurring at the surface of the dropping electrode. Its nature may be illustrated by a brief description of two possibilities that refer to the wave obtained when an electroactive species O is reduced to give R.

On the one hand, we may suppose that the processes $O + ne \rightarrow R$ and $R \rightarrow O + ne$ both proceed instantaneously at the electrode surface. Electrochemical equilibrium would then be established immediately upon the birth of a drop, and would be maintained throughout the drop life. The current obtained would reflect the position of the equilibrium, in accordance with the Nernst equation, and thus the "reversible" current–potential curve would conform to thermodynamic prediction.

On the other hand, we may suppose that the backward reaction, R →
O + ne, is so slow in the range of potentials under consideration that it
virtually does not occur at all. Then equilibrium in the thermodynamic
sense would be impossible, and the "totally irreversible" wave would reflect merely the effect of potential on the rate of the forward reaction,
O + ne → R.

Unfortunately, there are certain difficulties associated with the classification of waves into these categories. These difficulties are due in part to
the existence of a continuous spectrum of reaction rates ranging from extremely fast to extremely slow; this makes it impossible to draw any de-
fensible line of demarcation between "reversible" and "irreversible"
waves. Moreover, the above idealized description of a "reversible" process
is actually a description of a null class—although the equilibrium may be
established very rapidly, it cannot be truly instantaneous.

In practice, therefore, a "reversible" wave is generally taken as one that
conforms to the thermodynamic predictions within the accuracy attributed
to the measurements that have been carried out. This operational
definition leaves the question of reversibility at the mercy of the characteristics of the technique and the apparatus employed in the measurements
and of the temperament of the experimenter. There are many electrode
processes that are rapid enough to yield waves that obey the thermodynamic
predictions within the quite small errors of measurement inherent in the use
of precise equipment and careful technique, but that are nevertheless slow
enough to behave in a conspicuously irreversible fashion when inspected by
alternating-current or oscillographic polarography, in which a rapidly
varying potential is applied to the drop so that the existence of a small lag
in the attainment of equilibrium is much more apparent than it is in ordinary polarography.

Section 2 contains a brief outline of three major operational criteria of
polarographic reversibility and also of several auxiliary ones. Experience
has shown that considerable trust may be placed in thermodynamic de-
ductions from polarographic data when all of these criteria are obeyed.
The dangers present in other cases have been described by Berzins and
Delahay (16).

2. Properties of Reversible Waves

For a dropping electrode immersed in a solution containing C_O milli-
moles/liter of the oxidized form, O, and C_R millimoles/liter of the reduced
form, R, of the couple

$$O + ne = R$$

the assumption of instantaneous equilibrium is equivalent to stating the validity under all conditions of the Nernst equation

$$E = E^{0\prime} - \frac{0.05915}{n} \log \frac{C_R^0}{C_O^0} \tag{11}$$

where E is the potential of the drop, $E^{0\prime}$ is the formal potential of the half reaction, and the $C^{0\prime}$s are the concentrations of the two substances at the surface of the electrode. The flow of a positive current, i, causes the half reaction to proceed from left to right as written, so that $C_O^0 < C_O$ while $C_R^0 > C_R$. We assume that the current is proportional to the concentration gradient across the diffusion layer, so that

$$i = k_O(C_O - C_O^0) = k_R(C_R - C_R^0) \tag{12}$$

where k_O and k_R are the constants of proportionality in the equations for the cathodic and anodic diffusion currents

$$(i_d)_c = k_O C_O \tag{13}$$
$$(i_d)_a = k_R C_R$$

and where it is understood that the current i is corrected for the residual current at each potential. (Note that k_R is negative.) Combining equations (11), (12), and (13) yields the following equation for the wave (110, 155):

$$E = E^{0\prime} - \frac{0.05915}{n} \log \frac{k_O}{(-k_R)} - \frac{0.05915}{n} \log \frac{i - (i_d)_a}{(i_d)_c - i} \tag{14}$$

The potential at which

$$i = 1/2[(i_d)_c + (i_d)_a] \tag{15}$$

is the half-wave potential, $E_{1/2}$. Equations (14), (15), and (2) yield for the equation of the reversible wave

$$E = E_{1/2} - \frac{0.05915}{n} \log \frac{i - (i_d)_a}{(i_d)_c - i} \tag{16}$$

where

$$E_{1/2} = E^{0\prime} - \frac{0.05915}{2n} \log \frac{D_O}{D_R} \tag{17}$$

or

$$E_{5/2} = E^{0\prime} - \frac{0.05915}{n} \log \frac{I_O}{(-I_R)} \tag{18}$$

where I is defined by equation (3).

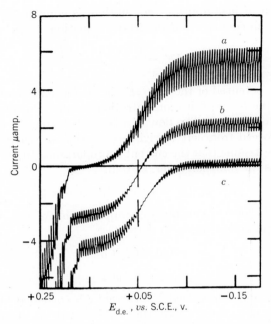

Fig. 46.7. Polarograms of saturated oxalic acid containing 0.0002% methyl red and (a) 1.4mM Fe(III), (b) 0.7mM Fe(III) and 0.7mM Fe(II), and (c) 1.4mM Fe(II). The short vertical lines indicate the half-wave potentials of the waves. Reproduced from Meites, *Polarographic Techniques* (225).

Similar derivations for the other cases that may arise have been presented in the literature (110,155,156,225,260).

The three fundamental operational criteria of polarographic reversibility follow directly from equations (16) and (18).

1. The half-wave potential must agree within experimental error with the value predicted by equation (18). As the diffusion coefficients of the two substances involved will rarely differ by a factor even as large as 2, the logarithmic term in equation (18) will almost always be less than 0.02 v. It can therefore be ignored unless $E_{1/2}$ differs by less than this amount from the potentiometrically determined formal potential. Because half-wave potentials are very much easier to measure than formal potentials, it is regrettably true that the formal potential needed for the application of this criterion will rarely be found in the literature.

2. The half-wave potential is a parameter characteristic of the half reaction involved, and does not depend on the direction from which equilibrium is approached. Therefore, the cathodic wave secured with

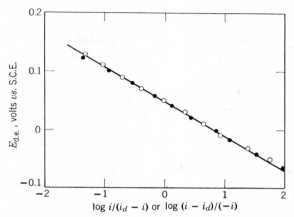

Fig. 46.8.   Plots of (a) $E_{d.e.}$ vs. log $i/(i_d - i)$ for the data of Fig. 46.7a $(open\ circles)$, and (b) $E_{d.e.}$ vs. log $(i - i_d)/(-i)$ for the data of Fig. 46.7c $(solid\ circles)$.   The straight line is drawn with the theoretical slope of -59.1 mv.

solutions of O alone, the anodic wave secured with solutions of R alone, and the cathodic–anodic wave obtained from solutions containing both O and R must all have the same half-wave potential (cf. Fig. 46.7).   Care must be taken when applying this criterion to eliminate or correct for iR drop in the circuit and for recorder lag.

3. The slopes of a plot of log $i/(i_d - i)$ vs. E for the cathodic wave of O alone, of a plot of log $(i - i_d)/(-i)$ for the anodic wave of R alone, and of a plot of log $(i - (i_d)_a)/((i_d)_c - i)$ for the cathodic–anodic wave of a mixture of O and R must all be equal to $-0.05915/n$ v. (cf. Fig. 46.8) (155,326). In applying this criterion it is necessary to obtain an independent estimate of n, which may be gotten from diffusion current constant data (e.g., equation (10)), from millicoulometry (22,59,80,84,220,341), from coulometry at controlled potential (23,64,183,186,193–195,224,236), or, in some simple cases, from purely chemical evidence.

In addition, it may be mentioned that, for a reversible wave, the half-wave potential is nearly, if not quite, independent of drop time or mercury pressure (313,323), and that the temperature coefficient of the half-wave potential is often much smaller (± 1 mv./deg. or less) than the range of values observed for some markedly irreversible waves (156).

The current-potential curve for the reversible couple involving a complex ion, $MX_p{}^{n-pb}$, and the amalgam of the metal M, according to the equation

$$MX_p{}^{n-pb} + x\text{Hg} + ne = M(\text{Hg})_x + pX^{-b}$$

obeys an equation very similar to equation (16):

$$E = (E_{1/2})_c - \frac{0.05915}{n} \log \frac{i - (i_d)_a}{(i_d)_c - i} \tag{19}$$

where $(E_{1/2})_c$ is given by

$$(E_{1/2})_c = E_c^{0\prime} - \frac{0.05915}{n} \log \frac{I_c}{(-I_M)} - \frac{0.05915p}{n} \log [X^{-b}] \tag{20}$$

Here $E_c^{0\prime}$ is the formal potential for the complex–metal amalgam couple and I_c and I_M are the diffusion current constants of the complex ion and of the metal in the amalgam, respectively. It is assumed that the concentration of X^{-b} is very much larger than the concentration of the complex ion. Hence,

$$\frac{\Delta(E_{1/2})_c}{\Delta \log [X^{-b}]} = -\frac{0.05915p}{n} \tag{21}$$

provided that $E_c^{0\prime}$ is unaffected by the changes in the concentration of the complexing agent (i.e., that the variation of the liquid-junction potential is inappreciable, and that the ionic strength either is kept constant or has a negligible effect on the formal potential). From equation (21) one can deduce the value of p, using half-wave potentials measured in the presence of different concentrations of the complexing agent. Moreover, by combining equations (18) and (20), one finds that the difference between the half-wave potential of the complex ion in a solution containing $1F$ ligand and the half-wave potential, $(E_{1/2})_s$, of the corresponding "simple" (aquo-complex) metal ion in a noncomplexing supporting electrolyte is

$$(E_{1/2})_c - (E_{1/2})_s = \frac{0.05915}{n} \log K - \frac{0.05915}{n} \log \frac{I_c}{I_s} \tag{22}$$

where K is the dissociation constant of the complex. The diffusion current constant term in this equation is usually smaller than the sum of the uncertainty in the liquid-junction potentials and the experimental errors involved in the half-wave potential measurements, and can be neglected except in work of the greatest precision.

The reasoning employed in the derivation of the above equations has been applied to the treatment of a number of other possible types of electrode reactions (110,155,159,177,178,246,260,306,309). Explicit equations have also been derived (42,118) for use when K is very small or when the solutions contain a number of complexes in equilibrium with each other. In evaluating the reliability of thermodynamic calculations based on half-wave potential measurements, it is of interest that the maximum precision with which a half-wave potential can be determined under optimum conditions seems to be close to ±0.2 mv. (215,323).

3. Properties of Irreversible Waves

The theory of irreversible polarographic waves has been developed by a number of authors (16,49,54,66,132,142,143,303,319,325) since Eyring, Marker, and Kwoh (67) first pointed out the significance of the rates of the electrochemical reactions. Here it is possible to present only a condensed summary of the principal conclusions.

Figure 46.9 illustrates the practical differences between reversible and irreversible waves. The formal potentials of the half reactions responsible

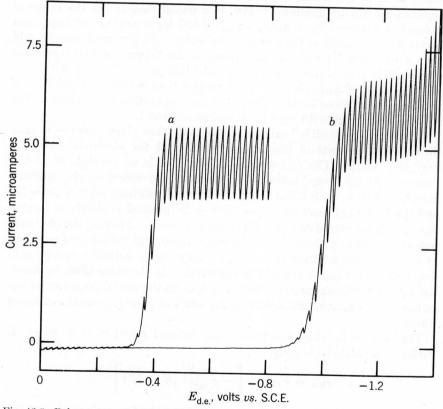

Fig. 46.9. Polarograms of (a) 0.4mM lead ion and (b) 0.5mM nickel ion in 0.1F sodium chloride–0.001F hydrochloric acid containing 0.002% Triton X-100.

for these two waves differ by only about 0.1 v., but whereas the half-wave potential of the reversible lead wave is very close to its formal potential, that of the irreversible nickel wave is several tenths of a volt more negative than the expected value.   In addition, the slope of the rising part of the nickel wave is much smaller than that of the lead wave.   The fact that irreversible waves are always spread over a greater range of potentials than reversible ones has an important bearing on practical polarographic analysis.   A difference of as little as 0.15 v. between the half-wave potentials of two successive waves may suffice to permit the accurate measurements of their wave heights if both are reversible and about the same height.   However, two irreversible waves whose half-wave potentials differed by this amount would be less well defined at best; at worst they might overlap so much as to be quite indistinguishable.   The value of $E_{3/4} - E_{1/4}$, whose significance will be discussed below, is a useful measure of the range of potentials occupied by a wave, and is listed for a number of important waves in Table 46.II at the end of this chapter.   In general it may be said that a reasonably precise measurement of the heights of two successive waves will be possible if they are equal and if $[(E_{1/2})_1 - (E_{1/2})_2] + 2[(E_{3/4} - E_{1/4})_1 + (E_{3/4} - E_{1/4})_2]$ is equal to or greater than $\sim$0.05 v., regardless of whether either wave is reversible.   Greater separation is required as the ratio of wave heights diverges more and more from 1.

A "totally irreversible" process is one that takes place under such conditions that the rate of the reverse reaction at the electrode surface is negligibly small.   The nickel wave in Fig. 46.9 is an example of such a process.   At the formal potential of the nickel ion–nickel couple (approximately -0.50 v. $vs.$ S.C.E.), both the forward reaction, $Ni^{+2} + 2e \rightarrow Ni$, and the backward reaction, $Ni \rightarrow Ni^{+2} + 2e$, proceed so slowly as to give rise to only an exceedingly small exchange current.   Making the electrode potential more negative than this increases the rate of the forward reaction; at a sufficiently negative potential, an appreciable cathodic current will flow and a reduction wave will be obtained.   At the same time, however, the rate of the backward reaction decreases as the electrode potential becomes more negative, and is vanishingly small at potentials on the cathodic wave.

The manner in which the rate of the forward reaction, $O + ne \rightarrow R$, varies with potential is given by

$$k_{f,h} = k'_{f,h} \exp\left[-\frac{\alpha n_a F_y}{RT}(E - E')\right]$$

where $k_{f,h}$ is the heterogeneous rate constant of the forward reaction at the potential E, α is the transfer coefficient for the electrode reaction, and n_a is the number of electrons involved in the rate-determining electron-transfer step. Although in principle n_a might have any integral value between 1 and n, no case in which n_a exceeds 2 has yet been found. The quantity $k'_{f,h}$ is obviously the value of $k_{f,h}$ when the potential is equal to the reference value E'. Two particular values of E' are of interest. One is the formal potential of the couple, which is more fundamental but which is intrinsically impossible to measure accurately by electrometric techniques for a totally irreversible half reaction. The value of $k'_{f,h}$ corresponding to the choice $E' = E^{0'}$ is given the symbol $k_{s,h}$. Much more frequently encountered, because it constitutes a fixed and readily usable reference point, is the choice $E' = 0$ v. vs. N.H.E.; the value of $k'_{f,h}$ corresponding to this choice is designated as $k^0_{f,h}$. By virtue of this choice, the preceding equation can be rewritten

$$k_{f,h} = k^0_{f,h} \exp\left[- \frac{\alpha n_a F_y}{RT} E \right] \tag{23}$$

where the potential E is now understood to be referred to the normal hydrogen electrode.

The current that flows at any potential is given by

$$i = n F_y A C^0_O k_{f,h} \tag{24}$$

where C^0_O is the concentration of reducible substance at the surface of the electrode. Near the foot of the wave, where $k_{f,h}$ is small, the current is so low that the concentration of O at the electrode surface is virtually unaffected and remains equal to its value in the bulk of the solution. In other words, the supply of O at the electrode surface is so great that the current is limited only by the slowness of the rate-determining electron-transfer step, and is therefore purely kinetic in nature. Current–potential data in this region have been used (170) for the evaluation of αn_a and $k^0_{f,h}$: in a relatively concentrated (e.g., 25 mM) solution of O, the maximum current during the drop life is measured, with the aid of a fast recorder, at each of a number of potentials such that the current is less than about 10% of the diffusion current. The logarithm of the current is then plotted against $E_{d.e.}$, and $k^0_{f,h}$ is obtained from the zero intercept of the resulting line while αn_a is obtained from its slope. The value of A—the area of the mercury drop at the instant of its fall—that is needed in the calculation of $k^0_{f,h}$ can be obtained easily from the measured values of m and t. The sole disadvantage of this technique appears to be its sensitivity to traces of impurities giving rise to waves in the range of potentials examined.

As the potential becomes more negative and the current increases, an increasing fraction of the ions or molecules of O reaching the electrode surface is reduced, and the resulting decrease of C_O^0 tends to counteract the ex-potential increase of $k_{f,h}$ with potential. Hence the current–potential curve passes through an inflection in the same way as does a reversible wave. The limiting current, which flows at potentials so negative that C_O^0 is virtually zero, displays exactly the same properties as the limiting current of a reversible wave, because $k_{f,h}$ in this region is so large that the ions or molecules of O are virtually instantaneously reduced as they reach the electrode surface, and the current therefore depends entirely on the rate of mass transfer.

The equation of a totally irreversible polarographic wave may be written

$$\frac{i'}{i_d'} = f(\mu) \tag{25a}$$

where

$$\mu = \left(\frac{12}{7}\right)^{1/2} \frac{k_{f,h} t^{1/2}}{D_O^{1/2}} \tag{25b}$$

Here t is the drop time (whose variation with potential over the limited range corresponding to the rising portion of the wave is almost always negligible), and D_O is the diffusion coefficient of O. The currents i' and i_d' are the instantaneous currents at the instants that the drops fall from the capillary tip at the potential E and on the plateau of the wave, respectively. They are most easily secured by measuring the maximum pen deflections on a polarogram obtained with a fast recorder. From the values of i'/i_d' at various selected potentials, the corresponding values of the parameter μ are obtained from Table 46.I, which was originally obtained by Koutecký (165) in a slightly different form. Plotting $\log \mu$ vs. $E_{d.e.}$ then

TABLE 46.I
Values of the Parameter μ for a Totally Irreversible Wave

i'/i_d'	μ	i'/i_d'	μ
0.1	0.124	0.55	1.18
0.15	0.195	0.6	1.42
0.2	0.270	0.65	1.72
0.25	0.355	0.7	2.10
0.3	0.450	0.75	2.63
0.35	0.557	0.8	3.44
0.4	0.677	0.85	4.71
0.45	0.819	0.9	7.35
0.5	0.983	0.95	15.1

permits values for both $k_{f,h}^0$ and αn_a to be secured. For this purpose it is convenient to combine the preceding equations into

$$\log_{10} \mu = \log_{10} \left(\frac{12}{7}\right)^{1/2} \frac{k_{f,h}^0 t^{1/2}}{D_O^{1/2}} - \frac{\alpha n_a F_y}{2.303 \; RT} E \qquad (26)$$

Thus a plot of $\log \mu$ *vs.* $E_{\text{d.e.}}$ should be linear; by extrapolating it to $E = 0$ (v. *vs.* N.H.E.) one can obtain the value of $k_{f,h}^0$. The value of D_O needed may be estimated with sufficient accuracy by an obvious application of equation (3). Meanwhile αn_a is obtained from the slope of the line; the numerical coefficient of the second term on the right-hand side of this equation is equal to $\alpha n_a/0.05915$ v. at 25°C.

The amount of labor involved in this process is excessive. It can be considerably decreased by taking advantage of the fact that, for values of i'/i_d' between about 0.1 and 0.95, Koutecký's values for μ and i'/i_d' correspond to a linear relationship between $\log \mu$ and $\log i'/(i_d' - i')$. The mean deviation from linearity is only ± 0.0043 in $\log i'/(i_d' - i')$. It would be a sanguine polarographer who would expect greater accuracy from such measurements.

In this way the equation of a totally irreversible wave involving only a single rate-determining electron-transfer step becomes, at 25°C. (230a),

$$E = E_{1/2} - \frac{0.05420}{\alpha n_a} \log \frac{i'}{i_d' - i'} \qquad (27a)$$

where

$$E_{1/2} = \frac{0.05915}{\alpha n_a} \log \left(1.349 \; k_{f,h}^0 t^{1/2}/D_O^{1/2}\right) \qquad (27b)$$

As is also true for a reversible wave, a plot of E *vs.* $\log i'/(i_d' - i')$ will be a straight line, but the slope will be equal to $-0.05420/\alpha n_a$ v., rather than to $-0.05915/n$ v. as is the case for a reversible wave. Very nearly the same results will be obtained if average currents rather than maximum currents are used, although the slope in the former case will be $-0.05915/\alpha n_a$ v. because the ratio of the average current to the maximum current varies from about 0.6 near the foot of the wave to about 0.82 on the plateau (143).

It is clear from equation (27b) that the half-wave potential of an irreversible wave is a purely kinetic function of no thermodynamic significance. It is also clear that the practice, which is still occasionally encountered, of concluding that a wave represents a one-electron reduction because the slope of its log plot is close to -0.059 v. is devoid of validity of any kind. Less often met nowadays, although still to be found in the older literature, is the equally incorrect conclusion that such a slope indicates that the rate-determining step involves one electron.

Tomes (326) showed that, for a reversible wave, the difference between the potentials $E_{3/4}$ (where $i = {}^3/_4\, i_d$) and $E_{1/4}$ (where $i = {}^1/_4\, i_d$) is

$$E_{3/4} - E_{1/4} = - \frac{0.05915}{n} \log 9 = - \frac{0.0564}{n} \text{ v. (at 25°C.)}$$

In exactly the same way it can be shown that, for a wave obeying equation (27a),

$$E_{3/4} - E_{1/4} = - \frac{0.05420}{\alpha n_a} \log 9 = - \frac{0.05172}{\alpha n_a} \text{ v. (at 25°C.)}$$

This provides what is doubtless the easiest and most convenient method of obtaining values of αn_a.

The measurement of $k^0_{f,h}$ and αn_a often provide much insight into the mechanism of the electrode reaction responsible for an irreversible wave. In this process it is important that, at least in the absence of any surface-active species, the value of α is rarely very far from 0.5. Hence a value of αn_a between about 0.3 and 0.6 may be considered to correspond to a rate-determining electron-transfer step involving one electron, whereas values of αn_a above about 0.8 may similarly be taken to correspond to $n_a = 2$.

A single example will suffice to illustrate the kind of information that can be extracted from this treatment. Data obtained by Karp (133) on the anodic wave representing the oxidation of hydrazine at pH values between 10 and 15.5 show that the average slope of a plot of E vs. $\log (i - i_d)/(-i)$ is -0.061 ± 0.002 v. Hence $0.0542/\alpha n_a = 0.061$, and $\alpha n_a = 0.89$, which leads to the conclusion that two electrons are involved in the rate-determining step. The rate of change of half-wave potential with respect to pH, which is experimentally equal to -0.0628 v. per pH unit, may be interpreted by differentiating equation (27b) to yield

$$\frac{\Delta E_{1/2}}{\Delta \text{pH}} = \frac{0.05915}{\alpha n_a} \frac{\Delta \log k^0_{f,h}}{\Delta \text{pH}}$$

With $\alpha n_a = 0.89$, this gives $\Delta \log k^0_{f,h}/\Delta \text{pH} = 0.95$. The variation of $k^0_{f,h}$ with pH results from the fact that $k^0_{f,h}$ is a quasi-first-order rate constant that includes the effects of variations in the concentration of hydrogen ion, hydroxyl ion, or any other species that enters into the rate equation. Writing $k^0_{f,h} = \mathbf{k}^0_{f,h}\, [\text{H}^+]^p$, where $\mathbf{k}^0_{f,h}$ is the true heterogeneous rate constant and p is the necessarily integral number of hydrogen ions consumed in the rate-determining step (or in fast processes preceding the rate-determining step), one immediately obtains $p = -1$. On this basis, the rate-determining step must be either $N_2H_4 + OH^- \rightarrow N_2H_3^+ + H_2O + 2e$ or something kinetically indistinguishable from it. The utility of such information in the interpretation of the electrochemical properties of a substance that is irreversibly reduced or oxidized is too apparent to require discussion.

Clearly this treatment is applicable only if the over-all electron-transfer process is known to involve just one slow step. Berzins and Delahay (16) showed that a plot of $\log k_{f,h}$ vs. E (or, which is essentially the same thing, a plot of E vs. $\log i/(i_d - i)$) can be resolved into two straight-line segments if the electrode reaction involves two slow steps whose $k^0_{f,h}$-values differ by a factor of 10 or more, provided that the corresponding αn_a-values are not too different. Even a far smaller difference could doubtless be detected by the curvature that it would produce in either of these plots; any such curvature over the range of potentials corresponding to $0.1\,i_d \leq i \leq 0.95\,i_d$ is a sensitive indication that more than one slow step is involved. In addition, this treatment should be eschewed unless αn_a is found to be constant (to, say, ±0.05 unit) over the range of conditions in question. Since both $k^0_{f,h}$ and αn_a are often drastically affected by the presence of surface-active materials (including long-chain tetraalkylammonium ions), whose adsorption on the drop alters the structure of the electrical double layer and may also prevent the appropriate orientation of the reducible group in a sterically hindered organic molecule on the drop surface, maximum suppressors should be avoided in work of this sort.

From the equations that have been written it is apparent that the half-wave potential of an irreversible wave varies with drop time (143), and that the magnitude of the variation depends on the value of αn_a. In a typical case (the reduction of nickel(II) from $0.2F$ potassium nitrate), $E_{1/2}$ varied from -1.016 to -0.959 v. vs S.C.E. as the drop time was increased from 2.09 to 7.66 seconds. Since it is readily shown from equation (27b) that $\Delta E_{1/2}/\Delta \log t = 0.02957/\alpha n_a$ v., it is possible in principle to obtain αn_a from data on the variation of half-wave potential with drop time. However, this requires a degree of accuracy difficult to obtain in ordinary work, and the previous procedure is therefore preferable.

Many authors have attempted to correlate half-wave potential with structure for groups of closely related organic compounds that yield totally irreversible waves. As the half-wave potential reflects variations in αn_a as well as in $k^0_{f,h}$, such correlations should be made with care. They should not be attempted if the values of αn_a differ appreciably for the different compounds investigated, or if the curvature of a plot of E vs. $\log i/(i_d - i)$ indicates that the electron-transfer process is a complex one.

The properties of polarographic waves for which the rate constants lie in the nebulous region between total irreversibility and apparent reversibility have been outlined by Delahay (46,49). Although there is not enough space to summarize them here, discussions of numerous other and more complex kinds of irreversible phenomena may be found in the original literature.

III. RELATED TECHNIQUES

A. AMPEROMETRIC TITRATIONS

The first amperometric titrations with a dropping mercury indicator electrode were carried out by Heyrovský and Berezicky (108). The theory and execution of such titrations were studied by Majer (206), Spalenka (305), Neuberger (250), Thanheiser and Willems (324), and, more extensively, by Kolthoff and his co-workers (146,148,153,154,160,301). Amperometric titrations are rapid, precise, and useful in many cases in which no other satisfactory electrometric system can be found for the detection of the end point.

Assume that V^0 ml. of a $C_A^0 M$ solution of a substance A is titrated with a $C_B M$ solution of a reagent B, and that a reaction occurs which results in the formation of a totally insoluble precipitate $A_m B_n$. Assume that the diffusion current is measured as a function of V_B, the volume of added reagent, at a potential at which, in accordance with equation (2),

$$(i_d)_A = k_A C_A$$

and

$$(i_d)_B = k_B C_B$$

Either k_A or k_B may be zero, but not both (i.e., at least one of the two reactants must yield a diffusion current at the potential employed). On the basis of these assumptions it is easily shown that a plot of $i_d(V^0 + V_B)/V^0$ against V_B consists of two straight lines whose point of intersection coincides with the equivalence point.

Of course, the solubility of the precipitate cannot be neglected near the equivalence point (156), but this is almost irrelevant in practical work, where it is a simple matter to construct the titration curve from data secured at points fairly far removed from the equivalence point. The latter is then found, as it is in conductometric titrations, by extrapolating the two straight lines obtained to their point of intersection. A typical titration curve is shown in Fig. 46.10.

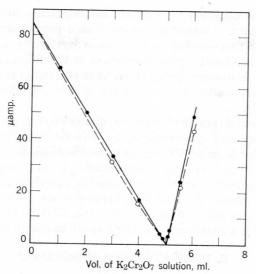

Fig. 46.10. Amperometric titration curve of 50 ml. of 0.01M lead nitrate with 0.05M potassium dichromate. Titrated at $E_{d.e.} = -1.0$ v. vs. S.C.E. The dotted curve shows the experimental points and the solid straight lines were obtained after correction for the dilution effect. Reproduced from Kolthoff and Lingane, *Polarography* (156).

Amperometric titrations are by no means restricted to precipitation reactions; they have also been used in redox (62,225,305,316) and chelometric (171,264,268) titrations, and even in certain cases (139,157,179,225) in which no chemical reaction takes place at all. The various kinds of titration curves that may be obtained are discussed in the original literature; they obviously depend on the polarographic characteristics of the reactants and products and on the potential applied to the dropping electrode. For an excellent review with many practical examples, see Reference 128a.

The range of concentrations to which amperometric titrations can be applied is about the same as for ordinary polarography, but under otherwise comparable conditions and in the absence of such purely chemical problems as coprecipitation, nonstoichiometric reactions, and the like, about a 10-fold gain in accuracy and precision can be achieved by the use of the titration technique.

B. DIFFERENTIAL POLAROGRAPHY

Differential polarography is a technique in which one measures the current flowing between two identical dropping electrodes at the same potential but in different solutions. This current is the difference between the two currents obtained by separate measurements with the two electrodes individually. Obviously any substance present at the same concentration in the two solutions will behave in exactly the same way at each electrode, and therefore it will have no effect on the differential polarogram. Thus it is possible to separate the small wave of a minor constituent of one solution from an overlapping large wave of a major constituent of both solutions (3,292).

The fundamental practical problem of differential polarography consists of matching and synchronizing the two dropping electrodes. It is not necessary for their $m^{2/3}t^{1/6}$-values to be identical, for a difference between these can be electrically compensated. What is essential is that the two electrodes have the same drop time and be exactly in phase to avoid the fluctuations of current that would otherwise result. Methods have been devised for solving this problem (249,297,311,327,338), but differential polarography has not found any considerable use in practical analysis.

C. DERIVATIVE POLAROGRAPHY

A derivative polarogram is a plot of di/dE vs. potential. For a wave described by the equation

$$E = E_{1/2} - \frac{RT}{kF_y} \log \frac{i}{i_d - i}$$

it is easily shown that di/dE passes through a maximum at the half-wave potential, and that for any particular species under fixed experimental conditions the maximum value of di/dE is proportional to concentration. The utility of derivative polarography stems from its ability to resolve waves that overlap to such an extent that they cannot be separated adequately by ordinary polarography.

Derivative polarograms may be secured in either of two ways. One involves the use of two identical dropping electrodes in the same solution, together with an electrical circuit that maintains a constant difference between the potentials of the two electrodes while the potential of one of them is varied over the range to be investigated (3,8,102,104). The problem of drop synchronization, mentioned above in connection with differential polarography, arises again in this technique. The other, and doubtless better, method involves the electrical differentiation of the current–potential curve obtained with a single dropping electrode (106, 134,175,298,335,336); this technique has been critically studied by Lingane and Williams (196), and has been employed in practical analysis by Pomeroy *et al.* (266) and by Říha (278,279). A different method (257) of achieving the same end has been proposed but seems not to have been used in practical work.

D. "OSCILLOGRAPHIC" POLAROGRAPHY

This term serves to denote a group of techniques in which the potential of the electrode is rapidly varied over the entire range of interest while the resulting variation of current is displayed on the screen of an oscilloscope. Although these techniques are of some theoretical interest, their analytical applications to date entitle them to only a cursory mention here. The interested reader should consult the original literature or Delahay's more comprehensive survey of principles and electrochemical applications (50).

The techniques that have been investigated may be classified according to the frequency of the voltage sweep employed. "Single-sweep" methods are those in which the voltage sweep is applied once during the life of each drop; since the current flowing at any particular instant during the sweep depends not only on the electrode potential at that instant but also on the area attained by the drop, it is necessary to synchronize the sweep with the drop formation if reproducible and meaningful data are to be obtained. In "multisweep" methods, on the other hand, the voltage sweep is repeated many times during the life of each drop with the aim of securing the curve corresponding to the maximum area of the drop.

In the first single-sweep method (210), the duration of the voltage sweep coincided exactly with the drop time ($1/30$ second). A more useful technique (2,269,270,304) is one in which a capillary of conventional (3 to 5 seconds) drop time is employed, and the sweep is begun at a predetermined instant near the end of the drop life. The rate of change of electrode area with time is then quite small, and this fact, together with the rapid depletion of the electroactive species in the layer of solution at the drop surface, leads to the appearance of a peak at the top of each wave. The peak current, which is proportional to the initial (i.e., bulk) concentration of the electroactive species, has been discussed by a number of authors (45,48,-251,270,295). Of advantage in practical analytical work is the fact that the rate of change of electrode area during the interval inspected is small; consequently the residual current is also small, and an appreciable improvement in the ratio of diffusion current to residual current is obtained. Hence the technique is somewhat more sensitive than conventional polarography; it is not uncommon for analyses of 10^{-4}mM solutions to be feasible. The rather complex instrument that the technique requires is commercially available as the "Polarotrace," manufactured by Southern Instruments, Ltd.

Multisweep methods employing sawtooth (i.e., unidirectional) voltage sweeps have been investigated by Delahay *et al.* (44,52,53). Bieber and Trumpler (19) and Sevcik (295) employed a triangular voltage sweep, which permits observation of the voltammetric properties of the reaction product formed at the electrode surface during the cathodic portion of the cycle. Such information is useful in deciding borderline questions of reversibility. Much the same end is served by the technique devised by Heyrovský *et al.* (101,103,109), who employed a streaming mercury electrode to obviate complications arising from periodic variations of electrode area.

E. ALTERNATING-CURRENT AND SQUARE-WAVE POLAROGRAPHY

In a.-c. polarography a small alternating voltage is superimposed on the slowly increasing direct voltage obtained from an ordinary polarograph, and the amplitude of the resulting alternating current is measured as a function of the direct potential. An a.-c. polarogram consists of a series of successive peaks; each peak occurs at the half-wave potential of a wave on the conventional polarogram, and its height is proportional to the concentration of the species responsible for the wave. Consequently, an a.-c. polarogram bears a superficial resemblance to a derivative polarogram, and the technique is occasionally useful in resolving two waves of nearly equal half-wave potentials. The detailed theory of a.-c. polarography has been examined by numerous authors (11,21,31–34,43,60,127,201,248,276, 287,293,318), and it has been shown that the peak height is dependent on both the concentration of the electroactive species and the rates of the forward and reverse electrode reactions. Thus, under otherwise identical conditions the peak height is a sensitive indication of the reversibility of the reaction, being much greater for a reversible process than for an irreversible one. This is extremely useful to the electrochemist, but it places the analyst at the mercy of any small variation of solution composition—the presence of a trace of surface-active material, for example—which alters the rates of the electrode reactions. The same thing is true of the results provided by the related technique of Kalousek (125,129,130,257,317).

In a.-c. polarography the potential of the dropping electrode is varied continuously, and this gives rise to an appreciable capacity current that poses some problems in dealing with very dilute solutions or with irreversible processes. This may be avoided by superimposing a square, rather than a sinusoidal, voltage wave on the steadily increasing direct potential. Immediately after each step in the square wave, an appreciable capacity current flows, but this decays rapidly to a very small value before the occurrence of the next step. The current is measured intermittently just before each step; the capacity current is practically eliminated. Square-wave polarography is claimed to be capable of high sensitivity and good resolution and to be particularly well adapted to the determination of traces of substances that give waves preceded on the polarogram by a much larger wave due to some other constituent of the sample (9,10,68–70,90, 131,240). This is a troublesome problem in ordinary polarography (cf. Section V-A), and the use of square-wave polarography will often greatly simplify the choice of a supporting electrolyte or eliminate the need for a preliminary chemical or electrolytic separation. Whether this is worth the cost and complexity of a square-wave polarograph is, of course, a matter for individual decision.

As in a.-c. polarography, the peak height in square-wave polarography depends on the kinetics of the forward and backward electrode reactions as well as on the factors that influence the height of an ordinary polarographic wave. The practical disadvantage of this fact has been mentioned above. On the other hand, in principle it should permit the determination of even a relatively small concentration of a substance yielding a reversible wave in the presence of a much larger concentration of another substance yielding an overlapping totally irreversible wave.

F. OTHER ELECTRODES

Various modifications of the conventional dropping electrode have been proposed. Capillaries prepared by drawing out thermometer tubing and those cut from commercial marine barometer tubing have similar characteristics and differ only in sturdiness and ease of preparation. Capillaries having markedly different properties are prepared by changing the shape of the lumen. Several authors (3,218,277,327) have employed flared capillaries, which give higher drop weights, and hence higher diffusion currents, than capillaries of uniform bore; unfortunately the increase of sensitivity thus obtained is partly overcome by a simultaneous increase of the residual current. L-shaped capillaries (218) are said (302) to have some advantages in work with non-aqueous solutions or at very negative potentials, but they suffer from gross deviations from the Ilkovič equation (218). Multiple dropping electrodes, in which four or more conventional capillaries are connected in parallel to the same mercury reservoir, have been employed (58,83,212,258), but not always with entirely satisfactory results (35). Vibrating dropping electrodes (15) may be useful in automatic amperometric titrations (50).

The most promising modification of the dropping electrode appears to be the rotated dropping mercury electrode described by Stricks and Kolthoff (315). Two forms of this electrode are shown in Fig. 46.11; directions for their preparation are given by Stricks and Kolthoff. The electrode is rotated at a speed of 150 to 300 r.p.m. by means of a synchronous motor. Droplets of mercury form at the tip, which has a diameter of about 0.05 mm., and are detached at regular intervals just as are the drops formed at a conventional dropping electrode. The value of m obtained with a rotated

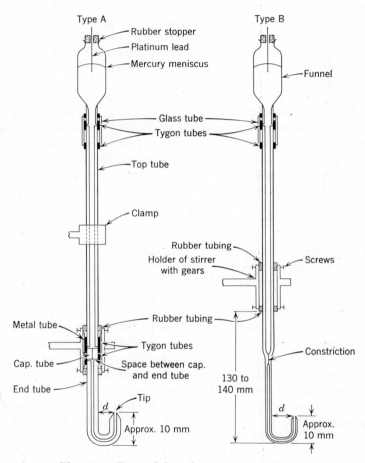

Fig. 46.11. Rotated dropping mercury electrodes.

electrode is governed chiefly by the height of the mercury column and the geometry of the capillary tube (in type A) or of the constricted portion of the tube (in type B), whereas the drop time depends on the interfacial tension between mercury and solution, on the rate of rotation of the electrode, and on the radius of the tip.   Partly because of the larger drop area, caused by the rotation of the electrode, and partly because of the decrease in the effective diffusion-layer thickness, diffusion currents are obtained that are about 10 times those measured with conventional electrodes under similar conditions.   As the concomitant increase of the residual current is considerably smaller (roughly a factor of 2), this represents an appreciable gain in sensitivity.

In the absence of a maximum suppressor the polarograms obtained with rotating electrodes are distorted by the streaming of the solution past the drop surface; because the rate of this streaming is considerably affected by electrode potential and salt concentration, and especially by the presence of traces of surface-active substances, the wave heights obtained in the absence of a maximum suppressor are somewhat difficult to measure and interpret.   For this reason Stricks and Kolthoff recommended the addition of at least 0.008% gelatin in practical work; it is not known how high a concentration can be tolerated, but by analogy with conventional polarography it would seem unwise to use a much higher concentration of gelatin without showing that this had no significant effect in the particular case at hand.

According to Okinaka and Kolthoff (256), the diffusion current under these conditions is described by

$$i_d = 1325\ nCD^{2/3}U^{1/2}\nu^{-1/6}(mt)^{1/2} \tag{28}$$

where U is the speed of rotation of the electrode tip (cm./second), ν is the kinematic viscosity of the solution (cm.^{2}/second), and the other quantities have their ordinary polarographic significance.   In practical analysis this would probably be used in the form

$$i_d = kC$$

where k, whose value would be constant for any particular wave under fixed experimental conditions (electrode rate of rotation, temperature, applied potential, etc.), would be determined by measurements with known solutions.

Many other indicator electrodes have been used in voltammetric measurements, including, among others, streaming mercury electrodes (87,88, 163,174,280–284,328,340), stationary mercury pool electrodes in quiet (314) and stirred (149,150,253,285) solutions, stirred mercury pool electrodes (227,228,265), rotating mercury electrodes (173), and hanging mercury drop electrodes (17,57,72,79,138,207,274,286).   These are discussed in Chapter 47.

IV. POLAROGRAPHIC APPARATUS

A. ELECTRICAL INSTRUMENTATION

There are two kinds of polarographs: manual and recording. With a manual polarograph the user must make point-by-point measurements of the current at each of a sufficient number of applied potentials to yield the desired information. A recording polarograph is an instrument that continuously varies the applied potential and draws a complete record of the resulting variations of the current. A manual polarograph is better suited to routine analysis, where the shapes and positions of the waves are known and all that is needed is the value of the current at one or two potentials. However, obtaining a complete polarogram with a manual instrument is a rather tedious operation, especially when the polarogram is a complicated one, and it is here that the recording instruments are worth their higher cost.

A laboratory doing only routine analyses of closely similar samples is usually best advised to select a manual polarograph. For general research, for methods development, or for analyses of highly dissimilar samples yielding complicated or not wholly predictable polarograms, on the other hand, a recording polarograph is essential. Laboratories that do both types of work should consider purchasing a manual instrument for the highly routine analyses and also a recording instrument for development work and for analyses of nonroutine samples. Manual polarographs are rarely found in industrial research laboratories.

The essential parts of a manual polarograph are diagrammed schematically in Fig. 46.12. In this circuit the variable resistor R_1 serves to adjust the voltage across R_2, which is indicated by the voltmeter V, to some convenient value such as 1.00 or 2.00 v. Any desired fraction of this total voltage can then be applied to the cell circuit by appropriate manipulation of the bridge R_2, which should be accurately linear, should have a resistance not exceeding 100 ohms (156), and must be fitted with an indicating dial to permit the measurement of the voltage being applied to the cell circuit. This consists of the cell itself in series with some current-measuring element. The reversing switches S_2 and S_3 are necessary because both the applied potential and the current may assume either positive or negative values; S_1 serves to prolong the life of the battery E.

A very simple instrument, which is suitable for much control work in which the solutions being analyzed are not too dilute and high accuracy is unnecessary, can be constructed by using a microammeter as the current-measuring element. An electrolytic capacitor, of 250 to 2000 $\mu f.$ capacity, depending on the characteristics of the microammeter, may be connected

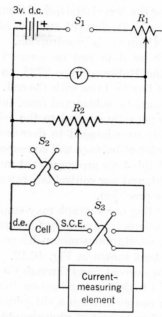

Fig. 46.12. Schematic diagram of a manual polarograph.

across its terminals to damp the oscillations resulting from the growth and fall of the drops. The range of the instrument may be extended to higher currents by shunting the microammeter, or a high-resistance millivoltmeter in series with a resistance box providing resistances between about 50 and 5000 ohms may be used instead of the microammeter. A shunted micro- • ammeter is employed in the American Optical Company's Model C-1 Electro-Polarizer.

When very small currents must be measured, or when greater accuracy is needed, the meter may be replaced by a galvanometer whose deflection is proportional to the current flowing through its coil. Kolthoff and Lingane (156) recommended a Rubicon Type 3514 taut-suspension box-type galvanometer; the writer has used a Leeds and Northrup Type HS galvanometer with complete satisfaction. The galvanometer sensitivity may be varied by means of an Ayrton-type shunt consisting of two decade resistance boxes in series across its terminals. A small, fixed resistor across the galvanometer terminals should be used to adjust its period to roughly three times the highest value of t likely to be encountered. The construction, calibration, and use of such circuits have been discussed by Kolthoff and Lingane (156). This principle is used in a number of commercially available instruments, including the American Optical Company's Model C-2 and R-1 Electro-Polarizers, the E. H. Sargent and Co. Model III Polarograph, and the Fisher Scientific Company's Elecdropode.

Very accurate and precise data can be secured by using a precision potentiometer, such as the Rubicon Type 2735, to measure the iR drop across a decade resistance box in series with the cell. The e.m.f. measured with the potentiometer must be subtracted from the output of the bridge R_2 to obtain the voltage actually applied to the cell. The galvanometer employed must be heavily overdamped to decrease the amplitude of its oscillations so that the point of balance will correspond to the true average current. Instruments of this type are somewhat more tedious to use than those previously described, and few control laboratories would derive much benefit from their extreme precision.

The conventional recording polarograph may employ either a galvanometer or a resistance-potentiometer assembly for current measurement, but invariably it contains a synchronous-motor-driven bridge differing in no important respect from that shown in Fig. 46.12. In a photographically recording polarograph the current flows through the coil of a galvanometer and causes a beam of light to deflect to an extent that is proportional to the current; the light beam passes through a slit perpendicular to the axis of rotation of a drum carrying a sheet of photographic paper. The drum is mechanically linked to the bridge so that the position of the spot of light with respect to the paper depends on both the applied voltage (along one axis) and the current (along the other axis). Such instruments have been described by several authors (1,74,112,184), and is sold by E. H. Sargent and Co. (Model XII Polarograph), and a number of other manufacturers in Germany, Czechoslovakia, and Japan.

To the necessity of processing the photographic record secured with these instruments is added the practical difficulty resulting from the sensitivity of the galvanometer to vibration (263). These problems do not occur with visible-recording polarographs, in which a standard resistor is connected in series with the cell and a strip-chart recording potentiometer is used to record the iR drop across this resistor. The voltage scale on the resulting polarogram is determined by the relation between the chart speed and the rate of rotation of the bridge. Most polarographs of this type are equipped with auxiliary circuits that permit starting the polarogram at any desired voltage, scanning any desired fraction of the maximum available voltage range, compensating the diffusion current of a preceding wave, recording current–time curves at constant voltage with the bridge disengaged, and other similar functions that are of considerable use in the research laboratory.

The commercially available visible-recording polarographs include the Radiometer (Copenhagen) PO3 and PO4 instruments, the LKB-Blomgren polarograph (LKB-Produkter, Stockholm), the Leeds and Northrup Type E Electrochemograph, the American Optical Company recording Electro-Polarizer, the E. H. Sargent and Co. Model XXI and XV Polarographs, the Fisher Scientific Company Elecdropode with auxiliary recording attachment, and the Metrohm Polarecord. Although a number of recording polarographs have been described in the original literature (78,135, 225,247,290,342), the writer is convinced that the construction of a recording polarograph in an industrial laboratory should not be considered except in the face of some (very improbable) requirement that cannot be met by any commercially available instrument.

B. DROPPING ELECTRODES AND CELLS

Dropping electrodes may be made by drawing out thermometer tubing, but it is both easier and, in the long run, less expensive to use "marine barometer tubing" obtainable from the Corning Glass Works. Suitable capillary tubing also can be purchased from several scientific supply houses, but at a much higher price. The conventional dropping electrode should give a drop weight of 7 to 10 mg. and a drop time of about 5 seconds when immersed in distilled water with the polarizing circuit disconnected. These desiderata are generally fulfilled by a 10- to 15-cm. length of marine barometer tubing with a mercury head of about 30 cm.

Many elaborate all-glass dropping-electrode assemblies have been devised, but no convincing proof has been offered that any real advantage is gained to offset their complexity. To permit easy reproduction of the mercury head in work with a single capillary while allowing this head to be varied to compensate for the differing characteristics of different capillaries, the writer uses the assembly shown in Fig. 46.13. The connections between the reservoir and capillary and the stand tube should be made with Tygon tubing or, less preferably, with neoprene or heavy-wall pure gum rubber tubing boiled in moderately concentrated aqueous sodium hydroxide to remove any trace of sulfur. Care must be taken that the tip of the capillary is cut off perfectly square and that the capillary is perfectly vertical (151,244). The original literature must be consulted for descriptions of the other arrangements that have been proposed (40,114,169,182,187,213, 242,248,310).

Especially when analyses are made by the standard solution method (*vide infra*), which necessitates the repetition of a substantial number of calibration experiments whenever the capillary is replaced, much time and effort can be wasted by careless treatment of the capillary. The funda-

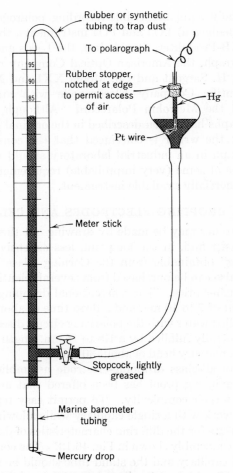

Rubber or synthetic
tubing to trap dust

To polarograph

Rubber stopper,
notched at edge
to permit access
of air

Hg

Pt wire

Meter stick

Stopcock, lightly
greased

Marine barometer
tubing

Mercury drop

Fig. 46.13. Typical dropping electrode assembly.

mental principle involved in the preservation of a capillary is that no solid matter of any kind must ever be permitted to enter its tip. To this end it is essential to avoid passing large anodic currents through a dropping electrode under such conditions that insoluble mercury salts are formed, to avoid crystallization of salts inside the capillary tip by scrupulously and thoroughly rinsing the capillary with distilled water whenever it is even momentarily removed from a solution, and to keep the capillary filled with mercury whenever it is not in use. Finally, a dropping electrode must never be lowered into a solution unless mercury is flowing through it.

Detailed directions for the care of capillaries have been given elsewhere (225).

Pure, clean mercury is essential to the successful use of polarography. Procedures for the purification of used mercury have been described by Meites (225), by Meites and Moros (237), and by Milner (239).

There are two general types of polarographic cells: those with an internal auxiliary electrode, such as a pool of mercury or a silver wire, whose potential depends on the composition of the solution being investigated, and those with an external reference electrode whose potential is fixed, known, and independent of sample composition.

Cells with internal auxiliary electrodes have two disadvantages. One is that the potential of the auxiliary electrode is not truly constant unless the solution is saturated with some slightly soluble salt of the metal from which the electrode is made; this is usually inconvenient, and in nitrate, per-chlorate, acetate, and other similar media, downright impossible. Hence such cells should not be used at all except in purely routine quantitative analyses, where the half-wave potentials obtained are of absolutely no concern. The other disadvantage is that reactions of the type

$$2Hg + \frac{1}{2}O_2 + H_2O + M^{+2} + 2Cl^- = Hg_2Cl_2 + M(OH)_2$$

or

$$Hg + 2Cl^- + O_2 + 2H_2O = HgCl_2 + H_2O_2 + 2OH^-$$

may considerably alter the composition of a sample before its polarogram can be recorded (145).

Cells of this type played an important part in early polarography, and a great many of them have been described (81,105,182,198,205,263), but in the writer's opinion they have long since outlived their usefulness.

Cells with external reference electrodes are of two main types: those in which the sample is separated from the solution in the reference electrode compartment by some sort of diaphragm, and those in which the two solutions are allowed to come into actual physical contact (61,111,144,254,334). The latter type seems to be preferred in Europe, but is almost never found in American laboratories. Apparently the proponents of each type consider that the other is likely to give rise to far more contamination of the solutions (61,156).

American practice strongly favors the H-cell designed by Lingane and Laitinen (189), in which the reference electrode (almost always a saturated calomel electrode) is separated from the sample by an agar plug held in place by a sintered glass disk. Directions for the preparation of the agar plug and reference electrode are given in the literature (156,225). Many

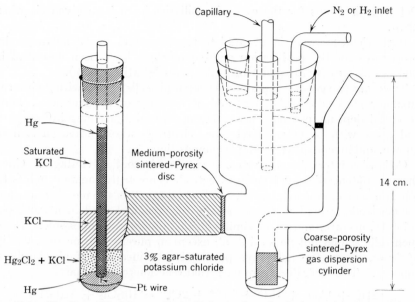

Fig. 46.14. H-cell modified to permit rapid deaeration of solutions. Reproduced from Meites, *Polarographic Techniques* (225).

modifications of this cell have been suggested (12,37,162,235,238,262)· the one preferred by the writer is shown in Fig. 46.14. The sintered glass gas-dispersion cylinder in this cell enables dissolved oxygen to be completely removed in only a minute or two by a rapid stream of nitrogen or hydrogen (167,235). Although space does not permit descriptions of the other diaphragm-type cells that have been proposed (14,76,172,200,294,347), attention should be called to the cells that have been designed for such special purposes as the determination of oxygen in biological fluids (12), the analysis of a few drops of solution (205,238), and the continuous monitoring of effluents from ion-exchange columns (20,136,137,140,208,271).

C. AUXILIARY EQUIPMENT

The effect of temperature on the diffusion current is large enough to necessitate the use of a thermostat in all but the crudest polarographic work. Temperature control to ±0.25°C. generally suffices and can be achieved quite inexpensively. It is convenient to be able to leave the thermostat stirrer on even while the measurements are being made, but to do this the thermostat must be set up carefully, because the dropping electrode is quite sensitive to vibration. The arrangement may be considered satisfactory if no change in the time required for 10 successive drops to form and fall results from turning the stirrer on.   Slow stirring and—especially— mechanical isolation of the stirrer will facilitate the achievement of this goal.

Dissolved oxygen is reducible at the dropping electrode, producing waves that would interfere with most polarographic measurements, and provision therefore must be made for its removal.   Occasionally this may be done by adding sulfite (152) or hydrazine (229) if the supporting electrolyte is neutral or alkaline, but this is impossible if the solution contains substances that decrease the rate of the chemical reduction of oxygen or that would react with the sulfite or hydrazine to give undesired products.   The re- moval of dissolved oxygen is therefore generally accomplished by passing a stream of a polarographically inert gas—nitrogen, hydrogen, argon, or, if the solution is acidic, carbon dioxide—through the solution.   Com- mercial compressed gases often are sufficiently free from oxygen for use without purification.   But in trace analysis, in work with powerful re- ducing agents, or in especially careful work of any kind they should be freed from the traces of oxygen they contain.   This can be done by passing the tank gas over finely divided metallic copper at 450 to 500°C. or through a train of efficient wash bottles filled with vanadous (231) or chromous (95,227) sulfate or chloride solutions.   In any case, the gas should be passed through a gas-washing bottle filled with water (or with a portion of the supporting electrolyte if this contains volatile substances such as ammonia, pyridine, ethanol, dioxane, and the like) and immersed in the thermostat before entering the cell; this prevents changes in the composi- tion of the sample during deaeration.   The gas train should be constructed entirely of Tygon and glass; rubber and polyethylene tubing are especially unsuitable because of their relatively high porosity to atmospheric oxygen.

The most important consideration in setting up a polarographic labora- tory is the sensitivity of the dropping electrode to vibration.   Although much good work has been done under conditions far from ideal, there is no question that the time required to locate a reasonably vibration-free spot will be well spent.   It is convenient to use a large thermostat, accessible from three or four sides, in which several cells can be placed (and deaerated) simultaneously.   The thermostat may conveniently be placed on a heavy table on which are mounted the gas-purification train and one or more dropping-electrode assemblies, while the thermostat stirrer and the polaro- graph are mounted on another table that does not touch the first.   The thermostat table should be equipped with a vacuum line (for emptying the cells without removing them from the thermostat), with running cold water (for replacing evaporation losses and for cooling in warm weather), and with electrical outlets (for the thermostat relay and heater, for use with rotating electrodes, and for other occasional purposes).

V. POLAROGRAPHIC METHODOLOGY

A. QUALITATIVE ANALYSIS

Qualitative polarographic analyses are performed by recording polarograms of the sample in a suitable number of appropriately chosen supporting electrolytes, and comparing the half-wave potentials and other characteristics of the waves obtained with the known polarographic characteristics of the various possible constituents of the sample. The number of polarograms needed, as well as the problems involved in selecting the supporting electrolytes, naturally depends on the complexity of the sample and the amount of previously available information regarding its composition.

The simplest possible kind of qualitative analysis is, of course, that in which all that is needed is an identification of the sample as one of a reasonably small number of fairly pure materials. For example, one might be called upon to decide whether a crystalline salt is cadmium nitrate or zinc nitrate. Reference to a table of half-wave potentials shows that in, say, $1F$ potassium chloride the half-wave potentials of cadmium and zinc are -0.64 and -1.00 v. vs. S.C.E., respectively. Recording a polarogram of a portion of the sample in $1F$ potassium chloride thus permits the immediate solution of the question at hand.

Although this situation is very nearly trivial, it does involve some subtleties worthy of mention. Suppose a sample is known to contain either copper or bismuth; since the half-wave potentials of these ions are both equal to -0.01 v. vs. S.C.E. in $1F$ nitric acid, it is evident that nothing worthwhile could be gained by recording a polarogram of the sample in that medium, because a wave having this half-wave potential would be observed in either case. One might instead use $0.1F$ potassium biphthalate, in which the half-wave potentials of copper and bismuth are -0.10 and -0.23 v. vs. S.C.E., respectively.

On the other hand, the half-wave potentials of thallous and lead ions in $1F$ hydrochloric acid are -0.48 and -0.44 v. vs. S.C.E., respectively; but despite this small difference no experienced polarographer would hesitate to undertake a decision as to which of these ions was responsible for a wave occurring in this range of potentials. This is because, as can be seen by differentiating equation (16), the lead wave, for which $n = 2$, is much steeper than the thallous wave, for which $n = 1$. The shape of a wave, or the presence of a characteristic maximum or minimum, is often of great utility in the course of a qualitative analysis.

The treatment of more complex mixtures may be illustrated by a single example. Suppose that a polarogram of a completely unknown sample is secured in $1F$ potassium cyanide and is found to consist of a single wave at about -1.4 v. $vs.$ S.C.E. Nickel ($E_{1/2} = -1.36$ v.), chromium(III) ($E_{1/2} = -1.38$ v.), and cobalt ($E_{1/2} = -1.45$ v.) might all be suspected. After consulting a table of half-wave potentials, one might perhaps secure a polarogram of another portion of the sample in $1F$ potassium thiocyanate. Here the respective half-wave potentials are -0.69, -1.05, and -1.08 v., so the presence or absence of nickel could easily be determined. However, it would still be impossible to decide between chromium and cobalt (or both) if a wave appeared at about -1.06 v.; one would then have to record a third polarogram in another supporting electrolyte, in which these two ions gave waves at distinctly different potentials.

Apart from the obvious problems associated with the choice of the successive supporting electrolytes—whose difficulty is largely dependent on one's experience—the chief practical problem arises in dealing with samples containing the various constituents in widely different concentrations. This problem, incidentally, also arises in quantitative polarographic analyses. Imagine first a sample containing a small concentration of copper, a higher concentration of lead, and a still higher concentration of zinc. In $1F$ potassium nitrate the half-wave potentials of these ions are -0.01, -0.40, and -1.01 v. $vs.$ S.C.E. A polarogram of such a mixture can easily be secured at such a sensitivity that the zinc wave is readily identifiable (or, for quantitative purposes, that the height of the zinc wave can be measured with satisfactory precision). At this sensitivity the lead wave may be too small for measurement or even for detection, but it is a simple matter to increase the sensitivity or to add a larger aliquot of the unknown. Either of these expedients will so magnify the zinc wave that it runs off the polarogram, but as zinc has already been identified (or determined) this is of no consequence. Repeating the same procedure will allow a copper wave of suitable height to be obtained.

From this discussion it may be concluded that the presence of a large concentration of one reducible substance, A, occasions no difficulty in the detection or determination of a second substance, B, if the half-wave potential of A is considerably more negative than that of B. (If the waves of A and B are anodic, the half-wave potential of A should be the more positive of the two.) Trouble arises when this order is reversed: when, for example, the concentration of copper is high and the concentrations of lead and zinc are successively smaller. This is, in fact, the most troublesome problem of practical polarographic analysis, and is the problem that has been primarily responsible for the development of differential, derivative, a.-c., and square-wave polarography. Each of these techniques serves to increase the ratio of A to B that can be tolerated in the determination of B in the unfavorable case. Many problems of this sort have been successfully handled by such expedients as differential oxidation, reduction, or complexation to reverse the order of the waves on the polarogram; by separating the two substances by precipitation, extraction into an immiscible solvent, electrolytic deposition, or ion-exchange chromatography; or by electrical compensation of the diffusion current of the earlier wave. The details of such procedures can be found in monographs on polarography (105,156,225,239). Here it can only be remarked that the problem has no completely general solution; the analytical chemist must exercise intelligent ingenuity.

B. QUANTITATIVE ANALYSIS

1. Selection of the Solvent and Supporting Electrolyte

This topic is of little importance to the analyst who wishes merely to use a method described in the literature for the analysis of samples similar to those for which the method was designed. But it should be apparent from the discussion just concluded that the choice of the medium is one of the most crucial points in the development of a new analytical method, or even in the modification of an existing method that must be applied to samples containing substances not taken into account in the original procedure.

Practically all inorganic polarographic analyses are carried out in aqueous solutions; only very rarely could one expect any advantage to result from the use of a non-aqueous solvent (345). On the other hand, the slight solubility of most organic compounds in water renders the use of a partially or wholly non-aqueous solvent an inescapable necessity in much organic polarography. The non-aqueous solvent must have two properties: it must obviously be a good solvent for the substance being determined and for the other constituents of the sample, and it must have a sufficiently high dielectric constant to permit adding reasonable concentrations of dissolved salts. The latter requirement serves two purposes: it gives rise to a conductance that is high enough to minimize the iR drop through the cell, and it allows the buffer capacity of the solution to be made great enough so that the pH of the solution at the electrode surface does not change from point to point along the wave (159). An excessive cell resistance always does, and an insufficient buffer capacity usually does, give rise to waves that are drawn out and rather unsuitable for accurate work. The first problem can be cured at the cost of some instrumental complexity (252, 261), but the second is immune to instrumental mitigation. By way of contrast to what was said in Section II-A-2, it may be mentioned that the migration-current problem does not exist in work with uncharged organic molecules.

Some of the solvents that have been employed in organic polarography are acetonitrile, ethanol, dioxane, tetrahydrofuran, formamide (and dimethylformamide), dimethyl sulfoxide, acetic acid (6), glycerol (288), ethylene glycol (77), and concentrated sulfuric acid (126,333). The first problem that must be overcome is that of dissolving the sample; to this end it may be necessary to experiment with varying the ratio of water to non-aqueous solvent, with mixing two or more polar solvents, or with mixing polar and nonpolar solvents (166). One then has the problem of finding a buffer system whose components are sufficiently soluble to provide sufficient buffer capacity and electrical conductance; for this purpose organic buffer systems are generally preferable to inorganic ones, whereas lithium, tetramethylammonium, and tetraethylammonium salts are more likely to be useful in non-aqueous media than sodium or potassium salts.

The chief problem in both inorganic and organic analysis is the selection of a supporting electrolyte in which the substance being determined gives a wave that is well defined—so that its height can be easily and accurately measured—and that is also well separated from the waves produced by the other constituents of the sample. For the reasons discussed in Section V-A, it is clearly preferable to arrange matters so that the wave of the desired constituent will precede the wave due to any other constituent; this can often be accomplished by the proper choice of complexing agent and pH. Otherwise, of course, one may always resort to a.-c. or square-wave polarography or to a prior chemical or electrolytic (most elegantly by the use of controlled-potential electrolysis (186,223)) separation.

The equivalent of differential complexation is rarely feasible in dealing with organic substances, and here one must usually fall back on attempts to separate waves or to alter their relative position by varying the pH or ionic strength (63) of the solution or the nature of the buffer system employed (75). In a few cases (e.g., with polyhydroxy compounds in borate buffers), the specific effects of the buffer system can be ascribed to purely chemical causes akin to complex formation in inorganic polarography. Far more often, however, such effects are to be attributed to changes in the structure of the electrical double layer that result in changes in the electrochemical kinetic parameters of the electrode reactions involving the different electroactive species in the solution. The unfortunate result of this fact is that there is no a priori way of selecting the conditions best adapted to the resolution of two waves of organic substances.   When one considers the additional fact that the waves of different substances containing the same functional group(s) are likely to be affected in much the same way by changes in the experimental conditions, it is evident that it is much more difficult to apply polarographic analysis to organic than to inorganic materials.

2. Preparation of the Sample

Preparing a sample for polarographic analysis sometimes involves nothing more than dissolving it in the medium selected, although in other cases a rather lengthy and laborious succession of preliminary steps may be required.   These steps are directed toward either or both of two ends: the separation of the substance being determined from other constituents of the sample that would give rise to interfering waves, and the adjustment of the oxidation state of the substance being determined.   A single, randomly chosen example will serve to illustrate the principles involved.

Suppose that one wished to determine vanadium in a mineral acid solution containing a small concentration of vanadium(IV) and a much larger concentration of iron(III).   In alkaline citrate or malonate, vanadium(IV) gives an anodic wave well separated from the ferric wave, but its ready air-oxidation in such media might lead one to prefer either:

1. Removal of the iron, e.g., by precipitation, electrolytic reduction to the metal at a mercury cathode, or ether extraction;

2. Reduction (either chemical or electrolytic) of the iron to the ferrous state, which in a dilute mineral acid solution gives no wave and thus does not interfere with the cathodic vanadium(IV) wave in such media; or

3. Oxidation of the vanadium to the +5 state (e.g., by lead dioxide, sodium bismuthate, or some other oxidizing agent of which any excess can be easily and completely removed), which in an acidic malonate buffer yields a wave preceding the ferric wave.

It is clear that the problems involved in the preparation of the sample are intimately related to the selection of the supporting electrolyte.   In the example just cited, oxidizing the vanadium to the +5 state would accomplish nothing if the polarogram of the oxidized solution were then obtained in a mineral acid supporting electrolyte, in which the vanadium(V) and iron(III) waves coincide.

The choice of techniques for accomplishing these two purposes is largely a matter of individual preference, so that general rules are difficult to give, especially since the elegance of any particular approach depends on the composition of the sample at hand.   It is worth pointing out, however, that controlled-potential electrolysis at a mercury cathode, which was first used for electroseparation prior to polarographic analysis by Lingane (181), occupies a place of honor among all of these techniques because of its ability to achieve both ends at once. For example, the polarographic characteristics of uranium, vanadium, copper, iron, etc., are such that a relatively lengthy separation of uranium from these other elements would probably be necessary before the uranium content of an ore could be determined polarographically. On the other hand, a single controlled-potential electrolysis of a solution of the sample in dilute mineral acid can be made to deposit copper, reduce iron and vanadium to innocuous lower oxidation states, and simultaneously convert uranium to the $+3$ state, which yields a well-developed anodic wave whose height can be measured easily without interference from any other element. Procedures of this kind involve a minimum of time and manipulation and should prove exceedingly valuable in dealing with complex samples.

Some of the techniques of sample preparation that have been mentioned will result in a solution containing the substance to be determined in the supporting electrolyte to be used. This is most likely to be feasible when the supporting electrolyte is relatively simple in composition, such as a mineral acid or a sodium hydroxide solution, and when the substance being determined is inert to air-oxidation in the medium in question; it is almost certain to be the case if the preparation of the sample has been carried out by controlled-potential electrolysis. In this event, all that is necessary is to thoroughly deaerate a portion of the solution in a suitable cell while allowing it to come to the temperature of the thermostat, insert the dropping electrode and adjust the height of the mercury column to the previously selected value, and finally record the polarogram over a range of potentials that includes the desired wave. Polarograms of solutions resulting from controlled-potential electrolyses can, of course, be secured without transferring them from the electrolysis cell, provided the latter is thermostated and so designed that a dropping electrode can be inserted into the working-electrode compartment.

For one reason or another, it may prove convenient or even necessary to carry out the analysis by preparing a stock solution of the sample in, say, dilute mineral acid, and then obtaining a polarogram of a mixture of an aliquot of this solution with a known volume of the supporting electrolyte. One substantial advantage of such a procedure is that it permits the residual current to be measured directly before the addition of the solution of the sample. This is conducive to greater accuracy than can otherwise be obtained because it eliminates the problems involved in extrapolation methods of correcting for the residual current and because it is the easiest and shortest method available for use with a manual polarograph. In this event it is obviously necessary to deaerate the supporting electrolyte alone so that the residual current can be measured before the sample is added.

To avoid the undesirable side reactions that may occur when metallic mercury is brought into contact with a solution containing dissolved oxygen, it is essential to deaerate the solution before the dropping electrode is inserted or the mercury pool (if one is used) is added. The gas stream is then diverted over the surface of the solution to avoid stirring while the measurements are being made.

The special problems that arise when the final solution contains powerful oxidizing or reducing agents, or substances that react with the components of the salt bridge leading to the reference electrode, have been discussed elsewhere (225).

3. Measurement of the Wave Height

As was indicated in the preceding section, the technique employed in measuring a wave height with a manual polarograph is somewhat different from that which is most suitable for use with a recording instrument.

We shall assume initially that one is dealing with a very well-defined wave, that is, a wave having a long plateau essentially parallel to the residual current curve. (See Fig. 46.1.) The best way to measure the diffusion current of a wave of this sort involves the selection of a potential somewhere on the plateau, preferably as near the potential of the electrocapillary maximum as possible in order to minimize the residual current and maximize the precision and sensitivity of the diffusion-current measurement. After deaerating the supporting electrolyte, the residual current is measured at this potential under exactly the same conditions (temperature, mercury pressure, etc.) as will be used in the subsequent measurement of the limiting current. A portion of a stock solution of the sample is then added and, after the mixture is deaerated, the limiting current is measured.

Provided that sufficient care is taken to ensure complete deaeration and that the same lot of each reagent is employed in preparing the solutions of a number of similar samples, it is often permissible to measure the residual current of a single blank solution and to apply this value as a correction to the limiting currents obtained with a number of sample solutions.

The so-called "increment method" (41,181) purports to eliminate or at least minimize the uncertainties due to possible variations in the residual current. It consists of measuring two currents with the final solution containing the sample. One of these (i_2) is obtained on the plateau of the wave; the other (i_1) is obtained at a potential at which the wave has not yet begun, for example at -0.45 v. in Fig. 46.1a. The difference between these currents, $i_2 - i_1$, is taken as a measure of the wave height. Obviously,

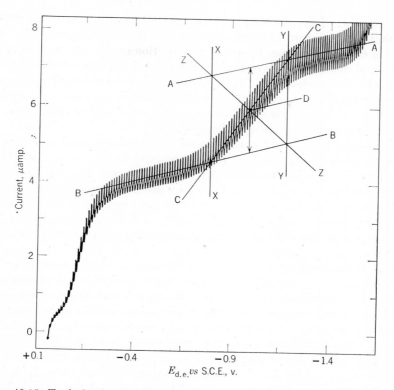

Fig. 46.15. Typical polarogram obtained with a recording polarograph, illustrating a graphical method of construction intended to correct for the residual current or (as illustrated here) for the diffusion current of a preceding wave. Reproduced from Meites, *Polarographic Techniques* (225).

this quantity cannot be exactly proportional to the concentration of the substance responsible for the wave, because the residual current is not independent of potential, so that $i_2 - i_1$ will not be zero even in the complete absence of the electroactive species. An empirical calibration curve is therefore necessary unless the diffusion current is so large that the change of the residual current between the two potentials used can be neglected.

This objection is overcome by a modification of the increment method in which a correction is applied for the difference between i_1 and i_2 obtained with a blank solution (255). That is, the wave height is taken as $(i_2 - i_1)_{sample} - (i_2 - i_1)_{blank}$. Here it is assumed that the residual-current curve of the solution of the sample is parallel, over the range of potentials in question, with that of the blank solution.

The analog of the direct method, as carried out with a recording polarograph, involves recording the residual current curve for the deaerated supporting electrolyte alone, then adding a portion of a stock solution of the sample, deaerating, and repeating the recording. This results in two curves like those shown in Fig. 46.1, from which the diffusion current can be measured directly. It is not necessary to obtain the entire polarogram, but even if the recording is confined to a relatively narrow range of potentials the procedure is somewhat lengthy.

Wave-height measurements with a recording polarograph are more commonly carried out by an extrapolation method illustrated by Fig. 46.15. The manner in which the lines AA and BB are constructed is obvious. When these are as nearly parallel as they are here, the exact potential at which the vertical distance between them is measured is of little importance. However, since $m^{2/3}t^{1/6}$ varies with potential (cf. Figs. 46.4 and 46.5), it is necessary to use a single predetermined potential throughout any series of analyses.

The chief difficulty with the extrapolation method arises when the plateau of the wave is not closely parallel to the residual-current portion of the polarogram; then the distance between AA and BB becomes sensitively dependent on potential, so the choice of potential becomes a matter for acute concern. The usual course is to measure the "wave height" at the potential at which the rising portion of the wave is exactly halfway between the two extrapolated lines. This corresponds roughly to the half-wave potential. The "wave height" thus obtained depends on both the diffusion current and the shape of the wave, and therefore it is not proportional to the concentration of the substance being determined (36, 232). Careful empirical standardization of the method with known solutions is therefore essential.

4. Interpretation of the Wave Height

In every polarographic analysis the concentration of the substance being determined is calculated with the aid of wave-height–concentration data obtained with known solutions. In the "absolute" method of interpreting the data, one makes use of information taken from the literature or obtained with a different capillary from that used in the analysis. In this method it is assumed that the diffusion current constant of any substance under identical experimental conditions is independent of the characteristics of the particular capillary employed. On the basis of this assumption, the concentration of the substance being determined can be found from the equation

$$C = i_d / I m^{2/3} t^{1/6}$$

The absolute method evidently requires the measurement of m and t for the capillary being used under the same conditions (especially at the same potential) as those involved in the measurement of the diffusion current. The limitations of the fundamental assumption are such that errors of about ± 3 to 5% may be encountered; this is not objectionable in much practical work and the method is particularly useful for occasional analyses, because it may then save much of the time required by a comparative method.

The simplest comparative method is the "standard solution" method, in which the relationship between wave height and concentration is established empirically by measurements with known solutions, using the same capillary that will be used in the analyses. A plot of C/i_d vs. i_d has been recommended on the grounds of convenience and precision (225). In applying the standard solution method it is unnecessary to measure m, but it is wise to check the value of t, under some arbitrarily selected set of conditions, in the course of each analysis or series of analyses; otherwise one is at the mercy of an unexpected change in capillary characteristics. The obvious necessity of repeating the calibration experiments for each substance being determined whenever the capillary has to be changed is the chief disadvantage of this method. On the other hand, no other procedure is capable of providing useful results if the wave height is not proportional to the concentration.

In the "standard sample" method (320), equal weights of the unknown and of a standard closely resembling it in composition are treated in exactly the same way, and the composition of the unknown is calculated from the ratio of the heights of the waves obtained with the two solutions. The method, which is capable of high accuracy if a suitable standard is available, is rather lengthy and is not often used.

The "standard addition" method (115) involves measuring the wave height as usual, using a known volume (say, V ml.) of solution. Then a known volume (v ml.) of a standard ($C_s M$) solution of the substance being determined is added, and the wave height is measured again. If i_1 and i_2 are the two wave heights, the concentration of the unknown is given by

$$C_u = i_1 v C_s / (i_2 v + (i_2 - i_1) V)$$

In deriving this equation it is assumed that the wave height is proportional to the concentration over the range in question. If i_1 is regarded as fixed, it is advantageous to have i_2 as large as possible, provided that this assumption is satisfied (226). However, if the current is proportional to the concentration only within a restricted range, i_2 should obviously not be above the upper limit of this range, and if i_1 is already very near that limit it may be advisable to dilute the sample solution before proceeding with the addition of the standard (273).

In the "pilot ion" method (71) a known concentration of a substance not present in the sample is added to the final solution. The wave heights of the substance being determined and the added or "pilot" substance are measured; provided that both are proportional to the respective concentrations one has

$$\frac{(i_d/C)_1}{(i_d/C)_2} = \frac{k_1}{k_2} = k$$

or

$$C_2 = k(i_d)_2 C_1/(i_d)_1 \tag{29}$$

The factors affecting k_1 and k_2 were reviewed in Section II-B-3-b; for the present purpose what is important is that changes in k_1 will be paralleled by very nearly equal changes in k_2, and will thus disappear from the ratio k. Because even fairly substantial variations of temperature, solution viscosity, mercury pressure, and other such quantities can be tolerated, the pilot ion method is excellently suited to routine analysis. The value of k is usually determined by applying equation (29) to data obtained with a solution containing known concentrations of the two substances. Evidently the wave due to the pilot substance must not coincide with or overlap the wave due to any possible constituent of the sample; the occasional difficulty of meeting this requirement when dealing with a complex sample is the only significant limitation to the use of this technique. Some care is necessary in choosing the concentration of the pilot substance to be added, and this must be done with due attention to the considerations outlined in Section V-A.

Some of the advantages of the pilot ion method are retained in the external standard method proposed by Porter (267), whose paper should be consulted for details.

5. Indirect Techniques

Although the great majority of polarographic analyses are performed by measuring the height of a wave due to the reduction or oxidation of the substance being determined, there are many examples of indirect methods in the literature. Sulfate has been determined after treatment with a known excess of lead ion by measuring the diffusion current of the excess lead (82,225); sodium has been determined by precipitation of the well-known triple acetate and measurement of the height of the uranium(VI) wave obtained on dissolving the precipitate in acid (38). Tartrate has been determined in the presence of citrate by measuring the wave height of a tartrato complex of antimony(III) (209), and aluminum can be determined by virtue of its complexation with an excess of the reducible dye, Pontachrome Violet SW (344). Chlorate can be determined by treatment with excess ferrous ion in a hydrochloric acid medium, followed by measurement of the diffusion current of the ferric ion formed during the chemical reduction of the chlorate (230).

These indirect procedures often involve questions of coprecipitation, stoichiometry, and chemical kinetics that do not arise in more conventional methods, but where they have been used they have generally constituted relatively simple solutions of difficult analytical problems.

VI. POLAROGRAPHIC DATA

Table 46.II is a highly condensed summary of the polarographic characteristics of a number of the commoner inorganic substances in a few of the most useful supporting electrolytes. For example, the entry "-0.46, w, II, -80, 1.44" has the following significance:

1. A cathodic wave is produced, and its half-wave potential is -0.46 v. *vs.* S.C.E. Parentheses around the value of $E_{1/2}$ indicate that the wave is anodic. The symbol ">0" denotes that $E_{1/2}$ is so positive that the rising part of the wave is masked by the anodic dissolution of the electrode mercury; clearly the height of such a wave cannot be obtained by any extrapolation method. The symbol "NR" indicates that no wave is observed.

2. The wave is well defined in the sense that its plateau is very nearly parallel to the residual-current curve and is sufficiently long (in a pure solution) to permit the easy and accurate measurement of the wave height. The symbol "i" indicates that the wave is ill defined in the sense that its height could not be measured with good accuracy; a very ill-defined ("vi") wave has a plateau so misshapen that neither its height nor that of any later wave could be estimated within usefully narrow limits. The symbols "fw" and "fi" mean fairly well-defined and fairly ill-defined, respectively.

3. The electrode reaction responsible for the wave produces the $+2$ state of the element in question.

4. $E_{3/4} - E_{1/4}$ is -80 mv., where, for example, $E_{3/4}$ is the potential at which $i - i_r = 3/4\ i_d$. For a reversible wave, $E_{3/4} - E_{1/4} = -56.4/n$ mv. The values of this quantity, together with the values of $E_{1/2}$, for two adjacent waves on a polarogram determine the extent of overlapping of the two waves.

5. The diffusion-current constant, $i_d/Cm^{2/3}t^{1/6}$, is 1.44. For multiple waves the diffusion-current constants refer to the total diffusion currents on the successive plateaus.

TABLE
Polarographic Characteristics of

Element and oxidation state	Sat'd. N₂H₄·2HCl	1F HCl	Sat'd. H₃C₆H₅O₇	Supporting 0.1F pyridine, 0.1F pyridinium chloride
Ag(I)	>0, vw, 0	Ppt.	>0, vw, 0	>0, i, 0
Al(III)	NR	NR	NR	NR
As(III)	−0.19, w, 0	−0.43, w, 0, —, 6.0	−0.58, vi, 0	−0.90, i
	−0.58, fw	−0.67, w, −III, —, 12.0	−0.73, i	−1.05, i
			−1.02, i, −III	
As(V)	NR	NR	NR	NR
Bi(III)	−0.20, vw, 0, −18	−0.09, vw, 0, −18, 5.2	−0.02, w, 0, −23	−1.00, i, 0, ppt.
Br(V)	—	+0.1, —, −I	—	—
Cd(II)	−0.73, fw, 0, −28	−0.64, vw, 0, −28, 3.58	−0.51, vw, 0, −28	−0.62, vw, 0, −28
Ce(IV)	Ce(III), NR	>0	Ce(III), NR	Ppt.
Co(II)	NR	NR	NR	−1.05, w, 0, −30
Cr(III)	NR	Ca. −1.0, vi, II	−0.78, i, II, −60	−0.99, fi, II
Cr(VI)	−0.59, fi, III, (?)	>0, —, III	>0, w, III	>0, w, III
				−1.19, fw, III
Cu(II)	>0, vw, I	+0.04, —, I	+0.03, vw, 0, −35	>0, w, I
	−0.33, vw, 0, −57	−0.22, —, 0, —, 3.39		−0.22, w, 0
Fe(II)	NR	NR	NR	NR
Fe(III)	>0, vw, II	>0, —, II	+0.23, w, II, −57	Ppt.
Hg(II)	>0, —, 0	>0, —, 0	—	—
I(V)	—	±0.0, —, −I, —, 12.0	—	—

46.II

Some Inorganic Substances[a]

electrolyte				
1F NH$_3$, 1F NH$_4$Cl	0.1F NH$_3$, 0.1F (NH$_4$)$_3$- C$_6$H$_5$O$_7$	0.5F Na$_2$- C$_4$H$_4$O$_6$, pH 9	1F KCN	1F NaOH
>0, w, 0	>0, w, 0	Ppt.	>0	Ppt.
NR	NR	NR	NR	NR
−1.41, fw, —,	−1.63, fw, −III,	NR	—	(−0.27, fw,
−110	−57			V, 34, −3.1
−1.64, fw, −III,				
−50				
NR	NR	NR	NR	NR
Ppt.	−0.43, vw, 0,	−0.7, i	Ppt.	−0.6 ppt.
	−45			
—	—	—	—	−1.6, —, −I
0.81, vw, 0, −28,	−0.71, vw, 0,	−0.64, w,	−1.18, w, 0	−0.76 ppt.
3.68	−42	0, —,		
		2.34		
Ppt.	>0, vw, III	—	Ppt.	Ppt.
−1.29, w, 0	−1.39, fw, 0,	−1.7	−1.45, w, I	Ppt.
	−82			
	−1.7 (small, i)			
−1.43, w, II	Ppt.	—	−1.38, w, II,	
−1.71, fi, 0			−58, 1.55	
−0.24, —, III	−0.24, vw, III,	—	—	−0.85, vw,
	−75		—	III, —, 5.72
−1.6, —, 0	−1.8, vi, 0, −60			
−0.24, fw, I, −57	−0.17, fi, I, −58	−0.30, vw,	Cu(I), NR	−0.41, fw, 0,
		0, −28		—, 2.91
−0.51, vw, 0,	−0.34, vw, 0,			
−57, 3.75	−58			
(−0.34), —, III	(−0.44), w, III,	—	NR	(−0.9), —,
	+35			III, +58
−1.49, —, 0	−1.63, vi, 0			1.46, —, 0
Ppt.	−0.46, vw, II,	—	>0, —, II	Ppt.
	−58	—	>0, —, 0	Ppt.
	−0.93, w, small			
	−1.61, i, 0			
Ppt.	—	—	—	—
−1.2, —, −I	—	—	—	−1.2, —, −I

(continued)

TABLE

Element and oxidation state	Sat'd. $N_2H_4 \cdot 2HCl$	$1F$ HCl	Sat'd. $H_3C_6H_5O_7$	Supporting $0.1F$ pyridine, $0.1F$ pyridinium chloride
In(III)	−0.65, w, I(?), −25 −0.91, fw, 0(?), −53	−0.6, w, 0	−0.54, w, 0	NR
Mn(II)	NR	NR	NR	NR
Mo(VI)	Mo(V) (formed by chem. reduction): >0, w, IV −0.43, w, III	−0.1, —, V −0.25, —, V −0.55, —, III	+0.04, vw, V, −57 −0.44, vw, III	−0.24, fw, small −0.68, w, ?
Ni(II)	NR	—	−0.98, i, 0	−0.75, vw, 0, −29 −1.17, w, ?, small
Pb(II)	−0.54, vw, 0, −27	−0.44, vw, 0, −28, 3.86	−0.36, w, 0, −27	−0.40, w, 0, −27
Sb(III)	−0.20, vw, 0, −21	−0.15, w, 0, −19, 5.57	−0.38, vw, 0	−0.47, i
Sb(V)	>0, i, III −0.21, vw, 0	−0.35, —, —, —, 1.9	NR	NR
Sn(II)	−0.25, fw, small	(−0.1), i, IV	(−0.05), fw, IV, 28	−1.12, fw, 0, ppt.
	−0.53, w, 0, −28	−0.47, —, 0, —, 4.07	−0.40, vw, 0, −27	
Sn(IV)	−0.21, vw, II	−0.1, —, II, small	NR	NR
	−0.52, w, 0, −26	−0.47, —, 0, —, 4.8		
Te(VI)	−0.75, w, small	—	NR	NR
Ti(IV)	—	$ca.$ −0.8	—	—
Tl(I)	−0.56, vw, 0, −57	−0.48, vw, 0	−0.44, vw, 0, −57	−0.45, vw, 0, −58

46.II (*continued*)

electrolyte

$1F$ NH_3, $1F$ NH_4Cl	$0.1F$ NH_3, $0.1F$ $(NH_4)_2$-$C_6H_5O_7$	$0.5F$ Na_2-$C_4H_4O_6$, pH 9	$1F$ KCN	$1F$ NaOH
Ppt.	−1.35, i, ?, −145, abnormally small	—	−−	−1.09
−1.66, w, 0	−1.62, i, 0, −71	—	−1.33, vw, I, −58	−1.70, ppt.
−1.71, fw, V(?), −57	−1.26, fw, V, −122; −1.70, i, IV	NR	—	—
−1.10, w, 0, —, 3.56	−1.09, i, 0	NR	−1.36, w, 0	Ppt.
Ppt.	−1.39, fw, 0; −0.53, w, 0, −28	−0.58, vw, 0, −28, 2.4	−0.72, w, 0	−0.76, vw, 0 −28, 3.40
—	−0.97, vw, 0, −114	−1.0, i; −1.2, i, —, —, 3.9	−1.09	(−0.45), vw, V; 1.15, —, 0; —, 6.0
—	NR	—	—	—
—	(−0.47), w, IV, 13	(−0.33), —, IV	—	(−0.73), —, IV, —, −3.45
	−0.75, vw, 0, −57	−0.92, —, 0		−1.22, —, 0, 3.45
—	NR	NR	—	NR
−1.21, —, −II, —, 17.5	−1.30, vw, −II, −73	—	−1.36	−1.57
—	—	—	—	NR
−0.48, vw, 0	−0.45, w, 0, −58	—	>0, vw, 0	−0.48, vw, 0

(*continued*)

TABLE

Element and oxidation state	Sat'd. N$_2$H$_4$·2HCl	1F HCl	Sat'd. H$_3$C$_6$H$_5$O$_7$	Supporting 0.1F pyridine, 0.1F pyridinium chloride
U(VI)	−0.16, vw, IV	−0.2, w, V + IV	−0.12, vw, IV(?), −63	−0.23, fw, V(?)
		−0.9, fw, III		−0.45, vi, IV
				−0.98, fw, III
V(IV)	−0.94, vi, II	−0.8, fi, II	−0.67, i, small	−0.63, vi, ?
			−1.05, i, II	
V(V)	−0.5, i, small	>0, fw, IV	+0.11, vw, IV, −58	−0.11, fw, IV
	−0.9, vi	−0.8, fi, II	−0.63, fi, II	−0.43, w, ?
				−0.77, w, II
W(VI)	NR, ppt.	NR, ppt.	NR	NR
Zn(II)	−0.98, i, 0, −28	—	−0.93	−1.03, fw, 0, −27

^{a} See text for key to abbreviations.

Most of the data in this table refer to solutions containing no maximum suppressor, but in a few cases gelatin, Triton X-100, or some other maximum suppressor was present. For information on such points the reader should consult the original literature or the writer's more extensive compilation (225). A more recent and much more extensive compilation of the polarographic characteristics of inorganic substances is available (228a) and is accompanied by summaries of a large number of critically selected methods of inorganic polarographic analysis (59a).

Table 46.III summarizes, in an even more condensed fashion, the polarographic characteristics of some of the more common organic functional groups. In so far as the original data permitted, the values cited refer to solutions containing no maximum suppressor and having ionic strengths of about 0.1. To a very rough first approximation, a molecule containing

46.II (*continued*)

electrolyte				
1F NH$_3$, 1F NH$_4$Cl	0.1F NH$_3$, 0.1F (NH$_4$)$_3$, C$_6$H$_5$O$_7$	0.5F Na$_2$-C$_4$H$_4$O$_6$, pH 9	1F KCN	1F NaOH
-0.8, —, V	-0.58, i, V(?), -49	—	—	—
-1.4, —, III	-1.06, vw, IV, -132			
(-0.32), fw, V, —, -0.94	(-0.05), vi, V	—	—	(-0.43), vw, V, —, -1.47
-1.28, fw, II, —, -1.82				
-0.96, fw, IV, —, 1.6	-0.27, i, IV, -51	—	—	-1.7, i, IV
-1.26, w, II, —, 4.72	-1.36, w, II, -101			
NR	-1.59, i, H$_2$, -53	—	NR	—
-1.35, vw, 0, —, 3.82	-1.24, w, 0, -50	-1.15, —, 0, —, 2.30	NR	-1.53, w, 0, -30, 3.14

two or more of the functional groups listed will yield a polarogram showing the characteristic waves of the separate groups, but the half-wave potentials may be considerably different from those listed here because of conjugation or other interactions between the groups. For this reason, and also because the effects of ionic strength, buffer and solvent natures, etc., are often pronounced, the information tabulated here represents only an indication of what may be observed with any particular compound. For information on the polarographic properties of specific compounds the reader should consult the compilations of Zuman (346), of Semerano and Griggio (291), and of Kabasakalian and McGlotten (128b), who also give summaries of a number of critically selected practical methods of inorganic polarographic analysis (128c).

TABLE 46.III. Half-Wave Potentials of Some Organic Functional Groups

Functional group	$E_{1/2}$, v. *vs.* S.C.E., at pH = 1	7	13	Product of electrode reaction
—C=C—		NR		
—C≡C—		NR		
ϕ—C=C—		−2.3		ϕ—CH—CH—
ϕ—C≡C—		−2.3		ϕ—CH$_2$—CH$_2$—
—C=C—C=C—		−2.6		—CH—C=C—CH—
(naphthalene structure)		−2.5		(dihydronaphthalene structure)
(anthracene structure)		−1.9		(dihydroanthracene structure)
—C=Cl		NR		
—C—Cl$_2$		−2.0		—CHCl
—C—Cl$_3$		−1.7		—CHCl$_2$
		−2.0		—CH$_2$Cl
—C—Br		−1.8		—CH
—C—Br$_2$		−1.5		—CHBr
		−1.8		—CH$_2$
—C—Br$_3$		−0.6		—CHBr$_2$
		−1.5		—CH$_2$Br
—C—I		−1.7		—CH
—C—I$_2$		−1.1		—CHI
		−1.5		—CH$_2$
—C—I$_3$		−0.5		—CHI$_2$
		−1.1		—CH$_2$I
		−1.5		—CH$_3$
—CHO			−1.6	—CH$_2$OH
—C=C—CHO			−1.0	—CH—CH—CHO
			−1.5	—CH—CH—CH$_2$OH
ϕ—CHO	−0.7	−1.1		ϕCHOH—CHOHϕ
		−1.4		ϕCH$_2$OH
—C=O		−2.2		—CHOH
—C=C—C=O	−0.9	−1.1		(—C—CH—C=O)$_2$
		−1.3	−1.5	—CH—CH—C=O
ϕ—C=O	−1.1			ϕ—C(OH)—C(OH)—ϕ
			−1.6	ϕCHOH
O=⟨ ⟩=O		−0.1		HO—⟨ ⟩—OH
—COOH		−1.8 (unbuffered)		H$_2$
—COOR		NR		
—C=C—COOH	−0.7	−1.3		—CH—CH—COOH
—CH—CHOH—CHOH		−2.5		—CH—CHOH—CHOH
O————C=O				O————CHOH

TABLE 46.III (*continued*)

Functional group	$E_{1/2}$, v. *vs.* S.C.E., at pH =			Product of electron reaction
	1	7	13	
—NO₂	−0.6	−0.9	−0.9	—NHOH
		−1.5	−1.7	—NH₂
—N=O		−0.2		—NHOH
—N=N—		−0.4	−0.7	—NH—NH—
φN₂⁺	−0.1	−0.1		
	−0.5	−0.9		φNHNH₂
—SH	−0.1	−0.4		(Anodic) —SHg
—OOH	−0.3		−0.7	—OH

GENERAL REFERENCES

1. Outlines of the polarographic method and its relationships with other electroanalytical methods:

Lingane, J. J., *Electroanalytical Chemistry*, 2nd ed., Interscience, New York–London, 1958.

Delahay, P., *New Instrumental Methods in Electrochemistry*, Interscience, New York–London, 1954.

2. Polarographic methodology and the interpretation of polarographic data:

Meites, L., *Polarographic Techniques*, Interscience, New York–London, 1955.

von Stackelberg, M., *Polarographische Arbeitsmethoden*, de Gruyter, Berlin, 1950.

Heyrovský, J., *Polarographisches Praktikum*, Springer-Verlag, Berlin, 1948.

Müller, O. H., "Polarography," in A. Weissberger, Ed., *Physical Methods of Organic Chemistry*, Vol. I of *Technique of Organic Chemistry*, 3rd ed., Part IV, Interscience, NewYork–London, 1960.

3. Comprehensive monographs:

Kolthoff, I. M., and J. J. Lingane, *Polarography*, 2nd ed., Interscience, New York–London, 1952.

Milner, G. W. C., *The Principles and Applications of Polarography and Other Voltammetric Processes*, Longmans, Green, London, 1957.

REFERENCES

1. Abichandani, C. T., and S. K. K. Jaktar, *J. Ind. Inst. Sci.*, **A23**, 131 (1941).
2. Airey, L., *Analyst*, **72**, 304 (1947).
3. Airey, L., and A. A. Smales, *Analyst*, **75**, 287 (1950).
4. Antweiler, H. J., *Z. Elektrochem.*, **43**, 596 (1937); **44**, 719,831,888 (1938).
5. Auerbach, C., *Anal. Chem.*, **30**, 1723 (1958).
6. Bachman, G. B., and M. J. Astle, *J. Am. Chem. Soc.*, **64**, 1303, 2177 (1942).
7. Bachofner, H. E., F. M. Beringer, and L. Meites, *J. Am. Chem. Soc.*, **80**, 4269, 4274 (1958).
8. Barendrecht, E., *Anal. Chim. Acta*, **15**, 484 (1956).

9. Barker, G. C., British Patent 709,826 (1954).
10. Barker, G. C., and I. L. Jenkins, *Analyst*, **77**, 685 (1952).
11. Bauer, H. H., and P. J. Elving, *Anal. Chem.*, **30**, 334, 341 (1948).
12. Beecher, H. K., R. Follansbee, A. J. Murphy, and F. N. Craig, *J. Biol. Chem.*, **146**, 197 (1942).
13. Benesch, R. E., and R. Benesch, *J. Phys. Chem.*, **56**, 648 (1952).
14. Berg, H., *Chem. Technol.*, **7**, 679 (1955).
15. Berman, D. A., P. R. Saunders, and R. J. Winzler, *Anal. Chem.*, **23**, 1040 (1951).
16. Berzins, T., and P. Delahay, *J. Am. Chem. Soc.*, **75**, 5716 (1953).
17. Berzins, T., and P. Delahay, *J. Am. Chem. Soc.*, **77**, 6448 (1955).
18. Bieber, R., and G. Trumpler, *Helv. Chim. Acta*, **30**, 706 (1947).
19. Bieber, R., and G. Trumpler, *Helv. Chim. Acta*, **30**, 971 (1947).
20. Blaedel, W. J., and J. W. Todd, *Anal. Chem.*, **30**, 1821 (1958).
21. Boeke, J., and H. van Suchtelen, *Philips Tech. Rev.*, **4**, 213 (1939).
22. Bogan, S., L. Meites, E. Peters, and J. M. Sturtevant, *J. Am. Chem. Soc.*, **73**, 1584 (1951).
23. Booman, G. L., W. B. Holbrook, and J. E. Rein, *Anal. Chem.*, **29**, 219 (1957).
24. Brasher, D. M., and F. R. Jones, *Trans. Faraday Soc.*, **42**, 775 (1946).
25. Brdicka, J., *Collection Czechoslov. Chem. Communo.*, **5**, 112, 148, 238 (1933).
26. Brdicka, J., *Z. Elektrochem.*, **48**, 278 (1942).
27. Brdicka, J., and K. Wiesner, *Naturwiss.*, **31**, 247, 391 (1943).
28. Bresle, A., *Science Tools*, **3**, 9 (1956).
29. Bresle, A., *Acta Chem. Scand.*, **10**, 951 (1956).
30. Bresle, A., *Science Tools*, **4**, 33 (1957).
31. Breyer, B., and F. Gutman, *Australian J. Sci.*, **8**, 21, 163 (1946); *Trans. Faraday Soc.*, **42**, 645, 650, 785 (1946).
32. Breyer, B., F. Gutman, and S. Hacobian, *Australian J. Sci. Research*, **A3**, 558, 567 (1950); **A4**, 595 (1951).
33. Breyer, B., and S. Hacobian, *Australian J. Sci. Research*, **A4**, 604 (1951).
34. Breyer, B., and S. Hacobian, *Australian J. Sci. Research*, **A4**, 610 (1951).
35. Bricker, C. E., and N. H. Furman, *Anal. Chem.*, **20**, 1123 (1948).
36. Buckley, F., and J. K. Taylor, *J. Research Natl. Bur. Standards*, **34**, 87 (1945).
37. Carritt, D. E., Ph.D. Thesis, Harvard University, 1947.
38. Carruthers, C., *Ind. Eng. Chem.*, *Anal. Ed.*, **15**, 70 (1943).
39. Colichman, E. L., *J. Am. Chem. Soc.*, **72**, 4036 (1950).
40. Cooper, W. C., and M. M. Wright, *Anal. Chem.*, **22**, 1213 (1950).
41. Copeland, L. C., and F. S. Griffith, *Anal. Chem.*, **22**, 1269 (1950).
41a. Cover, R. E., and L. Meites, *Anal. Chim. Acta*, **25**, 93 (1961).
42. DeFord, D. D., and D. N. Hume, *J. Am. Chem. Soc.*, **73**, 5321 (1951).
43. Delahay, P., *Rec. trav. chim.*, **67**, 165 (1948).
44. Delahay, P., *J. Phys. Colloid Chem.*, **53**, 1279 (1949); **54**, 402 (1950).
45. Delahay, P., *J. Phys. Colloid Chem.*, **54**, 630 (1950).
46. Delahay, P., *J. Am. Chem. Soc.*, **73**, 4944 (1951).
47. Delahay, P., *J. Am. Chem. Soc.*, **74**, 3506, 6315 (1952).
48. Delahay, P., *J. Am. Chem. Soc.*, **75**, 1190 (1953).
49. Delahay, P., *J. Am. Chem. Soc.*, **75**, 1430 (1953).
50. Delahay, P., *New Instrumental Methods in Electrochemistry*, Interscience, New York–London, 1954.
51. Delahay, P., *Instrumental Analysis*, Macmillan, New York, 1957, p. 87.

52. Delahay, P., and G. Perkins, *J. Phys. Colloid Chem.*, **55**, 586 (1951).
53. Delahay, P., and G. L. Stiehl, *J. Phys. Colloid Chem.*, **55**, 570 (1951).
54. Delahay, P., and J. E. Strassner, *J. Am. Chem. Soc.*, **73**, 5219 (1951).
55. Delahay, P., and J. E. Strassner, *J. Am. Chem. Soc.*, **74**, 893 (1952).
56. Delahay, P., and I. Trachtenberg, *J. Am. Chem. Soc.*, **79**, 2355 (1957); **80**, 2094 (1958).
57. DeMars, R. D., and I. Shain, *Anal. Chem.*, **29**, 1825 (1957).
58. DeVries, T., and W. S. Barnhart, *Ind. Eng. Chem., Anal. Ed.*, **19**, 934 (1947).
59. DeVries, T., and J. L. Kroon, *J. Am. Chem. Soc.*, **75**, 2484 (1953).
59a. Doležal, J., and J. Zýka, in L. Meites, Ed., *Handbook of Analytical Chemistry*, McGraw-Hill, New York, 1963, p. 5–113.
60. Doss, K. S. G., and H. P. Agarwal, *Proc. Indian Acad. Sci.*, **A33**, 66, 298 (1951).
61. Dousek, F. P., and V. Kalous, *Radiometer Polarographics*, **4**, 45 (1957).
62. Elofson, R. M., and P. A. Mecherly, *Anal. Chem.*, **21**, 565 (1949).
63. Elving, P. J., J. C. Komyathy, R. E. van Atta, C -S. Tang, and I. Rosenthal, *Anal. Chem.*, **23**, 1218 (1951).
64. Elving, P. J., and J. T. Leone, *J. Am. Chem. Soc.*, **80**, 1021 (1958).
65. Erdey-Gruz, T., and P. Szarvas, *Z. physik. Chem.*, **A177**, 277 (1937).
66. Evans, M. G., and N. S. Hush, *J. chim. phys.*, **49**, C159 (1952).
67. Eyring, H., L. Marker, and T. C. Kwoh, *J. Phys. Colloid Chem.*, **53**, 187 (1949).
68. Ferrett, D. J., and G. W. C. Milner, *Analyst*, **80**, 132 (1955); **81**, 193 (1956).
69. Ferrett, D. J., G. W. C. Milner, H. I. Shalgosky, and L. J. Slee, *Analyst*, **81**, 506 (1956).
70. Ferrett, D. J., G. W. C. Milner, and A. A. Smales, *Analyst*, **79**, 731 (1954).
71. Forche, E., *Mikrochemie*, **25**, 217 (1938).
72. Frankenthal, R. P., and I. Shain, *J. Am. Chem. Soc.*, **78**, 2969 (1956).
73. Frumkin, A., *Ergeb. exakt. Naturw.*, **7**, 239 (1928).
74. Furman, N. H., C. E. Bricker, and E. B. Whitesell, *Ind. Eng. Chem., Anal. Ed.*, **14**, 333 (1942).
75. Furman, N. H., and K. G. Stone, *J. Am. Chem. Soc.*, **70**, 3055 (1948).
76. Gawron, O., *Anal. Chem.*, **22**, 614 (1950).
77. Gentry, C. H. R., *Nature*, **157**, 479 (1946).
78. Gentry, C. H. R., and D. Newson, *Metallurgia*, **41**, 107 (1949).
79. Gerischer, H., *Z. physik. Chem.*, **202**, 302 (1953).
80. Gilbert, G. A., and E. K. Rideal, *Trans. Faraday Soc.*, **47**, 396 (1951).
81. Gisclard, J. B., *Ind. Eng. Chem., Anal. Ed.*, **17**, 196 (1945).
82. Gokhshtein, Ya. P., *Zavodskaya Lab.*, **17** (5), 1444 (1936).
83. Gokhshtein, Ya. P., *Zhur. Anal. Knim.*, **3**, 198 (1948).
84. Grabowski, Z. R., *Roczniki Chem.*, **27**, 285 (1953).
85. Grahame, D. C., E. M. Coffin, and J. I. Cummings, ONR Project NR-051-150, Tech. Report No. 2 (1950).
86. Grenier, J. W., Ph.D. Thesis, Yale University, 1955.
87. Griffiths, V. S., and W. J. Parker, *Anal. Chim. Acta*, **14**, 194 (1956).
88. Gyorbiro, K., and L. Poos, *Acta Chem. Acad. Sci. Hung.*, **9**, 185 (1956).
89. Hamamoto, E., *Collection Czechoslov. Chem. Communs.*, **5**, 427 (1933).
90. Hamm, R. E., *Anal. Chem.*, **30**, 450 (1958).
91. Hans, W., and W. Henne, *Naturwiss.*, **20**, 524 (1953).
92. Hans, W., and W. Jensch, *Z. Elektrochem.*, **56**, 648 (1952).
93. Harkins, W. D., and F. E. Brown, *J. Am. Chem. Soc.*, **41**, 499 (1919).

94. Harris, W. E., and I. M. Kolthoff, *J. Am. Chem. Soc.*, **67**, 1484 (1945).
95. Hersch, P., private communication (1953).
96. Heyrovský, J., *Chem. listy*, **16**, 256 (1922).
97. Heyrovský, J., *Trans. Faraday Soc.*, **19**, 785 (1924).
98. Heyrovský, J., *Arhiv. Hem. i Farm.*, **8**, 11 (1934).
99. Heyrovský, J., *Nature*, **135**, 870 (1935).
100. Heyrovský, J., "Polarographie," in W. Böttger, Ed., *Physikalische Methoden der Analytischen Chemie*, Leipzig, 1936, vol. 3.
101. Heyrovský, J., *Chem. listy*, **40**, 222,229 (1946); *Discussions Faraday Soc.*, **1**, 212 (1947).
102. Heyrovský, J., *Analyst*, **72**, 229 (1947).
103. Heyrovský, J., *Anal. Chim. Acta*, **2**, 533 (1948).
104. Heyrovský, J., *Anal. Chim. Acta*, **2**, 537 (1948).
105. Heyrovský, J., *Polarographisches Praktikum*, Springer-Verlag, Berlin, 1948.
106. Heyrovský, J., *Chem. listy*, **43**, 149 (1949).
107. Heyrovský, J., and J. Babicka, *Collection Czechoslov. Chem. Communs.*, **2**, 370 (1930).
108. Heyrovský, J., and S. Berezicky, *Collection Czechoslov. Chem. Communs.*, **1**, 19 (1929).
109. Heyrovský, J., and J. Forejt, *Chem. listy*, **35**, 155 (1941); *Z. physik. Chem.*, **193**, 77 (1943).
110. Heyrovský, J., and D. Ilkovič, *Collection Czechoslov. Chem. Communs.*, **7**, 198 (1935).
111. Heyrovský, J., and M. Kalousek, *Collection Czechoslov. Chem. Communs.*, **11**, 464 (1939).
112. Heyrovský, J., and M. Shikata, *Rec. trav. chim.*, **44**, 496 (1925).
113. Heyrovský, J., and I. Smoler, *Collection Czechoslov. Chem. Communs.*, **4**, 521 (1932).
114. Hodgson, H. W , and J. H. Glover, *Analyst*, **76**, 381 (1951).
115. Hohn, H., *Chemische Analysen mit dem Polarographen*, Springer-Verlag, Berlin, 1937.
116. Hohn, H., *Metall. u. Erz*, **40**, 197 (1943).
117. Hume, D. N., and W. E. Harris, *Ind. Eng. Chem., Anal. Ed.*, **15**, 465 (1943).
118. Hume, D. N., D. D. DeFord, and G. C. B. Cave, *J. Am. Chem. Soc.*, **73**, 5323 (1951).
119. Ilkovič, D., *Collection Czechoslov. Chem. Communs.*, **6**, 498 (1934).
120. Ilkovič, D., *Collection Czechoslov. Chem. Communs.*, **8**, 13 (1936).
121. Ilkovič, D., *Collection Czechoslov. Chem. Communs.*, **8**, 170 (1936).
122. Ilkovič, D., *J. chim. phys.*, **35**, 129 (1938).
123. Ilkovič, D., *Collection Czechoslov. Chem. Communs.*, **10**, 249 (1938).
124. Ilkovič, D., and G. Semerano, *Collection Czechoslov. Chem. Communs.*, **4**, 176 (1932).
125. Ishibashi, M., and T. Fujinaga, *Bull. Chem. Soc. Japan*, **23**, 261 (1950); **25**, 68 (1952).
126. James, J. C., *Trans. Faraday Soc.*, **47**, 1240 (1951).
127. Jessop, G., British Patent 640,768 (1948).
128. Johnson, M. G., and R. J. Robinson, *Anal. Chem.*, **24**, 366 (1952).
128a. Jordan, J., and J. H. Clausen, in L. Meites, Ed., *Handbook of Analytical Chemistry*, McGraw-Hill, New York, 1963, p. 5–155.
128b. Kabasakalian, P., and J. H. McGlotten, *ibid.*, p. 5–104.
128c. *Idem., ibid.*, p. 5–140.
129. Kalousek, M., *Collection Czechoslov. Chem. Communs.*, **13**, 105 (1948).
130. Kalousek, M., and M. Ralek, *Chem. listy*, **48**, 808 (1954).
131. Kambara, T , *Bull. Chem. Soc. Japan*, **27**, 523 (1954).
132. Kambara, T., and I. Tachi, *Bull. Chem. Soc. Japan*, **25**, 135 (1952).
133. Karp, S., and L. Meites, *J. Am. Chem. Soc.*, **84**, 906 (1962).
134. Kelley, M. T., and D. J. Fisher, *Anal. Chem.*, **30**, 929 (1958).

135. Kelley, M. T., and H. H. Miller, *Anal. Chem.*, **24**, 1895 (1952).

136. Kemula, W., *Roczniki Chem.*, **26**, 281, 694, 696 (1952); **29**, 653, 1157 (1955).

137. Kemula, W., and A. Gorski, *Roczniki Chem.*, **26**, 639 (1952).

138. Kemula, W., and Z. Kublik, *Roczniki Chem.*, **30**, 1005 (1956).

139. Kemula, W., and S. Siekierski, *Collection Czechoslov. Chem. Communs.*, **15**, 1069 (1950).

140. Kemula, W., and J. Witwicki, *Roczniki Chem.*, **29**, 1153 (1955).

141. Kern, D. M. H., *J. Am. Chem. Soc.*, **75**, 2473 (1953).

142. Kern, D. M. H., *J. Am. Chem. Soc.*, **76**, 4243 (1954).

143. Kivalo, P., K. B. Oldham, and H. A. Laitinen, *J. Am. Chem. Soc.*, **75**, 4148 (1953).

144. Kocent, A., *Chem. listy*, **47**, 174 (1953).

145. Kolthoff, I. M., *Ind. Eng. Chem., Anal. Ed.*, **14**, 195 (1942).

146. Kolthoff, I. M., and H. P. Gregor, *Anal. Chem.*, **20**, 541 (1948).

147. Kolthoff, I. M., W. E. Harris, and G. Matsuyama, *J. Am. Chem. Soc.*, **66**, 1782 (1944).

148. Kolthoff, I. M., and R. A. Johnson, *J. Electrochem. Soc.*, **98**, 231 (1951).

149. Kolthoff, I. M., and J. Jordan, *J. Am. Chem. Soc.*, **77**, 3215 (1955).

150. Kolthoff, I. M., J. Jordan, and S. Prager, *J. Am. Chem. Soc.*, **76**, 5221 (1954).

151. Kolthoff, I. M., and G. J. Kahan, *J. Am. Chem. Soc.*, **64**, 2553 (1942).

152. Kolthoff, I. M., and H. A. Laitinen, *Science*, **92**, 152 (1940).

153. Kolthoff, I. M., and A. Langer, *J. Am. Chem. Soc.*, **62**, 211, 3172 (1940).

154. Kolthoff, I. M., and A. Liberti, *Analyst*, **74**, 635 (1949).

155. Kolthoff, I. M., and J. J. Lingane, *Chem. Revs.*, **24**, 1 (1939).

156. Kolthoff, I. M., and J. J. Lingane, *Polarography*, 2nd ed., Interscience, New York–London, 1953.

157. Kolthoff, I. M., and C. S. Miller, *J. Am. Chem. Soc.*, **62**, 2171 (1940).

158. Kolthoff, I. M., and C. S. Miller, *J. Am. Chem. Soc.*, **63**, 1013 (1941).

159. Kolthoff, I. M., and E. F. Orlemann, *J. Am. Chem. Soc.*, **63**, 664 (1941).

160. Kolthoff, I. M., and Y. D. Pan, *J. Am. Chem. Soc.*, **61**, 3402 (1939).

161. Kolthoff, I. M., and E. P. Parry, *J. Am. Chem. Soc.*, **73**, 5315 (1951).

162. Komyathy, J. C., F. Malloy, and P. J. Elving, *Anal. Chem.*, **24**, 431 (1952).

163. Koryta, J., *Collection Czechoslov. Chem. Communs.*, **19**, 433 (1954).

164. Koutecky, J., *Ceskoslovensky cas. fys.*, **2**, 117 (1952).

165. Koutecky, J., *Chem. listy*, **47**, 323 (1953); *Collection Czechoslov. Chem. Communs.*, **18**, 597 (1953).

166. Koutecky, J., and R. Brdicka, *Collection Czechoslov. Chem. Communs.*, **12**, 337 (1947).

166a. Koutecký, J., and M. v. Stackelberg, in P. Zuman and I. M. Kolthoff, Eds., *Progress in Polarography*, Interscience, New York–London, 1962, Vol. I, p. 21.

167. Koyama, K., and C. E. Michelson, *Anal. Chem.*, **29**, 1115 (1957).

168. Krugers, J., *Chem. Weekblad*, **53**, 672 (1957).

168a. Kůta, J., and I. Smoler, in P. Zuman and I. M. Kolthoff, Eds., *Progress in Polarography*, Interscience, New York–London, 1962, Vol. I, p. 43.

169. Ladisch, R. K., and S. L. Knesbach, *Anal. Chem.*, **26**, 1251 (1954).

170. Laitinen, H. A., and W. J. Subcasky, *J. Am. Chem. Soc.*, **80**, 2623 (1958).

171. Laitinen, H. A., and R. F. Sympson, *Anal. Chem.*, **26**, 556 (1954).

172. Langer, A., *Ind. Eng. Chem., Anal. Ed.*, **17**, 454 (1945).

173. Lee, T. S., *J. Am. Chem. Soc.*, **74**, 269 (1952).

174. Leveque, P., *J. chim. phys.*, **49**, 269 (1952).

175. Leveque, P., and F. Roth, *J. chim. phys.*, **46**, 480 (1949).

176. Lewis, W. R., F. W. Quackenbush, and T. DeVries, *Anal. Chem.*, **21**, 762 (1949).
177. Lingane, J. J., *J. Am. Chem. Soc.*, **61**, 2099 (1939).
178. Lingane, J. J., *Chem. Rev.*, **29**, 1 (1941).
179. Lingane, J. J., *J. Am. Chem. Soc.*, **65**, 866 (1943).
180. Lingane, J. J., *Ind. Eng. Chem., Anal. Ed.*, **15**, 583 (1943).
181. Lingane, J. J., *Ind. Eng. Chem., Anal. Ed.*, **16**, 147 (1944).
182. Lingane, J. J., *Ind. Eng. Chem., Anal. Ed.*, **16**, 329 (1944).
183. Lingane, J. J., *Ind. Eng. Chem., Anal. Ed.*, **18**, 429 (1946).
184. Lingane, J. J., *J. Am. Chem. Soc.*, **68**, 2448 (1946).
185. Lingane, J. J., *J. Am. Chem. Soc.*, **75**, 788 (1953).
186. Lingane, J. J., *Electroanalytical Chemistry*, Interscience, New York–London, 1953.
187. Lingane, J. J., and I. M. Kolthoff, *J. Am. Chem. Soc.*, **61**, 825 (1939).
188. Lingane, J. J., and I. M. Kolthoff, *J. Am. Chem. Soc.*, **61**, 1045 (1939).
189. Lingane, J. J., and H. A. Laitinen, *Ind. Eng. Chem., Anal. Ed.*, **11**, 504 (1939).
190. Lingane, J. J., and B. A. Loveridge, *J. Am. Chem. Soc.*, **68**, 395 (1946).
191. Lingane, J. J., and B. A. Loveridge, *J. Am. Chem. Soc.*, **72**, 438 (1950).
192. Lingane, J. J., and L. Meites, *Ind. Eng. Chem., Anal. Ed.*, **19**, 159 (1947).
193. Lingane, J. J., and L. W. Niedrach, *J. Am. Chem Soc.*, **70**, 4115 (1948).
194. Lingane, J. J., and L. W. Niedrach, *J. Am. Chem. Soc.*, **71**, 196 (1949).
195. Lingane, J. J., and L. A. Small, *J. Am. Chem. Soc.*, **71**, 973 (1949).
196. Lingane, J. J., and R. Williams, *J. Am. Chem. Soc.*, **74**, 790 (1952).
197. Loveridge, B. A., Ph.D. Thesis, Harvard University, 1947.
198. Lykken, L., D. J. Pompeo, and J. R. Weaver, *Ind. Eng. Chem., Anal. Ed.*, **17**, 724 (1945).
199. Maas, J., *Collection Czechoslov. Chem. Communs.*, **10**, 42 (1938).
200. Maassen, G., *Angew. Chem.*, **50**, 375 (1937).
201. MacAleavy, G., Belgian Patent 443,003 (1941).
202. MacGillavry, D., *Rec. trav. chim.*, **56**, 1039 (1937); **57**, 33 (1938).
203. MacGillavry, D., and E. K. Rideal, *Rec. trav. chim.*, **56**, 1013 (1937).
204. Mackenzie, H. A., *J. Am. Chem. Soc.*, **70**, 3147 (1948).
205. Majer, V., *Collection Czechoslov. Chem. Communs.*, **7**, 146, 215 (1935); **9**, 360 (1937).
206. Majer, V., *Z. Elektrochem.*, **42**, 120, 122 (1936).
207. Mamantov, G., P. Papoff, and P. Delahay, *J. Am. Chem. Soc.*, **79**, 4034 (1957).
208. Mann, C. K., *Anal. Chem.*, **29**, 1385 (1957).
209. Mathers, A. P., J. E. Beck, and R. L. Schoeneman, *Anal. Chem.*, **23**, 1767 (1951).
210. Matheson, L. A., and N. Nichols, *Trans. Electrochem. Soc.*, **73**, 193 (1938).
211. Matsuyama, G., Ph.D. Thesis, University of Minnesota, 1948.
212. McGilvery, J., R. C. Hawkings, and H. G. Thode, *Can. J. Research*, **25**, 132 (1947).
213. McReynolds, R. C., *Ind. Eng. Chem., Anal. Ed.*, **14**, 586 (1942).
214. Meites, L., *J. Am. Chem. Soc.*, **71**, 3269 (1949).
215. Meites, L., *J. Am. Chem. Soc.*, **72**, 2293 (1950).
216. Meites, L., *J. Am. Chem. Soc.*, **73**, 1581 (1951).
217. Meites, L., *J. Am. Chem. Soc.*, **73**, 2035 (1951).
218. Meites, L., *J. Am. Chem. Soc.*, **73**, 3724 (1951).
219. Meites, L., *J. Am. Chem. Soc.*, **73**, 4115 (1951).
220. Meites, L., *J. Am. Chem. Soc.*, **75**, 3809 (1953).
221. Meites, L., *J. Am. Chem. Soc.*, **76**, 5927 (1954).
222. Meites, L., *Anal. Chem.*, **27**, 416 (1955).
223. Meites, L., *Anal. Chem.*, **27**, 977 (1955).

224. Meites, L., *Anal. Chem.*, **27**, 1116, 1531 (1955).

225. Meites, L., *Polarographic Techniques*, Interscience, New York–London, 1955.

226. Meites, L., *Anal. Chem.*, **28**, 139 (1956).

227. Meites, L., *Anal. Chim. Acta*, **18**, 364 (1958).

228. Meites, L., *Anal. Chim. Acta*, **20**, 456 (1959).

228a. Meites. L., in L. Meites, Ed., *Handbook of Analytical Chemistry*, McGraw-Hill, New York, 1963, p. 5–53.

229. Meites, L., and J. W. Grenier, *Anal. Chim. Acta*, **14**, 482 (1956).

230. Meites, L., and H. Hofsass, *Anal. Chem.*, **31**, 119 (1959).

230a. Meites, L., and Y. Israel, *J. Am. Chem. Soc.*, **83**, 4903 (1961).

231. Meites, L., and T. Meites, *Ind. Eng. Chem., Anal. Ed.*, **20**, 984 (1948).

232. Meites, L., and T. Meites, *J. Am. Chem. Soc.*, **72**, 3686 (1950).

232a. Meites, L., and T. Meites, *J. Am. Chem. Soc.*, **72**, 4843 (1950).

233. Meites, L., and T. Meites, *J. Am. Chem. Soc.*, **73**, 177 (1951).

234. Meites, L., and T. Meites, *J. Am. Chem. Soc.*, **73**, 395 (1951).

235. Meites, L., and T. Meites, *Anal. Chem.*, **23**, 1194 (1951).

236. Meites, L., and T. Meites, *Anal. Chem.*, **28**, 103 (1956).

237. Meites, L., and S. A. Moros, *Anal. Chem.*, **31**, 23 (1959).

238. Meites, T., and L. Meites, *Anal. Chem.*, **23**, 1893 (1951).

239. Milner, G. W. C., *The Principles and Applications of Polarography and Other Voltammetric Methods*, Longmans, Green and Co., London, 1957.

240. Milner, G. W. C., and L. J. Slee, *Analyst*, **82**, 139 (1957).

241. Moros, S. A., Ph.D. Thesis, Polytechnic Institute of Brooklyn, 1959.

241a. Moros, S. A., and L. Meites, *J. Electroanal. Chem.*, **5**, 90 (1963).

242. Mueller, E. F., *Ind. Eng. Chem., Anal. Ed.*, **12**, 171 (1940).

243. Müller, O. H., *J. Biol. Chem.*, **48**, 278 (1942).

244. Müller, O. H., *J. Am. Chem. Soc.* **66**, 1019 (1944).

245. Müller, O. H., *Trans. Electrochem. Soc.*, **87**, 441 (1945).

246. Müller, O. H., and J. P. Baumberger, *Trans. Am. Electrochem. Soc.*, **71**, 169, 181 (1937).

247. Müller, R. H., *Anal. Chem.*, **22**, 76 (1950).

248. Müller, R. H., R. L. Garman, M. E. Droz, and J. Petras, *Ind. Eng. Chem., Anal. Ed.*, **10**, 339 (1948).

249. Nesvabada, O., *Proc. 1st Intern. Polarogr. Congress, Prague*, Part III, p. 373, 1951.

250. Neuberger, A., *Z. anal. Chem.*, **116**, 1 (1939).

251. Nicholson, M. M., *J. Am. Chem. Soc.*, **76**, 2539 (1954).

252. Nicholson, M. M., *Anal. Chem.*, **27**, 1364 (1955).

253. Nikelly, J. G., and W. D. Cooke, *Anal. Chem.*, **29**, 933 (1957).

254. Novak, J. V. A., *Collection Czechoslov. Chem. Communs.*, **12**, 237 (1947).

255. Offutt, E. B., and L. V. Sorg, *Anal. Chem.*, **22**, 1234 (1950).

256. Okinaka, Y., and I. M. Kolthoff, *J. Am. Chem. Soc.*, **79**, 3326 (1957).

257. Paulik, J., and J. Proszt, *Acta Chim. Acad. Sci. Hung.*, **9**, 161 (1956).

258. Payne, S. T., *Anal. Chim. Acta*, **3**, 686 (1949).

259. Pech, J., *Collection Czechoslov. Chem. Communs.*, **6**, 126, 190 (1934).

260. Pecsok, R. L., *J. Am. Chem. Soc.*, **73**, 1304 (1951).

261. Pecsok, R. L., and R. W. Farmer, *Anal. Chem.*, **28**, 985 (1956).

262. Pecsok, R. L., and R. S. Juvet, Jr., *Anal. Chem.*, **27**, 165 (1955).

263. Philbrook, G. E., and H. M. Grubb, *Anal. Chem.*, **19**, 7 (1947).

264. Pickles, D., and C. C. Washbrook, *Analyst*, **78**, 304 (1953).

265. Pinches, P., and L. Meites, unpublished.
266. Pomeroy, P. R., R. A. White, and G. H. R. Gwatkins, *Metallurgia*, **46**, 157 (1952).
267. Porter, J. T., II, *Anal. Chem.*, **29**, 1638 (1957).
268. Přibil, R., and B. Matyska, *Collection Czechoslov. Chem. Communs.*, **16**, 139 (1951).
269. Randles, J. E. B., *Analyst*, **72**, 301 (1947).
270. Randles, J. E. B., *Trans. Faraday Soc.*, **44**, 322, 327 (1948).
271. Rebertus, R. L., R. J. Cappell, and G. W. Bond, *Anal. Chem.*, **30**, 1825 (1958).
272. Reimers, F., *Collection Czechoslov. Chem. Communs.*, **11**, 377 (1939).
273. Reinmuth, W. H., *Anal. Chem.*, **28**, 1356 (1957).
274. Reinmuth, W. H., *J. Am. Chem. Soc.*, **79**, 6358 (1957).
275. Reynolds, C. A., *Anal. Chem.*, **21**, 759 (1949).
276. Reynolds, C. A., *Anal. Chim. Acta*, **6**, 567 (1952).
277. Riches, J. P. R., *Nature*, **157**, 520 (1946).
278. Říha, J., *Collection Czechoslov. Chem. Communs.*, **16**, 479 (1951).
279. Říha, J., *Proc. 1st Intern. Polarog. Congr., Prague*, Part III, p. 743, 1951.
280. Ríus, A., *Fundamentals and Applications of the Streaming Mercury Electrode*, Academy of Sciences of Madrid, Bermejo, Madrid, 1949.
281. Ríus, A., J. Llopis, and S. Polo, *Anales real soc. Espan. fis. y quim. (Madrid)*, **45B**, 1039 (1949).
282. Ríus, A., and A. Marin, *Anales real soc. Espan. fis. y quim. (Madrid)*, **46B**, 55, 93 (1950).
283. Ríus, A., and M. J. Molera, *Anales real soc. Espan. fis. y quim. (Madrid)*, **43B**, 1074 (1947).
284. Ríus, A., and J. F. V. Serrano, *Anales real soc. Espan. fis. y quim. (Madrid)*, **45B**, 501 (1949).
285. Rosie, D. J., and W. D. Cooke, *Anal. Chem.*, **27**, 1360 (1955).
286. Ross, J. W., R. D. DeMars, and I. Shain, *Anal. Chem.*, **28**, 1768 (1956).
287. Sample, G. W., British Patent 599,409 (1945).
288. Sanko, A. M., and F. A. Manussova, *J. Gen. Chem. USSR*, **10**, 1171 (1940).
289. Schmid, R. W., and C. N. Reilley, *J. Am. Chem. Soc.*, **80**, 2087 (1958).
290. Schulman, J. H., H. B. Battey, and D. G. Jelatis, *Rev. Sci. Instr.*, **18**, 226 (1947).
291. Semerano, G., and L. Griggio, *Ricerca sci.*, **27**, Suppl. A, *Polarografia*, **3**, 243 (1957).
292. Semerano, G., and L. Riccoboni, *Gazz. chim. ital.*, **72**, 297 (1942).
293. Senda, M., M. Okuda, and I. Tachi, *Bull. Chem. Soc. Japan*, **28**, 31 (1957).
294. Serak, L., *Chem. listy*, **47**, 87 (1953).
295. Sevcik, A., *Collection Czechoslov. Chem. Communs.*, **13**, 349 (1948).
296. Siekierski, S., and E. K. Siekierska, *Roczniki Chem.*, **30**, 399 (1956).
297. Skobets, E. M., and N. S. Kavetskii, *Zavodskaya Lab.*, **15**, 1299 (1949).
298. Skobets, E. M., and V. D. Skobets, *Zavodskaya Lab.*, **23**, 167 (1957).
299. Slendyk, I., *Collection Czechoslov. Chem. Communs.*, **3**, 385 (1931).
300. Slendyk, I., *Collection Czechoslov. Chem. Communs.*, **4**, 335 (1932).
301. Smith, L. I., I. M. Kolthoff, and L. J. Spillane, *J. Am. Chem. Soc.*, **64**, 646 (1942).
302. Smoler, I., *Collection Czechoslov. Chem. Communs.*, **19**, 238 (1954).
303. Smutek, M., *Collection Czechoslov. Chem. Communs.*, **18**, 171 (1953).
304. Snowden, F. C., and H. T. Page, *Anal. Chem.*, **22**, 969 (1950).
305. Spalenka, M., *Collection Czechoslov. Chem. Communs.*, **11**, 146 (1939).
306. Stackelberg, M. v., *Z. Elektrochem.*, **45**, 466 (1939).
307. Stackelberg, M. v., *Z. Elektrochem.*, **57**, 338 (1953).

308. Stackelberg, M. v., H. J. Antweiler, and Kiesenbach, Z. Elektrochem., **44**, 663 (1938).
309. Stackelberg, M. v., and H. V. Freyhold, Z. Elektrochem., **46**, 120 (1940).
310. Stackelberg, M. v., P. Klinger, W. Koch, and E. Krath, Forschungsber Tech. Mitt. Krupp, Essen, **2**, 59 (1939).
311. Stankoviansky, S., Chem. Zvesti, **2**, 133 (1938).
312. Strehlow, H., O. Madrich, and M. v. Stackelberg, Z. Elektrochem., **55**, 244 (1951).
313. Strehlow, H., and M. v. Stackelberg, Z. Elektrochem., **54**, 51 (1950).
314. Streuli, C. A., and W. D. Cooke, Anal. Chem., **25**, 1691 (1953); **26**, 963, 970 (1954).
315. Stricks, W., and I. M. Kolthoff, J. Am. Chem. Soc., **78**, 2085 (1956).
316. Strubl, R., Collection Czechoslov. Chem. Communs., **10**, 475 (1938).
317. Suzuki, M., J. Electrochem. Soc. Japan, **21**, 264 (1953).
318. Tachi, I., and T. Kambara, Bull. Chem. Soc. Japan, **28**, 25 (1957).
319. Tanaka, N., and R. Tamamushi, Bull. Chem. Soc. Japan, **22**, 187, 1227 (1949); **23**, 110 (1950).
320. Taylor, J. K., Anal. Chem., **19**, 368 (1947).
321. Taylor, J. K., Anal. Chem., **19**, 478 (1947).
322. Taylor, J. K., R. E. Smith, and I. L. Cooter, J. Research Natl. Bur. Standards, **56**, 143 (1956).
323. Taylor, J. K., and S. W. Smith, J. Research Natl. Bur. Standards, **42**, 387 (1949).
324. Thanheiser, G., and J. Willems, Arch. Eisenhuttenw., **13**, 73 (1939).
325. Tockstein, A., Collection Czechoslov. Chem. Communs., **16**, 101 (1951).
326. Tomes, J., Collection Czechoslov. Chem. Communs., **9**, 12, 81, 150 (1937).
327. Tsimmergakl, V. A., Zavodskaya Lab., **15**, 1370 (1949).
328. Valenta, P., Collection Czechoslov. Chem. Communs., **16**, 239 (1951).
329. Van Rysselberghe, P., and J. W. McGee, J. Am. Chem. Soc., **67**, 1039 (1945).
330. Vavruch, I., Anal. Chem., **22**, 930 (1950).
331. Vesely, K., and R. Brdicka, Collection Czechoslov. Chem. Communs., **12**, 313 (1947).
332. Vlcek, A. A., Collection Czechoslov. Chem. Communs., **16**, 465 (1951).
333. Vlcek, A. A., Proc. 1st Intern. Polarogr. Congress, Prague, Part III, p. 373, 1951.
334. Vlcek, A. A., Chem. listy, **46**, 258 (1952).
335. Vogel, J., and J. Ríha, Czech. Patent No. P112–49 (1949).
336. Vogel, J., and J. Ríha, J. chim. phys., **47**, 5 (1950).
337. Voriskova, M., Collection Czechoslov. Chem. Communs., **12**, 607 (1947).
338. Wahlin, E., and A. Bresle, Acta Chem. Scand., **10**, 935 (1957).
339. Walkley, A., J. Am. Chem. Soc., **63**, 2278 (1941).
340. Weaver, J. R., and R. W. Parry, J. Am. Chem. Soc., **76**, 6258 (1954); **78**, 5542 (1956).
341. Weaver, R. D., and G. C. Whitnack, Anal. Chim. Acta, **18**, 51 (1958).
342. Whittem, R. N., and G. W. C. Milner, At. Energy Research Establ. Rept., **C/M 185** (1953).
343. Wiesner, K., Collection Czechoslov. Chem. Communs., **12**, 64 (1947).
344. Willard, H. H., and J. A. Dean, Anal. Chem., **22**, 1264 (1950).
345. Zlotowski, I., and I. M. Kolthoff, J. Am. Chem. Soc., **64**, 1297 (1942).
346. Zuman, P., Collection Czechoslov. Chem. Communs., **15**, 1107 (1950.)
347. Zuman, P., Chem. listy, **51**, 993 (1957).

Chapter 47

VOLTAMMETRY AT ELECTRODES WITH FIXED SURFACES

By Ralph N. Adams, *Department of Chemistry, University of Kansas, Lawrence, Kansas*

Contents

I. DEVELOPMENT OF ELECTRODES OTHER THAN THE D.M.E.

There would seem to be only three valid reasons for wishing to use electrodes other than the D.M.E. First, one might hope to improve on the accuracy and reproducibility of the D.M.E. Second, sensitivity could be increased. Third, a desire to expand the usable potential range would be sensible. Those who pursued the first cause by itself would soon be disappointed, for whereas electrode systems have been devised that match or even perform with higher precision in certain applications, the reproducibility of the D.M.E. in general applications bears no criticism. Indeed, it is the effort to exploit the second two points that has given rise to the now-extensive literature on other electrodes. The ordinary concentration levels of the D.M.E. are from 10^{-2} to $10^{-4}M$, and about $10^{-6}M$ is the limit of detection. An increased demand for accurate trace analyses over the past ten years has developed several electrodes with sensitivities at least 100-fold greater than the D.M.E. These have been generally, but not exclusively, mercury-type electrodes.

The greatest disadvantage of mercury electrodes is that the anodic range is severely limited. At best, dissolution of mercury occurs around 0.4 v. *vs.* S.C.E. This cut-off completely excludes the study of a wide variety of organic redox systems with mercury electrodes. The field of solid electrode voltammetry has grown as a result of this inadequacy of mercury.

It is convenient to group voltammetric electrodes other than the D.M.E. into two categories: (*1*) mercury-type electrodes, and (*2*) solid electrodes. This is an operational classification and is somewhat ambiguous. Thus, one finds a kind of mercury pool classified among solid electrodes. On the other hand, one has solid electrodes that are not solid at all in the physical sense. The classification is justified on the basis that it seems most important to group according to basic usage. Thus, mercury-type electrodes are primarily designed to *study the same electroactive systems as the D.M.E., only with increased sensitivity.* Solid electrodes also offer increased sensitivity, but their primary value is in the *study of anodic reactions.*

Historically, voltammetry began with solid electrodes, although the work bore little resemblance to present-day measurements. Le Blanc used solid electrodes in his classic measurements of the decomposition voltages of acid–base solutions and metal ions (65). Fundamental studies of electrolytic processes involving solid electrodes were initiated by several workers prior to 1910 (48,85,97). General interest in this area was dulled by the elegance of the D.M.E. Not until the 1940's was activity revived, when Laitinen and Kolthoff published their fundamental studies of platinum electrodes (61). The rotating platinum electrode (R.P.E.) became widely studied. In the late 1940's considerable work developed in the Soviet Union, and it has continued to the present. Although the total number of publications is much smaller, the increase (since about 1950) of papers dealing with solid electrodes parallels the rapid growth of the general polarographic literature.

The introduction of the mercury-pool cathode can be traced to the work of Gibbs (37). Analytical applications involving voltammetry were initiated only recently by Streuli and Cooke (103). Rotating amalgam electrodes were first used for analysis by Skobets and his co-workers (101), and mercury-plated electrodes, using platinum or silver as the supporting matrix, were examined by Marple and Rogers (78) and Cooke (16) at about the same time. Earlier, the streaming-mercury electrode had been introduced by Heyrovský and Forejt for oscillographic polarography (41). A very recent addition to the mercury-type electrode family is the hanging-drop type, developed for electrode kinetics by Gerischer (36). Very promising applications to analysis are indicated by the studies of Shain and his co-workers (96). (The newly developed rotating dropping mercury electrode is treated with the D.M.E. in the previous chapter and will not be considered here.)

Unfortunately, there is no single book with comprehensive coverage of electrodes other than the D.M.E. Delahay's excellent monograph (19) contains considerable information. Treatments of particular electrode systems are naturally contained in the polarographic treatises and monographs (15–19,40,53,79,84,98).

II. WORKING ELECTRODES AS ELECTROCHEMICAL TRANSDUCERS

A. RESPONSE AS A FUNCTION OF MASS TRANSFER AND APPLIED SIGNAL

Working electrodes in voltammetry may be considered as electrochemical transducers. The applied electrical signal (input signal) initiates the electrochemical reaction. The progress and behavior of this reaction are observed as an output or response signal. The magnitude and "wave form" of this response depend on the operating conditions of the transducer electrode. These transducer operating conditions may be subdivided as (1) the nature of the input signal; (2) the type and configuration of the electrode, i.e., its size and shape and whether it is used in quiet or stirred solution; and (3) the mass transport modes predominating in the particular electrode usage. Actually, the mass transport conditions are largely de-

TABLE 47.I Summary of Response Characteristics of Various Electrode Systems

Applied electrical signal	Electrode configuration	Predominant mass-transfer mode	Type of response signal	Equation of typical response signal	
A. Constant voltage	Stationary	Diffusion	Current–time	$i_t = \dfrac{nFAD^{1/2}c^{0b}}{\pi^{1/2}2t^{1/2}}$	(1)[a]
	Rotated (stirred)	Diffusion–forced convection	Steady current	$i_{lim} = \dfrac{nFADC^{0b}}{\delta_N}$	(2)[b]
B. Slow voltage sweep, 0–200 mv./min.[c]	Stationary	Diffusion, natural convection	Current–voltage	Variable	(3)
	Rotated[d]	Diffusion–forced convection	Current–voltage	$E = E_{1/2} + (RT/nF) \ln \dfrac{(i_L)_c - i}{i - (i_L)_a}$	(4)
C. Rapid voltage sweep, 200–1000 mv./min.[c]	Stationary	Diffusion	Current–voltage	$i_p = Kn^{3/2}AD^{1/2}c^{0b}V^{1/2}$	(5)[e]
	Rotated[d]	Diffusion–forced convection	Current–voltage	$E = E_{1/2} + (RT/nF) \ln \dfrac{(i_L)_c - i}{i - (i_L)_a}$	(4)
D. Constant current	Stationary	Diffusion	Potential–time	$E = E_{1/4} + (RT/nF) \ln \dfrac{\tau^{1/2} - t^{1/2}}{t^{1/2}}$	(6)[f]

[a] The bulk concentration of electroactive species is denoted by C.[b]
[b] The symbol δ_N is the thickness of the diffusion layer (Nernst).
[c] Single sweep only.
[d] About 600 r.p.m.
[e] In equation (5) V is the voltage sweep rate.
[f] In equation (6) τ is the transition time.

fined by (2) and indirectly by the nature of the input signal. Mass transport processes are treated elsewhere and will not be discussed in detail.

Table 47.I, which is not intended to be comprehensive, summarizes the variety of response signals commonly obtained. This summary is considerably simplified in that electrode configurations are only subdivided into stationary *vs.* rotated or stirred. Semi-infinite linear diffusion is assumed to be operative at all the stationary electrodes, which implies the use of planar electrodes. Different responses result with cylindrical (wire) or spherical electrodes, but these are not included in the abbreviated table. The response resulting from application of a *constant* voltage to a stationary electrode is not a voltammetric signal but rather is a current–time pattern. Such signals are properly classed under chronoamperometry. The limiting current obtained when a constant voltage is applied to a rotated electrode is the measurement used in amperometric titrations. Similarly, applying constant current to a stationary electrode gives a potential–time response. This technique is known as chronopotentiometry and should not be classed as voltammetry. Nevertheless, parts *A* and *D* of Table 47.I have been included, since these input signals are commonly used with pools and solid electrodes.

Parts *B* and *C* of Table 47.I illustrate an important point. If the electrode is rotated or operated in stirred solution, the response or current–voltage curve is relatively independent of the input signal sweep rate. On the other hand, with a quiet electrode and a slowly varying input signal, the response is listed as "variable." Using zero sweep rate (manual adjustment of input signal) or very slow rates gives ordinary polarograms. Slightly higher rates tend to give poorly defined peak-type polarograms. In addition, the term *variable* means that the response signals are not always consistent. This is due to the fact that, during the relatively long period of electrolysis, mass transfer by natural convection may develop. This mode of mass transfer is not reproducible and should be avoided (20,42).

With stationary electrodes, rapid sweep rates lead to well-defined peak polarograms of the general form given in the table. (Only single-sweep input signals are considered here.)

Several other restrictions apply to the data of Table 47.I. It should be noted that the third column does not include the mass transport conditions existing with so-called convection electrodes. These will be discussed later. Furthermore, all the listed response signals are for rapid (reversible) electroactive systems. Most important is the implication that the response signals arise only from a single, purely electrochemical reaction. In electrical terminology the signals are absolutely noise-free. This is obviously a situation met with only on the printed page. Real signals and their noise levels are discussed next.

B. SIGNAL/NOISE RATIO IN WORKING ELECTRODE RESPONSE

In analytical voltammetry we are interested only in the response signal that arises from the electrochemical reaction—the faradaic signal. It is hopeless to expect that the electrode will reproduce only this faradaic signal. In the case of a real current–voltage curve, the current is always composed of two portions: the faradaic current and the residual current. The term *residual current*, as ordinarily used in voltammetry, is made up of several factors: (*1*) capacity or charging current; (*2*) extraneous faradaic current from trace impurities in the test solution; and (*3*) environmental currents from interactions of the electrode surface with its present or past surroundings.

The second-named component of the residual current can be eliminated by very careful purification of all reagents used in preparing the test solution. Alternately, one can employ exhaustive pre-electrolysis of the supporting electrolyte prior to addition of the electroactive species. The environmental currents are somewhat more difficult to eliminate, but with proper choice of conditions they can be minimized, as is seen in the next section.

Capacity or charging current is present to some extent in every current–voltage curve. It cannot be eliminated since an electrode–solution interface has associated with it a double layer that behaves as a condenser of rather large capacity. Whenever the potential of the electrode is altered, part of the current flow is due to charging this capacitor to the new potential. Since the capacity component cannot be ignored, the ratio of faradaic to charging current (i_f/i_c) is an important parameter in analytical voltammetry. In the practical sense, this signal-to-noise ratio may be extended to include other unwanted signals. The experimental quantity to be examined critically is thus (i_f/i_r), where i_r is the entire residual current existing under the given conditions. For a thorough discussion of capacity currents and their relation to analytical voltammetry in trace analysis, the reader is referred to the review by Delahay (22).

C. ENVIRONMENTAL EFFECTS ON VOLTAMMETRIC RESPONSE

It has been noted that the past history and environment of solid electrodes often play a major role in their behavior. The idea that platinum and gold are inert and unattackable has been rendered completely false in the past few years. Both sorbed films of hydrogen (from exposure of the electrode to high-cathodic potentials) as well as surface oxidation (from anodic or chemical treatment) may contribute to the over-all voltammetric response.   In some cases, sorbed hydrogen or oxide films merely obscure the voltammetry under study, but they may also completely obliterate the response.   In any event, these films almost always initiate a mysterious sequence of current–time responses to those unfamiliar with solid electrodes. This is illustrated by the following set of polarographic operations with a platinum electrode.   Having completed an anodic polarogram of *ca.* $10^{-3}M$ iodide in, e.g., $1M$ sulfuric acid background (using an ordinary recording polarograph), the applied voltage is left momentarily at about $+1.2$ v. *vs.* S.C.E.   The voltage is then reset to zero, usually by manual adjustment of the polarographic bridge.   Normally a cathodic current is obtained, which decays slowly.   Depending explicitly on (*1*) how long the applied voltage remained at the anodic level, (*2*) how rapidly the bridge was reset to zero, and (*3*) the particular electroactive system and background media and other elusive experimental details, the magnitude and decay rate of the cathodic current will vary.   If another polarogram is to be run immediately, the inexperienced operator is concerned with reproducing the previous initial conditions.   Cathodic currents decaying with time also are obtained with platinum electrodes that have been pretreated with chromic acid or similar cleaning mixtures.   These "starting currents" are due to stripping of oxide films from the electrode surface, and it is not difficult to understand that their magnitude and decay rates depend on a large number of experimental details to which one ordinarily pays little attention.

All attempts to reproduce surface conditions prior to a polarographic run may be classed as pretreatment techniques.   It is not possible as yet to provide a concise, single set of directions for pretreatment that covers all situations.   I prefer the relatively simple technique given below, largely because it is particularly suited to anodic oxidations of organic materials at platinum electrodes.

If working with oxidizable organic compounds, in addition to surface oxides, polymerlike films of organic material are deposited frequently on the electrode.   Strong dichromate–sulfuric acid ("cleaning solution") is very effective in removing these films; a 30-second immersion usually suffices.   Prior to the first run of a series, and following every polarogram, the electrode is immersed for a few seconds in the chromic acid and then is rinsed thoroughly with distilled water.   The electrode surface is now thoroughly oxidized and, when immersed in the polarographic test solution, this surface will suffer reduction at a rate primarily controlled by the effective strength of the reductant present as electroactive material.   (Since platinum and gold electrodes are primarily used for anodic work, this discussion is not directed toward pretreatment for cathodic reductions.) Now, if the anodic polarogram is to be initiated at, say, +0.10 v., this applied voltage (or a somewhat lesser anodic value) can be placed on the electrode. The electrode system is then allowed to stand until the cathodic current decays to zero or to a very small value. If the reductant is strongly reducing, such as the ferrous ion or an aromatic diamine, this current decay will take a very short time. In almost all cases, 2 to 5 minutes will lower the cathodic current to an acceptable level. Under ordinary circumstances the amount of electroactive species consumed in this process is negligible. It is obvious that the oxide films also can be stripped in the absence of electroactive reductant by application of cathodic potentials. In the above technique the applied potential is used in addition to chemical reduction. No claim is made for the superiority of either technique. The important thing is that the starting current be reproduced for analytical purposes. The means of establishing this condition are a matter of choice.

A thorough discussion of the effect of oxides and sorbed hydrogen on recorded polarograms has been given by Kolthoff and Tanaka (54). Similar behavior at gold electrodes was studied by Bauman and Shain (6). The stepwise formation of platinum and gold oxides by both chemical and anodic oxidation of conventional voltammetric electrodes was demonstrated by Lee (66,67). Anson and Lingane later gave the first unequivocable chemical proof of oxide films on platinum (4). These works should be consulted for further information on pretreatment techniques.

The picture with regard to inclusion of foreign deposits on electrode surfaces, specific adsorption, and other factors, is far from complete. When using solid electrodes it is wise to adopt the attitude that the electrode is "dirty" at all times and to proceed with a pretreatment technique that gives reproducible results. This does not constitute a condemnation of solid electrodes for routine practical work. Indeed, the attention paid to pretreatment techniques represents no more work than the evaluation of capillary constants for precise application of the D.M.E.

III. MERCURY-TYPE ELECTRODES

A. MERCURY POOLS

1. Mercury Pools in Unstirred Solution

It is quite common to refer to electrodes used in unstirred solution as quiet. We will refer to the quiet mercury pool (Q.M.P.) for brevity. Fig. 47.1 shows a typical Q.M.P. electrolysis cell designed by Streuli and Cooke (104). The mercury rests on the fritted bottom of the cell. Re-

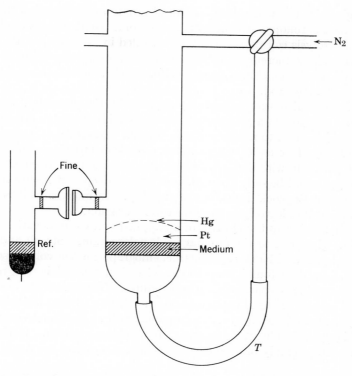

Fig. 47.1. Typical mercury pool electrolysis cell. Key: Hg is the mercury pool (added through the top opening); Pt is the platinum wire connection to the pool; Medium is the medium-porosity frit; *T* is the Tygon tubing connector; Fine are the fine-porosity frits; and Ref. is the reference half cell with ball-joint connector.

moval of oxygen is accomplished by forcing nitrogen up through the same frit. Very rapid and efficient deaeration is obtained in this manner. (Adding a small amount of absolute ethanol to the test solution speeds up oxygen removal through formation of fine bubbles. Streuli and Cooke found no detectable oxygen remaining after only 15 to 30 seconds under these conditions (104).) The entire cell was water-jacketed for temperature control.

Although the construction of mercury-pool electrodes appears very simple, there are several important design factors. First, the surface area must be reproducible. Solution must not creep down between the mercury and the cell wall. In the unit of Streuli and Cooke, the entire inner wall is coated with Desicote (Beckman Instrument Co.), which prevents wetting of the glass by the test solution. An alternate approach, that has been successful in chronopotentiometry is the use of a Lucite plug at the bottom of the electrolysis cell (93). A cavity is drilled in the center of the Lucite block to hold the mercury. Neither mercury nor water wet Lucite. The entire cell can be machined from Lucite, which is readily available in 2- to 3-inch diameter rod.

The interfacial tension of mercury depends on the potential; hence the curvature and area of a pool change with applied potential. A fairly large pool should be used to minimize these effects. According to Delahay, the diameter should be at least 2 cm. (19). Since electrical contact is made through platinum wire that can be bent flat against the bottom of the cavity, the pool need be only about 0.5 cm. or less deep. It is convenient to incorporate a stopcock drain for the mercury. In most cases it is wise to shock-mount the electrolysis unit on a rubber cushion.

The application to the Q.M.P. of an applied voltage that varies linearly with time gives rise to the familiar peak polarogram. Streuli and Cooke used the Leeds and Northrup Electrochemograph for the voltage scanning initially, but they found considerable electrical "hash" in the recorded polarograms due to coarse slide-wire windings. The polarizing bridge was replaced with an external voltage scanner made of a 10-turn Helepot driven through suitable gearing by a synchronous motor. A variable-speed scanner is highly desirable for voltammetry in unstirred solution. Components for versatile assembly of such electromechanical systems are readily available.

Restricting their initial study to metal ion reductions, Streuli and Cooke verified the linear dependence of peak current (i_p) on concentration. For concentrations of Tl(I), Pb(II), Cd(II), Cu(II), and Bi(III) varying between 10^{-4} and $5 \times 10^{-6}M$, the average deviation in i_p measurements was between 2 and 3%. Zinc ion reductions gave slightly higher deviations: around 6%. The variation of i_p with $V^{1/2}$ (square root of the voltage scan rate), predicted by the Randles (92) and Sevcik (99) equations, was excellent. The half-peak potential, $E_{p/2}$, generally was independent of concentration over the concentration range 10^{-4} to $10^{-6}M$, and it agreed well with conventional $E_{1/2}$'s at the D.M.E.

The true increased sensitivity of the mercury-pool electrode is reflected in the ratio of the measured current to the residual current, as compared with the same ratio for the D.M.E. Thus, Streuli and Cooke calculated $i_p/i_r = 24.0$, whereas for the D.M.E. the ratio i_d/i_r was only 2.3.

Studies of organic reduction at the Q.M.P. produced some very interesting results. In contrast to metal ion reductions, the $E_{p/2}$'s of typical organic compounds differed markedly from the $E_{1/2}$'s at the D.M.E. (104).

TABLE 47.II

Comparison of Reduction Potentials at Dropping Mercury and Mercury Pool Electrodes[a]

Compound	D.M.E.		Q.M.P.	
	1st	2nd	1st	2nd
Nitrobenzene	−0.22[b]	−0.68	−0.40	None
Dinitrobenzene	−0.27	−0.38	−0.30	−0.51
Benzophenone	−1.21	—	−1.15	—
Benzil	−0.93	—	−0.85	—
Azobenzene	−0.83	—	−0.72	—
1-Nitroso-2-naphthol	−0.27	—	−0.80	—
Cystine	−0.46	−0.87	−0.56	−1.11
1,6-Anthraquinone disulfonate	−0.67		−0.66	
Hydrazobenzene	−0.83		−0.76	

[a] Streuli, C. A., and W. D. Cooke, *Anal. Chem.*, **26**, 963 (1954).

[b] All potentials in volts *vs.* S.C.E.

Table 47.II shows some of the results. In general, $E_{p/2}$'s were reproducible to within 10 mv. and peak currents to ±7%.

The fact that different reduction potentials are obtained at the D.M.E. and the Q.M.P. leads to the idea that some new mixture problems might be attacked with the Q.M.P. Thus, Streuli and Cooke were able to determine *m*-dinitrobenzene in about 20-fold excess of nitrobenzene—a mixture that is not resolvable under the same pH conditions with the D.M.E. This capability of the Q.M.P. method is very attractive and should be explored further.

An important advantage of the mercury-pool electrode is that its increased sensitivity leads to the use of more dilute solutions. This can be of real value when solubility problems exist. For instance, although 80% ethanol was needed to solubilize enough organic material for the D.M.E., 5% ethanol gave enough electroactive material in solution for the Q.M.P. The analyses of anthraquinones and various insoluble dyestuff materials are hampered by solubility problems, and the mercury-pool technique may be of real value in such instances.

One of the disadvantages of the Q.M.P. is the appearance of hydrogen background waves earlier than with the D.M.E. With scan rates of 400 mv./minute, the cathodic limit is about −1.5 v. *vs.* S.C.E., decreasing to only −0.9 v. at scan rates of 600 mv./minute. Thus, conjugated double bonds, aldehydes, etc., cannot be done at the Q.M.P.

A particular analysis developed by Streuli and Cooke that illustrates the differences between the D.M.E. and the Q.M.P. is the determination of gamma-hexachlorocyclohexane is a mixture of isomers and other higher chlorination products.   At the D.M.E., heptachlorinated compounds overlap the gamma isomer wave.   No such interference exists with the Q.M.P., and excellent results on practical mixtures were obtained (105).

2. Mercury Pools in Stirred Solution

Arthur and his co-workers described an ingenious stirred mercury pool that used a small mercury-filled tube standing upright in the solution (5). Fig. 47.2 shows the apparatus.   The mercury surface is adjusted flush with

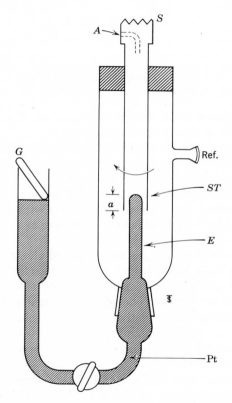

Fig. 47.2. Stirred mercury pool (after Arthur *et al.* (5)).   Key: *A* is an air vent; *S* is the stirrer shaft; Ref. is the connector to the reference half cell; *ST* is the rotating stirrer tube; *E* is the mercury tube electrode; ⚏ is a 10/30 standard-taper joint; Pt is the platinum wire connection; and *G* is a glass rod for adjusting the mercury.   Typical dimensions are as follows: stirrer tube—7.0 ± 0.1 mm., O.D.; electrode tube—1.72 mm. I.D.; and distance *a*—5 mm.

the inner upright tube.   Stirring is accomplished by the wider tube, which fits down over the pool.   It was found necessary to coat the inside of the mercury-filled tube with ceresin wax for reproducible results.   In addition, preconditioning of the electrode at cathodic potentials was necessary for a new electrode or one that had not been used for some time.

The magnitude of the limiting current with this electrode is a function of several variables: (1) the inner electrode diameter, (2) the depth the inner electrode extends into the hollow stirrer, and (3) the stirrer rotation speed.   The dimensions shown in Fig. 47.2 are typical of those used by Arthur *et al*.   Vertical positioning of the stirrer tube must be duplicated closely to reproduce limiting currents.   However, using only the unaided eye for such adjustments, results for limiting current *vs*. concentration of Cd(II), Pb(II), and Hg(II) were all linear within 1% (5).   Conventional polarograms were recorded on a Sargent polarograph.   The sensitivity of this electrode system is considerably higher than the D.M.E., and residual currents were reported to be quite low.   Half-wave potentials were found to be slightly more negative than at the D.M.E., as is to be expected.   In view of the relative ease with which Arthur *et al*. obtained reproducible results, it is surprising that this electrode system has not been used more widely.   On the other hand, mercury pools generally have found little acceptance among analytical chemists.   Peurifoy and Schrenk have reported some precise data using the Arthur-type electrode (91).

Rosie and Cooke added auxiliary stirring to the Q.M.P. in order to increase sensitivity (95).   The electrolysis vessel was identical with that used in the Q.M.P. studies and the operating techniques are similar.   The limiting currents were, of course, a critical function of the distance of the stirrer from the surface of the pool, the highest limiting currents being obtained when the stirrer actually touched the mercury surface.   Results were, however, erratic and very sensitive to position at this level.   A fixed distance of 6 mm. from the surface was chosen as the best compromise between sensitivity and reproducibility.

Here, where mass transfer is primarily by forced convection, voltage sweep rate has little effect on the shape of the polarograms.   Conventional waves were obtained with sweep rates of from 20 to 400 mv./minute. Half-wave potentials were found to be slightly more negative than those at the D.M.E., due primarily to accumulation of reduced metal in the electrode.   Rosie and Cooke studied a variety of inorganic and organic reductions.   As an example of long-term reproducibility, 17 runs on $10^{-5}M$ *o*-nitrotoluene during a one-month period gave a precision of 2.4% in limiting current.   The sensitivity of this electrode is about 300 times that of the D.M.E.   Two consequences of this increased sensitivity are important.

First, appreciable electrolysis occurs at the stirred pool. Wave heights decreased approximately 20% in ten minutes at a fixed potential on the plateau. This causes little trouble when using normal scanning speeds. The second effect, described previously, is an earlier cut-off due to hydrogen discharge, which constitutes the principal disadvantage of pool electrodes. The reduction of a variety of nitro and related aromatic compounds at stirred mercury pools was investigated by Bergman and James (7).

The rotating mercury electrode (R.M.E.), developed earlier by Lee, is a different form of stirred pool (68). A Bakelite cup attached to a precision steel stirring rod forms the electrode. A mercury "ring" is held in an annular space by centrifugal force. Electrical contact is provided by the platinum wire, which is insulated from the solution. A very thorough interpretation of the R.M.E. was given by Lee and has been reviewed by Delahay (19). The "wave equation" for the R.M.E. is of the form:

$$E = (E_{1/2})_{t\,=\,0} + \frac{RT}{nF} \ln \frac{i_L - i}{i + Q} \qquad (7)$$

where Q expresses the contribution to the $i-E$ curve of amalgam accumulated during the electrolysis period.

Residual currents are not negligible at the R.M.E.; because it is a fixed-area electrode the capacity-current portion of this residual current should be very small. The rather large observed residual currents have been interpreted as resulting from vibrational renewal of the surface—i.e., as largely capacitive (19). It is interesting to note that the stirred pool of Rosie and Cooke had quite low residual currents. An examination of the "noise" level of their polarograms indicated that considerable turbulence existed at the electrode surface, and one might expect movement of the pool surface with considerable charging current. Thus, it may be that the increased residual currents of the R.M.E. came from higher trace-impurity levels.

B. OTHER MERCURY-TYPE ELECTRODES

1. Streaming Mercury Electrodes

The streaming electrode was designed by Heyrovský and Forejt primarily for oscillographic polarography (41). It consists essentially of a mercury stream whose dimensions are defined by the distance between the capillary tip from which the mercury issues and the liquid level in the cell. It is immediately apparent that the area of such an electrode is difficult to reproduce. Furthermore, the streaming electrode uses an inordinate amount of mercury for practical purposes. Rius and his co-workers found that the streaming electrode can be used for ordinary polarograms and gave a thorough treatment of the limiting currents.   An account of their work has been given by Delahay (21).

Because of the lack of practicability of the streaming electrode, no analytical usage has developed.   An intriguing modification of potential analytical significance has been reported by Leveque (69).   The mercury flows from a reservoir down the length of an amalgamated platinum wire. The area of exposed mercury is adjusted by immersion into a layer of ethyl phthalate or other water-immiscible liquid.   Leveque reported proportionality between limiting currents and concentration for cadmium reduction over a fairly wide range of concentrations.   Limiting currents are about 30 times that of the D.M.E., but with an increased level of charging current. Volkov and Kus'kina have reported on electrolyses with mercury flowing along vertical metal surfaces (107).   It is difficult to see how streaming electrodes can compete with mercury pools in analytical applications.

2. Mercury Membrane Electrodes

Bowers and Wilson have discussed a new type of mercury electrode for voltammetry in which the electroactive material arrives at the electrode surface by diffusion through a cellophane membrane (12).   The cellophane, swollen in water, is placed over the end of a glass tube and held in place with a polyethylene ring.   A small pool of mercury inside the tube with a platinum external connection completes the electrode.

Polarograms at the mercury membrane electrode are quantitatively interpreted by assuming that a linear concentration gradient is established fairly rapidly within the membrane.   Linear dependence of limiting currents with concentrations of Cd(II) and Tl(I) were excellent (12).   The treatment of reversible and irreversible processes at the membrane electrode has appeared (12).

The rigid structure of the diffusion membrane minimizes convection problems, and the electrode has been found to be excellent for chronopotentiometry and current-scan voltammetry (11).   For instance, transition times of several minutes still obey the theoretical equations.   Work is in progress on the use of ion-exchange membranes as diffusion layers (11).   The analytical potentialities of the mercury membrane electrode are very promising indeed and will be forthcoming in the publications of Bowers and his co-workers.   Merely the isolation of the electrode proper from the solution offers some distinct advantages for in-line monitoring analysis.

In this connection, the platinum-type polyethylene and Teflon membrane electrodes used by Sawyer and his co-workers show real promise for the voltammetry of gases (97a).

3. Mercury-Plated Metal Electrodes

Amalgamated metal electrodes were studied in some detail by Skobets (101), as well as by Lydersen (76) and others (64,88). Cooke developed a silver amalgam electrode made very simply by dipping a large-diameter silver wire in mercury (16). The resultant film of dilute silver amalgam is very adherent and relatively insensitive to storage effects. The wire was used in a rotated (*ca.* 800 r.p.m.) configuration, giving an effective 50-fold increase in limiting current over the D.M.E. As with pool electrodes, the hydrogen discharge wave occurred at more positive potentials, somewhat limiting the useful range. Cooke studied the reduction of Co(III) to Co-(II), as well as Cd(II) to metal. In the former case, an ion–ion process, accumulation of deposited metal in the mercury, causes the half-wave potential to shift and depend on scanning rate, as is expected.

Marple and Rogers studied silver amalgam electrodes briefly but preferred to plate mercury on platinum (78). The mercury was plated from a mercuric nitrate medium onto small wires used as stationary electrodes. Several inorganic reductions as well as a variety of aromatic nitro compounds were examined with satisfactory results.

Mercury-plated electrodes seem to have found little usage among analytical chemists. Mong and Timnick used such an electrode recently for chronopotentiometric studies (80). The essential aim of this type of electrode is an increase of sensitivity over the D.M.E. However, it would seem that this goal can be better achieved with mercury pools or the hanging drop electrode which, although improving sensitivity, has few of the disadvantages associated with a solid matrix electrode.

IV. SOLID ELECTRODES

A large variety of electrode forms exist. The discussion of solid electrodes in this section will center around platinum, gold, and graphite as electrode materials, used in the form of wires or rods. In addition, some promising new types of electrodes will be discussed. Foil electrodes, although useful in chronopotentiometry, are rarely used for voltammetry, as noted previously.

A. PLATINUM AND GOLD WIRES

The conventional form of platinum wire electrode is easily constructed by sealing 16- or 18-gage wire in *soft* glass. The length of exposed wire is ordinarily 1 to 2 cm. It is advisable to melt a small amount of powdered wax on the inside of the glass seal (red sealing wax is excellent). An electrode that shows spurious signals or abnormal residual currents almost surely has developed minute cracks at the glass–metal seal. It is useless to attempt resealing a cracked electrode. It should be broken and a new electrode prepared. Electrical connection is normally made by filling the tube with mercury into which an external copper wire dips.

Gold seals to glass with great difficulty. Some workers have soldered gold to a brass rod that is then coated with insulating wax (72). Baumann and Shain pressure-fitted gold wires to Teflon rods, which proved very satisfactory (6).

Wire electrodes may be used in a stationary configuration, rotated or vibrated, or used in stirred solution. Vibrated electrodes have found only limited use, and the reader is referred to the original literature for construction details (29,38,71,88,94). Stationary and rotated wires will be discussed in greater detail since these are the most frequently used configurations.

1. Stationary Wire Electrodes

Cylindrical diffusion is operative at stationary wire electrodes. For *short periods of electrolysis* at ordinary-sized wires, the current-potential curves approximate linear diffusion conditions. Linear diffusion approximations are quite satisfactory using oscillographic sweep rates (8,87). Ordinary recording polarographic instruments require much longer periods of electrolysis. Nicholson considered the curvature of the wire using slow sweep rates and found excellent agreement with theory (87).

The distinction between linear and cylindrical diffusion is of minor importance in practical analysis. Equation (5) of Table 47.I predicts proportionality between the peak current i_p and concentration.

$$i_p = KC^b V^{1/2} \tag{5a}$$

In addition, the peak current is proportional to the square root of the voltage sweep rate. (Equation (5a) is identical with that used for quiet mercury pools.) For rapid (reversible) electrode reactions, the current–voltage curve shows a very sharp peak. Irreversible processes have a more drawn-out peak.

Excellent samples of practical voltammetry at stationary wire electrodes have been given by Nicholson (86,87). Nicholson found that the oxidation of ferrocyanide and the reduction of ferricyanide agreed closely with theory. Ferricyanide was recommended as a standard test ion for the calibration and comparison of electrode areas. An ordinary 20-mil platinum wire was used with a small glass bead sealed on the end to minimize end effects.

The oxidation of organic sulfides was examined in detail, using a background of $0.1M$ HCl in methanol. Coulometric data indicated a 2-electron oxidation to the sulfoxide. Plots of i_p vs. molecular weight of the various sulfides increased smoothly with molecular weight, indicating the same over-all electrode process for all compounds studied. Although the function i_p/c decreased slightly with increasing concentration, the analytical results were excellent. This study showed conclusively that natural convection interference can be made of minor importance in stationary voltammetry without undue precautions.

A more recent paper by Nicholson (86) describes the voltammetry of thiocyanate ion in pyridine–pyridinium ion backgrounds. Unlike the previous work, which used the standard voltage sweep rate of the Sargent polarograph, the thiocyanate oxidations were carried out by using a rate of 50 mv./minute. The apparatus was otherwise much the same. The oxidation of thiocyanate was found to be irreversible, and adsorption of an electrolysis product on the electrode surface was observed. However, the value i_p/c was constant within $\pm 1\%$ over the thiocyanate concentration range of 0.1 to 4mM. An extensive study of the process in the presence of several anions was also made.

Berzins and Delahay examined the deposition of metals on stationary wire electrodes (8). These studies were made using fast (oscillographic) sweep rates. Considerable discrepancies exist between theory and practice, due, apparently, to variations in the activity of freshly deposited metal surfaces, a problem common to metal electrodeposition.

Further utility of stationary wire electrodes in analytical applications is illustrated by the very interesting work of Crittenden and his co-workers (10). At constant applied potential, the transient current–time curves were integrated. Precise integrator circuits allowed the charge transferred over short periods of electrolysis to be measured to better than 0.5%. Convection effects were negligible. Plots of the diffusion-controlled charge vs. concentration were linear with concentration to within $\pm 1\%$ at ordinary wire electrodes. It is to be expected that further studies using this technique will be very fruitful. It would seem particularly adaptable to routine analysis coupled, perhaps, to a digital readout device.

Finally, in connection with stationary electrodes, the recent work on diffusion coefficient measurements should be mentioned. In practice, foil-type electrodes are used, with a restricting mantle to ensure semi-infinite linear diffusion (102). Verification of linear diffusion is obtained when the product $it^{1/2}$ is constant (at contant applied potential). Rather than obtain diffusion coefficients, this technique can be used to calibrate electrode areas or measure concentrations. In the latter connection, the rapid technique of Booman, Morgan, and Crittenden (10) is certainly preferable. Macero and Rulfs (77) have recently investigated diffusion coefficients by using much the same technique as von Stackelberg.

2. Rotated Electrodes

The rotated platinum electrode (R.P.E.) is by far the most widely used solid electrode configuration. It is constructed in much the same way as its stationary counterpart. The rotating device should operate at constant speed; 600 r.p.m. is a fairly standard speed. Stirring motors are, in general, unsatisfactory for this purpose. A geared-down synchronous motor should be used. The Synchronous Rotator marketed by Sargent, although expensive, is very satisfactory.

The wire itself should extend vertically downward. The various right-angle bends and twists introduced by individual workers have no particular advantages. Indeed, recent studies indicate that the turbulence with such forms is undesirable. A very practical reason for preferring the straight-downward wire is that it is least likely to be bent or twisted with handling. For analytical usage, the geometry of the electrode must be undisturbed for day-to-day reproducibility.

Limiting currents at the R.P.E. are proportional to concentration and obey the relationship:

$$i_L = \frac{nFADC^b}{\delta_N} \tag{2}$$

where δ_N is the effective thickness of the so-called Nernst diffusion layer. Mass transport to a rotating electrode is intermediate between diffusion and forced convection (51). Tsukamoto, Kambara, and Tachi have given a theoretical treatment of the limiting currents at the R.P.E. (106). Recent illuminating studies of mass transport conditions pertaining to forced convection have been given by Jordan's group (43). Equation (2), a simplification in that the thickness of the diffusion layer (δ_N) actually depends on the experimental hydrodynamic conditions, is useful in analysis since it is applicable to a wide variety of situations. Writing the equation in the form:

$$i_L = M_{\text{Rot}}C^b \tag{3}$$

where M_{Rot} is defined as the mass-transfer coefficient (44) for rotated electrodes (obviously not a constant for all electrodes), emphasizes the necessity of maintaining rigorous control over the mass-transfer process if reproducible limiting currents are to be obtained. This control can be exercised by rigidly fixing the over-all electrolysis cell geometry. Jordan and Jiminez have designed a "constant geometry" cell for the R.P.E. that showed a precision and accuracy of 1 to 3% over a 40-day period (45).

3. Convection Electrodes and Hydrodynamic Voltammetry

The application of hydrodynamic theory to electrodes with convective mass transport (rotated electrodes or stirred solution) was developed over the years by Levich and his co-workers (69a,70), culminating in the authoritative text by Levich in 1959 (70a). Important contributions to convective mass transport applied to electrodes of analytical significance have been made by the schools of Riddiford (7a,37a,85a) and Jordan (44a).

In the hydrodynamic treatment of voltammetry one relates the limiting current at a particular electrode to the pertinent hydrodynamic variables such as viscosity, solution velocity, diffusion coefficient, and characteristic dimension of the electrode. Provided laminar flow can be obtained, the limiting current equation can be treated rigorously. The use of dimensionless groups often facilitates the application of heat-transfer equations to the electrochemical situation (41a).

One electrode that can be treated in a rigorous fashion is the rotated-disk electrode. The equation for the limiting current at a rotated-disk electrode is:

$$i_{\text{lim}} = 0.617 \, nFAC^b_{\text{ox}} \, D_{\text{ox}}{}^{2/3} \, \omega^{1/2} \, \nu^{-1/6} \qquad (8)$$

where ω = angular velocity of the disk and ν = kinematic viscosity of the solution.

Rotating-disk electrodes have been used for the determination of diffusion coefficients (54a), kinetic currents, and other mechanism studies (70a). Rotated disks of carbon paste can be constructed easily and apparently perform well (33a).

Attempts to correlate the ordinary R.P.E. with hydrodynamic theory is difficult because of turbulent flow (106). Kolthoff and Jordan designed a platinum electrode with auxiliary stirring in the form of a four-blade paddle mounted above the wire, which showed a high degree of convective mass transport (50,51). Jordan, Javick, and Ranz constructed a microconical platinum electrode immersed as a probe in a precisely controlled flowing system. Rigorous hydrodynamic equations were derived for this electrode, and original literature should be consulted for details (43,44a).

Practically no analytical applications have been made of the rotating disk or similar convective transport electrodes possessing rigorous limiting-current equations. The indications are that such data will be forthcoming soon.

B. CARBON-ROD ELECTRODES

Limiting current studies at carbon rods were first made by Wilson and Youtz, who investigated fundamental diffusion principles at such electrodes (112).   Carbon rods in analytical voltammetry were examined by Lord and Rogers in a comparison study of various electrode materials (72).

Carbon or graphite rods are usually spectroscopic-grade rods, although pencil leads have been used.   Electrical connection is made through a small battery clip or the usual mercury well.

Untreated carbon rods have abnormally high residual currents.   Thorough impregnation with wax removes much of this unwanted current, and highly successful wax-impregnation treatments have been developed. Gaylor, Conrad, and Landerl showed the striking effect of impregnation on the ratio i_d/i_r, as illustrated in Table 47.III, taken from their data (34).

TABLE 47.III
Effect of Impregnating Agents on Carbon-Rod Electrodes $(34)^a$

Impregnating material	i_d/i_r
None	0.1
Saron resin	1.3
Sylon	2.0
Silicone resin	2.0
Lemon wax	2.5
Ceramid wax	3.7
Silicone 200	6.5
Opal wax	11.3
Ceresin wax	12.2
Castor wax	20.0

^{a} Polarographic test system: 10^{-4} dibutylphenylene-diamine in 1:1 alcohol–water acetate buffer.

Although castor wax showed the best response ratio, ceresin has been favored by later workers (31,32).   The wax-impregnation procedure usually consists of soaking the rod for one or more hours in the molten wax to thoroughly saturate the pores.   The rod is then withdrawn and allowed to cool. When the wax has hardened the outer surface of the rod is painted with a sealer such as Seal-All (Allen Products Corporation, Detroit, Mich.). The electrode surface is then prepared for use by cutting or breaking off the end.   Fresh surfaces are prepared in this manner after each run, if desired.

Morris and Schempf made a critical evaluation of impregnation procedures and concluded the waxing should be carried out under reduced pressure to aid the removal of entrapped gases (81).   These workers used a simple manual lathe to cut fresh working surfaces.   This procedure secures unsmeared surfaces and furthermore is less wasteful of electrode than manually breaking off a new end.   Morris and Schempf point out that about 15 to 20 fresh surfaces can be obtained from 1 inch of electrode.

TABLE 47.IV
Cathodic and Anodic Limits of Wax-Impregnated Graphite

Background system		Cathodic limit[a]	Anodic limit[a]
Buffer[b]	pH 1.20	−1.28	1.32
	pH 3.95	1.30	1.33
	pH 7.02	1.38	1.35
	pH 9.80	1.61	1.04
0.1M KCl		1.3	

[a] In volts *vs.* S.C.E.
[b] Clark and Lubs buffer.

Since some considerable effort is involved in waxing the electrode, the new cutting technique would seem to be worthwhile. The reproducibility of limiting currents with such electrodes was excellent, being of the order of ±1.4%. Recently Fox, Taft, and Schempf have completed a very interesting study of the oxidation potentials of some 15 to 20 substituted anilines and dimethylanilines at carbon rods prepared by the Morris and Schempf technique (33).

The potential range of carbon electrodes is considerably greater than that of platinum or gold. Table 47.IV shows the anodic and cathodic potential limits found by Morris and Schempf together with data reported by Gaylor and her co-workers for similar electrodes. It is evident that graphite electrodes are useful over a considerable cathodic region. Considerable use of this fact has been made for inorganic reductions, but relatively few organic reductions at carbon have been reported.

Carbon electrodes are most frequently used in quiet solution, but Gaylor, Conrad, and Landerl determined antioxidants in gasoline using stirred solution (35). Concentrations as low as 2 p.p.m. were determined very effectively.

C. RECENT DEVELOPMENTS ON SOLID ELECTRODES

Several workers have concerned themselves with developing new solid electrode systems whose performance would not be so dependent on past history as that encountered with the noble metals. This has resulted in several promising new electrodes whose properties are discussed briefly below. Details are to be found in the original literature or in forthcoming publications.

1. Tungsten Hemipentoxide Wire Electrodes

Jordan and Jiminez reasoned that an oxide-coated electrode should be well suited for anodic voltammetry in the region of potentials in which the oxide was stable (46).   Such an electrode should be ideal for the determination of oxidant species that would attack platinum and gold.   Accordingly they developed a tungsten hemipentoxide (W_2O_5) electrode that consists of a tungsten wire covered with a continuous coating of the oxide.   The tungsten hemipentoxide electrode (T.H.P.E.) was prepared by sealing a tungsten wire into Pyrex glass (ca. 0.8 mm. exposed).   The electrode was then precleaned by dipping in fused sodium nitrite until the surface was clean of colored oxides.   The adherent oxide film was then prepared by heating the electrode in a circulating air atmosphere for three hours at 475°C.   The electrode was rotated at 300 r.p.m. with a "constant geometry" type of electrolysis cell.   In $0.1M$ perchloric acid, the anodic potential limit was about 1.9 v. vs. S.C.E.   With suitable experimental conditions Ce(IV), Mn(VII), and Cr(VI) gave well-defined and reproducible polarograms at the T.H.P.E.   Limiting currents were directly proportional to concentration with very good reproducibility.   The concept of using fully oxidized electrode surfaces is an interesting one and well may produce significant new results in solid-electrode voltammetry.

2. Boron Carbide Electrodes

The writer and his co-workers have taken an opposite attack on the oxide problem, namely that of using materials that do not undergo surface oxidation.   The product Norbide (Norton Company) is commercial boron carbide that can be obtained molded in rods or other shapes.   This material is extremely inert to ordinary oxidizing agents, possesses almost metallic conduction, and appears well suited for solid electrode work.   A successful boron carbide (B_4C) electrode has been developed that shows no effects of surface oxidation (82,83).

Excellent results have been obtained on the anodic oxidation of organic materials at the B_4C electrode.   In addition, the hydrogen overpotential of polished B_4C is large and a considerable amount of cathodic work can be done.   For instance, the reduction of Zn(II) is easily accomplished at a polished B_4C electrode.   Since commercial B_4C contains some free carbon, the exact working mechanism of this electrode is not clear.   It may function as a carbon electrode.   There is no doubt, however, that the general voltammetric characteristics are a function of the boron carbide matrix. In general, half-wave potentials at B_4C are in close agreement with similar data at platinum anodes.

3. Mercury Chloride Film Anode

Kuwana developed an interesting mercury film electrode for the anodic oxidation of organic compounds (56,57).   A small mercury pool was scanned anodically to $+1.4$ v. *vs.* S.C.E. in a background medium $0.2M$ in potassium chloride and adjusted to *ca.* pH 2.5. An adherent film of mercurous chloride is formed on the mercury surface by this procedure. The applied potential is then set to $+0.1$ v. *vs.* S.C.E. and the electrode is ready for use. Another anodic scan in the absence of electroactive material produces a very flat residual current polarogram with less than 5 μamp. of current out to $+1.4$ v. (the electrode with the halide film acts essentially as an inert electrode). If, however, electro-oxidizable material is added, a peak polarogram is obtained whose half-peak potential is characteristic of the substance oxidized and whose peak height is directly proportional to its concentration. Excellent results were obtained for the oxidation of a wide variety of organic compounds. Under no circumstances were inorganic ions oxidized at the mercury chloride film anode (M.C.F.A.). The $E_{1/2}$'s of organic compounds are in close accord with those obtained at platinum.

One advantage of the M.C.F.A. is that its surface can be completely renewed by cathodic stripping of the halide film. In this connection, studies can be made of a molecule containing both oxidizable and reducible functions. The M.C.F.A. also can be operated advantageously using the chronopotentiometric technique. Further details are contained in the original literature.

4. Carbon Paste Electrodes

Since wax-impregnated electrodes have been quite successful, it was reasoned that a paste composed of powdered carbon or graphite and an organic liquid that was nonmiscible with water might be a useful "solid" electrode system. Such an electrode was developed and was found to be almost entirely free of residual currents while providing a very wide range of anodic and cathodic potentials (1). A paste of bromonaphthalene and high-purity powdered graphite has been found most advantageous. The paste is hand-packed into a pool cut from a Teflon rod, and electrical connection to the back of the pool is made with platinum wire.

Typical peak polarograms are obtained for the oxidation of a wide variety of organic compounds. The reproducibility of this electrode is excellent (83). Reductions of metal ions as well as of organic materials also can be accomplished (89).

5. Rotating Aluminum Electrode

All of the electrodes discussed previously have been relatively inert and, in general, are not to be classified as active electrodes in the corrosion sense. The rotating aluminum electrode (R.Al.E.) developed by Kolthoff and Sambucetti represents an extremely interesting new type of voltammetric electrode (53a). The R.Al.E. is apparently covered normally with an oxide film which, however, is permeable to both fluoride and hydroxide ions and, in a limited sense, to perchlorate, bromide, and chloride ions.

In acid solution, fluoride yields a well-defined anodic polarogram at about -1.5 v. *vs.* S.C.E. The limiting current is proportional to fluoride concentration, and the R.Al.E. can be used for amperometric determinations of fluoride at low concentrations. Hydroxide also yields reproducible limiting currents at highly negative potentials. The electrode functions as a pOH indicator electrode at pH 9. Even though the R.Al.E. is of real analytical value in the sense of trace fluoride analysis, more important contributions may develop from future fundamental studies of this and other film-covered electrodes.

V. ANALYTICAL APPLICATIONS

A. TYPICAL ANALYTICAL RESULTS

The quantitative determination of N,N'-tetramethylbenzidine (TMB) through measurement of i_p at a stationary Pt wire illustrates the ordinary analytical usage of solid electrodes. This compound was chosen at random from a series of aromatic amines under study in the writer's laboratory. No precautions were taken to ensure results of more than ordinary reliability—in fact, the aim was to provide a summary of a quick, "off-the-shelf" determination.

TMB was examined at a stationary Pt wire *ca.* 2 cm in length, extending vertically downward. Although the compound is readily air-oxidized, the work was performed in an open 50-ml. beaker. A conventional S.C.E. was used, and all polarograms were recorded on a Model E Electrochemograph. A stock solution of $0.01M$ TMB was prepared by dissolving the required weight of compound in a minimal quantity of concentrated HCl and then diluting with air-free distilled water to 1 liter.

Small portions of the stock TMB were added to a buffer background solution (Britton and Robinson buffer, pH *ca.* 2.0) and were polarographed to observe the general behavior of TMB. Fig. 47.3 shows these preliminary results, including the background scan. It is always worthwhile to run an initial survey of this sort. To avoid wasting time, the current range of the recording polarograph is set at a high level. Using 10^{-3} to $10^{-4}M$ solutions of electroactive species, the entire polarogram will fit into this range with any ordinary electrode size. All the polarograms of

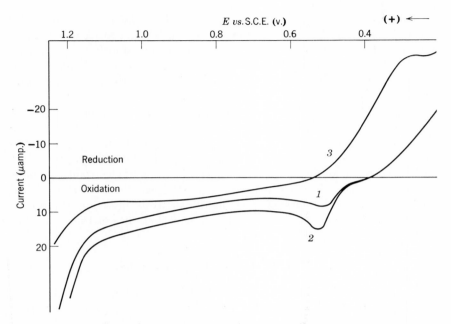

Fig. 47.3. Preliminary polarograms of TMB. Curve *1* = 1 ml. of 0.01*M* TMB; curve *2* = 2 ml. of 0.01*M* TMB; and curve *3* = background buffer solution.

Fig. 47.3 were started at 0.0 v. *vs.* S.C.E., although part of the potential range has been left out of the diagram for convenience. Using the Electrochemograph, anodic polarograms are best recorded by setting the selector switch to "Direct" and reversing the usual electrode connections; i.e., the connector marked "Polarized Electrode" is connected to the S.C.E. and "Reference" to the Pt or other form of anodic working electrode. The instrument zero is set at the right of the chart and the recording then follows the polarographic convention for anodic polarograms. Figs. 47.3 and 47.4 are actual chart papers taken from the instrument.

It can be seen easily that TMB oxidizes in this medium at about +0.5 v. *vs.* S.C.E. Also, the peak current is very roughly proportional to the concentration of TMB. Assuming that the problem at hand is the practical determination of small quantities of TMB, we can now state the conditions for the voltammetric determination.

Since the extra information is of no practical value, we need only scan from about +0.4 to 0.6 v. *vs.* S.C.E. Fig. 47.4 shows such polarograms for varying concentrations of TMB, with the lowest concentration carried out to somewhat more positive potentials than is necessary. Typical of

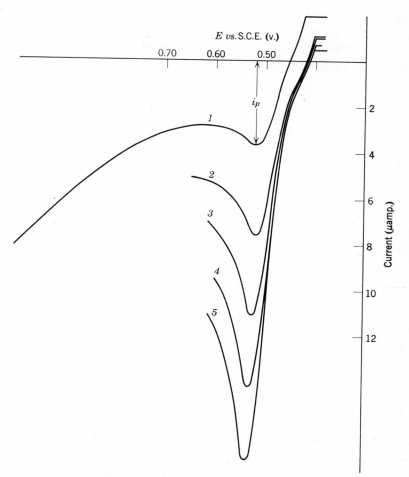

Fig. 47.4. Calibration polarograms for TMB. Curve _1_ = 4.0 × $10^{-5}M$ TMB; curve _2_ = 8.0 × $10^{-5}M$; curve _3_ = 1.2 × $10^{-4}M$; curve _4_ = 1.6 × $10^{-4}M$; and curve _5_ = 2.0 × $10^{-4}M$.

the anodic oxidation of organic amines at Pt, there is a very slight shift of peak potential with increasing concentrations. In the present case, this is of minor significance. The method of measuring i_p is shown on the diagram. Reference to Fig. 47.3 shows that the residual current for the background alone at the peak potential of TMB is slightly cathodic. This correction was ignored, and i_p was simply measured each time from the zero current line. Table 47.V shows the calibration data involving slightly more than a 10-fold range of TMB concentrations. At these relatively low concentration levels the results are quite satisfactory with this simple technique. These data are quite typical of results attainable at solid electrodes with a minimum of effort.

TABLE 47.V
Calibration Data for TMB

Conc. TMB (molarity)	i_p, mamp.	i_p/C
4.0×10^{-5}	3.6	9.00
8.0×10^{-5}	7.6	9.50
1.2×10^{-4}	11.1	9.25
1.6×10^{-4}	14.2	8.87
2.0×10^{-4}	17.4	8.70
3.2×10^{-4}	26.7	8.34
4.0×10^{-4}	32.7	8.18
	Mean	8.83
	Deviation, %	4.2

B. TRACE LEVEL ANALYSIS

Applications and critical discussions of the utility of voltammetry in trace analysis have been given by Cooke (17) and Delahay (22). The techniques of anodic-stripping voltammetry, among others, offer particular advantages in trace work, but these are discussed in other chapters of the Treatise.

C. CHRONOPOTENTIOMETRY AT SOLID ELECTRODES

The techniques of chronopotentiometry are fully covered in Chapter 44. An increasing awareness of the utility of chronopotentiometry at platinum and gold electrodes has developed recently, particularly in the area of organic oxidations, and only a brief mention of these will be made. A survey of the oxidations of aromatic amines, phenols, etc., indicated a wide range of applicability (2). Important contributions in this area have been made by Elving and Krivis (31) and by Voorhies and Furman (108,-109). Voorhies and Parsons have examined the chronopotentiometry of important dye intermediates with a view toward routine analysis (110). Kuwana and his co-workers have recently studied a variety of ferrocene derivatives in acetonitrile (14). The application of solid-electrode chronopotentiometry in nonaqueous media is particularly attractive.

D. FUSED-SALT VOLTAMMETRY

The fundamental polarography of fused-salt systems is the same as that of aqueous solutions, but the experimental techniques require a much greater degree of sophistication and are fraught with many practical difficulties. A detailed treatment of the techniques is beyond the scope of this section, and only a review of pertinent studies will be attempted.

TABLE 47.VI
Inorganic Reactions at Solid Electrodes[a]

No.	Electro-active species	Background electrolyte	Electrode	Type scan	$E_{1/2}$, $E_{p/2}$, or $E_{1/4}$ (v. vs. S.C.E.)	Reference
1	Ag(I)	0.1M KNO₃	W.I.G.E. (stirred)	E, 74.4 mv./min.	+0.21	(34)
		0.2M H₂SO₄	Pt (quiet)	E, 37	0.39	(72)
			Au (quiet)	E, 37	0.29	(72)
2	Pb(II)	0.1M KCl	W.I.G.E. (stirred)	E, 74.4	−0.61	(34)
		0.1M NaOH	R.P.E.	E, 222	+0.49 (anodic)	(52)
3	Zn(II)	0.1M NaOH	B₄C (quiet)	E, 200	−1.52	(83)
4	Cr(VI)	1M HClO₄	R.AuE.	E, 222	+0.674	(6)
5	Fe(II)	1M HCl	B₄C (quiet)	i, 3.7 μamp./min.	0.480	(82)
				E, 200	0.456	(82)
		0.1M HCl	R.P.E.	E, 37	0.484	(72)
6	I⁻	0.5M KCl	R.P.E.	E, 0.1–1 v./sec.	0.47, 0.75	(100)
		0.1M KNO₃	R.P.E.	E, 0.1–1 v./sec.	0.47	(100)
		1M H₂SO₄	R.P.E.	E,	0.50	(49)
			Pt for 1 (quiet)	Chrono	0.52	(2)
			B₄C (quiet)	E, 200	0.50	(82)
7	Fe(CN)₆⁻⁴	0.1M NaOH	R.P.E.	E, 0.1–1 v./sec.	0.26	(100)
		1M KCl	C.P.E. (quiet)	E, 200	0.21	(83)
		0.5M KCl	W.I.G.E. (quiet)	E, 74.4	0.21	(81)
			B₄C (quiet)	E, 200	0.19	(83)
8	Fe(CN)₆⁻³	0.5M KCl	W.I.G.E. (quiet)	E, 74.4	0.22	(81)
			B₄C (quiet)	E, 200	0.225	(83)
9	MnO₄⁻	1M H₂SO₄	R.P.E.	E,	0.82	(49)
10	Ce(IV)	1M H₂SO₄	R.P.E.	E	0.85	(49)

[a] Key to abbreviations: R.P.E., rotating platinum electrode; W.I.G.E., wax-impregnated graphite electrode; R.AuE., rotating gold electrode; B₄C, boron carbide electrode; C.P.E., carbon paste electrode (bromonaphthalene paste); E, voltage-scan measurement; i, current-scan measurement; and Chrono, chronopotentiometric measurement.

TABLE 47.VII

Organic Reactions at Solid Electrodes[a]

No.	Electroactive species	Background electrolyte	Electrolyte	Type scan	$E_{1/2}$, $E_{p/2}$, or $E_{1/4}$ (v. vs. S.C.E.)	Reference
A. Phenols						
1	Phenol	Buffer, pH 5.2	W.I.G.E.	E, 74.4	0.711	(34)
		Buffer, pH 9.0	Pt (quiet)	E, 200	0.515	(39)
2	p-tert-Butylphenol	Buffer, pH 9.0	Pt (quiet)	E, 200	0.41	(39)
3	Hydroquinone	Buffer, pH 5.2	W.I.G.E. (quiet)	E, 74.4	0.178	(34)
		Buffer, pH 5.5		Chrono	0.145	(31)
4	Resorcinol	Buffer, pH 5.2	W.I.G.E. (quiet)	E, 74.4	0.652	(34)
5	Catechol	Buffer, pH 5.2	W.I.G.E. (quiet)	E, 74.4	0.275	(34)
6	p-Aminophenol	Buffer, pH 11	Pt (quiet)	E, 20–40	0.124	(47)
7	N-n-butyl-p-amino-phenol	Buffer, pH 5.2	W.I.G.E. (quiet)	E, 74.4	0.170	(34)
B. Amines, Diamines						
8	p-Phenylenediamine	Buffer, pH 5.2	W.I.G.E. (quiet)	E, 74.4	0.212	(34)
		Acetonitrile, 0.1M LiClO₄	R.P.E.	i, 0	0.23	(90)
			Pt (quiet)	Chrono	0.40	(55)
9	N,N-Dimethyl-p-phenyl-enediamine	Buffer, pH 2.5	C.P.E. (quiet)	E, 200	0.45	(89)
		Buffer, pH 2.4	M.C.F.A. (quiet)	E, 400	0.46	(55)
		Buffer, pH 2.5	B₄C (quiet)	E, 200	0.39	(82)
		Acetonitrile, 0.1M LiClO₄	Pt (quiet)	Chrono	0.40	(55)
10	p-Hydroxydiphenylamine	Buffer, pH 4.4	C.P.E. (quiet)	E, 200	0.22	(89)

11	o-Dianisidine	Buffer, pH 2.4	C.P.E. (quiet)	E, 200	0.46	(89)
		1M H₂SO₄	B₄C (quiet)	E, 200	0.59	(83)
			Pt (quiet)	A.-c. polarograph	0.59	(111)
12	o-Tolidine	Buffer, pH 2.5	C.P.E. (quiet)	E, 200	0.51	(89)
			R.P.E.	i, 0	0.48	(90)
13	1-Naphthylamine	Buffer, pH 1.2	Pt (quiet)	Chrono	0.68	(2)
		Buffer, pH 9.0	Pt (quiet)	Chrono	0.50	(2)
14	Leuco crystal violet	Buffer, pH 1.1	R.P.E.	E, 200	0.824	(3)
	C. Sulfur compounds					
15	2-Thiabutane	Methanol–nitrobenzene–HCl	Pt (quiet)	E,	0.82 (E_p)	(30)
16	2-Mercaptobenzothiazole	Buffer, pH 10.4	Pt (quiet)	Chrono	0.60	(110)
	D. Miscellaneous					
17	Anthracene	Acetonitrile, 0.1M NaClO₄	Pt (quiet)	Chrono	1.2	(109)
		Acetonitrile, 0.1M LiClO₄			1.18	(55)
		Acetonitrile, 0.1M NaClO₄	Pt (vibrating)	E, 200	0.84 (vs. Ag/Ag⁺)	(73)
18	Furfuryl alcohol	Acetonitrile, 0.1M NaClO₄	Pt (vibrating)	E, 200	1.33 (vs. Ag/Ag⁺)	(73)
19	8-Hydroxyquinoline	Buffer, pH 2	B₄C (quiet)	E, 200	-1.16 (red'n.)	(82)

ᵃ Key to abbreviations: R.P.E., rotating platinum electrode; W.I.G.E., wax-impregnated graphite electrode; B₄C, boron carbide electrode; C.P.E., carbon paste electrode (bromonaphthalene paste); M.C.F.A., mercury chloride film anode; E, voltage-scan measurement; i, current-scan measurement; and Chrono, chronopotentiometric measurement.

Russian workers have pioneered fused-salt investigations since the 1940's. The group led by Delimarskii has contributed some 30 or more publications over this period. Reviews of this and other fused-salt work have been given by Delimarskii (23–25). The latter two reviews (24,25) summarize work on metal–metal ion electrode potentials or molten-salt systems and describe suitable reference half cells. Work in the United States using solid electrodes has been carried out mainly by Laitinen and his co-workers (58–60,62,63).

A wide variety of molten systems have been examined, with alkali halide eutectics perhaps most popular. Considerable care must be taken to remove traces of moisture from molten halide solvents (59). Molten mixtures of aluminum chloride with other alkali halides (15,28), nitrate mixtures (27), and fused borax (26) are among some of the systems reported.

Relatively conventional rotating or stationary wire electrodes have been used by most investigators. A serious disadvantage is the lack of good electrode materials, as pointed out by Laitinen et al. (63). Platinum, graphite, and tungsten have been widely used. An interesting "bubble" electrode was developed by Lyalikov and his co-workers (74,75). A platinum wire, dipping into the fused bath, is surrounded by an open-end glass mantle. A stream of nitrogen is slowly bubbled through the mantle and over the wire, causing the electrode to be alternately bathed and shielded from the solution. Although the advantages of this electrode system are somewhat obscure, Lyalikov reported very good results using it.

Reference electrodes have been a serious problem in molten-salt work. Flengas and Ingraham use a silver–silver chloride reference built like a conventional salt-bridge half cell (32). Bockris and his co-workers developed a silver wire immersed in about a 1% silver chloride solution in the particular eutectic melt. This reference electrode is contained in a tube with a simple glass membrance blown on the end (9). Laitinen et al. prefer a reference consisting of a platinum electrode in equilibrium with a dilute solution of Pt(II) dissolved in the molten salt. The reference system is a separate compartment of the cell.

One of the most promising new adventures in fused-salt work is the application of chronopotentiometry at platinum electrodes. The method has certain distinct advantages over slow-voltage sweep techniques, according to Laitinen and his co-workers (58,60). Thus, mass transport during the short electrolysis time can be rigidly controlled within the regime of linear diffusion. Furthermore, the amounts of metals deposited are so small as to cause very little surface build-up on the electrode. The latter effect is often a serious interference in obtaining smooth polarograms. In addition, the measurement of diffusion coefficients is very easily carried out by chronopotentiometry.

E. SELECTED VOLTAMMETRIC DATA AT SOLID ELECTRODES

Tables 47.VI and 47.VII of half-wave potentials have been compiled from literature data. They represent only a small part of the total number of materials studied and are intended only to indicate the scope of solid electrode applications. Data for mercury-type electrodes have not been included since the half-wave potentials, in general, can be estimated from corresponding studies at the D.M.E. The types of measurement are included in the tables, but the original literature should be consulted for details. Under the heading "Electrode," the solution conditions (quiet or stirred) are indicated unless the electrode designation indicates this (i.e., R.P.E.). The following abbreviations apply to the tables:

R.P.E.	Rotating platinum electrode
W.I.G.E.	Wax-impregnated graphite electrode
R.AuE.	Rotating gold electrode
B_4C	Boron carbide electrode
C.P.E.	Carbon paste electrode (bromonaphthalene paste)
M.C.F.A.	Mercury chloride film anode
E	Voltage-scan measurement
i	Current-scan measurement
Chrono	Chronopotentiometric measurement

All scan rates are given in millivolts per minute, unless otherwise noted. All potentials are referred to the S.C.E., except for a few nonaqueous systems, which are indicated.

Whereas these tables, as mentioned, contain only a very few of the compounds that have been examined at solid electrodes, an attempt has been made to select substances that have been studied by more than one investigator or that were polarographed at several types of electrodes.

REFERENCES

1. Adams, R. N., *Anal. Chem.*, **30**, 1576 (1959).
2. Adams, R. N., J. H. McClure, and J. B. Morris, *Anal. Chem.*, **30**, 471 (1958).
3. Allen, M. J., and V. J. Powell, *Trans. Faraday Soc.*, **50**, 1244 (1954).
4. Anson, F., and J. J. Lingane, *J. Am. Chem. Soc.*, **79**, 4901 (1957).
5. Arthur, P., J. C. Komyathy, R. F. Maness, and H. W. Vaughan, *Anal. Chem.*, **27**, 895 (1955).
6. Bauman, F., and I. Shain, *Anal. Chem.*, **29**, 303 (1957).
7. Bergman, I., and J. C. James, *Trans. Faraday Soc.*, **50**, 60 (1954).
7a. Bircumshaw, B. L., and A. C. Riddiford, *Quart. Rev.*, **6**, 157 (1952).
8. Berzins, T., and P. Delahay, *J. Am. Chem. Soc.*, **75**, 555 (1953).
9. Bockris, J. O'M., G. Hills, D. Inman, and L. Young, *J. Sci. Instr.*, **33**, 438 (1956).
10. Booman, G. L., E. Morgan, and A. L. Crittenden, *J. Am. Chem. Soc.*, **78**, 5533 (1956).
11. Bowers, R. C., personal communication (1959).

12. Bowers, R. C., and A. M. Wilson, *J. Am. Chem. Soc.*, **80**, 2968 (1958); **81**, 1840 (1950).
13. Bowers, R. C., A. M. Wilson, and C. Maggert, Abstracts, Am. Chem. Soc. Meeting, San Francisco, April 13–18, 1958.
14. Bublitz, D. E., G. Hoh, and T. Kuwana, *Chem. and Ind.*, **1959**, 635.
15. Chounyk, N. G., *Doklady Akad. Nauk S.S.S.R.*, **87**, 1033 (1952); through *Chem. Abstr.*, **47**, 6793 (1953).
16. Cooke, W. D., *Anal. Chem.*, **25**, 215 (1953).
17. Cooke, W. D., in *Physical Methods in Chemical Analysis*, W. G. Berl, Ed., Academic Press, New York, 1956, Vol. III.
18. Delahay, P., *Disc. Faraday Soc.*, **17**, 205 (1954).
19. Delahay, P., *New Instrumental Methods in Electrochemistry*, Interscience, New York–London, 1954.
20. *Ibid.*, p. 142.
21. *Ibid.*, pp. 235–236.
22. Delahay, P., "Polarography and Voltammetry," in J. Yoe and H. S. Koch, Eds., *Trace Analysis*, Wiley, New York, 1957.
23. Delimarskii, Y. K., *Ukrain. Khim. Zhur.*, **16**, 414 (1950); through *Chem. Abstr.*, **48**, 473b (1954).
24. Delimarskii, Y. K., *Uspekhi Khim.*, **23**, 766 (1954); through *Chem. Abstr.*, **49**, 1444e (1955).
25. Delimarskii, Y. K., *Zhur. Fiz. Khim.*, **29**, 28 (1955); through *Chem. Abstr.*, **49**, 8713c (1955).
26. Delimarskii, Y. K., and K. M. Kalabalina, *Ukrain. Khim. Zhur.*, **23**, 584 (1957); through *Chem. Abstr.*, **52**, 6081i (1958).
27. Delimarskii, Y. K., and I. D. Panchenko, *Doklady Akad. Nauk S.S.S.R.*, **91**, 115 (1953); through *Chem. Abstr.*, **49**, 8012 (1955).
28. Delimarskii, Y. K., E. M. Skobets, and L. S. Berenblyum, *Zhur. Fiz. Khim.*, **22**, 1108 (1948); through *Chem. Abstr.*, **43**, 8914d (1949).
29. Dirscherl, W., and K. Oho, *Leybold Polarograph. Ber.*, **1**, 49 (1953).
30. Drushel, H. V., and J. F. Miller, *Anal. Chem.*, **29**, 1956 (1957).
31. Elving, P. J., and A. F. Krivis, *Anal. Chem.*, **30**, 1645, 1648 (1958).
32. Flengas, S. N., and T. R. Ingraham, *Can. J. Chem.*, **35**, 1139, 1254 (1957).
33. Fox, I., R. W. Taft, and J. M. Schempf, private communication.
33a. Galus, G., C. Olson, H. Y. Lee, and R. N. Adams, *Anal. Chem.*, **34**, 164 (1962).
34. Gaylor, V. F., A. L. Conrad, and J. H. Landerl, *Anal. Chem.*, **29**, 224 (1957).
35. Gaylor, V. F., A. L. Conrad, and J. H. Landerl, *Anal. Chem.*, **29**, 228 (1957).
36. Gerischer, H., *Z. Physik. Chem.*, **202**, 302 (1953).
37. Gibbs, O. W., *Z. anal. Chem.*, **22**, 558 (1883).
37a. Gregory, D. P., and A. C. Riddiford, *J. Chem. Soc.*, **1956**, 3756.
38. Harris, E. D., and A. J. Lindsay, *Analyst*, **76**, 647, 650 (1951).
39. Hedenburg, J. F., and H. Freiser, *Anal. Chem.*, **25**, 1355 (1953).
40. Heyrovský, J., *Polarographie*, Springer, Vienna, 1941.
41. Heyrovský, J., and J. Forejt, *Z. Physik. Chem.*, **193**, 77 (1943).
41a. Ibl, N., *Electrochim. Acta*, **1**, 177 (1959).
42. Ibl, N., K. Buob, and G. Trumpler, *Helv. Chim. Acta*, **37**, 2251 (1954).
43. Javick, R. A., Ph.D. thesis, Penn. State Univ., 1958.
44. Jordan, J., *Anal. Chem.*, **27**, 1708 (1955); J. Jordan and R. A. Javick, *Electrochim. Acta*, **6**, 23 (1962).

44a. Jordan, J., R. A. Javick, and W. E. Ranz, *J. Am. Chem. Soc.*, **80**, 3846 (1958).
45. Jordan, J., and L. R. Jiminez, private communication.
46. Jordan, J., and L. R. Jiminez, unpublished data.
47. Julian, D. R., and W. R. Ruby, *J. Am. Chem. Soc.*, **72**, 4719 (1950).
48. Karaoglanoff, Z., *Z. Elektrochem.*, **12**, 5 (1906).
49. Kolthoff, I. M., and J. Jordan, *Anal. Chem.*, **25**, 1355 (1953).
50. Kolthoff, I. M., and J. Jordan, *J. Am. Chem. Soc.*, **75**, 4869 (1953).
51. Kolthoff, I. M., and J. Jordan, *J. Am. Chem. Soc.*, **76**, 3843 (1954).
52. Kolthoff, I. M., J. Jordan, and A. Heyndricky, *Anal. Chem.*, **25**, 884 (1953).
53. Kolthoff, I. M., and J. J. Lingane, *Polarography*, 2nd ed., Interscience, New York, 1952, Vol. I.
53a. Kolthoff, I. M., and Sambucetti, C. J., *Anal. Chim. Acta*, **21**, 17 (1959).
54. Kolthoff, I. M., and N. Tanaka, *Anal. Chem.*, **26**, 632 (1954).
54a. Kraichman, M. B., and E. A. Hogge, *J. Phys. Chem.*, **59**, 986 (1955).
55. Kuwana, T., Ph.D. thesis, Univ. of Kansas, 1959.
56. Kuwana, T., and R. N. Adams, *Anal. Chim. Acta*, **20**, 51, 60 (1959).
57. Kuwana, T., and R. N. Adams, *J. Am. Chem. Soc.*, **79**, 3609 (1957).
58. Laitinen, H. A., and W. S. Ferguson, *Anal. Chem.*, **29**, 4 (1957).
59. Laitinen, H. A., W. S. Ferguson, and R. A. Osteryoung, *J. Electrochem. Soc.*, **104**, 516 (1957).
60. Laitinen, H. A., and H. C. Gaur, *Anal. Chim. Acta*, **18**, 1 (1958).
61. Laitinen, H. A., and I. M. Kolthoff, *J. Phys. Chem.*, **45**, 1061, 1079 (1941).
62. Laitinen, H. A., and C. H. Liu, *J. Am. Chem. Soc.*, **80**, 1015 (1958).
63. Laitinen, H. A., C. H. Liu, and W. S. Ferguson, *Anal. Chem.*, **30**, 1266 (1958).
64. Langer, A., *Anal. Chem.*, **28**, 426 (1956).
65. Le Blanc, M., *Z. Physik. Chem.*, **12**, 333 (1893).
66. Lee, J. K., *Diss. Abstr.*, **16**, 249 (1956).
67. Lee, J. K., R. N. Adams, and C. E. Bricker, *Anal. Chim. Acta*, **17**, 321 (1957).
68. Lee, T. S., *J. Am. Chem. Soc.*, **74**, 5001 (1952).
69. Leveque, P., *J. Chim. Phys.*, **49**, 269 (1952).
69a. Levich, V. G., *Acta Physicochim.*, **17**, 257 (1942).
70. Levich, B., *Disc. Faraday Soc.*, **1**, 37 (1947).
70a. Levich, V. G., *Fiziko-khimicheskaya gidrodinamika* (*Physico-Chemical Hydrodynamics*), Godudarstvennoe, Izdatel'stvo Fizikomatematicheskoi Literatury, Moscow, 1959.
71. Lindsay, A. J., and E. D. Harris, *Anal. Chim. Acta*, **13**, 200 (1955).
72. Lord, S. S., and L. B. Rogers, *Anal. Chem.*, **26**, 284 (1954).
73. Lund, H., *Acta. Chem. Scand.*, **11**, 491, 1323 (1957).
74. Lyalikov, Y. S., and R. I. Glaser, *Zavodskaya Lab.*, **15**, 909 (1949); through *Chem. Abstr.*, **44**, 956e (1950).
75. Lyalikov, Y. S., and V. I. Karmazin, *Zavodskaya Lab.*, **14**, 138 (1948); through *Chem. Abstr.*, **43**, 8946i (1949).
76. Lydersen, D., *Acta. Chem. Scand.*, **3**, 259 (1949).
77. Macero, D. J., and C. L. Rulfs, *J. Am. Chem. Soc.*, **81**, 2942 (1959).
78. Marple, T. L., and L. B. Rogers, *Anal. Chem.*, **25**, 1351 (1953).
79. Milner, G. W. C., *The Principles and Applications of Polarography and Other Electroanalytical Processes*, Longmans, Green, London, 1957.
80. Mong, F. M., and A. Timnick, Abstracts, Pittsburgh Conf. on Analytical Chemistry, March 3–7, 1958.

81. Morris, J. B., and J. M. Schempf, *Anal. Chem.*, **31**, 286 (1959).

82. Mueller, T. R., and R. N. Adams, *Anal. Chim. Acta.*, **25**, 482 (1961).

83. Mueller, T. R., C. E. Olson, and R. N. Adams, in *Advances in Polarography*, I. S. Longmuir, Ed., Pergamon Press, London, 1960, p. 198.

84. Müller, O. H., *The Polarographic Method of Analysis*, 2nd ed., Mack Printing Co. Easton, Pa., 1951.

85. Nernst, W., and E. S. Merriam, *Z. physik. Chem.*, **53**, 235 (1905).

85a. Newson, J. D., and A. C. Riddiford, *J. Electrochem. Soc.*, **108**, 695 (1961).

86. Nicholson, M. M., *Anal. Chem.*, **31**, 128 (1959).

87. Nicholson, M. M., *J. Am. Chem. Soc.*, **76**, 2539 (1954).

88. Oehme, F., and D. Noack, *Chem. Tech. (Berlin)*, **1**, 270 (1955).

89. Olson, C. E., and R. N. Adams, unpublished data.

90. Parker, R. E., and R. N. Adams, *Anal. Chem.*, **28**, 828 (1956).

91. Peurifoy, P. V., and W. G. Schrenk, *Anal. Chem.*, **29**, 410 (1957).

92. Randles, J. E. B., *Analyst*, **72**, 301 (1947).

93. Reilley, C. N., G. S. Everett, and R. H. Johns, *Anal. Chem.*, **27**, 483 (1955).

94. Roberts, E. R., and A. J. Lindsay, *Analyst*, **76**, 647, 650 (1951).

95. Rosie, D. J., and W. D. Cooke, *Anal. Chem.*, **29**, 410 (1957).

96. Ross, J. W., R. D. DeMars, and I. Shain, *Anal. Chem.*, **28**, 1768 (1956).

97. Sand, H. J. S., *Phil. Mag.*, **1**, 45 (1901).

97a. Sawyer, D. T., R. S. George, and R. C. Rhodes, *Anal. Chem.*, **31**, 2 (1959).

98. Semerano, G., *Il Polarografa, Sua Theoria e Applicazioni*, A. Draghi, Padova, 1933.

99. Sevcik, A., *Collection Czechoslov. Chem. Communs.*, **13**, 349 (1948).

100. Shain, I., and A. L. Crittenden, *Anal. Chem.*, **26**, 281 (1954).

101. Skobets, E. M., L. S. Berenblyum, and N. N. Atamanenko, *Zavodskaya Lab.*, **14**, 131 (1948).

102. v. Stackelberg, M., M. Pilgram, and V. Toome, *Z. Elektrochem.*, **57**, 342 (1953).

103. Streuli, C. A., and W. D. Cooke, *Anal. Chem.*, **25**, 1691 (1953).

104. Streuli, C. A., and W. D. Cooke, *Anal. Chem.*, **26**, 963 (1954).

105. Streuli, C. A., and W. D. Cooke, *Anal. Chem.*, **26**, 970 (1954).

106. Tsukamoto, T., T. Kambara, and I. Tachi, *Sbornik, Mezinarad., Polarog. Sjezdu, Praze, 1st Cong., 1951*, Pt. I, *Proc.*, **524**, 1951.

107. Volkov, G. I., and E. I. Kus'Kina, *Zhur. priklad. Khim.*, **31**, 1755 (1958).

108. Voorhies, J. D., and N. H. Furman, *Anal. Chem.*, **30**, 1656 (1958).

109. *Ibid.*, **31**, 381 (1959).

110. Voorhies, J. D., and J. S. Parsons, *Anal. Chem.*, **31**, 516 (1959).

111. Walker, D., R. N. Adams, and A. Juliard, *Anal. Chem.*, **32**, 1526 (1960).

112. Wilson, R. E., and M. A. Youtz, *Ind. Eng. Chem.*, **15**, 603 (1923).

(References not complete after 1960)

Chapter 48

ELECTRODEPOSITION

By Nobuyuki Tanaka, *Tohoku University, Sendai, Japan*

Contents

Contents (*continued*)

I. INTRODUCTION

The term electrodeposition has been used for the electrochemical reaction in which the product is insoluble in the solution phase and deposits on or in an electrode. The electrodeposition is usually carried out in an electrolysis cell, which essentially consists of two metallic electrodes immersed either in the same electrolytic solution or in two different solutions with an electrolytic contact. In this cell, a reduction takes place at one electrode, which is called the cathode, and an oxidation at the other, which is called the anode. The electrodeposition may occur at either electrode. This process is governed by many factors, depending on the conditions under which the reactions proceed.

Let us consider an electrolysis cell that consists of a platinum electrode and a silver–silver chloride electrode, and which contains a dilute solution of thallous chloride in a relatively large concentration of potassium chloride. Oxygen in the solution is completely removed because it is reduced at the electrode. With this electrolysis cell, current–potential curves are obtained for the electrodeposition of thallium as the electrode potential of the platinum electrode is varied from zero to more negative potentials. Increasingly negative potentials eventually will result in the reduction of thallous ions; the current initially increases rapidly but then levels off to a limiting value when the solution is well stirred. This phenomenon is discussed in Chapter 43.

The reduction of thallous ions results in the electrodeposition of thallium metal on the platinum electrode. This phenomenon, "electrodeposition," was the first electrochemical technique applied to chemical analysis. In 1801, Cruikshank (14) electroanalyzed solutions containing silver and copper salts, and suggested that electrodeposition could be used for the qualitative identification of these metal ions present in solutions. Electrodeposition of metals was also the first application of the electrochemistry to quantitative analysis. In the 1860's, W. Gibbs (34) electrolyzed copper solutions, using a platinum cathode, and weighed the deposit of copper metal thus obtained. This technique, termed electrogravimetry, was developed rapidly during the nineteenth century, and by the 1890's it was well established as a useful analytical method for the determination of many metals.

Although the proportionality of the metal deposited on the electrode to the quantity of electricity used was recognized by Michael Faraday in 1833, this relation was not applied to chemical analysis until 1917 (40). It has been only in the last two decades that the application of Faraday's law to electrochemical analysis has been extensively investigated and well established under the name of "coulometry." Szebelledy and Somogyi (111), Lingane (77), Swift, Furman, and many other analytical chemists were involved in the development of the method. The technique of coulometry is discussed in Chapter 49 of this volume as well as in other reviews (17,80).

The limiting current on the current–potential curve is proportional to the concentration of the electroreducible metal ions present in the solution, provided the electrodeposition is carried out under proper conditions. This phenomenon was first applied to chemical analysis by the technique of polarography, which Heyrovský and his co-workers originally developed in the 1920's and from which voltammetry and other electroanalytical methods originated. For discussions of polarography and voltammetry the reader is referred to Chapters 46 and 47, as well as to other excellent publications (17,50,62,80,92,110).

Although electrogravimetry had been established as one of the most useful analytical methods for metals, it was often found to be difficult to apply when the solution contained several electroreducible metal ions, and there is a possiblity of simultaneous deposition of several metals. This difficulty has been overcome by maintaining the cathode at a potential at which the deposition of only one of the several metals takes place. This method is called "controlled-potential electrolysis" and has tremendous advantages over conventional electrolysis. The method was introduced by Sand (104) and Fischer (23) in 1907, but the manual operation of controlling the electrode potential was so laborious that the method was not widely used until the automatic potential-control device, the potentiostat, was invented. The adoption of the controlled-potential electrolysis technique increased to a great extent the usefulness of electrogravimetric methods and electrolytic separation in chemical analysis.

In this chapter, the electrodeposition of metals is considered from both theoretical and practical standpoints. The mechanism of the electrodeposition process is discussed in terms of electrode kinetics and electronic configurations of metal ions. Emphasis is given to the consideration of the electrode reactions of complex ions because metals are deposited, in most cases, from complexes rather than from simple or hydrated ions. Metal deposition from complex ions at the dropping mercury electrode is briefly discussed, and some typical examples of reaction mechanisms are presented. Recent advances in coordination chemistry are more or less taken into consideration for the interpretation of electrodeposition from complex ions.

Consideration of the kinetics of metal-deposition processes is followed by a discussion of the separation of metal ions by electrodeposition. Because of the increasing application of electrodeposition techniques to the separation of radioisotopes, consideration of the validity of the Nernst equation in the extremely dilute solutions employed in such cases is included. As for controlled-potential electrolysis, the principle is presented briefly but descriptions of the apparatus and the procedure are almost completely omitted. The selectivity of electrode reactions, the effects of pH, complex-forming substances, and surface-active substances also are discussed in connection with the controlled-potential technique.

In the section on electrogravimetric analysis, the discussion is centered on the relationship of the conditions of electrolysis to the physical properties of metal deposits. This subject, as well as that of controlled-potential electrolysis, has been discussed extensively by Lingane (80). The last two subjects dealt with in this chapter are internal electrolysis and electrography, of which only the principles are presented.

Readers who are interested in further discussion of the theoretical considerations of electrode processes may consult the monographs by Kortüm (63), by Delahay (17), and by Vetter (127). For further information on controlled-potential electrolysis and electrogravimetric analysis, the reader should refer to the monograph by Lingane (80).

The values of oxidation-reduction potentials that may be needed in the investigation of electrodeposition have been compiled by Latimer (71), and also by Charlot and his co-workers under the auspices of the International Union of Pure and Applied Chemistry (8).

II. ELECTRODE PROCESSES IN ELECTRODEPOSITION
A. TRANSFER OF IONS TO THE ELECTRODE SURFACE

In general, three processes may be considered for the transfer of ions to the electrode surface: (1) diffusion, (2) convection, and (3) electrolytic migration. Convection usually results from mechanical stirring. When an electrode reaction occurs in a stirred solution, the rate of transport (and hence the current) is not determined by convective transport alone, because an unstirred layer is considered to exist on the surface and ions must diffuse through this layer to reach the electrode. Transport by electrolytic migration is usually eliminated in electrodeposition by the addition of an excess of indifferent electrolyte. In an unstirred solution containing a large excess of indifferent electrolyte, the transfer of ions to the electrode is controlled by diffusion. The rate of electrodeposition will then be governed by the rate of diffusion, unless the electron-transfer process is rate-determining. An excellent discussion on the transport of ions is given by Kolthoff and Lingane (62) and by Delahay and his co-workers (17). The subject is also discussed in Chapter 42 of this volume.

B. POTENTIAL-ENERGY DIAGRAMS

The electrodeposition and the electrodissolution of a metal may be discussed from the standpoint of the energy variation of a metal ion in the region between the surface of the metal and a neighboring water molecule or molecules (5,41,99). The potential-energy diagram given in Fig. 48.1a represents the variation of the energy of a metal ion near the metal surface. The energy of the isolated ion $in\ vacuo$ is shown by the horizontal line, CC, and the energy that is lost when the ion is bound to the surface at an equilibrium distance d from the surface is denoted by $U_m{}^\circ$. The lowest horizontal line, AA, represents the energy of the ion at the ground state, and the other lines represent those at higher energy states.

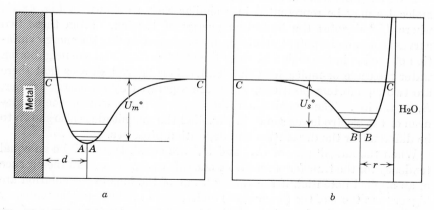

Fig. 48.1. Potential energy – distance diagrams of a metal ion at the surface of a metal (a) and in the hydrated state (b).

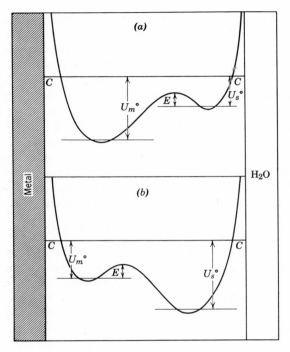

Fig. 48.2. Potential energy – distance diagrams of a metal ion in the region between the metal and the neighboring water molecule or molecules.

The energy of an ion in the vicinity of a water molecule or group of water molecules may be represented in a similar way, as shown in Fig. 48.1b, where U_s° denotes the hydration energy of the ion. From these two curves is obtained a potential-energy diagram representing the energy variation of the ion in the region between the metal surface and the neighboring water molecule or molecules (Fig. 48.2). This figure indicates that there are two equilibrium positions, which are separated by an energy barrier, E, for the ion. The magnitude of the barrier is dependent on the mechanism of the electrode reaction; in Fig. 48.2 the magnitude is also shown to be different for the dissolution and deposition processes.

When the magnitudes of U_m° and U_s° are equal, there will be an equal tendency for the transfer of ions from one side to the other. In the absence of an applied potential, if the energy levels of the ions in the solution are higher than those of the (uncharged) metal, there will be a greater tendency for ions to transfer from the solution to the metal than vice versa (Fig. 48.2a). Spontaneous transfer of ions will take place from the solution to the metal surface, provided the ions can pass over the energy barrier between them. The height of the barrier determines the activation energy of the process and consequently the rate of the transfer of ions. In many cases, when reversible electrodes are involved, this energy barrier is considered to be negligible, but in other cases it may limit the rate of the ion transfer, and the electrode process is then called "irreversible." If, as shown in Fig. 48.2a, the number of positive ions that are deposited on the metal surface exceeds the number of ions that leave the metal surface, a positive charge will accumulate on the surface of the metal that retards and finally stops further deposition of the positive ions on the metal surface. In electrodeposition, therefore, this accumulation of positive charge must be eliminated. This may be accomplished, as has been pointed out in Chapter 42, by applying a potential to the metal electrode that maintains a potential-energy curve favorable to the deposition process.

The potential diagram given in Fig. 48.2b indicates the reverse situation, where the energy levels of ions on the metal surface are higher than those in the solution. The rate of transfer of positive ions from the metal to the solution is greater than that in the opposite direction, and, therefore, a negative charge will accumulate on the metal surface until the depths of both potential-energy valleys become equal. If metal is to be dissolved from the electrode, a larger positive potential must be imposed on the electrode, so that the energy level of the metal is higher than that of the ions in the solution.

C. CONSIDERATION OF THE KINETICS OF ELECTRODE PROCESSES

1. General Considerations

Let us consider the simplest case of a first-order electrodeposition of the type:

$$M^{+n} + ne^- \rightleftharpoons M \tag{A}$$

From the discussion in the previous section, it can be said that the corresponding transfer of metal ions through an electrical double layer takes place simultaneously in both directions, from the metal to the solution and vice versa. The rates of these processes are represented in terms of the cathodic partial current, i_c ($i_c > 0$), and the anodic partial current, i_a ($i_a < 0$),[*] the directions of which are shown in Fig. 48.3 (126). The magnitudes of the cathodic and the anodic partial currents depend on the electrode potential, E (2). With increasingly positive potentials, $|i_a|$ becomes greater, whereas $|i_c|$ becomes smaller. The net rate of the charge-transfer

---

[*] The sign of current accords with that in conventional polarography.

process is obtained by combining the rates of the forward and backward reactions. Since the rates of both reactions are represented by the cathodic and the anodic partial current, respectively, the total current, i, is given by the algebraic sum

$$i = i_c + i_a \tag{1}$$

The magnitudes of i_c and i_a depend on the concentrations of metal ions involved and also on the potential difference at the electrode–solution interface. The expressions of i_c and i_a for reaction (A) can be obtained by applying the usual kinetic principle (17,22,29,126; also Chapter 42).

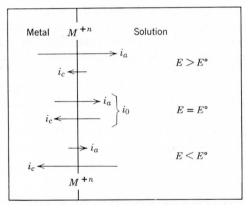

Fig. 48.3. Qualitative representation of the direction and magnitude of the charge transfer as a function of electrode potential (126).

Introducing the electrode potential, E (relative to the N.H.E.), the net current, i, is represented as follows:

$$i = nFA \left\{ k_f^\circ C_{M^{+n}}^\circ \exp\left[- (\alpha nF/RT)E \right] - \right.$$

$$\left. k_b^\circ C_M^\circ \exp\left[\frac{(1 - \alpha)nF}{RT} E \right] \right\} \tag{2}$$

where $C_{M^{+n}}^\circ$ = the concentration of metal ions at the solution interface, in moles/cm.³; C_M° = the concentration of metal atoms at the metal interface, in moles/cm.³; k_f° and k_b° = rate constants for the cathodic (forward) and anodic (backward) reactions; A = the area of the electrode, in cm.²; and α = the transfer coefficient, which has values ranging from 0 to 1.

At the equilibrium potential, $E = E_{eq.}$, currents in both directions are identical; that is,

$$i_c = i_a = i_0 \tag{3}$$

where i_0 is the so-called exchange current, which is one of the important measures of the kinetics of the charge-transfer reaction. In the system with the bulk concentrations, $C_{M^{+n}}$ and C_M, the exchange current at the equilibrium potential, $E_{eq.}$, is given by Gerischer and Tischer (32) as:

$$\begin{aligned} i_0 &= nFA\overset{\circ}{k_f}C_{M^{+n}} \exp\left[-(\alpha nF/RT)E_{eq.}\right] \\ &= nFA\ \overset{\circ}{k_b}C_M \exp\{[(1-\alpha)nF/RT]E_{eq.}\} \end{aligned} \tag{4}$$

If, for the sake of simplicity, concentrations are used instead of activities for the standard state, $^{\circ}C_M = {}^{\circ}C_{M^{+n}} = {}^{\circ}\overset{\circ}{C} = 1$ mole/liter, a relationship given by equation (5) holds at the standard potential, E°:

$$nFA\ \overset{\circ}{k_f}{}^{\circ}C_{M^{+n}} \exp[-(\alpha nF/RT)\ E^{\circ}] =$$
$$nFA\ \overset{\circ}{k_b}\ {}^{\circ}C_M \exp\{[(1-\alpha)nF/RT]E^{\circ}\} = {}^{\circ}i \tag{5}$$

where $^{\circ}i$ is the standard exchange current at equilibrium conditions for the standard state. Introducing the standard exchange current, equation (2) becomes

$$i = {}^{\circ}i\left\{(C_{M^{+n}}/{}^{\circ}C)\ \exp[-(\alpha nF/RT)(E-E^{\circ})]\ - \right.$$
$$\left. (C_M/{}^{\circ}C)\ \exp\left[\frac{(1-\alpha)nF}{RT}(E-E^{\circ})\right]\right\} \tag{6}$$

In the simple case of reaction (A) we have:

$$i_0 = {}^{\circ}i(C_M/{}^{\circ}C)^{\alpha}(C_{M^{+n}}/{}^{\circ}C)^{1-\alpha} \tag{7}$$

The exchange current i_0 and the charge transfer coefficient α are, in general, measurable parameters in electrochemical reactions, including electrodepositions.

Electrode reactions are usually not as simple as that shown in reaction (A). It is generally accepted that most metal ions exist in the form of complex ions in many electrolyte solutions, and a complete picture of the electrodeposition process must include consideration of the role the complexing species plays in the electrode reaction. Even in the case of a simple ion in aqueous solution, water molecules must be involved in the reaction since the metal ion exists in the hydrated form. It is not necessarily correct, however, to assume that all water molecules coordinated to a metal ion are involved in the electrode reaction. On the contrary, it is quite likely that $(p - q)$ water molecules dissociate from the hydrated ion (with p water molecules coordinated) before the electrode reaction, which involves q molecules of water, takes place. This process is represented in the following reaction:

$$\left. \begin{array}{l} [M(H_2O)_p]^{+n} \rightleftharpoons [M(H_2O)_q]^{+n} + (p - q)H_2O \\ [M(H_2O)_q]^{+n} + ne^- \rightleftharpoons M + qH_2O \end{array} \right\} \tag{B}$$

Complications also are expected on the metal side of the electrical double layer. In the deposition of a metal the incorporation of the metal atom into the electrode surface or lattice must be considered in addition to the dehydration steps noted above. On the surface of a liquid metal the reaction may be a two-step reaction in which the first step is the formation of an adsorbed atom on the surface, and the second step is the reaction of an adsorbed atom with a "hole" in the liquid. Conversely, it may be a single-step bimolecular reaction with a hole in the surface (29).

In the case of a solid metal, the electrode surface is not uniform, and the process of incorporation of the metal atom into the electrode lattice may be even more complex. Therefore, to complete the description of the deposition process, it becomes very important to know whether a one-step or a two-step reaction takes place.

2. Electrodeposition from Complex Metal Ions

The deposition of a metal from the complex ion state may be depicted in a manner analogous to that shown by reaction (B) (27,33). Denoting the ligands (complex-forming substances) as X, we have the following reactions:

$$[MX_p]^{+n} \rightleftharpoons [MX_q]^{+n} + (p - q)X \tag{C}$$

$$[MX_q]^{+n} + ne^- \rightleftharpoons M + qX \tag{D}$$

The charge-transfer reaction of reaction (D) has the reaction order q for the ligands X. The anodic current is then represented as:

$$i_a = i_0(C_M^{\circ}/C_M)(C_X^{\circ}/C_X)^q \exp[\{(1 - \alpha)nF\}/RT]\eta \tag{8}$$

where C_X° and C_X are the surface and the bulk concentrations of ligand X, respectively, and η is the overpotential defined as $E - E_{eq.}$. The relationship that corresponds te equation (7) is:

$$i_0 = {}^{\circ}i(C_M/{}^{\circ}C)^{\alpha}(C_X/{}^{\circ}C)^{\alpha q}(C_{MXq}/{}^{\circ}C)^{1 - \alpha} \tag{9}$$

Equation (9) indicates that from the measurement of the dependence of the exchange current, i_0, on the concentration C (26), the values of ${}^{\circ}i$, α, and q can be obtained. The value of q is considered to be especially important in analysis of the mechanism of this kind of reaction.

The existence of reaction (C) makes the above treatment somewhat more complicated. Applying the mass-action law, the following relationship is obtained:

$$(C_{MXq}/^{\circ}C) = K_{p,q}(^{\circ}C/C_X)^{(p-q)}(C_{MXp}/^{\circ}C) \tag{10}$$

where $K_{p,q}$ is the dissociation constant of $MX_p{}^{+n}$, according to reaction (C). From equations (9) and (10), the relationship

$$i_0 = {}^{\circ}i(K_{p,q})^{1-\alpha}(C_M/^{\circ}C)^{\alpha}(C_{MXp}/^{\circ}C)^{1-\alpha}(C_X/^{\circ}C)^{q-p(1-\alpha)} \tag{11}$$

is obtained. Equation (11) gives

$$\left(\frac{\partial \log i_0}{\partial \log C_X}\right)_{C_M,C_{MXp}=\text{const.}} = q - p(1-\alpha) \tag{12}$$

and

$$\left(\frac{\partial \log i_0}{\partial \log C_M}\right)_{C_{MXq},C_X=\text{const.}} = \alpha \tag{13}$$

or

$$\left(\frac{\partial \log i_0}{\partial \log C_{MXp}}\right)_{C_M,C_X=\text{const.}} = 1 - \alpha \tag{14}$$

The use of equations (12) and (13) or (14) makes it possible to determine the values of α and q from the measurement of the dependence of i_0 on the concentration C_X and C_M or C_{MXp}. The value of p usually is obtained either from calculation with the formation constant of $MX_p{}^{+n}$, as found in the literature, or directly from the experiments, such as by potentiometric measurement.

D. EXPERIMENTAL METHODS FOR THE STUDY OF ELECTRODE PROCESSES

A number of methods have been reported for the study of electrode processes in electrodeposition on solid and liquid metal electrodes (17,29,63, 67). It may be said that these methods are in general based on analysis of the functions that are composed chiefly of the quantities of potential (E), current (i), and time (t).

In these functions, if time is fixed, we have a correlation between potential and current,

$$i = f(E) \qquad \text{or} \qquad E = f(i)$$

In some cases, such as electrodeposition at the dropping mercury electrode, the relation may be expressed as

$$i = f(E,t) \qquad \text{or} \qquad E = f(i,t)$$

These potential–current relationships have been used for the study of electrochemical reactions. Most classic investigations of the electrodeposition of metals have employed the technique of measuring the relation between the electrode potential and the steady-state current. This kind of methodology has been called "voltammetry" or, in the special case of the dropping mercury electrode, "polarography." These methods, to which the reader should refer, are presented in Chapters 43, 46, and 47.

The relationship between the electrode potential and the time obtained at constant current (chronopotentiometry), and that between the current and the time obtained at constant potential (chronoamperometry), also have been employed for the study of electrodeposition. The terms "galvanostatic" and "potentiostatic" have been used by European electrochemists instead of the terms "constant current" and "constant potential," respectively. The principles of the measurement of galvanostatic transients (chronopotentiometry) and that of potentiostatic transients (chronoamperometry) are discussed in Chapter 44, as well as in the literature (26,29). A "double-impulse" method, which is in fact a combination of the potentiostatic and galvanostatic methods, has been devised and applied to the study of electrodeposition, especially in the reactions in which the charge-transfer reaction is extremely fast (30). The use of these techniques (in which a net current flow occurs) for exchange-current measurements is generally dependent on the extrapolation of the data obtained back to zero time, i.e., before a net current passes and the system is in the equilibrium state.

E. TYPICAL EXAMPLES OF REACTION MECHANISMS

1. One-Step Electrodeposition from a Stable Complex

In an ammoniacal silver solution, the ionic species, $[Ag(NH_3)_2]^+$, is the most predominant form unless the concentration of ammonia is extremely low. It has been found that the ionic species involved in the charge-transfer process is also $[Ag(NH_3)_2]^+$ (128).

In general, the charge-transfer process of the silver–ammine complex is written as

$$[Ag(NH_3)_q]^+ + e^- \rightleftharpoons Ag + qNH_3 \qquad \text{(E)}$$

From equation (8), the following relationships are easily seen:

$$(i_a)_i \sim C_{\mathrm{NH_3}}{}^q \tag{15}$$

and

$$\frac{\partial \log (i_a)_i}{\partial \log C_{\mathrm{NH_3}}} = q \tag{16}$$

where $(i_a)_i$ is the initial anodic partial current. The value of $(i_a)_i$ can be calculated from the observed initial current, i_i (33). Fig. 48.4 shows an example of the application of equation (16), and the result, $q = 2$, leads to the above conclusion.

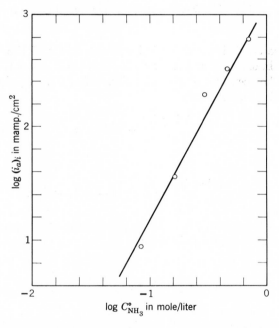

Fig. 48.4. Initial partial anodic current, $(i_a)_i$, as a function of $\mathrm{NH_3}$ concentration obtained with an $\mathrm{Ag^+}$–$\mathrm{Ag(NH_3)_2}{}^+$ system at constant electrode potential (128).

2. Two-Step Electrodeposition

It has been confirmed that the electrodeposition process from several complex ions occurs by a two-step reaction mechanism. In alkaline solution, zinc(II) exists in the form of the tetrahydroxozincate(II) ion, [Zn-(OH)$_4$]$^{-2}$. Measurements of the exchange current, i_0, at a zinc amalgam

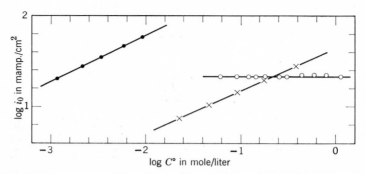

Fig. 48.5. Exchange current of a zinc amalgam–hydroxozincate(II) system obtained at varied concentrations of hydroxozincate (●), zinc metal in amalgam (✕), and OH⁻ ions (○)(27).

electrode were carried out at varied concentrations of the metal ion and hydroxyl ion in solution and at various concentrations of the metal in the amalgam. The results are shown in Fig. 48.5 (27). Applying equations (12), (13), and (14), we obtain

$$\frac{\partial \log i_0}{\partial \log C_{\mathrm{Zn}}} = 0.5 = \alpha$$

and

$$\frac{\partial \log i_0}{\partial \log C_{\mathrm{OH^-}}} = 0 = q - p(1 - \alpha)$$

As $p = 4$, $q = 2$ is obtained. The electrodeposition of zinc(II), therefore, proceeds in alkaline media as follows:

$$[\mathrm{Zn(OH)_4}]^{-2} \rightleftharpoons \mathrm{Zn(OH)_2} + 2\mathrm{OH^-}$$

$$\mathrm{Zn(OH)_2} + 2e^- \rightleftharpoons \mathrm{Zn} + 2\mathrm{OH^-}$$

A polarographic investigation gave the same result (88). A similar reaction mechanism was observed for the electrodeposition of zinc–ammine complexes (88).

In some cases, the electrodeposition proceeds along two simultaneous reaction paths. A tetracyanocadmate(II) ion, which is the most predominant species in cyanide solution, discharges through the following charge-transfer reactions:

$$[\mathrm{Cd(CN)_3}]^- + 2e^- \rightleftharpoons \mathrm{Cd} + 3\mathrm{CN^-}$$

$$[\mathrm{Cd(CN)_2}] + 2e^- \rightleftharpoons \mathrm{Cd} + 2\mathrm{CN^-}$$

The first reaction contributes predominantly to the total rate of the reaction in the higher-concentration region of cyanide ($[CN^-] > 0.1M$). In the lower-concentration region ($[CN^-] < 0.01M$), the second reaction becomes dominant (26).

In cyanide solution, zinc(II) forms a tetracyanozincate(II) ion. The electrodeposition of this species, however, was found to proceed through the intermediate $Zn(OH)_2$. This means that dihydroxozinc(II) discharges much faster than any of the cyano complexes and that, in spite of its low concentration, it contributes predominantly to the total rate of the reaction (26).

F. METAL DEPOSITION FROM COMPLEX IONS AT THE DROPPING MERCURY ELECTRODE

The electrodeposition of metals from complex ions at the dropping mercury electrode has been extensively investigated by a number of workers since the simplest case of diffusion-controlled metal deposition was interpreted by Heyrovský and Ilkovič (51). Electrodeposition in which the rate is controlled by the dissociation of the complex was first investigated by Tanaka and Tamamushi in the case of a completely labile complex (112,120). Since then, many types of electrodepositions from metal complexes have been dealt with from the theoretical standpoint, and the current–potential curves for those electrodepositions have been observed and explained (62,67,87,88).

In Table 48.I are summarized the schemes of the various electrode processes with the corresponding general equations (67). The assumptions and the meanings of the notations are as follows.

The complex ions, MX_j^{+n} ($0 \leq j \leq z$), are in equilibrium with the simple or hydrated metal ions, M^{+n}, and an excess of complex-forming substance X. The consecutive formation constant, k_j, is defined as

$$k_j = [MX_j^{+n}]/[MX_{j-1}^{+n}][X] \qquad (0 \leq j \leq z)$$

where, for simplicity, concentrations are used instead of activities. The reaction equilibrium given by

$$MX_j^{+n} \rightleftharpoons MX_{j-1}^{+n} + X$$

is perfectly labile, except for the equilibrium between MX_p and MX_{p-1}, which may be established at a limited rate of

$$MX_p^{+n} \underset{k^+}{\overset{k^-}{\rightleftharpoons}} MX_{p-1}^{+n} + X$$

TABLE 48.I

Scheme of Electrode Processes and General Equations

No.	Scheme of the electrode process[a]	General equation[b]	Examples
1	$MX_z \rightleftharpoons MX_q \overset{el}{\rightleftharpoons} M(Hg)$	$E = E° - (RT/nF) \ln i/(i_d - i)$ $\qquad - (zRT/nF) \ln [X]$ $\qquad - (RT/nF) \ln k_1 k_2 \ldots k_z$	Biplumbite ion (62,75) Cu(I)–ammine complex (62,75)
2	$MX_z \rightleftharpoons MX_q \overset{el}{\underset{k_f}{\rightharpoonup}} M(Hg)$	$i/(i_d - i) = \dfrac{0.886 k_f t_d^{1/2} D^{1/2}}{k_z k_{z-1} \ldots k_{q+1}[X]^{z-q}}$	Ni(II)–ammine complex (87)
3	$MX_z \rightleftharpoons MX_q \overset{el}{\rightleftharpoons} M(Hg)$ $\overset{k}{\rightleftharpoons} M(Hg)_{inact.}$	$E = E° - (RT/nF) \ln i/(i_d - i)$ $\qquad - (zRT/nF) \ln [X]$ $\qquad - (RT/nF) \ln k_1 \ldots k_z$ $\qquad + (RT/2nF) \ln k\, t_d$	
4	$MX_z \rightleftharpoons MX_p \overset{k^-}{\underset{k^+}{\rightleftharpoons}} MX_{p-1}$ $\overset{el_\infty}{\longrightarrow} M(Hg)$	$i_l/(i_d - i_l) = \dfrac{0.886(k\, t_d)^{1/2}}{k_z k_{z-1} \ldots k_p [X]^{n-p-0.5}}$	Cd-cyanide complex (4, 35,64) Cd–NTA complex (66, 97)
5	$M(Hg) \overset{el}{\rightleftharpoons} MX_{p-1} \overset{k^-}{\underset{k^+}{\rightleftharpoons}} MX_p$ $\rightleftharpoons MX_z$	$E = E° - (RT/nF) \ln i/(i_d - i) - (RT/nF)$ $\qquad \ln (0.886 k_1 \ldots k_{p-1})$ $\qquad - (RT/2nF) \ln k^+ t_d$ $\qquad - (RT/nF) \ln [X]^{p-0.5}$	

	Scheme	Equation	Complex
6	$MX_z \rightleftharpoons MX_p \overset{k^-}{\underset{k^+}{\rightleftharpoons}} MX_{p-1} \overset{el}{\rightleftharpoons} M(Hg)$	$E = E° - (RT/nF) \ln i/(i_l - i)$ $\quad - (RT/nF) \ln (k_1 \dots k_z[X]^z)$ $\quad - (RT/nF) \ln (i_l/i_d)$	Cd–NTA complex (65) Cd–EDTA complex (121)
7	$MX_z \rightleftharpoons MX_p \overset{k^-}{\underset{k^+}{\rightleftharpoons}} MX_{p-1}$ $\overset{el}{\rightleftharpoons} M(Hg) \overset{k}{\rightleftharpoons} M(Hg)_{inact.}$	$E = E° - (RT/nF) \ln i/(i_l - i)$ $\quad - (RT/nF) \ln (k_1 \dots k_z[X]^z)$ $\quad + (RT/2nF) \ln k\, t_d$ $\quad - (RT/nF) \ln (i_l/i_d)$	Cd–cyanide complex (64)
8	$MX_z \rightleftharpoons MX_p \overset{k^-}{\underset{k^+}{\rightleftharpoons}} MX_{p-1}$ $\rightleftharpoons MX_q \overset{el}{\underset{k_f}{\rightarrow}} M(Hg)$	$i/(i_d - i) = \dfrac{0.886 t_d^{1/2} D^{1/2} k_f}{k_z k_{z-1} \dots k_{q+1}[X]^{z-q}} (i_d/i_l)$	Cd–cyanide complex (64)
9	$MX_z \overset{MX_p \rightleftharpoons MX_{p-1} \overset{el}{\rightleftharpoons} M(Hg)}{\underset{MX_q \overset{k_f}{\nearrow}}{\rightleftharpoons}}$	$i/(i_d - i) = i_l/(i_d - i_l) + \dfrac{0.886 k_f t_d^{1/2} D^{1/2}}{k_z k_{z-1} \dots k_{q+1}[X]^{z-q}}$	Cd–NTA complex (66)

[a] The charge of the complex ion is omitted for simplicity.

[b] The notations i, i_l, and i_d indicate the average current, the average limiting current, and the average diffusion current, respectively. An exponential dependence of the electrode potential is assumed to be $k_f = k_f° \exp [-(\alpha nF/RT)E]$.

For the simplification of the mathematical treatment it is supposed that

$$1/(k^+[X]) \ll t_d$$

where t_d is the drop time of the dropping mercury electrode. To obtain a simple form of the resulting expressions, it is also assumed that

$$k_j[X] \gg 1$$

The problem is restricted, so that there are only three possibilities for the rates of the electrode reactions.

1. The rate of discharge of the complex, and that of ionization of metal followed by the formation of the same complex, are so great that during the electrolysis the concentrations of the reduced and the oxidized electroactive forms at the electrode surface are given by the Nernst equation. In Table 48.I, such a case is denoted by $\overset{el}{\rightleftharpoons}$, which corresponds to a polarographically reversible electrode reaction.

2. The ionization is incomparably slower and the rate of discharge is so great that the concentration of the electroactive form at the electrode surface falls to zero. In this case the condition for the limiting current is satisfied, and the notation $\overset{el\infty}{\rightarrow}$ is used in Table 48.I.

3. The discharge proceeds at a limited rate and the ionization can be neglected (a polarographically irreversible reaction). This case is denoted by $\overset{el}{\rightarrow}$.

For the electrode processes given in Table 48.I the following relationships are important: current vs. concentration of complex-forming substance; half-wave potential vs. concentration of complex-forming substance; half-wave potential vs. drop time; and instantaneous current vs. time.

G. ELECTRONIC CONFIGURATIONS OF IONS AND MECHANISMS OF ELECTRODEPOSITION

Electrodeposition processes for metal ions may be greatly influenced by their electronic configurations (83,129,132). For example, a hexaaquoiron(II) ion is readily electrodeposited from an aqueous solution, whereas a hexacyanoferrate(II) ion is reduced with difficulty. As is seen from the presence of four unpaired electrons indicated in the measurement of the magnetic moment, the hexaaquoiron(II) ion has an outer-electronic arrangement represented, in Pauling's sense, as follows:

$[Fe(H_2O)_6]^{+2}$

         3d   4s   4p   4d

The crosses denote the electrons donated from the coordinated water molecules. The hexacyanoferrate(II) ion, on the other hand, is known from magnetic studies to have no unpaired electron, and is given the following electronic configuration of d^2sp^3 hybrid orbitals:

$[Fe(CN)_6]^{-4}$

| $3d$ | $4s$ | $4p$ | $4d$ |

The *inner orbital complex*, $[Fe(CN)_6]^{-4}$, has much higher stability than the *outer orbital complex*, $[Fe(H_2O)_6]^{+2}$. The same situation will be found in the electrodeposition of other metal complexes. Lyons (83) classified

TABLE 48.II

Lyons' Classification of Metal Complexes According to Electronic Structure and Character of Electrodeposition from Aqueous Solutions (83)

Inner orbital complexes

No deposits obtained:[a] all complexes of Ti, Zr, Hf, V, Nb, Ta; most complexes of Cr, Mo, W; cyano complexes of Mn, Fe, Co, Ni, Ru, Rh, Pd, Os, Ir, Pt; o-phenanthroline complexes of Fe, Co, Ni, Cu, Rh, Ir, and other platinum metals; α,α'-bipyridine complexes of Fe, Co, Ni, Rh, Ir, and other platinum metals.

Deposits obtained only as amalgams: tetracyanonickelate.

Deposits obtained at low current efficiencies[b] and high activation overpotentials:[c] many complexes of the platinum metals.

Deposits obtained at high current efficiencies and low activation potentials: none.

Outer orbital complexes

No deposits obtained: Al, Be, Mg.

Deposits obtained as amalgams only: alkali metals, Ca, Sr, Ba; probably Sc, Y, lanthanide metals.

Deposits obtained only at low current efficiencies and high activation overpotentials: none.

Deposits obtained at high current efficiencies and low activation overpotentials: aquo and chloro complexes of Mn, Fe(II), Co(II), Ni, Cu(II), Zn, Cd, Hg, Ga, In, Tl, Pb, Sn; pyrophosphato complexes of Cu, Zn, Cd, Sn; ammine complexes of Ni, Cu, Ag, Zn, Cd; o-phenanthroline complexes of Zn and Cd; thiosulfato complexes of Cu and Ag; iodo complexes of Ag, Cd, and Hg; thiostannate; cyano complexes of Cu, Ag, Au, Zn, Cd, Hg, Tl, and In; hydroxo complexes of Zn and Sn; and others.

[a] Electrodeposition from certain ions, such as Cr(III) and Co(III), although it may appear to occur from an inner orbital complex, actually takes place from a lower valence state.

[b] Current efficiencies are considered high, for the purposes of this table, if they exceed about 50%.

[c] Activation overpotentials are considered low, for the purposes of this table, if they are markedly less than those commonly observed with the transition metals and the platinum group in general, i.e., if they are less than about 0.05 v.

metal complexes according to electronic structure and character of electrodeposition from aqueous solutions (Table 48.II).

The electrodeposition of the hydrated and the complex ion of a normal* metal is considered to be related to the dissociation of one or more coordinated groups from the metal ion (84). The ion formed serves as an activated intermediate and, therefore, has a coordination number that is lower than usual. It has been mentioned in the previous section that, in the electrodeposition of zinc from an alkaline solution, a $[Zn(OH)_4]^{-2}$ ion dissociates two hydroxyl groups to form an intermediate $Zn(OH)_2$, followed by the charge-transfer process from the intermediate. In many cases, such intermediates are regarded as being adsorbed onto the metal surface. Fig. 48.6 gives a schematic picture of this type of charge-transfer reaction (29).

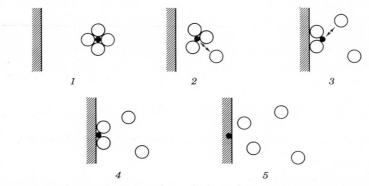

Fig. 48.6. Schematic representation of the discharge mechanism of $[Zn(OH)_4]^{-2}$ ion: processes $1 \rightarrow 2$ and $2 \rightarrow 3$ represent dissociation of ligands and formation of an activated intermediate, and process $3 \rightarrow 4$ represents the charge-transfer reaction; ● denotes Zn^{+2} and ○ is OH^{-}.

Zinc(II) is regarded as existing in the form of a tetraaquozinc(II) ion in the aqueous solution. The ion dissociates one molecule of water and forms a triaquozinc(II) ion, $[Zn(H_2O)_3]^{+2}$, which is regarded as an activated complex. The $[Zn(H_2O)_3]^{+2}$ ion may, of course, recombine with another water molecule and return to the original state or it may replace the lost coordinated group with a molecule on the aquated electrode surface. This water bridge is, then, eliminated, and a metallic bond is established. In the cases cited above, no rearrangement of the electronic configuration of the ion is required to attain the configuration of a metallic atom. This fact

* The word "normal" is used in the sense that electrode reactions are substantially reversible (after Piontelli (84)).

causes the low activation energy and, consequently, the higher reversibility of this type of reaction (84).

In the case of transition metals the mechanism is somewhat different. In many cases the transition metal ions form inner orbital complexes. Most of them are inert complexes in Taube's classification (122). This means that the dissociation mechanism cannot be applied to the electrode reactions of these complexes. A probable mechanism in this case is that the complex ion discharges at the electrode surface, dissociating no coordinated group and interacting with the electrode surface via an additional coordination, or through one of the coordinated groups to form a zero-valent complex. This, in turn, decomposes to the metal and the free ligands (130,132). One of the examples that have been thoroughly investigated is tetracyanoniccolate(0) (130).

In general, the transition metal ion in the +2 oxidation state, which has inner d-orbitals not fully occupied by electrons localized in the metal atom, is reduced through a univalent complex that is sufficiently stable to accept the second electron to form a zero-valent complex. The zero-valent complex thus formed may be reoxidized in solution or may decompose to the metal. This mechanism can be illustrated by the following scheme (130):

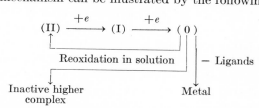

For further discussion on this subject, the papers by Vlček (129–132) should be consulted.

Transition-metal ions also form outer orbital complexes that are labile in substitution reactions. Electrodeposition of these complexes may take place by the dissociation of coordinated groups and the formation of the activated complex. In this case, however, some rearrangement of electronic configuration seems required before the charge transfer takes place. This causes higher activation energy and, consequently, irreversibility of the reaction.

The discharge process of ions at a solid electrode may be quite different from that at a liquid electrode. All surface sites of a liquid metal are, on the average, equivalent, whereas surface sites of a solid may vary in energy over a wide range. The growth of a crystal can take place only at the very few favorable surface sites at which the atom can be incorporated into the half-crystal position (13,29).

It has been confirmed experimentally that, at a solid mercury surface, the electrodeposition of mercurous ions

$$Hg_2^{+2} + 2e^- \rightleftharpoons Hg$$

proceeds by a two-step reaction mechanism in perchlorate solution. The first step is a transfer of ions to any surface sites on the crystal planes, and the second step is a transport of the ions to half-crystal positions by surface diffusion. Exchange currents measured with the double-impulse method as a function of mercurous ion concentration were not so different on liquid and the solid surfaces. In addition, the same charge-transfer coefficient, α, was obtained on both surfaces. These results indicate that the number of surface sites available for the charge-transfer reaction must be of the same order of magnitude on both the solid and the liquid mercury surfaces, and that the mechanism must not be different. A one-step mechanism, therefore, seems very improbable for the liquid mercury electrode (31).

The two-step reaction mechanism is also found in the electrodeposition and electrodissolution of silver near equilibrium condition. According to the measured exchange currents, which are of the same order of magnitude as those obtained for the mercury–mercurous ion electrode, the charge-transfer reaction is a very fast process. On the other hand, the exchange reaction between lattice atoms and adsorbed atoms has a rate that is about 1000 times smaller than that of the charge-transfer reaction. In the potential-equilibrium region, therefore, surface diffusion is considered to be a rate-determining step (28,32,91). At more negative potentials, however, the rate-determining step is attributed to the ionic-transfer process (13).

III. SEPARATION OF METAL IONS FROM SOLUTION BY ELECTRODEPOSITION—ELECTROLYSIS IN A UNIFORMLY STIRRED SOLUTION

A. CURRENT–ELECTRODE POTENTIAL CURVES

Consider the simple case of a metal electrodeposition that is represented by the equation

$$M^{+n} + ne^- \rightleftharpoons M \qquad \text{(F)}$$

or

$$M^{+n} + ne^- + Hg \rightleftharpoons M(Hg) \qquad \text{(G)}$$

where M^{+n} is the hydrated metal ion, and M and $M(Hg)$ are the corresponding metal and metal amalgam, respectively. Reactions (F) and (G) represent over-all electrode processes. Assume that reactions (F) and (G) proceed reversibly in the polarographic sense. The potential of the working electrode, E, is given by the Nernst equation, which can be derived from equation (6) for the equilibrium state:

$$E = E^\circ + \frac{RT}{nF} \ln \frac{C_{M^{+n}}^\circ}{C_M^\circ} \tag{17}$$

where C_M° and $C_{M^{+n}}^\circ$ are the concentrations of the metal and the metal ion at the electrode interface, and E° is the standard potential for reaction (F) or (G). Here concentration instead of activity is used again for the sake of simplicity.

When the metal, M, is used for the working electrode, or when an electrode of some other substance is completely covered with the metal M deposited from the solution, the value of C_M° may be assumed to be unity, and equation (17) is written as

$$E = E^\circ + (RT/nF) \ln C_{M^{+n}}^\circ \tag{18}$$

Equation (18) indicates that either an electrodeposition or an electrodissolution takes place at the working electrode unless E equals the equilibrium potential, $E_{eq.}$, which is given by the relationship

$$E_{eq.} = E^\circ + (RT/nF) \ln C_{M^{+n}} \tag{19}$$

where $C_{M^{+n}}$ is now the concentration of the metal ion in the bulk of solution, as there is no concentration polarization in this case. Assume that E is more positive than $E_{eq.}$. The value of $C_{M^{+n}}^\circ$ calculated from equation (18) is greater than the value of $C_{M^{+n}}$ in equation (19) and, consequently, an electrodissolution is taking place at the electrode surface. On the other hand, if E is more negative than $E_{eq.}$, $C_{M^{+n}}^\circ$ is smaller than $C_{M^{+n}}$ and, consequently, the electrode reaction is an electrodeposition. A current–electrode potential curve that is predicted from equation (18) is given in Fig. 48.7 (curve 1). In cases in which the charge-transfer step is kinetically limiting (17,63), equation (2) should be used instead of equation (18).

When the mercury electrode is used as a working electrode, equation (17) holds and C_M° represents the concentration of the metal at the surface of the amalgam. The current–electrode potential curve (given as curve 2 in Fig. 48.7) is obtained in this case, the characteristics of which are thoroughly discussed in Chapter 46 of this volume as well as in other polarographic references.

One type of electrolysis frequently encountered in electrochemical analysis is the electrodeposition of a metal, M, on a platinum cathode. In such a case the electrode is only partly covered with the metal for a cer-

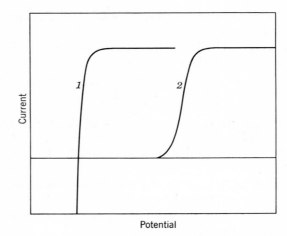

Fig. 48.7. Theoretical current–electrode potential curves for electrodeposition of metals: curve *1* is predicted by equation (18) and curve *2* is predicted by equation (17).

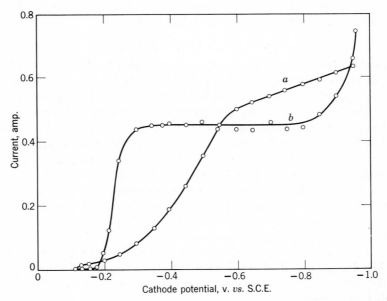

Fig. 48.8. Current – cathode potential curves for deposition of copper onto a platinum gauze cathode (area 160 cm.²) from 0.25M tartrate solution of pH 5.6 containing 50 mg./ 200 ml. of copper(II): curve *a* is without hydrazine and curve *b* is with 0.1M hydrazine present (80).

tain period after the initiation of electrolysis. If the assumption of unit activity of the metal is made ($C_M^\circ = 1$), obedience to equation (18) would be expected, and an abrupt increase in current should occur in the vicinity of the decomposition potential. This is not the case in the actual current–electrode potential curve, which shows a gradual rather than an abrupt increase in current (see Fig. 48.8 (7)). This fact indicates, as was first pointed out by Herzfeld (48), that the activity of the deposited metal on the incompletely covered platinum cathode is variable and smaller than unity.

B. ELECTRODEPOSITION FROM AN EXTREMELY DILUTE SOLUTION AND CRITICAL DEPOSITION POTENTIALS

Electrodeposition from an extremely dilute solution was first investigated by Hevesy and Paneth (49) with radioactive lead, ThB. They measured the deposition rate of ThB from a solution less than $10^{-8}N$ in the metal as a function of the electrode potential. The shapes of the curves obtained closely resemble those of polarographic current–potential curves. The deposition potential from the extremely dilute solution is called the "critical deposition potential."

The critical deposition potentials of bismuth, lead, silver, zinc, and other elements have been determined with radioactive isotopes of these elements for the purpose of examining the validity of the Nernst equation in dilute solution (6,10,24,45,58,59). In some cases the critical deposition potentials were found to be considerably more positive than the potentials that would be expected from the Nernst equation.

This important but difficult problem of the electrodeposition behavior of a trace metal on an inert electrode has been attacked by Haïssinsky (42), Rogers (6,7,38,39,102,103), and their co-workers, and a modified form of the Nernst equation has been derived by Rogers and Stehney (103) for a simple reversible electrodeposition of the type of reaction (F). The following assumptions are made in this derivation:

1. The area of the electrode is equal to that of a monolayer of deposit, which, to a first approximation, can be expressed as a mathematical product of the cross-sectional area of the deposited atom and the number of such atoms.

2. A second layer of atoms is not formed until the surface of the electrode has been completely covered with a monolayer.

If the number of atoms deposited is represented by N_M, the cross-sectional area of an atom of deposit by A_a cm.^{2}, the area of electrode by A_e cm.^{2}, and the activity coefficient of the metal by f_M, the activity of the metal on an incompletely covered inert electrode may be expressed as

$$a_M = (N_M A_a f_M)/A_e \tag{20}$$

Introducing equation (20) into equation (17) and replacing N_M by

$$N_M = (C'_{M^{+n}} - C^{\circ}_{M^{+n}}) \, V N_a \tag{21}$$

a modified Nernst equation for the electrodeposition of a metal in insufficient quantities to form a monolayer on an inert electrode is derived as

$$E = E^{\circ} + \ln [A_e/(A_a V N_a)] + \ln [C^{\circ}_{M^{+n}}/(C'_{M^{+n}} - C^{\circ}_{M^{+n}})] \tag{22}$$

where $C'_{M^{+n}}$ is the initial concentration of the metal ions, V is the solution volume, and N_a is Avogadro's number. The activity coefficients of M^{+n} and M are assumed, for simplicity, to be identical. If the fraction of the total quantity of M deposited when equilibrium is reached is denoted by x, equation (22) may be rewritten as

$$E = E_{1/2} + \ln (1 - x)/x \tag{23}$$

where

$$E_{1/2} = E^{\circ} + \ln A_e/(A_a V N_a) \tag{24}$$

Equation (23) is of the same form as that for the mercury electrode, but the expression for the half-wave potential (eq. (24)) is different. Equation (24) indicates that the value of $E_{1/2}$ is independent of the initial concentration of the reducible substance but is dependent on the area of the electrode, A_e, and on the volume of the solution, V.

A series of electrodeposition curves for silver (Fig. 48.9), which were obtained by Byrne, Rogers, and Griess (7) using radioactive silver, [111]Ag, and a platinum gauze electrode, represent very clearly the differences in the behavior of the deposition of "traces" of metal and the deposition of a "macro" quantity of metal. Curves *1* to *4* show the "trace" behavior, curve *8* the "macro" behavior, and curves *5* to *7*, with an intermediate plateau, correspond to the transition from the deposition of traces to normal behavior. The shapes of curves *1* to *4* agree with those predicted by equation (23). However, the potentials, where $x = 0.5$, are not the same but shift toward more negative potentials with an increasing concentration of silver ions. According to equation (24), those potentials corresponding to $E_{1/2}$ should be independent of the initial concentration of electrolyzed substance when less than a monolayer of deposit is formed. If the Nernst equation were applicable, the potential $E_{1/2}$ should shift toward more positive potentials with an increase in concentration of the electrolyzed substance. This is the case for curve *8* and the second step of curves *5*, *6*, and *7*.

In addition, the critical deposition potential depends on the electrode material on which the metal is deposited. Gold and silver electrodes

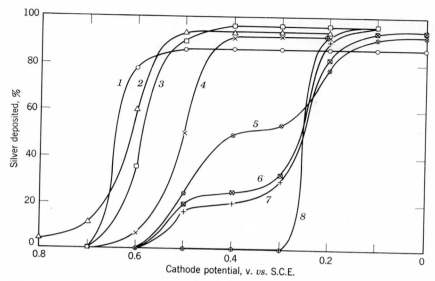

Fig. 48.9. Effect of initial concentration of silver on its deposition on a platinum electrode. Concentration of silver: curve *1*, trace; curve *2*, 2.3 $\times$ trace; curve *3*, 4.0 $\times$ $10^{-7}M$; curve *4*, 1.2 $\times$ $10^{-6}M$; curve *5*, 3.6 $\times$ $10^{-6}M$; curve *6*, $10^{-5}M$; curve *7*, 3.0 $\times$ $10^{-5}M$; and curve *8*, $10^{-4}M$ (7).

give different critical deposition potentials for bismuth deposited from a $3 \times 10^{-16}N$ solution. The critical deposition potential differs also before and after the pretreatment of the electrode.

These phenomena cannot be explained with the simple equations derived by Rogers and Stehney (103). The structure of the surface of metal must be taken into consideration. The heterogeneity of the metal surface has been confirmed by Haïssinsky and his co-workers from the radioautographs of deposits of polonium, radioactive bismuth, and lead (11,43,44). Adsorption of the metal ions on the metal surface also occurs in some cases. Considering these effects, Byrne and Rogers (6) revised the treatment given by Rogers and Stehney. This modified treatment represents an improvement, but still seems to be far from a satisfactory solution. N. Matsuura has critically reviewed this subject (89).

C. ELECTROLYSIS AT A CONTROLLED POTENTIAL

1. Electrolysis Current *vs.* Time

Consider the case of a stirred solution containing only one electroactive species, M^{+n}, which is reduced reversibly at the electrode according to reaction (F).   If the solution is electrolyzed at potentials sufficiently negative to yield an electrode reaction, the current, i, is expressed as

$$i = nFDA \ [(C_{M^{+n}} - C^\circ_{M^{+n}})/\delta] \tag{25}$$

where $C_{M^{+n}}$ is the concentration in the bulk of the solution, $C^\circ_{M^{+n}}$ is that at the electrode surface, D is the diffusion coefficient of M^{+n} ions, A is the area of the electrode surface, and δ is the effective thickness of the diffusion layer.   At sufficiently negative potentials, $C^\circ_{M^{+n}}$ is so small compared to $C_{M^{+n}}$ that equation (25) can be written as

$$i_l = nFDA \ (C_{M^{+n}}/\delta) \tag{26}$$

where i_l is the limiting current.

Equation (26) indicates that the current obtained at sufficiently negative potentials in a controlled-potential electrolysis is directly proportional to the concentration of M^{+n} ions in the bulk of the solution.   As the electrolysis proceeds, the bulk concentration of the M^{+n} ions decreases and, consequently, the current i_l decreases.   According to Lingane (77), the electrolysis current $vs.$ time relationship is expressed as

$$i_l = i_{t=0} \exp \ [(-DA/V\delta)t] \tag{27}$$

or

$$i_l = nFAD \ [(C_{M^{+n} \ (t=o)})/\delta] \exp \ [(-DA/V\delta)t] \tag{28}$$

where $i_{t=0}$ and $C_{M^{+n}(t=o)}$ are the initial current and initial concentration, respectively.

Combining equations (26) and (28), we obtain

$$\log \ [C_{M^{+n}}/C_{M^{+n}(t=o)} \ ] = (-0.43 \ DA/V\delta)t \tag{29}$$

The time required for the practical quantitative completion of an electrolysis can be calculated with equation (29).   It is independent of the initial concentration but is dependent on the diffusion coefficient, the area of the electrode, the volume of the solution, and the effective thickness of the diffusion layer.   The electrolysis time is shorter when the first two factors are greater and the last two are smaller.   For example, the electrolysis time required for 99.9% completion of the electrodeposition is given by

$$t_{99.9\%} = 7.0V\delta/DA \tag{30}$$

If V is expressed in cm.^{3}, δ in cm., D in cm.^{2}/second, and A in cm.^{2}, t is given in seconds.   For the values of 200 cm.^{3}, 2×10^{-3} cm. (69), 10^{-5} cm.^{2}/second, and 100 cm.^{2} for V, δ, D, and A in equation (30), respectively, $t_{99.9\%}$ is calculated to be 2.8×10^3 seconds (approximately 47 minutes).

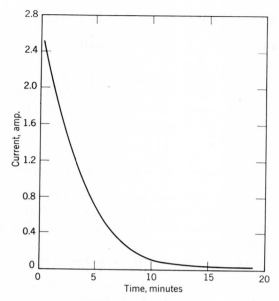

Fig. 48.10. Current decay in electrodeposition of copper onto a platinum cathode from 0.5M tartrate solution of pH 4.5 in the presence of hydrazine.

Operation at higher temperatures, and with more effective stirring, shortens the time required for the electrolysis because the former increases the diffusion coefficient and the latter decreases the effective thickness of the diffusion layer. The relationships mentioned above have been confirmed by Lingane (77) and by MacNevin and Baker (85). An example of the current–time curve is reproduced in Fig. 48.10 (79).

2. The Relationship of Potential to Reaction Completion

a. DEPOSITION ON AN INERT ELECTRODE

In the case of such a reversible metal deposition as that in reaction (F), the equilibrium electrode potential, $E_{eq.}$, is given by equation (19) if the electrodeposition takes place at the electrode of the same metal as the metal ions present in the solution, or at an inert electrode that is covered completely with the metal deposited from the solution. If a 99.99% completion of the deposition is required, the final concentration of the metal ions in the solution is 0.01% of the initial one. The equilibrium electrode potential in the final state is different from that in the initial state by the magnitude

$$(E_{eq.})_i - (E_{eq.})_f = (RT/nF) \ln [(C_{M^{+n}})_i]/[(C_{M^{+n}})_f] \qquad (31)$$

$$= (0.0591/n) \log [(C_{M^{+n}})_i]/[(C_{M^{+n}})_f] \qquad (32)$$

(at 25°C.), where subscripts i and f are the initial and final states, respectively. In the case of 99.99% completion, $(E_{eq.})_i - (E_{eq.})_f$ equals 0.24 v. for $n = 1$ and 0.12 v. for $n = 2$ at 25°C. This indicates that, in most reversible reactions, the electrode potential need not be more than 0.2 v. more negative than the decomposition potential to obtain practically complete deposition (80).

b. Deposition on a Mercury Electrode

Consider the reversible electrode reaction given by equation (G). The electrode potential is represented by equation (17). If the volume of solution is $V_{sol.}$ and that of the mercury of the electrode is V_{Hg}, the equilibrium electrode potential may be written

$$E = E_a° + (RT/nF) \ln (V_{Hg}/V_{sol.}) + (RT/nF) \ln (1 - x)/x \qquad (33)$$

where x denotes the degree of completion of electrolysis and varies from 0 to 1. Equation (33) can be written in the form

$$E = E_{1/2} + (RT/nF) \ln (1 - x)/x \qquad (34)$$

The half-wave potential depends on the ratio of the volume of solution to that of the mercury electrode. The potential $E_a°$ in equation (33) is practically equal to the half-wave potential in polarography, which, therefore, is utilized in the selection of the appropriate potential for the electrolytic separation (77). Equation (34) clearly indicates that the quantity (1 − x) is as small as 10^{-4} when E is made more negative than $E_{1/2}$ by $(0.059 \times 4)/n$ v. at 25°C.

It should be noticed that equations (33) and (34) hold only when the metal deposited is soluble in mercury. If the amount of metal electrolyzed exceeds the limit of the solubility of the metal in mercury, the relation between the electrode potential and the degree of completion is that shown by Fig. 48.11 (101). When x is smaller than x_l, the x vs. E curve agrees with the one that is predicted from equation (33). At x_l, the amalgam is saturated with the metal. When x is greater than x_l, reaction (F) takes place at the electrode instead of reaction (G). The x vs. E curve, therefore, is shifted toward more negative potentials because, in general, $E_a°$ is less negative than $E°$ (74,109). If the concentration of the metal ion is so low that the amount of metal deposited is not enough to form a monolayer, the x vs. E curve for $x > x_l$ is not determined directly by the ordinary Nernst

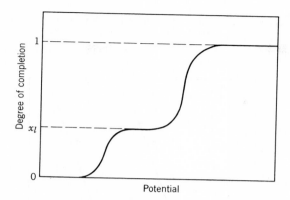

Fig. 48.11. Variations of the degree of completion with potential. A film of metal is formed when x exceeds the value of x_l (101).

equation (equation (18)), but seems to be determined by equations (23) and (24).

3. Separation of Electrode Reactions: Selective Deposition

The use of controlled-potential electrolysis is especially advantageous when it is applied to solutions that contain two or more electroactive species. In Fig. 48.12 are shown schematic current–electrode potential curves for two reducible metal ions, M^{+n} and $M'^{+n'}$, curve 1 being for M^{+n} ions and curve 2 for $M'^{+n'}$ ions. To cause the electrodeposition of M by the reduction of M^{+n}, the cathode potential must be more negative than the decomposition potential of the M^{+n} ion (a in Fig. 48.12). If the electrode potential is less negative than the decomposition potential of the $M'^{+n'}$ ion (b in Fig. 48.12), the electrodeposition of M takes place only at the electrode. In conclusion, it can be said that, at the potentials between a and b, the metal M can be electrodeposited selectively from the solution containing two reducible metal ions, M^{+n} and $M'^{+n'}$.

It may be thought from the foregoing discussion that the optimum potential to separate two or more electrode reactions can be predicted readily from theoretical considerations. This is true in some cases but not in others. The potential at which a metal codeposits with some other metal may be considerably different from the potential at which it deposits in the absence of other metals. This may make the selection of the optimum potential for the separation of two or more metals difficult. The most reliable method in this case is to determine the current–electrode potential curve of the particular reaction under exactly the same conditions as in the actual electrolysis.   In the case of an electrodeposition on a platinum electrode, measurement of the current–potential curve with a platinum-wire microelectrode under the same conditions is helpful and convenient.

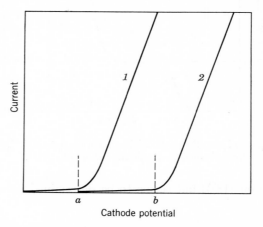

Fig. 48.12. Schematic current – cathode potential curves for M^{+n} (curve *1*) and $M'^{+n'}$ (curve *2*) ions when their separation is desired.

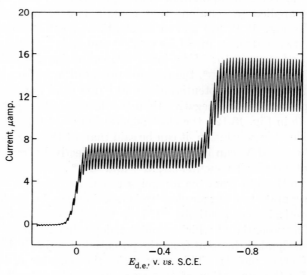

Fig. 48.13. Polarogram recorded with the dropping mercury electrode of a solution containing about 1mM each of copper(II) and cadmium(II) in a supporting electrolyte composed of 0.2M potassium nitrate and 0.01% gelatin.

For electrodeposition on the mercury electrode, the polarographic current–potential curves can be utilized to select the desired potential for the separation of two reducible metal ions. In Fig. 48.13 is reproduced a polarogram that was obtained with a solution containing about 1 millimolar each of copper(II) and cadmium(II) in a supporting electrolyte of 0.2M potassium nitrate. This polarogram suggests that if the potential of the working electrode is controlled at any potential between 0 and -0.4 v. only copper will be deposited from the solution. For further details on this subject the reader should refer to the literature (80).

4. Factors Affecting the Selectivity

Again, consider the case of the reversible electrodepositions of metals M and M' from $M(H_2O)_p^{+n}$ and $M'(H_2O)_{p'}^{+n'}$ ions, according to the reactions:

$$M(H_2O)_p^{+n} + ne^- \rightleftharpoons M + pH_2O \tag{H}$$

$$M'(H_2O)_{p'}^{+n'} + n'e^- \rightleftharpoons M' + p'H_2O \tag{I}$$

Assume that the decomposition potential of reaction (H), $E_{dec.}(M)$, is less negative than that of reaction (I), $E_{dec.}(M')$. If the difference between $E_{dec.}(M)$ and $E_{dec.}(M')$ is sufficiently large, the separation of both metals by electrodeposition of metal M is readily completed by electrolyzing at any potential more negative than $E_{dec.}(M)$ but less negative than $E_{dec.}(M')$. When $E_{dec.}(M)$ is nearly equal to $E_{dec.}(M')$, it is difficult to electrodeposit M in the absence of any codeposition of M'. In order to perform this separation, therefore, it is necessary to change the conditions of electrolysis in such a way as to separate adequately the potentials at which M and M' are deposited. The parameters discussed below are commonly manipulated to achieve this goal.

a. Effects of pH

In many cases an increase of pH will cause the ionization of one or more protons from a hydrated metal ion to form a hydroxo complex. Assume that the hydroxo complexes, $M(OH)_q(H_2O)_{p-q}^{+(n-q)}$ and $M'(OH)_{q'}(H_2O)_{p'-q'}^{+(n'-q')}$ exist at a given pH and are reversibly reduced to the corresponding metals, according to the equations

$$\left.\begin{array}{l} M(OH)_q(H_2O)_{p-q}^{+(n-q)} + qH^+ \rightleftharpoons M(H_2O)_p^{+n} \\ M(H_2O)_p^{+n} + ne^- \rightleftharpoons M + pH_2O \end{array}\right\} \tag{J}$$

and

$$M'(OH)_{q'}(H_2O)_{p'}^{+(n'-q')} + q'H^+ \rightleftharpoons M'(H_2O)_{p'}^{+n'} \Big\}$$
$$M'(H_2O)_{p'}^{+n'} + n'e^- \rightleftharpoons M' + p'H_2O \quad\quad \Big\} \quad (K)$$

We may now represent the sum of the concentrations of $M(H_2O)_p^{+n}$ and $M(OH)_q(H_2O)_{p-q}^{+(n-q)}$ with $[M^{+n}]_t$ and define the dissociation constants of $M(H_2O)_p^{+n}$ as (3):

$$*\beta_q(M^{+n}) = \left\{ [M(OH)_q(H_2O)_{p-q}^{+(n-q)}][H^+]^q \right\}/[M(H_2O)]_p^{+n} \quad (35)$$

where, for simplicity, concentrations are used instead of activity. From equation (35), $[M^{+n}]_t$ is given as

$$[M^{+n}]_t = [M(H_2O)_p^{+n}] \left\{ 1 + *\beta_q(M^{+n})/[H^+]^q \right\} \quad (36)$$

From equations (19) and (36), the equilibrium potential $E_{eq.}(M)$ may thus be expressed as

$$E_{eq.}(M) = E^\circ(M) - (RT/nF) \ln \left\{ 1 + *\beta_q(M^{+n})/[H^+]^q \right\}$$
$$+ (RT/nF) \ln [M^{+n}]_t \quad (37)$$

Equation (37) indicates that the value of $E_{eq.}(M)$ varies with the pH of the solution. When $*\beta_q(M^{+n}) \ll [H^+]^q$, however, the second term of the right-hand side of equation (37) is zero and $E_{eq.}(M)$ is independent of the pH of the solution. When $*\beta_q(M^{+n}) \gg [H^+]^q$, equation (37) is written as

$$E_{eq.}(M) = E^\circ(M) - (RT/nF) \ln \left\{ *\beta_q(M^{+n})/[H^+]^q \right\}$$
$$+ (RT/nF) \ln [M^{+n}]_t \quad (38)$$

The value of $E_{eq.}(M)$ shifts to more negative potentials by $0.059q/n$ v. (at 25°C.) with an increase of one pH unit.

Similar relationships also may be derived for reaction (K), and the equilibrium potential $E_{eq.}(M')$ is given as

$$E_e(M') = E^\circ(M') - (RT/n'F) \ln \left\{ 1 + *\beta_{q'}(M'^{+n'})/[H^+]^{q'} \right\}$$
$$+ (RT/n'F) \ln [M'^{+n'}]_t \quad (39)$$

and when $*\beta_{q'}(M'^{+n'}) \gg [H^+]^{q'}$,

$$E_{eq.}(M') = E^\circ(M') - (RT/n'F) \ln \left\{ *\beta_{q'}(M'^{+n'})/[H^+]^{q'} \right\}$$
$$+ (RT/n'F) \ln [M'^{+n'}]_t \quad (40)$$

Under the conditions for which equations (38) and (40) hold, the separation of $E_{eq.}(M)$ and $E_{eq.}(M')$ depends primarily on the difference of the magnitudes of $*\beta_q(M^{+n})/[H^+]^q$ and $*\beta_{q'}(M'^{+n'})/[H^+]^{q'}$.

A typical example of this type is the electrodeposition of thallium and lead on a mercury electrode. It is known that in alkaline solution thallium(I) forms only a monohydroxo complex, TlOH, whereas lead(II) forms higher hydroxo complexes, probably $Pb(OH)_3^-$ and $Pb(OH)_4^{-2}$. Considering the dissociation constants of these complex species, it can be said that $*\beta_q(Pb^{+2})/[H^+]^q$ is much greater than $*\beta_{q'}(Tl^+)/[H^+]^{q'}$. The electrode reactions of lead and thallium, which are not separated in acid or neutral solution, thus can be separated in alkaline solution. These considerations agree well with the experimental observations (62,75) and obviously have practical applicabilities.

b. Effects of Complex-Forming Substances

The effects of a complex-forming substance on the potential for the electrodeposition of a metal may be predicted from discussions of the voltammetric waves of complex metal ions (62,75). Assume that, in a solution containing a complex-forming substance, X^-, the metal ion, M^{+n}, forms a perfectly labile complex, $MX_p^{+(n-p)}$. If the electrodeposition of $MX_p^{+(n-p)}$ takes place reversibly at the electrode according to the reactions

$$\left.\begin{array}{l} MX_p^{+(n-p)} \rightleftharpoons M^{+n} + pX^- \\ M^{+n} + ne^- \rightleftharpoons M \end{array}\right\} \tag{L}$$

the equilibrium potential is represented in a way similar to that of equation (37):

$$E_{eq.}(M) = E°(M) - (RT/nF) \ln\left\{1 + \beta_p(MX_p)[X^-]^p\right\}$$

$$+ (RT/nF) \ln [M^{+n}]_t \tag{41}$$

where $\beta_p(MX_p)$ is the over-all formation constant of $MX_p^{+(n-p)}$ (3) and $[M^{+n}]_t$ is the total concentration, given by

$$[M^{+n}]_t = M^{+n} + MX_p^{+(n-p)}$$

In most cases, $\beta_p(MX_p)[X^-]^p$ is sufficiently larger than unity so that equation (41) can be written as

$$E_{eq.}(M) = E°(M) - (RT/nF) \ln \beta_p(MX_p)[X^-]^p$$

$$+ (RT/nF) \ln [M^{+n}]_t \tag{42}$$

The difference between $E_{eq.}(M)$ and $E°(M)$ depends chiefly on the magnitude of $\beta_p(MX_p)[X^-]^p$. Similar considerations may be applied to the electrodeposition of a metal, M′, from a complex ion, $M'X_{p'}^{+,(n'-p')}$, which proceeds reversibly according to the reaction

$$M'X_{p'}^{+,(n'-p')} \rightleftharpoons M'^{+n'} + p'X^- \left.\right\}$$

$$M'^{+n'} + n'e \rightleftharpoons M' \qquad\qquad\qquad \left.\right\} \qquad (N)$$

If the standard potentials of reactions (L) and (N) are almost identical, the separation of both reactions with the aid of complex formation is dependent primarily on the difference in magnitudes of $\beta_p(MX_p)[X^-]^p$ and $\beta_{p'}(M'X_{p'})[X^-]^{p'}$. Separation of the electrode reactions based on this principle is frequently employed.

There may be cases in which no appropriate complex-forming substance, X^-, is found that makes $\beta_p(MX_p)[X^-]^p$ and $\beta_{p'}(M'X_{p'})[X^-]^{p'}$ sufficiently different from each other. In such cases the addition of two complex-forming substances, X^- and Y^-, causes a successful separation when the following conditions are satisfied: (1) $\beta_p(MX_p)[X^-]^p$ and $\beta_{p'}(M'X_{p'})[X^-]^{p'}$ are almost identical; (2) $\beta_q(MY_q)[Y^-]^q$ is much larger than $\beta_p(MX_p)[X^-]^p$; and (3) in a solution containing only Y^- as a complex-forming substance no appreciable amount of $M'^{+n'}$ can remain in solution because of precipitation or other reasons. The separation of the polarographic wave for bismuth from that of copper was thus successful when a supporting electrolyte containing potassium cyanide and ethylenediaminetetraacetate was used (56). This technique may be applied to the separation of bismuth from copper by controlled-potential electrolysis, and similar possibilities may be considered for other electrode reactions.

c. EFFECTS OF SURFACE-ACTIVE SUBSTANCES

Although surface-active substances often are added to electrolytic solutions from which metal deposition is to take place, the effects of such materials on the separation of electrode reactions have not been investigated systematically. It is well known that the addition of surface-active substances sometimes affects to a great extent the shape (reversibility) of the current–potential curve in polarography. This fact suggests that the separation of electrode reactions may be improved or worsened by the addition of a surface-active substance. If electrodepositions such as those given by reactions (H) and (I) are considered, a situation favorable to the separation of these reactions would be one in which the reaction taking place at more negative potentials is less reversible and more sensitive to the surface-active substance than the other more reversible reaction taking place at less negative potentials.

In a supporting electrolyte containing ethylenediaminetetraacetate, bismuth(III) gives a polarographic wave that results from the reduction of the bismuth(III)–ethylenediaminetetraacetate complex. This wave is completely suppressed by the addition of 0.033% of gelatin (100). Similarly, the reduction waves of PbY^{-2} and CdY^{-2} (Y^{-4} is the ethylenediaminetetraacetate anion), which are observed in acetate buffer solutions in the absence of surface-active substances, are obliterated upon the addition of gelatin. These and similar phenomena may be utilized effectively for the separation of two electrode reactions.

D. APPLICATIONS

1. Controlled-Potential Methods

The technique of controlled-potential electrolysis has been applied successfully to the separation of large amounts of interfering metals from small amounts of metals that are to be determined. One of the important advantages of electrolytic separation over precipitation and extraction methods is that it does not require the addition to the solution of any extraneous reagents which might complicate the treatment of the residual solution for the subsequent determinations. Another important advantage is that the electrolytic method avoids the loss of minor constituents by coprecipitation and, also, when a potentiostat is used, shortens operator time.

Controlled-potential electrolysis also has been applied in electrogravimetric analysis. By this method, the metal to be analyzed may be deposited on the electrode in the presence of other metals that might be codeposited if the electrolysis were carried out without controlling the potential. This subject is discussed in Section IV of this chapter.

Many kinds of electrodes, in principle, can be used as working electrodes for electrolytic separation at controlled potential. In practice, however, platinum and mercury electrodes are most commonly employed; the mercury electrode is restricted to use in separations. Cells, other electrodes, and electrical apparatus are also discussed in Section IV.

As the subject has been discussed extensively by Lingane (80), the following presentation of one typical example will suffice for illustrating the use of a controlled-potential electrolytic separation.

The separation of large amounts of silver from small amounts of bismuth by controlled-potential electrolysis has been investigated as a means for determining minute quantities of bismuth impurity in metallic silver (55). A solution of silver nitrate corresponding to 200 to 500 mg. of silver metal

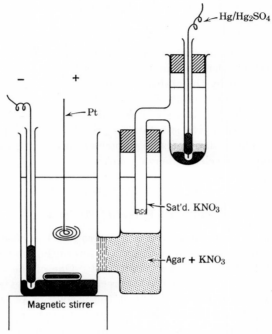

Fig. 48.14. Mercury cathode cell used for the controlled-potential separation of silver from bismuth (55).

is prepared in 50 ml. of $0.2N$ nitric acid containing 5 ml. of ethyl alcohol. The solution is transferred to the H-type electrolysis cell shown in Fig. 48.14 and is electrolyzed with the potential of the mercury electrode at -0.20 v. *vs.* a mercury–mercurous sulfate electrode in $1N$ sulfuric acid. This controlled potential is 0.32 v. more negative than the standard potential of silver and 0.44 v. less negative than the polarographic half-wave potential of bismuth. The electrolysis is continued until the current falls below 5 mamp., which usually requires about 1 hour. The bismuth(III) content in the residual solution is determined by either a polarographic or a colorimetric method.

2. Elements that are Deposited at the Mercury Electrode

The electrodeposition behavior of an element depends on the nature of the supporting electrolyte, the nature of the electrode, the structure of the electrolysis cell, and other electrolysis conditions. In Table 48.III are presented the elements that may be deposited at a mercury electrode upon

TABLE 48.III

Metals Deposited at a Mercury Electrode (90)

Ia	IIa	IIIa	IVa	Va	VIa	VIIa	VIII			Ib	IIb	IIIb	IVb	Vb	VIb	VIIb	0
H																	He
Li	Be											B	C	N	O	F	Ne
Na	Mg											Al	Si	P	S	Cl	A
K	Ca	Sc	Ti	V	Cr	Mn	Fe	Co	Ni	Cu	Zn	Ga	Ge	As	Se	Br	Kr
Rb	Sr	Y	Zr	Nb	Mo	Tc	Ru	Rh	Pd	Ag	Cd	In	Sn	Sb	Te	I	Xe
Cs	Ba	La[a]	Hf	Ta	W	Re	Os	Ir	Pt	Au	Hg	Tl	Pb	Bi	Po	At	Rn
Fr	Ra	Ac[b]															

Note: Heavy solid lines enclose elements that can be quantitatively deposited in the mercury cathode. Broken lines enclose elements that are quantitatively separated from the electrolyte, but are not quantitatively deposited in the mercury. Light lines enclose elements that are incompletely separated.

[a] Also elements 58 to 71 (partial deposition of lanthanum and neodymium has been reported).

[b] Also elements 90 to 103.

electrolysis in a weakly acid solution with conventional electrolysis cells (90).

IV. ELECTROGRAVIMETRIC ANALYSIS

A. CONTROLLED-POTENTIAL METHODS

1. Apparatus

A simple manual circuit for controlled-potential electrolysis is shown schematically in Fig. 48.15. The applied voltage between the working and the auxiliary electrode is adjusted by means of a rheostat acting as a voltage divider in order to keep the working-electrode potential at a

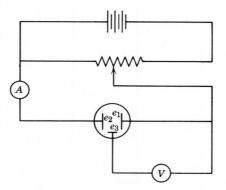

Fig. 48.15. Simple circuit for controlled-potential electrolysis: e_1, working electrode; e_2, auxiliary electrode; e_3, reference electrode; A, current measuring device; and V, potential measuring device.

desired value or within a desired range relative to that of the reference electrode. The potential of the working electrode *vs.* the reference electrode is observed with a potentiometer or a vacuum-tube voltmeter, and the electrolysis current is indicated by a milliammeter connected in series with the working electrode.

In electrolysis at a controlled potential, equation (29) holds in most cases. The time required for the practical completion of the electrolysis, therefore, depends on the magnitudes of the diffusion coefficient of the electrolyzed substance, D, the area of the electrode, A, the volume of the solution, V, and the effective thickness of the diffusion layer, δ. If reduction of the electrolysis time is desired, the first two factors, D and A, must be increased and the last two factors, V and δ, must be decreased. Cells and electrodes should be designed accordingly. In Fig. 48.16 is shown the essential features of a very simple cell that may be used for most electrogravimetric determinations of metals. The cell vessel is an ordinary 250 to 300-ml. beaker, which is covered loosely by a split watch glass so that spray loss can be prevented when gas evolution occurs vigorously at the anode.

Cylindrical platinum gauze electrodes with reinforced edges are used in most cases. The outer cylinder serves as the cathode on which the metal

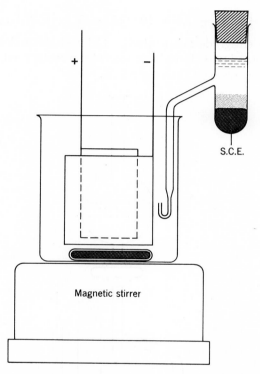

Fig. 48.16. Simple cell for controlled-potential electrolysis with a platinum cathode.

is deposited. Convenient dimensions for this electrode are 5 cm., both for diameter and for height, the gross area being approximately 160 cm.² and the weight about 27 g. The inner cylinder, which serves as the anode, is sometimes replaced by a platinum wire electrode. The anode should be placed concentrically within the cathode so that the electrical field between the electrodes is as uniform as possible. This is essential in obtaining uniform metal deposition over the entire cathode. Effective stirring also is essential for this purpose as well as for decreasing the diffusion-layer thickness and, consequently, accelerating the rate of deposition.

The reference electrodes most frequently used are a saturated calomel electrode and a silver–silver chloride electrode. The potential of the saturated calomel electrode (S.C.E.) is defined as the e.m.f. of the cell

$$-H_2 \text{ (1 atm.) } \big| H^+(a = 1) \big\| KCl(s), Hg_2Cl_2(s) \big| Hg +$$

which is given by

$$E = +0.242 - 7.6 \times 10^{-4} (t - 25) \text{ v. } vs. \text{ N.H.E.} \qquad (43)$$

where t is the Centigrade temperature. Calomel electrodes prepared with $0.1M$ or $1M$ potassium chloride solutions also may be used, but they seem to be much less convenient than the S.C.E.

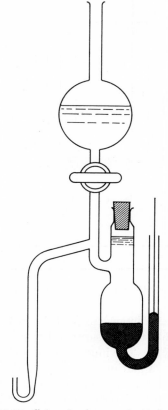

Fig. 48.17. Calomel reference electrode (80).

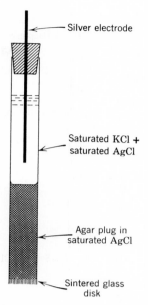

Fig. 48.18. Silver – silver chloride reference electrode, especially useful for electrolysis with the mercury electrode (80).

Many designs of calomel electrodes have been reported by electrochemists and electroanalytical chemists. In Fig. 48.17 is shown the saturated calomel electrode that Lingane recommended for use with a platinum gauze working electrode (80).

A mercury–mercurous sulfate electrode may be used when chloride ion is not permissible in the test solution but sulfate ion is. The potential of the electrode with saturated potassium sulfate solution is +0.64 v. *vs.* N.H.E., or +0.44 v. *vs.* S.C.E.

The calomel reference electrode shown in Fig. 48.17 is not considered suitable for electrolysis with the mercury electrode. In this case, various forms of silver–silver chloride electrodes, such as those shown in Figs. 48.18 and 48.19, are recommended (80,93). The potential of these electrodes is +0.197 v. *vs.* N.H.E., or −0.045 v. *vs.* S.C.E. at 25°C.

In principle, it is not impossible to keep the potential of the working electrode at a desired value or within a desired range by manual operation. In practice, however, it is extremely tedious and, sometimes, difficult or impossible because the applied voltage required changes rapidly, especially in the beginning of an electrolysis. A completely automatic instrument for controlling the potential of a working electrode, called a "potentiostat,"

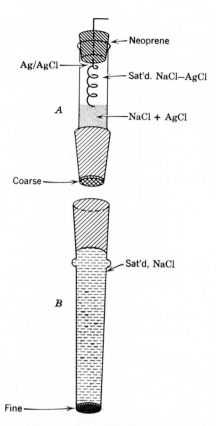

Fig. 48.19. Low-resistance silver – silver chloride electrode for controlled-potential electrolysis (93).

has been devised by Hickling (52). Since Hickling's work, many kinds of potentiostats have been constructed and applied to controlled-potential electrolysis. Their control principles and performance characteristics have been summarized by Lingane. The readers should refer to his book (80) and a review by Meites (94) for details of the apparatus and the general technique of controlled-potential gravimetric analysis.

2. Conditions of Electrolysis and the Physical Characteristics of Metal Deposits

It is desirable that the physical characteristics of a metal deposit fulfill certain qualifications that are determined by the anticipated subsequent use of the deposit. For example, it is necessary that metal platings and deposits to be used for analysis (by means of weighing) be smooth and adherent.

Metal deposits obtained from solutions of complex ions frequently have better physical properties than those obtained from solutions of simple (uncomplexed) ions. The addition of small amounts of surface-active substances (called "brighteners") often improves remarkably the physical properties of the deposited metal. Although the causes of these phenomena are not completely understood, they are of substantial technological importance. In addition, hydrogen evolution must be prevented during the electrolysis if adherent and smooth deposits are desired.

a. Crystal Structures of Electrodeposits (99)

The relation between the brightness of metal deposits and their crystal structures has been the topic of some discussion. Some researchers have emphasized the importance of crystal orientation and suggested that copper deposited from cyanide complexes is dull not because of crystal size but because of random crystal orientation. Others, however, do not agree with this. Clark and Simonsen (9) and Denise and Leidheiser (18) have stated that neither crystal size nor orientation is related to brightness, but that the surface must be smooth enough for specular reflection.

The surface structures of metals deposited from solutions of complexed and uncomplexed ions have been investigated by means of microscopy. These investigations show that, from perchlorate or nitrate solutions in which uncomplexed silver ions exist, silver is not deposited uniformly over the face of a silver crystal, but only on a number of active centers on the crystal face. The number of such active centers varies with many factors. When silver is electrodeposited from solutions of complexes such as cyanide, on the other hand, an entire face of the crystal may develop. In general, the materials present in the solution determine which crystal face develops.

It has been suggested that the nature of the coordinating group as well as the thermodynamic stability of the complex ions is important in determining whether deposits having good physical properties will be formed (68). In general, large coordinating substances, or those containing aromatic ring systems, give deposits having poor physical properties. It has also been observed that complexes that are reduced either with great difficulty, or very easily, do not give good plates. Complexes in an intermediate range of stability give metal deposits of good physical properties.

b. ADDITION OF SURFACE-ACTIVE SUBSTANCES (BRIGHTENERS)

As has been mentioned above, the addition of small amounts of surface-active substances, or brighteners, may improve to a great extent the physical properties of metal deposits. Although it has been suggested that this was due to the ability of brighteners to form complexes with the metal ions present in solution, this concept has not been accepted because of the lack of experimental support. A survey of more than 100 organic addition agents used in the plating of nickel failed to reveal any relation between the structure of the compounds and their efficacy as brighteners. As a matter of fact, it seems unreasonable to suppose that all addition agents used as brighteners form Werner-type coordination compounds with metal ions in solution. On the other hand, various substances, such as glycine, tartaric acid, citric acid, and metaphosphoric acid, which were found to function as brighteners in the electrodeposition of silver and copper, are able to form complexes with silver or copper ions. This fact suggests that, for some compounds, some close correlation may exist between the efficacy as a brightener and its ability to form complex compounds with metal ions. However, no single simple interpretation is able to reconcile all of the observed experimental facts with the structural characteristics of the wide variety of brighteners now in use (99).

Some brighteners have little tendency to form complexes with metal ions in solution, but possess a tendency to be adsorbed strongly on the surfaces of metal electrodes. The smoothing action of these surface-active brighteners is possibly explained as follows: such substances are adsorbed to a greater extent on the incipient "high spots" of the surface than in the "valleys," and consequently they prevent the build-up of crystals at high spots and hinder the further growth of high spots themselves.

In electrogravimetric analysis of lead, the addition of 0.1% gelatin was recommended by Tutundzic (125) and Schleicher (107) to improve the adherence and smoothness of lead deposited from acetate buffer solution. The smoothness of cadmium deposited from an ammoniacal medium was found to be markedly improved by the addition of only 0.01% gelatin; a more coarsely crystalline deposit of cadmium is obtained in the absence of gelatin. It has been confirmed that the smoother cadmium deposit obtained in the presence of gelatin contains no appreciable amount of gelatin in it. However, the occlusion of organic substances in metal deposits that are obtained by the classic constant-current electrolysis method has been reported. This occlusion may cause not only a significant deterioration of the physical characteristics of the metal deposit, but also serious positive errors in electrogravimetric analysis. In this connection, Lingane expressed the opinion that this kind of occlusion of organic matter in the deposit appears to result from the lack of potential control in the classic methods. His investigation (76) clearly shows that copper—deposited by controlled-potential electrolysis from solutions containing 1 g. of urea and as much as 23 g. of sodium tartrate per 200 ml.—contains no appreciable amount of organic substances. Under similar conditions, Skowronski obtained by the classic method copper deposits in which considerable amounts of carbon compounds seemed to be occluded. The controlled-potential technique is superior to the constant-current method in this respect (76).

c. OTHER CONDITIONS

The prevention of hydrogen evolution at the electrode also is one of the important conditions for obtaining a smooth metal deposit. Controlled-potential electrolysis is advantageous in this respect, because the cathode potential can be kept by this technique below the value at which hydrogen ion is reduced. The only way to prevent hydrogen evolution when employing the classic "constant-current" technique is by the use of an appropriate cathodic depolarizer.

Roughness caused by codeposition of hydrogen is explained by some researchers as due to the formation of hydrides and their decomposition at the electrode surface. Other workers, however, consider it to be the result of a purely mechanical phenomenon. Further investigation will be necessary to reach a conclusion.

The value of the current density is another factor that must be taken into consideration to prevent deterioration of the physical properties of metal deposits. At very large current densities, deposits tend to be rougher and less adherent than at small current densities. The value of the controlled potential, especially in the beginning of electrolysis, must be sufficiently positive so that the permissible current density is not exceeded. Methods for automatically limiting the current density in the early stages of electrolysis have been developed (80).

Besides the deterioration of the physical characteristics of metal deposits, serious positive errors in electrodeposition often are observed when the classic "constant-current" technique is applied. After extensive studies of nickel deposition by the constant-current method, Yokosuka (133) concluded that positive errors in deposition of nickel were due to the codeposition of platinum resulting from the electrodissolution of the platinum anode. The addition of hydrazine sulfate to the electrolysis solution is very effective in suppressing the anodic dissolution of platinum, whereas the addition of hydroxylamine is less effective (133). Similar phenomena

TABLE 48.IV

Deposition Potentials at a Platinum Electrode

Metal[a]	Supporting electrolyte[b]								
	1	2	3	4	5	6	7	8	9
Au	+0.60	+0.70	+0.70	$(+0.50)^c$	—	−1.00	+0.60	+0.40	−0.15
Hg	+0.15	+0.40	+0.40	$(+0.25)^c$	−0.05	−0.80	+0.20	+0.30	−0.30
Ag	—	+0.40	+0.40	$(+0.30)^c$	−0.05	−0.80	+0.40	+0.30	−0.05
Cu	−0.15	−0.05	−0.05	−0.30	−0.45	−1.55	−0.45	−0.60	−0.70
Bi	−0.15	−0.08	−0.05	−0.35	—	$(−1.70)^c$	−0.50	−0.60	−0.70
Sb	−0.20	−0.33	$(−0.30)^c$	−0.75	—	−1.25	−0.70	−0.70	—
Sn	−0.50	—	—	—	—	—	—	—	—
Pb	−0.55	—	—	−0.50	—	—	−0.65	−0.65	—
Cd	−0.80	−0.80	—	−0.90	−0.90	−1.20	—	−0.65	−1.00
Zn	—	—	—	−1.10	−1.40	−1.50	—	—	—
Ni	—	—	—	—	−0.90	—	—	—	—
Co	—	—	—	—	−0.85	—	—	—	—

[a] The concentration of metal ions was 0.1 g./200 ml.

[b] Supporting electrolyte:

1. $0.3M$ HCl + $0.14M$ NH₂OH·HCl.
2. $0.2M$ H₂SO₄.
3. $0.7M$ HNO₃.
4. $0.4M$ Na tartrate + $0.1M$ NaH tartrate.
5. $1.2M$ NH₄OH + $0.2M$ NH₄Cl.
6. $0.4M$ KCN + $0.2M$ KOH.
7. EDTA + 5 g. NH₄NO₃ + 2 g. NH₂OH·HCl + 200 ml. H₂O (pH ≐ 3).   Molar ratio of metal to EDTA is 1 to 3.
8. EDTA + 5 g. CH₃COONH₄ + 200 ml. H₂O (pH ≐ 5).   Molar ratio of metal to EDTA is 1 to 3.
9. EDTA + 2 g. NH₄Cl + 20 ml. NH₄OH + 180 ml. H₂O.   Molar ratio of metal to EDTA is 1 to 3.

[c] These indicate that metal deposits obtained are not suitable for electrogravimetric analysis.

may be expected to take place in controlled-potential electrolysis, and appropriate measures must be taken to prevent serious interference.

3. Applications

The controlled-potential gravimetric method is most effective when it is applied to the analysis of a mixture of several depositable metals. When a solution contains a single depositable metal, there is little need, other than to obtain a good deposit, for controlling the electrode potential. In mixture several metals often can be determined successively simply by appropriate regulation of the electrode potential. For example, copper, bismuth, and lead can be deposited successively at −0.30, −0.40, and −0.60 v. vs. S.C.E., respectively, from a tartrate solution of pH 5 to 6. If tin(IV) also is present it is deposited at a cathode potential of −0.60 v. vs. S.C.E. after the solution is acidified with concentrated hydrochloric acid so that the stannic–tartrate complex is completely decomposed.

For effective application of controlled-potential electrolysis to the separation and determination of metals, it is desirable to know the values of the deposition potentials of those metals in various electrolytes. This subject has been investigated by Tanaka, and the values given in Table 48.IV were obtained (113–119).

A number of applications of controlled-potential gravimetric analysis have been reported in the literature, and the subject has been discussed extensively by Lingane (80). Examples of metals that can be separated and determined are given in Table 48.V. For further information, the reader should consult the monograph by Lingane (80) and several reviews in *Analytical Chemistry* (1,15,16).

B. INTERNAL ELECTROLYSIS (SPONTANEOUS ELECTROGRAVIMETRIC ANALYSIS)

An electrogravimetric method that employs no external voltage source, but is based on the use of the spontaneous electromotive force of the electrolysis cell itself, has been developed and named "internal electrolysis." Lingane, however, has recommended the name "spontaneous gravimetric analysis," which would be more truly descriptive (80). Consider an electrolysis cell that consists of a tared platinum cathode immersed in a copper solution and a zinc electrode in a solution of zinc sulfate separated from the copper solution by a porous diaphragm. If the two electrodes are short-circuited, the cell reaction

$$Zn + Cu^{+2} \rightleftharpoons Zn^{+2} + Cu \tag{44}$$

TABLE 48.V

Controlled-Potential Separations and Determinations of Various Metals

Metal	Separated from	Electrolyte	Control potential, E_c, v. vs. S.C.E.	Ref.
Sb	Pb, Sn, etc.	HCl + NH₂OH·HCl; 50–70°C.	−0.40	(108)
	Sn	H₂SO₄ + N₂H₄	−0.07 ~ −0.22	(21)
	Sn	Na₂S + NaOH + KCN; 60°C.	−1.32	(107)
	Cd	HCl + NH₂OH·HCl; 60°C.	−0.25	(113)
Bi	Cu	Alk. tartrate + KCN + NH₂OH	−0.75 → −0.90	(60)
	Pb	HNO₃ + N₂H₄; 80–85°C.	−0.10 → −0.25	(12,73)
	Sn, Pb	HCl + H₂C₂O₄ + N₂H₄; 80–85°C.	−0.15 → −0.30	(60)
	Sb	H₂SO₄	−0.10	(114)
	Pb, Sn, Sb, etc.	Na tartrate + N₂H₄ (pH 5.2–6.0)	−0.40	(81)
	Pb, Sn, Sb, etc.	Na tartrate + succinic acid + N₂H₄ (pH 5.8)	−0.40	(53)
	Cd	H₂SO₄	−0.15	(114)
Cd	Zn	CH₃COOH	−0.75	(105)
	Zn	CH₃COOH + CH₃COONa (pH 4)	−0.80	(106)
	Zn	HCl + NH₂OH (pH 1.0–1.5)	−0.80	(70)
	Zn	NaCN(KCN) + NaOH(KOH)	−1.30	(19,118)
	Zn	NH₄OH + N₂H₄ + gelatin	−0.95 → −1.15	(80)
	Zn	NH₄OH + NH₄Cl	−1.0	(117)
Cu	Sn, Cd	HCl + NH₂OH	−0.20	(113)
	Pb	HNO₃	−0.15	(115)
	Pb	Na tartrate + NaH tartrate + NH₂OH·HCl	−0.35	(116)
	Pb, Sn, etc.	HCl + NH₂OH	−0.40	(108)
	Pb, Sn, etc.	1M HCl + N₂H₄·2HCl (1 g./150 ml.)	−0.40	(70,123)
	Pb, Sn, etc.	HCl (<0.5M) + N₂H₄	−0.35	(19,20)
	Pb, Sn, etc.	1M HCl + NH₂OH·HCl (4 g./250 ml.)	−0.40	(78,96)
	Sb, Cd	H₂SO₄	−0.15	(114)

	Pb, Sb, Sn, Ni, etc.	Na tartrate + urea + N$_2$H$_4$·2HCl (pH 4–6)	−0.36	(76)
	Pb, Sb, Sn, Ni, etc.	Na tartrate + N$_2$H$_4$·2HCl (pH 5.2–6.0)	−0.30	(81)
	Ni	NH$_4$OH + NH$_4$Cl	−0.60	(117)
	Bi, Cd, Zn	Na tartrate + NaH tartrate	−0.3	(116)
	Bi, Pb, Sn, Sb, As, etc.	Na tartrate + succinic acid + N$_2$H$_4$·2HCl (pH 5.8)	−0.30	(53,54)
	Bi	EDTA + NH$_4$NO$_3$ + NH$_2$OH·HCl (pH 3.1); 60–70°C.	−0.41	(46)
Pb	Sn, Zn, etc.	HCl + NH$_2$OH·HCl	−0.36	(98)
	Sb	HNO$_3$ + HF + K$_2$Cr$_2$O$_7$	−0.40	(72,123,124)
	Cd	Na tartrate + NaH tartrate + NH$_2$OH·HCl	−0.4	(116)
	Cd, Sn, etc.	HCl + NH$_2$OH; 60–70°C.	−0.60	(108)
	Cd, Sn, Ni, etc.	Na tartrate + N$_2$H$_4$ (pH 4–6)	−0.60	(81)
Hg	Cu	KCN + KOH	−1.00	(118)
Ni	Zn, Al, Fe	Na tartrate + NH$_4$OH + Na$_2$SO$_3$; 70°C.	−1.10	(124)
	Zn	(NH$_4$)$_2$SO$_4$ + Na$_2$SO$_3$ + NH$_4$OH; 80–90°C.	−0.95	(57)
Rh	Ir	NH$_4$Cl + HCl + NH$_2$OH	−0.25 ∼ −0.40	(86)
Ag	Cu	NH$_4$OH + H$_2$O$_2$	−0.1 ∼ −0.2	(19,21,95)
	Cu	NH$_4$OH + NH$_4$Cl	−0.05	(117)
	Cu	CH$_3$COOH + CH$_3$COONH$_4$	+0.1	(106)
	Cu	H$_2$SO$_4$	+0.35	(114)
	Cu, Bi	HNO$_3$	+0.30	(115)
	Cu	KCN + KOH	−0.85	(118)
	Pb	HNO$_3$; 10°C.	+0.30	(115)
	Cd	NH$_4$OH + NH$_4$Cl	−0.05	(117)
	Cd, Zn	KCN + KOH	−0.90	(118)
Sn	Cd	HCl + NH$_2$OH·HCl; 70°C.	−0.70	(61,108)
	Cd	HCl + NH$_2$OH·HCl	−0.60	(113)
	Zn, etc.	HCl + N$_2$H$_4$·2HCl	−0.70	(72,123,124)

proceeds spontaneously. The copper is deposited on the platinum electrode and the zinc anode is dissolved to form zinc(II) ions. This net reaction is equivalent to the reaction that takes place when metallic zinc is
placed in a solution of copper sulfate. A difference between the two cases
is that, in the latter case, the deposited copper does not adhere well to the
metallic zinc because the surface of the latter is continually disintegrating.
In an internal electrolysis cell, however, the copper is not deposited on the
surface of metallic zinc but on the surface of a platinum electrode. This
condition is exactly the same as that for electrodeposition taking place with
an external voltage source, and, consequently, the deposited metal can be
obtained in an adherent form.

Since electrolysis is driven by the electromotive force of a cell of the type
given in equation (44), it is a type of controlled-potential electrolysis. The
cell is represented more generally as

$$-M_1 \mid M_1{}^{+2} \parallel M_2{}^{+2} \mid M_2(Pt) + \qquad (45)$$

where it is assumed that both M_1 and M_2 form bivalent ions, and that M_1
is less noble than M_2. The cell reaction is

$$M_1 + M_2{}^{+2} = M_1{}^{+2} + M_2 \qquad (46)$$

The reversible galvanic e.m.f. at zero current is given by

$$E = E^{\circ}_{M_1, M_1{}^{+2}} + E^{\circ}_{M_2{}^{+2}, M_2} + (0.059/2) \log (C_{M_2{}^{+2}}/C_{M_1{}^{+2}}) \qquad (25°C.) \quad (47)$$

The e.m.f. of the cell, therefore, depends on the concentration ratio of
$M_2{}^{+2}$ and $M_1{}^{+2}$. As the cell reaction proceeds, the concentration of $M_2{}^{+2}$
decreases while that of $M_1{}^{+2}$ increases, and, correspondingly, the e.m.f.
decreases and approaches zero. Since the electrolysis current depends on
the e.m.f. and the cell resistance, it decays gradually with the decrease
of the e.m.f. The electrolysis current, that is, the rate of metal deposition,
generally is not so large because of the relatively high cell resistance and the
relatively small driving voltage. Therefore, the time required to deposit
a given metal is considerably longer, compared with electrolysis with external potential control. This is the most serious disadvantage of the internal electrolysis technique.

Devices that decrease the time required for deposition have been reported. For example, the use of a coarse fritted glass plate with very low
internal resistance is recommended for the separation of the anolyte from
the catholyte (134).

Internal electrolysis also can be carried out in such a way that an electrodeposition takes place at the anode instead of at the cathode. For
example, thallic oxide deposits on a platinum anode when a catholyte

that consists of a paste of lead dioxide and dilute sulfuric acid is employed (82).

A number of studies have been performed for the purpose of increasing the applicability of internal electrolysis. The use of an electrolysis cell that permits continuous renewal of the anolyte has been recommended for electrodeposition at the cathode. This technique may assure a more nearly constant potential during the electrolysis and, therefore, may have a higher separation efficiency than conventional methods (36).

The details of this technique as well as cells, methodology, and applications have been discussed by Lingane (80). Excellent reviews concerning advances in theory, instrumentation, and methodology have appeared every other year in *Analytical Chemistry* (1,15,16).

V. ELECTROGRAPHY

The technique of electrography is essentially based on an electrolysis that takes place in a specially arranged electrolysis cell. The cell usually consists of an electrode of a metal specimen, a porous medium containing an

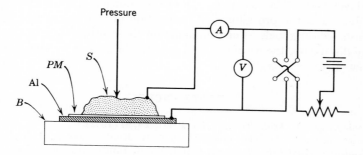

Fig. 48.20. Schematic arrangement for electrographic measurements: S, specimen, PM, printing medium; Al, aluminum plate for the second electrode; B, insulating base; A, milliammeter; and V, voltmeter.

appropriate electrolyte on which the metal specimen is placed, and the second electrode on which the porous medium rests. The cell arrangement and electrical circuit are shown schematically in Fig. 48.20, where the porous medium containing the electrolyte is designated as a printing medium. The metal-specimen electrode functions in most cases as the anode, in which instance an electrodissolution of the specimen metal occurs and, as a result, metal ions are transferred into the printing medium. This is the exact opposite of the above-mentioned electroanalytical methods, which are based on electrodeposition.

Electrography originated from investigations that were made independently by Fritz (25) and by Glazunov (37). Fritz was interested in the determination of the sensitivity of various spot tests, and he employed electrodissolution with a known current for a known time in order to transfer small known quantities of metal ions to solutions held in porous paper. He termed his technique the "Elektro-Tüpfel-Methode."

Glazunov applied electrodissolution to the study of the macrostructure of metal specimens, particularly of ferrous metals. In the technique he developed, the polished specimen surface is pressed firmly against paper moistened with an electrolyte containing a color-producing reagent, e.g., potassium ferrocyanide. The paper is placed on a piece of aluminum or stainless steel plate, which serves as the cathode. After a few seconds of electrolysis with a relatively small voltage, a structural pattern of the surface is produced. The differentiation is due to different rates of electrodissolution of iron from different parts of the surface. This technique for the study of the surface structure of metals was called the "electrographic method" by Glazunov.

Electrographic techniques for qualitative and quantitative analysis have been developed. The technique of electrotransfer, the function of the electrolyte, and the procedure for recognition of the transferred products have been investigated. For comments on these subjects, with a comprehensive discussion, the reader should consult the review by Hermance and Wadlow (47).

REFERENCES

1. Ashley, S. E. Q., *Anal. Chem.*, **21**, 70 (1949); **24**, 91 (1952).
2. Bates, R. G., "Electrode Potential," in I. M. Kolthoff and P. J. Elving, Eds., *Treatise on Analytical Chemistry*, Part I, Vol. 1, Interscience, New York–London, 1959.
3. Bjerrum, J., G. Schwarzenbach, and L. G. Sillén, *Stability Constants*, Part II, The Chemical Society, London, 1958.
4. Breiter, M., M. Kleinerman, and P. Delahay, *J. Am. Chem. Soc.*, **80**, 5111 (1958).
5. Butler, J. A. V., *Electrocapillarity*, Methuen, London, 1940, Chapter III.
6. Byrne, J. T., and L. B. Rogers, *J. Electrochem. Soc.*, **98**, 457 (1951).
7. Byrne, J. T., L. B. Rogers, and J. C. Griess, Jr., *J. Electrochem. Soc.*, **98**, 452 (1951).
8. Charlot, G., *Selected Constants: Oxidation-Reduction Potentials*, Pergamon, London, 1958.
9. Clark, G. L., and S. H. Simonsen, *J. Electrochem. Soc.*, **98**, 110 (1951).
10. Coche, A., *Compt. rend.*, **225**, 936 (1947).
11. Coche, M. A., H. Faraggi, P. Avignon, and M. Haïssinsky, *J. Phys. Radium*, **10**, 312 (1949).
12. Collin, F. M., *Analyst*, **54**, 654 (1929).
13. Conway, B. E., and J. O'M. Bockris, *Proc. Roy. Soc. London*, **A248**, 394 (1958).

14. Cruikshank, W., *Ann. Physik.*, **7**, 105 (1801).
15. DeFord, D. D., *Anal. Chem.*, **26**, 135 (1954); **28**, 660 (1956); **32**, 31R (1960).
16. DeFord, D. D., and R. C. Bowers, *Anal. Chem.*, **30**, 613 (1958).
17. Delahay, P., *New Instrumental Methods in Electrochemistry*, Interscience, New York–London, 1954.
18. Denise, F., and H. Leidheiser, *J. Electrochem. Soc.*, **100**, 490 (1953).
19. Diehl, H., *Electrochemical Analysis with Graded Cathode Potential*, G. F. Smith Chemical Co., Columbus, Ohio, 1948.
20. Diehl, H., and R. Brouns, *Iowa State Coll. J. Sci.*, **20**, 155 (1945).
21. Diehl, H., and J. P. Butler, *Analyst*, **77**, 268 (1936).
22. Eyring, H., S. Glasstone, and K. J. Laidler, *J. Chem. Phys.*, **7**, 1053 (1939).
23. Fischer, A., *Z. Angew. Chem.*, **20**, 134 (1907).
24. Flagg, J. F., and W. E. Bleidner, *J. Chem. Phys.*, **13**, 269 (1945).
25. Fritz, H., *Z. Anal. Chem.*, **78**, 418 (1929); *Mikrochemie*, **19**, 6 (1935); **21**, 47 (1936); **22**, 34, 168 (1937); **23**, 61 (1937); **24**, 22, 171 (1938).
26. Gerischer, H., *Z. Elektrochem.*, **57**, 604 (1953).
27. Gerischer, H., *Z. Physik. Chem.*, **202**, 302 (1953).
28. Gerischer, H., *Z. Elektrochem.*, **62**, 256 (1958).
29. Gerischer, H., *Anal. Chem.*, **31**, 33 (1959).
30. Gerischer, H., and M. Krause, *Z. Physik. Chem.*, N. F., **10**, 264 (1957).
31. Gerischer, H., and M. Krause, *Z. Physik. Chem.*, **14**, 184 (1958).
32. Gerischer, H., and R. P. Tischer, *Z. Elektrochem.*, **61**, 1159 (1957).
33. Gerischer, H., and W. Vielstich, *Z. Physik. Chem.*, N. F., **3**, 16 (1955).
34. Gibbs, W., *Z. Anal. Chem.*, **3**, 327 (1864).
35. Gierst, L., *Cinétique d'approche et réactions d'électrodes irréversibles*, thèse d'aggrégation, Université Libre de Bruxelles, Brussels, 1958.
36. Giordani, M., P. Ippoliti, and E. Scarano, *Ricerca Sci.*, **24**, 2316 (1954).
37. Glazunov, A., *Chim. & Ind. (Paris)*, Spec. No. 425 (1929); Spec. No. 247 (1930); Spec. No. 332 (1932); *Oesterr. Chem. Ztg.*, **41**, 217 (1938).
38. Griess, J. C., Jr., J. T. Byrne, and L. B. Rogers, *J. Electrochem. Soc.*, **98**, 447 (1951).
39. Griess, J. C., Jr., and L. B. Rogers, *Trans. Electrochem. Soc.*, **95**, 129 (1949).
40. Grower, G. G., *Am. Soc. Testing Mater. Proc.*, **17**, 129 (1917).
41. Gurney, R. W., *Ions in Solution*, Cambridge University Press, London, 1936, Chapter IV.
42. Haïssinsky, M., *J. Chim. Phys.*, **32**, 116 (1935); **43**, 21 (1946).
43. Haïssinsky, M., and A. Coche, *J. Chem. Soc.*, *Suppl.*, **2**, 397 (1949).
44. Haïssinsky, M., H. Faraggi, A. Coche, and P. Avignon, *Phys. Rev.*, **75**, 1963 (1949).
45. Hanney, C., *Helv. Chim. Acta*, **31**, 633 (1948).
46. Hayakawa, H., M. Ishibashi, and T. Fujinaga, *Japan Analyst (Bunseki Kagaku)*, **4**, 610 (1955).
47. Hermance, H. W., and H. V. Wadlow, "Electrography and Electro Spot Testing," in W. G. Berl, Ed., *Physical Methods in Chemical Analysis*, Academic Press, New York, 1951.
48. Herzfeld, K. F., *Physik. Z.*, **13**, 29 (1913).
49. Hevesy, G. V., and F. Paneth, *Physik. Z.*, **15**, 797 (1914).
50. Heyrovský, J., *Polarographisches Praktikum*, Springer-Verlag, Berlin, 1948.
51. Heyrovský, J., and D. Ilkovič, *Collection Czech. Chem. Commun.*, **7**, 198 (1935).
52. Hickling, A., *Trans. Faraday Soc.*, **38**, 27 (1942).
53. Ishibashi, M., and T. Fujinaga, *Japan Analyst (Bunseki Kagaku)*, **2**, 342 (1953).

54. Ishibashi, M., T. Fujinaga, and Y. Kusaka, *J. Chem. Soc. Japan, Pure Chem. Sect.* (*Nippon Kagaku Zasshi*), **75**, 13 (1954).
55. Ishibashi, M., T. Fujinaga, and M. Sato, *Japan Analyst* (*Bunseki Kagaku*), **5**, 77 (1956).
56. Ishibashi, M , T. Fujinaga, and M. Sato, *J. Chem. Soc. Japan, Pure Chem. Sect.* (*Nippon Kagaku Zasshi*), **77**, 696 (1956).
57. Ishibashi, M., T. Fujinaga, T. Tatsumi, and K. Hirose, *Japan Analyst* (*Bunseki Kagaku*), **4**, 365 (1955).
58. Johnson, G. L., R. F. Leininger, and E. Segré, *J. Chem. Phys.*, **17**, 1 (1949).
59. Joliot, F., *J. Chim. Phys.*, **27**, 119 (1930).
60. Kny-Jones, F. G., *Analyst*, **64**, 172, 575 (1939); **66**, 101 (1941).
61. Kny-Jones, F. G., A. J. Lindsey, and A. C. Penny, *Analyst*, **65**, 498 (1940).
62. Kolthoff, I. M., and J. J. Lingane, *Polarography*, 2 vols., Interscience, New York–London, 1952.
63. Kortüm, G., *Lehrbuch der Elektrochemie*, Verlag Chemie, Weinheim, 1957.
64. Koryta, J., *Z. Elektrochem.*, **61**, 423 (1957).
65. Koryta, J., *Collection Czech. Chem. Commun.*, **24**, 2903 (1959).
66. Koryta, J., *Collection Czech. Chem. Communs.*, **24**, 3057 (1959).
67. Koryta, J., *Electrochim. Acta*, **1**, 26 (1959).
68. Kramer, M. D., S. Swann, Jr., and J. C. Bailar, Jr., *Trans. Electrochem. Soc.*, **90**, 55 (1946).
69. Laitinen, H. A., and I. M. Kolthoff, *J. Phys. Chem.*, **45**, 1079 (1941).
70. Lassieur, A., *Bull. Soc. Chim. France*, [4], **39**, 1167 (1926).
71. Latimer, W. M., *The Oxidation States of the Elements and Their Potentials in Aqueous Solutions*, 2nd ed., Prentice-Hall, New York, 1952.
72. Lindsey, A. J., and H. J. S. Sand, *Analyst*, **59**, 328 (1934).
73. Lindsey, A. J., and H. J. S. Sand, *Analyst*, **60**, 744 (1935).
74. Lingane, J. J., *J. Am. Chem. Soc.*, **61**, 976 (1939).
75. Lingane, J. J., *Chem. Revs.*, **29**, 1 (1941).
76. Lingane, J. J., *Ind. Eng. Chem., Anal. Ed.*, **17**, 640 (1945).
77. Lingane, J. J., *J. Am. Chem. Soc.*, **67**, 1916 (1945).
78. Lingane, J. J., *Ind. Eng. Chem., Anal. Ed.*, **18**, 430 (1946).
79. Lingane, J. J., *Anal. Chim. Acta*, **2**, 589 (1948).
80. Lingane, J. J., *Electroanalytical Chemistry*, Interscience, New York–London, 1958.
81. Lingane, J. J., and S. L. Jones, *Anal. Chem.*, **23**, 1798 (1951).
82. Lipchinskiĭ, A., *Zhur. Anal. Khim.*, **12**, 83 (1957).
83. Lyons, E. H., Jr., *J. Electrochem. Soc.*, **101**, 363 (1954).
84. Lyons, E. H., Jr., *J. Electrochem. Soc.*, **101**, 376 (1954).
85. MacNevin, W. M., and B. B. Baker, *Anal. Chem.*, **24**, 986 (1952).
86. MacNevin, W. M., and S. M. Tuthill, *Anal. Chem.*, **21**, 1052 (1949).
87. Matsuda, H., and Y. Ayabe, *Bull. Chem. Soc. Japan*, **29**, 134 (1956).
88. Matsuda, H., and Y. Ayabe, *Z. Elektrochem.*, **63**, 1164 (1959).
89. Matsuura, N., *Japan Analyst* (*Bunseki Kagaku*), **5**, 411 (1956).
90. Maxwell, J. A., and R. P. Graham, *Chem. Revs.*, **46**, 471 (1950).
91. Mehl, W., and J. O'M. Bockris, *J. Chem. Phys.*, **27**, 818 (1957).
92. Meites, L., *Polarographic Techniques*, Interscience, New York–London, 1955.
93. Meites, L., and S. A. Moros, *Anal. Chem.*, **31**, 23 (1959).
94. Meites, L., "Controlled-Potential Electrolysis," in A. Weissberger, Ed., *Physical Methods of Organic Chemistry*, Interscience, New York–London, 1960.
95. Miller, H., *Ind. Eng. Chem., Anal. Ed.*, **8**, 431 (1936).

96. Milner, G. W. C., and R. N. Witten, *Analyst*, **77**, 11 (1952).
97. Morinaga, K., *J. Chem. Soc. Japan, Pure Chem. Sect.* (*Nippon Kagaku Zasshi*), **79**, 200 (1958).
98. Oka, S., G. Muto, and S. Nagatsuka, *Japan Analyst* (*Bunseki Kagaku*), **2**, 198 (1953).
99. Parry, R. W., and E. H. Lyons, Jr., "Coordination Compounds in Electrodeposition," in J. C. Bailar, Jr. and D. H. Busch, Eds., *The Chemistry of the Coordination Compounds*, Reinhold, New York, 1956.
100. Reilley, C. N., W. G. Scribner, and C. Temple, *Anal. Chem.*, **28**, 450 (1956).
101. Rogers, L. B., *J. Electrochem. Soc.*, **99**, 267 (1952).
102. Rogers, L. B., D. P. Krause, J. C. Griess, Jr., and D. B. Ehrlinger, *Trans. Electrochem. Soc.*, **95**, 33 (1949).
103. Rogers, L. B., and A. F. Stehney, *Trans. Electrochem. Soc.*, **95**, 25 (1949).
104. Sand, H. J. S., *J. Chem. Soc.*, **91**, 373 (1907).
105. Sand, H. J. S., *J. Chem. Soc.*, **91**, 401 (1907).
106. Sand, H. J. S., *Electrochemistry and Electrochemical Analysis*, Blackie and Sons, London, 1940, Vol. II.
107. Schleicher, A., *Elektroanalytische Schnellmethode*, F. Enke, Stuttgart, 1947.
108. Schoch, E. P., and D. G. Brown, *Trans. Am. Electrochem. Soc.*, **22**, 265 (1913); *J. Am. Chem. Soc.*, **38**, 1660 (1916).
109. Stackelberg, M. von, *Z. Elektrochem.*, **45**, 466 (1939).
110. Stackelberg, M. von, *Polarographische Arbeitsmethoden*, W. de Gruyter, Berlin, 1950.
111. Szebelledy, L., and Z. Somogyi, *Z. Anal. Chem.*, **112**, 313 (1938).
112. Tamamushi, R., and N. Tanaka, *Bull. Chem. Soc. Japan*, **23**, 110 (1950).
113. Tanaka, M., *Japan Analyst* (*Bunseki Kagaku*), **6**, 344 (1957).
114. Tanaka, M., *Japan Analyst* (*Bunseki Kagaku*), **6**, 409 (1957).
115. Tanaka, M., *Japan Analyst* (*Bunseki Kagaku*), **6**, 413 (1957).
116. Tanaka, M., *Japan Analyst* (*Bunseki Kagaku*), **6**, 477 (1957).
117. Tanaka, M., *Japan Analyst* (*Bunseki Kagaku*), **6**, 482 (1957).
118. Tanaka, M., *Japan Analyst* (*Bunseki Kagaku*), **6**, 617 (1957).
119. Tanaka, M., *Japan Analyst* (*Bunseki Kagaku*), **8**, 501 (1959).
120. Tanaka, N., and R. Tamamushi, *Sbornik Meziárod. Polarog. Sjezdu, Praze, 1st Congr.*, 1951, Pt. I. Proc., p. 486.
121. Tanaka, N., R. Tamamushi, and M. Kodama, *Z. Physik. Chem.*, N. F., **14**, 141 (1958).
122. Taube, H., *Chem. Revs.*, **50**, 69 (1952).
123. Torrance, S., *Analyst*, **62**, 719 (1937).
124. Torrance, S., *Analyst*, **63**, 488 (1938).
125. Tutundzic, P. S., *Z. Anorg. Allgem. Chem.*, **237**, 38 (1938).
126. Vetter, K. J., *Z. Elektrochem.*, **59**, 596 (1955).
127. Vetter, K. J., *Elektrochemische Kinetik*, Springer-Verlag, Berlin, 1961.
128. Vielstich, W., and H. Gerischer, *Z. Physik. Chem.*, N. F., **4**, 10 (1955).
129. Vlček, A. A., *Collection Czech. Chem. Commun.*, **20**, 894 (1955).
130. Vlček, A. A., *Nature*, **177**, 1043 (1956).
131. Vlček, A. A., *Collection Czech. Chem. Commun.*, **22**, 948 (1957).
132. Vlček, A. A., *Z. Elektrochem.*, **61**, 1014 (1957).
133. Yokosuka, S., *Japan Analyst* (*Bunseki Kagaku*), **6**, 695, 753 (1957).
134. Zhdanov, A. K., V. A. Khadeev, and F. M. Mirzabekov, *Zhur. Anal. Khim.*, **13**, 661 (1958); *Zhur. Priklad. Khim.*, **31**, 640 (1958).

Chapter 49

COULOMETRIC ANALYSIS

By Donald D. DeFord, *Northwestern University, Evanston, Illinois,* and John W. Miller, *Phillips Petroleum Company, Bartlesville, Oklahoma*

Contents

Contents (*continued*)

I. INTRODUCTION

A. FUNDAMENTAL PRINCIPLES OF COULOMETRIC ANALYSIS

A coulometric analysis is one in which the desired substance is made to undergo a quantitative, stoichiometric reaction with electrons. The quantity of material present is then calculated with the aid of Faraday's law from a measurement of the number of electrons (i.e., the number of coulombs of electricity) required to effect the reaction. Since all types of coulometric analyses involve a titration with electrons, the term *coulometric titration* is commonly used as a synonym for coulometric analysis. This term is used in this sense throughout this chapter, although it should be pointed out that some investigators (50) prefer to restrict its usage to denote only analyses involving secondary processes, in accordance with the original usage (186) of the term.

In all coulometric titrations electrons are added to (or removed from) the system at a suitable electrode in an electrolysis cell. The electrons may be taken up (or given up) directly by the substance being titrated (primary process); for example, ferric ion may be titrated at a cathode according to the reaction

$$Fe^{+3} + e^- \rightarrow Fe^{+2} \tag{1}$$

Alternatively, an electron carrier or *coulometric intermediate* may be used (secondary processes) as in the titration of ferric ion with electrolytically generated titanous ion.

Electrode reaction:

$$Ti^{+4} + e^- \rightarrow Ti^{+3} \tag{2a}$$

Secondary reaction:

$$\underline{Fe^{+3}} + Ti^{+3} \rightarrow \underline{Fe^{+2}} + Ti^{+4} \tag{2b}$$

Over-all reaction:

$$Fe^{+3} + e^- \rightarrow Fe^{+2} \tag{2c}$$

In both cases the over-all reactions are identical; the Ti^{+4}–Ti^{+3} redox couple in the second example serves essentially as a catalyst and is not involved in the stoichiometry of the over-all reaction.

Although many coulometric titrations can be carried out by either a primary or a secondary process, only one of these alternatives may be applicable to certain titrations. In the titration of olefins with electrolytically generated bromine, for example, the coulometric intermediate is incorporated into the final product, and the desired over-all reaction can be accomplished only by a secondary process.

Electrode reaction:

$$2Br^- \rightarrow Br_2 + 2e^- \tag{3a}$$

Secondary reaction:

$$\underline{R_2C{=}CR_2} + Br_2 \rightarrow \underline{R_2CBrCBrR_2} \tag{3b}$$

Over-all reaction:

$$R_2C{=}CR_2 + 2Br^- \rightarrow R_2CBrCBrR_2 + 2e^- \tag{3c}$$

In some cases the titration is performed by addition of electrons to the system at the cathode, as in equations (1) and (2), and in other cases by withdrawal of electrons at the anode, as in equation (3). All electrolysis cells must have both a cathode and an anode, but usually only one of these electrodes, the *working electrode*, is directly involved in the over-all titration reaction. The other electrode, the *auxiliary electrode*, is necessary to complete the electrical circuit but is not involved in the titration reaction itself.

If the *over-all* titration reaction proceeds with 100% current efficiency—that is, if all of the electricity entering the cell is consumed in the desired titration reaction—the weight of the substance being determined is given by

$$W = QM/nF \tag{4}$$

where Q is the quantity of electricity (coulombs) required for complete reaction, M is the molecular weight of the substance, n is the number of faradays involved in the reaction with one mole of substance, and F is the value of the faraday (96,491 coulombs per equivalent) (40,41).

A quantitative over-all titration reaction that proceeds with 100% current efficiency is essential for the successful employment of the coulometric method. The problems involved in the application of the method consist almost entirely in the selection and maintenance of experimental conditions that will insure the fulfillment of this requirement within the limits of error that can be tolerated in the analysis. Although it is usually possible to determine and to apply some correction for deviations from ideal behavior, the ultimate sensitivity and accuracy of the method are determined in large measure by the degree of success realized in minimizing all such deviations.

If the titration involves only a primary electrochemical reaction, as in equation (1), one need be concerned only that this electrochemical reaction is quantitative. On the other hand, if the titration is carried out by a secondary process, one must insure that the secondary chemical reactions, equations (2b) and (3b), as well as the electrode reactions, equations (2a) and (3a), are quantitative. The problems involved in obtaining quantitative secondary chemical reactions are substantially identical with those encountered in classic titrimetry and are discussed fully in other chapters of this Treatise. Only the electrode reactions will be treated in detail in this chapter.

The nature of the reactions that occur at the surface of a particular electrode in any given solution and the extent to which these reactions proceed to completion are determined by the potential of the electrode. It is apparent, then, that the potential of the working electrode must be controlled within limits that insure the realization of the desired quantitative electrochemical reaction. In the technique which has come to be known as *controlled-potential* coulometric analysis, the potential is controlled in a direct fashion by continuously monitoring the potential of the working electrode with respect to a suitable reference electrode and adjusting the output of the electrolysis power supply as necessary to maintain the desired potential. Automatic instruments, called *potentiostats*, may be employed for this purpose. The second general technique for controlling the electrode potential consists in adding to the solution an excess of a suitable electroactive substance that can act as a redox buffer. In this case it is the current rather than the potential that is subjected to external control, and the technique is known as *controlled-current* coulometric analysis. The added substance must not only maintain the desired potential, but also its

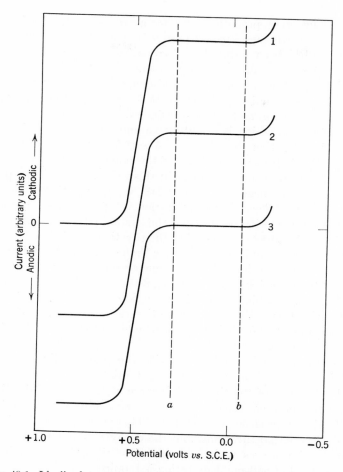

Fig. 49.1. Idealized current–potential curves for the ferric–ferrous system.

electrolysis product must serve as a coulometric intermediate for the substance being titrated. Except for certain types of film-stripping coulometry, the controlled-current technique is applicable only when a secondary process is involved; the controlled-potential technique is usually applicable to both primary and secondary processes.

A qualitative understanding of the basic features of these two fundamental techniques of potential control can be gained by an examination of the pertinent current–potential curves. The coulometric titration of ferric iron will serve as an illustrative example. In Fig. 49.1, curve 1 represents the current–potential curve for a sample containing iron in the ferric state only, whereas curve 2 represents the situation when one-half the ferric ion has been reduced to ferrous ion (50% completion of the coulometric titration), and curve 3 represents complete reduction. At all stages of the titration a reasonably well-defined limiting current plateau, corresponding to reduction of ferric ion to ferrous, exists in the region between +0.30 v. (line a) and −0.05 v. (line b). In this potential range the reduction of the ferric ion is quantitative and this reduction is the only electrochemical reaction that occurs. A satisfactory controlled-potential coulometric titration can be achieved if the potential of the working electrode is maintained at any point within this range. Should the potential become much more negative than −0.05 v., quantitative reduction of ferric ion can be achieved, but the titration will fail because simultaneous reduction of hydrogen ion occurs, and the current efficiency for the desired reaction falls below 100%. Likewise, the titration will fail if the potential is allowed to become much more positive than +0.3 v.; the failure in this case results not from a low current efficiency but rather from incomplete reduction of the ferric ion. For example, if the potential is set at +0.50 v., a cathodic current, which results in reduction of ferric ion, exists at the start of the titration. However, as the titration proceeds this current decreases; when half the ferric ion has been reduced the current has fallen to zero and no further reaction occurs.

When the titration is carried out with the potential in the optimum range, it is apparent from the current–potential curves that the current (hence also the rate of the titration) is large at the start of the titration. As the titration proceeds the current falls, approaching zero asymptotically as the titration approaches completion. This general behavior is typical of controlled-potential titrations, and the decay of the current to a negligibly small value serves to indicate that the titration is complete. No auxiliary method of end-point detection is required.

The controlled-current technique may be used for the coulometric titration of ferric ion if titanic ion is added to the sample solution. Current–potential curves for this system corresponding to 0, 50, and 100% completion of the titration are shown by curves 1, 2, and 3, respectively, in Fig. 49.2. With this system the impression of a current corresponding to line a results initially only in the direct reduction of ferric ion (intersection of line a with curve 1); the electrode potential is approximately +0.50 v. When about half of the ferric ion has been reduced, the rate at which ferric ion diffuses to the electrode surface is no longer sufficient to maintain the impressed current. The potential shifts to the vicinity of 0.0 v., where simultaneous reduction of ferric and titanic ions occurs (intersection

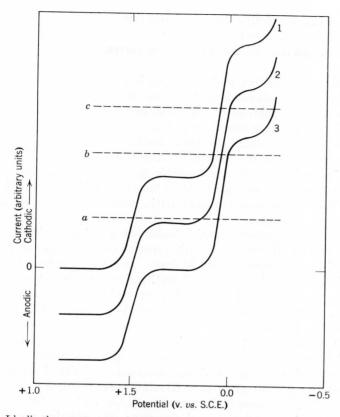

Fig. 49.2. Idealized current–potential curves for the coulometric titration of ferric iron with electrolytically generated titanous ion.

of line a with curve 2). However, as the titanous ion that is produced diffuses from the electrode surface and is mixed with the body of the solution, it reacts with the ferric ion, as indicated by equation (2b). The overall reaction, equation (2c), is identical with that for the controlled-potential case, and the over-all titration efficiency is 100%. The same situation obtains even if a larger current (line b) is employed. In this case the potential of the working electrode remains in the vicinity of 0.0 v., and simultaneous reduction of ferric and titanic ions occurs during the entire course of the titration. It is clear that the titration will fail, however, if a very large constant current corresponding to line c is employed. This current exceeds the limiting diffusion current of the titanic ion, and the potential moves to values sufficiently negative to reduce hydrogen ion as the titration approaches completion (intersection of line *c* with curve *3*). A current corresponding to line *c* could be used if the concentration of the titanic ion were increased so that its limiting diffusion current exceeded the impressed current.

When the controlled-current technique is employed, the titration system itself gives no indication of the degree of completion of the titration. and some auxiliary method of end-point detection must be employed so that the titration may be terminated when the equivalence point is reached. In general, any end-point detection method suitable for locating the equivalence point for the secondary chemical reaction involved in the titration is applicable. In the example discussed above, any indication method that may be used satisfactorily for the titration of ferric ion with titanous ion by the standard volumetric method may be used for the coulometric method also.

Neither the controlled-potential technique nor the controlled-current technique can be said to be generally superior to the other. Each has its own peculiar advantages and limitations. In some cases no suitable coulometric intermediate is available; these titrations must be performed by the controlled-potential technique. Whenever coulometric intermediates are employed, the controlled-current technique is usually, but by no means always (222a), the preferred method. Frequently the controlled-potential technique possesses greater selectivity because of the greater precision of potential control that can be achieved. On the other hand, the decay of the current during the course of controlled-potential titrations makes this method relatively slow; often 15 to 60 minutes are required for completion of the titration. Because high currents may be employed throughout the entire course of controlled-current titrations, the titration may be completed in a very few minutes. The shorter times required with the controlled-current method are advantageous not only because of the greater speed of analysis but also because relative errors arising from background currents, side reactions, and other similar causes are frequently minimized if the time required for the titration is kept as short as possible. The apparatus required for the controlled-current technique is usually simpler and less expensive than that required for the controlled-potential technique. This is particularly true if a constant titration current is employed so that the number of coulombs may be evaluated from the current–time product, thus obviating the need for a separate coulometer.

B. HISTORICAL

The fundamental principle of electrochemical equivalence was first stated by Faraday in 1833. Chemical coulometers, which are based on this principle and which depend upon a measurement of the number of equivalents of an electrolysis product to estimate the quantity of electricity passed through an electrolytic cell, have been in common use for more than a century. It is rather strange that the reverse application of this law, the technique of coulometric analysis, has been developed only relatively recently. The origins of the coulometric method can be traced back to Grower (87) who, in 1917, determined the thickness of tin coatings on copper wire by measuring the number of coulombs required to strip the coating from the wire when the latter was made the anode in an electrolytic cell. Little further interest in the method was evident for 20 years following Grower's work, although a few additional papers dealing with the determination of coatings and films on metals appeared in the literature. In 1938, Szebelledy and Somogyi (233) published a series of classic papers that greatly broadened the scope of coulometric analysis by introducing the use of coulometric intermediates. Further studies of this powerful new technique were initiated by Professor E. H. Swift and his collaborators in 1946; their results demonstrated the versatility, simplicity, and accuracy of the method and stimulated many further investigations and applications.

Coulometric analysis with controlled potential was first explored in 1942 by Hickling (101). In 1945, Lingane published the first of a series of papers that established this technique as a practical analytical method (139).

Since 1950, interest in the coulometric method has been widespread, and several hundred papers on the subject have appeared in the literature. Coulometry now constitutes one of the major branches of electroanalytical chemistry.

II. FACTORS INVOLVED IN THE CONTROL OF CURRENT EFFICIENCY AND THE DEGREE OF COMPLETION OF THE TITRATION REACTION

A. SELECTION OF THE ELECTRODE POTENTIAL IN CONTROLLED-POTENTIAL TITRIMETRY

1. Reversible Processes

If the electrochemical reaction that occurs at an electrode surface is strictly reversible, that is, if a condition of redox equilibrium exists at the electrode surface, the Nernst equation may be used to describe the relationship between the electrode potential and the degree of completion of the reaction at the conclusion of the titration. A generalized redox reaction may be represented by the equation

$$wO + xX + ne \rightleftharpoons yR + zZ \tag{5}$$

where O and R represent the oxidized and reduced forms of the redox couple, X and Z are any other substances involved in the reaction, and w, x, n, y, and z are stoichiometric coefficients. For this reaction the Nernst equation is

$$E = E^0 - \frac{RT}{2.3nF} \log{(\gamma_R^y C_R^y \gamma_Z^z C_Z^z)/(\gamma_O^w C_O^w \gamma_X^x C_X^x)} \tag{6}$$

where E is the electrode potential, E^0 is the standard potential for the reaction, R is the gas constant, T is the absolute temperature, the γ's are the activity coefficients, and the C's are the concentrations. For any given set of experimental conditions the activity coefficients are approximately constant and it is convenient to write equation (6) in the form

$$E = E^{0\prime} - \frac{RT}{2.3nF} \log{(C_R^y C_Z^z)/(C_O^w C_X^x)} \tag{7}$$

where $E^{0\prime}$ is the formal potential of the redox reaction and is given by

$$E^{0\prime} = E^0 - \frac{RT}{2.3nF} \log{(\gamma_R^y \gamma_Z^z)/(\gamma_O^w \gamma_X^x)} \tag{8}$$

A few specific examples will serve to illustrate the application of equation (7). In these examples, a temperature of 25°C., at which the factor $RT/2.3F$ has a value of 0.059 v., will be assumed. For the titration of ferric ion according to equation (1), the Nernst equation takes the form

$$E = E^{0\prime} - \frac{0.059}{1} \log{\frac{[\mathrm{Fe}^{+2}]}{[\mathrm{Fe}^{+3}]}} \tag{9}$$

The degree of completion of the titration reaction—that is, the fraction of the original sample that undergoes the desired titration reaction—is given by

$$\lambda = \frac{[\mathrm{Fe}^{+3}]^0 - [\mathrm{Fe}^{+3}]}{[\mathrm{Fe}^{+3}]^0} \tag{10}$$

where $[\mathrm{Fe}^{+3}]^0$ represents the initial concentration of the ferric ion and $[\mathrm{Fe}^{+3}]$ the concentration at the conclusion of the titration. Since $[\mathrm{Fe}^{+2}] = \lambda[\mathrm{Fe}^{+3}]^0$, equation (9) may be written in the form

$$E = E^{0\prime} - \frac{0.059}{1} \log{\frac{\lambda}{1 - \lambda}} \tag{11}$$

If it is desired that the titration be at least 99.9% complete ($\lambda = 0.999$), it is apparent that the electrode potential must be at least 3×0.059 or 0.177

v. more negative than the formal potential. Had the electrode process involved a 2-electron change ($n = 2$) rather than a single electron process, an electrode potential only $3 \times 0.059/2$ or 0.089 v. more negative than the formal potential would have been sufficient to achieve quantitative titration.

For the determination of copper by the plating of copper at a platinum cathode from a solution of cupric ion according to the reaction

$$Cu^{+2} + 2e^- \rightleftharpoons Cu \tag{12}$$

the Nernst equation takes the final form

$$E = E^{0\prime} - \frac{0.059}{2} \log \frac{1}{[Cu^{+2}]^0} - \frac{0.059}{2} \log \frac{1}{1 - \lambda} \tag{13}$$

For this particular reaction, the degree of completion of the titration is a function not only of the applied potential but also of the initial concentration of cupric ion in the sample. If the preceding reduction is carried out at a mercury cathode, in which the deposited copper is soluble, the Nernst equation becomes

$$E = E_a^{0\prime} - \frac{0.059}{2} \log \frac{V_s}{V_{Hg}} - \frac{0.059}{2} \log \frac{\lambda}{1 - \lambda} \tag{14}$$

Here the degree of completion of the reaction does not depend upon the original concentration of cupric ion but is influenced by the ratio of the volume of the aqueous solution, V_s, to the volume of mercury, V_{Hg}. The subscript on the symbol for the formal potential indicates that the formal potential to be used in this calculation is that of the amalgam electrode. Since formal potentials, including amalgam potentials, at a mercury electrode are virtually the same as polarographic half-wave potentials for reversible processes carried out in the same media, the wealth of polarographic data available is extremely valuable in selecting suitable conditions and potentials for coulometric analyses that employ mercury electrodes.

Although only primary processes were used in the preceding illustrative examples, the same approach may be employed for secondary processes also. For the titration of chloride ion at a silver anode according to the over-all reaction

$$Ag + Cl^- \rightleftharpoons AgCl + e^- \tag{15}$$

the appropriate form of the Nernst equation is

$$E = E^{0\prime} - \frac{0.059}{1} \log [Cl^-]^0 - \frac{0.059}{1} \log (1 - \lambda) \tag{16}$$

The influence of complexing agents and of pH on the potentials at which electrochemical reactions occur has already been discussed in earlier chapters. By judicious selection of complexing agents and by proper adjustment of pH and the concentration of the complexing agents, it is usually possible to devise an electrolysis system that will permit quantitative titration of the desired substance without serious interference from other components in the sample.

Although most of the coulometric titrations that have been investigated have been carried out in aqueous solvents, the use of nonaqueous solvents also is feasible, provided the solution has a sufficient electrical conductivity. If the use of nonaqueous solvents is contemplated, it should be remembered that the formal potentials of electrochemical reactions in these solvents are frequently very different from those in water.

If a substance is to be titrated in the presence of a potentially interfering substance and if both react at the electrode by a single electron process, it is clear from equation (11) that the formal potentials of the two substances must be separated by at least 0.354 v. if quantitative ($\lambda = 0.999$) titration of the one is to be accomplished with negligible ($\lambda = 0.001$) titration of the other. Smaller differences are permissible if the value of n for one or both reactions is greater than unity (0.177 v. if the value of n is 2 for both reactions, etc.). If the concentration of the potentially interfering substance is considerably less than that of the desired substance, values of λ somewhat greater than 0.001 may be tolerated without introducing serious errors into the desired determination. This would allow satisfactory titrations with slightly smaller differences in formal potentials than those calculated above. Conversely, greater differences in formal potentials are necessary if the concentration of the potentially interfering substance exceeds that of the desired substance.

If a solid is deposited on an inert electrode from extremely dilute solutions, the total deposit may be less than a monolayer even when the entire sample has been plated. Since the activity of a fractional monolayer is usually quite different from that of a bulk deposit, the calculations outlined above are invalid (89,212); a modified form of the Nernst equation usually may be applied, however.

2. Irreversible Processes

The rates of totally irreversible electrode processes are extremely slow in the vicinity of their equilibrium potentials. Calculations of the type outlined in the preceding section are of little value in selecting suitable potentials for analyses. The use of the current–potential curves for the particular system under consideration, as outlined in Section I-A, constitutes the only practical method for selecting an appropriate potential and for estimating the degree of completion of the desired reaction and the extent of interference from undesired reactions. Even this approach is only semiquantitative at best, and the preliminary conclusions drawn from an examination of the current–potential curves must be verified by actual coulometric titrations of standards.

B. BACKGROUND CURRENTS

Any current that does not contribute to the desired electrochemical reactions may be called a background or residual current. Since any background current causes the current efficiency to fall below 100%, such currents should be eliminated to the maximum extent possible, and corrections must be applied for those that cannot be eliminated.

Leaks in the electrical circuit constitute one possible source of background currents. This source of trouble is easily eliminated by keeping the equipment in good condition and maintaining good insulation between the electrical leads to the cell. Only one type of leakage current deserves any special comment. When mercury electrodes are used it is common practice to make electrical contact with the mercury through a platinum or nickel wire. Even though the contact wire may be sealed into the electrolysis cell well below the surface of the mercury, it is possible that a film of solution may creep between the mercury and the wall of the container and reach the contact wire. When this situation exists, a portion of the current may pass from the auxiliary electrode through the film of solution directly to the contact wire, by-passing the mercury completely. The tendency of aqueous solutions to creep between mercury and glass is particularly pronounced when the electrode is operated at quite negative potentials. Under these conditions, large background currents resulting from reduction of water at the platinum or nickel contact may occur. Treatment of the glass surfaces with silicones or other water-repellent films is helpful in minimizing creepage. Placement of the contact wire in a tube or leveling bulb that is far removed from the mercury–solution interface is also effective. Although problems of the type discussed above are encountered most often with mercury electrodes, it must be emphasized that films of solution that reach the contact point between electrodes and connecting wires may cause trouble in any system.

Background currents, other than those resulting from electrical leaks, may be grouped into five different categories—charging, impurity faradaic, continuous faradaic, kinetic, and induced (6a,173). Each of these types will be considered individually.

The interface between the solution and the surface of the working electrode constitutes an electrolytic capacitor. The capacity of this interface may vary between wide limits, depending on the particular electrode used, the composition of the solution, and the electrode potential, but a capacity of 10 to 100 microfarads per square centimeter is typical. If the potential of the working electrode before the titration is started is different from that which it assumes during the titration, a portion of the current entering the cell is consumed in charging the interfacial capacity. The number of coulombs required for the charging process may be estimated from the relationship

$$Q = C \Delta E \tag{17}$$

If one assumes a change in potential of 1 v., an electrode area of 10 cm.², and a double-layer capacity of 20 μf./cm.², then 2×10^{-4} coulombs are required. This constitutes a negligibly small error when one is titrating 1 meq. of sample, which requires approximately 100 coulombs. Normally, charging-current errors become significant only in the titration of extremely small quantities of material. There are several ways in which these errors may be minimized or eliminated when necessary. In controlled-potential analyses, the working electrode may be brought to its operating potential in the presence of supporting electrolyte before the sample is added. In controlled-current methods, pretitration of the supporting electrolyte accomplishes the same result. In either method, the contribution of charging currents is included in a blank run; blanks thus constitute an effective method of compensating for errors from this source.

Impurity faradaic currents are those resulting from the more-or-less quantitative titration of impurities present in the solution or on the electrode surface. If the current results from an impurity on the electrode surface—for example, an oxide film that is reduced during the course of the titration—proper pretreatment of the electrode to remove the impurity is generally effective. Similarly, interferences caused by impurities in the reagents and solvents can be eliminated by prior treatments designed either to remove the impurities or to convert them to a noninterfering form. Purification of reagents and solvents by electrochemical methods is often particularly effective, especially in controlled-potential methods (166). Pretitration of reagent solutions will eliminate interferences in many cases. Blanks may be used effectively to correct for small errors arising from impurities in the solvents or reagents employed.

The reduction of dissolved oxygen is one of the most commonly encountered sources of impurity faradaic currents when the working electrode is operated at potentials sufficiently negative to cause this reduction to occur. Fortunately, oxygen can be removed easily by bubbling an inert gas such as nitrogen through the solution.   In some cases a reagent, such as sulfite ion, may be used to destroy the dissolved oxygen.

Impurity faradaic currents that arise from constituents of the sample itself cannot be eliminated or corrected for by the techniques described above. Interferences from this source can be eliminated only by removal of the offending species or by conversion to some noninterfering state.

Continuous faradaic currents are those that arise from the slow, irreversible oxidation or reduction of some major component in the system, usually the solvent.   The discussion below will be restricted to oxidation and reduction of water, but similar considerations hold for other solvents. The formal potential for the reduction of water under a pressure of 1 atmosphere of hydrogen varies from about -0.25 v. vs. S.C.E. at pH 0 to about -1.07 v. at pH 14.   Similarly, the formal potential for the oxidation of water under a pressure of 1 atm. of oxygen varies from about $+0.98$ v. at pH 0 to about $+0.16$ v. at pH 14.   Formal potentials for the reduction are less negative if the hydrogen pressure is less than 1 atm., whereas those for the oxidation are less positive if the oxygen pressure is less than 1 atm. Water is thermodynamically stable only if the electrode potential lies between the formal potential for reduction and that for oxidation.   Whenever the electrode is operated at potentials outside this range of stability, water will be reduced or oxidized at a finite rate at the electrode surface.   The current consumed in these processes is the continuous faradaic current. The rate of reduction or oxidation of water, hence also the magnitude of the current, depends on the value of the overpotential for the particular electrode–solution system used, the area of the electrode, and also upon the potential at which the electrode is maintained.

Since the continuous faradaic current is usually an exponential function of the potential when the electrode is operated in the unstable region, it is advantageous to select conditions for the titration that require the minimum possible excursion of the potential into the unstable region.   If possible, the electrode chosen should be the one with the highest available overpotential.   Overpotentials vary extremely widely between different electrode materials; the overpotential for the reduction of water is only a few millivolts on platinized platinum but is about 1 v. on mercury.

In a constant-potential coulometric titration, the continuous faradaic current is substantially constant throughout the entire course of the titration.   A blank determination, carried out at the same potential and for the same length of time as the sample titration, enables a proper correction for this background current to be made.   On the other hand, the potential may vary between rather wide limits in a controlled-current titration (see Section I-A); this variation in the potential causes the continuous faradaic current to vary during the course of the titration also. Even if the potential of the electrode were constant, the magnitude of the correction to be applied for the continuous faradaic background current depends upon the time required for the titration, and a blank determination would be of no value since it would require a shorter time than the titration of the sample. The only really satisfactory way to eliminate errors arising from the continuous faradaic current in controlled-current titrations is to select operating conditions under which these errors are negligible. If this proves to be impossible, the only other alternative available is to obtain a set of empirical calibration factors by titrating known standards over the same concentration ranges as those encountered in the samples.

Kinetic background currents, which are of concern primarily in controlled-potential titrations, result from slow chemical reactions that regenerate the starting material. In the determination of manganese by reduction of Mn(II) ion to Mn(I) ion in cyanide solution, for example, the Mn(I) ion is slowly oxidized back to Mn(II) by water. This component of the background current rises from zero at the start of the titration, when no Mn(I) is present, to a final steady-state value after extensive prolongation of the titration. Blanks are of no value in correcting for errors from this source, since the current results from titration of the sample itself. If the kinetics of the interfering reaction are known, it is possible, in principle, to calculate the magnitude of the error, but this is seldom a practical solution.

Induced background currents result from oxidations or reductions that do not normally proceed at the electrode surface under the ambient conditions employed, but that are induced by the main electrochemical reaction. In some cases these induced reactions may occur because of changes in the electrode surface. For example, during the deposition of nickel ion at a mercury cathode, the overpotential for the reduction of water may be reduced to such an extent that water is reduced at a much greater rate than it is in the absence of simultaneous reduction of nickel. In other cases the induced reaction may be a side reaction involving transient intermediates produced in the main electrolysis.

C. SIDE REACTIONS

Side reactions that can in any way alter the stoichiometry of the desired over-all titration reaction are always potential sources of error in all types of coulometric analysis. The reactions occurring during the controlled-potential oxidation of the tetraphenylborate ion in unbuffered solution will serve to illustrate one type of system that may be encountered (82). Although the primary electrode process is a two-electron oxidation, the oxidation product, presumably the diphenylboronium ion, undergoes a further slow reaction with water to liberate hydrogen ions, which in turn react slowly with tetraphenylborate ions to produce electrochemically inactive products. The number of faradays of electricity required for complete removal of 1 mole of tetraphenylborate varies from as little as 1 to as much as 2 faradays, depending on the initial concentration of the ion and other experimental conditions. Geske and Bard (83) have given a general classification of side reactions of this sort and a mathematical evaluation of the errors that may be encountered in each case. Generally speaking, side reactions are more frequently encountered and usually prove to be more troublesome in the titration of organic compounds than in the titration of inorganic materials.

D. THE AUXILIARY ELECTRODE

Since the auxiliary electrode is not involved in any way in the titration, any convenient electrode material and any desired electrode reaction may be employed, provided only that the electrode reactions or the products of electrolysis are not allowed to interfere in any way with the titration reaction. The most generally applicable method of preventing such interference consists in the use of separate compartments for the working electrode and the auxiliary electrode. These compartments must be connected through a salt bridge, porous plug, or some other device that will allow the conduction of the current but that will prevent gross mixing of the contents of the two chambers.

In many cases it is possible to devise auxiliary electrodes that can be placed in the sample solution along with the working electrode without giving rise to any interfering reactions. If the auxiliary electrode is to be the anode, and if it is permissible to add chloride ion to the solution, a silver wire usually may be made to serve as the auxiliary electrode. The product of the electrode reaction in this case is solid silver chloride, which deposits on the surface of the electrode and which does not interfere with the titration reaction in most cases. Platinum anodes are seldom satisfactory as auxiliary electrodes because of the probable interference resulting from the evolved oxygen; in some cases they may be used if a depolarizer such as hydrazine, the oxidation of which yields nitrogen, can be added to the solution. Platinum cathodes frequently can be employed as auxiliary electrodes, however, since the usual electrolysis product, hydrogen, seldom interferes in the titration reaction.

E. THE WORKING ELECTRODE

Although the material of construction and the nature of the surface of an inert electrode have no influence on the *equilibrium* composition of a solution in contact with it, the rates of electrochemical reactions are profoundly affected by these factors. A few examples will serve to illustrate this point. The deposition of bismuth from tartrate solution at pH 6.0 onto a clean platinum cathode at -0.3 v. is immeasurably slow; yet the deposition proceeds rapidly if the electrode is previously coated with bismuth (138). The reduction of stannic tin to the stannous state cannot be made to proceed with 100% current efficiency at a clean platinum electrode in acidic bromide solution because hydrogen ion is reduced simultaneously. If a film by hydrous stannic oxide is allowed to form on the electrode surface, the hydrogen overpotential rises sufficiently to permit 100% efficiency for the desired reduction (9). The iron(II)–iron(III) couple is substantially reversible at an oxidized platinum surface but behaves quite irreversibly at a clean platinum surface (118).

In selecting and preparing an electrode for any particular titration, one hopes, of course, to achieve a surface at which undesired reactions proceed

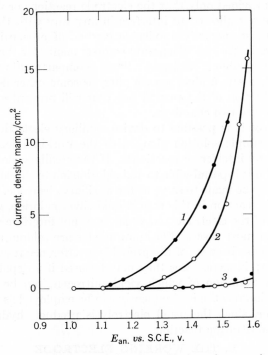

Fig. 49.3. Current-potential curves for the oxidation of cerous ion at a platinum anode (146): (*1*) 0.025*M* cerous sulfate in 1*M* sulfuric acid; (*2*) 0.05*M* cerous perchlorate in 1*M* perchloric acid; and (*3*) 1*M* perchloric acid or 1*M* sulfuric acid alone.

at minimal rates and desired reactions at conveniently rapid rates. Unfortunately, there is at the present time no theoretical basis for predicting in advance the effect of changes in the electrode surface on the rates of electrochemical reactions at those surfaces.

The magnitude of the current for diffusion-controlled processes is directly proportional to the electrode area if all other experimental conditions remain constant. A high ratio of electrode area to solution volume in controlled-potential titrations favors minimum analysis times and is generally to be desired (see Section III-C-1).

In controlled-current titrations, also, large electrode areas permit the use of large generation currents. However, in titrations of this type one does not normally wish to employ the largest possible current, but rather a current that will permit completion of the titration in reasonable time; this time must be long enough to minimize the danger of overrunning the end point. Usually there is an optimum current for any given titration. In many cases the current efficiency is a function of the current density at the electrode surface, and frequently there is an optimum current density for maximum current efficiency. The data of Lingane et al. (146) on the current efficiency for the generation of ceric ion at a platinum anode in

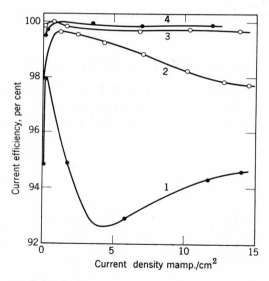

Fig. 49.4. Current efficiencies for electrogeneration of ceric ion as a function of current density and solution composition (146): (1) 0.05M cerous perchlorate in 1M perchloric acid; (2) 0.025M cerous sulfate in 0.9M sulfuric acid; (3) 0.1M cerous sulfate in 0.9M sulfuric acid; and (4) 0.1M cerous sulfate in 3M sulfuric acid.

acidic solutions of cerous salts illustrate this point. Pertinent current density–potential curves for this oxidation are shown in Fig. 49.3, and current efficiencies as a function of current density for several different sets of experimental conditions are shown in Fig. 49.4. The low current efficiency at very low current densities in sulfuric acid solutions reflects the fact that the continuous faradaic current due to the oxidation of water is quite significant even at the lowest potentials at which oxidation of cerous ion occurs. As the current density is raised, the potential moves to more positive values. The increasing potential causes the rate of both electrode reactions to increase, but the rate of cerous ion oxidation increases more rapidly than that of water, and the current efficiency increases. The converse is true if the current density is raised to still higher values; the efficiency then falls with increasing current density. It is clear from Fig. 49.4 that satisfactory generation in perchloric acid solution is impossible at any current density. These data clearly indicate the fact that there is an optimum electrode area that depends upon the magnitude of the current to be used in the titration. A marked dependence of current efficiency on current density is usually noted only at the extreme ends of the potential range, where oxidation or reduction of the solvent may occur. In the intermediate range of potentials, where the solvent is stable, high generation efficiencies can usually be maintained over a very broad range of current densities.

F. THE EFFECT OF TEMPERATURE

Since the rate of reactions, both chemical and electrochemical, increases with increasing temperature, it is sometimes possible to enhance the rate of desired reactions or to suppress undesired reactions by proper adjustment of the temperature. For example, the generation of silver(II) as a coulometric intermediate by oxidation of silver(I) in nitric acid solution proceeds with much greater efficiency at 0°C. than at room temperature (46). The rate of the interfering electrode reaction, the oxidation of water, decreases more rapidly with temperature than the rate of the desired reaction. Low temperatures are doubly advantageous in this particular case because the rate of the side reaction by which the argentic ion oxidizes the solvent is also greatly reduced at low temperatures, although the reaction of the titrant with reductants such as cerium(III) or vanadium(IV) remains very fast.

Since diffusion coefficients increase with increasing temperature, the rate at which controlled-potential titrations proceed to completion is considerably enhanced at elevated temperatures.

G. THE EFFECT OF AGITATION

As the agitation of the solution or electrode is increased, the thickness of the diffusion layer decreases and the limiting current for diffusion-controlled processes rises. The rate of controlled-potential titrations, which are normally diffusion controlled, is thus directly increased by more effective agitation (see Section III-C-1). Kinetically controlled electrode reactions, such as those that contribute to the continuous faradaic background current, are substantially unaffected by the rate of stirring. Vigorous stirring thus minimizes the total fraction of the current that is due to background currents in controlled-potential titrations and improves the current efficiency as well as decreasing the time required for the titration.

In controlled-current titrations, rapid stirring permits the use of higher generation currents without danger of exceeding the limiting diffusion current of the redox buffer. Rapid mixing of the electrically generated intermediate with the body of the solution increases the rate of the desired reaction and minimizes the danger of overrunning the end point.

III. APPARATUS AND TECHNIQUES

The essential apparatus for any coulometric titration consists of (1) an electrolysis cell in which the desired reactions may be carried out, (2) a power supply to furnish the electrolysis current, and (3) a coulometer for measuring the quantity of electricity used. In analyses in which the potential of the working electrode is not controlled directly, some means of end-point detection is also required. Still other auxiliary equipment and control devices are frequently desirable in order to make the analyses more convenient and to provide for automatic operation.

A. COULOMETERS

The problem of evaluating the number of coulombs used in an analysis consists in an evaluation of the time integral of the electrolysis current. Any device that determines this integral with adequate accuracy and precision is suitable as a coulometer. A large variety of such instruments has been described. These instruments vary widely in accuracy, precision, cost, complexity, operating range, and convenience. No single coulometer can be said to be the ideal instrument for all applications, and the analyst should select the one most suited to his own particular requirements.

1. Coulometry at Constant Current

Whenever it is possible to maintain the electrolysis current at a constant value, the time integral of the current is equal to the current–time product.

The apparatus for determining the number of coulombs in this case consists of a galvanostat to provide a constant electrolysis current and a chronometer for measuring the total time of electrolysis.

a. GALVANOSTATS

The simplest type of galvanostat consists of a high-voltage battery that is connected to the electrolysis cell through a large series resistance, as illustrated in Fig. 49.5. For a circuit of this type the electrolysis current is given by

$$i = (E_B - E_C)/R \tag{18}$$

where E_B is the battery voltage, E_C is the potential across the electrolysis cell, and R is the total series resistance ($R_1 + R_2 + R_M$, where R_M is the ammeter resistance). If E_C is very small in comparison with E_B, it is apparent that small fluctuations in the cell potential during the course of the analysis will have little effect on the current, which will remain substantially constant if the battery voltage and the series resistance remain

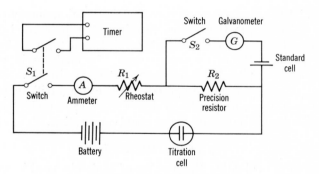

Fig. 49.5. Simple galvanostat.

constant. Standard radio B batteries of 45 to 300 v. are suitable for electrolysis currents up to about 10 mamp.; with higher currents battery life is very short, and a line-operated, constant-voltage power supply is more convenient. The current can be set at the desired value by adjusting R_2 until the meter reads the desired current. More precise settings can be achieved by adjustment to a null galvanometer deflection when S_2 is closed; in this case R_2 should be set at a value such that $R_2 = E_S/i$, where E_S is the standard cell potential and i is the desired current. The standard cell may, of course, be replaced by a precision potentiometer. A double-pole switch, S_1, which insures that the electrolysis current and timer are turned on and off in synchronism, is desirable.

Although the simple galvanostat described above is adequate for many purposes, an automatically regulated constant-current supply is much more convenient and more precise. A large number of such instruments have been described (8,26,53,78,175,206,207,253). These instruments can be designed to furnish currents from the microampere range (90) up to several amperes (247). Lingane's (136) electromechanical servo instrument can be assembled very easily from commercially available components and is capable of maintaining constant currents from 1 to 100 mamp. with a precision of ±0.01%. Most of the other instruments that have been described are electronically regulated and can control the current to within ±0.1% or better. One instrument that is capable of regulation to 1 p.p.m. has been described (152). The electronic instruments have response times that are considerably faster than the electromechanical instruments and are the preferred choice whenever rapid corrective action is necessary. However, the speed of response of the electromechanical instruments is quite adequate for most of the cases encountered in practical work. Several excellent galvanostats are available commercially.

When using any self-regulating galvanostat, a suitable dummy resistor should be switched into the circuit in place of the cell whenever the electrolysis current is interrupted. In order to avoid errors due to the failure of the galvanostat to respond instantly to changes in load impedance, the value of the dummy resistor should be such that the voltage drop across it is equal to that across the cell. When the response time of the galvanostat is relatively long, a very careful matching is required to avoid significant errors; if the response time is very fast (of the order of 0.001 second or less), which is usually the case with the electronic instruments, matching is unnecessary and the dummy resistor may be replaced by a short circuit.

b. CHRONOMETERS

An electric timer is the most convenient and popular device for measuring electrolysis times in constant-current coulometric work. A timer that can be read to the nearest 0.1 second and that can totalize up to 1000 seconds is the most generally useful. The timing error should not exceed ±0.02 second per operation if several on–off cycles must be employed in approaching the end point of the titration; for this reason a clutch-operated timer is preferable to other types. The timer should be turned on and off with the same switch or relay that is used to initiate and terminate the electrolysis current.

The accuracy of an electric timer operating from a synchronous motor depends upon the accuracy of the power line frequency. In most localities this frequency is maintained with sufficient accuracy and constancy to insure negligible timing errors. In laboratories where the power line frequency is not sufficiently stable, the timer may be operated from a precision tuning-fork oscillator (79).

Whenever the total time to be measured is very short or whenever a very large number of on–off operations is required, even the best electric timers may not be capable of adequate timing accuracy. In these cases a counter chronometer may be used (175,243).

2. Chemical Coulometers

A chemical coulometer is an instrument in which the current to be integrated is passed through an electrolysis cell to generate some chemical compound with a known and reproducible current efficiency (preferably 100%). The compound generated is then determined by any appropriate analytical method and the quantity of electricity passed through the coulometer is calculated with the aid of Faraday's laws.

a. GRAVIMETRIC COULOMETERS

The primary standard coulometer is the silver coulometer, in which the quantity of silver deposited on a platinum cathode from a silver nitrate solution is weighed (209). Although this coulometer and certain of its modifications (69) are excellent for calibration because of their high accuracy, they are inconvenient to use and are not direct-reading; hence they find little application in routine work. All other types of gravimetric coulometers suffer from the same disadvantage.

In some cases it is possible to make one of the electrodes in the cell in which the coulometric titration is being carried out serve as a coulometer electrode as well as the auxiliary electrode of the titration cell. For example, in the controlled potential coulometric titration of thallium by oxidation of Tl^+ to Tl_2O_3 at a platinum anode, the number of coulombs may be determined by adding Ag^+ to the sample and determining the deposited silver from the gain in weight of the platinum cathode of the titration cell (70).

b. TITRATION COULOMETERS

Several types of coulometers that involve titration of electrode products have been proposed. For example, the iodine coulometer involves titration of the iodine formed at a platinum anode in potassium iodide solution (249), and the alkali coulometer involves titration of the base produced at a platinum cathode ($2H_2O + 2e^- \rightarrow H_2 + 2OH^-$) in potassium bromide solution (103,148). Like the silver coulometer, many of these coulometers are capable of high precision, but they are almost as inconvenient to use as the gravimetric coulometers if manual titration procedures are used. This inconvenience is greatly reduced if the titration is done with an automatic titrator.

c. "COULOMETRIC" COULOMETERS

One of the most serious drawbacks of the gravimetric coulometers is the relatively large amount of operator time involved in washing, drying, and weighing the electrode and its deposit. This disadvantage can be eliminated by determining the quantity of the deposit by coulometric stripping rather than by weighing (57). In one specific instrument that has been described, copper is plated onto a platinum cathode during the integration process. At the conclusion of the experiment, the deposited copper is determined by anodic oxidation at constant current; the time required for stripping is then a measure of the coulombs used in the plating process. The entire stripping process can be made completely automatic. Besides the added convenience that is offered by an instrument of this type, much smaller quantities of deposit, and hence fewer coulombs, can be determined accurately than is possible by weighing the deposit. Precisions of $\pm 0.1\%$ in the range from 0.01 up to 75 coulombs can be achieved.

A coulometric titration coulometer employing the quinone–hydroquinone couple, capable of a precision of 1 part in 100,000, has been described (225). Many other titration coulometers also could be adapted for coulometric titration of the electrolysis products.

d. GAS COULOMETERS

Coulometers in which a gas is produced at one or both electrodes can be read easily and directly by measuring the quantity of gas evolved. The hydrogen–oxygen coulometer (139) has been used extensively in coulometric analysis, but because it is subject to significant negative errors at low current densities, it is not well suited for many coulometric determinations. The more recently developed hydrogen–nitrogen coulometer (193) does not suffer from this disadvantage and is to be preferred in most cases.

In using a gas coulometer, it is possible to determine the quantity of evolved gas not only by measurement of volume, but also by measurement of pressure at constant volume (24,217). The latter technique of measurement is generally preferable when a continuous indication or recording of coulombs is desired, since pressure is more easily measured continuously than is volume.

It is possible to devise gas coulometers that are capable of measuring extremely small quantities of electricity. An accuracy of $\pm 1\%$ for measurements in the range from 0.001 to 0.1 coulomb is claimed for one such device (200).

e. OTHER TYPES OF CHEMICAL COULOMETERS

The use of analytical methods other than those listed above for the determination of the products of the electrode reactions in a coulometer offer many interesting possibilities with respect to improving the convenience and the sensitivity of chemical coulometers. For example, several types of "colorimetric coulometers" have been described (73,86). One coulometer of this general type (73) involves oxidation of a copper anode in triethanolamine solution followed by colorimetric determination of the resulting copper complex. This coulometer performs quite satisfactorily in the range from 1 to 10 coulombs. By generating base at the working electrode of the coulometer, the electrolyte of which contains a suitable acid–base indicator, the sensitivity can be increased to permit measurements in the 0.01 to 1.0 coulomb range. By appropriate selection of electrode reactions and proper adjustment of the volume of electrolyte used, it should be possible to obtain easily measurable absorbances for any quantity of electricity that must be measured in coulometric analysis. These coulometers are attractive not only because they are simple, convenient, and direct-reading, but also because they can be adapted to give a continuous record of coulombs versus time if a recording spectrophotometer is employed for the continuous measurement of absorbance.

3. Electromechanical Coulometers

Several different types of electromechanical devices may be employed for the evaluation of current–time integrals.

a. RECORDED CURRENT–TIME CURVES

Current may be recorded as a function of time with a strip-chart recorder. The area under the recorded curve, which is equal to the desired integral, may then be evaluated by measuring with a planimeter or by weighing the excised portion of the chart. The accuracy of this method of measurement is limited by the accuracy of the recorder, which is usually of the order of ± 0.5 to 1.0%. Because of the relatively slow response of most recorders (1 to 5 seconds), this method is not generally applicable in cases in which the current may change rapidly with time, e.g., when on–off cycling is employed in approaching the end point.

b. Ball and Disk Integrators

Since the evaluation of the area under a recorded time curve by the method outlined above is rather time-consuming, it is more convenient to attach to the recorder a ball-and-disk integrator, which permits the number of coulombs to be read directly and continuously (144). Several instruments of this type are commercially available. The response time and the precision of integration are usually determined by the recorder, and are about the same as those given above. Position servomechanisms other than a recorder may be used to position the ball carriage of the integrator.

c. Velocity Servomechanism Integrators

By means of a suitable velocity servo system it is possible to operate a direct-current tachometer generator at a speed such that the output voltage of the generator is directly proportional to the instantaneous value of the current to be integrated (168). Since the generator output voltage also is directly proportional to its rotational velocity, the total number of revolutions, which can be read by means of a revolutions counter coupled to the generator shaft, is proportional to the time integral of the current. Instruments of this type are reasonably rapid in response and may be used to integrate currents from the order of 0.1 mamp. or less up to several amperes. In a properly designed instrument the calibration factor (coulombs per revolution) is constant within ±0.1% over at least a tenfold range of currents; this permits the achievement of over-all integration accuracies of the order of ±0.2% in controlled-potential applications, in which the current decreases from a relatively large value at the start of the titration to nearly zero at the end. A coulometer of this type is available commercially.

d. Integrating Motors and Relays

An integrating motor is a small direct-current motor that operates on very small currents (of the order of a few tenths of a milliampere) and that has an armature with a very low moment of inertia. Over restricted voltage ranges, the motor speed is directly proportional to the voltage applied to its input terminals, and hence the total number of revolutions of the armature is proportional to the time integral of the input voltage. By connecting a suitable resistor in parallel with the motor, currents may be integrated (12,76,195). The rapid response of the motor permits its use even in applications that involve many on–off cycles during the course of a titration (195). Calibration for operation in different current ranges is easily accomplished (76) and integration accuracies of the order of ±0.1 to 0.2% can be achieved. Unfortunately, the calibration factor for typical motors changes by about 0.2% for a twofold change in the current; unless corrections for this nonlinearity are applied, precise integrations are possible only when the current to be integrated remains roughly constant. Since the deviation from linearity is approximately proportional to the applied voltage, the number of coulombs is given by the equation

$$Q = (N + k_1 t)/k_2 R \tag{19}$$

where N is the number of revolutions, t is the total operating time, R is the shunt resistance, and the k's are constants for any given motor. If this method of calculation is used, an integrating motor is capable of an accuracy of ±0.3% over a 100-fold current range (137). Alternatively, a small compensation current may be added to the current to be integrated in order to extend the range over which linear response can be achieved (181).

An integrating relay is essentially an integrating motor, the armature of which is constrained to oscillate between fixed limits rather than to rotate continuously in one direction. Although these relays may be employed in coulometric analyses in which the current is nearly constant (14), the precision is less than that which can be obtained with an integrating motor, and the calibration factor depends very markedly upon the current.

4. Electronic Coulometers

a. ANALOG INTEGRATORS

The integrators that are commonly used in analog computers consist of a high-gain operational amplifier with a fixed input resistor and a fixed capacitor in the feedback loop. Integrators of this type, the components of which are readily available commercially, are capable of excellent performance when used as coulometers. A schematic representation of the circuitry involved is shown in Fig. 49.6. The current to be integrated is passed between the input terminals; the output voltage is proportional to the time integral of the input current and is given by

$$e_{\text{out}} = - \frac{R_1}{(R_1 + R_2)C} \int i \, dt \tag{20}$$

A detailed discussion of the principles of operation of this type of integrator is beyond the scope of this chapter, but may be found in any textbook on analog computers.

By proper selection of the resistors, R_1 and R_2, and the capacitor, C, almost any desired scale factor can be secured. Integration accuracies of the order of $\pm 0.1\%$ for currents ranging from less than one microampere to several amperes can be realized. The output voltage, and hence the number of coulombs, may be read with an ordinary voltmeter or, more precisely, with a potentiometer or digital voltmeter. If desired, the output may be connected to a recorder to obtain a continuous record of coulombs as a function of time.

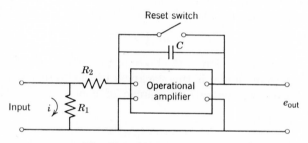

Fig. 49.6. Analog integrator.

Analog integrators are among the most versatile, accurate, and generally useful coulometers that have yet been used for coulometric analysis (15,112,113).

b. Relaxation Oscillators

Several types of relaxation oscillators, the frequency of which is proportional to the input current, have been described (74,120,161,232). If the output of such an oscillator is connected to a suitable counter, the number of counts recorded is proportional to coulombs. These devices are relatively simple but are neither sufficiently reliable nor sufficiently precise to be used in analyses requiring a high degree of accuracy.

5. Coulometric Techniques

The determination of the number of coulombs consumed in a controlled-current coulometric titration ordinarily presents no special problems; the titration is continued until the end-point detection system indicates that the equivalence point has been reached. The titration is terminated at this point, and the coulometer is read. In controlled-potential analyses, on the other hand, the current decays during the course of the electrolysis and approaches the background current asymptotically as the titration approaches completion. The slow approach to completion is not only time-consuming, but there is often considerable uncertainty in knowing when to terminate the electrolysis unless the value of the background current is known in advance. For these reasons it is often advantageous to terminate the electrolysis when the titration is 90 to 99% complete and to estimate the coulombs required for 100% completion from data taken during the titration of the first 90 to 99%.

If a controlled-potential electrolysis is carried out under conditions such that the current is diffusion-controlled, which is the usual practice, the current, i_t, at any time t is related to the concentration by the expression

$$i_t = nFADC_t/\delta \tag{21}$$

where C_t is the concentration in the body of the solution at time t, A is the area of the electrode, and δ is the thickness of the Nernst diffusion layer. From Faraday's law, the rate of change of concentration with time is given by

$$dC_t/dt = -i_t/nFV \tag{22}$$

where V is the volume of the solution. Combination and integration of equations (21) and (22) gives

$$C_t = C_0 \exp (-kt) \tag{23}$$

$$i_t = i_0 \exp (-kt) \tag{24}$$

where C_0 and i_0 are the initial concentration and current, respectively, and where k is given by

$$k = DA/V\delta \tag{25}$$

The number of coulombs, Q_t, consumed from the initiation of the electrolysis up to time t, is given by

$$Q_t = \int_0^t i_t \, dt = (i_0/k) - (i_t/k) \tag{26}$$

It is clear from equation (26) that a linear relationship exists between Q_t and i_t. This relationship may be used as a basis for estimating the total number of coulombs required for complete electrolysis without actually carrying the analysis to completion. It is necessary only to obtain corresponding values of Q_t and i_t at two or more different times during the course of the electrolysis. The straight line obtained when Q_t is plotted as a function of i_t may then be extrapolated to its intercept on the coulombs axis to obtain the value of Q_∞, the number of coulombs that would be required to complete the titration and to reduce the current to zero. In order to minimize errors in the extrapolation it is common practice to obtain a number of points in the region of 90 to 99% completion of the titration (i.e., at currents between 10% and 1% of the initial value) in order to define the best possible line and to keep the length of the extrapolated portion of the line small. Under some circumstances it may be permissible or even desirable to work outside this range, however. In particular, when background currents are comparatively large, better results often are obtained by defining the line to be extrapolated from points taken at smaller degrees of completion.

If a direct-reading coulometer with an electrical output signal is available, an X-Y recorder may be used to plot Q_t versus i_t automatically during the course of the electrolysis (91). In this case the operator need only terminate the electrolysis at an appropriate point and extrapolate the recorded curve to obtain the desired result. This method is limited by the accuracy of the recorder (usually of the order of 1%) unless the full scale of the recorder is used to plot only the data taken during the last 10% or so of the determination.

It is possible to obtain the data required for the desired plot from a series of coulometer readings only (169), but the method outlined above is usually more convenient.

B. POTENTIOSTATS

The principles of operation and the general characteristics of potentiostats have been treated in Chapter 48. Most of the potentiostats that have been designed and used for controlled-potential electroseparations are also suitable for use in controlled-potential coulometric analysis, although the requirements for the latter are slightly more stringent. Several instruments are commercially available, and many others have been described in the literature. The following references describe a few of those which have been designed particularly for coulometric analyses (8,15,112,113,144,175).

The success of a coulometric analysis depends upon the maintenance of the potential of the working electrode between limits that insure the achievement of 100% current efficiency. The gain of the potentiostat must be high enough and its speed of response sufficiently rapid to maintain the set potential with the required precision. However, if gain and speed of response are made too high, the entire system becomes unstable and may even break into oscillation. Because the electrolysis cell itself is an integral part of the control loop, it is impossible to predict performance on the basis of the characteristics of the potentiostat alone. Since cell capacity and resistance, control potential, and current and voltage requirements may vary between wide limits from one type of analysis to another or even during the course of a single analysis, it is quite possible that regulation may be satisfactory under some conditions and completely inadequate under others. The most satisfactory method of checking the system to be sure that control requirements are being met is to connect an oscilloscope between the working and reference electrodes and to observe the trace on the oscilloscope screen. Oscillations or any other evidence of instability can be detected easily, and the precision of potential control can be observed. This test should be performed whenever experimental conditions are changed in any way. Most potentiostats have controls for adjusting gain and frequency response so that the instrument can be matched to the cell being used with it.

The details of the problems of stability, response time, precision of control, and other similar factors have been fully treated in the literature (13,21,80,81,85,113,244,251), but are beyond the scope of this chapter.

C. TITRATION CELLS

1. Cells for Controlled-Potential Coulometry

All cells for controlled-potential coulometry must be provided with a suitable vessel for containing the electrolyte, a working electrode, an auxiliary electrode, a reference electrode, and a stirrer or some other device for providing agitation. Provisions for adding or removing reagents and solutions, gas dispersion tubes for deoxygenation and for providing an inert atmosphere, salt bridges or permeable membranes for isolating anode and cathode compartments, and other similar features are usually desirable and often essential. There is no single cell that is ideal for all determinations. Many different cells, most of them designed for specific applications, are described in the literature. A single-compartment cell that has proved to be quite generally useful in analyses employing a mercury cathode is shown in Fig. 49.7. A more elaborate cell with isolated anode and cathode compartments is shown in Fig. 49.8.

A fiber-type saturated calomel electrode is the most generally useful type of reference electrode if the potentiostat will tolerate the resistance (1000 to 5000 ohms) of such an electrode. The tip of the reference electrode should be placed as close to the working electrode as possible in order to minimize the effect of IR drop in the solution.

In order to minimize the load on the potentiostat and to minimize resistive heating of the cell solution, the anode–cathode resistance of the cell should be kept as small as possible. Resistive heating may be a very serious problem when nonaqueous solvents of low conductivity are used. With aqueous solutions, high cell resistances are usually encountered only with dual-compartment cells and can be minimized by using short, large-diameter salt bridges filled with highly conductive solutions.

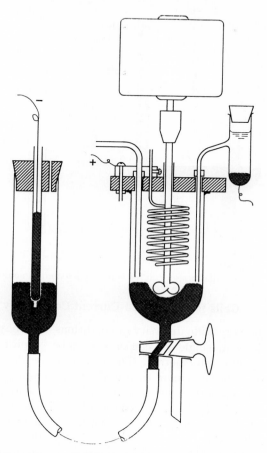

Fig. 49.7. Single-compartment cell for controlled-potential coulometry with a mercury cathode (139).

It is apparent from equation (23) that electrolysis proceeds at a maximum rate when the value of k, equation (25), is as large as possible. In order to keep analysis times at minimal values, electrolysis cells that have a high ratio of electrode area to solution volume and that permit vigorous agitation to minimize the thickness of the diffusion layer are highly desirable.

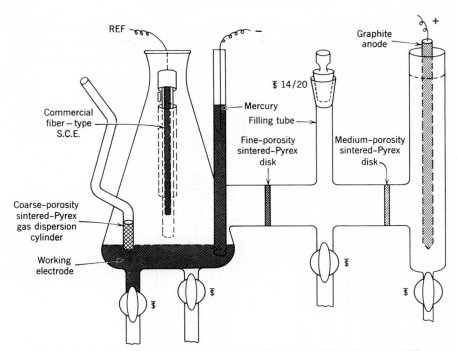

REF

−

Graphite anode

+

⚡ 14/20

Commercial fiber—type S.C.E.

Mercury

Filling tube

Fine-porosity sintered-Pyrex disk

Medium-porosity sintered-Pyrex disk

Coarse-porosity sintered-Pyrex gas dispersion cylinder

Working electrode

Fig. 49.8.   Double-diaphragm cell for controlled-potential coulometry (168).

2. Cells for Controlled-Current Coulometry

Because of the very wide diversity of conditions that may be required in different titrations, no single cell can be said to be "typical" of those used in controlled-current coulometry.   The cell must be designed to fit the requirements of each particular titration.   For example, the titration of acids in a halide supporting electrolyte with visual end-point indication may be carried out in an ordinary beaker into which a silver anode and a platinum cathode are dipped.   On the other hand, the rather elaborate cell shown in Fig. 49.9 was designed for titrations with titanous ion at an elevated temperature.   This titration requires an inert atmosphere, isolation of the auxiliary electrode, a potentiometric end-point indication system, and a heater for maintaining the desired temperature.   Many other cells designed to meet the special requirements of specific titrations are described in the literature.

When isolation of the auxiliary electrode is required, a simple sintered glass disk, as shown in Fig. 49.9, is adequate if some leakage of electrolyte from the auxiliary electrode compartment can be tolerated.   If the prod-

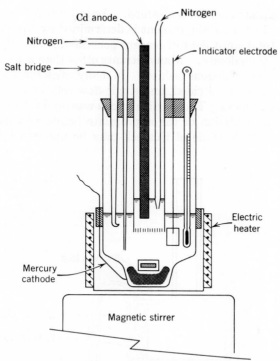

Fig. 49.9. Cell for coulometric titrations with electrolytically generated titanous ion (143).

ucts of the auxiliary electrode reaction interfere seriously in the titration, agar plugs or long salt bridges may be required to prevent intermixing of the two solutions. Ion-exchange membranes often can be used to advantage in preventing deleterious ions from entering the solution being titrated (65).

In most coulometric titrations it is possible to generate the desired intermediate in a separate generator cell and then to allow the reagent to flow into the test solution (48,49). Except for the fact that the titrant is generated electrolytically, titrations of this type are substantially identical with conventional volumetric titrations. For example, if a neutral sodium perchlorate solution is allowed to flow into the top of the generator cell shown in Fig. 49.10, the solution divides and flows out of the two delivery tubes. If now an electric current is passed between the two platinum electrodes of the cell, an equivalent amount of acid will be generated at the anode and an equivalent amount of base at the cathode. If the effluent from the appropriate delivery tube is allowed to flow into the test solution, acid–base titrations may be performed.   As in any coulometric titration, the rate of production of the reagent is determined by the electrolysis current, and the total equivalent of reagent generated is directly proportional to the number of coulombs.   Many titrants other than acids and bases can be generated in an analogous fashion.   In many cases the flow of generator electrolyte need not be divided, and single-flow cells of the type shown in Fig. 49.11 may be used.   This particular cell was used for the generation of the halogens by oxidation of the appropriate halide salts or acids.   The platinum working electrode of this cell may be replaced by mercury for

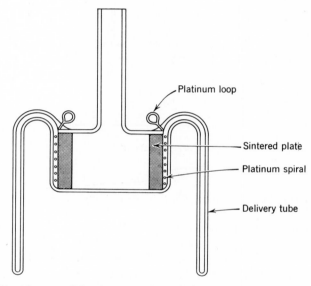

Fig. 49.10. Double-arm cell for the external generation of coulometric intermediates (12).

titrations that require the use of a mercury electrode (194).   Titrations with externally generated reagents are obviously more cumbersome than those in which the working electrode is placed directly in the test solution. However, the technique does permit titrations that cannot be carried out in the normal fashion because of the presence of substances in the test solution that interfere in the desired electrode reaction; for example, acidimetric titrations employing internal generation cannot be applied when the test solution contains substances more easily oxidized than water at the generator anode.

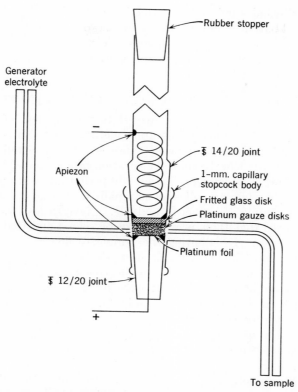

Fig 49.11 Single-arm cell for the external generation of coulometric intermediates (197).

D. AUTOMATIC COULOMETRIC TITRATORS

Controlled-potential coulometric analyzers employing self-correcting potentiostats are inherently automatic in the sense that attention from the operator during the course of the analysis is not required. Controlled-current titrations, on the other hand, do require operator attention unless provision is made within the instrument to automatically terminate the titration when a preset end point has been reached. Fortunately, the process is very easy to automate, since the titrant is an electric current, which may be readily adjusted, regulated, measured, and controlled by standard electrical and electronic components and circuitry. No complex valves, pumps, storage vessels, and volume-measuring equipment are required, as is the case with liquid titrants. Many different investigators have designed and described fully automatic titrators for single- or multiple-purpose uses (12,28,29,48,79,114,128,157,210,226,253). The preceding list of references includes only a small fraction of the instruments that have been described but includes examples of most types of titration and of most end-point indication systems. A discussion of the problems of instrument design is beyond the scope of this chapter and the reader is referred to the original literature for details.

E. CONTINUOUS COULOMETRIC TITRATIONS

Very little attention has been devoted to the problem of developing controlled-potential coulometric titration methods that can be applied to the continuous analysis of flowing samples. The controlled-potential method is inherently slow because the titration rate is limited by diffusion, and the problems of designing cells that will permit quantitative titrations of flowing samples and that will respond rapidly to changing concentrations in the flowing sample are rather formidable. Nevertheless, Eckfeldt (55) has demonstrated that these problems can be solved and that continuous analysis is feasible. By allowing the sample to flow through a shallow labyrinthine channel in the working electrode he was able to achieve an effective cell volume of 1.5 ml. and an effective working electrode area of 38 sq. cm. Current efficiencies of nearly 100% could be maintained at flow rates up to several milliliters per minute. This technique offers considerable promise for a wide variety of applications in which a continuous analysis of a flowing sample is desired (e.g., analysis of column effluents, continuous process analysis, etc.) and is deserving of further study and exploitation.

The problems involved in the design of continuous automatic analyzers employing the controlled-current method and making use of coulometric intermediates are considerably less rigorous because the rate of titration is not limited by slow diffusion of the substance being titrated. Titrations of this type were first explored by Shaffer, Briglio, and Brockman (221), who designed an instrument for the continuous determination of mustard gas in the atmosphere. Their instrument consisted of an electrolysis cell, fitted with two generator electrodes and two indicator electrodes and filled with acidified potassium bromide, through which the sample was bubbled. The mustard gas was titrated as it entered the cell by bromine formed at the generator anode. The indicator electrodes were connected to a control system that automatically adjusted the electrolysis current to maintain a small fixed concentration of bromine in the cell, regardless of the rate of bromine consumption by the sample. With an instrument of this type, it is clear that the electrolysis current is directly proportional to the rate (moles/second) of delivery of titratable component to the electrolysis cell. If sample is delivered to the cell at a constant rate, the current must be directly proportional to the concentration of the titrate in the sample stream. A continuous record of concentration as a function of time may be obtained by connecting a recording ammeter in series with the generator electrodes.

An improved version of the Shaffer, Briglio, and Brockman instrument was designed by Austin and his associates (6). The Austin instrument and later modifications thereof have been available commercially for several years and have been widely used for the determination of oxidizable components such as hydrogen sulfide, mercaptans, and sulfur dioxide in gas streams. Other instruments operating on the same general principles have been used in organic elemental analysis for the titration of products such as hydrogen chloride and sulfur dioxide produced on combustion. When a gas chromatography column is placed ahead of the combustion furnace to separate the sample into its individual components, these instruments become capable of determining each individual halogen- or sulfur-containing compound without interference from other compounds that may be present in the sample but that do not contain the element being titrated (39,116, 132). Some of the continuous titrators are extremely sensitive; an instrument for monitoring boranes in the atmosphere is capable of determining boranes at the 0.2 p.p.m. level (19). A coulometric pH-stat, which is a type of continuous titrator, has been employed for studying reaction rates in aqueous solutions (133).

IV. APPLICATIONS

The coulometric method has been applied to the solution of a wide variety of practical analytical problems. The survey of applications that is included in this section is not comprehensive but illustrates the types of problems amenable to solution by coulometry and points out some of the advantages and limitations of the method.

A. CONTROLLED-POTENTIAL COULOMETRY

Although the theoretical foundation of controlled-potential coulometry has been highly developed, the technique has not been extensively exploited in practical analysis. Although many reasons for the limited use of the method could be cited, the most cogent of these is the fact that voltammetric and polarographic methods usually can be used for the same types of determinations to which the controlled-potential coulometric method is applicable. Although coulometry usually offers a significant advantage over voltammetry in the precision which can be achieved in an analysis, voltammetry is considerably more rapid, is easier to apply, and requires simpler apparatus.   If the precision which is required in an analysis can be realized by employing voltammetry or polarography, the use of coulometry in preference to these methods is seldom justified except in a few special cases.

1. Deposition of Metals

Coulometric determinations of many metal ions may be accomplished by plating the metal onto a solid inert electrode such as platinum (101) or into a mercury cathode (139).   Mercury is generally preferred as a cathode material because of its higher hydrogen overpotential and because polarographic data may be employed in selecting optimum conditions for the analysis (139).   Metal ions that have been determined in this way include copper (101,139,168,254), cadmium (139), lead (139), nickel (147), cobalt (147), and silver (175).   In many cases, successive determinations of several metal ions in a single sample can be made (147,175).   Average errors of less than $\pm 0.1\%$ have been realized in the determination of 2 to 600 mg. of copper (168); many other metals can be determined with similar accuracy.   Under ideal circumstances this technique can be made extremely sensitive; precisions of $\pm 4\%$ or better have been reported for the determination of copper in the 1 to 100 γ range (254).   Submicrogram analyses are possible if the capacity current is reduced to a small fraction of the total current; less than 0.1 γ of lead was measured within $\pm 10\%$ (171).

Sometimes controlled-potential coulometry may be used to advantage in combination with some other measurement technique to obtain analyses of mixtures that cannot be resolved easily by either method alone.   For example, mixtures of cadmium and zinc (155) or of lead and tin (54) can be determined by plating the two components simultaneously and measuring both the coulombs required for the deposition and the weight of the deposit (coulogravimetry).   Similarly, mixtures of lead and thallium can be resolved by polarographic measurement of the total diffusion current of the two overlapping waves combined with coulometric measurements (167).

2. Deposition of Insoluble Salts

Halide ions can be determined by deposition as their silver salts at a silver anode, the potential of which is controlled so as to achieve the desired reactions (148).   Both components in iodide–chloride, iodide–bromide, and iodide–thiocyanate mixtures can be determined by successive determinations on the same sample (148,187).   Bromide–chloride mixtures cannot be resolved accurately because of coprecipitation problems, although the resolution is improved if an alcoholic solvent is used (187).

Coulogravimetry may be employed to advantage in the analysis of this particular mixture (154). Most workers have preferred the use of controlled-current techniques (see Section IV-B-3) rather than the controlled-potential technique for the determination of halides.

3. Oxidations or Reductions in Which Both Initial and Final Species are Soluble in a Solvent

Controlled-potential coulometric titrations of a number of soluble species that are oxidized or reduced to soluble products have been described. Methods are available for the determination of iodide (101), iron (153), arsenic (153), chromium (104), molybdenum (104), manganese (173), europium (222), uranium (16,17,63,223,258), neptunium (231), and plutonium (218). Successive determinations of several species are often possible; for example, both iron(III) and chromium(VI) in mixtures can be determined by simultaneous reduction to iron(II) and chromium(III) followed by coulometric reoxidation of the iron(II) (151). A striking example of the selectivity that can be achieved is afforded by the determination of chromium in the presence of 19 other metals (170); interferences are eliminated by a series of potentiostatic preoxidations and prereductions that precede the final coulometric determination.

Controlled-potential coulometric methods have been worked out for a few organic halogen and nitro compounds (58,122), including trichloroacetic acid in the presence of dichloroacetic acid (174), picric acid in the presence of dinitrophenol (139,172), and the γ-isomer of hexachlorocyclohexane (216). Ascorbic acid has been oxidized in a two-electron process at a platinum electrode (213a). Although it would appear that controlled-potential coulometry could be profitably exploited in many other determinations of organic compounds, there are several practical difficulties that limit the applicability of the method. Chief among these is the fact that most of the over-all titration reactions are quite irreversible; hence it is frequently extremely difficult to find suitable experimental conditions under which the desired reactions will proceed rapidly and quantitatively while undesired reactions are suppressed (see Section II).

B. CONTROLLED-CURRENT COULOMETRY

In contrast to the controlled-potential methods, controlled-current coulometric methods have been widely applied in practical analysis. Most titrations that can be carried out by classic volumetric techniques also can be performed coulometrically if the titrant can be generated as a coulometric intermediate with 100% current efficiency. Table 49.I lists most of the

TABLE 49.I

Summary of Electrogenerated Titrants and Coulometric Analyses

Titrant generated	Material titrated	References
1. Acid-base		
Hydrogen ion	Bases	49,95,162,163,189,233,253
Hydroxide ion	Acids	12,30,31,59,96,131,233,235,255
2a. Oxidizing agents		
Bromine	Arsenic(III)	127,186
	Uranium(IV)	27
	Ammonia	3,134
	Olefins	20,130,182,246
	Organic compounds	6,44,119,190
Iodine	Arsenic(III)	49,205
	Water–Karl Fischer	11,114,176,177
	Organic compounds	107
	Sulfur dioxide	84,100
	Boranes	19
Chlorine	Arsenic(III)	197
	Iron(II)	60,64
	Unsaturation	43,108
Cerium(IV)	Iron(II)	35a,66
	Iodide ion	146
	Titanium(III)	51
	Organic compounds	75
Manganese(III)	Iron(II)	67,220,238
	Hydrogen peroxide	239
Silver(II)	Cerium(III)	165
	Arsenic(III)	46
Iron(III)	Vanadium(II)	124
Chromium(VI)	Iron(II)	184
Dithionate ion $(S_2O_6^{-2})$	Organic dyes	185
Ferricyanide ion	Thallium(I)	142
Vanadium(V)	Iron(II)	105
Molybdenum(V)	Cobalt(II)	121
Palladium(II)	Copper(I)	149
2b. Reducing agents		
Iron(II)	Oxidizing agents $(Cr_2O_7^{-2}, MnO_4^-, VO_3^-, Ce^{+4})$	35,36,66,77,99,234
	Plutonium(VI)	22,32
Titanium(III)	Iron(III)	5,33,158
	Vanadium(V,IV)	145,156
	Uranium(VI)	115,143
	Organic dyes	194
Copper(I)	Oxidizing agents	2,23,140,164
Tin(II)	Halogens	9
	Platinum(IV)	7

TABLE 49.I (*continued*)

Titrant generated	Material titrated	References
Iron(II)–EDTA	Iron(III)	214
Uranium(V)	Iron(III)	56
	Vanadium(V)	196
Uranium(IV)	Chromium(VI)	224
Vanadium(IV)	Manganese(VII)	45
Chromium(II)	Oxygen	106,213

3. Precipitation titrations

Silver(I)	Halide ions	37,39,135,192
	Mercaptans	128,129,131
Mercury(I)	Halide ions	47,202
Mercury(II)	Sulfide ion	203
	Mercaptans	204
Ferrocyanide ion	Zinc(II)	141
Halide ions	Silver(I)	94
Cerium(III)	Fluoride ion	250

4. Complexing agents

Mercury(II)	Cyanide ion	201
	Amines (as dithio-carbamic acid derivs.)	204
Ethylenediamine-tetraacetate ion	Metal ions	208,229
Thioglycollate ion	Metal ions	179
Monothioethylene-glycolate ion	Metal ions (noble)	180
Cyanide ion	Gold(III,I); silver(I); nickel(II)	1

5. Film stripping
a. Plating thickness

Tin(II)	Tin plate	71,87,109,123,219
Zinc(II)	Zinc plate	71
Lead(II)	Lead plate	71
Cadmium(II)	Cadmium plate	71
Copper(II)	Copper plate	71
Chromium(III)	Chromium plate	71

b. Oxide and other films

Silver(0)	Silver iodide	61
	Silver oxide	25,199
	Silver sulfide	25,199
Iron(0)	Iron oxides	62,92,178
Copper(0)	Copper oxides	18,25,42,126,199
	Copper sulfides	25,199
Tin(0)	Tin oxides	72,102,252
Boron(0)	Boron oxides	211

(*continued*)

TABLE 49.I (*continued*)

Titrant generated	Material titrated	References
c. Deposition–coulometric stripping		
Copper(II)	Copper on platinum	256,257
Lead(II)	Lead on platinum	256
Silver(I)	Silver on platinum	150
Cadmium(II)	Cadmium in mercury	159,188,198
Lead(II)	Lead in mercury	188
Copper(II)	Copper in mercury	188
6. Miscellaneous		
Hydrogen	Unsaturation	68,160,183
Oxygen	Surface adsorption	24
—	Water	4,34,110
—	Oxygen	111,240
Alkali metal ions	—	241
Sulfate, phosphate ions	—	241

titrants that have been generated thus far, together with typical determinations in which they have been used.   It will be noted that most of the titrants that enjoy widespread use in classic volumetric analysis can be satisfactorily generated for use in coulometric titrations also.   A few of the more common titrants, such as permanganate and thiosulfate, cannot be generated, but reagents that can be substituted for these in many titrations can be generated.   Some reagents, such as silver(II) and uranium(V), which are too unstable to be used in volumetric analysis, can be employed satisfactorily in coulometric analysis.

In general, controlled-current coulometric titrimetry and classic volumetric titrimetry are comparable in precision and accuracy.   Both methods are limited to equal extents by such common features as problems arising in the precise location of the equivalence point, unfavorable reaction kinetics, side reactions, etc.   The precision that can be achieved in measuring the number of coulombs is of the order of $\pm 0.1\%$ if relatively simple galvanostats and chronometers are used; more sophisticated equipment permits precisions comparable with those achieved when a weight buret is used.   In both methods, sample sizes are limited primarily by difficulties involved in the manipulation of very small volumes of solution; excellent results in the titration of acids and bases in solution volumes as small as 10 μliters have been reported (215).   Because of the greater ease with which reagents may be pretitrated and with which very small amounts of reagents may be added, the coulometric method is generally somewhat superior in the titration of very dilute solutions; for example, titration of mercaptans in the part-per-million range is readily accomplished (128), and under ideal conditions manganese (as permanganate) has been satisfactorily titrated in the part-per-billion range (36). The coulometric method presents definite advantages by obviating the necessity for preparing, standardizing, and storing solutions of titrants; this advantage is particularly pronounced if unstable titrants or very dilute solutions of titrants are required. Because the solution suffers no change in volume during a coulometric titration, amperometric, conductometric, and photometric titration curves can be plotted or recorded directly without the necessity of applying the volume corrections required when volumetric methods are used. The advantages of the coulometric method with respect to the ease of automation of the titration process have been pointed out in Section III-D. The ease with which the rate of titrant addition can be varied is useful in kinetic studies (52,245,246).

The wide applicability of the coulometric method, together with its high precision and accuracy, has led Tutundžič (236,237) to propose that the coulomb be adopted as the primary standard for all titrimetry. However, the Commission on Electrochemical Data of the Analytical Chemistry Section of the International Union of Pure and Applied Chemistry has suggested that this proposal is premature because of the lack of adequate data on the ultimate accuracy of a large number of coulometric methods as compared with the best volumetric methods available (117). In addition, since the coulomb is based on the atomic weight of silver, silver is the primary standard, and not the coulomb.

1. Acid–Base Titrations

Bases may be generated by the reduction of water and acids by the oxidation of water at a platinum or other inert electrode:

$$H_2O + e^- \rightarrow OH^- + \tfrac{1}{2}H_2$$

$$\tfrac{1}{2}H_2O \rightarrow H^+ + \tfrac{1}{4}O_2 + e^-$$

The sample solution must not contain any substance that is more easily reduced (when acids are being titrated) or oxidized (when bases are being titrated) than the solvent, water. External generation (Section III-C-2) eliminates difficulties that arise from the presence of other oxidizable or reducible species. Isolation of the auxiliary electrode is obviously required when internal generation is employed unless the auxiliary electrode reaction is nonprotolytic. Silver–silver halide auxiliary electrodes have been widely used, especially in the titration of acids. The coulometric method can be applied to the titration of most acids and bases that are amenable to assay by conventional acidimetry and alkalimetry. Titrations in nonaqueous solvents such as acetonitrile (95,230) and glacial acetic acid (162) are feasible.

2. Redox Titrations

Because of the ease with which they can be generated with 100% current efficiency and because of their wide applicability, the halogens have been more widely used than any other intermediates as oxidizing agents in coulometric titrimetry. Bromine, in particular, can be generated in both aqueous and nonaqueous solvents under a wide range of experimental conditions. This intermediate is useful not only as an oxidizing agent but also for the titration of olefins, phenols, and other compounds by bromination. The use of cupric bromide as a supporting electrolyte provides the $Cu(I)-Br_2$ dual intermediate system (23). With this system an excess of bromine may be generated for the titration of materials that react slowly with the reagent; the excess may be back-titrated by electrogenerated cuprous ion by reversing the flow of current through the cell. Iodine works well as a coulometric intermediate in the same types of titrations to which classic iodimetry is applicable. The Karl Fischer titration also may be done with electrolytically generated iodine (10,11,114,176,177), but the method has not been widely applied.

Coulometric titrations that require the transfer of oxygen atoms for the generation of the reagent have not met with much success. Permanganate cannot be generated at all (67,220), and current efficiencies are low in the generation of dichromate (184). However, other strong oxidizing agents, such as dipositive silver, ceric ion, and manganic ion, which can replace permanganate or dichromate in many titrations, can be generated satisfactorily.

Most of the standard reducing reagents can be generated satisfactorily, although careful attention must be paid to experimental conditions to avoid simultaneous reduction of the solvent when the stronger reducing agents such as titanous ion are being generated. The successful generation of chromous ion with 100% current efficiency has been claimed on the basis that the titration of oxygen in trace quantities agreed with the results by another method (106). Reproducible chromous ion generation has made it useful in an automatic oxygen analyzer (213). Thiosulfate ion cannot be generated, but stannous ion can be used as a substitute for thiosulfate in carrying out many conventional iodometric titrations (9).

3. Precipitation Titrations

Silver ion can be generated easily with 100% current efficiency by oxidation of a silver metal anode and has been widely applied to the titration of halides and mercaptans. The American Association of Clinical Chemists has adopted the coulometric titration of chloride ion in biological materials as a standard method (37,38). In acidic solution, mercurous ion can be generated by oxidation of a mercury anode; this intermediate offers some advantages over silver ion as a titrant for halides in some cases. In alkaline solution, mercuric ion is formed by the anodic oxidation of mercury and may be used as an intermediate for the titration of sulfides and mercaptans.

4. Complexation Titrations

Electrolytically generated silver ion may be used for the complexometric titration of cyanide, but mercuric ion is a more satisfactory intermediate, especially for the titration of small amounts of cyanide (201). Mercuric ion also has been used successfully for the complexometric titration of materials such as thiourea and amines; in the latter case the amines were converted to their dithiocarbamic acid derivatives prior to titration (204).

Ethylenediaminetetraacetate can be generated by reduction of the mercuric complex at a mercury electrode (208).

$$HgY^{-2} + 2e^- \rightarrow Hg + Y^{-4}$$

The cadmium complex may be used as the supporting electrolyte in place of the mercuric complex in many cases (229). Metal ions, such as calcium, zinc, and lead, can be titrated with the ligand, which is released by the reduction of the supporting electrolyte. Other complexation reagents such as thioglycollic acid (179) and monothioethylene glycol (180) may be generated in a similar fashion.

5. Film-Stripping Coulometry

Several examples of the application of constant-current coulometry to the determination of the thickness of protective metal coatings and of oxide and corrosion layers on a variety of base metals are given in Table 49.I. In many cases it is possible not only to determine the total coating thickness but also to obtain considerable information on the nature of the coating. For example, in the determination of the thickness of tin coatings on copper it is possible to determine both the external coating of pure tin and the copper–tin alloy that exists at the interface (87). Likewise it is possible to estimate both the oxide and sulfide in mixed oxide–sulfide films on copper and silver (25,199). It must be remembered, however, that the stripping process is not carried out under thermodynamically reversible conditions and care must be exercised in interpreting the experimental data unless the method has been proved on known samples (18,72,126,178,252). The method is extremely sensitive; less than one monolayer of a film can be determined under very carefully controlled conditions (126).

A modification of the film-stripping coulometric method may be applied to the determination of metal ions in solution. For example, copper in an aqueous solution may be plated quantitatively on a platinum cathode by exhaustive electrolysis using either controlled potential or controlled current. The amount of copper plated, which is equal to that originally present in the sample solution, may then be determined by film-stripping coulometry. This approach offers a distinct advantage over direct controlled-potential coulometric analysis, since stripping can be carried out in a short time with a relatively large controlled current, thus minimizing errors arising from background currents. This approach has been used very successfully for the determination of copper at the microgram level (150,256,257), but it has not been explored extensively for the determination of other metal ions. Difficulties are sometimes encountered in achieving quantitative deposition of metal ions when this method is applied to the analysis of extremely dilute solutions, but nevertheless analyses can be made in the submicrogram range if empirical calibration curves are employed (150). Unfortunately, constant-current stripping methods cannot be used generally if the metal ions are plated into a mercury electrode rather than onto the surface of a solid electrode, and one must usually resort to controlled-potential electrolysis for the stripping process. In some cases, however, interrupted constant-current techniques may be used for the stripping step if the solution contains halide ions; in this case the mercurous halide formed at the electrode surface acts as a coulometric intermediate (198).

If carefully controlled conditions are employed in both the plating and stripping processes, it is possible to perform practical analyses by measuring the number of coulombs consumed in the stripping process even though neither process is quantitative (150,159,188). Analyses of this type are basically anodic-stripping voltammetric methods (see Chapter 50) rather than coulometric titration methods, however.

6. Miscellaneous Applications

Electrolytically generated hydrogen may be employed as a coulometric intermediate for the determination of unsaturated compounds that are susceptible to assay by conventional hydrogenation methods (68,160,183). An automatic apparatus that permits a continuous recording of the rate of the hydrogenation has been described (183). Water in gases may be determined by quantitative electrochemical conversion into hydrogen and oxygen in a special cell containing phosphorus pentoxide absorbent (4,34, 110,227). This method has proved to be particularly popular for the continuous determination of moisture in the parts-per-million range. The water cell has been applied to the determination of carbon and hydrogen in organic materials by a direct measurement of the water formed by combustion (191). The carbon dioxide from combustion can be converted to water by a catalytic system and the water determined as above (88). Trace quantities of oxygen in gases may be coulometrically reduced at a porous silver electrode (111,240). This technique has been employed as a very sensitive detector in continuous gas analyzers.

The preparation of standard solutions of reagents that can be generated electrolytically with 100% current efficiency is an obvious extension of the coulometric method. This technique has proved to be particularly useful for the preparation of standard solutions of metals in fused salts (124,125). Known concentrations of hydrogen or oxygen can be readily introduced into other gases by electrolytic generation; this technique is applicable also to flowing systems and is especially convenient for calibration purposes in the parts-per-million range, where conventional techniques are extremely cumbersome (98,228,242).

Hanselman and Rogers (94) have described a very versatile technique for the "generation" of reagents by controlling the passage of the titrant through highly permselective ion-exchange membranes under the influence of an electric current. A solution of the reagent is isolated from the solution to be titrated by a suitable ion-exchange membrane; the desired ion in the reagent solution is then caused to migrate through the membrane at a constant rate by passing a constant current through the membrane. If the membrane is perfectly selective, the passage of one faraday will cause exactly one equivalent of the reagent ion to be transported from the reagent reservoir into the solution being titrated. Actually, no presently available membrane is perfectly selective, but current efficiencies that are close to 100% and that are reproducible to within 1 to 2% are readily attained. This technique is particularly attractive when no electrode system is available for generation of the reagent in the normal manner or when the solution to be titrated contains components that interfere with normal generation. The application of this technique to the generation of vanadyl, lithium, thorium, and phosphate ions as well as to other ions has been described (241).

Although they are not titrations in the strict sense, several other extensions of the coulometric method deserve mention. The maintenance of constant gas pressures by electrochemical generation of gases on demand has proved to be useful in studying rates of oxidation by molecular oxygen (24) and for studying surface adsorption (93). Displacement of liquids by electrochemically generated gases offers a convenient means of precisely controlling the rate of delivery of these liquids through control of the electrolysis current (97). Flow rates as low as 0.1 ml./hour can be maintained readily (248).

GENERAL REFERENCES

Most of the fundamental principles that underlie the coulometric method are covered in other chapters of this Treatise. The basic theories and techniques discussed in Chapters 42 and 43 are particularly pertinent. Much of the material presented in Chapters 46 to 48 also is directly applicable to the theory and practice of coulometric analysis.

The following references may be consulted for further details on the theory and applications of the coulometric method. The list is by no means comprehensive.

G1. Charlot, G., and J. Badoz-Lambling, *Chim. mod.*, **3**, 353 (1958). A comprehensive review.

G2. DeFord, D. D., *Anal. Chem.*, **26**, 135 (1954); **28**, 660 (1956); **32**, 31R (1960); D. D. DeFord and R. C. Bowers, *Anal. Chem.*, **30**, 613 (1958); A. J. Bard, *Anal. Chem.*, **34**, 57R (1962). Periodic reviews of the current literature.

G3. Delahay, P., *New Instrumental Methods in Electrochemistry*, Interscience, New York–London, 1954. An excellent treatment of the basic theory.

G4. Lingane, J. J., *Electroanalytical Chemistry*, 2nd ed., Interscience, New York–London, 1958. Particularly valuable as a source of detailed information on instruments, techniques, and practical analytical procedures.

G5. Meites, L., "Controlled-Potential Electrolysis," in A. Weissberger, Ed., *Technique of Organic Chemistry*, 3rd rev. ed., Interscience, New York–London, 1960, Vol. I, Part IV. A comprehensive treatment of both the theoretical and practical aspects of controlled-potential electrolysis, including controlled-potential coulometry, with special emphasis on applications in the field of organic chemistry.

G6. Reinmuth, W. H., "Theory of Electrode Processes," in C. N. Reilley, Ed., *Advances in Analytical Chemistry and Instrumentation*, Interscience, New York–London, 1960, Vol. I, p. 241. The practical implications of current theories of electrode processes, as well as the theories themselves, are covered.

REFERENCES

1. Anson, F. C., K. H. Pool, and J. M. Wright, *J. Electroanal. Chem.*, **2**, 237 (1961).
2. Arcand, G. M., *Anal. Chim. Acta*, **19**, 267 (1958).
3. Arcand, G. M., and E. H. Swift, *Anal. Chem.*, **28**, 440 (1956).
4. Armstrong, R. G., K. W. Gardiner, and F. W. Adams, *Anal. Chem.*, **32**, 752 (1960).
5. Arthur, P., and J. F. Donahue, *Anal. Chem.*, **24**, 1612 (1952).

6. Austin, R. R., *Am. Gas Assoc., Proc.*, **31**, 505 (1949); Austin, R. R., L. E. Percy, and E. E. Escher, *Gas*, **26** (No. 5), 47 (1950); *Ibid.*, (No. 6), p. 3; Austin, R. R., G. K. Turner, and L. E. Percy, *Instruments*, **22**, 588 (1949).

6a. Badoz-Lambling, J., *J. Electroanal. Chem.*, **1**, 44 (1959).

7. Bard, A. J., *Anal. Chem.*, **32**, 623 (1960).

8. Bard, A. J., *Anal. Chim. Acta*, **21**, 365 (1959).

9. Bard, A. J., and J. J. Lingane, *Anal. Chim. Acta*, **20**, 463 (1959).

10. Barendrecht, E., *Nature*, **183**, 1181 (1959).

11. Barendrecht, E., and J. G. F. Doornekamp, *Z. Anal. Chem.*, **186**, 176 (1962).

12. Bett, N., W. Cook, and G. Morris, *Analyst*, **79**, 607 (1954).

13. Bewick, A., A. Bewick, M. Fleischmann, and M. Liler, *Electrochim. Acta*, **1**, 83 (1959).

14. Bogan, S., L. Meites, E. Peters, and J. M. Sturtevant, *J. Am. Chem. Soc.*, **73**, 1584 (1951).

15. Booman, G. L., *Anal. Chem.*, **29**, 213 (1957).

16. Booman, G. L., and W. B. Holbrook, *Anal. Chem.*, **31**, 10 (1959).

17. Booman, G. L., W. B. Holbrook, and J. E. Rein, *Anal. Chem.*, **29**, 219 (1957).

18. Bouillon, F., J. Piron, and M. DeLil, *Nature*, **178**, 1406 (1956).

19. Braman, R. S., D. D. DeFord, T. N. Johnston, and L. J. Kuhns, *Anal. Chem.*, **32**, 1258 (1960).

20. Bratzler, K., and H. Kleeman, *Erdoel Kohle*, **7**, 559 (1954).

21. Breiter, M., and F. G. Will, *Z. Elektrochem.*, **61**, 1177 (1957).

22. Brunstad, A., *U.S. At. Energy Comm.*, **TID-7516**, 137 (1956); through *Chem. Abstr.*, **51**, 1770 (1957).

23. Buck, R. P., and E. H. Swift, *Anal. Chem.*, **24**, 499 (1952).

24. Button, J. C. E., and A. J. Davies, *J. Sci. Instr.*, **30**, 307 (1953).

25. Campbell, W. E., and U. B. Thomas, *Trans. Electrochem. Soc.*, **76**, 303 (1939).

26. Carson, W. N., Jr., *Anal. Chem.*, **22**, 1565 (1950).

27. Carson, W. N., Jr., *Anal. Chem.*, **25**, 466 (1953).

28. Carson, W. N., Jr., *Anal. Chem.*, **25**, 1733 (1953).

29. Carson, W. N., Jr., *Anal. Chem.*, **26**, 1673 (1954).

30. Carson, W. N., Jr., and H. S. Gile, *Anal. Chem.*, **27**, 122 (1955).

31. Carson, W. N., Jr., and R. Ko, *Anal. Chem.*, **23**, 1019 (1951).

32. Carson, W. N., Jr., J. W. Vanderwater, and H. S. Gile, *Anal. Chem.*, **29**, 1417 (1957).

33. Clemency, C. V., and A. F. Hagner, *Anal. Chem.*, **33**, 888 (1961).

34. Cole, L. G., M. Czuha, R. W. Mosley, and D. T. Sawyer, *Anal. Chem.*, **31**, 2048 (1959).

35. Cooke, W. D., and N. H. Furman, *Anal. Chem.*, **22**, 896 (1950).

35a. Cooke, W. D., C. N. Reilley, and N. H. Furman, *Anal. Chem.*, **23**, 1662 (1951).

36. Cooke, W. D., C. N. Reilley, and N. H. Furman, *Anal. Chem.*, **24**, 205 (1952).

37. Cotlove, E., "Chloride," in D. Seligson, Ed., *Standard Methods of Clinical Chemistry*, Vol. III, Academic Press, New York, 1961.

38. Cotlove, E., and H. H. Nishi, *Clin. Chem.*, **7**, 285 (1961).

39. Coulson, D. M., and L. A. Cavanagh, *Anal. Chem.*, **32**, 1245 (1960); Coulson, D. M., L. A. Cavanagh, J. E. deVries, and B. Walther, *J. Agr. Food Chem.*, **8**, 399 (1960).

40. Craig, D. N., and J. I. Hoffman, *Natl. Bur. Std. (U.S.), Circ.*, **524**, 13 (1953).

41. Craig, D. N., J. I. Hoffman, C. A. Law, and W. J. Hamer, *J. Res. Natl. Bur. Std.*, **64A**, 381 (1960).

42. Cruzan, C. G., and H. A. Miley, *J. Appl. Phys.*, **11**, 631 (1940).
43. Čůta, F., and Z. Kučera, *Chem. Listy*, **47**, 1166 (1953); *Chem. Abstr.*, **48**, 3850 (1954).
44. Čůta, F., and Z. Kučera, *Chem. Listy*, **52**, 595 (1958); through *Chem. Abstr.*, **53**, 5978 (1959).
45. Davis, D. G., *Anal. Chem.*, **31**, 1460 (1959).
46. Davis, D. G., and J. J. Lingane, *Anal. Chim. Acta*, **18**, 245 (1958).
47. DeFord, D. D., and H. Horn, *Anal. Chem.*, **28**, 797 (1956).
48. DeFord, D. D., C. J. Johns, and J. N. Pitts, Jr., *Anal. Chem.*, **23**, 941 (1951).
49. DeFord, D. D., J. N. Pitts, and C. J. Johns, *Anal. Chem.*, **23**, 938 (1951).
50. Delahay, P., G. Charlot, and H. A. Laitinen, *Anal. Chem.*, **32**, No. 6, 103A (1960).
51. Dilts, R. V., and N. H. Furman, *Anal. Chem.*, **27**, 1596 (1955).
52. Dubois, J. E., *Z. Elektrochem.*, **64**, 143 (1960).
53. Dunn, F. J., J. B. Mann, and J. R. Mosley, *Anal. Chem.*, **27**, 167 (1955).
54. DuRose, A. H., and D. M. Hutchinson, *Plating*, **40**, 470, 630 (1953); through *Chem. Abstr.*, **47**, 9820 (1953).
55. Eckfeldt, E. L., *Anal. Chem.*, **31**, 1453 (1959).
56. Edwards, K. W., and D. M. Kern, *Anal. Chem.*, **28**, 1876 (1956).
57. Ehlers, V. B., and J. W., Sease, *Anal. Chem.*, **26**, 513 (1954).
58. Ehlers, V. B., and J. W. Sease, *Anal. Chem.*, **31**, 16 (1959).
59. Einsel, D. W., H. J. Trurnit, S. D. Silver, and E. C. Steiner, *Anal. Chem.*, **28**, 408 (1956).
60. Emrick, E. R., *Dissertation Abstr.*, **20**, 3039 (1960); *Chem. Abstr.*, **54**, 9600 (1960).
61. Evans, U. R., and L. C. Bannister, *Proc. Roy. Soc. (London), Ser. A*, **125**, 370 (1929).
62. Evans, U. R., and H. A. Miley, *Nature*, **139**, 283 (1937).
63. Farrar, L. G., P. F. Thomason, and M. T. Kelley, *Anal. Chem.*, **30**, 1511 (1958).
64. Farrington, P. S., W. P. Schaefer, and J. M. Dunham, *Anal. Chem.*, **33**, 1318 (1961).
65. Feldberg, S. W., and C. E. Bricker, *Anal. Chem.*, **31**, 1852 (1959).
66. Fenton, A. J., Jr., and N. H. Furman, *Anal. Chem.*, **29**, 221 (1957).
67. Fenton, A. J., Jr., and N. H. Furman, *Anal. Chem.*, **32**, 748 (1960).
68. Flaschka, H., and M. Hochenegger, *Mikrochim. Acta*, **1957**, 587.
69. Foley, W. T., *J. Electrochem. Soc.*, **104**, 638 (1957).
70. Foley, W. T., and R. F. Pottie, *Anal. Chem.*, **28**, 1101 (1956).
71. Francis, H. T., *Trans. Electrochem. Soc.*, **93**, 79 (1948).
72. Frankenthal, R. P., T. J. Butler, and R. T. Davis, Jr., *Anal. Chem.*, **30**, 441 (1958).
73. Franklin, T. C., and C. C. Roth, *Anal. Chem.*, **27**, 1197 (1955).
74. Fuchs, W., and O. Veiser, *Arch. Eisenhuettenw.*, **27**, 429 (1956).
75. Furman, N. H., and R. N. Adams, *Anal. Chem.*, **25**, 1564 (1953).
76. Furman, N. H., and A. J. Fenton, Jr., *Anal. Chem.*, **28**, 515 (1956).
77. Furman, N. H., C. N. Reilley, and W. D. Cooke, *Anal. Chem.*, **23**, 1665 (1951).
78. Furman, N. H., L. J. Sayegh, and R. N. Adams, *Anal. Chem.*, **27**, 1423 (1955).
79. Gerhardt, G. E., H. C. Lawrence, and J. S. Parsons, *Anal. Chem.*, **27**, 1752 (1955).
80. Gerischer, H., *Proc. Intern. Comm. Electrochem. Thermodyn. Kinet.*, 9th Meeting (1959), p. 243.
81. Gerischer, H., and K. E. Staubach, *Z. Elektrochem.*, **61**, 789 (1957).

82. Geske, D. H., *J. Phys. Chem.*, **63**, 1062 (1959).
83. Geske, D. H., and A. J. Bard, *J. Phys. Chem.*, **63**, 1057 (1959).
84. Glass, J. R., and E. J. Moore, *Anal. Chem.*, **32**, 1265 (1960).
85. Greene, N. D., *Corrosion*, **15**, 369*t* (1959).
86. Gresz, S., *Periodica Polytech.*, **3**, 105 (1959); *Chem. Abstr.*, **54**, 7245 (1960).
87. Grower, G. G., *Proc. Am. Soc. Testing Mater.*, **17** (II), 129 (1917).
88. Haber, H. S., and K. W. Gardiner, *Microchem. J.*, **6**, 83 (1962).
89. Haissinsky, M., *Electrochimie des Substances Radioactive et des Solutions Extrement Diluées*, Hermann, Paris, 1946.
90. Haisty, R. W., *Rev. Sci. Instr.*, **31**, 1297 (1960).
91. Hanamura, S., *Talanta*, **2**, 278 (1959).
92. Hancock, P., and J. E. O. Mayne, *J. Chem. Soc.*, **1958**, 4167.
93. Hannah, K. W., M. J. Joncich, and N. Hackerman, *Rev. Sci. Instr.*, **25**, 636 (1954).
94. Hanselman, R. B., and L. B. Rogers, *Anal. Chem.*, **32**, 1240 (1960).
95. Hanselman, R. B., and C. A. Streuli, *Anal. Chem.*, **28**, 916 (1956).
96. Head, W. F., and M. M. Marsh, *J. Chem. Educ.*, **38**, 361 (1961).
97. Heckly, R. J., *Science*, **127**, 233 (1958).
98. Hersch, P. A., *Anal. Chem.*, **32**, 1030 (1960).
99. Hetman, J. S., *Analyst*, **81**, 543 (1956).
100. Hibbs, L. E., and D. H. Wilkins, *Anal. Chim. Acta*, **20**, 344 (1959).
101. Hickling, A., *Trans. Faraday Soc.*, **38**, 27 (1942).
102. Hothersall, A. W., and W. N. Bradshaw, *J. Iron Steel Inst. (London)*, **133**, 225 (1936).
103. Hoyer, H. W., *J. Phys. Chem.*, **60**, 372 (1956).
104. Ibrahim, S. H., and A. P. M. Nair, *J. Madras Univ.*, **26B**, 521 (1956); through *Chem. Abstr.*, **52**, 12668 (1958).
105. Iinuma, H., and T. Yoshimori, *Gifu Daigaku Kogakubu Kenku Hokoku* No. 6, 88 (1956); through *Chem. Abstr.*, **51**, 4200 (1957).
106. James, G. S., and M. J. Stephen, *Analyst*, **85**, 35 (1960).
107. Kalinowski, K., *Roczniki Chem.*, **30**, 269 (1956); through *Chem. Abstr.*, **50**, 12166 (1956).
108. Kalinowski, K., and Z. Sykulska, *Acta Polon. Pharm.*, **15**, 179 (1958); through *Chem. Abstr.*, **52**, 17617 (1958).
109. Katz, W., *Stahl Eisen*, **76**, 1672 (1956); through *Chem. Abstr.*, **52**, 5160 (1958).
110. Keidel, F. A., *Anal. Chem.*, **31**, 2043 (1959).
111. Keidel, F. A., *Ind. Eng. Chem.*, **52**, 490 (1960).
112. Kelley, M. T., H. C. Jones, and D. J. Fisher, *Anal. Chem.*, **31**, 488 (1959).
113. Kelley, M. T., H. C. Jones, and D. J. Fisher, *Anal. Chem.*, **31**, 956 (1959).
114. Kelley, M. T., R. W. Stelzner, W. R. Laing, and D. J. Fisher, *Anal. Chem.*, **31**, 220 (1959).
115. Kennedy, J. H., and J. J. Lingane, *Anal. Chim. Acta*, **18**, 240 (1958).
116. Klass, P. J., *Anal. Chem.*, **33**, 1851 (1961).
117. Kolthoff, I. M., *Anal. Chim. Acta*, **18**, 386, 391 (1958).
118. Kolthoff, I. M., and E. R. Nightingale, *Anal. Chim. Acta*, **17**, 329 (1957).
119. Kowalski, K., Z. Sykulska, *Acta Polon. Pharm.*, **14**, 255 (1957); through *Chem. Abstr.*, **52**, 12683 (1958).
120. Kramer, K. W., and R. B. Fischer, *Anal. Chem.*, **26**, 415 (1954).
121. Kratochvil, B., and H. Diehl, *Talanta*, **3**, 346 (1960).

122. Kruse, J. M., *Anal. Chem.*, **31**, 1854 (1959).
123. Kumze, C. T., and A. R. Willey, *J. Electrochem. Soc.*, **99**, 354 (1952).
124. Laitinen, H. A., and B. B. Bhatia, *Anal. Chem.*, **30**, 1995 (1958).
125. Laitinen, H. A., and J. W. Pankey, *J. Am. Chem. Soc.*, **81**, 1053 (1959).
126. Lambert, R. H., and D. J. Trevoy, *J. Electrochem. Soc.*, **105**, 18 (1958).
127. Lee, J. K., and R. N. Adams, *Anal. Chem.*, **26**, 240 (1958).
128. Leisey, F. A., *Anal. Chem.*, **26**, 1607 (1954).
129. Leisey, F. A., *Instr. Soc. Am. J.*, **7**, 67 (1960).
130. Leisey, F. A., and J. F. Grutsch, *Anal. Chem.*, **28**, 1553 (1956).
131. Liberti, A., *Anal. Chim. Acta*, **17**, 247 (1957).
132. Liberti, A., and G. P. Cartoni, *Chim. Ind. (Milan)*, **39**, 821 (1957); Liberti, A., G. P. Cartoni, and U. Pallotta, *Ann. Chim. (Rome)*, **48**, 40 (1958); *Chem. Abstr.*, **52**, 2664 (1958).
133. Liberti, A., and L. Ciavatta, *Gazz. Chim. Ital.*, **87**, 1337 (1957); *J. Inorg. Nucl. Chem.*, **8**, 365 (1958).
134. Liberti, A., and P. Lazzari, *Ric. Sci.*, **26**, 825 (1956); through *Chem. Abstr.*, **50**, 9930 (1956).
135. Lingane, J. J., *Anal. Chem.*, **26**, 622 (1954).
136. Lingane, J. J., *Anal. Chem.*, **26**, 1021 (1954).
137. Lingane, J. J., *Anal. Chim. Acta*, **18**, 349 (1958).
138. Lingane, J. J., *Electroanalytical Chemistry*, 2nd ed., Interscience, New York–London, 1958, p. 405.
139. Lingane, J. J., *J. Am. Chem. Soc.*, **67**, 1916 (1945).
140. Lingane, J. J., and F. C. Anson, *Anal. Chem.*, **28**, 1871 (1956).
141. Lingane, J. J., and A. M. Hartley, *Anal. Chim. Acta*, **11**, 475 (1954).
142. Lingane, J. J., and A. M. Hartley, *Anal. Chim. Acta*, **13**, 183 (1955).
143. Lingane, J. J., and R. T. Iwamoto, *Anal. Chim. Acta*, **13**, 465 (1955).
144. Lingane, J. J., and S. L. Jones, *Anal. Chem.*, **22**, 1169 (1950).
145. Lingane, J. J., and J. H. Kennedy, *Anal. Chim. Acta*, **15**, 465 (1956).
146. Lingane, J. J., C. H. Langford, and F. C. Anson, *Anol. Chim. Acta*, **16**, 165 (1957).
147. Lingane, J. J., and J. A. Page, *Anal. Chim. Acta*, **13**, 281 (1955).
148. Lingane, J. J., and L. A. Small, *Anal. Chem.*, **21**, 1119 (1949).
149. Liu, C. H., *Anal. Chem.*, **33**, 1477 (1961).
150. Lord, S. S., Jr., R. C. O'Neill, and L. B. Rogers, *Anal. Chem.*, **24**, 209 (1952).
151. Lüdering, H., *Arch. Eisenhuettenw.*, **29**, 173 (1958); through *Chem. Abstr.*, **52**, 9860 (1958).
152. MacInnes, D. A., C. Yang, and L. R. Pray, *J. Phys. Chem.*, **61**, 662 (1957).
153. MacNevin, W. M., and B. B. Baker, *Anal. Chem.*, **24**, 986 (1952).
154. MacNevin, W. M., B. B. Baker, and R. D. McIver, *Anal. Chem.*, **25**, 274 (1953).
155. MacNevin, W. M., and R. D. McIver, *Anal. Chem.*, **27**, 1994 (1955).
156. Malmstadt, H. V., and C. B. Roberts, *Anal. Chem.*, **27**, 741 (1955).
157. Malmstadt, H. V., and C. B. Roberts, *Anal. Chem.*, **28**, 1412 (1956).
158. Malmstadt, H. V., and C. B. Roberts, *Anal. Chem.*, **28**, 1884 (1956).
159. Mamantov, G., P. Papoff, and P. Delahay, *J. Am. Chem. Soc.*, **79**, 4034 (1957).
160. Manegold, E., and F. Peters, *Kolloid-Z.*, **85**, 310 (1938); *Chem. Abstr.*, **33**, 1993 (1939).
161. Masui, M., and H. Sayo, *Yakugaku Zasshi*, **75**, 1515 (1956); through *Chem. Abstr.*, **50**, 4561 (1956).

162. Mather, W. B., Jr., and F. C. Anson, *Anal. Chim. Acta*, **21**, 468 (1959).
163. Mather, W. B., Jr., and F. C. Anson, *Anal. Chem.*, **33**, 132 (1961).
164. Meier, D. J., R. J. Myers, and E. H. Swift, *J. Am. Chem. Soc.*, **71**, 2340 (1949).
165. Meier, D. J., and E. H. Swift, *J. Am. Chem. Soc.*, **72**, 5331 (1950).
166. Meites, L., *Anal. Chem.*, **27**, 416 (1955).
167. Meites, L., *Anal. Chem.*, **27**, 1114 (1955).
168. Meites, L., *Anal. Chem.*, **27**, 1116 (1955).
169. Meites, L., *Anal. Chem.*, **31**, 1285 (1959).
170. Meites, L., *Anal. Chim. Acta*, **18**, 364 (1958).
171. Meites, L., *Anal. Chim. Acta*, **20**, 456 (1959).
172. Meites, L., and T. Meites, *Anal. Chem.*, **28**, 103 (1956).
173. Meites, L., and S. A. Moros, *Anal. Chem.*, **31**, 23 (1959).
174. Meites, T., and L. Meites, *Anal. Chem.*, **27**, 1531 (1955).
175. Merritt, L. L., Jr., E. L. Martin, Jr., and R. D. Bedi, *Anal. Chem.*, **30**, 487 (1958).
176. Meyer, A. S., Jr., and C. M. Boyd, *Anal. Chem.*, **31**, 215 (1959).
177. Meyer, A. S., Jr., and C. M. Boyd, *U. S. At. Energy Comm.*, **ORNL–1899** (1955).
178. Miley, H. A., and U. R. Evans, *Iron Steel Inst. (London), Spec. Rept.* **21**, 243 (1938); through *Chem. Abstr.*, **32**, 5760 (1938).
179. Miller, B., and D. N. Hume, *Anal. Chem.*, **32**, 524 (1960).
180. Miller, B., and D. N. Hume, *Anal. Chem.*, **32**, 764 (1960).
181. Miller, J. W., Thesis, Northwestern University, Evanston, Illinois, 1956; *Dissertation Abstr.*, **16**, 2012 (1956).
182. Miller, J. W., and D. D. DeFord, *Anal. Chem.*, **29**, 475 (1957).
183. Miller, J. W., and D. D. DeFord, *Anal. Chem.*, **30**, 295 (1958).
184. Monnier, D., and P. Zwahlen, *Helv. Chim. Acta*, **39**, 1865 (1956); *Anal. Abstr.*, **4**, 3647 (1957).
185. Munemori, M., *Talanta*, **1**, 110 (1958).
186. Myers, R. J., and E. H. Swift, *J. Am. Chem. Soc.*, **70**, 1047 (1948).
187. Nair, A. P. M., and S. H. Ibrahim, *J. Sci. Ind. Res. (India)*, **15B**, 703 (1956); through *Chem. Abstr.*, **51**, 16200 (1957).
188. Nikelly, J. G., and W. D. Cooke, *Anal. Chem.*, **29**, 933 (1957).
189. Oelsen, W., and G. Graue, *Angew. Chem.*, **64**, 24 (1952).
190. Olson, E. C., *Anal. Chem.*, **32**, 1545 (1960).
191. Olson, E. C., R. L. Houtman, and W. A. Struck, *Microchem. J.*, **5**, 611 (1961).
192. Olson, E. C., and A. F. Krivis, *Microchem. J.*, **4**, 181 (1960).
193. Page, J. A., and J. J. Lingane, *Anal. Chim. Acta*, **16**, 175 (1957).
194. Parsons, J. S., and W. Seaman, *Anal. Chem.*, **27**, 210 (1955).
195. Parsons, J. S., W. Seaman, and R. M. Amick, *Anal. Chem.*, **27**, 1754 (1954).
196. Phillips, S. L., and D. M. Kern, *Anal. Chim. Acta*, **20**, 295 (1959).
197. Pitts, J. N., D. D. DeFord, T. W. Martin, and E. A. Schmall, *Anal. Chem.*, **26**, 628 (1954).
198. Porter, J. T., II, and W. D. Cooke, *J. Am. Chem. Soc.*, **77**, 1481 (1955).
199. Price, L. E., and G. J. Thomas, *Trans. Electrochem. Soc.*, **76**, 329 (1939); through *Chem. Abstr.*, **33**, 8159 (1939).
200. Proszt, J., and L. Poos, *Periodica Polytech.*, **1** (No. 1), 25 (1957); through *Chem Abstr.*, **52**, 7005 (1958).
201. Przybylowicz, E. P., and L. B. Rogers, *Anal. Chem.*, **30**, 65 (1958).
202. Przybylowicz, E. P., and L. B. Rogers, *Anal. Chem.*, **28**, 799 (1956).
203. Przybylowicz, E. P., and L. B. Rogers, *Anal. Chem.*, **30**, 1064 (1958).

204. Przybylowicz, E. P., and L. B. Rogers, *Anal. Chim. Acta*, **18**, 596 (1958).
205. Ramsey, W. J., P. S. Farrington, and E. H. Swift, *Anal. Chem.*, **22**, 332 (1950).
206. Reilley, C. N., *J. Chem. Educ.*, **31**, 543 (1954).
207. Reilley, C. N., R. N. Adams, and N. H. Furman, *Anal. Chem.*, **24**, 1044 (1952).
208. Reilley, C. N., and W. W. Porterfield, *Anal. Chem.*, **28**, 443 (1956).
209. Richards, T. W., and G. W. Heimrod, *Proc. Am. Acad. Arts Sci.*, **37**, 415 (1902); **44**, 91 (1908); *J. Am. Chem. Soc.*, **37**, 692 (1915).
210. Richter, H. L., Jr., *Anal. Chem.*, **27**, 1526 (1955).
211. Robson, H., and T. Kuwana, *Anal. Chem.*, **32**, 567 (1960).
212. Rogers, L. B., *Record Chem. Progr.* (*Kresge-Hooker Sci. Lib.*), **16**, 197 (1955).
213. Sakamaki, I., and S. Yuki, *Bunseki Kagaku*, **7**, 33 (1958); through *Anal. Abstr.*, **5**, 3698 (1958); *Chem. Abstr.*, **54**, 163 (1960).
213a. Santhanam, K. S. V., and V. R. Krishnan, *Anal. Chem.*, **33**, 1493 (1961).
214. Schmid, R. W., and C. N. Reilley, *Anal. Chem.*, **28**, 520 (1956).
215. Schreiber, R., and W. D. Cooke, *Anal. Chem.*, **27**, 1475 (1955).
216. Schwabe, K., *Naturwissenschaften*, **38**, 458 (1951); through *Chem. Abstr.*, **46**, 11554 (1952).
217. Schwarz-Bergkampf, E., and R. Reichert, *Mikrochim. Acta*, **1955**, 1031.
218. Scott, F. A., and R. M. Peekema, *Proc. U. N. Intern. Conf. Peaceful Uses At. Energy, 2nd, Geneva, 1958*, **28**, 573.
219. Seddon, P. W., *Metal. Ind.* (*London*), **62**, 37 (1943); through *Chem. Abstr.*, **37**, 2273 (1943).
220. Selim, R. G., and J. J. Lingane, *Anal. Chim. Acta*, **21**, 536 (1959).
221. Shaffer, P. A., Jr., A. Briglio, Jr., and J. A. Brockman, Jr., *Anal. Chem.*, **20**, 1008 (1948).
222. Shults, W. D., *Anal. Chem.*, **31**, 1095 (1959).
222a. Shults, W. D., *Anal. Chem.*, **33**, 15 (1961).
223. Shults, W. D., and P. F. Thomason, *Anal. Chem.*, **31**, 492 (1959).
224. Shults, W. D., II, P. F. Thomason, and M. T. Kelley, *Anal. Chem.*, **27**, 1750 (1955).
225. Smith, S. W., and J. K. Taylor, *J. Res. Natl. Bur. Std.*, **63C**, 65 (1959).
226. Smythe, L. E., *Analyst*, **82**, 228 (1957).
227. Souček, J., M. Přibyl, and K. Novák, *Collection Czech. Chem. Communs.*, **27**, 400 (1962).
228. Stafford, C., J. E. Puckett, M. D. Grimes, and B. J. Heinrich, *Anal. Chem.*, **27**, 2012 (1955).
229. Stein, H. H., Thesis, Northwestern University, Evanston, Illinois, 1956; *Dissertation Abstr.*, **16**, 2326 (1956).
230. Streuli, Carl A., *Anal. Chem.*, **28**, 130 (1956).
231. Stromatt, Robert W., *Anal. Chem.*, **32**, 134 (1960).
232. Sykut, K., *Ann. Univ. Mariae Curie-Sklodowska, Lubin-Polonia, Sect.* AA, **9**, 91 (1954); through *Chem. Abstr.*, **51**, 5473 (1957).
233. Szebelledy, L., and Z. Somogyi, *Z. Anal. Chem.*, **112**, 313, 323, 332, 385, 391, 395, 400 (1938); *Chem. Abstr.*, **32**, 5325, 6179 (1938).
234. Takahashi, T., and H. Sakurai, *J. Chem. Soc. Japan, Ind. Chem. Sect.*, **63**, 608 (1960); through *Anal. Abstr.*, **8**, 2888 (1961).
235. Taylor, J. K., and S. W. Smith, *J. Res. Natl. Bur. Std.*, **63A**, 153 (1959).
236. Tutundžič, P. S., *Anal. Chim. Acta*, **8**, 182 (1953).
237. Tutundžič, P. S., and S. Mladenovič, *Anal. Chim. Acta*, **8**, 184 (1953).

238. Tutundžič, P. S., and S. Mladenovič, *Anal. Chim. Acta*, **12,** 390 (1955).
239. Tutundžič, P. S., and M. M. Paunovič, *Anal. Chim. Acta*, **22,** 291 (1960).
240. U.S. Patent 2,898,282 (Aug. 4, 1959), W. M. Flock, Jr., and F. A. Keidel (to duPont Co. Inc.).
241. U.S. Patent 2,954,336 (Sept. 27, 1960), J. F. Grutsch (to Standard Oil Co., Indiana).
242. U.S. Patent 2,900,317 (Aug. 18, 1959), F. A. Keidel (to duPont Co., Inc.).
243. Vorstenburg, F., and A. W. Loffler, *J. Electroanal. Chem.*, **1,** 422 (1960).
244. Wadsworth, N. J., *Analyst*, **85,** 673 (1960).
245. Walisch, W., *Ber.*, **93,** 1481 (1960).
246. Walisch, W., and J. E. DuBois, *Ber.*, **92,** 1028 (1959).
247. Walkiden, G. W., *Chem. Ind. (London)*, **1961,** 1614.
248. Ware, G. C., *Sewage Ind. Wastes*, **30,** 1121 (1958); through *Chem. Abstr.*, **52,** 19263 (1958).
249. Washburn, E. W., and S. J. Bates, *J. Am. Chem. Soc.*, **34,** 1341 (1912).
250. Weaver, J. L., and W. C. Purdy, *Anal. Chim. Acta*, **20,** 376 (1959).
251. Will, F. G., *Z. Electrochem.*, **63,** 484, 689 (1959).
252. Willey, A. R., and D. F. Kelsey, *Anal. Chem.*, **30,** 1804 (1958).
253. Wise, E. N., P. W. Gilles, and C. A. Reynolds, Jr., *Anal. Chem.*, **25,** 1344 (1953); *Ibid.*, **26,** 779 (1954).
254. Yamada, T., *Bunseki Kagaku*, **3,** 215 (1954); through *Anal. Abstr.*, **3,** 344 (1956).
255. Yasuda, S. K., and R. N. Rogers, *Microchem. J.*, **4,** 155 (1960).
256. Zakhar'evskiĭ, M. S., *Vopr. Pitaniya*, **7,** No. 4/5, 180 (1938); through *Chem. Abstr.*, **34,** 1083 (1940).
257. Zbinden, C., *Bull. Soc. Chim. Biol.*, **13,** 35 (1931); through *Chem. Abstr.*, **25,** 5642 (1931).
258. Zittel, H. E., L. B. Dunlap, and P. F. Thomason, *Anal. Chem.*, **33,** 1491 (1961).

Part I
Section D-2

Chapter 50

STRIPPING ANALYSIS

By Irving Shain, *University of Wisconsin, Madison, Wisconsin*

Contents

I. INTRODUCTION

A. SCOPE OF STRIPPING ANALYSIS

In recent years, much of the research in electroanalytical methods has been directed toward increasing the sensitivity of the various techniques. The realization of the importance of traces of electroactive metal ions in biological and electronic research, for example, has catalyzed many attempts to extend the sensitivity of polarography and related methods   In no case, however, can the sensitivity be extended indefinitely, since in the analysis of extremely dilute solutions one encounters residual current that can be significantly larger than the analytical current to be measured.   The problem, then, is one of developing electroanalytical methods in which the sample current is enhanced without particularly increasing the residual current simultaneously.   Perhaps the most successful approach to this problem is *stripping analysis*.

Stripping analysis is a combination of various electrochemical techniques that have one characteristic in common.   The sought-for material is concentrated before analysis by some sort of an electrolysis step: by electro-deposition of the metal ions into a mercury electrode, forming an amalgam, or by electroplating onto a solid electrode.   The concentrated material is then electrolytically redissolved (stripped) from the electrode, and the analysis is performed by following the electrodissolution process with one of several applicable electrochemical methods.   By concentrating the sample in this manner before analysis, it is possible to analyze very dilute solutions, in the range of $10^{-6}M$ to $10^{-9}M$, with excellent precision.   The limit of detectability has been extended about two orders of magnitude further. These remarkable sensitivities can be obtained using procedures that are relatively simple and rapid and, as a result, stripping analysis has become a very important electroanalytical method.

B. SURVEY OF EARLY APPLICATIONS

1. Surface Films and Oxide Layers

Fundamentally, stripping analysis is a very old technique.   It is closely related to the early research on surface films, oxide layers, and plated coatings.   Probably the earliest example of stripping analysis was reported by Grower (27) who investigated tin coatings on copper wires.   An electrolysis cell was set up using the sample wire for the anode and a platinum wire as a cathode, with a gas coulometer in series with the cell and the voltage source. As the current passed through the cell, the potential of the anode was measured with respect to a pure tin wire used as a reference electrode.   The first potential shift occurred when the pure tin coating had been stripped off. Then an intermediate layer of tin–copper alloy was stripped off and another potential shift indicated that the copper wire itself had started to oxidize. The coulometer reading at each potential shift was correlated with the thickness of the particular coating.

This general approach is closely related to both coulometry and chrono-potentiometry. It was further developed by several investigators (1,20), who described coulometric devices for measuring the thickness of coatings on steel and copper. Constant-current methods were used and, from the measured transition times, the quantity of electricity involved in the stripping process could be calculated.

A similar approach has been used to investigate tarnish films on silver (8,59) and oxides on tin plate (21). In these cases, however, the electrode process of interest is a *cathodic* stripping reaction. The reduction of oxidized surface layers to metal is followed coulometrically.

2. Trace Analysis

The first application of stripping analysis to an actual determination was made by Zbinden (75). The method, reported to be accurate to 3% for 0.0006 mg. of copper, was very simple. The copper in the solution was plated onto a platinum cathode in a manner analogous to that used in electrogravimetric analysis. However, it was not possible to weigh the electrode because of the small amount of copper present. When the electrodeposition was complete, therefore, the current was reversed and the copper was stripped back off the electrode into the solution. When all copper had redissolved, the stripping current dropped to zero and the copper content could be determined from the quantity of electricity used during the stripping process.

After Zbinden's work, application of the stripping technique to trace analysis received relatively little attention (19,74). More effort was devoted to the development of methods for the analysis of minor electroactive constituents in rather large samples that contained other interfering electroactive material. Large mercury pool electrodes were used for electro-separation of the sample, and then, after either distillation of the mercury (9,23) or electrodissolution of the sample in a fresh electrolyte solution (43,66,71), the analysis could be made using conventional methods.

A more versatile and rapid type of stripping analysis was introduced by Rogers and his co-workers (25,49,51), who showed that it was not necessary to carry the electrodeposition step to completion as long as a fixed, reproducible portion of the sample could be electrodeposited. They worked with very small volumes of solution, and showed that microelectrodes could be used for stripping analysis. These workers analyzed extremely dilute solutions ($\sim 10^{-8} M$) by following the stripping process coulometrically (with solid electrodes) or voltammetrically (with mercury-plated silver and platinum electrodes). At about the same time Barker and Jenkins (5) indicated the extreme sensitivity and versatility of the method. Several metal ions were electrodeposited into a stationary mercury electrode, and the resulting amalgam was analyzed by using square-wave polarography on the stripping process.

Various other approaches to stripping analysis have developed rapidly in the last few years. Many simple and rapid analyses have been reported at extremely low concentrations levels. The literature on the theory and application of these methods is scattered widely, however, since the methods are related to both the voltammetric techniques (polarography, chronopotentiometry, etc.) and the stoichiometric techniques (electrodeposition, coulometry). In the remainder of this chapter, therefore, an attempt will be made to classify and correlate the various approaches to stripping analysis. It is expected that bringing these methods to the attention of analysts in an orderly and useful manner will result in stripping analysis taking its place among the standard electrochemical methods of analysis.

II. THEORY AND APPLICATION OF STRIPPING ANALYSIS

A. GENERAL CORRELATION AND DEFINITIONS

In all types of stripping analysis, the first step involves a pre-electrolysis or initial electrodeposition for the purpose of concentrating the sample. Several cases can be considered, depending on the type of electrode reaction; in addition, the methods can be classified as *stoichiometric* or *nonstoichiometric*, depending on whether the pre-electrolysis is carried to completion.

Among the various electrode reactions are electroplating on solid electrodes, such as the deposition of silver on a platinum electrode; precipitation of an insoluble electrode oxidation product, such as that formed when a silver electrode is oxidized in a halide solution; and, finally, amalgam formation, as obtained when many of the common metals (Pb, Cd, Zn, etc.) are reduced on mercury electrodes. In all cases the techniques used in these pre-electrolysis steps are essentially the same as those used in electrogravimetric analysis with controlled cathode potential (Chapter 48). The general effects of many experimental parameters (stirring, temperature, electrode area, etc.) can be extrapolated readily from the previous discussion. The major differences are the result of the dilute solutions encountered and, in some cases, the use of microelectrodes.

The subsequent step in stripping analysis, the electrodissolution of the concentrated sample, also can be classified as *stoichiometric* or *nonstoichiometric*, and the choice depends primarily upon the type of electrode used and the character of the initial electrodeposition reaction. Whenever the stripping process involves electrodissolution of a precipitate or a plated coating, the reaction must be carried to completion. Thus stoichiometric methods related to coulometry are used. On the other hand, when mercury electrodes are used, it is possible to use either stoichiometric or non-stoichiometric methods.

B. STRIPPING ANALYSIS WITH MERCURY ELECTRODES

The form of stripping analysis that has received the most attention in recent years has involved the use of mercury electrodes. The types of stripping analysis with mercury electrodes can be classified by whether the pre-electrolysis is carried to completion. In addition, the stripping process can be carried to completion or can be followed by some nonstoichiometric method. Practically all of the applications that have involved carrying the electrodeposition step to completion also have involved carrying the stripping process to completion. These stoichiometric methods have used relatively large electrodes in order to reduce the time required for the analysis. On the other hand, when the electrodeposition step has not been carried to completion, ordinarily neither has the stripping process. Microelectrodes are used for these nonstoichiometric methods, since relatively high concentrations of the sample can be accumulated in short times.

1. Nonstoichiometric Methods

The most versatile, rapid, and sensitive form of stripping analysis that has been developed involves the use of mercury microelectrodes in methods wherein neither the pre-electrolysis nor the stripping process is carried to completion. The pre-electrolysis is carried out at constant potential while the solution is stirred to increase the rate of electrodeposition. After a carefully timed interval, the stirring is stopped and the electrodeposited metals are stripped from the amalgam. The stripping process can be followed by any of the available nonstoichiometric techniques. Among them are square-wave polarography (3,4,5), chronopotentiometry (50), potentiostatic methods (50), oscillographic polarography (30,36), and voltammetry with linearly varying potential (18,37,38,40,54a,57). The last method has been investigated most extensively because the cells, apparatus, and working procedures are simple extensions of polarographic techniques.

a. ELECTRODEPOSITION

When the pre-electrolysis step of a stripping analysis involves the formation of an amalgam, the procedures are similar to mercury pool electrodeposition (Chapter 48) or to coulometry with controlled cathode potential using mercury pool electrodes (Chapter 49). The major differences arise from the fact that only a carefully reproducible portion of the sample must be deposited. Thus precautions must be taken to ensure that the rate of stirring, placement of the cell and stirrer, and volume of solution are fairly reproducible.

In general, the sensitivity of a stripping analysis depends on how concentrated an amalgam can be formed during the pre-electrolysis step. Thus, the hanging mercury drop electrode is especially suitable for stripping analysis applications. Relatively high amalgam concentrations can be obtained in the limited volume of the hanging drop electrode in reasonable pre-electrolysis times. Effective applications of the hanging mercury drop electrode to stripping analysis (18,40) have used pre-electrolysis times on the order of 5 minutes for $10^{-6}M$ and $10^{-7}M$, 15 minutes for $10^{-8}M$, and 60 minutes for $10^{-9}M$ solutions.

(1) Amalgam Concentrations and Sensitivity

Useful estimates of the amalgam concentrations can be obtained by considering the diffusion processes within the hanging mercury drop electrodes. In the usual procedure, a pre-electrolysis potential is selected that is sufficiently cathodic so that the rate of deposition is controlled only by the rate of mass transfer. Thus, if the stirring is kept constant, the flux of material at the surface of the electrode also will be constant. Such a case was discussed by Delahay and his co-workers (50) who applied a treatment, suitable for semi-infinite diffusion at a plane electrode, to the hanging mercury drop electrode. This is valid for short pre-electrolysis times, but for the times normally used for analytical purposes the limited volume of the electrode must be considered.

By solving Fick's second law for spherical diffusion (with the appropriate initial and boundary conditions), it can be shown that, for the pre-electrolysis times used in analytical work, the concentration of metal within the hanging drop electrode is relatively uniform (68). Thus the concentration can be calculated from the approximate equation

$$C_{\text{amal.}} = (3i_c t)/(4\pi n F r_0^3) \tag{1}$$

where $C_{\text{amal.}}$ is the concentration of the metal in the amalgam, i_c is the pre-electrolysis current, t is the pre-electrolysis time, n is the number of electrons involved in the electrode reaction, F is the Faraday value, and r_0 is the radius of the electrode. A typical value of i_c for a $10^{-5}M$ solution is the order of 0.5 μamp., and a 5-minute electrolysis would produce an amalgam approximately $5 \times 10^{-3}M$, a concentration increase (over the original solution) of about 500. A similar 500-fold increase in the sensitivity of the analysis could be expected during the subsequent stripping process.

Pre-electrolysis currents cannot be measured accurately for solutions more dilute than about $10^{-5}M$. However, measurements at higher concentrations can be used to calibrate the mass-transfer process, and i_c for the lower concentrations can be obtained from a linear extrapolation. Thus equation (1) can be used to predict the sensitivity of a stripping analysis for a particular cell–electrode–stirring arrangement and to help select the proper pre-electrolysis time.

(2) Selection of Pre-Electrolysis Potential

Equation (1) also can be used to help select the proper pre-electrolysis potential. Although the polarographic literature serves as a useful guide, the half-wave potentials cannot be used directly. The equilibrium potential of an amalgam electrode immersed in a solution depends on the ratio of the concentration of metal ions in the solution ($C_{soln.}$) to the concentration of the metal in the amalgam ($C_{amal.}$). The polarographic half-wave potentials are essentially equilibrium potentials for equal concentrations of metal ion in the solution and metal in the amalgam. On the other hand, the amalgams formed in stripping analysis are much more concentrated than the solution, and as a result equilibrium potentials are shifted markedly cathodic of the polarographic half-wave potentials.

In general, this cathodic shift amounts to approximately $0.06/n$ v. for each order of magnitude that the ratio $C_{soln.}/C_{amal.}$ is decreased below unity. The lower limit of $C_{soln.}$ expected frequently can be estimated, and $C_{amal.}$ can be calculated from equation (1). The actual pre-electrolysis potential should not be less than $0.12/n$ v. cathodic of the estimated equilibrium potential (16). However, care must be taken not to exceed the decomposition potential of any possible interfering substances that are reduced at more cathodic potentials.

(3) Mercury-Plated Electrodes

If the volume of the mercury electrode could be decreased without markedly decreasing the electrode area, higher amalgam concentrations could be obtained for the same pre-electrolysis times. This, in turn, should lead to more sensitive analyses. The mercury plated platinum and silver microelectrodes used by Rogers and his co-workers (25,51) should be extremely sensitive for stripping analysis. Unfortunately, the properties of such electrodes change with time, causing major variations in electrode sensitivity. Mercury-plated platinum electrodes were more recently investigated by Kemula and his co-workers (34), who also found them to be unreproducible and not suitable for stripping analysis applications. On the other hand, Neeb (54a) was able to overcome some of the unreproducibility of mercury-plated platinum electrodes by cleaning the electrode in nitric acid and replating prior to each determination. Bruckenstein and Nagai (7) were able to overcome some of the nonreproducible characteristics of mercury-plated platinum electrodes by continuously plating mercury onto the platinum during the course of plating and stripping experiments with other metals, such as thallium and lead. The technique will be useful in studying certain types of electrode reactions since the stripping process appears to involve direct oxidation of the amalgam by Hg(II). Although analyses were reported to the $10^{-7}M$ concentration level, the complex electrode reactions may limit the applicability of the technique in trace analysis. At the present time, therefore, the hanging mercury drop electrode is probably the most suitable form of mercury electrode for use in nonstoichiometric stripping analysis.

b. ELECTRODISSOLUTION

After the pre-electrolysis step, the resulting amalgam must be analyzed. This can be accomplished by almost any of the electroanalytical methods, as was mentioned above. Among the theoretical treatments were those reported by Delahay and his co-workers (50), who studied the stripping process under conditions of constant applied potential and constant applied current. However, most of the important analytical applications of the method have used the technique of voltammetry with linearly varying potential for analysis of the amalgams (18,40,57). After the carefully timed pre-electrolysis period, the stirring is stopped and the solution is allowed to come to rest. Usually 30 seconds is sufficient. Then the potential is scanned toward anodic values, using the general techniques of voltammetry with linearly varying potential (15) (Chapter 44). A typical rate of voltage scan is in the range of 30 mv. per second. Characteristic peak-shaped current–voltage curves are obtained, and the peak height for the anodic stripping current is proportional to the concentration of the sample in the amalgam. This, in turn, can be correlated with the original concentration of the sample in the bulk of the solution. A typical anodic stripping curve for a $10^{-8}M$ solution of Cd^{+2} after a 15-minute electrolysis is shown in Fig. 50.1. The anodic and cathodic residual-current curves are

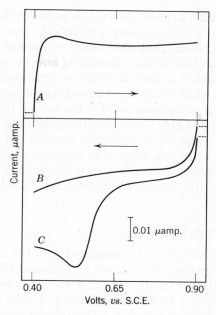

Fig. 50.1. Current–voltage curves for anodic stripping of $10^{-8}M$ cadmium solution in $0.1M$ potassium chloride, using voltammetry with linearly varying potential (18). The rate of voltage scan is 21 mv. per second. Key: A is the cathodic residual current; B is the anodic residual current after the 15-minute pre-electrolysis; and C is the anodic stripping current for $10^{-8}M$ cadmium solution after the 15-minute pre-electrolysis. Reproduced by courtesy of *Analytical Chemistry*.

TABLE 50.I

Peak Current as a Function of Pre-Electrolysis Time and Concentration, Using Voltammetry with Linearly Varying Potential and a Hanging Mercury Drop Electrode (18) (Courtesy of *Analytical Chemistry*)

Ion	Concn., mole/liter	i_p/t^a, μamp./min.	Av. dev.,[a] %	Electrolysis time, min.
Cd^{+2}	1.00×10^{-6}	2.10×10^{-1}	1.9	5
(0.1M KCl)	1.00×10^{-7}	2.09×10^{-2}	2.4	5
	1.00×10^{-8}	2.10×10^{-3}	2.4	15
	1.00×10^{-9}	2.10×10^{-4}	3.0	60
Tl$^+$	1.00×10^{-6}	1.18×10^{-1}	2.0	5
(0.1M KCl)	1.00×10^{-7}	1.17×10^{-2}	3.0	5
	1.00×10^{-8}	1.21×10^{-3}	4.1	15

[a] Average and average deviation of six determinations.

also shown.   Under these conditions the cathodic peak current for a conventional analysis using voltammetry with linearly varying potential would be about 1.5×10^{-8} μamp., and thus would be masked entirely by the residual current.   This is a striking example of how the pre-electrolysis step concentrates the sample so that it produces significantly higher currents under conditions in which the residual current is not particularly enhanced.

Normal analytical procedures involve the use of standard samples for calibration.   Table 50.I (18) shows that the product of the pre-electrolysis time and the anodic peak height is directly proportional to the bulk concentration of the sample over a very wide range of concentrations (10^{-6} to $10^{-9}M$).   If reasonable care is taken to reproduce the conditions of pre-electrolysis the average deviations range from 2% at $10^{-6}M$ to 4% at $10^{-9}M$.

(1) Current–Voltage Curves

The anodic peak height can be correlated with the amalgam concentration only if the stripping process is not complicated by the effects of irreversibility, precipitate formation, or intermetallic compound formation. These interferences may be difficult to detect, and in the development of new methods of stripping analysis a comparison of experimental and theoretical current–voltage curves can save considerable time and effort.

An equation for such current–voltage curves has been derived by Reinmuth (61), who considered both the limited volume of the hanging mercury drop electrode and the curvature of the electrode surface.   For the times and scanning rates normally used in stripping analysis, only the effect of surface curvature need be considered.   The equation is similar to that derived for voltammetry with linearly varying potential at a hanging mercury drop electrode (22,60), except that since the diffusion process in stripping analysis is divergent the spherical correction term acts to decrease the current.

The equation can be written in the form

$$i = nFAC_{amal.}\sqrt{aD}\psi(E) - nFADC_{amal.}(1/r_0)\phi(E) \qquad (2)$$

where i is the anodic current, n is the number of electrons involved in the electrode reaction, A is the area of the electrode, $C_{amal.}$ is the concentration of the metal in the hanging mercury drop electrode, D is its diffusion coefficient, r_0 is the radius of the electrode, $a = nFv/RT$, v is the rate of voltage scan, and R, T, and F have their usual significance. $\psi(E)$ and $\phi(E)$ are both functions of potential and can be obtained from the literature (22,60).

A comparison of the theoretical and experimental current–voltage curves is shown in Fig. 50.2, which indicates that this approach will be useful in the development of new methods of stripping analysis.

The polarographic literature serves as an excellent source of data applicable to the pre-electrolysis step, but the electrodissolution of amalgams has not been studied very extensively.   Data on specific interactions of the indifferent electrolyte with the metal as it is stripped from the amalgam are not available, and these parameters must be considered carefully when developing new techniques.   For example, metal ions that produce irreversible polarographic waves on reduction (such as Fe, Co, and Ni) are usually

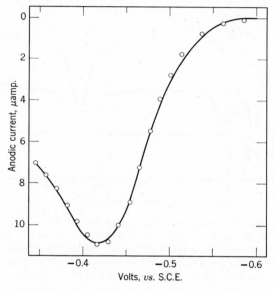

Fig. 50.2. Current–voltage curve for anodic stripping of thallium, using voltammetry with linearly varying potential (68).   The solution is $1.00 \times 10^{-8}M$ Tl$^+$, $0.1M$ KCl. The rate of voltage scan is 33.3 mv. per second and the pre-electrolysis time is 5 minutes at -0.7 v. *vs.* S.C.E.   The line is experimental, the points are theoretical.   Reproduced by courtesy of *Analytical Chemistry*.

difficult to electrooxidize from amalgams.   However, no thorough study of complexing and pH has been made in order to develop specific methods of stripping analysis.   Most of the information that is available can be obtained from studies of dropping amalgam electrodes (10,24,42,70) and amalgam pool electrodes (28,29,58) and, in addition, from studies of certain mercury cathode electroseparations in which the sample has been recovered by electrooxidation of the amalgams (Section II-B-2).

(2) Intermetallic Compounds

In recent work on the analysis of mixtures using the hanging mercury drop electrode, Kemula and his co-workers reported that in some cases intermetallic compounds apparently are formed in the amalgam (31–33). The effects of such compound formation are to change the potential for the dissolution of the metal, to produce a separate peak for the oxidation of the compound, and to change the sensitivity calibration as determined from single-component systems.

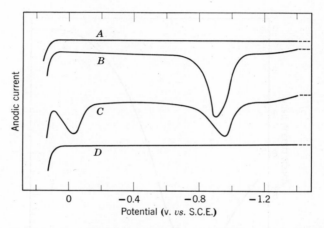

Fig. 50.3. Portion of anodic stripping curves for Ni–Zn mixed amalgams, using voltammetry with linearly varying potential (33). The pre-electrolysis time is 2 minutes; the rate of voltage scan is 6.7 mv. per second; and the indifferent electrolyte is 0.1M KCl. Key: A is the indifferent electrolyte only; B is $5 \times 10^{-4}M$ Zn^{+2}; C is $5 \times 10^{-4}M$ Zn^{+2} and $5 \times 10^{-4}M$ Ni^{+2}; and D is $5 \times 10^{-4}M$ Ni^{+2}.

An example of intermetallic compound formation with nickel and zinc is shown in Fig. 50.3. On addition of equal amounts of nickel to zinc solutions, the peak current for anodic stripping of zinc decreases. A new peak appears at more anodic potentials, which probably is caused by the oxidation of an intermetallic compound since this potential is not associated with any particular process in the individual solutions.

These effects are most serious when working with relatively high concentrations ($10^{-5}M$) of one of the components of the intermetallic compound, and the precision and accuracy of many analyses of mixtures could be seriously affected. Therefore known solutions with composition similar to the sample should be used for calibration.

Many other binary mixtures of metals in mercury have been investigated by Kemula and his co-workers. Among them are Au–Cd and Au–Zn (33,35,39), Sn–Ni (31), and Zn–Cu, Cd–Cu, Ag–Cd, and Zn–Ag (33). It has also been pointed out (33) that stripping analysis with the hanging mercury drop electrode is a very powerful tool for the investigation of these intermetallic compounds.

(3) Analysis of Mixtures

Stripping analysis of mixtures of reducible materials is very effective. Two approaches are possible, depending on the relative concentrations of the components of the mixture.

In the first approach, the analysis is carried out successively on the individual species present, starting with the one most easily reduced. A pre-electrolysis potential is selected that is cathodic of the reduction potential of the first component, but not so cathodic as to permit electrolysis of significant amounts of the next reducible substance. After the pre-electrolysis, the potential is scanned anodically and the determination is made as in a single-component system. Then, using a new hanging drop electrode, the procedure is repeated, this time selecting a pre-electrolysis potential that exceeds the reduction potential of the first two components, but not the third. On the anodic scan, two peaks are obtained, but only the first is required for analysis, and it can be measured accurately. The method is rather time-consuming, since a complete pre-electrolysis procedure is required for each component of a mixture.

The second approach to the analysis of mixtures was used by Kemula and his co-workers (40), who combined a nonstoichiometric pre-electrolysis step with a stoichiometric stripping process. Using a hanging mercury drop electrode, the method was applied to the analysis of complex mixtures of trace impurities in high purity zinc. Only one pre-electrolysis was used, at a potential cathodic enough so that all the components of the mixture were deposited into the same electrode. Then, during the stripping step, the anodic scan was stopped just after the first peak was measured. During this period at constant potential, the first component to be stripped from the amalgam was entirely removed from the mercury. When the stripping current for this first component had decayed to very low values, the anodic scan was resumed until the next peak appeared, when the process was repeated. In this way, interfering currents from the more easily oxidized components of a mixed amalgam could be eliminated. It was possible to determine Cu, Sn, Pb, Cd, Sb, Bi, and Tl in high-purity zinc at concentrations as low as $10^{-6}\%$ (in $0.3M$ zinc; corresponding to a 0.2-g. zinc sample in 10 ml. of solution). The precision of this method suffers because the electrodeposition of the more easily reduced components of the mixture continues during the stripping process, and thus, the pre-electrolysis times depend on the sample composition.

Most other examples of nonstoichiometric methods of stripping analysis with mercury electrodes have not involved actual samples, but have been performed on specially prepared solutions to demonstrate the method. The method has been used, however, to determine very low concentrations of Cu, Pb, and Zn in urine samples that had been digested with sulfuric acid (67). In addition, traces of impurities in reagent-grade chemicals (3,51) have also been determined (see Section III-C).

2. Stoichiometric Methods

a. ELECTRODEPOSITION

If the pre-electrolysis step of stripping analysis is to be carried to completion, using a relatively large mercury pool electrode, the procedure is again identical in all respects to mercury pool electrodeposition (Chapter 48) or to coulometry with controlled cathode potential using mercury pool electrodes (Chapter 49). It should only be noted that since the actual analysis and/or separation of components will take place on the subsequent electrodissolution step, critical control of all the experimental parameters is not required during the pre-electrolysis step. Reference can be made to the above-mentioned chapters for detailed discussion; also see Section II-C-1-a.

b. ELECTRODISSOLUTION

After the pre-electrolysis procedure has been carried to the point at which the concentrations of all components of interest have been reduced the required degree, the actual analysis can take place. Two major approaches have been reported to date. In one, the stripping process takes place into a new, "clean" solution of an indifferent electrolyte, of much smaller volume than the original solution. The analysis then is made on this new solution by any of a number of classical or instrumental techniques. The second approach involves the quantitative coulometric stripping of the sample back into solution.

(1) Concentration and Separation Methods

It was recognized early that controlled-potential electrolysis with a mercury pool electrode was a versatile method for separating and concentrating samples of reducible metal ions. The original procedures were inconvenient, however, in that they required a distillation to remove the mercury prior to the actual analysis (9,23). Volatilization of certain metals

(Cd, for example) made the method inaccurate. The development of electrolytic stripping techniques (11,43–45,66,72) greatly increased the convenience of the method and made additional separations possible. For example, in many cases it is possible to separate various metals from large quantities of iron, since the oxidation of iron from a mercury electrode is very irreversible (12,45,66).

An example of the use of stripping analysis for the purpose of concentrating and separating the components in a mixture was reported by Taylor and Smith (71). The polarographic analysis of lead and cadmium in zinc-base alloys is difficult because of the presence of large amounts of zinc and moderate amounts of copper. Since the copper wave precedes the lead and cadmium waves, the interference prevents an accurate analysis for lead and cadmium. In addition, the low concentrations of lead and cadmium present require that relatively large samples be dissolved in quite small volumes. The supporting electrolyte therefore contains large and variable amounts of zinc salts, which affect the diffusion-current constants of lead and cadmium. Thus the calibration factors vary with the size of the sample.

These difficulties were overcome by the application of stripping analysis after dissolving the sample in hydrochloric acid. A pre-electrolysis potential (-0.9 v. vs. S.C.E.) was chosen beyond the decomposition potential of copper, lead, and cadmium, but not so cathodic as to permit electrodeposition of any zinc. Thus a complete separation of the copper, lead, and cadmium from the zinc was accomplished during the pre-electrolysis step. When the pre-electrolysis step was complete the remainder of the original sample solution was removed and it was replaced by a small volume of a fresh solution of potassium chloride. An anodic stripping potential was then selected (-0.35 v. vs. S.C.E.) at which both lead and cadmium were oxidized back into the solution, but which was not so anodic as to permit the oxidation of copper. The resulting solution thus contained only the lead and cadmium, sufficiently concentrated so that they could be analyzed polarographically.

Although the usefulness of this approach is obvious, only a few additional applications have been reported (65,66). Again, specific information on electrodissolution of amalgams is rather limited (see Section II-B-1-b), but the development of additional applications of this type of stoichiometric stripping analysis should be relatively easy.

(2) Quantitative Coulometry

In assessing attempts to extend ordinary coulometry with controlled cathode potential to exceedingly low concentration levels, Meites and

Moros (54) discussed the various sources of errors and how they can be minimized. Among the sources of errors were the quantities of electricity associated with (1) charging of the electrical double layer, (2) electrolysis of impurities in the solution, and (3) continuous electrolysis current due to decomposition of the indifferent electrolyte or the solvent. The first source of error can be corrected for by assuming that the capacity of the electrical double layer in the presence of the indifferent electrolyte does not change appreciably on addition of a sample at very low concentration. The second source of error can be minimized by purification of the reagents, mercury, etc. However, the continuous electrolysis current due to the decomposition of the indifferent electrolyte or solvent is very difficult to correct for, particularly when very small samples are to be analyzed. Electrolysis times of 15 to 20 minutes frequently are required, and the relatively large quantity of electricity associated with the decomposition of the indifferent electrolyte or solvent seriously limits the sensitivity of the method.

Meites (53) has found, however, that if the sample is pre-electrolyzed to form an amalgam, a coulometric method can be applied to the stripping process with a much greater sensitivity. In particular, the time required to strip the amalgam quantitatively back into the solution is much less than the time required for electrodeposition, and thus the errors caused by the continuous decomposition of the solvent are minimized. In addition, the stripping process takes place at less cathodic potentials than the electrodeposition, and interfering currents are less at these potentials. Meites applied this method to the analysis of zinc solutions and found that samples containing at least 10γ of zinc in 50 ml. of solution $(3 \times 10^{-6}M)$ could be determined at the 0.1% error level. With somewhat greater errors, analyses could be made with samples containing as little as 0.1γ.

C. STRIPPING ANALYSIS WITH INERT ELECTRODES

Although much of the recent interest in stripping analysis has involved the use of mercury electrodes, there are several reports of precise and sensitive applications involving solid electrodes. Whenever stripping analysis is to be used for a sample that later must be stripped from the electrode at very anodic potentials, it is necessary to use inert electrodes. This includes stripping analyses of all metals more noble than mercury. Platinum electrodes also can be used for stripping analysis of other easily reducible metals, such as Cu and Pb, but there are no major advantages over the use of mercury electrodes in most cases. However, some irreversible reactions result in amalgams that cannot be reoxidized. In such cases (e.g., nickel), platinum electrodes are more useful for stripping analysis than mercury electrodes.

As with mercury electrodes, the electrodeposition process can be either stoichiometric or nonstoichiometric. However, the stripping process always must be carried to completion since the only correlation possible between the original sample concentration and the electrodeposited film is through some type of coulometric measurement.

1. Electrodeposition

The problems involved in electroplating onto a platinum or other inert electrode from solutions containing $10^{-6}M$ or less of the active species require special attention. As with mercury electrodes, the residual current is as large or larger than the electrolysis current, but, in addition, large deviations from the expected electrodeposition potentials are frequently observed.

a. STOICHIOMETRIC ELECTRODEPOSITION

The electrodeposition procedure is identical to that used in electrogravimetric analysis with controlled potential (Chapter 48). The potential is set at a preselected value, the solution is stirred, and the electrodeposition is allowed to proceed until the current falls to very low values, depending on the degree of completion of electrodeposition that is desired. But since the residual current may be much larger than the electrolysis current, other means of predicting when the electrolysis is complete must be used.

Lingane (47) has discussed a semiempirical equation that is useful in relating the current flowing in a convection electrolysis cell to the experimental parameters:

$$i_t = i_0 \exp(-kt) \tag{3}$$

where i_t is the instantaneous electrolysis current flowing, i_0 is the initial electrolysis current, k is an empirical constant related to the cell geometry, and t is the time from the start of the electrolysis. Although the use of this equation has never been extended to the extremely low concentration levels considered here (because of residual current interferences), there is no reason to suspect that the mass-transfer effects would be any different from those at somewhat higher concentration levels. Thus, if the constant k is determined empirically for a particular cell–electrode–stirring arrangement using relatively more concentrated solutions ($\sim 10^{-4}M$), equation (3) can be used to estimate the required electrolysis time.

By considering the mass-transfer process at the electrode in terms of the Nernst diffusion-layer theory, the empirical constant k can be related to several of the experimental parameters (47)

$$k = DA/V\delta \tag{4}$$

where D is the diffusion coefficient of the reacting species, A is the area of the electrode, V is the volume of the solution, and δ is the thickness of the diffusion layer, dependent on the efficiency of the stirring. The applicable conclusions that can be drawn from this relation are similar to those in electrogravimetric analysis, since increased stirring, decreased solution volume, and increased electrode area all help to increase k, thus decreasing the required electrolysis time.

Two additional effects must be considered in connection with the electrode area. First, the goal of the electrodeposition step in the stripping analysis procedure is to concentrate the sample and then to analyze under conditions in which the effect of the residual current is minimized. Because the residual current increases with the electrode area, a small electrode would decrease the effect of this interference. The second major effect involves the fact that, at the low concentrations under consideration, there may not be enough sample in the solution to cover the surface of a large electrode completely. Under these conditions, peculiar "undervoltage" and "overvoltage" effects may occur.

b. Undervoltage and Overvoltage Effects

In relatively concentrated solutions the potentials involved in the reaction

$$M^{+n} + ne \rightarrow M \text{ (ppt.)} \tag{5}$$

can be described in terms of a simple form of the Nernst equation

$$E = E^0 + (RT/nF) \ln a_{M}^{+n} \tag{6}$$

on the assumption that the activity of the solid deposit is unity. Using this approach the equilibrium potential for a particular concentration of metal in the solution can be calculated readily. When comparisons are made between such calculations and experimental results for very dilute solutions, equilibrium potentials are sometimes found to be anodic of the expected values. This indicates that the metal ions involved are easier to reduce than predicted by equation (6), and such effects are sometimes referred to as "undervoltage." Rogers (62) has reviewed the various effects observed on electrolysis of very dilute solutions and points out that attempts to explain the phenomena in terms of variable activity due only to the partial coverage of the electrode (64) cannot account for all the observations. In fact, many additional effects such as adsorption, physical structure of the electrode surface, and possibly intermetallic bonding between the electrode and the deposit play an important part.

Rogers and his co-workers have studied the electrodeposition of silver (63) and copper (14) from very dilute solutions. With $10^{-7}M$ silver solutions, electrodeposition occurred at potentials several tenths of a volt more anodic than expected. Dilute copper solutions showed smaller deviations.

In addition, peculiar overvoltage effects are sometimes noted. For example, the electrodeposition of bismuth from tartrate solution proceeds at a higher rate on bismuth than on platinum (48). This results in a rather high overvoltage at the start of the electrolysis, which decreases as the bismuth plates out, i.e., until the effective area of the electrode covered by the bismuth equals the total electrode area. In a case in which very dilute solutions are involved, there may not be sufficient bismuth in the solution to attain complete coverage of a large electrode.

Very little quantitative information is known about these effects and, in most cases, the proper selection of potential for the electrodeposition step in stripping analysis must be determined by experiment. This is particularly true when an attempt must be made to separate traces of reducible metal ions in a mixture, since these unexpected undervoltage and overvoltage effects may prevent a separation that is relatively straightforward at higher concentration levels. Thus it is desirable to use the smallest possible electrodes for stripping analysis since predictions of electrode behavior on the basis of observations made with more concentrated solutions are more likely to be valid. On the other hand, as the electrode area decreases the time required for the electrodeposition to go to completion increases. The ultimate selection of the electrode size must represent a compromise between these various effects.

c. NONSTOICHIOMETRIC ELECTRODEPOSITION

In general, the observations made in connection with stoichiometric electrodeposition hold for the case in which only a reproducible portion of the sample is to be deposited. The major difference is that the reproducibility of the electrodeposition step now limits the precision of analysis, rather then the completeness of the electrodeposition. The stirring efficiency and the time of electrolysis are the two most critical factors for a particular electrode–cell arrangement. Since no attempt is made to carry the electrodeposition to completion, the pre-electrolysis times are much shorter. Microelectrodes are ordinarily employed.

It is possible to analyze only the most noble component of a mixture of reducible metal ions when using the nonstoichiometric method, since mixed electrodeposition would occur at very cathodic potentials.

2. Electrodissolution

The process of stripping a surface layer from an electrode has not been studied very intensively, and only a few applications have been described that involve anodic stripping from inert electrodes (19,49,56,74,75).

The ultimate goal of the stripping process is to determine how much sample has been plated onto the electrode, so that this quantity can be related to the original concentration of the sample in the bulk of the solution. Several experimental approaches are possible, including constant-potential and constant-current methods and voltammetry with linearly varying potential. However, in each case the final correlation with bulk concentration must be through coulometry, and the stripping process must be carried to completion.

a. Constant-Potential Methods

One of the simplest ways to strip a plated coating from an inert electrode is to shift the potential suddenly to some anodic value after the electrodeposition step. If this were done the current would go to a rather high value, determined primarily by the potential and the rate of mass transfer of the product of the electrode reaction away from the electrode surface. Ordinarily, a reasonably steady state diffusion-convection process would be set up, and the current would remain relatively constant until the bulk of the deposit had been stripped off, at which point the current would decay to very low values. It would be possible to record these current–time curves and then to obtain the number of coulombs involved in the electrodissolution by integration. Alternatively, the current could be integrated directly using electronic or mechanical integrators. This method has been used very little, however, probably because it is inconvenient to correct for the residual current. The origin of the residual current and ways of handling the problem have been discussed in connection with stripping analysis on oxidizable electrodes (69).

b. Constant-Current Methods

The determination of the number of coulombs required in the electrodissolution process can be obtained more directly if the stripping current is held constant. Then, by measuring the time required to strip the layer completely, the quantity of electricity can be obtained. This process can be considered either an example of a primary coulometric titration (Chapter 49) or as an experimental approach similar to chronopotentiometry (Chapter 44). In either case, the potential of the working electrode is measured as a function of time during the stripping process, and when the

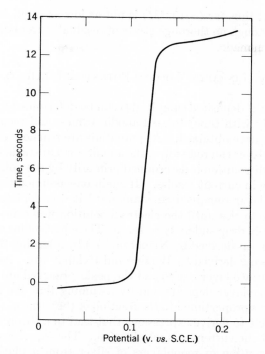

Fig. 50.4. Potential–time curve for the constant-current anodic stripping of silver from a platinum electrode. The solution is $10^{-5}M$ Ag^+ in $0.1M$ KCl and $0.1M$ NH$_4$OH. The pre-electrolysis time is 1 minute and the stripping current is 10 μamp.

electrodissolution of the surface layer is complete the potential shifts toward more anodic values and some other electrode reaction takes place. This can be a second electroplated layer under the first one, decomposition of the indifferent electrolyte, or evolution of oxygen from water.

For certain metals, e.g., silver, the electrodissolution process is relatively uncomplicated, the transitions are sharp, and it is easy to measure the transition times. A potential–time curve for the electrodissolution of silver from a platinum electrode is shown in Fig. 50.4. For the best accuracy, it is usually necessary to select by experiment a constant stripping current such that errors due to uncertainty in the transition time are minimized.

Although the constant-current method of stripping analysis was the first to be developed, it has not received much attention. The only analytical applications have involved copper, primarily in food products (19,74). These methods are essentially extensions of Zbinden's work (75), previously described in Section I-B-2. It should be pointed out that the limit of sensitivity reported thus far ($\sim 10^{-6} M$) is not as low as could be expected for the method, although no thorough study of residual current and other interferences has been made.

c. Linearly Varying Potential Methods

The quantity of deposited sample also can be determined by scanning the voltage (linearly with time) toward anodic values, and recording the current–potential curve obtained. As potentials are reached at which the deposited surface layer can redissolve, the anodic current starts to flow. Since the rate of the dissolution is determined primarily by the potential, an exponential increase in current results. If again one assumed that the activity of the surface layer remained constant until it was depleted, the current would continue to rise until the electrodissolution was complete, and then the current would drop suddenly to zero. The equation for such a current–potential curve was derived by Nicholson (55) by adapting the equation for the reverse process derived by Berzins and Delahay (6). Actually, the activity of the surface layer varies and the peaks observed are rounded. By considering monolayer deposits and by assuming that the activity of the surface layer was proportional to the fraction of the surface covered, Nicholson (55) was able to derive expressions that lead to a theoretical prediction of the shape of the current–potential curve. The experimental results for the electrodissolution of monolayers of silver from a platinum electrode checked the theory very closely. However electrodissolution of both lead and copper monolayers showed major deviation.

In any analytical procedure, it would not be possible to control the electrodeposition so that only monolayer deposits would form. On the contrary, deposits varying from fractional monolayers to rather massive coatings could be obtained from various samples. The electrodissolution of a multilayer silver deposit is shown in Fig. 50.5, and such a process does not check well with either the bulk electrode dissolution or monolayer dissolution theory.

As a result of these studies it is apparent that although the shape of the current–potential curve obtained resembles the typical peaked curve obtained when using stationary electrodes with voltammetry with linearly varying potential, there is no theoretical basis for a correlation between peak height and quantity of sample deposited unless it is certain that less than a monolayer deposit is present. In an actual stripping analysis no such assurance is possible, and the only valid procedure is to integrate the area under the current–potential curve (which is also a current–time curve) to obtain the total number of coulombs involved in the electrodissolution.

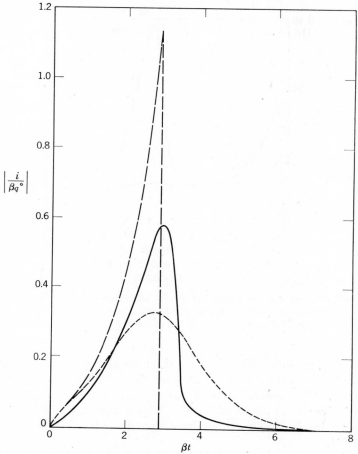

Fig. 50.5. Current–potential curve for the electrodissolution of a multilayer silver coating from a platinum electrode, using voltammetry with linearly varying potential (55). Key: ——— is experimental; - - - - - - is by monolayer dissolution theory; and — — — — is by bulk metal dissolution theory. The function plotted on the ordinate is related to the stripping current, and the peak current for the experimental curve is 84.8 μamp. The units on the potential axis correspond to approximately 25.6 mv. The initial potential ($\beta t = 0$) is 0.320 v. Reproduced by courtesy of the *Journal of the American Chemical Society*.

An excellent example of the sensitivity of this procedure was described by Rogers and his co-workers (49), who used platinum electrodes for the stripping analysis of dilute silver solutions. A current–potential (time) curve for the electrodissolution of 5.6×10^{-9} g. of silver from a platinum electrode

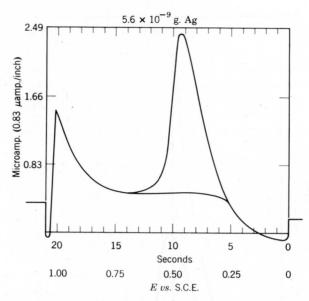

Fig. 50.6. Current–voltage curve for anodic stripping of silver from a platinum electrode, using voltammetry with linearly varying potential (49). Reproduced by courtesy of *Analytical Chemistry*.

is shown in Fig. 50.6. The simple and convenient correction for residual current also is shown. The area under the curve was obtained with a planimeter. This general method was applied to as little as 2.5×10^{-12} moles of silver in 20 μliters of solution with a reproducibility of 2 to 5%. In larger volumes of solution, analyses were made in solutions as dilute as $5 \times 10^{-6}M$.

Stripping analysis using a solid inert electrode also has been applied to the analysis of dilute nickel solutions (56). Although nickel cannot be reoxidized from a mercury electrode easily, it is readily stripped into thiocyanate solution from a platinum electrode. Accurate and precise analyses on solutions as dilute as $10^{-7}M$ were reported.

In this method the rate of scan of the potential must be selected so as to obtain an optimum ratio of the dissolution current to the charging current. Ordinarily this must be determined by experiment. If successive layers are to be stripped off an inert electrode, care must be taken to ensure that the most easily oxidized material has been completely dissolved and that the current due to this process has decreased to zero before continuing the voltage scan to more anodic potentials.

D. ELECTRODE OXIDATION METHODS

A form of stripping analysis that has been developed quite recently involves the oxidation of a silver (69) or a mercury (2) electrode in the presence of an anion (halide, sulfide, etc.) to form an insoluble silver or mercurous salt on the surface of the electrode. This oxidized layer is subsequently reduced and the cathodic stripping current forms the basis of the analysis. Since the success of the method depends on exceeding the solubility product of the desired precipitate at the electrode surface, it is not possible to carry the pre-electrolysis to completion.

1. Electrodeposition of Oxidized Films

The pre-electrolysis procedure involved in this type of stripping analysis is much the same as any other nonstoichiometric method. Thus, careful timing of the pre-electrolysis and reproducible stirring are among the important experimental parameters.

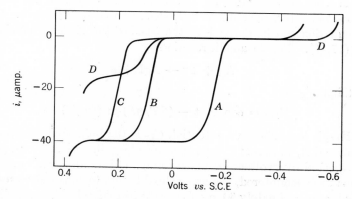

Fig. 50.7. Current–voltage curves for the oxidation of a silver electrode in stirred halide solutions (69). Each solution is $10^{-3}M$ in the halide and $0.1M$ acetate buffer. Key: A is KI; B is KBr; C is KCl; and D is KCl in 80% ethanol. Reproduced by courtesy of *Analytical Chemistry*.

In addition, the selection and control of the potential at which the formation of the oxidized film takes place is very critical. For example, if the method is to be used for the determination of iodide ion, using a silver electrode, a potential must be selected at which silver can be oxidized to AgI readily, but it must not be so anodic as to permit appreciable oxidation of the silver to free silver ion. Although it is sometimes possible to obtain an indication of the proper range of potentials from polarographic data, it is best to select the optimum potential from a current–voltage curve obtained under conditions as close as possible to those used in the stripping analysis. Ordinarily, it is necessary to use somewhat higher concentrations, however. Fig. 50.7 shows such current–voltage curves obtained on $10^{-3}M$ solutions of halides using a stationary silver electrode in stirred solution (69). Except for the higher concentration of halide ion, all conditions (electrode, stirring, cell arrangement, etc.) were the same as those used in subsequent stripping analyses. For the stripping analysis of iodide, for example, it should be possible to select any potential within the range -0.1 v. to $+0.3$ v. for pre-electrolysis, since a rather broad limiting-current region for the formation of AgI is present. The final selection of the proper potential must, however, include considerations on shifts in the potential of the wave as the method is applied to more dilute solutions.

In order to predict changes in the shape of the current–voltage curve as the concentration of iodide is varied, it is necessary to know the variation of the activity of the deposit during the course of the electrolysis. As before, this is not generally known, but it can be assumed that the activity of the deposit is unity, since microelectrodes are used in this work. Thus, a useful equation can be derived on the basis of the Nernst diffusion-layer theory (17,41). For the anodic reaction

$$Ag + I^- \rightarrow AgI + e \tag{7}$$

one obtains

$$E_{1/2} = \text{constant} - (RT/nF) \ln (C_{I^-}/2) \tag{8}$$

where $E_{1/2}$ is the half-wave potential, C_{I^-} is the bulk concentration of iodide ion, and R, T, n, and F have their usual significance. Thus, provided no unexpected overvoltage or undervoltage effects appear as more dilute solutions are encountered, the wave should shift toward more anodic potentials by approximately 60 mv. for every 10-fold reduction in iodide concentration. By using these calculations, an estimate of the maximum limit of sensitivity of the method can be obtained (ignoring residual current and effects of other interferences), which, in the case of AgI, is probably about $10^{-9}M$.

It is apparent that the method would be less sensitive for the case of a more soluble deposit, e.g., AgCl, and this is reflected in the much narrower limiting current range for the formation of AgCl in Fig. 50.7.

2. Reduction of Surface Films

The reduction of an oxidized layer of precipitate on the electrode surface is very similar to the anodic stripping processes discussed in connection

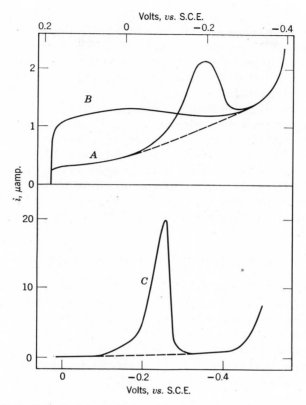

Fig. 50.8. Cathodic stripping of silver iodide films using voltammetry with linearly varying potential (69). Concentrations and pre-electrolysis times were A, $4 \times 10^{-8}M$ at 30 minutes; B, blank; and C, $4 \times 10^{-6}M$ at 10 minutes. Reproduced by courtesy of *Analytical Chemistry*.

with inert electrodes. Thus all correlations between the quantity of precipitate and the bulk concentration of sample must be made on the basis of a coulometric cathodic stripping process. Again, this process can be carried out by means of constant-potential, constant-current, or linearly varying potential methods.

In each case, the cathodic stripping process is analogous to the corresponding method discussed in connection with inert electrodes (Section II-C-2). Thus, for each method, it is relatively difficult to correct for the residual current when the amount of material deposited on the electrode becomes small, and this, in turn, is another factor that limits the sensitivity of the method. Because the stripping process is a reduction, frequently taking place at potentials just cathodic of the saturated calomel electrode, an additional interference arises because of the reduction of traces of oxygen in the solution. Nevertheless, studies (69) indicate that each of the methods is applicable at least to the $10^{-8}M$ concentration level for the determination of iodide with a silver electrode. An example of the use of cathodic stripping with linearly varying potential is shown in Fig. 50.8.

Cathodic stripping with linearly varying potential has also been applied to halide films on mercury electrodes (2). A 15 minute pre-electrolysis at +0.4 v. (vs. S.C.E.) of a chloride solution containing relatively large amounts of U(VI) was followed by a cathodic scan of 100 mv. per minute. Peak-shaped curves were obtained, and it was found that the peak height (corrected for the large residual current) was directly proportional to the bulk concentration of chloride. These results may be due in some way to the "passivation" of the mercury electrodes (46) by the mercurous chloride surface layer.

III. EXPERIMENTAL PROCEDURES

In general, the cells, electrodes, circuits, and associated equipment used for stripping analysis are simple extensions of the apparatus required for the polarographic techniques. Although the detailed arrangement depends on the particular form of stripping analysis used, the changes are relatively straightforward. Therefore this discussion will emphasize the procedures used in stripping analysis with the hanging mercury drop electrode using voltammetry with linearly varying potential.

A. APPARATUS

The cells, electrodes, and related equipment are the same as used for voltammetry with linearly varying potential. Several versions of the hanging mercury drop electrode have been described. In one type, drops of mercury, as they fall from a conventional dropping mercury electrode capillary, are caught in a small glass or Teflon scoop, and then are hung on a gold-plated (26) or mercury-plated (18) platinum wire. In another type, the hanging mercury drop electrode is formed by displacing a small amount of mercury through a capillary (37). The electrode shown in Fig. 50.9 has proved to be very useful for general analytical work. The electrode consists of a small platinum wire (0.010- to 0.016-inch diameter) sealed into a piece of 6-mm. soft glass tubing. The tip of the glass and the metal are polished flat with fine emery, or preferably a polishing wheel of the type used for final polishing of metallographic samples. Then the platinum is dissolved back a few thousandths of an inch with hot aqua regia. Next, the electrode

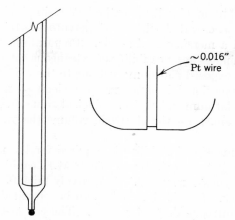

Fig. 50.9. Hanging mercury drop electrode and detail of the tip.

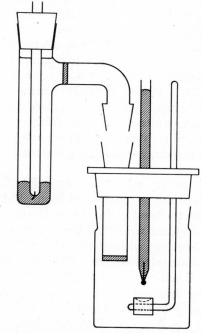

Fig. 50.10. Hanging mercury drop electrode and cell assembly. The nitrogen inlet and dropping mercury electrode capillary are not shown. A 14/20 standard-taper joint is used in the salt bridge; the 19/22 joint at the top of the reference electrode compartment is convenient. The sintered glass disks are 10 mm., fine or ultrafine. The mercury transfer scoop is Teflon.

is mercury plated by making it the cathode of a simple electrolysis cell containing a fairly concentrated solution of mercurous perchlorate, dilute perchloric acid, and a mercury pool anode. Preparation of the electrode in this manner eliminates any possibility of extraneous currents due to hydrogen evolution on exposed platinum; yet one to three drops of mercury collected from a conventional dropping mercury electrode may be hung on the mercury-plated platinum wire easily. Typical values for the electrode area are 0.04 to 0.07 cm.^{2}; for the electrode volume the values are 0.0006 to 0.0018 cm.^{3}.

Reasonable dimensional stability is required for the mounting arrangement of the hanging drop electrode, the D.M.E. capillary, and the scoop used to transfer drops of mercury. A relatively thick (0.5-inch) Teflon cell top is satisfactory. In addition, holes can be provided for the reference electrode and a nitrogen dispersing tube. The cell assembly is shown in Fig. 50.10.

When solid electrodes are required for stripping analysis, they also can be mounted on 6-mm. soft glass tubing, and thus will fit in the same cell assembly as the hanging mercury drop electrode.

The reference electrode shown in the cell assembly is a double-junction type, which is useful when it is necessary to separate the saturated calomel electrode from the sample solution. Other reference electrodes, with a single junction or with a flowing electrolyte compartment, can be constructed in a similar fashion. The sintered glass disks used in these reference electrodes are fine or ultra fine. With fairly concentrated electrolyte in the salt bridge, the cell resistance seldom exceeds 1000 ohms. Since the total current flowing is usually quite small, the resulting IR drop is negligible.

Although standard gas dispersing tubes are satisfactory, a somewhat less bulky nitrogen inlet tube can be constructed from a 10-mm. filter stick, bent in the shape of a J, with the bend as close to the glass frit as possible.

The cell itself is a standard weighing bottle body, which can be removed easily for changing solutions without disturbing the electrode assembly. For work with very dilute solutions, adsorption phenomena (Section III-B) on the walls of the cell can cause serious errors. These can be minimized by using a polystyrene drinking glass for the cell body. A Teflon cell cap can be machined readily to fit the tapered sides of such a cell, which is quite satisfactory for handling very dilute solutions.

Much smaller sample volumes can be handled by constructing a similar cell, but with a 10/18 standard taper joint for the cell body (73). Using this cell, stripping analysis can be performed with samples as small as 0.5 ml.

Several of the stoichiometric methods of stripping analysis also can be applied to very small volumes of solution. Rogers and his co-workers (49) described a cell with a platinum working electrode that was suitable for determinations with as little as 0.02 ml. of solution. Stripping analysis with mercury electrodes has not been extended to such small volumes, although several simple extensions of polarographic techniques that were developed for small sample volumes are promising (Chapter 46).

At this time the only instrument suitable for voltammetry with linearly varying potential that is available commercially is the Sargent Model FS Polarograph (E. H. Sargent Company, Chicago, Ill.). Several rates of voltage scan are available; ranging from 16.7 to 50 mv. per second.

For coulometric stripping, Meites (53) used the equipment available from Analytical Instruments Co., Bristol, Conn. Other equipment designed for constant-potential coulometry has been described in Chapter 49. However, for most of the other techniques used for stripping analysis instruments are not commercially available. Perhaps the most versatile approach to the instrumentation problem involves the use of analog computer amplifiers (13), and circuits suitable for any approach to stripping analysis (as well as to electrochemical measurements in general) can be developed.

The stirrer used during the pre-electrolysis step of the stripping analysis must have a very constant and reproducible speed, independent of solution volume, amount of mercury in the cell, line voltage, etc. Excellent results are obtained by using a synchronous motor, approximately 300 r.p.m., with a magnet attached to the shaft. This provides a constant-speed magnetic stirrer that is convenient to use and that provides reproducible stirring if positioned properly each time the cell is moved.

B. ADSORPTION PHENOMENA

One of the most serious problems encountered in stripping analysis involves adsorption phenomena. When working with very dilute solutions ($10^{-8}M$ or less) equilibration of the sample solution with the container can seriously change the concentrations. At these low concentrations, a major portion of the sample can be lost on the walls of the container in a very short time. Conversely, contamination of the sample can occur when a flask that previously contained some other material is used.

In general, all glassware used for stripping analysis must be carefully leached with very high quality distilled water (at least three distillations, with proper precautions to prevent particulate carry-over and creeping). Then each container should be equilibrated 2 or 3 times with portions of the solution it is to contain. Even with these precautions, glassware is usually not suitable for long contact with $10^{-8}M$ solutions. Silicone coating (Desicote) of the glassware does seem to decrease the amount of adsorption (desorption) and/or decrease the rate of these processes.

Well-leached plastic containers are usually satisfactory, provided they are inert to the solutions used. It is hoped that new transparent types of Teflon will soon be available for use in fabrication of more inert laboratory utensils and possible electrolysis cells.

C. REAGENT PURIFICATION

A second major difficulty encountered with stripping analysis at the very lowest concentration levels involves the indifferent electrolyte. Rather

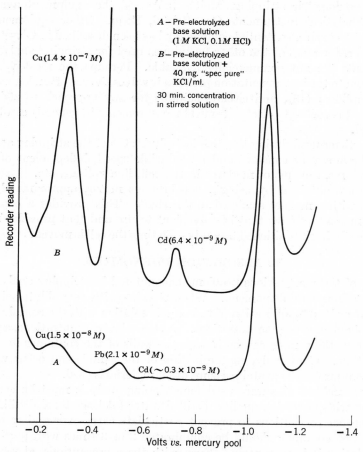

Fig. 50.11. Stripping analysis of potassium chloride solutions, using square-wave polarography (3). Reproduced by courtesy of *Analytica Chimica Acta*.

high concentrations of electrolytes such as potassium chloride or potassium nitrate must be added to the sample to reduce migration currents and to decrease the cell resistance. Unfortunately, the best available reagent-grade chemicals contain enough lead and other electroactive metals so that a 0.1M solution frequently contains the order of $10^{-7}M$ of three or four impurities. An example is shown in Fig. 50.11, a stripping analysis of a solution of potassium chloride obtained by a modified square-wave polarographic method (3). Thus, it is ordinarily necessary to purify the reagents used in stripping analysis.

Although ion-exchange techniques seem promising as a technique for purification of reagents, very few results have been reported. A few attempts to utilize the technique in this laboratory did not yield conclusive results. On the other hand, electrolysis with a mercury pool cathode (52) has proved to be satisfactory for purification of a wide range of reagents that are not too acid. It may be necessary to purify certain acids by redistillation. Although zone purification techniques have not yet been used to prepare high-quality reagents for stripping analysis, the method offers many advantages that probably should be investigated.

IV. SUMMARY

The choice of a particular form of stripping analysis depends on the type of sample and on the sensitivity and accuracy required. In general, the nonstoichiometric methods of analysis are faster, more versatile, and more sensitive than the corresponding methods in which the pre-electrolysis is carried to completion. For example, when using voltammetry with linearly varying potential, with a hanging mercury drop electrode, it is possible to make analyses at the 10^{-6} or $10^{-7}M$ concentration level in less than 10 minutes, including removal of dissolved oxygen, pre-electrolysis, and the anodic scan. Since the voltage is being scanned, a single preliminary stripping analysis curve shows individual peaks for each component, and gives an indication of the various concentrations. Thus, it is possible to design the final analytical procedure very easily, including selection of instrument sensitivity, potential range, pre-electrolysis time, etc. In addition, the extremely small volume of the hanging mercury drop electrode makes it possible to obtain relatively concentrated amalgams in very short times, thus accounting for the sensitivity of the method. Other types of stationary mercury microelectrodes possess these advantages, but to a lesser degree.

On the other hand, this last feature makes these microelectrodes unsuitable when it is necessary to use a stoichiometric pre-electrolysis procedure.

The small surface area of the microelectrodes would require impossibly long pre-electrolysis times. Thus, relatively large electrodes, with the associated higher residual current, must be used, and the sensitivity seldom exceeds $10^{-6}M$ in methods that employ stoichiometric pre-electrolysis procedures. Nevertheless, they are indispensable when it is necessary to accomplish a separation and recovery of the sample simultaneously with the analysis, or when the extreme accuracy of the coulometric method is required.

There are many other combinations of methods that could be applied to stripping analysis but, in general, these are relatively obvious extensions of the methods mentioned here. Further work on the applications of stripping analysis, particularly to commercial samples, will be developed easily as extensions of the corresponding polarographic techniques.

In conclusion, it should be noted that analytical methods that are accurate to 0.1% at $10^{-6}M$ or 4% at $10^{-9}M$ are rare. The sensitivity of stripping analysis can be made even more striking by converting these molar concentrations to units more frequently used in trace analysis: a $10^{-9}M$ solution corresponds to about 0.1 part per billion. The limit of detectability for many materials is about $10^{-11}M$, or about 1 part per trillion.

REFERENCES

1. Anderson, S., and R. W. Manuel, *Trans. Electrochem. Soc.*, **78**, 373 (1940).
2. Ball, R. G., D. L. Manning, and O. Menis, *Anal. Chem.*, **32**, 621 (1960).
3. Barker, G. C., *Anal. Chim. Acta*, **18**, 118 (1958).
4. Barker, G. C., *At. Energy Res. Estab. (Gt. Brit.)*, **C/R-1563** (1957).
5. Barker, G. C., and I. L. Jenkins *Analyst*, **77**, 685 (1952).
6. Berzins, T., and P. Delahay, *J. Am. Chem. Soc.*, **75**, 555 (1953).
7. Bruckenstein, S., and T. Nagai, *Anal. Chem.*, **33**, 1201 (1961).
8. Campbell, W. E., and U. B. Thomas, *Trans. Electrochem. Soc.*, **76**, 303 (1939).
9. Casto, C. C., "Electrolytic Separation Methods," in C. J. Rodden, Ed., *Analytical Chemistry of the Manhattan Project*, McGraw-Hill, New York, 1950, p. 520.
10. Cooper, W. C., *J. Am. Chem. Soc.*, **77**, 2074 (1955).
11. Coriou, H., J. Gueron, H. Hering, and P. Leveque, *J. Chim. Phys.*, **48**, 55 (1951).
12. Coriou, H., J. Hure, and N. Meunier, *Anal. Chim. Acta*, **9**, 171 (1953).
13. DeFord, D. D., Division of Analytical Chemistry, 133rd Meeting, American Chemical Society, San Francisco, Calif., April, 1958.
14. DeGeiso, R. C., and L. B. Rogers, *J. Electrochem. Soc.*, **106**, 433 (1959).
15. Delahay, P., *New Instrumental Methods in Electrochemistry*, Interscience, New York–London, 1954, Chapter 6.
16. Delahay, P., *ibid.*, p. 40.
17. Delahay, P., *ibid.*, p. 221.
18. DeMars, R. D., and I. Shain, *Anal. Chem.*, **29**, 1825 (1957).
19. Elema, B., *Antonie van Leeuwenhoek. J. Microbiol. Serol.*, **12**, 243 (1947); through *Chem. Abstr.*, **44**, 4367 (1950).

20. Francis, H. T., *J. Electrochem. Soc.*, **93**, 79 (1948).
21. Frankenthal, R. P., T. J. Butler, and R. T. Davis, Jr., *Anal. Chem.*, **30**, 441 (1958).
22. Frankenthal, R. P., and I. Shain, *J. Am. Chem. Soc.*, **78**, 2969 (1956).
23. Furman, N. H., C. E. Bricker, and B. McDuffie, *J. Wash. Acad. Sci.*, **38**, 159 (1948).
24. Furman, N. H., and W. C. Cooper, *J. Am. Chem. Soc.*, **72**, 5667 (1950).
25. Gardiner, K. W., and L. B. Rogers, *Anal. Chem.*, **25**, 1393 (1953).
26. Gerischer, H., *Z. Physik. Chem.*, **202**, 302 (1953).
27. Grower, G. G., *Am. Soc. Testing Mater., Proc.*, **17**, II, 129 (1917).
28. Hickling, A., and J. Maxwell, *Trans. Faraday Soc.*, **51**, 44 (1955).
29. Hickling, A., J. Maxwell, and J. V. Shennan, *Anal. Chim. Acta*, **14**, 287 (1956).
30. Kalvoda, R., *Anal. Chim. Acta*, **18**, 132 (1958).
31. Kemula, W., and Z. Galus, *Bull. Acad. Polon. Sci., Ser. Sci. Chim.*, **7**, 553 (1959).
32. Kemula, W., Z. Galus, and Z. Kublik, *Nature*, **182**, 1228 (1958).
33. Kemula, W., Z. Galus, and Z. Kublik, *Bull. Acad. Polon. Sci., Ser. Sci. Chim.*, **6**, 661 (1958).
34. Kemula, W., Z. Galus, and Z. Kublik, *Bull. Acad. Polon. Sci., Ser. Sci. Chim.*, **7**, 723 (1959).
35. Kemula, W., Z. Galus, and Z. Kublik, *Roczniki Chem.*, **33**, 1431 (1959).
36. Kemula, W., and Z. Kublik, *Roczniki Chem.*, **30**, 1005 (1956).
37. Kemula, W., and Z. Kublik, *Anal. Chim. Acta*, **18**, 104 (1958).
38. Kemula, W., and Z. Kublik, *Chem. Anal. (Warsaw)*, **3**, 483 (1958); through *Chem. Abstr.*, **53**, 12923 (1959).
39. Kemula, W., Z. Kublik, and Z. Galus, *Nature*, **184**, 56 (1959).
40. Kemula, W., Z. Kublik, and S. Glodowski, *J. Electroanal. Chem.*, **1**, 91 (1959).
41. Kolthoff, I. M., and J. J. Lingane, *Polarography*, Interscience, New York–London, 1952, Vol. 2, p. 578.
42. Kossler, I., *Collection Czech. Chem. Communs.*, **15**, 723 (1950).
43. Koslovskii, M. T., and P. P. Tsyb, *J. Appl. Chem. U.S.S.R.*, **23**, 1285 (1950); through *Chem. Abstr.*, **46**, 8991 (1952).
44. Kozlovskii, M. T., P. P. Tsyb, and E. I. Ruzina, *J. Appl. Chem. U.S.S.R.*, **24**, 1003 (1951); through *Chem. Abstr.*, **47**, 6279 (1953).
45. Kozlovskii, M. T., P. P. Tsyb, and E. F. Speranskaya, *Trudy Komissii Anal. Khim., Akad. Nauk S.S.S.R., Otdel. Khim. Nauk*, **4**(7), 255 (1952); through *Chem. Abstr.*, **48**, 1878 (1954).
46. Kuwana, T., and R. N. Adams, *Anal. Chim. Acta*, **20**, 51, 60 (1959).
47. Lingane, J. J., *Electroanalytical Chemistry*, 2nd ed., Interscience, New York–London, 1958, pp. 222–228.
48. Lingane, J. J., and S. L. Jones, *Anal. Chem.*, **23**, 1798 (1951).
49. Lord, S. S., Jr., R. C. O'Neill, and L. B. Rogers, *Anal. Chem.*, **24**, 209 (1952).
50. Mamantov, G., P. Papoff, and P. Delahay, *J. Am. Chem. Soc.*, **79**, 4034 (1957).
51. Marple, T. L., and L. B. Rogers, *Anal. Chim. Acta*, **11**, 574 (1954).
52. Meites, L., *Anal. Chem.*, **27**, 416 (1955).
53. Meites, L., *Anal. Chim. Acta*, **20**, 456 (1959).
54. Meites, L., and S. A. Moros, *Anal. Chem.*, **31**, 23 (1959).
54a. Neeb, R., *Z. Anal. Chem.*, **171**, 321, 330 (1959); **180**, 161 (1961).
55. Nicholson, M. M., *J. Am. Chem. Soc.*, **79**, 7 (1957).
56. Nicholson, M. M., *Anal. Chem.*, **32**, 1058 (1960).
57. Nikelly, J. G., and W. D. Cooke, *Anal. Chem.*, **29**, 933 (1957).

58. Porter, J. T., II, and W. D. Cooke, *J. Am. Chem. Soc.*, **77**, 1481 (1955).
59. Price, L. E., and G. J. Thomas, *Trans. Electrochem. Soc.*, **76**, 329 (1939).
60. Reinmuth, W. H., *J. Am. Chem. Soc.*, **79**, 6358 (1957).
61. Reinmuth, W. H., *Anal. Chem.*, **33**, 185 (1961).
62. Rogers, L. B., *Record Chem. Progr.* (*Kresge-Hooker Sci. Lib.*), **16**, 197 (1955).
63. Rogers, L. B., D. P. Krause, J. C. Griess, Jr., and D. B. Ehrlinger, *J. Electrochem. Soc.*, **95**, 33 (1949).
64. Rogers, L. B., and A. F. Stehney, *J. Electrochem. Soc.*, **95**, 25 (1949).
65. Scacciati, G., and A. D'Este, *Chim. Ind.* (*Milan*), **37**, 270 (1955).
66. Schmidt, W. E., and C. E. Bricker, *J. Electrochem. Soc.*, **102**, 623 (1955).
67. Shain, I., unpublished results (1960).
68. Shain, I., and J. Lewinson, *Anal. Chem.*, **33**, 187 (1961).
69. Shain, I., and S. P. Perone, *Anal. Chem.*, **33**, 325 (1961).
70. Stromberg, A. G., and A. I. Zelyanskaya, *Trudy Komisii Anal. Khim., Akad. Nauk S.S.S.R. Otdel. Khim Nauk*, **4**(7), 5 (1952); through *Chem. Abstr.*, **47**, 11032 (1953).
71. Taylor, J. K., and S. W. Smith, *J. Res. Natl. Bur. Std.*, **56**, 301 (1956).
72. Tsyb, P. P., and M. T. Kozlovskii, *J. Appl. Chem. U.S.S.R.*, **24**, 955 (1951); through *Chem. Abstr.*, **47**, 6278 (1953).
73. Underkofler, W. L., and I. Shain, *Anal. Chem.*, **33**, 1966 (1961).
74. Zakharevskii, M. S., *Khim. Referat. Zhur.*, **2**, 84 (1939); through *Chem. Abstr.*, **34**, 1083 (1940).
75. Zbinden, C., *Bull. Soc. Chim. Biol.*, **13**, 35 (1931).

Chapter 51

CONDUCTOMETRY AND OSCILLOMETRY

By J. West Loveland, *Research and Engineering Department, Sun Oil Company, Marcus Hook, Pennsylvania*

Contents

Contents (*continued*)

I. INTRODUCTION

The conduction of electricity takes place through the net movement of electric charges. An applied electrostatic field may, for example, give rise to the flow of electrons as in a metallic conductor, to the differential migration of suspended or dissolved charged particles in solution as in electrophoresis (Chapters 28 and 36), or to the migration of positive and negative ions in an electrolyte solution. The field of conductometry embraces the latter phenomenon. Other things being constant, the conductance of an electrolyte solution depends on the number of ions present, their charge, and their intrinsic mobilities. Because the net electrical conductance of a solution is a summation of the individual conductances of all ionic species present, this property is not a specific one. Thus, an infinite variety of combinations of concentration of two strong electrolytes may be selected to yield solutions with identical conductances. A single conductance measurement is, therefore, analytically useful only as an estimate of the total salt content.

Because of the linear relationship between the concentration of a given ion and its contribution to the total conductance, it is possible to ascertain the degree of completion of a chemical reaction by performing a series of conductance measurements. This principle is the essential basis for *conductometric titrations*, in which the increase or decrease in conductance is related to concentration changes of the ionic species involved in the titration reaction. Conductometric titrations are used to determine many organic and inorganic compounds by employing acid–base, precipitation, and complex-forming reactions. In some cases, particularly for mixtures of acids or bases, the technique is often superior to other methods of analysis, such as potentiometry. In addition, conductance measurements may be used for the determination of ionization constants, solubilities, equivalent conductances, ion-pair and complex formation, and solvent effects in solution. Because conductance measurement lends itself readily to instrumentation, the technique has been employed in process control of streams containing electrolytes and in special analytical equipment.

The past several years have seen the utilization of radio-frequency methods in which external electrodes are employed for conductance and capacitance measurements (*oscillometry*) (12,13,46,47). Although oscillometry may be used for the titration of ionic species, ordinary conductometric titration is preferred in most cases because of its relative simplicity both in instrumentation and interpretation. The oscillometric technique, however, offers advantages when contamination of electrodes is a problem, such as in precipitation titrations. The external placement of the electrodes is also of utility in following concentration changes as they occur in chromatographic columns, or for determining reaction rates in solutions contained in a closed system.

For a supplementary coverage of the fields of conductometry, oscillometry, and theory of electrolytes, the reader should consult the bibliography given at the end of the chapter.

II. THEORY

A. CONDUCTOMETRY

1. Units of Conductance

Under the influence of an electrostatic field (applied potential), ions in a solution are almost instantaneously accelerated to the point at which the viscous drag of the solvent limits their speed. As the applied potential is doubled the velocity is also doubled, which results in twice the number of charges being transferred past a given point per unit of time. Hence, electrolyte solutions obey Ohm's law in that the current, I, flowing in an electrical conductor is directly proportional to the electromotive force, E, and inversely proportional to the resistance, R, of the conducting medium.

Where a potential, E_p, is required to overcome polarization effects at the electrodes, the applicable form of Ohm's law is $I = (E - E_p)/R$.

As in the case with metallic conductors, the resistance, R, of a solution depends not only on its intrinsic properties but also directly on the length, l, and inversely on the area, A, of the conducting sample. Thus,

$$R = \rho l / A \text{ ohms} \tag{1}$$

where the constant, ρ, in ohm cm., is the *specific resistance* of the material, i.e., the resistance between opposite faces of a cube one centimeter in length. The value of ρ is usually much greater for electrolytes than for metals. The ratio l/A for a conductometric cell is known as the *cell constant*, $\mathbf{K}$, and its determination is discussed in Section III-A-5.

The reciprocal of specific resistance is the *specific conductance*, κ, with units of ohm^{-1} cm.$^{-1}$ or mho cm.$^{-1}$. From equation (1):

$$1/R = A/\rho l = \kappa(A/l) = (\kappa/\mathbf{K}) \text{ mhos} \tag{2}$$

When A and l are unity and one volt is applied to the cell, the current in amperes equals $1/R$ or κ.

For electrolyte solutions the specific conductance is a function also of the concentration of the electrolyte; for very dilute solutions of strong electrolytes the conductance is essentially proportional to concentration. The units of conductance are conventionally established on an equivalents basis. The *equivalent conductance*, Λ, is related to specific conductance and concentration, C, in gram equivalents per 1000 cc. as follows:

$$\Lambda = 1000\kappa/C \text{ mhos cm.}^2 \tag{3}$$

Thus, Λ represents the specific conductance of a hypothetical solution of the electrolyte containing one gram-equivalent per cubic centimeter. An experimental value of Λ may be determined from measurements of R, $\mathbf{K}$, and C by means of the relationship

$$\Lambda = 1000\mathbf{K}/CR \tag{4}$$

2. Forces Acting on Ions

Essentially four primary factors govern the mobility of ions in solutions of finite concentration. At infinite dilution, only two of these need be considered: the electrical force of an ion of valence z and charge ze caused by the applied voltage, E, and the frictional force caused by the movement of the ion through the solvent. Because these forces are equal and opposing,

$$zeE = K_f v \tag{5}$$

where K_f is the coefficient of frictional resistance for an ion and v is the velocity of the ion. At finite concentrations two other effects also become important and equation (5) is not strictly valid. These are the electrophoretic and relaxation effects, which are a direct result of the existence of an ionic atmosphere around a central ion.

The present quantitative treatment of the ionic atmosphere and its effects on conductance is chiefly the result of the early work of Debye and Hückel (22) and the subsequent work of Onsager (62). From their theoretical treatment, in which the electrical potential, ψ, and the charge density, $\rho_\pm$, caused by a central ion at any point in solution were calculated as a function of the concentration and charges of the ions and the dielectric constant of the solvent, it was deduced that every ion is surrounded by a spherically symmetrical ionic atmosphere of equal charge and opposite sign. From further considerations the magnitude of the electrophoretic and relaxation effects on the conductance of electrolytes was calculated.

The *electrophoretic effect* arises from the fact that under the force of an applied potential the ionic atmosphere with charge $\rho_\pm$ will tend to move in a direction opposite to that of the central ion and carry with it solvent molecules. Thus, the mobility of the central ion is retarded by this opposing flow of solvent. As a simple model, the ionic atmosphere may be considered to have an effective radius of r and a charge of z. The velocity of the ionic atmosphere may then be calculated by Stoke's law:

$$v' = zeE/6\pi\eta r \tag{6}$$

where E is the applied potential, zeE is the electrical force, and η is the viscosity of the medium. The electrophoretic effect may be considered as an added viscous resistance.

Under an applied external potential, the central ion initially migrates more rapidly than its surrounding ionic atmosphere, destroying the spherical charge symmetry of the atmosphere. The resulting charge dissymmetry causes a charge of opposite sign to be built up behind the moving ion and hence exerts a retarding effect on its velocity, giving rise to the *relaxation effect*.

3. Equivalent Conductance: Effect of Concentration and Ionic Charge

The theoretical treatment of the factors discussed above yields the Onsager equation for equivalent conductance (62):

$$\Lambda = \Lambda^0 - \left[\frac{41.3\,(z_1 + z_2)}{\eta(\epsilon T)^{1/2}} + \frac{2.8 \times 10^6 z_1 z_2}{(\epsilon T)^{3/2}\,(1 + q^{1/2})}\Lambda^0\right]\left[\sum \frac{C_i z_i^2}{2}\right]^{1/2} \tag{7}$$

where Λ^0 is the *limiting equivalent conductance* at infinite dilution, ϵ is the dielectric constant, T is the absolute temperature, and q is a factor depending on the charges and limiting conductances of the ions. Equation (7) can be simplified to the familiar form

$$\Lambda = \Lambda^0 - (A + B\Lambda^0)\sqrt{C} \tag{8}$$

where A and B are the factors expressing the electrophoretic and the time of relaxation effects, respectively.

Equations (7) and (8) predict with reasonable accuracy the equivalent conductances for strong electrolyte solutions up to about $0.005M$ for $1:1$ electrolytes. For $2:2$ electrolytes, deviations from theory occur at a much lower concentration, mainly because of ion-pair formation.

As equation (7) indicates, the equivalent conductance decreases with increasing concentration and increasing ionic charge. Table 51.I illustrates these effects for the chlorides of potassium, barium, and lanthanum.

TABLE 51.I

Effect of Concentration and Ionic Charge on Equivalent Conductance of Various Chlorides at 25°C.

	Mhos cm.^{2}		
Moles/liter	K^+	Ba^{+2}	La^{+3}
0.0	149.9	140.3	145.3
0.001	147.0	132.3	131.2
0.01	141.3	119.1	111.3
0.1	129.0	98.7	88.0
1.0	111.9	70.0	51.2
Reference	[a]	[b]	[c]
% Reduction in Λ from 0.0 to $1.0M$/liter	25	50	65

[a] Shedlovsky, T., *J. Am. Chem. Soc.*, **54**, 1411 (1932).

[b] Jones, G., and M. Dole, *J. Am. Chem. Soc.*, **52**, 2245 (1930).

[c] Jones, G., and C. R. Bickford, *J. Am. Chem. Soc.*, **56**, 602 (1934).

The equivalent conductance depends strongly on the type and concentration of electrolyte, as depicted in Fig. 51.1a. The deviations are somewhat less apparent when the data are plotted in terms of specific conductance (Fig. 51.1b). For example, hydrochloric acid and potassium chloride then show fairly linear concentration dependency. Lanthanum chloride displays a greater degree of nonlinearity. For this reason, $1:1$ electrolytes are preferred titrants for precipitation, acid–base, or complexation reactions.

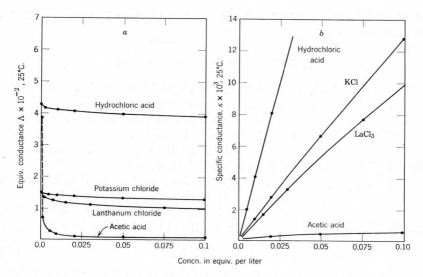

Fig. 51.1. Variation of equivalent conductance (*a*) and specific conductance (*b*) with concentration: a comparison of several different strong electrolytes and a weak electrolyte (acetic acid).

4. Absolute Velocity and Mobility of Ions

For dilute solutions of strong electrolytes the current, and hence the conductance, will depend on the charge of the ion, on the number of ions, and on their ease of movement. When a unit potential gradient, i.e., 1 v. per cm., is applied, the resulting velocity of the ion is known as the *mobility, u,* in cm. per second. At infinite dilution—where no ionic interaction occurs—the mobility attains a limiting maximum value, the *absolute mobility, u^0.* For all completely ionized salts, the limiting equivalent conductance, Λ^0, is proportional to the absolute mobilities of the ions; hence:

$$\Lambda^0 = F(u^0_+ + u^0_-) \tag{9}$$

where F is the Faraday. Furthermore, the limiting *ionic* equivalent conductances must have the relationships:

$$\lambda^0_+ = Fu^0_+ \quad \text{and} \quad \lambda^0_- = Fu^0_- \tag{10}$$

The absolute mobility of an ion is thus equal to the limiting ionic equivalent conductance divided by the Faraday (96,500 coulombs). The absolute velocity then is the product of the absolute mobility and the potential gradient in volts per centimeter. At finite concentrations, values of $\lambda_\pm$ are substituted for $\lambda^0_{\pm}$, and ionic velocities and mobilities will decrease with increasing concentration.

5. Ionic Equivalent Conductances

Although equivalent conductances of electrolytes are significant to the analytical chemist, perhaps more pertinent are the *ionic* equivalent conductances of the individual ions. In a conductometric titration the concentration of some particular ionic species is altered, rather than that of the electrolyte as a whole. This requires insight as to the relative contribution of the individual ionic species to the total conductance.

Kohlrausch in 1876 observed that each ion contributes a definite amount to the total conductance irrespective of the nature of the other ions. This *law of independent migration* of ions is strictly true only at infinite dilution, at which interionic effects can be ignored, and this law may be expressed as

$$\Lambda^0 = \lambda^0_+ + \lambda^0_- \tag{11}$$

where λ^0_+ and λ^0_- are the ionic equivalent conductances at infinite dilution of the cation and anion, respectively.

At concentrations other than those at infinite dilution, the equivalent conductance of an electrolyte may still be expressed as the sum of the ionic equivalent conductances of the two ions. However, the values of ionic equivalent conductances will be less than those at infinite dilution and, with increasing concentration, may even change their relative contributions to the total conductance. The contribution of a particular ion to the equivalent conductance of a salt at a given concentration is given by the equations

$$\lambda_+ = t_+\Lambda = \frac{u_+}{u_+ + u_-} \tag{12}$$

and

$$\lambda_- = t_-\Lambda = \frac{u_-}{u_+ + u_-} \tag{13}$$

where t_+ and t_- are the *transference numbers* and u_+ and u_- are the mobilities of the cation and anion, respectively, at the prescribed concentration. Because transference numbers can be determined by independent methods, $\lambda_{\pm}$ values may be obtained at any desired concentration. The t_+ and t_- values may be plotted versus concentration and extrapolated to obtain $t^0_{\pm}$ values at infinite dilution: these values and that of Λ^0 may be used to determine the ionic equivalent conductance at infinite dilution by means of equations (12) or (13).   The ionic equivalent conductances of several ions at infinite dilution are given in Table 51.II.

From the $\lambda_{\pm}^0$ values of Table 51.II it is seen that the mobilities, and, hence, by way of equation (10), the currents carried by each ion differ. The hydrogen ion and, to a lesser degree, the hydroxyl ion have extraordinarily high mobilities, which is attributed to the ability of the hydrogen and hydroxyl ions to use water molecules as transmitters of the ions. The mechanism involves the transfer of a proton from one hydronium ion to a neighboring water molecule; subsequently any one of the three protons on the newly formed hydronium ion is free to transfer to a second neighboring water molecule, etc.   Because this process, in which the identity of the originally migrating proton is lost, is rapid, the net mobility of charge is actually greater than could be achieved through the mobility of an intact ion.   This proton-transfer process may account for 80% or more of the current in solutions of acids.   Thus, conductometric titrations of strong acids with bases are readily performed with good accuracy because of the large change in conductance resulting from the replacement of the highly mobile hydronium ion with a less mobile cation.

Values of $\lambda_{\pm}^0$ are useful in the selection of titrants and in the prediction of the shapes of conductometric titration curves, as discussed in Section IV-A. Although a more exact approach would be to use $\lambda_{\pm}$ values for the actual concentrations in question, this procedure usually is not necessary for general interpretative purposes.   The $\lambda_{\pm}^0$ values also permit calculation of the ionic or salt equivalent conductance because the values of Λ^0, λ_{+}^0, and λ_{-}^0 for different salts and ions are additive.   Hence, the necessity for experimental measurements is avoided.   For example, if the value of Λ_{MX}^0 is desired, and the values of λ_{M+}^0 or λ_{X}^0 are unknown, the equations

$$\Lambda_{MX}^0 = \lambda_{M+}^0 + \lambda_{X-}^0$$

$$\lambda_{M+}^0 = \Lambda_{MCl}^0 - \lambda_{Cl-}^0$$

$$\lambda_{X-}^0 = \Lambda_{NaX}^0 - \lambda_{Na+}^0$$

may be combined to yield

$$\Lambda_{MX}^0 = \Lambda_{MCl}^0 + \Lambda_{NaX}^0 - \lambda_{Cl-}^0 - \lambda_{Na+}^0$$

Furthermore, the additivity of conductances of mixtures of electrolytes may be assumed for purposes of approximation.   For example, for a mixture of MX, MY, and NZ,

$$\Lambda(MX, MY, NZ) = 2\lambda_{M+} + \lambda_{N+} + \lambda_{X-} + \lambda_{Y-} + \lambda_{Z-}$$

TABLE 51.II
Ionic Equivalent Conductances of Ions at Infinite Dilution at 25°C.[a]

Cations	λ^0_+	Anions	λ^0_-
H^+	349.8_1	OH^-	198.6
Li^+	38.6_8	F^-	55.4
Na^+	50.10	Cl^-	76.35
K^+	73.50	Br^-	78.14
Rb^+	77.8_1	I^-	76.8_4
Cs^+	77.2_6	N_3^-	69
Ag^+	61.9_0	NO_3^-	71.46
Tl^+	74.7	ClO_3^-	64.6
NH_4^+	73.3_5	BrO_3^-	55.7_4
$CH_3NH_3^+$	58.7_2	ClO_4^-	67.3_6
$(CH_3)_2NH_2^+$	51.8_7	IO_4^-	54.5_5
$(CH_3)_3NH^+$	47.2_5	ReO_4^-	54.9_7
NMe_4^+	44.9_2	HCO_3^-	44.5_0
NEt_4^+	32.6_6	Formate	54.5_9
NPr_4^+	23.4_2	Acetate	40.9_0
NBu_4^+	19.4_7	Cyanoacetate	41.8_1
NAm_4^+	17.4_7	Propionate	35.8
Be^{+2}	45	Butyrate	32.6
Hg^{+2}	53.0_5	Benzoate	32.3_8
Ca^{+2}	59.50	Picrate	30.3_9
Sr^{+2}	59.4_5	SO_4^{-2}	80.0_2
Ba^{+2}	63.6_3	$C_2O_4^{-2}$	74.1_5
Cu^{+2}	53.6	CO_3^{-2}	69.3
Zn^{+2}	52.8	$Fe(CN)_6^{-3}$	100.9
Co^{+2}	55	$P_3O_9^{-3}$	83.6
La^{+3}	69.7	$Fe(CN)_6^{-4}$	$110._5$
Ce^{+3}	69.8	$P_4O_{12}^{-4}$	$93._7$
Pr^{+3}	69.6	$P_2O_7^{-4}$	$95._9$
Nd^{+3}	69.4	$P_3O_{10}^{-5}$	109
Sm^{+3}	68.5	$(Co(NH_3)_6)^{+3}$	101.9
Eu^{+3}	67.8	$(Co_2tri\text{-}en_3)^{+6}$	68.7
Gd^{+3}	67.3		
Dy^{+3}	65.6		
Ho^{+3}	66.3		
Er^{+3}	65.9		
Tm^{+3}	65.4		
Yb^{+3}	65.6		

Note: The number of significant figures given is such that the last figure, if printed normally, is considered reliable within 1 or 2; if it is printed below the line of the other figures, it is considered reliable within about 5.

[a] Table taken from R. A. Robinson and R. H. Stokes, *Electrolyte Solutions*, 1st ed., Butterworths, London, 1955, Appendix 6.1, page 452, by permission of the publishers; references to the original literature are given there.

Thus, the total salt content of solutions may be estimated from conductivity measurements. The presence of small concentrations of acids or bases may lead to appreciable errors in such determinations. The ash content of sugar is commonly determined by conductometric measurements because the mineral matter present in sugar is usually soluble and completely ionized in aqueous solutions (31). The determination of individual ions in mixtures may be achieved simply by measuring the specific conductance before and after the addition of the proper reagent (63).

6. Effect of Temperature, Solvent, and Degree of Ionization

Temperature. Ionic equivalent conductance for most ions increases approximately 2% per degree in the vicinity of room temperature. The hydrogen ion is an exception, having a $d \lambda/dT$ value of about 1.4% per degree. Whereas the temperature should be controlled to within 0.01°C. for theoretical studies, for ordinary titrations the temperature need be controlled to within only 1°C.

Viscosity of Solvent. One of the main factors governing conductance of ions in solution is the viscosity of the solvent, as indicated in equation (7) and implied in the coefficient of frictional resistance in equation (5). Generally, the greater the viscosity of the solvent, the smaller is the conductance for a given electrolyte. Assuming Stoke's law of viscous flow to hold for ions in solution and assuming all ions to have the same radii, the product of viscosity, η, and mobility, u, should be a constant. Walden observed that, for some salts in various solvents, including water, the limiting equivalent conductance indeed conformed to the formula $\Lambda^0 \eta^0 =$ constant. In the case of tetraethylammonium iodide, $\Lambda^0 \eta^0$ varies between 0.65 and 0.73 for solvents such as acetone ($\eta^0 = 0.0032$ poises), methanol ($\eta^0 = 0.0058$), acetic anhydride ($\eta^0 = 0.0086$), and nitrobenzene $\eta^0 = 0.018$). However, this rule should be taken only as a qualitative guide in view of the assumptions involved.

Dielectric Constant of Solvent. Another factor, particularly important in nonaqueous conductance work, is the dielectric constant of the solvent. Solvents having a dielectric constant lower than water usually have less solvating power for salts. As a result, strong electrolytes (in water) are much less soluble in these solvents* and weak electrolytes are less dissociated. According to equation (7), as the dielectric constant decreases, the electrophoretic and relaxation effects increase. Thus, the equivalent

---

* It should be noted that, when solvents are used that form complexes or solvate with ions, an increase in the solubility of a salt may occur. Thus, silver chloride is more soluble in pyridine than in water because Ag^+ is solvated by pyridine.

conductance decreases more rapidly with an increase in concentration in solvents of lower dielectric constant. A further consequence of decreasing the dielectric constant, hence leading to increased electrostatic attraction between ions, is the possible formation of ion pairs and a substantial reduction in the concentration of ionized species. The ion pairs, being highly polar in nature, effectively increase the dielectric constant of the medium, diminishing the electrophoretic and relaxation effects. Because this effect is smaller in magnitude than that arising from the loss of ionized species, the net conductance decreases although the equivalent conductance of the remaining ionic species increases (45). Consequently, most non-aqueous titrations of organic species are performed in solvents that have dielectric constants above 10 (such as methanol). However, it is possible to carry out successful conductometric titrations in solvents of very low dielectric constant, such as toluene (15).

Although it is generally agreed that viscosity affects the mobility of ions to a greater extent than dielectric constant, the exact magnitude of the contribution of each is difficult to ascertain even under the best of conditions. Table 51.III-A shows that, as the weight per cent of methanol in water increases, ϵ decreases in a near-linear fashion, η goes through a maximum, and Λ^0 exhibits a minimum. However, the minimum in Λ^0 does not occur at the maximum η as might be expected from Walden's rule. The decrease in Λ^0 over the 0 to 40% methanol range can be attributed mainly to viscosity effects. The influence of ϵ becomes evident when the data are compared at equal viscosity values. Table 51.III-A shows two such sets, one occurring at $\eta = 13.85$ (% methanol = 20.2 and 58.8) and the other at $\eta = 8.49$ (% methanol = 0 and 88.5). The decrease in Λ^0 for both cases can be attributed in part to dielectric constant. Moreover, the decrease of Λ^0 in the latter case and, to a certain extent, in the former is undoubtedly influenced by the variations in the effective radius of the ions as methanol replaces water molecules in the solvated ions. In finite solutions the association of ions also must be considered. In pure methanol, for example, at 25°C., a 0.053M KCl solution is about 5.5% associated (27a).

Interpretations are even more difficult when acid and base solutions are considered, for in addition to viscosity, dielectric constant, solvation, and ion-pair association, there are dissociation and proton-transfer changes taking place. As solvents decrease in dielectric constant, acids will tend to be less dissociated. Furthermore, with decreasing water content fewer water molecules will be available to participate in the proton-transfer mechanism, thus reducing the effective mobility of the proton. These latter effects for acids and bases may be of greater magnitude than the combined effects present for KCl or other salt solutions. For example, the equivalent conductance of a $0.05M$ KCl varies no more than 10% over the range of 40 to 100% methanol. In ethanol–water solutions (Table 51.III-B) having similar dielectric constant values, the Λ of a $0.3N$ sulfuric acid solution decreases by over 200% over the range of 54 to 90% ethanol.

TABLE 51.III-A

The Viscosity, Dielectric Constant, and Limiting Equivalent Conductance of Potassium Chloride in Water–Methanol System at 25°C. (27a)

Methanol, wt. %	Dielectric constant	Viscosity, millipoise	Λ^0_{KCl}
0	78.5	8.49	150.3
20.2	69.2	13.85	99.2
40.2	59.6	15.9	78.2
58.8	50.8	13.85	74.0
60.7	49.8	13.5	74.2
80.7	39.1	10.3	91.5
88.7	36.3	8.49	96.9
100	31.5	5.45	104.8

TABLE 51.III-B

Dielectric Constant and Equivalent Conductance of $0.306N$ Sulfuric Acid in Water–Ethanol System (65a)

Ethanol, wt. %	Dielectric constant of solvent at 20°C.[a]	Equivalent conductance at 22.5°C.
53.5	47.5	100.4
79.2	34.5	48.3
90.6	29.5	30.7

[a] Interpolated values from National Research Council, *International Critical Tables*, McGraw-Hill, New York, 1929, Vol. VI, p. 101.

Degree of Ionization: The incomplete ionization of weak electrolytes such as acetic acid causes a considerably greater reduction in the equivalent conductance than that due to interionic effects. This is readily apparent from the comparison of the equivalent conductances for a strong acid (hydrochloric) and a weak acid (acetic) as a function of concentration, as shown in Fig. 51.1a. Only in very dilute solutions, in which acetic acid approaches complete ionization, does Λ approach its limiting equivalence conductance value of 390.7.

Although the conductance ratio, $\alpha = \Lambda/\Lambda^0$, (often called the degree of ionization) has no special significance for strong electrolytes, for weak electrolytes α offers a reasonably good measure of the extent of ionization. With corrections for mobilities as indicated in Section IV-A-4, exact values of the ionization constants may be calculated from the observed values of α.

The effect of incomplete ionization of the species titrated or of the titrant itself on titration curves is of great importance in determining the shape of the conductometric titration curves obtained. Specific examples illustrating the selection of titrants for weak acids and bases are given in Section IV-A-1-b.

7. Electrical Analog of Cell and Solution

In a conductometric titration in which two metal electrodes are placed in direct contact with an electrolyte solution, the electrical circuit may be represented as:

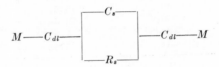

where M is the metal electrode, C_{dl} is the electrical double-layer capacitance that exists at the metal–solution interface, C_s is the solution capacity that depends on the dielectric nature of the solution, and R_s is the electrical resistance of the solution. The double-layer capacitance depends not only on the electrode material but also on the nature and concentration of the anions and cations present and on the potential existing across the double layer. For example, the capacity of the double layer at a smooth, bright platinum electrode in a saline solution is of the order of 20 μf. per square centimeter. This capacity may be increased many fold by platinization, a process that results in a larger microscopic surface area. The two C_{dl} capacitances in series with the parallel combination of the solution resistances (R_s) and capacitance (C_s) may be considered as one capacitance to give an equivalent circuit identical to that depicted in Fig. 51.2c. In this figure, C_1 corresponds to the combined interfacial capacitances and C_2 to the solution capacitance. Because most conductivity measurements employ alternating voltages of 60 and 1000 cycles per second, it is of interest to consider the relative effects of the two different capacities, C_{dl} and C_s, on the a.-c. resistance measurements.

The solution capacitance, C_s, in micromicrofarads ($\mu\mu f$.), is given as

$$C_s = (0.0885 A \epsilon)/d$$

where A is the area of the electrodes, ϵ is the dielectric constant of the solution, and d is the distance between the electrodes. When A equals 1 cm.^{2}, d is 1 cm., and ϵ is 80 (as for water), C_s will be 7.1 $\mu\mu$f.

The capacitative reactance, X_{C_s} (i.e., the effective impedance that C_s exhibits to the flow of an alternating current), is given by $X_{C_s} = 1/(2\pi f C_s)$, where f is the frequency (c.p.s.) and C_s is the capacitance in farads. At 1000 c.p.s. the reactance of the solution capacitance for the example above is 2.2×10^7 ohms. For a $0.1N$ KCl solution the purely resistive component, R_s, would be 78 ohms. In a parallel arrangement the total impedance is governed mainly by the lower of the two values, X_{C_s} or R_s. Therefore, in this example, X_{C_s} has essentially no effect on the measurement of R_s. However, X_{C_s} at megacycle and higher frequencies may be of sufficiently low magnitude that its contribution to the over-all measurement would have to be taken into account.

On the other hand, the capacitive reactance of C_{dl} at 1000 c.p.s., assuming a double-layer capacitance of 100 μf., is 1.6 ohms. Because C_{dl} is in series with R_s, the total opposition to alternating current flow, i.e., the impedance, Z, is given by:

$$Z = \sqrt{R_s{}^2 + X_{C_{dl}}{}^2}$$

The reciprocal of Z is known as the admittance of the solution. In the example cited, Z is only a few hundredths of an ohm greater than R_s. However, if C_{dl} or f were much smaller, Z could become appreciably greater than R_s. Further, for a series capacitance–resistance network, the current leads the voltage by an amount equal to arc tan X_C/R_s, which in this particular instance is negligible but which becomes appreciable in cases in which R_s or C_{dl} are small. Chapter 42 discusses the current–voltage phase-angle relationships in more detail. By proper balancing of capacitances and resistances in a Wheatstone bridge, the current and voltage can be brought into phase at the null point and a pure resistance, and hence conductance, of the solution measured separately and hence accurately.

The process of current flow is such that the electrical double layer of one of the electrodes is charged on one half of the alternating-current cycle while that of the second electrode is discharged. During the second half of the cycle the charging and discharging processes reverse themselves at each of the electrodes. Cations will increase in concentration and displace anions at the electrode surface on the negative cycle but will be incrementally displaced by anions during the positive cycle. During this non-Faradaic process the anions and cations are conducting the current through the solution in an alternating fashion.

The charge, q, which the electrical double layer acquires, is related to the potential E_{dl} across the double layer and the capacity by

$$q = C_{dl} \times E_{dl}$$

When E_{dl} varies with respect to time, a capacitance current, i_c, is obtained (55):

$$i_c = dq/dt = C_{dl} dE_{dl}/dt$$

For alternating-current conditions, dE_{dl}/dt is a sinusoidal function given by $E\omega \cos \omega t$, where ω equals $2\pi f$ where f is the frequency. Capacity currents, therefore, are directly proportional to the capacity of the electrical double layer, the magnitude of the applied potential, and its frequency. As $X_{C_{dl}}$ increases, a greater portion of the applied potential will be dropped across the electrode–solution interface; if large potentials are used, the possibility of undesirable Faradaic processes is enhanced.

A limiting case occurs when d.-c. potentials are applied. Capacitive reactance under this condition is infinite and i_c equals zero (an instantaneous charging current occurs upon application of the potential, for dE/dt is finite at that time). Potentials sufficiently great must be applied to the electrodes for a Faradaic process to take place, such as the evolution of hydrogen and oxygen from water or the oxidation of metals. Conductance processes require cations in solution to move toward the cathode and the anions to move toward the anode while the electrochemical processes at the electrode surfaces carry the current into and out of the solution.

B. OSCILLOMETRY

1. Solution Property Measurements

Oscillometry differs from conductometry in that the electrodes are not in intimate contact with the solution, usually being separated from the solution by the glass walls of the container. This cell design necessitates the use of high-frequency applied potentials (several megacycles) in order to achieve a suitable response for changes in the solution composition. In such a system we are measuring a composite of essentially two effects. One is *conductance*, in which the conducting ions absorb energy that is translated into motion and heat. The other effect deals with *dielectric constant* or *capacitance*, in which energy is absorbed but is then returned to the oscillating circuit during each frequency cycle. This latter effect arises from the induced polarization and alignment of electrically unsymmetrical molecules under the influence of an electrical field.

The earliest uses of high frequency were not in oscillometry but in the measurement of dielectric constant or capacitance changes, in which a capacitor was immersed in the solution to be tested. By noting frequency, capacitance, or dielectric constant changes, two-component mixtures can be analyzed. This method is discussed in detail in Chapter 52.

In oscillometric methods the response of an instrument will, in general, be a combined response due to both the conductance and the dielectric properties of the solution. However, if one is working with solutions of high dielectric constant and no salts are present, the response will be mainly capacitive or dielectric in nature. On the other hand, if the solution is of low dielectric constant and contains electrolyte, the response will be mainly due to conductance. The combined responses can be separately measured with a General Radio Twin-T impedance bridge (65). For a discussion of the response characteristics of oscillators to capacitance and conductance loads, the reader is referred to Section III-B.

2. Factors Affecting Titration Curves

In practice, high-frequency conductometric titrations give, in addition to the usual V-shaped curves, nonlinear intersecting curves and, in some cases, inverted V-shape curves (1,37,38,42). These effects may occur for a number of reasons: (1) instrument response may or may not be a linear function of either the concentration of the electrolyte or the dielectric constant of the solution at a given frequency; (2) different responses are obtained at a given concentration or dielectric constant at different frequencies, (3) different cell designs cause differences in total capacitances and hence differences in capacitance response; (4) various makes of instruments may give different responses when other conditions (cell geometry and sample composition) are the same; and (5) for electrolyte solutions the conductance response will be affected by electrolyte concentration and will be a function of variables such as temperature, solution viscosity, and the degree of dissociation of the electrolyte.

3. Equivalent Circuit of Cell and Solution: Conductance and Capacitance Relationships

Although there are several variables influencing the shape of the titration curves, it has been shown (65) that the curves can be predicted if one relates the high-frequency conductance and capacitance responses in terms of the low-frequency conductance of the solution. To do this requires the mathematical analysis of the equivalent circuit of the cell and solution for the condenser type of cell arrangement. Shown in Fig. 51.2 is a cross section of the cell and solution (a), its equivalent circuit (b), and the fundamental circuit (c) that combines the two capacities C_w of the cell walls into one and assumes that the resistance of the cell walls, R_w, is so high as to have negligible effect on the response. Schematic (d) is a simplified parallel *equivalent* circuit of (c). Although circuits (c) and (d) do not represent the exact conditions of distributed capacities or resistances

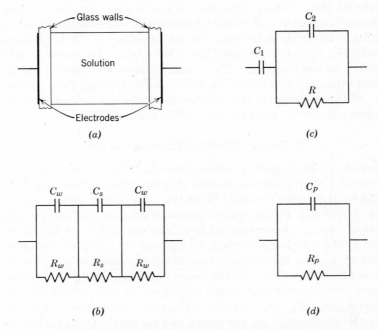

Fig. 51.2. Equivalent circuits for cell and solution of the condenser type: (a) is the physical arrangement; (b) shows C_w, the capacitance, and R_w, the resistance of the cell walls; and C_s, the capacitance, and R_s, the resistance of the solution; (c) is the fundamental equivalent circuit; and (d) is a simplified parallel equivalent circuit.

they do offer a reasonable analogy in which theory and experiment can be checked.

The admittance, Y, (or $1/Z$, the impedance) of the parallel equivalent circuit is the sum of the conductance, G_p (or $1/R_p$) plus the susceptance, C_p, ($1/X_{C_p}$, the reactance), all in mhos, as given in equation (14), where j equals $\sqrt{-1}$:

$$Y = G_p + jC_p \tag{14}$$

The conductance term, G_p, is given by:

$$G_p = \frac{1}{R_p} = \frac{\kappa\omega^2 C_1^2}{\kappa^2 + \omega^2(C_1 + C_2)^2} \tag{15}$$

where ω is $2\pi f$ and κ is the actual low-frequency specific conductance of the solution, equal to $1/R$. The quantities C_1, C_2, and R are the same as in Fig. 51.2c.

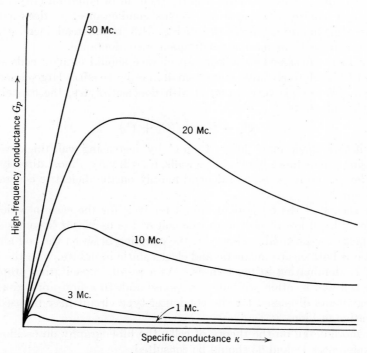

Fig. 51.3. Relationship of high-frequency conductance, G_P, versus low-frequency conductance, κ, at several frequencies.

Equation (15) indicates that (1) as the cell capacity, C_1, increases (cell has greater area and dielectric constant and smaller thickness), the value of G_p increases; (2) as the frequency decreases, G_p decreases and becomes zero at zero frequency; (3) G_p is a unique function of the low-frequency conductance, κ, and independent of the type of electrolyte; and (4) when κ is very small or very large, G_p approaches zero and hence a peak occurs at a given frequency. Fig. 51.3 shows the G_p response as a function of κ at several different frequencies. By knowing on which side of the peak the conductance of a solution lies, it is possible to plot the high-frequency conductance response during a titration.   Working with solutions at very high conductivities in the vicinity of the peaks will lead to partially inverted curves.   In this respect, it is helpful to obtain a plot of the high-frequency response versus low-frequency conductance in order to select the best conditions for high-frequency titrations.

The susceptance (capacitance, C_p) term of equation (14) involves the same κ, C_1, and C_2 values as appear in the G_p term of equation (15).   However, the response of capacitance versus conductance, κ, does not go through a maximum as for G_p vs. κ of Fig. 51.3, but instead increases and then levels off with increasing low-frequency conductance.

Instruments designed to follow capacitance should employ cells whose value of C_1 is relatively large and C_2 small in order to effect large changes in response.   When κ is very small, as with nonelectrolytes, the capacitance term, C_p, reduces to

$$C_p = (C_1 C_2)/(C_1 + C_2) \qquad (16)$$

Thus, if C_1 is made much larger than C_2 by decreasing wall thickness and increasing the distance between the walls, C_p will vary almost directly with C_2.   Hence, the response will depend mainly on the dielectric constant of the sample.

The theory of the equivalent circuit analysis for the case in which the sample and cell are placed inside the coil of the oscillator becomes somewhat more complicated.   However, the coupling between the coil and the solution is both electromagnetic and electrostatic in nature, with the latter probably dominating in most cases.   As a result, capacitative properties of the cell and solution will affect response and, to a first approximation, the arguments discussed for the condenser-type circuit may be used in a qualitative fashion.

For more detail on the theory of cells, the bibliography on oscillometry and References 18 and 65 should be consulted.

III. APPARATUS AND TECHNIQUE

A. LOW-FREQUENCY CONDUCTANCE

1. Wheatstone Bridge—Alternating-Current Measurements

The Wheatstone bridge is the classic apparatus for measuring resistances or conductances and is considered in detail in the following discussion. The fundamental arrangement of the Wheatstone bridge for equal-arm (a) or opposite-arm (b) balance for conductance measurements is shown in Fig. 51.4.   In the equal-arm arrangement (a), R_S is the resistance of the cell solution, R_1 is a variable resistance, usually a decade box, and R_2 and R_3

are variable resistances that may be two portions of a linear slide wire on which contact at point a can be moved back and forth; alternatively, they may be separate decade boxes. A variable capacitor C is placed across R_1 to balance out any phase shifts in the alternating signal caused by the capacity effects present in the cell, and it is adjusted to give the sharpest minimum in the null detector of the bridge. The capacitor is usually unnecessary in ordinary titration work.

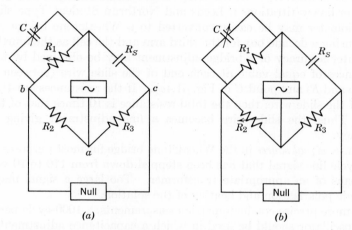

Fig. 51.4. Wheatstone bridge arrangements for measuring conductance: (a) equal-arm balance; (b) opposite-arm balance.

In practice, R_1 is made roughly equal to R_S. Resistances R_2 and R_3 are adjusted so that a minimum is observed in the null detector. At balance there is zero potential difference between points b and c. This condition requires that the potential drop across R_1 equal that across R_S and the potential drop across R_2 equal that across R_3.

Equating potentials: $i_1R_1 = i_sR_s$ and $i_2R_2 = i_3R_3$

Taking ratios of equals: $i_1R_1/i_2R_2 = i_sR_s/i_3R_3$

In the above relationship, $i_1 = i_2$ and $i_s = i_3$, so that all currents cancel. Rearranging resistances shows that the resistance of the solution is as follows:

$$R_S = (R_1R_3)/R_2 \qquad (17)$$

Therefore, with R_1 set, only the ratio of R_3 and R_2 need be known. If a slide wire is used, it is good practice to vary R_1 so that only the center portion of the slide wire is used. This eliminates the possibility of large errors when the ratio R_3/R_2 is high or low. It is quite convenient for titration work to set R_2 equal to R_3, in which case R_1 is varied to obtain a minimum; then the resistance of the solution can be read directly since it is equal to R_1.

In the opposite-arm bridge arrangement, Fig. 51.4b, the same principles of equating potential drops and resistances are used in obtaining a balance. In this case, when $R_1 = R_3$ the bridge is at balance and $R_S = R_2$.

For ordinary titrations a Leeds and Northrup Student Type slide-wire potentiometer may be easily converted to a Wheatstone bridge arrangement, using a decade box for the third arm and the cell as the fourth arm.

Greater accuracy of a bridge adjustment may be obtained by inserting resistances of equal value at each end of the slide wire (between R_2 and point b and R_3 and point C of Fig. 51.4a). If the resistances are $4^1/_2$ times that of the slide wire, then the total resistance is 10 times that of the slide wire. Thus, the slide wire becomes a fine adjustment giving greater accuracy.

An a.-c. *signal source* in the Wheatstone bridge for most purposes may be a 60-cycle line signal that has been stepped down from 110 to 10 v. or less by means of an appropriate transformer. Too large a signal may cause electrode polarization and heating of the solution.

For more precise conductometric measurements, a 1000-cycle-per-second audio oscillator should be used in which a capacitance adjustment is provided in the Wheatstone circuit for balancing out the cell capacitance. Frequencies greater than 1000 cycles per second may be used, but stray capacities and cell capacitance make it more difficult to obtain a precise minimum in the null detector. In addition, inductive effects become more pronounced and each resistance in equation (17) must be replaced by the corresponding Z or impedance term. The inductive and stray-capacity effects of the wire resistors can be made almost negligible by proper mechanical design, but cell capacitance can never be eliminated. For proper design of Wheatstone bridges for precise measurements of conductance the reader is referred to the literature (52,68).

The *null detector* may be any device capable of converting a few micro- or millivolts of signal into an audio or readable signal. The earphone is a sensitive null-point indicating device, as is a sensitive a.-c. galvanometer. The oscilloscope has in recent years found wide application as a null detector, and in commercial conductance units the "magic eye" tube is in use.

Vacuum-tube oscillator circuits may be used to supply the a.-c. signal to the cell, and also to amplify the null signal (20). In some cases the bridge unbalance can be amplified so that the output of the amplifier (as indicated by a meter) gives the resistance of the solution directly (29).

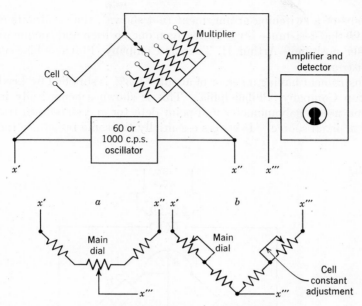

Fig. 51.5. Simplified schematic of (*a*) Industrial Instruments, Inc., Model RC-16B2 Conductance Bridge, and (*b*) the Serfass Bridge. Courtesy of Industrial Instruments, Inc., and A. H. Thomas Co.

Although it is possible to devise Wheatstone bridges suitable for conductance measurements from readily available laboratory components, several inexpensive conductivity bridges are commercially available. Industrial Instruments Inc., Cedar Grove, New Jersey, manufactures an easily operated vacuum-tube instrument, Model RC-16B2, having less than 1% error.   The instrument comes either as a line- or as a battery-operated unit.   Another useful instrument, also employing vacuum tubes, is the line-operated Serfass Bridge, having less than 1% error.   Both units use a "magic eye" for null-point indication and cover the range of resistances encountered from pure water to concentrated acid solutions.   Fig. 51.5 shows a simplified schematic diagram of the two instruments.   The cell arm, the multiplier arm (1 to $10^5 \times$ in 6 steps), the a.-c. signal, and the amplifier and detector are similar in both units.   However, they differ in the manner of balancing the bridge.   Model RC-16B2 (part *a* of Fig. 51.5) uses a slide wire (main dial) that is split between the two balancing arms. The dial itself is calibrated to read directly in either resistance or conductance units.   The Serfass unit (part *b* of Fig. 51.5) uses a slide wire (main dial) in one arm, and a cell-constant adjustment in the opposite arm.

By means of a switching arrangement (not shown), the quadrants are reversed so that resistance is read directly in one position and conductance in the other position. Arthur H. Thomas Company, Philadelphia, supplies both instruments.

An instrument having an error of about ±0.3% is supplied by Leeds and Northrup Company, Philadelphia. This is shown schematically in Fig. 51.6, and uses a galvanometer null-point detector and step-down transformer as a signal source. It covers essentially the same resistance range as

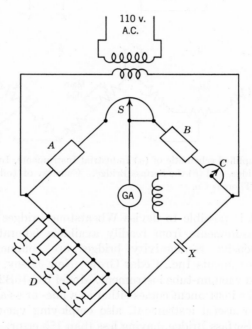

Fig. 51.6. Simplified circuit of Leeds and Northrup Conductance Meter. Courtesy of Leeds and Northrup Co.

the two other instruments mentioned. Ivan Sorvall, Inc., Norwalk, Connecticut, supplies an instrument in which the output can be fed to a recorder for the continuous measurement of conductance.

When very precise conductance measurements, accurate to ±0.01% or better, are necessary (as in theoretical physical chemical studies on electrolyte solution), the bridge described by Jones and Joseph (52) should be used. Such an instrument is available from Leeds and Northrup Company.

2. Direct-Current Measurements and Polarization (D.C. and A.C.)

The direct-current method for measuring conductivity is simpler in principle than the a.-c. Wheatstone bridge method. Two identical probe electrodes are inserted into the solution between the two working electrodes and are used to measure the difference in potential between two points in the solution. A known, small current is passed at the two working electrodes. Knowing the impressed current, the measured ΔE enables a calculation of the solution resistance from Ohm's law. Platinum, tungsten, and

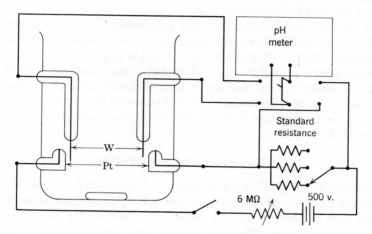

Fig. 51.7. Cell and apparatus for direct-current conductivity titrations, according to Taylor and Furman (71).

silver–silver chloride probe electrodes may be used to measure the potential drop. To reduce the possibility of polarization of the probe electrodes during the potential measurement, a high-input impedance instrument such as a pH meter or vacuum-tube voltmeter should be used.

It is necessary that the working electrodes be reversible and nonpolarizable (34), such as are properly designed silver–silver chloride and mercury–mercurous sulfate electrodes (3). The restriction of nonreactivity of all these electrodes with the electrolyte solution, of course, applies. Because the electrode reactions arising from the impressed current may result in the consumption of the electrolyte or the liberation of new ions, it is necessary to employ small impressed currents and to apply the current only so long as is needed to measure the potential.

Direct-current techniques have been used for conductometric titrations (71) in a beaker cell in which small currents are impressed on platinum working electrodes. Tungsten probe electrodes and a pH meter are used for the potential measurement. Fig. 51.7 shows a convenient circuit for d.-c. conductometric titrations.

In nonaqueous solvents, in which resistances of the order of 10^8 to 10^{10} ohms are observed, a single pair of working electrodes may be used in series with a large external resistance (10^8 ohm) and a d.-c. battery (1.5 v.). A vibrating-reed electrometer is used to measure the small potential drop across the external resistor arising from the flowing direct current. Such an arrangement may be used successfully in conductometric titrations in solvents of low dielectric constant (15).

The possibility of harmful electrode polarization is present in both a.-c. and d.-c. conductometric measurements and proper steps must be taken to minimize its effects. Higher frequencies and large-area electrodes (such as platinized platinum) reduce electrode polarization; however, both of these increase capacity effects, making it more difficult to obtain a sharp null minimum in the a.-c. technique. Proper choice of frequency and electrode surface area is therefore required for optimum results, as discussed in Section II-A-7.

3. Instruments for Industrial Use

Conductivity often offers a good analytical approach to control in a process stream in which electrolytes are present either as impurities or as an integral part of the process. A variety of conductivity instruments are available for such uses. For spot checking on a process stream or tank, the

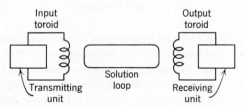

Fig. 51.8. Electrodeless method for measuring conductivity. Courtesy of Industrial Instruments, Inc.

conductivity bridges shown in Figs. 51.5 and 51.6 are quite adequate and are used with dip-type conductivity cells. Where continuous monitoring is required, both Leeds and Northrup Company and Industrial Instruments, Inc., supply conductivity-control instruments that furnish continuous recording of conductivity or furnish a signal to actuate a valve, alarm, etc., when the solution deviates from some preset conductivity value.

A rather unique instrument that does not rely on the use of electrodes is available from Industrial Instruments, Inc. Fig. 51.8 shows the basic principle on which it works. In this case the conducting solution acts as an induction loop that couples the two toroidal coils. With constant input voltage the output of the system is proportional to the conductivity of the solution. The use of such a technique is recommended only under certain conditions, such as when cells tend to clog with fibers or sludge or when hot, highly conductive, or extremely corrosive solutions are involved.

4. Electrodes and Conductivity Cells

Platinum electrodes are generally about 1 cm.^{2} in area and preferably are vertical so as to prevent the collection of precipitate on the electrode surface in precipitation reactions. The electrodes are welded to heavy-gage platinum wires, which are sealed rigidly to the cell walls or glass walls. Since heavy platinum wire is difficult to seal tightly in Pyrex, graded seals should be used to prevent leakage of solution and movement of the electrodes. The leads protruding externally from the cell provide a means for connection to the conductivity bridge.

Platinization of the electrodes may be accomplished by cleaning the platinum in dichromate–sulfuric acid cleaning solution, rinsing thoroughly in distilled water, immersing in a platinizing solution containing about 3% chloroplatinic acid and 0.001% lead acetate (which increases the rate of deposition of platinum), and applying of a slowly alternating potential. The two electrodes are connected to a 3- or 4-v. battery with a variable resistor in series. The electrolysis proceeds with a moderate evolution of gas and the polarity of the electrodes is manually reversed every 15 to 20 seconds until a light gray (not black) deposit forms. The electrodes are then washed and placed in a $1N$ sulfuric acid solution and electrolyzed with polarity reversal every 15 seconds or so for several minutes to remove occluded impurities. A thick platinum deposit should be avoided because of absorption effects. The electrodes should be thoroughly washed and stored under distilled water. Platinizing solutions may be purchased from a number of supply houses.

Conductivity-titration cells are probably as varied in design as there are workers in the field. Fig. 51.9 depicts two possible designs. Other possibilities are discussed in the bibliography. In some cases an open beaker with fixed electrodes is sufficient. However, for fairly dilute solutions an open beaker would not be satisfactory because atmospheric contamination of the solution, particularly from carbon dioxide in the air, may alter the conductance appreciably.

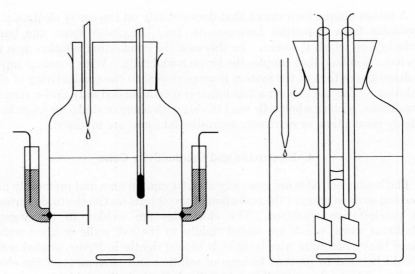

Fig. 51.9. Conductance cells for titrations.

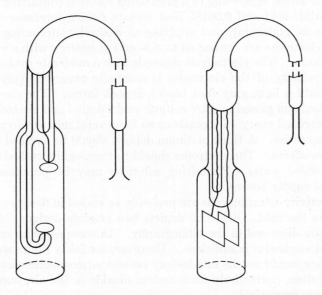

Fig. 51.10. Dip-type conductance cells for concentration measurements.

Dip cells with conductance-calibration curves are quite often used in a direct measurement of concentration. Fig. 51.10 shows two such cells. For laboratory work, Pyrex dip cells are convenient and are available from Leeds and Northrup Company, Industrial Instruments, Inc., and apparatus supply houses such as A. H. Thomas, Emil Greiner, and others. For industrial use cells may be constructed of Pyrex, various plastics, or metals. Designs are available having different cell constants for different solution strengths and operating temperatures. For precision work, special cells are available from Leeds and Northrup Company that incorporate the essential details described by Shedlovsky (68) and others.

5. Cell Constants

For titrations it is not necessary to obtain precise values for the cell constant. However, the cell constant should be high ($\sim$5 to 10) for concentrated solutions and low ($\sim$0.1) for very dilute solutions so as to keep the cell resistance in an easily measurable range. When specific conductance or specific resistance is used as a direct measure of the concentration of the electrolyte, the cell constant should, of course, be accurately known.

In order to determine experimentally the constant for a given cell, it may be seen from equation (2) that the resistance of the cell might be measured when containing a solution for which the specific conductance is known. This may be expressed by:

$$\mathbf{K} = \frac{l}{A} = R\kappa \qquad (18)$$

Standard potassium chloride solutions are commonly used because the specific conductances of solutions of this salt are very accurately known. Table 51.IV gives some specific conductances of potassium chloride solutions over a range of temperatures. It is best to select a standard solution

TABLE 51.IV

Specific Conductances of Standard Potassium Chloride Solutions, in ohm^{-1} cm.$^{-1}$, for Cell-Constant Determination[a]

Temperature, °C.	KCl (g.) in 1000 g. of solution		
	71.1352	7.41913	0.745263
0	0.06517	0.007137	0.0007736
18	0.09783	0.011166	0.0012205
25	0.11134	0.012856	0.0014087

[a] Jones, G., and B. C. Bradshaw, *J. Am. Chem. Soc.*, **55**, 1780 (1933).

having a specific conductance in the same range as that of the solutions to be measured.

6. Titration Techniques

A conductometric titration may require 10 minutes or longer, depending on the complexity of the system being titrated. To minimize the necessity for correction of the measured conductance values for dilution, the titrant should be at least 10 and preferably 20 times as concentrated as the solution to be titrated. With microburets, concentrations 50 times as concentrated can be used to advantage. With less-concentrated titrants it is necessary to correct for dilution to maintain the linear relation between conductance and titrant volume. The values of resistance are multiplied by $V/(V + v)$, where V is the original volume of solution and v is the volume of titrant added. If conductance values are used, these are corrected by multiplying by $(V + v)/v$. Conductance values are preferred for plotting titration curves, since resistance values, being the reciprocal of the conductance values, result in nonlinear curves.

For most titrations, thermostating of the cell is unnecessary. However, for titrations involving high heats of reaction (such as acid–base reactions at high concentrations) it is advisable to provide a constant-temperature arrangement for the titration cell. A reasonable precaution is to place a thermometer in the solution and to maintain the temperature to within $1°C.$ of the starting temperature throughout the titration. For more precise work requiring conductance errors not greater than $\pm 0.2\%$, the temperature should be held constant to within $\pm 0.1°C.$

Stirring of the solution after each addition of titrant may be accomplished manually or with mechanical or magnetic stirrers. In any case, care should be taken to minimize transfer of heat to the cell. After insuring that a homogeneous solution has been obtained, stirring is discontinued or reduced to prevent bubble formation before the conductance measurement is made.

7. Purity of Solvent

The *purity* of the solvent is important in conductivity work. The specific conductance of high-purity water (*conductivity water*) is less than 0.1×10^{-6} mho cm.$^{-1}$ at $25°C.$ Distilled water in equilibrium with carbon dioxide of the atmosphere (*equilibrium water*) has a specific conductance of about 1×10^{-6} mho cm.$^{-1}$. In most titrations the specific conductance of the solution will have values greater than 1×10^{-3} mho cm.$^{-1}$, and the specific conductance of water can be neglected. Water redistilled from alkaline permanganate with collection of the middle portion under an inert gas will suffice for most titrations. Purification by mixed-bed ion exchange also is a common technique. For solutions having a κ less than 1×10^{-3} mho cm.$^{-1}$, the conductance of water should be subtracted from that of the solution for accurate results (74). However, it should be realized that, if the impurities in the water react in any way with any of the electrolytes in solution, the corrections are more involved.

In nonaqueous conductance work, pure solvents usually have a specific conductance much less than that of water. However, the specific conductances of the nonaqueous electrolyte solutions generally are also less than those in water, so that for very dilute solutions solvent corrections are again important. At the same time, however, obtaining very pure nonaqueous solvents is quite often more difficult than obtaining very pure water.

B. HIGH FREQUENCY (OSCILLOMETRY)

1. Oscillators and Measurement of Response

Because there are many variations in oscillator design and mode of measuring response, we shall attempt to describe only their essential features. A general characteristic of an oscillator is that a feedback voltage from the tank circuit must be supplied to the input circuit of an amplifier tube in order to maintain oscillations. This feedback must be in phase with the oscillations in the input circuit. Although many oscillator circuit designs are available, they differ essentially only in the manner in which feedback is supplied. Several have been found satisfactory for oscillometry; the examples include the Clapp (8), grid-dip (Colpitts) (1,51), tuned-plate tuned-grid (27,47), crystal (38), and others (37).

In an oscillator the resonance frequency, f_r, is independent of the equivalent series or parallel resistance and is determined by the equivalent capacitance, C, and equivalent inductance, L, of the circuit as follows:

$$f_r = 1/(2\pi\sqrt{LC}) \qquad (19)$$

where f_r is in cycles per second, L in henries, and C in farads. Fig. 51.11 shows the parallel arrangement of the oscillator components. The L and C also could be arranged in series fashion, but this is little used in oscillometry and will not be discussed here.

Both L and C resist changes in alternating current to give effective resistance factors, called the capacitive reactance, $X_C = 1/(2\pi fC)$, and the inductive reactance, $X_L = 2\pi fL$. Both are 180° out of phase and equal at the resonant frequency. Assuming all the resistance, R_L, is in the coil and is small (very nearly true in practice), the impedance, Z, of the parallel circuit to alternating current is

$$Z = L/[C\sqrt{R_L^2 + (X_L - X_C)^2}] \tag{20}$$

or at resonance $Z = L/(CR_L)$. At resonance the circuit in Fig. 51.11 has the following properties: (1) the line current, I_d, is at a minimum; (2) the impedance, Z, presented to the line is a maximum; (3) the line current is in phase with the line voltage; and (4) the current, I_a, circulating in the LC tank circuit is usually much larger than the line current by an amount equal to X_L/R_L, which is referred to as the Q of the circuit, and is a power-loss factor. For more details on oscillators and their characteristics, textbooks on radio fundamentals should be consulted (72).

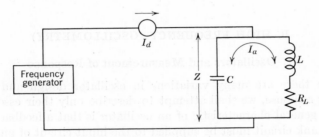

Fig. 51.11. Parallel oscillator circuit.

Figure 51.12 shows schematically the capacitance and conductance loading of an oscillator in terms of frequency and impedance. Curve 1 is with a reference sample and curve 2 is with a sample in which the change is mainly capacitive due to the higher dielectric constant of the sample. In this case, by increasing the effective capacity the resonant frequency f_r^1 is shifted to f_r^2, as indicated by equation (19). If the oscillator is not returned to this new resonance frequency, the impedance will decrease according to equation (20), and a change in current or voltage response will be observed.

A change in frequency of the oscillator may be determined by the use of beat-frequency methods, in which the working frequency is compared to that of a standard frequency and the difference is recorded (75). The frequency difference can be read directly from a frequency meter (9) or converted to a voltage that is proportional to frequency by a discriminator circuit similar to that used in "FM" radios. Also, capacity may be added or subtracted from a calibrated dial to restore the frequency to its original value (69).

Curve *3*, on the other hand, occurs when the sample contains electrolyte and provides a resistive load on the oscillator. For this case f_r is not changed to any great extent but the effective impedance is decreased. The resistance of the solution, R_S, acts essentially as a load in parallel with the

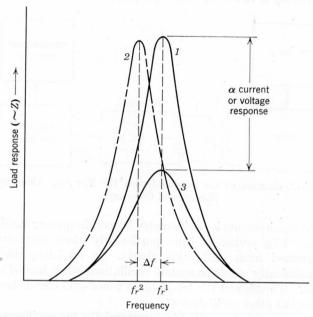

Fig. 51.12. Variation of load (impedance) and frequency for capacitance change (curves *1* and *2*) and for conductance change (curves *1* and *3*).

impedance. For this simplified situation the total impedance, Z_T, at f_r can be given by the approximate equation:

$$Z_T \approx ZR_S/(Z + R_S) \qquad (21)$$

The decrease in impedance causes I_d to increase in Fig. 51.11 and in general current or voltage changes in the plate, grid, or cathode circuits (1,13,38,47), which can be related to the concentration changes of the electrolyte.

Blake introduces the term *Q-metrics* to describe the effect of resistance on the oscillating system. This, of course, stems from the use of X_L/R_L or Q as a measure of power loss, where the smaller the ratio the greater is the power loss and the greater the line current required to supply energy to sustain oscillations.

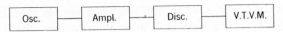

Fig. 51.13. Block diagram of Sargent's Oscillometer Model V. Key: Osc., oscillator; Ampl., amplifier; Disc., discriminator, set at 5 Mc.; and V.T.V.M., vacuum-tube voltmeter. Courtesy of E. H. Sargent and Company.

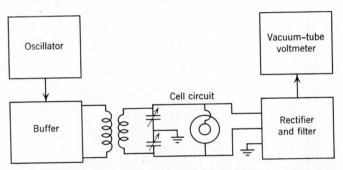

Fig. 51.14. Block diagram of the Sargent-Jensen HF Titrator. Courtesy of E. H. Sargent and Company.

One of the requirements in oscillometry is good frequency stability of the oscillator over long periods of time, particularly when concentrations are being determined from calibration charts. In addition, the oscillator should be sufficiently stable to sustain oscillations when loaded by the cell and solution. To this end the tuned-plate tuned-grid circuit has not been as satisfactory as other oscillators (8).

A few instruments are available commercially for oscillometric work. E. H. Sargent and Company, Chicago, Illinois, has marketed an instrument called the Chemical Oscillometer Model V, a block diagram of which is shown in Fig. 51.13. Capacitance or dielectric constant is the main function being measured, although titrations involving conductance changes can be performed (7,43). The instrument covers a wide range of dielectric constant from 0 to about 100 on a scale having 32,000 units. The same dial units can be used over smaller dielectric-constant ranges to give increased sensitivity (69).

E. H. Sargent and Company also markets a "Sargent-Jensen HF Titrator" (66), which is quite responsive to conductivity changes. A block diagram of this instrument is shown in Fig. 51.14. The oscillator is a crystal-controlled tuned-plate tuned-grid type, with a buffer stage inserted between it and the cell to give added stability. The cell is located in the secondary of a tuned transformer and the high-frequency voltage changes due to loading are rectified and observed on a d.-c. vacuum-tube voltmeter.

When studies require the determination of both conductance and capacitance values (39,65), the General Radio Type 821-A Twin T impedance bridge can be used.

2. Cells

The ideal geometry and location of a cell in a high-frequency apparatus will vary from one instrument to another and on the range of conductance and dielectric constant of the samples to be tested. Variables such as the thickness of cell walls and the size and spacing of electrodes must be considered in any design, as discussed in Section II-B. Usually, more than one type cell will be needed to make full use of an instrument.

Cells to be inserted in the inductance coil of the oscillator should fit snugly and extend above and below the ends of the coil. With concentrated solutions the oscillator may overload and not sustain oscillations. By using cells of smaller diameter, the loading may be reduced to a practical point.

Cells placed in the condenser part of an oscillator require that the electrode plates fit tightly against the walls either by mechanical means or with cement. The electrodes may be made of any metal to which leads may be easily attached. The cell material may be of glass or plastic or any material that is a nonconductor. For a given instrument in which small differences in dielectric constant are to be measured, cells with larger electrode areas and thinner walls are required than when a wide range of dielectric constants are to be compared. By varying the electrode-separation distance the useful concentration region of the response curves can be shifted as required (18).

3. Requirements in Use

For titration or single-measurement work the sample should always extend slightly above and slightly below (1 cm. or more) the external electrodes. Any metal parts used for stirring, titrating, or holding equipment in place should be kept either several inches from the cell or else in a rigid fixed position to avoid unwanted variations in capacity and loading effects. Temperatures should be held relatively constant, particularly when conducting solutions are involved. Where dielectric measurements are being made, temperature variation is not as important since the dielectric constant varies about 0.2% per degree for most liquids, i.e., about 10 times smaller than the temperature coefficient for conductance. Although it is possible to design cells that are thermostated with water jackets, this is quite often undesirable because of the effect of water on the measurements being made. However, low-dielectric-constant solvents can be used as the thermostating liquids, which avoids this problem to a large extent. Air thermostating is satisfactory in most cases, except when temperatures should be held to within a few tenths of a degree, such as in the determination of rates of reaction.

Of particular importance in nonaqueous work, where single measurements are being made, is the preparation and storage of water-free samples. This is especially important with samples of low dielectric constant.

IV. USES OF TECHNIQUES

A. LOW-FREQUENCY CONDUCTANCE

Because of the nonspecificity of conductance, it is not a very useful qualitative tool. On the other hand, it is quantitative for (1) a known single electrolyte in solution, or (2) for a change in the concentration of an ionic species when present in solution with other ions of constant concentration. Both conditions lead to single measurements for determining concentrations that find wide application in laboratory and process control, and the latter condition leads to the use of multiple measurements, as in conductometric titrations.

1. Conductometric Titrations

In conductometric titrations the manner of variation in the conductance of the solution prior to and after the end point is dependent on the nature of the sample, the titrant, and the particular type of reaction that these undergo. Prior to the end point the conductance may decrease, as in strong acid–base reactions. The conductance may remain the same, as in precipitation and complexing reactions, in which the ions remaining in solution have about the same conductance as those originally in solution. Thirdly, conductance may increase, as in the case of neutralization of weak or very weak acids with bases. Typical curves are shown in Figs. 51.15a, b, and c. Beyond the equivalence point the conductance generally either increases, as in Fig. 51.15b (curve 1) and c, or remains essentially constant, as in Fig. 51.15a. Special cases in which conductance decreases after an end point occur in certain complexing titrations, as indicated in Fig. 51.15b (curve 2). Conductance may decrease after an end point in a two-end-point titration, as shown in Fig. 51.16, in which acetic acid and ammonium chloride are titrated with sodium hydroxide.

The analytical chemist, in determining whether a particular species can be titrated conductometrically, is faced with the problems of (1) the chemical reactions the species will undergo, i.e., with what titrant will it re-

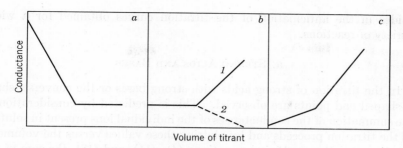

Fig. 51.15. Various forms of conductometric titration curves before and after equivalence point: *a*, strong acid with weak base; *b* (curve *1*), precipitation, $AgNO_3$ + NaCl, and (curve *2*), complexation, $Hg(NO_3)_2$ + KCN in acid solution; and *c*, very weak acid with strong base.

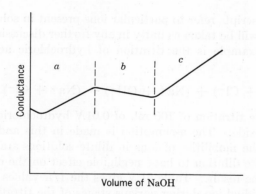

Fig. 51.16. Double end point conductometric titration curve with a decrease in conductance after the first end point. Acetic acid and NH_4Cl titrated with NaOH:

Portion *a*. $HOAc + NaOH \rightarrow NaOAc + HOH$
        b. $NH_4Cl + NaOH \rightarrow NH_4OH + NaCl$
        c.   Excess NaOH

act, and (*2*) the physical chemistry of the reaction, i.e., the differences in mobilities of the ions before and after the equivalence point, and whether dissociation, complexation, hydrolysis, etc., effects are present that would complicate the titration. Quite obviously there need be little thought given to these latter aspects in strong acid–base titrations. However, these considerations become quite important when working with slightly dissociated compounds or with mixtures in which the effects of solvent and other ions present must be taken into account. In the ensuing discussion are considered various types of conductometric titrations that may serve as guides in the anticipation of the titration curves obtained for a wider variety of reactions.

a. STRONG ACIDS AND BASES

In the titration of strong acids with strong bases or the converse, sharp V-shaped end points are observed. This is predicted by consideration of the summation of the conductances of the individual ions present in solution as the titration proceeds and by plotting these values versus the volume of the titrant. By combining equations (4), (11), and (18), the sum of the conductances may be expressed in the following manner:

$$\frac{1}{R} = \frac{1}{R_1} + \frac{1}{R_2} + \cdots = \frac{\lambda^0_1 C_1}{1000\mathbf{K}} + \frac{\lambda^0_2 C_2}{1000\mathbf{K}} + \cdots \tag{22}$$

where the subscripts refer to particular ions present in solution and $\mathbf{K}$, the cell constant, will be taken as unity in any further discussion.

A typical example is the titration of hydrochloric acid with sodium hydroxide:

$$(H^+ + Cl^-) + (Na^+ + OH^-) \rightarrow (Na^+ + Cl^-) + H_2O$$

Consider the titration of 100 ml. of $0.01N$ hydrochloric acid with $1.0N$ sodium hydroxide. The assumption is made in this and subsequent examples that the mobilities of ions in dilute solutions are close enough to those at infinite dilution to have negligible effect on the qualitative interpretation of the result. Table 51.V gives the $1/R$ values of equation (22) for each individual ion during various stages of the titration. Because of the concentrations chosen, the effects of dilution are negligible. Fig.

TABLE 51.V

Specific Conductances of Ions During the Titration of 100 ml. of $0.01N$ HCl with $1.0N$ NaOH

1.0N NaOH, ml.	Specific conductance $\times 10^3$, in mhos cm.$^{-1}$ (25°C.)					
	H^+	Cl^-	Na^+	OH^-	NaCl	Total
0.0	3.50	0.76	0.00	0.00	0.00	4.27
0.2	2.80	0.76	0.10	0.00	0.25	3.66
0.5	1.75	0.76	0.25	0.00	0.63	2.76
0.8	0.70	0.76	0.40	0.00	1.01	1.86
1.0	0.00	0.76	0.50	0.00	1.26	1.26
1.5	0.00	0.76	0.75	0.99	1.26	2.50
2.0	0.00	0.76	1.00	1.98	1.26	3.74

51.17 shows the specific conductance plotted against the volume of titrant, using the data of Table 51.V. The dashed line represents the contribution of the salt formed (NaCl) to the total conductance. The salt line becomes of interest when working with weak acids or bases, since the conductance of these solutions on titration follows the salt line (see Section IV-A-1-b). When strong acids or bases are to be titrated in the presence of salts, the curve of Fig. 51.17 would be pushed upward and the relative change in conductance would be decreased. If the salt content is very high, then inaccuracies due to small relative changes in conductances occur and the accuracy of the titration decreases.

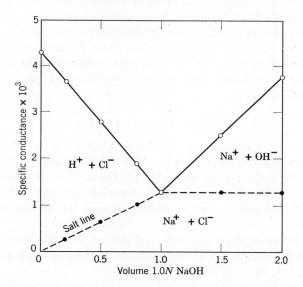

Fig. 51.17. Conductometric titration of 100 ml. of $0.01N$ HCl with $1.0N$ NaOH.

It is of only theoretical interest that the end point does not exactly coincide with the equivalence point at pH 7. This is because the hydrogen ions have a greater mobility than the hydroxyl ions and require a slight excess of base to reach minimum conductance. However, this cannot be detected experimentally.

One of the particular advantages of conductometric titration of strong acids and bases is the fact that both very concentrated as well as very dilute solutions may be titrated. Thus, solutions that are $0.0001N$ can be titrated with about the same precision as can be more concentrated solutions. However, very dilute solutions must be protected from the atmosphere so to prevent contamination from acidic gases, such as HCl or SO₂, and from basic gases, such as NH₃.

In general, conductometric titrations of strong acids and bases are not widely used because of the relative simplicity of other techniques.

Moderately strong acids and bases with pK's of 1 to 3 may be titrated with strong bases. Thus, trichloroacetic acid, $K_a = 3 \times 10^{-1}$, and dichloroacetic acid, $K_a = 5 \times 10^{-2}$, both give reasonably good V-shaped curves on titration with a strong base. Monochloroacetic acid, $K_a = 1.6 \times 10^{-3}$, and salicylic acid, $K_a = 1 \times 10^{-3}$, and other acids and bases with pK's of about 3 are sufficiently undissociated so as to give a curved line before the end point, and considerable care must be taken in locating the end point. Titration of such acids is improved in very dilute solutions because of more complete ionization or by addition of excess ammonia and subsequent titration with a strong base. An alternate approach for improving end points is to add alcohol to decrease the ionization sufficiently so that the last portion of the neutralization curve may follow the salt line, as is the case for weaker acids.

b. Weak Acids and Bases

For purposes of discussion, weak acids and bases will be defined as those having pK's over the range of 4 to 7. The theory for calculating the exact hydrogen ion or hydroxyl ion concentration for weak acids or bases is given in Chapter 12. The aspects of conductometric titrations of weak acids only will be considered, as similar considerations will apply for the titration of weak bases.

Consider, for example, the titration of 100 ml. of $0.01N$ acetic acid with $1.0N$ sodium hydroxide. The approximate conductance for a solution of a weak acid, HA, may be given by:

$$1/R = \frac{K_a^{1/2} C_{HA}^{1/2} (\lambda_{H^+}^0 + \lambda_{A^-}^0)}{1000 \mathbf{K}} \tag{23}$$

where K_a is the ionization constant of the acid. For $0.01N$ acetic acid the conductance, from equation (23), is 0.17×10^{-3} mhos cm.$^{-1}$, which is considerably lower than 4.3×10^{-3} mhos cm.$^{-1}$, the conductance of a $0.01N$ hydrochloric acid solution. Thus, the titration starts out with a fairly low conductance. As base is added, the neutralization frees acetate ion, which reduces the hydrogen ion concentration further according to the ionization constant equation, $K_a = [(H^+)(A^-)]/(HA)$. During the first several per cent of the neutralization the hydrogen ion conductance decreases more rapidly than the acetate and sodium ion conductances increase. The net result is a minimum in conductance during the first portion of the titration, after which the conductance increases and follows the salt line because of the sodium and acetate ions generated by the titration reaction. Table 51.VI gives the results of calculations for a few points of the conductometric titration of acetic acid. The specific conductance of the individual ions at

TABLE 51.VI

Specific Conductances of Ions During the Titration of 100 ml. of 0.01N Acetic Acid with 1.0N NaOH

1.0N NaOH, ml.	Specific conductance $\times$ 10³ (25°C.)					
	H$^+$	OAc$^-$	Na$^+$	OH$^-$	NaOAc	Total
0.0	0.15	0.02	0.00	0.00	0.00	0.17
0.1	0.06	0.04	0.05	0.00	0.09	0.15
0.2	0.02	0.08	0.10	0.00	0.18	0.20
0.5	0.01	0.20	0.25	0.00	0.45	0.46
0.8	0.00	0.33	0.40	0.00	0.73	0.73
1.0	0.00	0.41	0.50	0.01	0.91	0.92
1.5	0.00	0.41	0.75	0.99	0.91	2.15
2.0	0.00	0.41	1.00	1.98	0.91	3.39

the various stages of titration was calculated according to equation (22); that for acetic acid with zero ml. of titrant from equation (23). The curve obtained is shown in Fig. 51.18. In this figure the dotted line indicates the shape of the curve after the end point when ammonia hydroxide is used as a titrant. In this case the ammonium ions produced during neutralization suppress the dissociation of ammonia hydroxide so that there is very little increase in conductance beyond the equivalence point. In general, slightly sharper end points may be obtained for weak acids with a pK_a in the range of 4 to 7 when ammonia hydroxide is used as titrant, rather than a strong base. For acids with a pK_a greater than 7, ammonia hydroxide becomes unsatisfactory because hydrolysis of the salt formed produces appreciable rounding of the curve at the equivalence point. Even in the case of the neutralization of acetic acid with ammonium hydroxide there is a slight hydrolysis that, however, is not serious since straight lines before and after the end point permit accurate extrapolation of the end point.

A general rule is that satisfactory curves will be obtained when the last 25% of the neutralization follows the salt line. This occurs when the conductance of the acid equals about 1% of the conductance of the salt at 75% neutralization. Kolthoff (General References) calculates that the dissociation constant should be equal to or less than $6.7 \times 10^{-3} \times C_0$, where C_0 is the initial concentration of the acid. Thus, if a 0.1N solution is titrated,

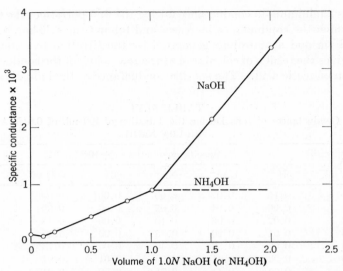

Fig. 51.18. Conductometric titration of 100 ml. of 0.01N acetic acid with 1.0N NaOH or 1.0N NH$_4$OH.

the dissociation constant should be 6.7×10^{-4} or less. In the case of acetic acid, solutions less than 0.002N will give poor end points. Similar conditions hold for weak bases being titrated with strong acids.

Very weak acids having pK_a's of 8 to 10 may be titrated with a strong base. Such acids contribute a negligible amount to the conductance and the titration follows the salt line from the start of the titration. Rounding of the curve occurs in the vicinity of the end point due to the increasing hydroxyl ion concentration from the hydrolysis of the salt. This effect becomes more serious the weaker the acid. Beyond the equivalence point the conductance curve increases more rapidly due to the excess hydroxide. Extrapolation of the initial straight portion of the neutralization line and the latter part of the excess base line give curves similar to that of Fig. 51.15c.

Acids or bases having pK values greater than 11 or 12 may not be titrated because hydrolysis increases the conductivity to such an extent during the titration that no inflection point can be observed.

A general expression developed by Kolthoff, which gives the smallest dissociation constant a very weak acid may have and still give a straight line during the first portions of the neutralization, is

$$K_a = \frac{2.6 \times 10^{-12}}{(1 - X)C} \tag{24}$$

where X is the fraction to be neutralized. Thus, in titrating a $0.01N$ solution in order to have the first 25% of the titration follow the salt line, the acid should have a K_a value of 3×10^{-10} or more. Further, equation (24) indicates it is best for very weak acids to titrate fairly concentrated solution.

It is possible to titrate such very weak species as boric acid ($K_a = 6 \times 10^{-10}$), phenol ($K_a = 1 \times 10^{-10}$), and pyridine ($K_b = 1.2 \times 10^{-9}$). The conductometric titration of phenolic material in lignins (67) is a practical application of this type of titration. Also, the conductometric titration of alkaloids, which are usually very weak bases, and their salts has been used for many years. Kolthoff has shown that codeine, atropine, and other alkaloids are titratable and that the purity of quinine or its hydrochloride salt might be determined conductometrically. In many cases alkaloid salts are more easily and more accurately determined by conductometry than by the phenolphthalein indicator method.

A very marked improvement in the shape of the titration curves for weak and very weak acids is obtained by the addition of an excess amount of a weak base such as ammonia (30). The presence of a weak base, B, shifts the equilibrium of the dissociation of the weak acid, HA, to the right.

$$HA + B \rightleftharpoons HB^+ + A^-$$

The large increase in the dissociation of the acid leads to more acute angles at the equivalence point and makes it possible to titrate acids not revealed by the usual conductometric approach. The titration with a strong base becomes one of the changes in conductance due to the replacement of the BH^+ cation by the cation of the strong base up to the end point and after the end point, an increase in conductance due to excess hydroxyl ions. There will be a slight rounding at the end point, depending on the dissociation constant of the weak base. Several weak bases can be used, such as ammonia, pyridine, ethyl amine, etc. However, because of the greater mobility of the NH_4^+ ion, ammonia is preferred. Phenol, which gives a curve similar to that of Fig. 51.15c by the ordinary procedure, gives in the presence of excess ammonia and potassium hydroxide as titrant, a curve similar to that of Fig. 51.15b. More acute angles are obtained with lithium hydroxide, since the neutralization curve decreases due to the lower mobility of the lithium ion. It is possible by using this technique to observe two inflection points for multifunctional compounds such as resorcinol, pyrogallol, and salicylic acid. An additional advantage of the use of a weak base is its ability to solubilize many water-insoluble compounds that ordinarily must be titrated in an aqueous–nonaqueous solvent, in which poorer end points are generally obtained.

c. Mixtures of Acids or Bases

When mixtures of a *strong acid* and a *moderately strong acid* ($K = 10^{-3}$) are titrated with strong base, a reasonably well-defined end point will be obtained for the total acids. However, the moderately strong acid will be sufficiently dissociated so that a portion of it will be titrated as a strong acid and the curve will be rounded at the first end point. Extrapolation of the straight-line portion on either side will give an end point that will be slightly high for the strong acid. Sometimes alcohol or another nonaqueous

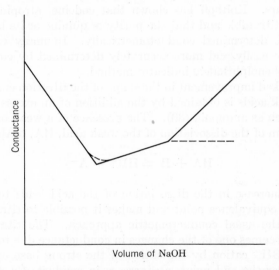

Fig. 51.19. Conductometric titration of a mixture of a strong acid (hydrochloric) and a weak acid (acetic) with NaOH or NH₄OH (*dotted line*).

solvent can be added to suppress the ionization of the weaker acid and improve the sharpness of the first end point. Section IV-A-1-f discusses the use of nonaqueous solvents for differentiating two strong acids.

For a *strong acid* mixed with a *weak acid*, two end points are obtained by titrating with a strong or a weak base. In the titration the conductivity at first decreases in a straight line, due to the neutralization of the strong acid. Then, near the first equivalence point, the weak acid will be neutralized and the conductivity increases and soon follows the salt line up the second end point, after which excess strong base increases the conductivity still further. Fig. 51.19 shows the conductivity changes taking place for the titration of a mixture of hydrochloric and acetic acids. Fig. 51.19 also shows (*dotted line*) the use of a weak base such as ammonium hydroxide for the same titra-

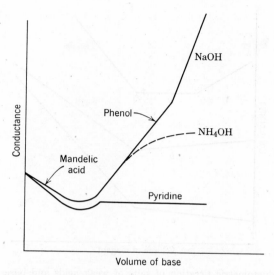

Fig. 51.20. Conductometric titration of a mixture of a moderately strong acid (mandelic, $K_a = 4.3 \times 10^{-4}$) and a very weak acid (phenol, $K_a = 10^{-10}$).

tion. This has practical use in the determination of the mineral acid content of vinegar.

The method can be used on sulfonphthaleins, in which the sulfonic acid is first titrated and then the phenolic group gives a second break in the titration curve. Oxalic acid acts as a dibasic acid.

When a *very weak acid* ($K_a = 10^{-10}$) is present with a *strong acid*, a strong base must be used for the titration if both end points are to be observed. A weak base cannot be used because the hydrolysis of the salt of the very weak acid and weak base gives indistinct end points. However, if a very weak base ($K_b = 10^{-9}$) is used as a titrant, a single end point is observed, which is for the strong acid.

The use of a very weak base as titrant is useful when a *very weak acid* is present with a *moderately strong acid*. Often the ionization of the moderately strong acid is such that a rounding at the first end point occurs when a strong base is used. In such cases it is useful to titrate first with a strong base to get total acids and then separately with a very weak base to obtain the moderately strong acid. Fig. 51.20 illustrates this for the titration of a mixture of mandelic acid, $K_a = 4.3 \times 10^{-4}$, and phenol, $K_a = 10^{-10}$, with (*a*) sodium hydroxide and (*b*) pyridine. The dotted line shows the course the titration would take with ammonium hydroxide. The first end point is obtained with pyridine and the second end point with sodium hydroxide.

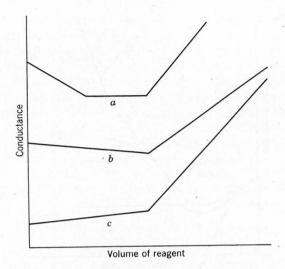

Fig. 51.21. Conductometric titration of salts of weak acids and bases: *a*, Na$_2$S with HCl; *b*, NH$_4$Cl with NaOH; and *c*, Na acetate with HCl.

A mixture of a *weak acid* ($K_a = 10^{-5}$) and a *very weak acid* ($K_a = 10^{-10}$) with careful work can be titrated conductometrically with a strong base, provided that the anions of the acids have different specific conductivities. However, since both acids will follow their salt lines, sharp breaks never occur at the first end point and the titration of mixtures of weak and very weak acids finds little application.

d. Salts of Weak Acids or Bases

Weak acids or bases are replaced from their salts by strong acids or bases, respectively. The replacement reaction is exemplified for acids by:

$$HCl + NaOAc \rightarrow NaCl + HOAc$$

and for bases by:

$$NaOH + NH_4Cl \rightarrow NaCl + NH_4OH$$

Typical titration curves are shown in Fig. 51.21. It is to be noticed that, for the titration of sodium acetate with hydrochloric acid (curve *c*), two rectilinear curves are formed, giving an easily calculated end point. As sodium acetate is titrated, the acetate ion is replaced by the chloride ion, which has a higher ionic mobility. As a result, the conductivity increases slightly until the acetic acid is completely liberated, after which the excess hydrochloric acid causes a large increase in conductance. Because of the dissociation of the acetic acid, the curve will be slightly rounded at the equivalence point but extrapolation of the straight-line portions yields correct end points. Accurate titrations can be performed on salts, for which the liberated acid has an ionization constant as large as 5×10^{-4} if the solution concentration is about $0.1N$. Where salts of polyfunctional acids are concerned, if the K_a's of the acids are sufficiently different ($\sim 10^{-5}$) for the first and second stages, two end points may be observed, as in the case of the titration of sodium sulfide with hydrochloric acid (curve a).

Replacement titrations are useful in the titration of salts of acids such as benzoates, succinates, oxalates, and phosphates. Ammonium chloride in the presence of weak acids can be determined, as indicated in Fig. 51.16, as can the ammonium content of fertilizer.

e. Precipitation and Complexation

The use of conductance in *precipitation reactions* is basically the replacement of one ion with another. The accuracy depends upon the speed of precipitate formation, upon the purity and the solubility of the precipitate, as well as upon the conductance measurement. A precipitate having a very small solubility product, K_{sp}, e.g., 10^{-12}, will contribute little to the total conductivity; whereas one with a larger K_{sp}, e.g., 10^{-6}, would contribute ions to the solution and in the vicinity of the end point would cause considerable rounding. The solubility before and after the end point is reduced because of the common-ion effect, so that extrapolation of the end portion of the curves gives reliable end points.

Kolthoff calculates that the solubility products of the precipitate should not be greater than 5×10^{-5} when titrating $0.1N$ solutions. For $0.001N$ solutions the solubility product should not be greater than 5×10^{-9}. This is based on the assumption that satisfactory curves will be obtained if at the titration midpoint the conductance arising from the soluble precipitate is no more than 1% of that of the salts. The solubility of most slightly soluble substances can be effectively reduced by adding alcohol.

At the equivalence point the contribution of the soluble portion of the precipitate to the conductance may be calculated from the following equation:

$$1/R = [K_{sp}^{1/2}(\lambda_{M^+}^0 + \lambda_{X^-}^0)]/1000K \qquad (25)$$

where K_{sp} is the solubility product and K is the cell constant. Thus, for silver chloride ($K_{sp} = 1.7 \times 10^{-10}$) the specific conductance is ($0.8 \times 10^{-6} + 1.0 \times 10^{-6}$) = 1.8×10^{-6}. For a solution of $0.001N$ silver nitrate titrated with $0.1N$ lithium chloride, this amounts to 1.6% of the total conductance at the equivalence point.   Fig. 51.22 shows the effect of the solubility of silver chloride on the end point for various silver nitrate concentrations.   The dotted lines show the actual values.

A titrant should be selected that will give the sharpest angle at the equivalence point.   Consider, for example, the determination of silver in a solution of silver nitrate.   Silver ion may be precipitated with lithium, sodium, or potassium chloride.   In all cases the nitrate concentration remains unchanged, and up to the end point lithium, sodium, or potassium ion is replacing silver ion in the solution.   From Table 51.II it is observed that the ionic equivalent conductance of lithium ion, $\lambda^0_{Li^+} = 39$, is less than that of sodium ion, $\lambda^0_{Na^+} = 50$, both of which are smaller than that of silver

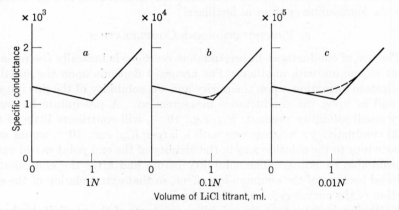

Fig. 51.22. Effect of concentration on conductometric titration curves in precipitation reactions: a, 0.01N AgNO$_3$ with 1.0N LiCl; b, 0.001N AgNO$_3$ with 0.1N LiCl; and c, 0.0001N AgNO$_3$ with 0.01N LiCl.

ion, $\lambda^0_{Ag^+} = 62$.   Thus, if either lithium or sodium chloride are used, the conductance would decrease during the precipitation of silver ion.   The use of potassium chloride, $\lambda_{K^+} = 74$, would result in an increase in conductance. The differences obtained in the angle of the end points are illustrated in Fig. 51.23.

In general, to obtain the sharpest end points possible it can be stated that (1) when a cation is being precipitated by the anion of the titrant, the titrant anion should give the most insoluble salt and have the highest mobility possible and the titrant cation should have the lowest mobility possible; and (2) conversely, when an anion is being precipitated by the cation of the titrant, the titrant cation should give the most insoluble salt and have the highest mobility possible, and the titrant anion should have

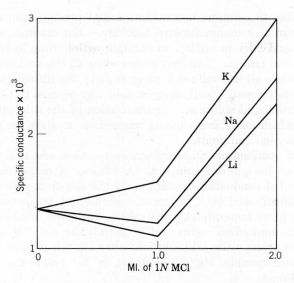

Fig. 51.23. Effect of cation on angle at end point in conductometric titration of silver nitrate with chloride ion.

the lowest mobility possible. Thus, lithium salts and acetate salts are used when possible for titrating cations and anions, respectively.

Errors in conductometric titrations of precipitation reactions can occur in several ways:

1. Contamination of electrodes due to adhering precipitate, resulting in erratic conductance measurements.

2. Occlusion of ions by precipitate, resulting in lower readings and possible curvature of curves.

3. Incomplete precipitation during the course of titration due to slowness of the precipitation reaction, resulting in incorrect end points.

4. Inconstant composition of precipitate.

The first error can be minimized by occasional tapping of the electrode to dislodge the precipitate. The second error is minimized by working in dilute solutions and working at elevated but constant temperatures. The third error can be minimized by working at higher temperature and sometimes by adding alcohol. The fourth error is difficult to overcome, particularly if two forms of the precipitate are stable under the conditions used. Solvent, temperature, and choice of titrant would be variables to explore to reduce this error. Chapter 18 will be helpful in understanding the anomalies occurring during precipitation reactions.

It is possible to combine neutralization and precipitation reactions to analyze mixtures by conductometric titration. For example, a mixture of sulfuric acid and calcium sulfate, on titration with barium hydroxide, gives two distinct end points. The first comes when all the acid is neutralized, the second when all the sulfate is precipitated; the difference equals the calcium sulfate present. Sodium hydroxide may be used to titrate certain metal salts from acid solution. Neutralization of the acid gives one end point, after which metal ions such as magnesium or silver are precipitated to yield the second end point.

The use of conductance in *complexation reactions* requires that the reaction product be a stable complex. A number of metals can be satisfactorily titrated conductometrically using the disodium salt of ethylenediaminetetraacetic acid (41). Mercuric perchlorate, when used to titrate chloride ion, gives mercuric chloride, which, although soluble, is a sufficiently stable nonionized compound to permit the use of conductometric titration. In excess nitric acid solution, when Hg^{+2} is present and titrated with potassium cyanide, Hg^{+2} is replaced by K^+ before the equivalence point, as follows:

$$Hg^{+2} + 2K^+ + 2CN^- \rightarrow Hg(CN)_2 + 2K^+$$

After the end point the conductivity decreases (Fig. 51.15b, curve 2), according to the reaction:

$$H^+ + CN^- + K^+ \rightarrow HCN + K^+$$

A number of titrants used in precipitation and complexation titrations are silver nitrate for chloride, bromide, cyanide, thiocyanide, and molybdate ions; mercuric perchlorate for chloride, acetate, and cyanide ions; lead nitrate for sulfate, sulfite, benzoate, and oxalate ions; barium acetate for sulfate, chromate, and tartrate ions; lithium oxalate or sulfate for alkaline earths and lead or sodium chromate for barium and silver ions; sodium sulfide for zinc, copper, etc.; potassium ferrocyanide for cobalt, nickel, and cadmium ions; disodium salt of ethylenediaminetetraacetic acid for copper (11), zinc, and lead (41) ions.

The above list is by no means exhaustive either in the anions or cations titrated or in the number of titrants used. The bibliography (Kolthoff and Laitinen) should be consulted for a more complete list, as well as references on conductometric titrations in precipitation and complexation reactions.

f. Conductometric Titration in Nonaqueous Solvents

Although the general instrumental techniques for conductometric titrations in nonaqueous solvents are the same as in aqueous solutions, the inter-

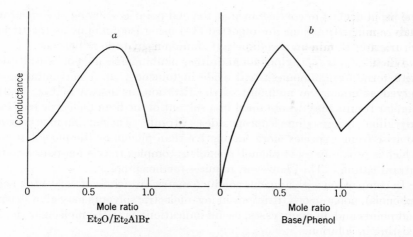

Fig. 51.24. Conductometric titrations in nonaqueous solvents: *a*, titration of Me$_2$-AlCl with Me$_2$O in MeBr solvent; and *b*, titration of phenols with Bu$_4$NOH in toluene solvent.

pretation of the curves obtained in nonaqueous solutions is, in many cases, more complex.

Acid–base titrations in aqueous solutions are easily explained on the basis of their ionization and on the free hydroxyl and hydronium ions. In non-aqueous solvents, one must consider not only the suppression or enhancement of ionization of acids or bases depending on the solvent, but also, for example, Lewis acid–base relations (28), ion-pair and triple-ion formation, hydrogen bonding, and solvent–solute and solute–solute interactions (16).

One such example is the addition of dimethyl ether (Lewis base) to dimethyl aluminum bromide (Lewis acid) in methyl bromide solvent. A maximum in the conductance occurs at about 0.7 mole of ether per mole of solute, as shown in Fig. 51.24*a*. The maximum is probably due to the fact that the solute exists in dimer form and the dissociation of this form, when complexed with ether, is greater than that of the monomolecular complex (45,54). The fact that a sharp break occurs at a mole ratio of 1:1 indicates the feasibility of conductometric titrations of aluminum halides with Lewis-type bases in a quantitative fashion. This has been verified to a certain extent by the good agreement obtained between potentiometric and conductometric results on the titration of diethyl aluminum chloride with diethyl ether in a cyclohexane solvent (14). In this case the conductance increases linearly during the latter half of the complexing reaction, decreases abruptly at the end point, and levels off shortly afterward. The reason for the rapid decline in conductance at the end point is still one of conjecture. Other similar titrations are reported (14) using isoquinoline as the titrant for triethyl aluminum and dimethyl aluminum hydride in benzene.

When 2,3,5-trimethylphenol and other nonhindered phenols are titrated with tetrabutylammonium hydroxide in toluene (15), a maximum is observed at about the midpoint of the titration, as shown in Fig. 51.24b. Similar results may be obtained in a solvent of medium dielectric constant (pyridine), using sodium isopropoxide as titrant. The maximum is believed to arise from a species more conductive than phenol or the phenolate ion, which is probably a 1:1 phenol–phenolate complex that is ion-paired to the titrant cation. This, however, requires further proof.

In comparison with aqueous conductometric titrations of very weak acids (phenols), nonaqueous titrations in low-dielectric solvents may give sharper end points and, in many cases, useful indications as to the molecular species existing in solution.

The conductometric titrations of weak bases such as 8-quinolinol and p-bromaniline are sharper in a 1:1 mixed solvent (1,4-dioxane-formic acid) than in acetic acid (56). In this mixed solvent, mixtures of weak bases may be titrated if the pK's of the protonized bases differ by one unit.

Strong acids may be titrated in glacial acetic acid using a strong base or a weak base, such as sodium acetate (44,53). In the case of sulfuric acid the dissociation of the second hydrogen is reduced sufficiently so that HSO_4^- acts as a weak acid in the glacial acetic acid. As a result, two end points are observed, the first corresponding to the formation of sodium bisulfate and the second to the formation of sodium sulfate. When hydrochloric acid is present with sulfuric acid, three end points are observed using lithium acetate as titrant (44), and both acids can be determined in one titration.

Conductometric titrations in nonaqueous solvents should prove useful for many acids or bases, including the Lewis type, when titration in aqueous solution or nonaqueous potentiometric titration fails or is inadequate.

2. Elemental Analyses Using Conductance as a Finishing Step

Conductance, since it offers a rapid method for determining concentrations of conducting species in solution, has been used effectively as a finishing step in the determination of various elements. The element, usually in some organic compound, is pyrolyzed, oxidized, or converted by some method into a gas, which is swept into an absorbing solution of known conductance. The adsorbed gas will either increase or decrease the conductance of the solution and, from suitable calibration curves, the amount of the unknown may be determined.

Thus, total sulfur in hydrocarbons is determined by burning the hydrocarbons in a wick burner and absorbing the sulfur dioxide in peroxide solution (64). The percentage of sulfur is measured as sulfuric acid from a calibration curve. The method compares favorably to the nephelometric finishing step (36). Carbon in steel (6) and organic carbon in sea water (61) are converted to CO_2, which is then determined conductometrically after absorption in a barium hydroxide solution. Nitrogen is determined in organic material by converting the nitrogen to ammonia, which is then absorbed in boric acid solution and is measured conductometrically (4).

A Conductometric Oxygen Analyzer is commercially available from Laboratory Equipment Corporation, St. Joseph, Michigan, for oxygen in steel and other metals. Oxides in the sample are reduced to carbon monoxide and converted to carbon dioxide, which is absorbed in a conductivity cell containing barium hydroxide. The change in resistance of the solution is related to the oxygen concentration. Small amounts of oxygen in titanium can be determined conductometrically after conversion of the oxygen to carbon dioxide (19).

In general, conductance may be used to determine any element occurring in a compound when that element can be converted into an ionized species and titrated as an acid or base or can undergo precipitation or complexation.

3. Determination of Critical Micelle Concentration

Salts with one ion containing a long hydrocarbon chain (soaps) exhibit properties of inorganic electrolytes at low concentrations. As the concentration of a soap increases, the conductance increases. However, a point is reached at which a discontinuity occurs and the conductance increases at a

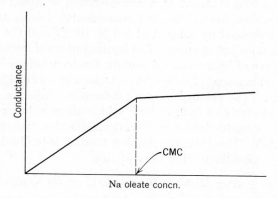

Fig. 51.25. Conductometric determination of the critical micelle concentration (CMC) of soap solutions.

slower rate. The concentration at the inflection point is called the critical micelle concentration (CMC). It is generally believed that above the CMC the long-chain ions associate to form aggregates or micelles. At the same time, the number of free ions remains essentially constant or at least does not increase in numbers as rapidly as at concentrations less than the CMC. Fig. 51.25 shows a curve that is typical for sodium oleate (26). Sodium dodecylsulfate gives a similar curve (32). Other soaps may not give straight lines before and after the CMC point. Some workers have interpreted the shape of the curves to give such information as the size distribution and molecular weight of micelles and mechanism of their formation (25,70). It would appear that other approaches to micelle formation would be needed to confirm conclusively some of the interpretations.

4. Determination of Ionization Constants

The theory of Arrhenius is approximately valid when applied to solutions of weak electrolytes. Actually, by careful consideration of all factors involved, conductance measurements may be used to obtain rather precise measurements of the ionization constants of weak acids.

Using acetic acid as an example, the limiting equivalent conductance would be: 349.8 $(\lambda_{H^+}^0)$ + 40.9 $(\lambda_{OAc^-}^0)$ or 390.7 (Λ_{HOAc}^0).

At $0.02N$ the equivalent conductance is 11.57 and the conductance ratio, α, is 0.0296. To the first approximation the dissociation constant will be 1.806×10^{-5}, as given by the equation

$$K_a = [(H^+)(OAc^-)]/(HOAc) = \alpha^2 C/(1 - \alpha) \qquad (26)$$

The value of α was obtained at a concentration of about $5.9 \times 10^{-4}N$ hydrogen and acetate ions, although it was calculated using Λ^0. The value must now be corrected by using Λ at $5.9 \times 10^{-4}N$ and the operation repeated until α does not change. The equivalent conductance can be obtained by the use of hydrogen and acetate ion-transference numbers and equivalent conductances of $0.00059N$ solutions of hydrochloric acid and sodium acetate. The value also can be determined from the conductances of the strong electrolytes hydrochloric acid, sodium chloride, and sodium acetate at this concentration by combining empirical equations, as discussed in Section II-A-5. However, the simplest method is to obtain α values by successive approximations using the equation

$$\Lambda_i = \Lambda^0 - (B_1\Lambda^0 + B_2)\sqrt{\alpha C}/(1 + Ba'\sqrt{\alpha C}) \qquad (27)$$

where Λ_i is the equivalent conductance at concentrations of αC, B, B_1, and B_2 are constants, and a' is estimated to be about 4A. Robinson and

Stokes (see bibliography) discuss the use of equation (27) in more detail and give values for the constants.

The ionization constant determined from the last α value must then be corrected for the activity coefficient, $f_\pm$, at the concentration of (αC) as follows: $K_a(\alpha^2 f^2_\pm C)/(1 - \alpha)$.

The activity coefficient may be obtained from the Debye-Hückel expression for activity coefficients (Robinson and Stokes, General References) or, alternately, K_a may be plotted versus $C^{1/2}$ and K_a extrapolated to infinite dilution. Values of K_a obtained by either approach agree with 0.3% of the potentiometric value of 1.754×10^{-4}. Shedlovsky (see bibliography) gives several ionization constants calculated from conductance measurements.

5. Determination of Solubility Products

By rearranging equation (3) and substituting $\mathbf{K}/R$ from equation (18) for κ in equation (3), the concentration of a sparingly soluble salt, MX, in solution may be determined. Thus,

$$C = 1000\mathbf{K}/(R\Lambda_{MX}) = 1000\mathbf{K}/[R(\lambda_{M^+} + \lambda_{X^-})] \tag{28}$$

where C is the concentration of the salt in equivalents per liter, $\mathbf{K}$ is the cell constant, and R is the measured resistance. For salts with low solubility products of 10^{-10} or less, the concentrations of the ions will be sufficiently low ($\sim 10^{-5}N$) that λ_{M^+} and λ_{X^-} will be very nearly equal to $\lambda^0_{M^+}$ and $\lambda^0_{X^-}$, respectively. For such salts the solubility product can be calculated directly from the conductance of a saturated solution, but with a correction for the conductance of the water (74).

For example, suppose a saturated solution of silver chloride gives a resistance of $57,000\Omega$, after correction for the contribution of water, $\mathbf{K}$ is 0.1, and ($\lambda^0_{Ag^+} + \lambda^0_{Cl^-}$) = 138.3; the concentration of silver chloride as calculated from equation (28) is $1.29 \times 10^{-5}N$. The solubility product is $K_{sp} = (Ag^+)(Cl^-) = 1.66 \times 10^{-10}$. If the soluble portion of the precipitate is not completely ionized, this approach will lead to errors.

For salts that are more soluble, the concentration of the ions becomes high enough so that the limiting ionic conductances should no longer be used and the ionic conductances at the concentration involved must be used if an accurate K_{sp} is to be determined. The $\lambda^0_\pm$'s are used first to obtain the approximate concentration and then the $\lambda_\pm$'s for that concentration are used from available data. If $\lambda_\pm$ values are not available, the technique of substitution of equivalent conductances of the cation and anion salts at that concentration may be used, as illustrated in Section II-A-5.

6. Application to Single and Continuous Measurement

a. LABORATORY USES

Conductance is one of the best methods for determining the purity of laboratory distilled water. On large distillation units a continuous recording of conductance for purity is helpful. Water purified by means of ion-exchange resins may be monitored for purity by inserting electrodes at the bottom of the ion-exchange column.

Rates of combustion of carbonaceous material to carbon dioxide may be determined by a continuous recording of the decrease in conductivity of an absorbing base solution (33,35).

It is possible to use conductance as a standardization procedure for solutions (59). For this, the calibration should be over a limited normality range and compensated for any temperature change of the solution. Determining concentrations by single conductance measurement is one of the most rapid techniques available for this purpose and is the basis of the finishing steps for elemental analysis discussed earlier.

In general, whenever a change in conductance can be related to the corresponding change in the concentration of an electrolyte, the method can be used for following composition or reaction rates.

b. INDUSTRIAL USES

Conductance measurements find wide use in industry. In some cases, a spot check on a solution is made with a dip electrode cell and meter and in other cases a continuous recording of conductance is employed. Conductance measurements are used in power plants to check the purity of steam distillate, demineralized water, raw water, and solid contents of boiler water. In the textile industry the yarn-scouring baths are tested for soda ash content. The caustic content of solutions for pretzel making and for fruit- and vegetable-peeling baths are easily measured by conductance. In the metal industries solutions in pickling baths, caustic degreasing baths, anodizing baths, and rinse baths are monitored by conductance methods. Moisture content of soils is also easily done in the field with portable instruments.

B. HIGH FREQUENCY (OSCILLOMETRY)

1. Titration of Ionic Species

The employment of external electrodes in high-frequency titrations has certain advantages over conventional conductometric methods of titration. The use of costly platinum and all the associated requirements of platinizing and washing are obviated. Undesirable catalytic effects from platinum for certain materials are not present, and polarization of electrodes and changing electrode areas due to the adherance of solid materials are eliminated.

Several acid–base, precipitation, and complexation titrations have been performed by high-frequency methods. Almost all of these depend primarily on changes in the conductance of the solution.

The following examples are indicative of the possibilities of high-frequency titrations.

In aqueous solutions the acid–base titrations include the mixture of hydrochloric and acetic acids with ammonium hydroxide (46); phosphoric acid with sodium hydroxide (50); and sodium hydroxide (11,37,47), barium hydroxide (8), and sodium carbonate (39) with hydrochloric acid. In non-aqueous solutions, the acid–base reactions are o-phthalic or benzoic acid with sodium methoxide in acetone (47); boric acid with sodium hydroxide or diethylamine in methanol (plus glycerol) (40); and salicylic, o-nitrophenol, and benzoic acid with sodium methoxide in dimethylformamide (21). The precipitation and complex-ion titrations in aqueous solutions are silver ion with chloride ion (8,47) and with thiocyanate ion (8,39); chloride or thiocyanate ions with mercuric ion (8); sulfate ion with barium chloride (57) or barium acetate (7); beryllium with sodium hydroxide (2); and oxalate with thorium nitrate (10) and the reverse titration (38). Several different metal ions can be titrated in very dilute solutions using salts of ethylenediaminetetraacetic acid (43). A titration of the oxidation-reduction reaction of permanganate and ferrous ammonium sulfate is possible (47). A more extensive bibliography is given in the literature (66).

The oscillometric titration curves may be curved in many cases, as discussed in Section II-B-3, thus necessitating taking several readings close to the end point. Although there is this disadvantage, it appears that by proper selection of concentration, frequency, cell arrangement, and type of instrument most titrations done by conventional conductometric methods can be performed by high-frequency methods. However, finding all the proper conditions is a limitation of the technique.

2. Determination of Concentrations of Nonionic Species

High-frequency measurements have been used to analyze two-component and in some cases three-component mixtures. Such analyses rely mainly on the dielectric properties of the compounds. Analysis of mixtures based on dielectric properties has been done for many years, using capacity measurements in which the electrodes are inserted in the mixture (see Chapter 52). However, the use of high-frequency techniques has the advantage of using external electrodes, thus avoiding any fouling of electrodes.

The analysis of a two-component mixture requires the use of a standard curve. If the dielectric constants of the two components are far apart, the accuracy may be better than that of most other techniques. When the dielectric constants are close together the accuracy falls off. However, even a mixture of benzene and toluene that differ by about 0.1 dielectric constant can be determined with a fair degree of accuracy if a very stable instrument is used. Hexane-benzene, acetone–water, and o- and p-xylene mixtures can be determined (60), as can an aniline–nitrobenzene mixture (75). Alcohol–water mixtures are easily analyzed (77).

Three-component mixtures can be determined if one of the components can be quantitatively removed. For example, methyl ethyl ketone, benzene, and water can be determined (76) in mixture. In this case frequency is measured before and after dehydration to obtain water, then benzene and methyl ethyl ketone are obtained from the frequency after dehydration from a working curve.

3. Application to Continuous Measurements

a. RATES OF REACTION

High-frequency techniques may be uniquely used for measuring relatively rapid rates of hydrolysis of esters (23,27,48) and neutralization of nitroparaffins (24). Polymerization reactions have been studied by high-frequency techniques (17). An essential criterion is that the change observed be an accurate indication of the corresponding change in the composition of the solution. The technique would, therefore, work well for many two-component systems but not as well on a several-component mixture in which many variables might be involved.

Recording of the response with time is possible. In the case of the hydrolysis of ethyl acetate with sodium hydroxide, values obtained of the rate constant from the recording agreed well with those obtained by other techniques (27). In this reaction the response is mainly one of conductance due to the difference in the mobilities of the hydroxyl and acetate ions.

b. ZONE DETECTOR IN COLUMN CHROMATOGRAPHY

Changes in composition of eluates from chromatographic columns may be recorded continuously (5,49,58) using oscillometric methods. The electrodes are usually placed on the sides of the outlet tube of the chromatographic column, although it would be possible to move the electrodes up and down a column and obtain a recording of the chromatographic bands. The sensitivity of the high-frequency method for detection of chromatographic zones is reduced when eluants are used containing high concentrations of buffers or electrolytes.

c. PROCESS CONTROL

In general, it is possible to follow changes in composition if the high-frequency instrument response is related to the conductance or dielectric constant properties of the desired material. The continuous monitoring of toluene in refinery streams (73) is possible with a specially designed high-frequency instrument. With the increasing use of special electronic devices in instrumenting plants, it would appear that high-frequency oscillometry with its advantage of external electrodes will find wider application in the future.

GENERAL REFERENCES

Theory of Electrolytes

Glasstone, S., *Introduction to Electrochemistry*, Van Nostrand, New York, 1942.
Harned, H. S., and B. B. Owen, *The Physical Chemistry of Electrolyte Solutions*, 2nd ed., Reinhold, New York, 1950.
Robinson, R. A., and R. H. Stokes, *Electrolyte Solutions*, Butterworths, London, 1955.
Potter, E. C., *Electrochemistry*, Cleaver-Hume, London, 1956.
Fuoss, R. M., and F. Accascina, *Electrolytic Conductance*, Interscience, New York–London, 1959.

Conductometry

Britton, H. T. S., *Conductometric Analysis*, Van Nostrand, New York, 1934.
Britton, H. T. S., "Conductometric Analysis," in W. G. Berl, Ed., *Physical Methods in Chemical Analysis*, Academic Press, New York, 1951, Vol. II, pp. 51–104.
Kolthoff, I. M., *Konduktometrische Titrationen*, Steinkopf, Dresden, 1923.
Kolthoff, I. M., and H. A. Laitinen, *pH and Electro Titrations*, Wiley, New York, 1941.
Lingane, J. J., *Electroanalytical Chemistry*, Interscience, New York–London, 1953.
Shedlovsky, T., "Conductometry," in A. Weissberger, Ed., *Physical Methods of Organic Chemistry* (Vol. I of *Technique of Organic Chemistry*), 2nd ed., Interscience, New York–London, Part II, pp. 1651–1683.

Oscillometry

Blake, G. G., *Conductometric Analysis at Radio Frequency*, Chemical Publishing Co., New York, 1953.
Reilley, C. N., "High-Frequency Methods," in P. Delahay, Ed., *New Instrumental Methods in Electrochemistry*, Interscience, New York–London, 1954, pp. 319–345.

REFERENCES

1. Anderson, K., E. S. Bettis, and D. Revinson, *Anal. Chem.*, **22**, 743 (1950).
2. Anderson, K., and D. Revinson, *Anal. Chem.*, **22**, 1272 (1950).
3. Andrews, L. W., and W. E. Martin, *J. Am. Chem. Soc.*, **60**, 871 (1938).

4. Appleton, L., *Chemist Analyst*, **42**, 4 (1953).

5. Baumann, F., and W. J. Blaedel, *Anal. Chem.*, **28**, 2 (1956).

6. Bennett, E. L., J. H. Harley, and R. M. Fowler, *Anal. Chem.*, **22**, 445 (1950).

7. Bien, G. S., *Anal. Chem.*, **26**, 909 (1954).

8. Blaedel, W. J., and H. V. Malmstadt, *Anal. Chem.*, **22**, 734 (1950).

9. Blaedel, W. J., and H. V. Malmstadt, *Anal. Chem.*, **24**, 450, 455 (1952).

10. Blaedel, W. J., and H. V. Malmstadt, *Anal. Chem.*, **23**, 471 (1951).

11. Blaedel, W. J., H. V. Malmstadt, D. L. Petitjean, and W. K. Anderson, *Anal. Chem.*, **24**, 1240 (1952).

12. Blake, G. G., *J. Sci. Instr.*, **22**, 174 (1945).

13. Blake, G. G., *Analyst*, **75**, 32 (1950).

14. Bonitz, E., *Chem. Ber.*, **88**, 742 (1955).

15. Bruss, D. B., and G. A. Harlow, *Anal. Chem.*, **30**, 1836 (1958).

16. Bryant, P. J. R., and A. W. H. Wardrop, *J. Chem. Soc.*, **1957**, 895.

17. Burrell, C. M., T. G. Majury, and H. W. Melville, *Proc. Roy. Soc. (London)*, **205**, 309, 323 (1952).

18. Clayton, J. C., J. F. Hazel, W. M. McNabb, and G. L. Schnable, *Anal. Chim. Acta*, **14**, 269 (1956).

19. Codell, M., and G. Norwitz, *Anal. Chem.*, **30**, 324 (1958).

20. Creamer, R. M., and D. H. Chambers, *Anal. Chem.*, **26**, 1098 (1954).

21. Dean, J. A., and C. Cain, Jr., *Anal. Chem.*, **27**, 212 (1955).

22. Debye, P., and E. Hückel, *Phys. Z.*, **24**, 185, 305 (1923).

23. Elving, P. J., *Discussions Faraday Soc.*, **17**, 156 (1954).

24. Elving, P. J., and J. Lakritz, *J. Am. Chem. Soc.*, **77**, 3217 (1955).

25. Evans, H. C., *J. Chem. Soc.*, **1956**, 579.

26. Flockhart, B. D., and H. Graham, *J Colloid Sci.*, **8**, 105 (1953).

27. Flom, D. G., and P. J. Elving, *Anal. Chem.*, **25**, 541 (1953).

27a. Foster, N. G., and E. S. Amis, *Z. Physik. Chem.*, N. F., **3**, 365 (1955).

28. Fritz, J. S., *Acid–Base Titrations in Nonaqueous Solvents*, G. F. Smith Chemical Co., Columbus, Ohio, 1952.

29. Garman, R. L., *Ind. Eng. Chem.*, *Anal. Ed.*, **8**, 146 (1936).

30. Gaslini, F., and L. Z. Nahum, *Anal. Chem.*, **31**, 989 (1959).

31. Gillett, T. R., *Anal. Chem.*, **21**, 1081, 1084 (1949).

32. Goddard, E. D., and G. C. Bensen, *Can. J. Chem.*, **35**, 986 (1957).

33. Goodwin, R. D., *Anal. Chem.*, **25**, 263 (1953).

34. Gunning, H. E., and A. R. Gordon, *J. Chem. Phys.*, **10**, 126 (1942).

35. Hale, C. H., and M. N. Hale, *Anal. Chem.*, **23**, 724 (1951).

36. Hale, C. C., E. R. Quiram, J. E. McDaniel, and R. F. Stringer, *Anal. Chem.*, **29**, 383 (1957).

37. Hall, J. L., *Anal. Chem.*, **24**, 1236 (1952).

38. Hall, J. L., *Anal. Chem.*, **24**, 1244 (1952).

39. Hall, J. L., and J. A. Gibson, Jr., *Anal. Chem.*, **23**, 966 (1951).

40. Hall, J. L., J. A. Gibson, Jr., H. O. Phillips, and F. E. Critchfield, *Anal. Chem.*, **26**, 1539 (1954).

41. Hall, J. L., J. A. Gibson, Jr., P. R. Wilkinson, and H. O. Phillips, *Anal. Chem.*, **26**, 1484 (1954).

42. Hamme, H. W., E. L. Grove, and J. L. Kassner, *J. Chem. Phys.*, **22**, 944 (1954).

43. Hara, R., and P. W. West, *Anal. Chim. Acta*, **11**, 264 (1954); **12**, 72, 285 (1955); **13**, 189 (1955); **14**, 280 (1956).

44. Higuchi, T., and C. R. Rehm, *Anal. Chem.*, **27**, 408 (1955).
45. Jacober, W. J., and C. A. Kraus, *J. Am. Chem. Soc.*, **71**, 2409 (1949).
46. Jensen, J. W., and A. L. Parrack, *Texas Eng. Expt. Sta. Bull.*, **92** (1946).
47. Jensen, J. W., and A. L. Parrack, *Ind. Eng. Chem., Anal. Ed.*, **18**, 595 (1946).
48. Jensen, J. W., G. M. Watson, and J. B. Beckham, *Anal. Chem.*, **24**, 1770 (1951).
49. Johansson, G., K. J. Karrman, and A. Norman, *Anal. Chem.*, **30**, 1397 (1958).
50. Johnson, A. H., and A. Timnick, *Anal. Chem.*, **28**, 889 (1956).
51. Johnson, A. H., and A. Timnick, *Anal. Chem.*, **30**, 1324 (1958).
52. Jones, G., and R. C. Joseph, *J. Am. Chem. Soc.*, **50**, 1049 (1928).
53. Kolthoff, I. M., and A. Willman, *J. Am. Chem. Soc.*, **56**, 1007 (1934).
54. Kraus, C. A., *J. Phys. Chem.*, **60**, 129 (1956).
55. Loveland, J. W., and P. J. Elving, *J. Phys. Chem.*, **56**, 250 (1952).
56. McCurdy, W. H., Jr., and J. Galt, *Anal. Chem.*, **30**, 940 (1958).
57. Milner, O. I., *Anal. Chem.*, **24**, 1247 (1952).
58. Monaghan, P. H., P. B. Moseley, T. S. Burkhalter, and O. A. Nance, *Anal. Chem.*, **24**, 193 (1952).
59. Muller, R. H., and A. M. Vogel, *Anal. Chem.*, **24**, 1590 (1952).
60. Nance, O. A., T. S. Burkhalter, and P. H. Monaghan, *Anal. Chem.*, **24**, 214 (1952).
61. Noll, C. A., and J. W. Polsky, *Tappi*, **39**, 51 (1956).
62. Onsager, L., *Phys. Z.*, **28**, 277 (1927).
63. Polsky, J. W., *Ind. Eng. Chem., Anal. Ed.*, **19**, 657 (1947).
64. Quiram, E. R., *Anal. Chem.*, **27**, 274 (1955).
65. Reilley, C. N., and W. H. McCurdy, Jr., *Anal. Chem.*, **25**, 86 (1953).
65a. Sanghi, I., D. S. Datar, and S. H. Zaheer, Jr., *J. Chem. Phys.*, **18**, 1415 (1950).
66. Sargent, E. H. and Co., *Sci. Apparatus and Methods*, **9** (No. 1) (1957).
67. Sarkanen, K., and C. Schuerch, *Anal. Chem.*, **27**, 1245 (1955).
68. Shedlovsky, T., *J. Am. Chem. Soc.*, **52**, 1793 (1930).
69. Sherrick, P. H., G. A. Dawe, R. Karr, and E. F. Ewen, *Manual of Chemical Oscillometry*, E. H. Sargent and Co., Chicago, 1954.
70. Stigter, D., *Rec. Trav. Chim.*, **73**, 611 (1954).
71. Taylor, R. P., and N. H. Furman, *Anal. Chem.*, **24**, 1931 (1952).
72. Terman, F. E., *Radio Engineering*, 2nd ed., McGraw-Hill, New York, 1937.
73. Thomas, B. W., F. J. Faegin, and G. W. Wilson, *Anal. Chem.*, **23**, 1750 (1951).
74. Washburn, E. W., *J. Am. Chem. Soc.*, **40**, 106 (1918).
75. West, P. W., T. S. Burkhalter, and L. Broussard, *Anal. Chem.*, **22**, 469 (1950).
76. West, P. W., T. Robichaux, and T. S. Burkhalter, *Anal. Chem.*, **23**, 1625 (1951).
77. West, P. W., P. Senise, and T. S. Burkhalter, *Anal. Chem.*, **24**, 1250 (1952).

Chapter 52

MEASUREMENT OF CAPACITY: ANALYTICAL USES OF THE DIELECTRIC CONSTANT

By B. W. Thomas, *Thomas Instrumentation & Research Co.*, and Richard Pertel, *University of Houston, Houston, Texas*

Contents

Contents (*continued*)

I. INTRODUCTION

Emphasis in this chapter will be placed primarily on practical utilization of the dielectric constant as a simple and direct means for the characterization and analysis of many compounds and compound types. Some attention will be devoted in passing to the basic fundamentals of the dielectric constant and to methods employed for its measurement. Dielectric constant is by no means a new or unique property. It is an electrical property possessed by all materials regardless of whether they are in the solid, liquid, or gaseous form. Dielectric constant is basically a structural property depending on the form, orientation, and arrangement of the atoms and/or molecules that constitute the substance (10,18,21,29,32,37,39,43,44, 53).

As an analytical tool, dielectric constant has the same limitation as density or refractive index. If used alone, it permits measurement of an individual compound or a compound type only in those mixtures containing two compounds or two types of compounds. For certain compound types, there is a general correlation between dielectric constant, refractive index, and density, but this is by no means true for all substances. It generally applies to hydrocarbons only, and for most hydrocarbons the dielectric constant value is approximately equal to the square of the refractive index. For most hydrocarbon types, dielectric constant increases with density and molecular weight. For many other compounds, such as nitrogen, chlorine, bromine, and, especially, hydrocarbons to which oxygen has been added, the dielectric constant decreases with density and molecular weight.

Measurement of dielectric constant is often simpler and more accurate than determinations of refractive index or density. This is especially true for the equipment required for continuous measurement, recording, and control of these properties. Compensation for temperature variations of a flowing chemical or petroleum stream is easily accomplished in equipment designed to measure dielectric constant, but this is not true for either density or refractive index. Although dielectric-constant measurement devices have been in laboratory use for many years, they have been employed to monitor and/or control dynamic chemical or petroleum processes only in the past five to ten years.   This extension of an important analytical tool has been brought about by instrumentation improvements and developments and by a continuing effort on the part of the process-control engineer to find simpler, more economical, and more appropriate ways to monitor specific properties in the control of a process.

II. THEORETICAL CONCEPTS AND FUNDAMENTAL ASPECTS OF THE DIELECTRIC CONSTANT

A. CAPACITY AND DIELECTRIC CONSTANT

When a conductor is placed in a small, direct-current electrical field, current will flow as a result of the movability of electrons or ions.   A nonconductor, or insulator, under similar conditions will not show such an effect since it does not contain charges capable of free movement.   Our discussion in this chapter is concerned with the behavior of homogeneous nonconductors in small electrical fields.

Experimentally, we can consider a parallel-plate condenser, or capacitor, in which the dimensions (area, A) of the plates are large compared to the distance, d, between them; we measure its capacitance (in e.s.u.) as the ratio of the stored electrical charges on the plates to the applied potential difference:

$$C = Q/V \qquad (1)$$

where the capacitance C is measured in farads, the quantity of electrical charge Q in coulombs, and the potential V in volts.   In principle, a capacitor may hold its charge indefinitely.   Thus, a capacitor is essentially an electrical device that will block the steady flow of electricity in a direct-current circuit.   A nonsteady flow of electricity, e.g., in an alternating-current circuit, will not be blocked by the capacitor.

A capacitor may consist of two or more surfaces that can be arranged as parallel flat plates or as a combination rod-and-cylinder arrangement. Three typical capacitors are shown in Fig. 52.1, in which a represents one pair of plates, b represents three pairs of plates, and c represents a cylindrical capacitor in which a solid rod is placed concentrically inside a cylinder.

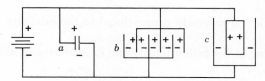

Fig. 52.1. Condenser types.

When we evacuate the space between the capacitor plates, the resulting capacitance of such a system may be designated by C_0. If we now introduce an insulator into the electrical field between the plates the capacitance of the resulting system will be increased by a factor ϵ:

$$C = \epsilon C_0 \tag{2}$$

An insulator also is called a dielectric material; hence, ϵ is called the dielectric constant of the substance in question. Rewriting equation (2), we get

$$\epsilon = C/C_0 \tag{2a}$$

From this it can be seen that ϵ is a dimensionless quantity and that its value for a vacuum, ϵ_0, must be equal to 1. It is found that for all substances $\epsilon > 1$, but for most gases it is only slightly higher than 1. Dry air at standard temperature and pressure has the dielectric constant $\epsilon_{air} = 1.0005364$ (25). Thus, for all but the most accurate measurements, air can be used as a reference instead of vacuum.

The first measurements of dielectric constants were made by Faraday and, in general, his interpretations are still valid. A good historical review is given by Partington (37).

B. ELECTRIC FIELD OF A CAPACITOR

In an evacuated parallel-plate capacitor, the intensity of the electrical field between the two oppositely charged plates is given by

$$E_0 = 4\pi\sigma \tag{3}$$

where σ is the surface density of charge per square centimeter on either the positive or the negative plate. A nonvector notation will be used in our discussion. If the space between the plates now is filled with a homogeneous dielectric material and the charge density on the plates is kept constant, the capacitance of such a system, as we have already pointed out, is increased by the factor ϵ. Therefore, the intensity of the electrical field must be decreased by the factor ϵ to:

$$E = E_0/\epsilon = (4\pi\sigma)/\epsilon \tag{4}$$

since capacitance is inversely proportional to the intensity of the electrical field.

The reduction of the field intensity can be written as a difference between the two fields:

$$E_0 - E = 4\pi\sigma - (4\pi\sigma)/\epsilon \tag{5}$$

or

$$E_0 - E = 4\pi\sigma[1 - (1/\epsilon)] \tag{6}$$

Comparing equation (3) with equation (6), we see that

$$\sigma[1 - (1/\epsilon)] = P \tag{7}$$

where P appears to be the net reduction of charge density on the plates or of the total field-producing charge. Since the charge density, σ, was kept constant on the plates between which the dielectric material was inserted, it seems that charges were induced on the surfaces of the dielectric material that are opposite to the plates they face. The net effect thus will be an apparent lowering of σ, as if a fraction of the original charges on the plates had become "neutralized." P is called, therefore, the induced polarization of the dielectric material. Since we defined σ as the surface density of the total charge per unit area, $\sigma = \sigma_{\text{total}}/A$, then P represents the total induced charge per unit area, $P = \sigma_{\text{ind.}}/A$. Multiplying the numerator and the denominator by the distance between the plates, d, we see that P is also the electric moment per unit volume for the substance in question.

Instead of comparing electrical-field intensities between charged plates under conditions of a vacuum and in the presence of a dielectric material, respectively, we can also say that, in the presence of a dielectric material, there is a total "true" charge on the plates that includes the "neutralized" portion. The field intensity induced from these total charges at charge density σ is given by

$$D = 4\pi\sigma \tag{8}$$

where D is called the electric displacement. It is obvious that in vacuum

$$D = E_0 \tag{9}$$

and, in the presence of a dielectric material,

$$D = \epsilon E \tag{10}$$

Substituting equations (7) and (9) into equation (6), we obtain

$$D = E + 4\pi P \tag{11}$$

Dividing both sides by E, we obtain

$$D/E = 1 + (4\pi P)/E \tag{12}$$

or

$$\epsilon = 1 + (4\pi P)/E \tag{13}$$

from which we obtain

$$P = (\epsilon - 1)(E/4\pi) \tag{14}$$

Thus, the induced polarization of a dielectric material can be obtained by measuring its dielectric constant at a given field intensity.

C. CLAUSIUS-MOSSOTTI EQUATION AND MOLAR POLARIZATION

Instead of showing the magnitude of the electrical-field intensity on the bulk dielectric material, we can also inquire about the magnitude of forces on individual atoms and molecules contained in the dielectric material. To this end, we shall make use of a relationship found by Mossotti (30) and by Clausius (4), which expresses the field at the center of a sphere. Such a field can be calculated exactly for macroscopic systems. For molecular systems, the assumption will be made that each molecule occupies a small sphere. The error can be shown to be insignificant when, in the absence of an external field, the molecules in the dielectric material are oriented at random. The polarization of a single molecule, α_0, under these conditions can be shown to be connected to the dielectric constant by

$$(\epsilon - 1)/(\epsilon + 2) = (4\pi/3)N_1\alpha_0 \tag{15}$$

where N_1 is the number of molecules per cubic centimeter. Multiplying both sides of the equation by the molar volume, M/ρ, where M is the molecular weight and ρ is the density of the substance, we obtain the molecular Clausius-Mossotti formula:

$$(\epsilon - 1)/(\epsilon + 2)(M/\rho) = (4\pi/3)N\alpha_0 = P_M \tag{16}$$

where N is Avogadro's number and P_M is the molar polarization.

From the above equation, it is obvious that both α_0 and P_M have the dimensions of volume.

At this point we should examine the polarization of molecules in more detail. Since all matter consists of positive nuclei surrounded by negative electron clouds, we can distinguish three different types of reversible polarization when an electric field is applied:

1. Electronic polarization, P_E, in which the electrons will be displaced with respect to the nuclei toward the positive pole of the electric field.

2. Atomic polarization, P_A, in which, because of the electron-cloud displacement, the nuclei also will be displaced with respect to each other.

3. Orientational polarization, P_O, in which, because of permanent dipole moments of molecules, the external field will tend to orient the molecules along the direction of the lines of force.

The first two polarizations will give a temporary or induced dipole moment to the molecule as long as the field is applied.   The total molar polarization, P_M, is given by the sum of these three polarizations:

$$P_M = P_E + P_A + P_O \tag{17}$$

D. TIME-DEPENDENT ELECTRIC FIELDS

Thus far, we have discussed dielectric material in a static or direct-current field.   Consider now that the charge densities on the plates, and hence the electric field between them, are functions of time.   The most commonly used field for this purpose is a periodically changing one in which the electric-field intensity is given by

$$E = E_0 \cos \omega t \tag{18}$$

and in which E_0 is independent of the time, t, ω is the angular frequency, and $\omega/2\pi$ is the frequency in cycles per second, ν.

A dielectric material also will show polarization in this case, and displacement of electron clouds and nuclei with respect to each other will show some inertia toward the field change.   At low frequencies this will be unimportant, and the molecules are capable of oscillating in phase with the periodically changing field.   The dielectric constant, ϵ, will remain constant under these conditions.   As the frequency of the field increases, the molecules will eventually begin to lag in the attainment of equilibrium. This lag is commonly called relaxation.   There will be a decrease in polarization and in the value of ϵ.   The frequency range at which this occurs is called the anomalous dispersion region.   The relative extent of the electronic, atomic, and orientational polarization will be dependent on the frequency of the alternating field.

Thus, inertia of electrons is very small and the polarizing distortion of electron orbits is capable of following the oscillating field to high frequencies in the ultraviolet.   The atomic polarization, P_A, is considerably slower, due to the heavier nuclear masses, and it is capable of following the oscillating field only up to the infrared frequencies.   Atomic polarization is usually comparatively smaller than the electronic contribution and constitutes about 5 to 15% of the P_E.   The third polarization, which is that due to the orientation of permanent dipoles in molecules, P_O, is fairly slow, corresponding to the frequency of microwaves and radio waves.   This last process will be opposed by the thermal motion of the molecules and, hence, P_O decreases as the temperature increases.

The general dependency of the polarization upon frequency may be seen in Fig. 52.2.   A similar graph is obtained when the dielectric constant,

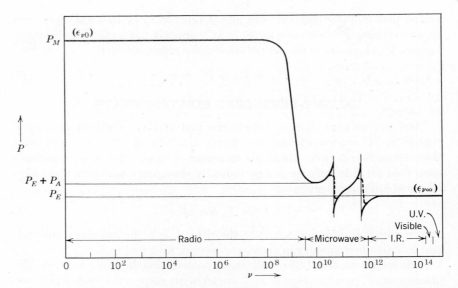

Fig. 52.2. Schematic representation of dependence of total polarization of a molecule with permanent dipole moment upon frequency ranging from radio waves through the ultraviolet region. Arbitrary absorption or anomalous dispersion regions are indicated.

ϵ_ν, or the refractive index, n_ν^2, is plotted against frequency; on such a plot we have the value for the optical (or high-frequency) dielectric constant, $\epsilon_{\nu\infty}$, at one end of the graph and the static (or low-frequency) dielectric constant, ϵ_{ν_0}, at the other end.

E. DIPOLE MOMENTS

The temperature dependency of orientational polarization, which is not explicitly expressed in the Clausius-Mossotti equation and is inherent in the total polarization, led Debye (6) to express the total molecular polarization as

$$P_M = (\epsilon - 1)/(\epsilon + 2)(M/\rho) = (4\pi/3)N[\alpha_0 + (\mu^2/3kT)] \qquad (19)$$

where k is the Boltzmann constant, T is the absolute temperature, and μ is the permanent dipole moment. Dipole moments are measured in Debye units, which are multiples of 10^{-18} e.s.u. The other symbols have already been defined.

From equations (17) and (19) we obtain

$$(4\pi/3)N\alpha_0 = P_E + P_A \qquad (20)$$

and

$$(4\pi/9kT)N\mu^2 = P_O \tag{21}$$

$P_E + P_A$ in equation (20) is called the induced polarization, P_i.

According to Maxwell (27), in substances whose magnetic susceptibilities are very close to unity—which includes almost all transparent materials—the dielectric constant, ϵ, and the refractive index, n, are related by

$$\epsilon_\nu = n_\nu^2 \tag{22}$$

where the subscript ν denotes that they must be measured at the same frequency as the field. Substituting this value into equation (16), we obtain the Lorentz–Lorenz equation (Lorentz (23); Lorenz (24)) for the molar refraction:

$$R_M = [(n^2 - 1)/(n^2 + 2)](M/\rho) = (4\pi/3)N\alpha_0 \tag{23}$$

The refractive index is measured in the range of the so-called optical frequencies, at which only electronic and atomic polarizations occur. Therefore, equation (23) can be used to calculate $P_E + P_A$:

$$P_E + P_A = [(n^2 - 1)/(n^2 + 2)](M/\rho) \tag{24}$$

The total molar polarization may be obtained from the dielectric constant measurement in the microwave or radio-wave region by the use of equation (19) at the same temperature at which the molar refraction was obtained. This will permit the determination of the dipole moment of the molecules in question. The dipole moment of a diatomic molecule is directed along the length of the bond. In a polyatomic molecule we can measure only the resultant dipole moment obtained from the vector addition of the individual bond moments. The calculation of dipole moments for polyatomic molecules from individual bond moments is possible, but should be used as an approximation since many discrepancies exist in the numerical values for the bond moments.

Since P_A can occur in the infrared, it is necessary to obtain refractivity data in that region. This poses experimental difficulties. For qualitative purposes, one may include an estimate of 5 to 15% of P_E for the value of P_A, but for more quantitative work it is necessary to calculate it from vibrational infrared absorption frequencies, ν (5):

$$P_A = N/9\pi \sum_i [e_i^2/(m_i\nu_i^2)] \tag{25}$$

Here e is the effective charge, m is the reduced mass, and the summation is carried out over all the vibrational degrees of freedom, i.

Another method that will permit the calculation of resultant molecular dipole moments makes direct use of equation (19). Since P_E and P_A are seen to be independent of temperature, we can measure molar polarization, P_M, at different temperatures and plot it against $1/T$. A straight line will be obtained whose slope will permit the calculation of the dipole moment and whose intercept will give $P_E + P_A$. This method is very accurate but it can be used only when the molecule is polar, i.e., with an associated permanent dipole moment, and when the latter is constant with respect to temperature.

In using the Debye equation, certain restrictions should be kept in mind. The predicted linear dependency between the total molar polarization and the reciprocal of the absolute temperature is expected to apply only when the polar molecules are interacting with the applied field and not with each other. This is realized when the polar molecules are sufficiently separated from each other. Thus, the Debye equation is applicable to gas-phase and dilute-solution studies, in which, in the latter case, the polar substance is diluted by a nonpolar solvent. But even under these conditions discrepancies sometimes can be found between measurements in the gas phase and the dilute solutions, indicating that Debye's formula is useful as a first approximation only. An extension of Debye's theories that is in better agreement with experimental observations has been presented by numerous scientists. Notable contributions to this work have been made by van Arkel and Snoek (52), Onsager (36), and Kirkwood (19).

In principle, however, we are in a position to elucidate structures of polar compounds by determining their dipole moments, and in instances in which the latter are known we can use the dielectric constant measurements for chemical analysis. Thus, the purity control of nonelectrolytes and the analysis of binary, and sometimes even multicomponent, mixtures may be solved by these methods.

Most molecules that contain oxygen atoms, as well as the general classification of halogen compounds, have large permanent dipole moments and exhibit strong dielectric properties. The presence of permanent dipole moments is responsible for the dielectric effects that are of interest to the analytical chemist, and these embrace a major portion of this chapter. Such effects have been found to be measured most easily and satisfactorily in the frequency range of 1 to 10 million cycles per second.

F. SOLUTIONS AND MIXTURES

In a dilute solution of a polar substance and a nonpolar solvent, the dipoles are sufficiently separated from each other and we may use the Debye equation. Under these conditions, the individual polarizations are, as an approximation, independent of each other, and the total molar polarization may be written as (7):

$$P_{12} = [(\epsilon_{12} - 1)/(\epsilon_{12} + 2)][(x_1 M_1 + x_2 M_2)/\rho_{12}] = x_1 P_1 + x_2 P_2 \quad (26)$$

where x is the mole fraction and the subscripts 1 and 2 denote the solvent and solute, respectively; hence subscript 12 refers to the mixture of 1 and 2. In the case of dilute solutions, ρ_{12} approaches ρ_1 in the limit, and the density of the solvent may be substituted as a good approximation.

Since

$$x_1 + x_2 = 1 \quad (27)$$

we may write

$$P_{12} = (1 - x_2)P_1 + x_2 P_2 \quad (28)$$

from which

$$x_2 = (P_{12} - P_1)/(P_2 - P_1) \quad (29)$$

Thus, if the total molar polarizations of the pure components and the mixtures are known, we can use this to calculate the composition of the mixture from the dielectric constant measurements. Similarly, if the composition is known, we can calculate the molar polarization of the solute. To this end, we plot P_2 vs. x_2 and extrapolate the resulting curve to infinite dilution. This will have eliminated any possible dipole interactions in the solution, and the molar polarization at infinite dilution, $P_{2\infty}$, now can be used to calculate the dipole moment of the polar solute (45):

$$\mu = 0.01281 \times 10^{-12}[(P_{2\infty} - R_{M2})T]^{1/2} \quad (30)$$

where R_{M2} is the molar refraction of the solute and the measurements were all done at the same temperature.

The dielectric constant of the binary mixture, ϵ_{12}, is, in general, a function of composition. A linear correlation,

$$\epsilon_{12} = y_1 \epsilon_1 + y_2 \epsilon_2 \quad (31)$$

where y designates the volume fraction of a given component, is in most cases not to be expected. There are, however, numerous empirical formulas to account for specific cases. A number of these are presented by Oehme (34). For practical purposes it is found to be expedient to use calibration curves for the system to be analyzed.

To analyze for multicomponent systems, we need, in principle, $(n - 1)$ different measurable properties to determine n components. For systems with three components, we can use the dielectric constant and the density

or the refractive index and evaluate the data with the help of a calibration
diagram in a triangular coordinate system. In general, the measurable
properties should be so chosen as to result in calibration-curve families
that intersect approximately at right angles. This will minimize the error
in determining compositions of unknown systems with the help of these
graphs. Oehme (35) presents an example for the system methanol–
isopropanol–water, in which the dielectric constant and the density were
measured at 20°C.

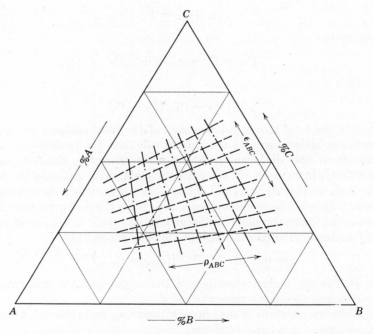

Fig. 52.3. Calibration diagram of a hypothetical three-component system (A, B,
and C). The dielectric constants, ϵ_{ABC}, and densities, ρ_{ABC}, of various concentrations of
the three components have been used as measurable properties.

Figure 52.3 will illustrate the principle of this method for three hypothetical components, A, B, and C. Each apex of the triangle is taken as
100% of the component with which it is labeled. Superimposed on this
triangular diagram are experimentally found calibration curves of the
dielectric constant and the density for different compositions.

The subscripts on the ϵ and ρ indicate different numerical values in this case. An unknown mixture can be determined by finding the intercept of the measured dielectric constant and the density curve obtained at the same temperature.

For practical application, dielectric constant can be used effectively for determining compound types if only two types are present and if their average values are sufficiently different. Furthermore, if it is known that a given component in a complex mixture possesses a dielectric property considerably different from all other components, and all the other compounds have essentially the same dielectric property, the key compound can be measured with reasonable reliability. A good example of this application is the measurement of toluene only in admixture with paraffins and naphthenes, all within a narrow boiling range (46).

A requirement for accurate analyses of mixtures by dielectric constant is that all components of the mixtures be completely miscible with each other. For completely miscible liquids, the dielectric constant of the mixture is equal to the volumetric sum of dielectric constants for the various components. For example, using equation (31) we have for a mixture $\epsilon_{12} = y_1\epsilon_1 + y_2\epsilon_2 + \ldots$, where y_1 is the volume fraction of component 1 and ϵ_1 is the dielectric constant for component 1, etc.

Suppose, for example, that it is desired to analyze a mixture of toluene ($\epsilon_1 = 2.379$) and benzene ($\epsilon_2 = 2.284$) by measurement of dielectric constant. Suppose further that the mixture is found to have a dielectric value of 2.350 by means of a suitable measuring device. From the above equation we have 2.350 = volume fraction of toluene × 2.379 + volume fraction of benzene × 2.284, or 2.350 = 2.379 (y_1) + 2.284 (1.00 − y_1). Solving for y_1, we have $y_1 = (2.350 − 2.284)/(2.379 − 2.284) \times 1.00$, or $y_1 = (0.066/0.095) \times 1.00 = 0.695$ volume fraction of toluene. Hence, 1.00 − $y_1 = 0.305$ volume fraction of benzene. The accuracy of the above analysis is plus or minus 1% toluene (or benzene) for an error of plus or minus 0.001 in the dielectric-constant measurement of the mixture. If the dielectric-constant measurement error is no larger than plus or minus 0.0001, then the analysis is accurate to plus or minus 0.1% toluene or benzene. These accuracies assume that the dielectric constant data used for pure toluene and benzene are correct to three decimal places and that temperature effects are negligible.

For known miscible liquids or for liquids absorbed in solids, the above method of computation does not apply. In the measurement of water in water–oil mixtures, in which oil is the continuous phase and water is in the form of small spheres, the water contribution toward an increase in dielectric constant is quite small. On the other hand, if water is mixed with alcohol or acetone, in which it is soluble, its contribution toward the dielectric constant of the mixture is large and can be handled by the volumetric formula above.

For oil and water emulsions, the dielectric constant increases about 3% for each 1% of water added to the mixture (15). This is true only in the range of zero to 50% water in which oil is the continuous phase. Above 50% water, the water becomes the continuous phase and there is a large increase of the dielectric constant of the mixture. Addition of 1% water to an oil whose dielectric constant is 2.50 will increase the dielectric constant of the oil mixture to 2.575. If the two were normally miscible liquids, the dielectric constant would be 99% of 2.50 plus 1% of 80 = 3.28. At a 10% water content in the same oil, the dielectric constant of the mixture is actually only 3.347, and addition of another 1% water increases the dielectric constant to only 3.449.

Thus, it is seen that for nonmiscible liquids analysis methods depend very largely on development of a correlation between measurement of dielectric constant and independent analytical methods for composition determinations.

For the measurement of water in paper, a special technique involving several electrodes and a spray-type electrical field is required (15). In general, it has been found that 1% water in paper will cause a 6 to 20% increase in dielectric constant in the range of zero to 20% water. In measuring the dielectric constant of conducting liquids or electrolytes, special precautions are required to prevent conductivity from overshadowing dielectric effects. Obviously, a conducting liquid will produce a short between the plates of a condenser; hence, it is necessary to insulate the plates. Use of such insulating films makes measurement of the dielectric constant for a conducting liquid possible but, at the same time, it makes troublesome corrections and modifications of the circuit necessary, in order to obtain a linear function between composition and dielectric constant. This is particularly true in the application of high-frequency circuitry to aqueous solutions having unusually high dielectric values (16).

G. BASIC MEASUREMENT TECHNIQUES

The basic method for measurement of dielectric constant is concerned with determination of the capacitance of a condenser in which the material in question constitutes the medium separating the plates. Capacitance can be measured in terms of the frequency of a standard oscillator in which an inductance is in series with the capacitance. An equation relating frequency, inductance, and capacitance for a resonant, oscillating, electrical circuit is:

$$f = \frac{1}{2}\pi \sqrt{LC} \tag{32}$$

where f is frequency in cycles per second, L is inductance, and C is capacitance. A simple circuit to which this equation applies is shown in Fig. 52.4, where the capacitance, C, is made up of a variable known capacitance, C_v, and an unknown measurement-cell capacitance, C_x. Since C_v and C_x are connected in parallel, the total capacitance C is equal to $C_v + C_x$. The capacitance C_x of the measurement cell depends upon its physical dimensions as outlined above and the dielectric constant of the material separating its plates.

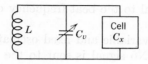

Fig. 52.4. Oscillating circuit.

Physically speaking (47), the capacitance of the parallel-plate condenser can be expressed as follows in micromicrofarads:

$$C = (0.884\epsilon A N)/D \tag{33}$$

where A is the plate area in square centimeters, D is the separation distance between adjacent plates in centimeters, N is one less than the number of plates, and ϵ is the dielectric constant of the separating medium between the plates. For a cylindrical condenser, Fig. 52.1c, the formula becomes:

$$C = 0.2416\epsilon[L/\log_{10}(r_1/r_2)] \tag{34}$$

where C is capacitance in $\mu\mu$f., L is the inside length, in cm., r_1 and r_2 are outer and inner radii respectively, of annular space, in cm., and ϵ is the dielectric constant.

If the physical size, shape, and distance between the condenser plate are held fixed, capacitance is a linear function of the dielectric material between the plates. As the cell capacitance, C_x, is increased by an amount ΔC_x as a result, for example, of an increase in dielectric constant of the filling material, the variable known capacitance, C_v, must be reduced by a corresponding amount, ΔC_v, in order to maintain a constant frequency in the oscillating circuit. Thus, it is clear that the frequency of an oscillating circuit is coupled with and depends upon the dielectric constant of the separating material.

Numerical values of the dielectric constant can be measured in terms of frequency shift of a sensitive oscillator or of the capacitance that is required in parallel with the measurement cell to restore the original frequency. In either case, a general circuit of the type shown in Fig. 52.5 can be used for such measurements (46). This apparatus can be employed to measure (*1*) the change in frequency of a variable-frequency oscillator or (*2*) the capacitance required to restore frequency in a variable-frequency oscillator. A variable-frequency oscillator usually consists of a vacuum tube, an inductance coil, a variable known capacitance, and a cylindrical capacitance-measurement cell. Signals from this oscillator are mixed with the signal from a crystal-controlled oscillator and are passed to a mixer oscillator. The mixer oscillator will, in turn, supply an output signal to a recorder and meter equal to the beat frequency or difference between the two input circuits.

If frequencies of the variable and fixed oscillators are equal, the mixer output signal is zero. No signal is sent to the frequency meter and no

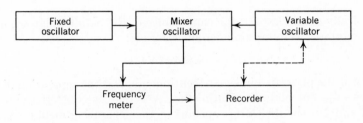

Fig. 52.5. General capacitance-measuring circuit.

deflection is indicated on the recorder. As dielectric constant of the material in the measuring cell increases, capacitance in this cell increases and causes a frequency decrease in the measurement-circuit oscillator in accordance with equation (32). This difference frequency is arranged to send a positive signal to the frequency meter and to drive the recorder up the scale in proportion to the change in dielectric constant of the material in the measuring cell.

In industrial-measurement circuitry, this general principle is employed, but in most cases the recorder operates to maintain a zero signal from the mixer oscillator (46). Hence, as dielectric constant of a flowing stream changes, the recorder moves up or down the scale to add or subtract capacitance to the measuring circuit to counterbalance the signal caused by a change in dielectric constant. This deflection of the recorder can be calibrated for direct measurement of change in dielectric constant for the flowing material.

III. PRACTICE OF MEASURING: METHODS AND EQUIPMENT

Because of the many ways in which measurement of dielectric constant and capacitance have been applied successfully, in both laboratory and industrial processes, there are many variations in arrangement and design of high-frequency dielectric equipment (32,39,44). In practically all cases, use is made of an oscillating circuit with a frequency in the range of 1 to 10 megacycles per second.

A. APPARATUS ARRANGEMENTS

1. Foxboro Capacitance Dynalog

The most widely used instrument for continuous measurement and recording of capacitance is the Foxboro Capacitance Dynalog (9,28). A simplified block diagram of the dynalog instrument is shown in Fig. 52.6. It

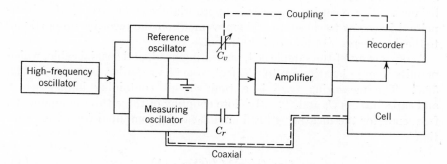

Fig. 52.6. Foxboro Capacitance Dynalog.

consists of a high-frequency oscillator and a sample cell connected by a coaxial cable, a measuring head, reference and measuring circuits, reference and variable condensers, an amplifier, and a recorder.

The crystal-controlled, high-frequency oscillator furnishes a 1.6-Mc. a.-c. voltage with 60-cycle amplitude modulation to both the reference and measuring circuits. Output voltages from these circuits pass identical radio-frequency detectors and the 1.6-Mc. frequencies are converted to 60-cycle voltages without loss of power. The 60-cycle voltages from the reference and measurement detectors are fed to the variable condenser, C_v, and the reference condenser, C_r, respectively. The output signal from these condensers represents a mixture of the two 60-cycle voltages and is

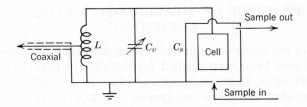

Fig. 52.7. Measuring head and sample cell.

sent through a voltage amplifier, a phase detector, and a power amplifier
to the recorder dynapoise drive.

In a balanced condition, the reference and measurement-detector output
voltages are equal, the dynapoise drive is in balance, and the recorder pin
remains stationary. If a d.-c. increase occurs in the flowing sample, the
output reference and measurement voltages are no longer equal and, as a
result of this imbalance, the dynapoise drive moves the variable condenser C_v to the extent and in such a direction as may be required to restore
balance. The recorder pin arm is appropriately connected to the dynapoise drive so as to cause up-scale movement on the recorder proportional
to the d.-c. increase of the flowing stream.

Arrangement of the sample cell, measuring head, and coaxial cable, which
permits remote location up to 517 feet from the recorder, is shown in Fig.
52.7. The measuring head is a tank circuit containing inductance L
and capacitances C_v and C_s. By close coupling of these three components,
frequency for the measuring-head circuit can be computed from the equation

$$f = (1/2\pi)\sqrt{L(C_v + C_s)} \tag{35}$$

Energy of oscillation in the measuring head is supplied by the coaxial cable,
which, in turn, reflects a frequency signal to the dynalog circuitry in the
recorder.

2. Hallikainen-Shell

Another d.-c. instrument designed primarily for operation on flowing
streams is the Hallikainen-Shell (12,40). A block diagram of this apparatus
is shown in Fig. 52.8. It includes a constant-frequency oscillator, sample
cell, variable condenser, amplifier, balancing motor, and signal transmitter.
One basic difference between the Hallikainen-Shell and Foxboro units is
that the Hallikainen does not permit remote location of the sample cell.
The crystal-controlled oscillator employs only one vacuum tube and has a

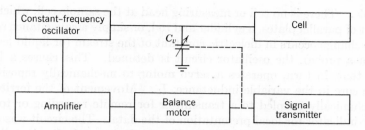

Fig. 52.8. Hallikainen-Shell dielectric constant meter.

resonant frequency of 7 Mc. An inductance coil in the plate circuit of the vacuum tube oscillates in resonance with the sample cell and the variable capacitance, C_v. At resonance conditions, an increase in capacitance due to a change in d. c. of the stream, causes a rapid increase in plate current and cathode voltage. By feeding a fixed reference voltage and a portion of the variable cathode voltage into a servo amplifier, it is possible to employ a motor-driven variable capacitance, C_v, to retain resonance even with a d.-c. change of the sample. A shaft on the variable capacitor actuates a pneumatic transmitter that, in turn, provides an air signal to the remote recorder. Adjustments in plate spacing and/or the stator position in the variable condenser, C_v, permit changes in instrument range or zero settings.

3. Instruments, Incorporated

A third type of d.-c. meter is manufactured by Instruments, Incorporated (16,17). A simple sketch of this apparatus is shown in Fig. 52.9. It consists of an oscillator with variable inductance, L_v, coaxial cable and cell amplifier, servo motor, and recorder. The oscillator is the standard Hartley type and is crystal-controlled to a frequency of 3.5 Mc. A cathode-follower amplifier is used between the balanced bridge and the oscillator and a coaxial cable makes remote location of the sensing element

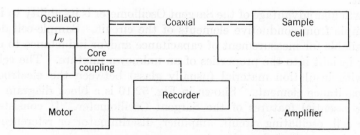

Fig. 52.9. Instruments, Inc., dielectric constant meter.

possible. There is no coil or measuring head at the sample cell, which may consist of parallel plates, a cylinder and rod, or simply a capacitance rod.

If a change occurs in dielectric constant of the stream (or liquid level, in case of a probe), the oscillator circuit is detuned. This causes a bridge upset that, in turn, operates a servo motor to mechanically reposition a ferrite core in the variable inductance, L_v. Movement of the ferrite core is mechanically coupled to a transmitter for remote recording or to a recorder-indicator for local presentation of the data. The circuit was developed by Gulf Oil Co. and has been used extensively on pipeline installations for the measurement of sediment and water in crude oil. It also has been used successfully in liquid-level and interface service by means of simple capacitance probes.

4. Sargent Oscillometer

A fourth apparatus worthy of mentioning is the laboratory Sargent Oscillometer (42). It represents development work at Louisiana State University and the A & M College of Texas. Although original efforts were

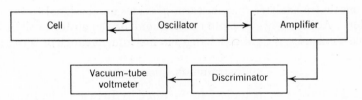

Fig. 52.10. Sargent Oscillometer.

directed toward chemical titrations, the Sargent Oscillometer has found use in the study of a wide variety of organic and inorganic chemicals. It is equally suited for measurement of conductivity or dielectric constant, since these properties contribute to the capacitance, resistance, or energy loss of a circuit.

A particular advantage of the Sargent Oscillometer is its ability to isolate the sample from conductive elements of the circuit. Sample-cell designs are available for measurement of capacitance and/or inductance to obtain greater insight into the properties of an unknown mixture. The cells are built with insulation material (usually glass) between the electrodes of the capacitance elements. Shown in Fig. 52.10 is a block diagram representing essential features of the Sargent Oscillometer. It consists of a sample cell, oscillating circuit, amplifier, discriminator or reference oscillator, and a vacuum-tube voltmeter.

High-frequency signals from the measurement oscillator are amplified and compared with a constant frequency of 5 Mc. from a discriminator circuit.   When these two frequencies are matched precisely, output of the vacuum-tube voltmeter drops sharply to zero.   The oscillator contains a high-precision variable capacitance having a range of 1000 dial units and a bank of multiple-selector capacitors to obtain a total scale of 0 to 32,000 units.   This provides measurement of dielectric constant in the range of 1 to 100; correct matching of two circuits is indicated by a zero reading of a null-indicator meter in the vacuum-tube voltmeter circuit.

5. Sun Oil Dielectric Meter

Although a d.-c. meter developed by Sun Oil Company is not being marketed, its ability to make highly precise measurements warrants its inclusion in this Treatise (41).   A block diagram of the apparatus is shown

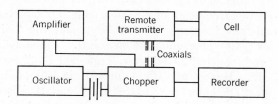

Fig. 52.11. Sun Oil Co. dielectric constant meter.

in Fig. 52.11.   The remote transmitter and sample cell are mounted at the stream, which may be one mile from the other circuitry.   Basic parts of the instrument include a sample cell, transmitter, chopper, amplifier, oscillator, and recorder.

Operation of the Sun Oil meter is as follows: low-frequency voltage is chopped by means of a polarized relay superimposed on a high-frequency voltage and is fed into a remote transmitter by means of coaxial cables. Diodes in the transmitter pass the low-frequency voltage alternately to a reference condenser and a measurement-cell capacitor. The amplifier sees only the r.-f. voltage, which is a function of the capacitance difference between the reference and measurement cells.   Output from the amplifier is rectified and sent alternately to two integrating condensers by the same chopper mechanism used to control the low-frequency voltage.   Hence, the charge on one integrating condenser is proportional to the remote reference capacitor whereas that on the other condenser depends on the dielectric constant of the sample.   Amplitude control is built into the r.-f.

oscillator for circuit stabilization, and recorder zero and span are resistance controlled. Output voltage from the integrating condensers is proportional to the capacity difference in the sample cell and reference condenser, and this d.-c. voltage passes directly into the recorder. Span adjustment can change this proportionality factor over a wide range without changing the recorder zero.

6. Other D.-C. Meters

There also are a number of commercial instruments available in Germany for the measurement of dielectric constant and dielectric loss. The Wissenschaftlich-Technische Werkstätten in Weilheim/Obb. produces a number of instruments capable of measurements in the range from 30 cycles to 6000 megacycles per second in the microwave range. Among this firm's instruments are the "Multi-Dekameter, Type DK-06," for the frequency range of 100 kc. to 12 Mc.; the "NF-Dekameter, Type DK-05," for the frequency range of 30 cycles to 100 kc.; the "Dekameter, Type DK-03," for the constant frequency of 1.8 Mc.; the "Dipolmeter, Type DM-01," for the constant frequency of 1.8 Mc.; and the "Ultra-Hygrofix, Type Hy-5," for water determination in solids. Franz Küstner Nachf., Dresden A21, produces the "DK-Meter, Type 600 RL," for the constant frequency of 7 Mc. Haardt und Co., G.m.b.H., in Köln, Gürzenichstrasse 21, produces the "Dielkometer, Type CAN," and "Dielkometer, Type CRV." All the above-mentioned instruments are discussed critically by Oehme (33).

B. CAPACITANCE SAMPLE CELLS AND PROBES

Capacitance-measurement cells to be used for analyses depending on dielectric properties are of major importance. Because of the many ways in which the dielectric property can be measured to obtain basic information about an operation, a process, or a product, there also are a large number of sample-cell designs available for use. The particular application for which a cell is to be used, in general, dictates the physical size, shape, strength, and electrical-property specifications to which the cell must be built. A few general remarks are pertinent to the planning and design of satisfactory capacitance cells for the measurement of dielectric constant.

The physical size of an enclosed sample cell is of little consequence except as required for a specific application. If the cell is to be used in a laboratory, its size should be restricted to minimize sample requirements. For use on a flowing stream, space in the cell must permit easy flow of the test material. It is desirable to operate a process test cell under the same temperature and pressure conditions prevailing in the flowing stream.

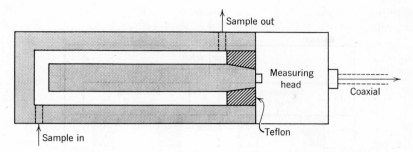

Fig. 52.12. Cylindrical capacitance cell.

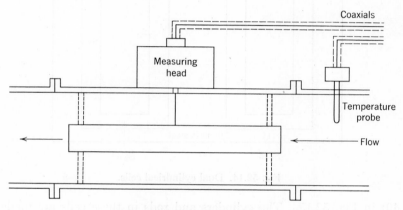

Fig. 52.13. In-line sample cell.

Capacitance of the cell, when filled with the test liquid, as well as expected variations in capacitance, must be compatible with the range built into the measuring circuitry. Cell shape should be designed for easy mounting and cleaning and it should be installed for elimination of gas bubbles, with minimum of dead space, in order to prevent accumulation of sediment or rust. Some turbulence should be present in the flowing stream to maintain good thermal and composition mixing.

The strength of the cell must be compatible with stream pressure, the electrical insulation material in the cell component must be capable of withstanding operation pressures and temperatures, and the cell materials must be free from attack by the test stream. A few typical sample cells and probes are shown in Figs. 52.12 to 52.16.

The single-stream cylindrical cell shown in Fig. 52.12 was developed by Humble (47) and later was modified for use on two streams, as shown

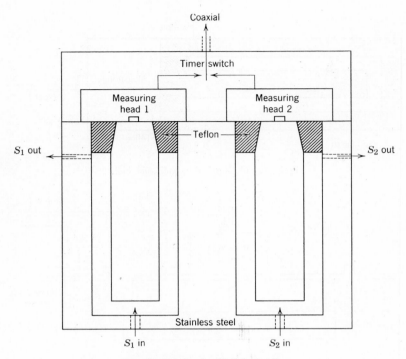

Fig. 52.14. Dual cylindrical cells.

(3,49) in Fig. 52.15. The cylinders and rods in these cells are made of stainless steel, and Teflon washers provide insulation between the grounded cylinder and the oscillating-rod electrode. These cells are capable of operation at temperatures up to 400°F. and pressures up to 1000 psig. For comparison of two flowing streams, Sun Oil (41) makes use of matched cylindrical cells mounted in the same constant-temperature bath. Prior to entering the capacitance cells, both streams flow through coiled metal tubes for equilibration of temperature. One cell is used in the remote transmitter as the reference cell and the other as the measurement cell.

The in-line sample cell shown in Fig. 52.13 has been used by Humble in many plant applications (48). It is especially applicable when conditions favor direct measurement on the flowing stream and temperature fluctuations are within control of a temperature compensator. Instead of the solid rod used by Humble (Fig. 52.13), Instruments Inc. (16) and Gulf Oil (8) have developed and used one or more hollow concentric cylinders mounted centrally inside flowing pipelines. The concentric cell has been found best for measurement of basic sediment and water in crude oil.

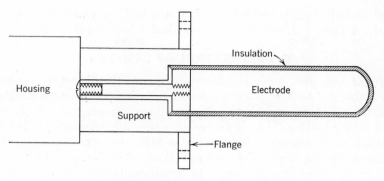

Fig. 52.15. Dielectric probe-level.

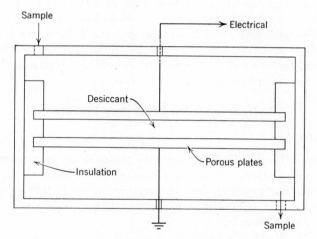

Fig. 52.16. Dielectric moisture cell.

A sketch of Sun's moisture cell is shown in Fig. 52.16. It consists of two insulated porous metal plates separated by a suitable desiccant. The desiccant absorbs or desorbs water from and to the flowing stream until equilibrium is reached, and the high dielectric property of water, relative to hydrocarbons, permits measurement to as low as 5 p.p.m. of water. Absolute measurement of water in flowing hydrocarbon streams can be achieved best by the use of two such cells operating on dried and undried portions of the stream.

For measurement of liquid level or interface level between two miscible liquids, use is made of a capacitance probe shown in Fig. 52.15. Developed by Instruments Inc. (16), this probe accommodates a wide temperature range for both liquids and solids. It is available in a variety of sizes and lengths and can be installed in either vertical or horizontal positions.

C. PREPARATION OF SAMPLES

Sample preparation for the determination of the dielectric constant in either laboratory-measuring or process-monitoring equipment is simple and straightforward, but proper techniques are quite important. Sample precautions required for chemical analyses are normally adequate for dielectric-constant measurements. Test samples must be representative of the stream or mixture from which they are taken. This is especially true if the mixture embraces a wide range of densities, boiling points, molecular weights, or compound types.

Proper sampling becomes even more difficult if the test mixture contains two phases that are not miscible. For dielectric-constant measurement of solids, viscous liquids, and two-phase systems, it is often advantageous to employ a solvent in which the test material can be dissolved. The following are recommended practices for handling samples in the laboratory or in process applications of dielectric constant.

1. Recommended Laboratory Practices

Temperature

Means must be provided for accurate temperature measurement, control, or compensation. It is often easier to develop a temperature–dielectric-constant gradient, for temperature compensation or for correction of results to a reference temperature, than it is to maintain precise temperature of the sample.

Agitation

Proper agitation of the sample should be maintained throughout the test period to insure homogeneity of both composition and temperature.

Vapor Loss

Samples containing light or gaseous compounds must be measured at sufficiently low temperatures or high pressures to prevent loss of vapor.

Calibration

Calibration samples from a variety of known compounds must be prepared and tested on the apparatus before it is ready for use in studying unknown mixtures.   Calibration samples should be similar in composition and dielectric constant to the materials to be tested.

Solvents

Solvents that may be employed for dissolving solids or for breaking emulsions prior to measurement of dielectric constant should be standardized, in so far as is practical.   They should have high solubility, low vapor pressure, and negligible toxicity.

2. Recommended Process Practices

Correlation

Usable and realistic correlation data should be established between the dielectric constant and the concentration of key components in the process stream for which control is desired.

Key Component

If a single key component does not exist it will be necessary to correlate the instrument measurement with some other property of the stream, such as compound type, density, boiling range, or molecular weight.   The last correlation requires unusual care to prevent inaccuracies and unreliable results.

Contaminants

The stream on which dielectric-constant measurements are to be made must be kept free of small contaminants that may result in large variations in dielectric constant.   For example, hydrocarbon streams must be kept free of water or molecules containing oxygen, nitrogen, chlorine, bromine, or iodine atoms.

Sample Flow

Sample flow should be sufficient to afford good mixing plus thermal equilibrium of the sample with the temperature bath or compensation element.

Pressure

Sample pressure must be sufficient to prevent formation of gas bubbles in the measuring cell.   In general, sample pressure as near as possible to process pressure is desirable.

Temperature

Proper temperature control or temperature compensation is of major importance in process-stream monitoring. Automatic temperature compensation is usually preferable to precise control at some specific temperature. Good compensation for temperature can be achieved, in general, over a range of plus or minus $8°C$. In conjunction with temperature compensation, it is often desirable to use a tap-water bath for smoothing stream variations.

On-Stream Measurements

If process-stream variations are less than plus or minus $8°C$., the measuring cell and compensator may be placed directly in the process flow line.

Two-Phase Streams

Except under special cases of high sample-flow rates and good turbulence, measurement of dielectric constant should not be attempted on streams containing two phases. Greater maintenance and personal attention are usually required on d.-c. installations on two-phase systems unless results are used only to indicate trends or major changes.

D. OPERATIONAL TECHNIQUES

Since dielectric constant is not a unique property and most applications are concerned with mixtures of more than two components, measurement techniques and interpretation of results require knowledge of the mixture and good judgment. Two operational techniques, calibration of test equipment and control of temperature, need further emphasis and clarification.

1. Calibration of Test Equipment

Dielectric constant is an electrical property not easily measured as an absolute value. Instead of direct measurement, dielectric constant is used for comparison of unknown mixtures with pure compounds or mixtures that are known. Useful comparisons require identical operating conditions and equipment.

If an instrument is to be used for direct measurements of dielectric constant, it must be calibrated with two or more pure compounds. For per cent concentrations of key components or compound types, it will usually suffice to determine instrument response to a series of known mixtures.

These known mixtures, however, must have key compounds and background materials that are compatible with the stream or samples to be analyzed.

Calibration curves are required for each kind of stream or series of test samples. In these curves, known dielectric constant values for pure compounds are plotted against dial numbers or recorder-response values. For process applications, only one calibration curve is needed for each application. In pipeline interface monitoring, typical samples of each product to be monitored may be used to establish calibration data. It is advisable to establish systematic recheck procedures for all calibration data. This is especially true for plant or pipeline applications in which equipment is subject to severe atmospheric conditions.

2. Temperature—Its Importance and Control

Temperature is the most important variable for which control or compensation is required in the measurement of dielectric constant. The precision with which temperature must be controlled depends upon the temperature coefficient of dielectric constant (rate of change with temperature) and the accuracy desired in the measured value. High accuracy in the measurement of dielectric constant does not mean high accuracy in the analysis, except for binary mixtures. For a single-compound type in a mixture, precision of analysis is often limited more by the necessity of using average dielectric constant values for the several compounds than it is through inaccurate temperature-control measurement of dielectric constant. In general, temperature control to plus or minus 0.05°C. is sufficient for laboratory testing, whereas control to plus or minus only 0.2°C. is satisfactory for a stream analyzer. Temperature control of the test sample is best in laboratory work, but temperature compensation is more suitable for on-stream applications. Either manual or automatic temperature corrections of test results often become impractical and difficult to administer. On the other hand, precise temperature control for process monitoring under all weather conditions is often difficult and unreliable.

Compensation of temperature for plus or minus 7°C. variations has been found satisfactory for most on-stream dielectric-constant instruments. This order of compensation is accomplished electrically with inexpensive auxiliary equipment, usually available from the manufacturer. For plant installations in which the streams have relatively constant temperature (plus or minus 7°C. variations from an average), it is common practice to install both the measuring cell and the temperature compensator directly in the main flow line. In this case, no provision is made for temperature control of the stream or for protection of the measurement element from the weather.

IV. SURVEY OF APPLICATIONS

Dielectric constant is a physical property of gases, liquids, and solids that can be used to aid in the identification and determination of purity for individual compounds. As a single property it compares in value with such other physical characteristics as density and refractive index. Dielectric constant can be used specifically for determining per cent composition only for binary mixtures and for mixtures in which only two types of compounds are present. Success of the latter application depends on the degree of closeness of dielectric values for the several compounds in either of the two types. If the compounds of one type encompass a wide range of values, accuracy of percentages of either type is correspondingly impaired. Some improvement in the accuracy of the type analysis can be achieved by use of weighted averages of dielectric constant values for the compounds of each type. This approach, however, requires knowledge of the percent of each compound within a type, and such information is not usually available. Dielectric constant can be used equally well for laboratory bench-scale research or for continuous monitoring and automatic control of pilot units or of semicommercial or full-scale industrial processes.

A. LABORATORY USES

Perhaps the greatest laboratory uses of the dielectric constant are determination of purity and identification of compounds. This is evidenced by the large volume of dielectric constant data found in handbooks and in special publications. A few selected dielectric constant values for chemical compounds are presented for easy reference in Tables 52.I, 52.II, and 52.III (26,33,51). For the most part, these data were obtained under conditions of carefully controlled temperature and through the use of relatively simple, standardized, high-frequency electrical circuitry.

1. Pure Compounds

Dielectric data for paraffinic, olefinic, diolefinic, naphthenic, and aromatic types of hydrocarbons are tabulated in Table 52.I. Data for oxygenated compounds such as alcohols, ethers, ketones, and acids are shown in Table 52.II. In Table 52.III are listed dielectric data for organic compounds containing nitrogen, bromine, chlorine, and iodine.

Although it is practical to measure the dielectric constant for a pure compound in terms of a comparison of capacitances when the cell is first filled with the compound in question and then with air, a more common practice is to use suitable reference compounds to develop calibration curves from which data for unknown materials may be obtained directly. Quantitative

TABLE 52.I
Dielectric Properties of C₅ to C₁₁ Hydrocarbons[a]

Carbon atoms	Paraffins	ε	Olefins	ε	Naphthenes	ε	Diolefins	ε	Aromatics	ε
C_5	n-Pentane	1.844	Pentene-1	2.100	Cyclopentane	1.965	13-Pentadiene	2.32 (25°C.)	—	—
C_6	n-Hexane	1.890	cis-Hexene-3	2.062	Cyclohexane	2.023	2,4-Hexadiene	2.22	Benzene	2.284
C_7	n-Heptane	1.924	Heptene-1	2.050	m-Cyclohexane	2.020	—	—	Toluene	2.391
C_8	n-Octane	1.948	cis-Octene-3	2.062	—	—	—	—	o-Xylene	2.568
C_9	n-Nonane	1.972	4-Ethyl-3-heptene	2.48	—	—	—	—	Propylbenzene	2.36
C_{10}	n-Decane	1.991	cis-5-Decene	2.071 (25°C.)	cis-Decahydronaphthalene	2.10	Dicyclopentadiene	2.43	t-Butylbenzene	2.38
C_{11}	n-Undecane	2.005	—	—	—	—		(40°C.)	1-Methyl-4-t-butylbenzene	2.33

[a] All data are drawn from A. A. Maryott and E. R. Smith, "Table of Dielectric Constants of Pure Liquids," *Natl. Bur. Std. (U.S.) Circ. No.* **514** (1951); N. A. Lange, Ed., *Handbook of Chemistry*, 9th ed., Handbook Publishers, Inc., Sandusky, Ohio, 1956; and C. D. Hodgman, Ed., *Handbook of Chemistry and Physics*, 40th ed., Chemical Rubber Publishing Co., Cleveland, 1958. Data were obtained at 20°C. unless otherwise indicated.

TABLE 52.II

Dielectric Properties of Oxygenated Compounds[a]

Carbon atoms	Alcohols	ϵ	Ethers	ϵ	Aldehydes	ϵ	Ketones	ϵ	Acids	ϵ
C$_1$	Methanol	32.63 (25°C.)	—	—	—	—	—	—	Formic	58.5 (16°C.)
C$_2$	Ethanol	24.3 (25°C.)	Methyl ether	5.02 (25°C.)	Acetaldehyde	21.8 (10°C.)	—	—	Acetic	6.15
C$_3$	1-Propanol	20.1 (25°C.)	—	—	Propionaldehyde	18.5 (17°C.)	Acetone	20.7 (25°C.)	Propionic	3.30 (10°C.)
C$_4$	1-Butanol	17.8 (25°C.)	Ethyl ether	4.335	Butyraldehyde	13.4 (26°C.)	2-Butanone	18.5	Butyric	2.97
C$_5$	1-Pentanol	13.9 (25°C.)	—	—	Valeraldehyde	10.1 (17°C.)	2-Pentanone	15.4	Valeric	2.66
C$_6$	1-Hexanol	13.3 (25°C.)	Propyl ether	3.39 (26°C.)	—	—	2-Hexanone	14.6 (14.5°C.)	Caproic	2.63 (71°C.)

[a] All data are drawn from A. A. Maryott and E. R. Smith, "Table of Dielectric Constants of Pure Liquids," *Natl. Bur. Std. (U.S.) Circ. No.* **514** (1951); N. A. Lange, Ed., *Handbook of Chemistry*, 9th ed., Handbook Publishers, Inc., Sandusky, Ohio, 1956; and C. D. Hodgman, Ed., *Handbook of Chemistry and Physics*, 40th ed., Chemical Rubber Publishing Co., Cleveland, 1958. Values were obtained at 20°C. unless otherwise indicated.

TABLE 52.III

Dielectric Properties of Miscellaneous Organic Compounds[a]

Carbon atoms	Amines	ϵ	Bromo compounds	ϵ	Chloro compounds	ϵ	Iodo compounds	ϵ
C_1	Methylamine	9.40 (25°C.)	Bromomethane	9.82 (0°C.)	Chloromethane	12.6 (−20°C.)	Iodomethane	7.00
C_2	Ethylamine	6.94 (10°C.)	Bromoethane	9.32	Chloroethane	6.2 (170°C.)	Iodoethane	7.82
C_3	Isopropylamine	5.5	1-Bromopropane	8.09 (25°C.)	1-Chloropropane	7.7	Iodopropane	7.00
C_4	Butylamine	5.3	1-Bromobutane	7.07	1-Chlorobutane	7.39	1-Iodobutane	6.22
C_5	Amylamine	4.5 (22°C.)	1-Bromopentane	6.32 (25°C.)	1-Chloropentane	6.6	1-Iodopentane	5.81

[a] All data are drawn from A. A. Maryott and E. R. Smith, "Table of Dielectric Constants of Pure Liquids," Natl. Bur. Std. (U.S.) Circ. No. 514 (1951); N. A. Lange, Ed., Handbook of Chemistry, 9th ed., Handbook Publishers, Inc., Sandusky, Ohio, 1956; and C. D. Hodgman, Ed., Handbook of Chemistry and Physics, 40th ed., Chemical Rubber Publishing Co., Cleveland, 1958. Values were obtained at 20°C. unless otherwise indicated.

evaluation of new research materials, whether they are gas, liquid, or solid, can be achieved quickly and easily through the use of dielectric-constant measurements.

Another important laboratory application is continuous monitoring of pilot-unit streams. For this type of monitoring a small-volume sample cell and precise temperature control are required. Many of today's industrial uses of the dielectric constant have resulted from trial operations in laboratory or pilot-unit applications.

Impurity monitoring of water in the production of acetone has made successful use of the dielectric constant in the range of 0 to 0.5 weight per cent of water (38). Measurement of water in this low range is made possible by virtue of the large difference in the dielectric property between water and acetone (21.4 for acetone and 80 for water at 20°C.). It has been found that neither temperature nor pressure, nor a combination of the two, plus density and refractive index measurements are as satisfactory as the dielectric constant for controlling a distillation in which high-purity acetone is separated from water. The water content of acetone at this level is usually determined by the Karl Fischer method, but both sampling and analysis time favor dielectric-constant monitoring.

2. Kinetic Investigations

In addition to the importance of the dielectric constants of solvents in the solution reactions, in which, in particular, the activities of ions are strongly influenced by a change in ϵ, we can also follow reaction rates by the measurement of the dielectric constant. If the cell surface and the electrical field of the capacitor have no influence on the rate of the reaction, we may incorporate the capacitor directly into the reaction chamber and follow the reaction rate continuously with suitable recording devices. Thus, Axtmann (1) studied the esterification of ethyl alcohol by acetic anhydride in carbon tetrachloride. The rate of the reaction was followed by measuring the over-all dielectric constant.

The reaction was carried out in a closed vessel in which 13 equally spaced metal plates formed an electrical capacitor and at the same time served as a reaction chamber. Completely enclosed in glass, the combination capacitance cell and reaction chamber was submerged in a constant-temperature oil bath prior to introduction of the samples to be reacted. Compensation of capacitance changes in the cell resulting from the reaction were achieved by means of an adjustable micrometer-spindle capacitance in an auxiliary circuit. Progress of the reaction could be followed and read directly from the micrometer position through use of an appropriate calibration curve. In this application, dielectric constant appears to be considerably more suitable for following the high-speed reaction than were other monitoring techniques such as polarimetry, spectrophotometry, or conductometry.

Obtained data indicated that the dielectric constant of this multicomponent solution of polar molecules in a nonpolar solvent was directly proportional to the concentrations of the individual species and followed the empirical linear relationship of Heston et al. (14):

$$\epsilon = \epsilon_1 + ax_2 \tag{37}$$

where ϵ_1 is the dielectric constant of the solvent, a is the slope of the line, and x_2 is the mole fraction of the polar solute. Axtmann assumed that there was no interaction between the four solute molecules, and since there is no change in the total number of moles present the mole fractions of any one substance would be directly proportional to their respective concentrations. Equation (37) may then be written as:

$$\epsilon = \epsilon_1 + a_2x_2 + a_3x_3 + a_4x_4 + a_5x_5 \tag{38}$$

Subscripts 2 to 5 indicate the four polar-solute molecules. The sum of the mole fractions is a constant; from the stoichiometry of the reaction we have $x_2 = x_3$ and $x_4 = x_5$. Hence, the a's will be the individual slopes of the dielectric constant–concentration curves. From these relationships, it can be seen that the change of concentration of any one component may be followed by observing the change in the over-all dielectric constant. Second-order specific rate constants were evaluated with an average deviation of 0.12% between them.

Kinetics of cis-trans isomerizations may be followed very conveniently by measuring the dielectric constant. Thus, Dickinson and his co-workers (31) studied the isomerization of diiodoethylene by elementary iodine, both thermally and photochemically, in hydrocarbon solvents.

3. Miscellaneous Uses

Efficiency and progress in the separation of compound types by means of liquid-phase chromatography have been monitored with the dielectric constant (20). This application is based on the average difference in dielectric-constant values among compounds in the paraffin, naphthene, and aromatic groups. Since the sample volume was relatively small in liquid-phase chromatography, it was necessary to develop a small-volume capacitance cell through which the liquid effluent was caused to flow during this application. The capacitance cell arrangement for testing low-volume samples consisted of a metal-coated glass tube with a central wire electrode.

Minimum sample volumes for the test cell developed for this application were no more than 0.3 ml. Null-point meter readings were used in following the chromatographic separation; upon reaching a predetermined deviation from zero, the meter needle deflection was caused to activate a relay that, in turn, operated a buzzer system to alert an operator to change the product receiver.

Dielectric constant has been used as a research tool in the laboratory to measure power factors and thermal-expansion coefficients of solids and liquids (2). Designed primarily for studying plastics in liquid or solid form, a variable-temperature–variable-frequency dielectric apparatus has been used in the ranges of minus 25 to plus 150°C. and 50 cps to 600,000 cps, respectively. Two flat-surfaced Invar cups served as the test-cell electrodes and flexible stainless steel bellows provided electrical connections for the cups. Such an arrangement made accurate electrode spacing possible. Hot oil circulated through the electrode supports provided a means for precise temperature control. The entire measurement unit was mounted inside a thermally insulated case. Wide-range frequency measurements on both liquid and solid plastics were achieved through use of a tight-fitting glass cylinder in which the electrodes could slide, producing a variation in capacitance through changes in cell thickness.

A laboratory dielectric meter originally designed for measurement of moisture in a wide variety of materials has been employed to monitor the solvent content of plant samples containing oil and wax (22). Synthetic mixtures of the MEK–toluene dewaxing solvent were prepared in waxy oil stocks for calibration of the equipment. Contamination effects of dissolved water in the oil–solvent samples were eliminated by operation of the equipment at a temperature above 40°C. This application was made possible for a wide variety of oil and wax mixtures because of the large difference in dielectric constant between the solvent employed and the wax–oil portion of the test samples.

Using a stainless steel cylindrical capacitance cell with Teflon insulators and quartz spacers, successful use has been made of dielectric properties in studying mixtures of water and hydrogen peroxide. Because of the high-conductivity problem encountered in these studies on highly similar materials, it was necessary to employ electrical rather than mechanical polishing and cleaning of the stainless steel cell surfaces (11).

B. INDUSTRIAL USES

Tremendous progress has been made in the past 15 years in the development and application of dielectric equipment for control of flowing streams in the chemical and petroleum industry (46,47,50). Prior to 1949 it was necessary for the user to design and build both the high-frequency oscillator circuitry and the capacitance sample cell.   These hand-made units were expensive in both design and construction and were difficult to install in hazardous areas.   Close-proximity location of the measuring cell and the oscillator was usually required.   After 1949, however, an apparatus known as the capacitance dynalog, with both high accuracy of performance and simplicity of installation, became available.   As a result of these favorable qualities, increased interest developed in the use of the dielectric constant for process monitoring.   Sample cells were not available on early-model dynalogs, but suitable cells were built by the user.   A coaxial cable furnished with the dynalog made remote location of the sample cell practical. Hence the need for explosion-proofing the oscillator was eliminated, since it could be located in the control room.

1. Toluene Analyzer

An early dielectric constant instrument was custom-built by Humble for monitoring toluene in a stream containing paraffins and naphthenes (46). This measurement depended on a dielectric constant value of 2.41 for toluene, as compared to a value of 2.0 for the paraffin–naphthene portion. The electric circuit of this analyzer consisted of a constant-frequency, crystal-controlled oscillator operating at 2,000 kc., a variable-frequency oscillator containing the sample cell, a mixer oscillator, a frequency meter, and a voltage-regulated power supply (see Fig. 52.5).   The frequency meter measured the difference in frequency between the constant-frequency oscillator and the variable-frequency oscillator containing the sample cell. Signals from the meter were fed to a recorder for monitoring the toluene concentration in the flowing stream.

The flowing stream was passed through the stainless steel cell at a pressure of 15 pounds per square inch and a rate of 3 liters per minute.   The sample passed through a temperature-controlled 40°C. water bath, the sample cell, and back into the main flow stream.

Laboratory-analyzed plant samples were employed for calibrating the plant apparatus for the range from 40 to 90% toluene.   Each recorder division was equivalent to 0.5% change in toluene.   Credits accruing to the use of an analyzer on process streams depend to a large extent upon the type of application, but it is not unusual to achieve a savings of $10,000 per year.

2. Detection of Interface

Movement of products by pipeline often has been hampered by the difficulty of detecting arrival of the interface between two products.   Use of dispatch directives, color tests, hydrometers, and recording gravitometers to determine interface arrival has not been successful. In an effort to reduce pipeline costs, Gulf Research has made use of dielectric constant to monitor interface movement (8). Application has been made to fuel oils, kerosenes, and a wide variety of gasolines.

In interface monitoring, Gulf placed a concentric cylinder or a probe directly in the line through which the material was flowing. Dielectric constant was found to be one minute faster than a recording gravitometer and three minutes faster than a hydrometer or color test in detecting interface changes. The dielectric-constant method was sufficiently sensitive to detect interface for some 17 products, whereas no other procedures were applicable.

3. Basic Sediment and Water Detection

Gulf also applied dielectric constant to the detection of basic sediment and water (BS & W) in crude oil (8). A cylindrical probe was mounted in the center of the pipe flow line for a continuous record of BS & W contaminations. If the recorder indicated excess BS & W contamination, an automatic sampler was activated to withdraw samples for further study in the laboratory. Individual samples taken under off-specification conditions were composited and processed later to determine average contamination during a given period. Gulf also has made use of dielectric constant in pipeline service to detect differences between crude oils produced from different zones and of different qualities although they had identical API gravities and widely different viscosities.

4. Phenol Extraction

Phenol extraction of a lubricating oil to improve the viscosity index has been monitored with the dielectric constant. Aromatics having a low viscosity index are removed from the oil in the improvement process. Since the dielectric constant for aromatics is higher than for paraffins and naphthenes, the dielectric-constant meter is ideally suited for monitoring the phenol-extraction process. A plant installation by Humble made use of a dual-cell capacitance element to compare feed and finished oil (49). Prior to passing the cells, the two streams were passed through constant-temperature water and into the cell block also submerged in the bath. The temperature of the bath is normally maintained at or near the boiling point of water by direct steam injection. An advantage in this system is that the steam flow rate did not vary the bath temperature.

The recorder difference between feed and product in this application was a measure of extraction efficiency; thus, at a quick glance, the operator could detect changes in feed or efficiency of the extraction process.   It was observed that low-viscosity-index stocks experienced a larger change in viscosity index during phenol extraction.   In addition to improvement in oil quality monitoring, the recorder was used to indicate lined-out performance of the extraction process.   A switch in feed stock was observed quickly, although several hours were required to reach equilibrium on a new feed (3).   U. S. Patent No. 2,737,469, covering this application, has been assigned to Esso Research and Engineering Company.

5. MEK Dewaxing

Dielectric monitoring of lubricating-oil dewaxing, with MEK–toluene as solvent, has been employed successfully by Humble (3,48).   The ratio of oil to the solvent mixture was found to be critical in the dewaxing operation and was easily monitored with dielectric constant.   In this application a comparison is made between the wax removed and that fed to the process. An apparatus similar to that used in the phenol-extraction application is employed for this test, but a temperature near 100°C. was required.

6. SO$_2$ Extraction of Aromatics

Because of the large difference in dielectric constant between the aromatics and the paraffin–naphthene mixture in which they are contained, Humble uses dielectric constant as a means for monitoring the feed composition (3,48).   In this application, flow of the feed stream was required through one sample cell only.   Rather than employ precise temperature control, an electrical compensating device was found satisfactory if stream-temperature fluctuations were less than 6°C.   A two-cell metal block and series flow were employed, but the second cell served as a holder for the compensator-thermister element.   Initially, reproducibility of the instrument was checked automatically for ten minutes every four hours by injection of a known reference liquid.   Such testing indicated high stability of the instrument, and calibration checking every four hours was eliminated.   The dielectric meter in this application often detected feed changes sufficient to upset the process operation; they would have been missed with the customary 2-hour spot sampling.

7. Propane-to-Oil Ratio

Control of the propane-to-oil ratio in the deasphalting process is of prime importance in preparation for the dewaxing of lube oils (50).   High propane contents result in fast filtering, but this means a loss in oil throughput capacity, and insufficient propane makes for excess filtering time.   Using dielectric-constant measurements for typical oils and a literature value for propane, it was possible to establish the mixture dielectric-constant levels that should be maintained for best dewaxing filter rates. Calibration data were established in terms of filtering performance for a given stock, and through plant experience it was possible to establish optimum propane–oil ratios and, hence, to achieve maximum dewaxing rates. U. S. Patent No. 2,905,616, covering this application, has been issued to Esso Research and Engineering Company.

8. Octane Monitoring

One of the most rewarding current uses for continuous measurement of dielectric constant in the petroleum industry is the monitoring of octane improvement in catalytic reforming of gasolines. Since catalytic reforming converts naphthenic compounds to aromatics, and aromatics in general have higher dielectric-constant values than paraffins and naphthenes, octane improvements resulting from catalytic reforming are easily monitored by dielectric constant. In this application, Humble makes use of a dual-cell capacitance element in which the feed and the reformed product are compared (50). In this use of dielectric constant, catalyst degradation during the reaction period also was observed, and differences between the low- and high-octane feeds could be determined. Typical calibration curves of research octane number versus recorder readings were developed for stocks having end points of 130, 150, and 180°C. (50). Average accuracy for octane-number improvements through use of the dielectric constant was ±1 octane number. U. S. Patent No. 2,903,417, covering this application, has been issued to Esso Research and Engineering Company.

9. Miscellaneous Applications

Level measurements for liquids, liquid interfaces, and solids have been made with the dielectric constant through the use of suitable probe arrangements (16,42). The water content of such materials as clay, wheat, paper, cereals, and catalysts has been measured with the dielectric constant. Reaction products from oxidation, hydrogenation, or dehydrogenation of hydrocarbons can be compared with feed stocks, and important properties of liquid media have been measured by submerging high-frequency circuit components directly in the medium to be studied (53). Isomer ratios between toluene–2,4-diisocyanate and toluene–2,6-diisocyanate mixtures have been measured with the dielectric constant to an accuracy of 0.2% in the manufacture of urethane polymers.

Heating by means of the dielectric property has been used as a new separation process for certain heat-sensitive materials, and salt crystals in admixture with ice have been preferentially melted with high-frequency electric fields so that the salt can be removed with negligible contamination by water (13). Water in hydrocarbons has been measured in a pilot-unit application (51). Detectability of changes in capacitance as low as 0.00265 $\mu\mu$f. or 1 p.p.m. of water is claimed for this application.

REFERENCES

1. Axtman, R. C., *J. Am. Chem. Soc.*, **73**, 5367 (1951); *Anal. Chem.*, **24**, 783 (1952).
2. Baker, E. B., *Rev. Sci. Instr.*, **20**, 716 (1949).
3. Chamberlain, N. F., B. W. Thomas, J. B. Beaugh, and P. B. Land, *Ind. Eng. Chem.*, **48**, 1990 (1956).
4. Clausius, R., *Die mechanische Wärmetheorie*, 2nd ed., Vieweg, Braunschweig, 1879, Vol. 2, p. 62.
5. Coop, T. E., and L. E. Sutton, *J. Chem. Soc.*, **1938**, 1269.
6. Debye, P., *Polar Molecules*, Chemical Catalog Co., New York, 1929, p. 36.
7. *Ibid.*, p. 44.
8. Endean, H. J., and R. M. Howard, *Preprint* **53**-Pet-**14**, Petroleum and Mechanical Engineering Conference, A.S.M.E., Houston, Texas, September, 1953.
9. Foxboro Company, "Foxboro Capacitance Dynalog," *Bulletin No. 20-11* and *Technical Information Sheet 25-A-52a*, Foxboro, Mass., 1958.
10. Frölich, H., *Theory of Dielectrics*, 2nd ed., Oxford University Press, London, 1958.
11. Gross, P. M., Jr., and R. C. Taylor, *J. Am. Chem. Soc.*, **72**, 2075 (1950).
12. Hallikainen Instruments Co., *Hallikainen-Shell Bulletin: Dielectric Constant Recorder*, Berkeley, Calif., 1958.
13. Heisig, C. G., and K. A. Kobe, *Ind. Eng. Chem.*, **50**, 1517 (1958).
14. Heston, W. M., A. D. Franklin, E. J. Hennelly, and C. P. Smyth, *J. Am. Chem. Soc.*, **72**, 3443 (1950).
15. Howe, W. H., *Inst. Radio Engrs. Trans. Ind. Electronics*, **PGIE-5**, 56 (1958).
16. Instruments, Inc., *Bulletin 256, Model B-04 Electr-O-Probe*, Tulsa, Okla., 1958.
17. Instruments, Inc., *Bulletin CP-758, Bulletin 154-H1, Model H-04 Capacity Product Analyzer*, Tulsa, Okla., 1958.
18. Jelatis, J. G., *J. Appl. Phys.*, **19**, 419 (1948).
19. Kirkwood, J. G., *J. Chem. Phys.*, **7**, 911 (1939).
20. Laskowski, D. W., and R. E. Putscher, *Anal. Chem.*, **24**, 965 (1952).
21. Lattey, R. T., and W. G. Davies, *Phil. Mag.*, **12**, 111 (1931).
22. LeRosen, H. D., L. V. Wike, and S. W. Denton, *Anal. Chem.*, **24**, 1620 (1952).
23. Lorentz, H. A., *Verhl. K. Akad. Wetens. Amsterdam*, **18**, 60, 85 (1879); *Ann. Phys.*, **9**, 641 (1880).
24. Lorenz, L., *Kgl. Dansk. Videns. Selsk. Skrift.*, **8**, 205 (1869); *Ann. Phys.*, **11**, 70 (1880).
25. Maryott, A. A., and F. Buckley, "Table of Dielectric Constants and Electric Dipole Moments of Substances in the Gaseous State," *Natl. Bur. Std. (U.S.) Circ., No.* **537** (1953).
26. Maryott, A. A., and E. R. Smith, "Table of Dielectric Constants of Pure Liquids," *Natl. Bur. Std. (U.S.) Circ., No.* **514** (1951).

27. Maxwell, J. C., *A Treatise on Electricity and Magnetism*, Oxford University Press, London, 1873, Vol. 2, p. 388.
28. Moore, F. E., *Oil Gas J.*, 56, 96 (1958).
29. Moore, W. J., *Physical Chemistry*, 3nd ed., Prentice-Hall, Englewood Cliffs, N.J. 1962, p. 554.
30. Mossotti, O. F., *Mem. di Math. e Fisica di Modena*, 24, II, 49 (1850).
31. Noyes, R. M., R. G. Dickinson, and V. Shomaker, *J. Am. Chem. Soc.*, 67, 1319 (1945).
32. Oehme, F., *Dielektrische Messmethoden*, Verlag Chemie, Weinheim/Bergstr., 1958.
33. *Ibid.*, p. 30.
34. *Ibid.*, p. 102.
35. Oehme, F., *Farbe Lack*, 65, 498 (1959).
36. Onsager, L., *J. Am. Chem. Soc.*, 58, 1486 (1936).
37. Partington, J. R., *Advanced Treatise on Physical Chemistry*, Longmans, Green, London, 1953, Vol. IV, p. 404; 1954, Vol. V, p. 287.
38. Pompeo, D. J., J. Parker, and S. S. Smith, *World Petrol. Congr. 3rd, The Hague*, Sect. VI, *Preprint* 28 (1951).
39. Powles, J. G., and C. P. Smyth, "Dielectric Constant and Loss," in A. Weissberger, Ed., *Technique of Organic Chemistry*, 2nd ed., Interscience, New York–London, 1954, Vol. 1, Part III, pp. 2279–2320.
40. Rolfson, F. B., Shell Development Co., Emeryville, Calif., private communication (1957).
41. Shawhan, E. N., H. L. Bachofer, J. Lerner, and J. R. Wright, "Versatile Capacity Measuring System for Level Control and Stream Analysis," paper presented to American Petroleum Institute meeting, New York, May, 1959.
42. Sherrick, P. H., G. A. Daive, R. Karr, and E. F. Ewen, *Manual of Chemical Oscillometry*, E. H. Sargent and Co., Chicago, 1954.
43. Smyth, C. P., *Dielectric Behavior and Structure*, McGraw-Hill, New York, 1955.
44. Smyth, C. P., "Dipole Moments," in A. Weissberger, Ed., *Technique of Organic Chemistry*, 2nd ed., Interscience, New York–London, 1949, Vol. 1, Part II, pp. 1611–1650.
45. *Ibid.*, p. 1621.
46. Thomas, B. W., F. J. Faegin, and G. W. Wilson, *Anal. Chem.*, 23, 1750 (1951).
47. Thomas, B. W., *Proc. Instr. Soc. Am.* 7, 61 (1952).
48. Thomas, B. W., and J. B. Beaugh, *Petrol. Refiner*, 35, 133 (1956).
49. Thomas, B. W., N. F. Chamberlain, O. J. Howell, and R. L. Martin, *Proc. Instr. Soc. Am.*, 10, 55-18-3 (1955).
50. Wherry, T. C., and R. E. Wrightman, *Proc. Symp. Process Fluid Analyzers, Instr. Soc. Am.*, 12 (1957).
51. Wyman, J., *Phys. Rev.*, 35, 623 (1930).
52. Van Arkel, A. E., and J. L. Snoek, *Physik. Z.*, 33, 662 (1932).
53. Von Hippel, A. R., *Dielectric Materials and Applications*, Wiley, New York, 1954.

SUBJECT INDEX

A

Absolute mobility of ions in conductometry, 2575, 2576

Absolute velocity of ions in conductometry, 2575, 2576

Absorption-mode spectrum in NMR, 1924

Accelerator, van de Graaf, 2076

Acetal mass spectra, 2026, 2027

Acetate esters, mass spectrometry of, table, 2028

Acetone-water mixtures, oscillometric determination of, 2626

Acid-base titrations, coulometric, 2519, 2520

Acids, C_1–C_4, MS analysis of, table, 2047
  dielectric constants of, table, 2662
  organic, mass spectra, 2027

Acids and bases, oscillometric determination of, 2625

Activation overpotential, 2125

Activity in e.m.f. measurements, 2271

Adsorption currents, 2323
  of surface-active materials, 2128
  waves, 2323

Age study of minerals, by MS, table, 2059

Alcohol, mass spectra of, 2020, 2022

Alcohols, C_1–C_4, MS analysis of, table, 2047
  C_{16}–C_{27}, MS analysis of, table, 2048
  dielectric constants of, table, 2062
  MS analysis of, table, 2052
  primary, mass spectra of, 2020–2022
  secondary, mass spectra of, 2021, 2022
  tertiary, mass spectra of, 2022

Alcohol–water mixtures, analysis by MS, 2055
  oscillometric determination of, 2626

Aldehydes, dielectric constants of, table, 2662
  mass spectra of, 2023, 2024
  parent-ion intensities, figure, 2023

Aliphatic ether, mass spectra of, table, 2031

Aliphatic paraffins, ion sensitivities of, table, 2016
  mass spectra of, 2014

Aliphatic sulfide, mass spectra of, table, 2036

Alkyl benzenes, mass spectra of, 2019
  MS analysis of, table, 2047
  NMR constants of, figure, 1927

Alloys, magnetic properties of, 1754

Alternating-current polarography, 2206–2208, 2340, 2341

Alternating magnetic field in NMR, 1910, 1911

Aluminum electrode, rotating, 2404, 2405

Aluminum, polarographic characteristics of, table, 2364

Amalgamated metal electrodes, 2396

Amides, MS analysis of, table, 2048

Amines, aliphatic, MS analysis of, table, 2048
  coulometry of, table, 2517
  dielectric constant of, table, 2663
  identification of radicals from, 1953
  MS analysis of, table, 2047

p-Aminophenol, polarographic characteristics of, table, 2410

Ammonia, coulometry of, table, 2516

Amperometric titration, 2187–2191, 2307, 2336, 2337
  accuracy of, 2307
  curves for, 2337
  definition of, 2307
  precision of, 2307

Analyzer tube, double-focusing, figure, 1979
  magnetic, sector field, figure, 1976

Aniline-nitrobenzene mixtures, oscillometric determination of, 2626

Anisotropy, magnetic, 1760, 1866–1868; figures, 1867, 1868

2673

Mercury tetrathiocyanotocobalt, susceptibility of, 1829

Mercury–mercurous electrodes, 2290, 2459

Mercury-type electrodes, 2388–2396
    mercury-membrane electrodes, 2395
    mercury-plated metal electrodes, 2396
    streaming mercury electrodes, 2394, 2395

Metal deposition from complex ions at the D.M.E., 2431–2434

Metal electrodeposits, crystal structure of, 2461–2465
    effect of surface-active agents on, 2462, 2463
    physical characteristics of, 2460–2465

Metamagnetism, table, 1763

Metastable transition chart, 1971

Methods for analysis of mixtures by MS, table, 2047, 2048

Methyl butanoate, dissociation of, 2029

3-Methyl butyl ethers, dissociation of, table, 2031

Methyl ethers, dissociation of, table, 2031

Methyl ethyl ketone–benzene–water mixtures, determination of, 2626

Methyl ethyl ketone–toluene mixture, in dewaxing, 2669

Methyl hydrogen peroxidase, magnetochemistry of, 1871

2-Methyl styrene, identification of radicals from, 1953

Migration, of ions, law of independent, 2576
    in mass transport, 2129, 2130
    See also Conductance *and* Ionic equivalent.

Migration currents, definition of, 2309
    in quantitative analysis, 2306, 2307
    suppression of, 2309

Mobility, absolute, of ions in conductometry, 2575, 2576

Molecular structure, correlation of, in NMR spectrometry, figure, 1927
    determination of, by NMR spectrometry, 1928–1931
    proof of, by NMR spectrometry, figure, 1928

Molecular weight measurement, by rate of effusion with MS, 2058

Molybdenum, coulometry of, 2515
    electrode, 2278
    polarographic characteristics of, table, 2366

Mono-olefins, mass spectra of, 2017–2019

Multicomponent mixtures, NMR characterization of, 1934–1941

Multicomponent quantitative analysis, calculations of, 1932–1934
    by NMR spectrometry, 1931–1934
    spectral requirements, 1931, 1932; figure, 1932

Multiple-charged ions, study of by MS, 1968–1970

Multiplet intervals in magnetochemistry, classification of, 1774

Multiplets, produced in NMR by chemical shift, figure, 1901
    produced by spin-spin, 1905, 1906

N

n, estimation of value of, 2319, 2327
    factors affecting value of, 2327

Naphtha, nonolefinic, mass spectrometric analysis of, table, 2052

Naphthalenes, condensed aromatic, NMR constants of, figure, 1927
    dielectric constants of, table, 2661
    uncondensed aromatic, NMR constants of, figure, 1927

1-Naphthylamine, polarographic characteristics of, table, 2411

Natural gas, mass spectrometric analysis of, table, 2047

Néel point, 1765

Neptunium, coulometry of, 2515

Nernst diffusion layer, 2145–2147, 2172; figure, 2146

Nernst equation, 2118, 2166–2168, 2270, 2271
    in coulometry, 2483–2485
    in stripping analysis, 2550

Nickel, coulometry of, 2514
    deposition potential of, table, 2464
    electrodetermination of, table, 2467